# GOOD BEER GUIDE 1997

**EDITED BY JEFF EVANS**

**BOOKS**

**Campaign for Real Ale Ltd.**
230 Hatfield Road, St Albans,
Hertfordshire AL1 4LW

# CONTENTS

**Editor:** Jeff Evans. **Deputy Editor:** Jill Adam. **The HQ Team:** (Campaigns) Stephen Cox, Iain Loe,
Mike Benner, Ben Wardle; (Administration) Richard Smith, Malcolm Harding, Jo Bates, Su Tilley,
Cressida Feiler, Jean Jones, Gary Fowler, Mandi Gilling, Clare Stevens, Mick Green, Nick Verlaine,
Steve Powell. **Design:** Rob Howells. **Cover Photograph:** Carl Warner. **Hops:** The Hop Pocket (Craft
Shop), Bishop's Frome, Worcestershire. **Maps:** Perrott Cartographics, Machynlleth.

**Published by** Campaign for Real Ale Ltd., 230 Hatfield Road, St Albans, Hertfordshire AL1 4LW.
Tel. (01727) 867201. E-mail: camra@camra. org.uk Home Page: http://www. camra.org.uk **Typeset
by** Tradespools Ltd., Frome, Somerset. **Printed by** Clays Ltd., Bungay, Suffolk.

**ISBN 1 85249 009 8**    © **Campaign for Real Ale Ltd. 1996/97**

This guide is the result of thousands of hours' work by CAMRA members: it is a true labour of love.
Thanks to all who conducted pub surveys and contributed facts and figures about breweries and
beers, and in particular to CAMRA's Regional Directors for co-ordinating the flow of information.

# INTRODUCTION

**W**ELCOME to the 24th edition of CAMRA's *Good Beer Guide* and to a beer industry which, to the casual viewer, is more than a touch confusing at the moment. On the one hand, small microbreweries are opening up faster than one a week, the national brewers are investing in alehouse pub chains and selling beers from independent producers, and regional brewers are treating their customers to exciting, new 'special' brews every month. On the other hand, major brewing sites are being closed, the nationals seem intent on devouring each other, and nitrokeg – smoothflow, creamflow, call it what you will – continues to eat into real ale's share of the market.

It's certainly true that there are more real ales out there today than there have been for many a year, though finding them all may prove difficult. This year's *Good Beer Guide* is delighted to welcome no less than 68 new micro-breweries and brew pubs and we wish them well in a market which is still dominated by national brands and well-promoted beers from regional breweries. Some micros' beers may find their way into the new alehouses. This concept, whilst it is a welcome recognition by the big brewers of the enormous interest there is in real ale, serves just one purpose for them – it is the latest theme pub fad, designed to milk the ale craze while it lasts. That this is the case is evident from their other activities in the past year. First they pumped pubs full of nitrokeg. Nitrokeg – unlike real ale, fresh, living beer which contains yeast and ferments in the cask – is a processed, pasteurised beer which is served using nitrogen and carbon dioxide gases, giving it a creamy texture. Unfortunately, being pasteurised and heavily chilled, it doesn't have a lot of flavour. For its producers, however, it is hugely profitable, thanks to its long shelf-life and low wastage. Its gimmicky initial cloudiness that takes time to settle in the glass, makes it an adman's dream. It has been pushed relentlessly in flashy TV commercials, sometimes alongside cask-conditioned beer to suggest that it's all the same stuff, really. This may explain why, as the 1996 CAMRA prices survey showed, nitrokeg beers are on average 13 pence a pint dearer than cask ale, despite being cheaper to produce and handle.

## —— CARVING UP THE MARKET ——

Of even more concern is the way in which the giant breweries have once more begun to carve up the market. The last *Good Beer Guide* condemned Scottish & Newcastle's take-over of Courage and how the deal was largely nodded through by the Office of Fair Trading. It predicted that, by creating a new market leader with some 30 per cent of the UK's beer production, jobs would be lost, breweries would close and the other big brewers would not stand idly by and allow their standing to be eroded. All this has sadly come to fruition. Scottish Courage has already announced the closure of the Webster's brewery in Halifax and the Home brewery in Nottingham, and there is little evidence to suggest that its closure programme is complete. Carlsberg-Tetley has also tried to make economies and has shut down the Tetley Walker brewery in Warrington and the Plympton brewery in Devon. Now, as the 1997 *Good Beer Guide* goes to press, news is breaking that Bass is about to buy up Carlsberg-Tetley in a bid to once more become the UK's biggest brewer. The consequences of such a deal are considered in the breweries section of this book, starting on page 418.

## ── ISSUES THAT MATTER ──

The beer industry has changed remarkably in the seven years since the Government's Supply of Beer Orders were introduced. Pub groups have been established, breweries have merged, the guest beer has become established and hundreds of new micro-breweries have set up shop. It looks like the next few years will be just as eventful and, more than ever, it is vital that the consumer's voice is heard. That is why CAMRA will continue to speak out on issues that matter.

**Issues like beer tax.** It's ludicrous that our brewers pay so much more beer tax than our partners in the European Union. This high Government take is reflected in the price of beer (about a third of the cost of a pint goes to the Treasury through beer tax and VAT), so it's obvious why so many people (both legally and illegally) have joined the booze cruises, flooding the UK with cheap beer from France, where brewers pay seven times less beer duty. CAMRA is campaigning for a reduction in the level of UK beer duty to the European average, to give our brewers a chance to compete and to preserve jobs in breweries and pubs.

**Issues like beer quality.** The introduction of nitrokeg brands which are, if nothing else, always consistent in their condition and taste, together with some scorching summer weather, has focused drinkers' minds on the quality of real ale on sale in our pubs. The misuse of the swan neck and sparkler system – designed to whip up a thick, creamy head on northern beers, but applied to beers which are not brewed to stand such vigorous treatment – is just as damaging to beer flavour and texture. It's commonplace now to discover a pub with half-a-dozen or more cask beers available, but choice means nothing if the beers are not drinkable. Some brewers have responded with initiatives to improve the quality of their beers in pubs (as Roger Protz reveals on page 14), and CAMRA is actively supporting these moves.

**Issues like pub preservation.** Central to the pleasure of a good pint is having a good pub in which to drink it. In the 1960s and 1970s, the trend towards creating large, cavernous, one-bar establishments resulted in the loss of many characterful pub interiors. Snugs and smoke-rooms were demolished, parlours and vaults were lost. Drinkers today demand segregation. Not everyone wishes to hear the jukebox, smell the food or breathe in other people's cigarette smoke. But try isolating noises, smells and fumes in an open bar. Heritage also demands respect from the pub re-fitters. This year's *Good Beer Guide* includes, for the first time, a special star symbol for pubs which have outstanding original interiors, pubs which must be preserved for their historic value. A National Inventory of such important pubs has been drawn up and is printed in full at the end of Pubs to Save, an explanatory feature beginning on page 21.

**Issues like licensing reform.** The introduction of extended Sunday hours in 1995 was long overdue. Now we need to see some logic in the application of late-night hours. Is it really sensible to turn hundreds of buoyed up youths onto the streets of a town at the stroke of eleven? Allowing pubs to decide their own opening times would stagger the pub

# MAKING BEER: PART ONE
## THE INGREDIENTS

**MALT:** Sometimes referred to as 'the soul of beer', malt is the grain which gives beer its sweetness, its body and much of its fruitiness. Malt is partially germinated barley. The germination breaks down unwanted proteins and releases vital starches which will become sugars during brewing, but to prevent full germination the barley is kilned. This roasts the grains, turning them various shades of brown and leaving them with greater or lesser degrees of sweetness, nuttiness and coffee- and chocolate-like flavours. Brewers select the malts which best suit the style of beer they wish to create. First they decide which strain of barley they need (Maris Otter is recognised as being the best of the British), then they choose how much kilning it should have: paler, biscuity malts for pale ales; dark malts for colouring milds and old ales; highly roasted malts (and even roasted, unmalted barley) for stouts and porters.

**WATER:** Strictly known as 'liquor' in the trade, the water used has to suit the type of beer being produced. Certain beer styles demand certain kinds of mineral composition. Classic pale ales, for instance, were developed from the hard, gypsum- and Epsom salt-rich spring water of Burton upon Trent, and many brewers now 'Burtonise' their local supplies to emulate the chemical make up of Burton's natural water.

**HOPS:** Contrary to popular belief, hops – the flowers of the hop bine, a member of the nettle and cannabis family – do not provide the substance of beer: that is the duty of the malt. Hops, instead, act as a seasoning, adding bitterness to the sweet malt and giving beer a refreshing taste balance and some dryness. Hops also bring with them herby, peppery and even citrus flavours and aromas. As with the malt, the brewer will take care to choose his hops. He may adopt classic bittering strains like Fuggles, or opt for the more aromatic and less robust varieties like Goldings. An additional bonus of hops is their preserving quality: they help keep beer free from infection. Hop flowers are supplied to brewers dried and squeezed into sacks called hop pockets. In recent years, the hop pellet – made from ground and compressed hops – has been introduced. Some brewers controversially use hop oils and extracts which can leave an unpleasant bite at the back of the throat.

**YEAST:** Yeast is the agent which turns sweet, malty wort (unfermented beer) into an alcoholic drink. A single-cell fungus, it attacks sugar and transforms it into alcohol and carbon dioxide. Yeast develops its own character from the environment in which it lives and the combinations of malt with which it works, which is why brewers go to great lengths to preserve and protect the yeast strains which have characterised their beers for generations. Ale yeast mostly sits on top of the wort during fermentation and works at a higher temperature than lager yeast, which drops to the bottom. Hence ale is often referred to as a top-fermented beer and lager as bottom-fermented.

**ADJUNCTS:** These extra ingredients replace or complement the standard beer constituents mentioned above. Sugar is the most common, helping brewers gain more fermentable material in their brew, to achieve a higher alcohol content but with less malty body in the finished beer. Other cereals may also be introduced: wheat, maize and rice are familiar in certain beer styles and have some benefits in reducing hazes or in head retention, but are frowned upon by purists.

exodus and ensure there was less friction. In any case, why aren't drinkers in England and Wales trusted to drink later, as they are in Scotland?

**Issues like the tied house.** The right of a small brewery to tie pubs it owns to the beers it produces is fundamental to its survival. Free up all Britain's pubs and a Pandora's box of discounting and heavy advertising will be thrown open, resulting in the breweries with the financial muscle and brand name presence dominating the market. It could mean goodbye to the likes of Fuller's, Adnams, Brains and Timothy Taylor, and all the wonderful beers they brew, with pub after pub stocking only the wares of Scottish Courage and Bass-Carlsberg. As Stephen Cox explains on page 8, the EC is currently reviewing the position of the tied house in the context of the European free market. Its conclusions will be important and CAMRA will be making sure that the EC is aware of the consequences of abolishing the tie.

**Issues like beer choice.** The guest beer law, whilst it has had its successes, continues to be circumvented by the big brewers. Under the law, tenants of national brewers' pubs can sell one cask-conditioned ale from another supplier, a brewer of their own choosing. The nationals, however, encourage tenants to take a beer from their own list of 'approved' guest beers. For an easy life, many publicans agree, leaving the nationals firmly in control of the beer sold in their pubs and resulting in the same familiar guest beers being sold across the country. Pub Groups, with some notable exceptions, also fall down on beer choice. Supply deals are agreed between their head offices and the major breweries, leaving pub managers with only a handful of unexciting national brands to sell. CAMRA wishes to see the guest beer law applied to pub-owning companies, which are, at present, exempt, and is also campaigning to ensure that the definition of a guest beer is preserved as a real ale and not widened to include processed beers, a move which would further boost big brewers producing well-known keg bitters, lagers and stouts, and seriously threaten the small craft ale brewers who have gained from the guest beer law.

**Issues like good trade practice.** CAMRA condemns the use of fake handpumps to serve keg beer or keg cider in an effort to dupe the public into thinking they are traditional brews. The Campaign is also adamant that when you pay for a pint you should get a pint; short-measuring, at today's beer prices, is ripping off beer drinkers to the tune of thousands of pounds each year. It seems that drinkers are often not aware of the price of their pint in any case, as nearly ten per cent of pubs still do not display price lists.

CAMRA has been fighting on issues like these for 26 years. The Campaign for Real Ale was formed in 1971, as a response to the widescale take-over and closure of small brewers by the big boys, who then used the pubs they inherited for the sale of mass-produced, fizzy keg beer. Watneys Red, Courage Tavern and Whitbread Tankard were not just poor substitutes for local beers; they were downright insults to the pub customer. What began as a jokey little drinking club quickly turned into a powerful pressure group, as thousands of pub-users raced to join up and express their support. CAMRA stills needs that support today. Our membership currently stands at just under 50,000, but the more members we have, the more pub-users we can claim to represent and the more clearly our voice is heard. If you agree that action is needed on the issues outlined above, please join us and give us your support.

# MAKING BEER: PART TWO
## THE PROCESS

**THE MASH:** Sieved malt is crushed and fed into a giant receptacle known as a mash tun which already contains hot water (liquor). The mash tun is fitted with a stirring mechanism to turn the mash and to ensure the malt and liquor combine into a thick, sweet, porridgey stew, with all the starches in the malt turning into sugars. The process takes up to two hours. The sweet liquid, now known as wort, is drained off from the bottom of the mash tun, with the husks of the malt acting as a filter. The malt remaining in the tun is then sprayed – or sparged – with hot water by revolving sprinklers in order to extract any remaining sugars which may be in the grain and to wash out the last of the wort. The grain is then deemed to be spent and is sold off for animal fodder.

**IN THE COPPER:** The wort is next run into a large boiler known as a kettle or copper. Hops are added at various stages and the hopped wort boils for up to an hour and a half, absorbing the oils, aromas and flavours of the hops, killing bacteria and separating out unwanted proteins (which haze up the beer). When the brew is ready it is run off through a device called the hop back which collects the spent hops and waste proteins. If hop pellets have been used a centrifuge is employed to separate the gungy bits of hops from the wort.

**FERMENTATION:** Before yeast is added ('pitched' is the trade term), the hot wort is cooled by passing it through heat exchangers on its way to the fermenting vessel. Modern breweries have stainless steel, tall, conical fermenters; traditional producers still have high-sided oak vessels lined with copper. The yeast is pitched and fermentation begins immediately. After a few days, the yeast has worked so vigorously with the sugars in the wort that it has greatly increased its own volume. The excess yeast is scooped off the top and fermentation continues for another few days. When the yeast is tired and begins to clump together, the brewer deems that primary

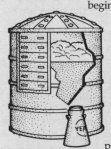

fermentation is complete and runs the beer out into conditioning tanks, where the beer's harsher flavours are rounded off. The beer is then racked into casks and small amounts of a glutinous substance called finings (made from the swim bladder of the sturgeon fish) are added to draw the yeast to the bottom of the cask, so clearing the beer (the finings sink with the yeast, so you don't drink them). Keg beers (including nitrokeg beers) are not fined but are pasteurised and filtered, to kill off and remove any remaining yeast and so prevent further fermentation.

**IN THE CASK:** Cask-conditioned beer (real ale) continues to ferment until it is served in the pub, ensuring a fine, fresh, mature flavour. It has its own natural effervescence and can be served straight from the cask by gravity, or by using a simple suction pump, like a handpump. Its temperature is kept at about 12.5 degrees C/55 degrees F. Keg beer is pressurised, inert and has to be pumped to the bar with gas. It is usually heavily chilled to mask its absence of real flavour. It has a long shelf-life, making it massively profitable. Cask beer, as a living substance, must be consumed within about three days, or it will spoil (see Best Cellars, page 14). But, taste-wise, there is no comparison between keg and cask.

# DON'T LET THE TIE DIE

*STEPHEN COX looks at the European Commission's review of the tied house system and argues that this form of restricted trading must continue.*

AMONGST MANY ISSUES, the European Commission is currently looking at one of the fundamentals of the British pub scene – the tied house system. A European-wide review of tying arrangements is expected to be concluded in 1997, and it could lead to drastic changes. Your local pub, the pint you drink, your favourite brewer – all could be swept away.

That prospect has brought together a curious coalition of pub-owning brewers, tenants and CAMRA. All of these groups can see room for improvement in the tied house system as it stands, but all are united around the belief that the principle of the tie has to stay. The myth is that abolition of the tie will lead to a new era of freedom, when every licensee will be able to choose whichever beer they want from whichever supplier. A Utopia is promised of lower prices and wider choice.

In truth, the market would only be freer on the terms of the largest companies. On the brewing side, there would be a brief and bloody price war, with many casualties as larger companies, consolidating their positions, bought up smaller producers and closed their breweries. We could end up with no more than two companies brewing 90 per cent of our beer. This is precisely what happened in Australia when the tie was abolished. The giant brewers would have a range of tactics to secure their

## The market share of big breweries in European countries without British-style ties

|  | Biggest Brewer | Biggest Two Brewers |
|---|---|---|
| Belgium | 73% | 90% |
| Denmark | 76% | 87% |
| France | 47% | 76% |
| Netherlands | 52% | 65% |
| (UK at present | 30% | 53%) |

Note: the top two brewers in Canada have 92% of the market. In Australia, the biggest two have 90%.

trade – ever higher spends on advertising, discounts, and the use of loans to tie the free trade. Most countries without British-style ties have much more restricted markets, dominated by a very limited number of brewers.

So what, exactly, is a tied house? In short, it is a pub which is rented by a tenant from the owning company, a brewery. As part of his contract, the tenant agrees to buy beer, and often other drinks and services, from the company. That agreement is the 'tie'. As an independent business, the tenant keeps any profit he makes, but he doesn't have the freedom to shop around and his rent is supposedly discounted to compensate for this restriction in choice. However, the extent of the tie is already less than it used to be – national brewers' tenants are only tied for beer, and even then they are entitled to buy a guest cask-conditioned beer from the supplier of their choice.

The tied house system is the backbone of Britain's family brewers. By and large these companies depend on running traditional, tenanted pubs selling cask-conditioned beer – over three-quarters of their production is real ale. Anthony Fuller, of Fuller, Smith and Turner, estimates that half of those companies would leave brewing if the tie went. They would be unable to compete on price with the powerful big breweries and would retreat into pub ownership. The remainder might only survive on a much reduced scale. That amounts to a massive loss of local choice.

Abolishing the tie would deprive these smaller pub-owning brewers of their core business, the pubs they can use to advertise their beers to the world, the pubs which guarantee a regular turnover of their products. Certainly some would survive – probably in strategic alliances with bigger companies and without control over their own destiny.

---

**Other ways in which pubs are run**

**Free house:** A much abused term. In theory, a free pub can buy any product from anyone. Owned and run by the licensee, a free house should be beholden to no-one. In practice, many are tied to big breweries in return for financial loans used to purchase or upgrade the property. Some pubs which claim to be free houses are owned by pub chains who use the term in a cynical marketing exercise.

**Managed pub:** Here the owning company simply puts an employee in to run the place. He is paid a salary – just as the manager of your local Boots is paid by Boots to run the shop. The manager is told what to sell and can only choose beers from a list provided by the company.

**Leased pub:** A long lease is like a tenancy but lasts for ten or 20 years rather than the standard three. It involves the payment of a much higher rent and shifts more of the responsibility for matters such as repairs onto the lessee.

---

## —— PUB GROUPS ——

The abolition of the tied tenancy would not end the dominance of large pub-owning companies. Chains of managed pubs would remain, run directly by company HQ. These chains would have massive buying power and would thrive in the new market, negotiating the best deal with the biggest companies. Whether customers used to individuality and local choice would benefit is another matter. You only have to consult the Pub Groups section of this book to discover how much beer choice some pub chains offer their licensees.

All in all 28,000 pubs are run as tenancies of one sort or another. If the tie went then those pubs would see their rents raised still further, as brewers looked to compensate for what they lost in tied beer sales. Some might end up managed; some might be sold to individuals. Some might be considered unviable and close, becoming sites for property development. In short, the abolition of the tie threatens more domination by national brands, fewer pubs, less choice and higher prices.

# ── Face The Facts ──

Is all this a realistic threat? Would the Commission scrap the pub tie? Many concerned parties feel that Britain's unique pub is just not understood. On the Continent matters are very different – more beer is consumed in bottles than on draught, and bars account for a lower proportion of sales than in Britain. Brewery ownership of pubs is rare – more bars are tied by loans or distribution agreements, and these often differ significantly from their British equivalents. In recent months, Brussels has seen brewers, tenants, and CAMRA delegations explaining their case to the Commission. It is a strong case, and we think the Commission is listening. Consider the facts:

Britain's beer market is not particularly closed to competition. We import a higher proportion of our beer than any of the other great beer drinking nations of Europe – there are well over 200 different imported beers from over 40 countries, possibly the highest total in Europe. Brewery-owned pubs only account for a quarter of all beer sales. The pubs of brewers and other pub retailers put together account for only around a third of beer sales.

British pubs offer the widest choice of draught beers in Europe and the second widest choice of bottled beers. In addition, British pub prices are amongst the lowest in Europe when our ludicrous levels of beer tax are taken into account.

Support for the principle of the tie is not saying that the industry is perfect. Of course there are problems with particular companies and of course the tie is not fair to everyone all the time. Many tenants feel that the long leases introduced in recent years are so onerous that they cannot be justified as fair to the tenant. It's a point worth making because European law only permits a tie if both sides benefit. Tenants' organisations are stressing this point and proposing changes to improve their lot, in particular by arguing for new systems of adjudication to settle what is a genuinely fair rent. Such changes might temper the hunger for rent of the larger companies and ensure that leased pubs aren't drained of their lifeblood.

Smaller, pub-less brewers argue, quite fairly, that they start at a disadvantage compared with the long-established brewer which owns pubs. Managed pubs, tied pubs and loans between big breweries and other pubs tie up two-thirds of the on-trade, and leave the minnows battling for the rest. It's not even a fair fight for that last remaining third, they say. But CAMRA does not believe that this is sufficient reason for scrapping the tied house system. The guest beer law, introduced in 1990, has widened choice and helped these smaller brewers win new markets. We want the guest beer safeguarded and its application extended to non-brewing pub companies, who are perversely exempt, so that the small brewers are given a further boost. Who knows, some of the smaller brewers may well get into the pub-owning business themselves.

We do not have long to wait for the European Commission's verdict. If the arguments are listened to we should soon hear that the future of Britain's regional and smaller breweries has been safeguarded and that the tenant will remain pivotal to the British brewing industry. We might even see versions of the British law applied in other EC countries and that can only extend the choice of beers on the Continent.

*Stephen Cox is CAMRA's Campaigns Manager.*

# ROSY WITH CIDER

*Back in 1978 the* Good Beer Guide *began carrying information about traditional cider, as the need to protect the cider industry – suffering the same problems as the brewing world – was realised. Nineteen years later, things are looking up, as TED BRUNING explains.*

HAVING, more on faith than evidence, been trumpeting a real cider revival for two years now, I'm relieved to find that it's actually happening. More and more people are making real cider, many of them fruit-growers or winemakers looking for a sideline and lured by a 7,000-litre duty-exempt annual allowance. There's more and more media interest: in the weeks before the *Good Beer Guide* went to press *The Independent* and the *Daily Mail* both gave the topic some coverage, and Julian Temperley of Burrow Hill Cider in Somerset was on TV twice.

More and more supermarkets are stocking something like an authentic cider: Sainsbury takes the honours with a specially-commissioned range from Weston's of Much Marcle – carbonated, alas, but at least made mainly of apples. And more and more pubs are stocking real ciders: *The CAMRA Guide to Real Cider*, published in autumn 1996, lists 2,500 real cider pubs – 700 more than appeared in the *Good Cider Guide* six years ago.

The people who seem not to have caught on are the brewers, especially regionals. Ale house chains – Wetherspoons, Tap & Spile, and Whitbread's Hogshead – are in the van of the real cider revival: how long before the stuffy old regionals catch up?

## ——— CORE ISSUES ———

So what is real cider? Let's start with what it isn't. It isn't mass-produced from apple concentrate, fermented to 12 per cent alcohol with additional sugar, watered down by half or more, filtered, pasteurised, and artificially carbonated to suit palates too immature even for British lager. It isn't Woodpecker or Dry Blackthorn or Olde English. It isn't Scrumpy Jack or Taunton Cidermaster. It most certainly isn't Diamond White or K.

Real cider is, essentially, apple wine, and what Bulmers, Gaymer's and Taunton tried to do in the 1950s was reinvent it as cheaper, stronger lager. To understand why commercial cider is, by and large, so bloody awful, take half a pint of cheap Liebfraumilch, water it down to half its starting strength, and fizz it up in the kids' Sodastream. What cider should be is just the freshly pressed juice of apples – either special cider varieties or, in the East, ordinary cookers and eaters – fermented either with its own natural yeast or a cultured wine yeast if necessary, and matured. It's normally fairly dry, since the natural sugars are easily accessible to the yeast; it's usually still, unless it has been dosed with additional yeast either in a champagne-type bottle or, less often, in the cask; and it tends to be stronger than the average beer but weaker than table wine, in the

5.5–8.5 per cent alcohol range. It's also radically different from anything you've ever tasted – certainly, nothing from Bulmers or Taunton will prepare you for the variety of treats in store. (And incidentally: *don't* get taken in by Bulmers Scrumpy Jack or Taunton Cidermaster served, apparently, by handpump. These are keg ciders, artificially carbonated, and the 'handpump' is a fancy keg tap. CAMRA campaigns uncompromisingly against this cheap deception, and pubs which serve keg beers or ciders by fake handpump are barred from a listing in this book.)

OVER 2000 SPECIALIST PUBS

GUIDE TO
**REAL CIDER**

TED BRUNING   CAMRA

Real ciders vary as dramatically in taste as wines, and for the same reasons: each apple variety has its own character, which is in turn affected by the *terroir* and the method of cultivation. Throw in the variables of weather, blend, and fermentation technique and you end up with a huge range of possibilities: rich, musky Heck's Kingston Black; dry, tannic Dunkerton's Breakwell Seedling; shockingly spicy Perry's Redstreak; floral, aromatic James White; perfumy, subtle Franklin's. And that's before you've tried perry, the drink fermented from the juice of pears!

## —— PRESERVING A TRADITION ——

Given the fantastic riches of Britain's cidermaking heritage and the inventiveness and vitality of the revivalists, it's a cause for deep shame that the cider tradition has become so submerged. Real cider has been written off as a rustic curio, available only in narrowly-defined regions and demanded only by tourists and maniacal farmworkers. All that has been on sale in the rest of the country is a mass-produced imitation so debased as to be unrecognisable.

It was up to CAMRA to reintroduce the drinking public to real cider and exhume the reputation of a fine drink which once delighted monarchs and labourers alike. CAMRA saw that real cider was no less a part of the nation's pub heritage for being largely regional, that it was under threat, and that as no-one else was in a position to defend it, CAMRA would. It was a decision which has been spectacularly successful: cider bars at beer festivals have introduced the genuine article to members of the public in droves; almost everyone who has tasted it has been converted; and for the alehouse chains stocking real ciders has proved a powerful enhancement of their 'authentic' image. But CAMRA acted in the nick of time. Every tidal wave that has lashed the shores of the brewing industry has also hit cider, with even more dramatic effects.

12

For years we had the Big Three – Bulmers, Taunton and Gaymer's – a small second division headed by Weston's, Inch's and Merrydown, and a substratum of tiny local companies, many of them farmers turning out a few hundred gallons a year as an insignificant descant to their main businesses. Then came the Monopolies Commission enquiry of the late 1980s, which included a clause (largely ignored at the time but highly significant in the long run) freeing national brewery tenants from the cider tie. Bulmers, the only independent of the Big Three, alone had the strength to survive the end of the tie. Gaymer's was sold by owner Allied Breweries to its management, who before long had to sell to drinks distribution giant Matthew Clark at a loss. The same fate befell Taunton, owned by a consortium of brewers including Bass and Courage, which was also sold to its own management, who also couldn't cope and who also sold out to Matthew Clark at a loss.

The cider industry continues to hold up a mirror to the brewing industry's closures and mergers. In 1995, Matthew Clark closed the Gaymer factory at Attleborough near Norwich, ending at the stroke of an accountant's pen an eight-century-old tradition of volume cidermaking in East Anglia. Then, early in 1996, Bulmers took over Inch's, the largest of the independents with a seven per cent market share and debts of nearly £5 million. If Bulmers hadn't bought it – thus securing over 50 per cent of the national cider market to Matthew Clark Taunton's 41 per cent – Inch's would have been liquidated.

These manoeuvres leave the second division of cidermakers smaller than ever: Merrydown has two per cent of the market but makes no traditional cider; Weston's is making inroads on the supermarket trade, but this has notoriously low margins; Thatcher's, Broadoak, and Biddenden are only gradually becoming more widely distributed.

What is really needed to secure a future for traditional cidermakers, both medium-sized and small, is recognition from the retail trade. Regional brewers must acknowledge that real cider is a product with every bit as much quality, authenticity and heritage as real ale, and allow their tenants to stock superior products from small makers. National brewery tenants and lessees must exploit the fact that they are no longer tied on ciders and are free to offer a competitive range of traditional products which have a proven public appeal. Pub operating companies must take a leaf out of the JD Wetherspoon book and stock real ciders. Supermarkets and off-licence chains must realise that bottled cider does not stop at two-litre PETs of fizzy sugar-water. And hoteliers and restaurateurs must be persuaded that a selection of fine ciders can enhance even the most distinguished wine list.

## —— PIP! PIP! ——

Good-quality traditional cider is a central part of Britain's gastronomic heritage, one of our great contributions to the world of food and drink. But its appeal for the support of drinkers and retailers is not based on ideology, but on the fact that it tastes ... great!

*Ted Bruning, assistant editor of CAMRA's monthly newspaper,* What's Brewing, *is author of* The CAMRA Guide to Real Cider, *published by CAMRA Books at £7.99.*

# BEST CELLARS
## (HANDS OFF REAL ALE!)

*Quantity or quality? As pubs extend their choice of real ales, the focus is more than ever on the quality of the beer on sale. ROGER PROTZ looks at how brewers are striving to ensure that good beer leaving the brewery is still good beer when it reaches the glass – whatever the weather.*

IN A PERFECT WORLD, the only enemy of good beer is the human hand. A good publican will take every possible measure to ensure his beer is kept in a spotless, cool cellar. He will clean his 'lines' – the plastic tubes that link cask to bar – so that no microbes lurk to infect the precious fluid, and he will regularly wash all the moving parts of the simple suction-pump beer engine. And then you stick your great warm mitt around the glass and the temperature of the beer soars.

In the long, torrid summer of 1995, warm beer led thousands of drinkers away from real ale and over to nitrokeg. Sales of cask-conditioned ale fell by between seven and ten per cent. Sales of Draught Bass, far and away the country's biggest selling premium real ale, fell by a staggering 22 per cent as Bass put all its considerable weight behind its soar away nitro brand, Caffrey's.

As I write this one year later, with the temperature touching 30 degrees Celsius, it is too early to say whether nitrokeg will continue to cut a swathe through sales of real ale. But brewers who are as devoted to the quality of their cask beers as much as profit graphs are leaving nothing to chance. Strenuous efforts are being made by producers big and small to make sure the pint delivered to your glass is cool, tasty and refreshing and that only the drinker's hand can be blamed if things go wrong.

Pub tenants, a doughty but conservative breed, are being cajoled into dumping decades of received wisdom about real ale and are being instilled with the need to keep their cellars cool, their lines clean and their casks free from possible infection.

It is likely that within a year or two the fad for nitrokeg will have faded. But the damage to cask ale could be incalculable unless steps are taken now to ensure consistent quality. And consistency means rejecting myths and legends about real ale, what the quality control managers at Marston's of Burton upon Trent call the 'we've always done it that way' mentality among publicans, which includes assurances to bemused customers that there's nothing wrong with a pint of warm, cloudy beer.

> **Nitrokeg**
> Nitrokeg is a filtered and pasteurised beer that is a development from canned 'widget' beer. It is served by a mix of nitrogen and carbon dioxide at a low temperature, between 6–8C/42–46F. The smooth, creamy quality of nitrogenised beer masks most of the aromas and flavours of ale, especially hop character. The beer is cold but characterless.

## —— IN THE ENGINE ROOM ——

Few users of the *Good Beer Guide* get the chance to see a pub cellar. It is the engine room of the pub and it is where everything can go wrong. Cask-conditioned ale is a delicate drink that needs careful nurturing. It is a living product, with a secondary fermentation in the cask that ensures ripe aromas and flavours and a sparkle created as yeast turns remaining brewing sugars into alcohol and carbon dioxide. In order to control the level of carbonation, a cask is vented through an opening on the top – the shive – using soft and hard wooden pegs called spiles. Once a cask has been vented and is open to the atmosphere it should be served within three days, before oxidation sets in. This is where many pubs fall down. In attempting to stock too many real ales than turnover justifies, the three-day rule is too often breached, leaving drinkers with a selection box of beers well past their best instead of a sensible two or three well-kept ales.

Cellars must be clean, the floors scrubbed and walls and ceilings whitewashed. Some deep cellars remain cool whatever the outside temperature: the sandstone caves deep beneath England's oldest pub, the Trip to Jerusalem in Nottingham, for example, are a constant ten degrees C even if the city is in the grip of a tropical heatwave. But most cellars are nearer the surface and can soak up heat from the bars and kitchens above. All sensible brewers and free trade publicans are now installing cellar coolers, usually in the form of cold-air blowers. The recommended cellar temperature for cask ale is 12.5C or 55F – old man Fahrenheit is still popular in the pub trade – though many breweries now suggest a temperature range to allow for high summer and low winter variations. Marston's, for example, suggests a range of 11.5–14C/53–57F.

> **Gravity Dispense**
> Even cask-conditioned ale served straight from the cask by gravity should be cool. Whitbread's Hogshead chain of pubs, for instance, always have four or more ales behind the bar in a specially-designed cabinet. The beer is kept at the correct temperature by powerful fans which keep a constant flow of cold air circulating around the casks.

At McMullen of Hertford, production director Tony Skipper is a firm believer in 12.5C/55F. He should be listened to with considerable respect. He not only brews superb beer but was named *Head Brewer of the Year* in 1995 in a poll of members of the British Guild of Beer Writers and his Country Bitter came first in its class in the 1996 Brewing Industry International Awards. 'Fifty-five degrees Fahrenheit is right for draught beer,' Mr Skipper says. 'Below that, beer becomes thin and loses its complexities of flavour.'

## —— ON TO THE BAR ——

It is comparatively easy to maintain a cellar at 12.5/55 degrees. But as the beer is drawn through the lines and up to the bar it will warm up during the journey. McMullen has taken several steps to ensure the beer stays cool as it snakes its way along walls and up to the bar. 'Snakes' is a useful term, for the beer is helped by a curious device known as a python. A python looks more like a giant black German sausage than a reptile.

Inside the thick casing of foam are the beer lines from several casks and in the centre is another, wider line which contains cold water driven from the cellar by a pump known as the ale driver. The python was developed to keep keg beers and lagers cold as they rose from cellar to bar. It has now been adapted to come to the aid of cask ale, with water kept at a higher temperature than the 6.5/43 degrees used for keg. If the water is too cold, the beer will be equally frigid.

McMullen, in common with many other breweries, now uses narrow-bore piping and quarter-pint beer engines to serve cask ale. With wider pipes and half-pint engines, several pints of beer stayed in the lines between pub sessions. The amount of beer in line has been halved but it is absolutely essential that it is pulled off and thrown away at opening time to avoid handing the first few customers alcoholic Ovaltine.

## —— CHILLING OUT ——

Hot summers have led to a debate about just how low the temperature of cask beer can be taken. Below 11/52 degrees, unfiltered draught beer will develop what is called a chill haze, as proteins in the malt make the liquid cloudy. This can be avoided by using low nitrogen malts but the end result is a beer in which the natural, rounded flavours of biscuity malt and tangy, citric hops are masked by the chill. I drank Marston's Pedigree at several temperatures as part of the research for this article and found that this subtle and complex ale lost some of its sublime character if served too cold.

At the turn of the 20th century the recommended cellar temperature for cask ale was 65 degrees F (17.5C). It was pulled through glass or lead pipes and left to stand for hours in lead beer engines. The beer was not only warm but dangerous. Things have changed. Modern technology and cooling systems have been harnessed to deliver beer that is refreshing and quenching yet which still retains the aromas and flavours that make cask-conditioned ale the wonder of the world of brewing. If the brewers and the publicans have done their job, only the customer, with his hot palms, can spoil it.

The best advice is: keep your hands off. If you drink from a straight glass or 'sleeve', leave it on the bar or table untouched when you're not actually supping and hold it close to the top when you pick it up. There's a lot to be said for the 'jug' – the glass with a handle, developed specifically to keep hot, sweaty hands out of contact with the beer. But what do most drinkers do when confronted with a jug? Why, they turn the handle away from them and hold the glass round the middle. And then complain about warm beer.

### Cellarmanship

CAMRA has produced a new comprehensive guide to caring for cask beer. *Cellarmanship* is an invaluable manual for all publicans and brewers and will soon be available from good bookshops or direct from CAMRA, 230 Hatfield Road, St Albans, Hertfordshire AL1 4LW. Further information and credit card orders on (01727) 867201. Discounts will be available for CAMRA members.

*Roger Protz edits CAMRA's national newspaper,* What's Brewing, *and is author of numerous books on beer, including* The Ultimate Encyclopedia of Beer *and* The Ale Trail.

# HOW TO KEEP AND SERVE REAL ALE

## DO

● Keep casks at the correct temperature (53-55° F) whenever possible

● Avoid unnecessary movement of casks between delivery and venting

● Wedge casks securely and tap in good time – 24 to 48 hours before serving

● Ensure that the beer has cleared by checking at the tap before attempting to serve it

● Clean beer lines at least once a week and keep taps and/or extractor rods sterile

## DON'T

● Return beer to a cask; it is likely to turn good beer 'off'

● Tilt casks too steeply, you may actually get less saleable beer as a result

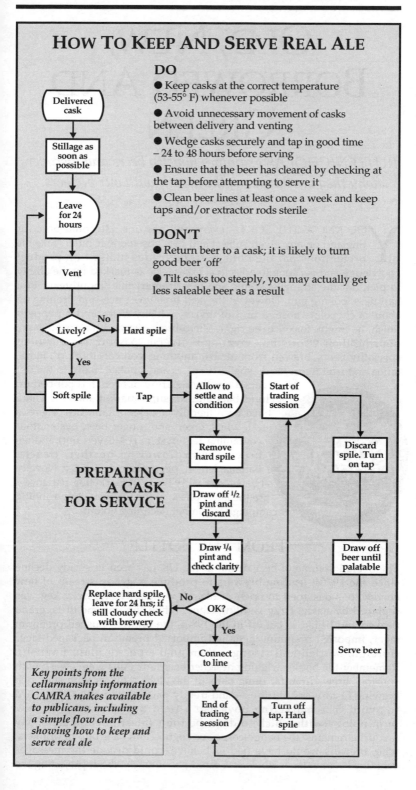

**PREPARING A CASK FOR SERVICE**

*Key points from the cellarmanship information CAMRA makes available to publicans, including a simple flow chart showing how to keep and serve real ale*

# OLD, NEW, BORROWED AND GREEN

*RUTH NICHOLAS examines novelty beers and discovers why they are flavour of the month with our brewers.*

YOU KNOW THE SORT – every pub has one. He could bore for England on any given subject and his chosen one is bitter. Like his pretentious pal the wine buff, he prides himself on product knowledge and is prone to adjectival excess. He is marked by the ability to pick out the strangest scents and most remarkable 'mouthfeels' in a harmless looking pint. However, the next time you catch him droning on about a chocolate nose, a hint of myrrh, whisky notes and a peppery finish, he might, for once, be right. Micro-breweries and majors alike are pouring their efforts into creating a diverse, nay bizarre, range of speciality beers, brewed from almost anything you can think of. Flora, fauna and fruit figure, as do shellfish, spices and smoked malts. In the last two years a mystifying array of beers has popped up behind bars and on supermarket shelves. There have been literally dozens of launches. There is red, white, green and ginger beer, oyster stout containing real oysters (I kid you not) and ale brewed with flowering heather, treacle, banana, lemon, pepper and coriander. Novelty beers – speciality beers in marketing parlance – are the latest phase of the brewers' long-running campaign to combat declining volume.

## —— FROM THE BOTTLE ——

The overall volume of beer drunk in the UK has been in steady decline since the 1970s, leading brewers to produce a steady stream of new concoctions designed to open drinkers' pockets. Nasty, fizzy keg was replaced by nasty, fizzy swilling-lager. When the volume of lagerade peaked and began to tail off in the 1980s, the brewers pushed premium lager, imported premium lager and imported premium packaged lager (foreign, bottled and stronger than gnat's pee in plain English). Remember the bottle-swigging designer beer fad? Pubs were awash with spurious brews from far flung parts of the globe – places with such rich brewing history as Mauritius – and trendy names and bottles were hard to avoid. The marketing boys had a field day dreaming up new terminology with which to describe their latest phenomenon. My favourite remains 'the badge-conscious cognoscenti', a group of drinkers, who, brewers would have had us believe, could decode the messages contained within lager labels and cared passionately about projecting the right image through what they were drinking.

The last ten years have seen no- and low-alcohol beer; 'lite', 'dry' and 'ice' lager; and widget and cream ale. Each has been hailed as the holy grail by a PR machine that grinds out predictable hyperbole. 'Revolution' is ever a popular word.

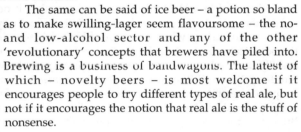

Take dry beer. Although it sounded like a contradiction in terms, it was hailed as the next really big thing: the pils of the 1990s. Invented by Japanese brewing giant Asahi in 1987, it took its home market by storm (a 25 per cent share within three years) and made reasonable inroads into the world's biggest market, the US. By 1990 there were 36 brands on sale in 11 countries, all derived from a brewing process that produced a strong lager with no aftertaste. The idea was based on getting lathered without getting halitosis, a matter of great concern for Japanese office workers, apparently. British brewers imported the concept lock, stock and liver, launched 'dry' versions of existing brands and threw money at marketing them. They successfully created a blip in the UK market that lasted all of about five minutes.

The same can be said of ice beer – a potion so bland as to make swilling-lager seem flavoursome – the no- and low-alcohol sector and any of the other 'revolutionary' concepts that brewers have piled into. Brewing is a business of bandwagons. The latest of which – novelty beers – is most welcome if it encourages people to try different types of real ale, but not if it encourages the notion that real ale is the stuff of nonsense.

## —— SPECIAL EDITIONS ——

Whitbread has been the most active brewer by far and the company believes it is doing a fine job promoting different brewing styles to the public in general and women in particular. These are not novelty beers, it protests, but a serious attempt to enliven the market and to demonstrate the depth of variety and range of techniques possible in traditional British beer. 'We get a hell of a lot of positive feedback,' says Colin Westcott-Pitt who is assistant brand manager of ales. 'We are doing something a bit different that is creating real interest and involvement.'

Whitbread launched its programme of limited edition, speciality ales three years ago with Ryman's Reserve, produced by British winemaker Hugh Ryman using Czech Saaz hops. Other beers have included Fuggles Chocolate Mild (containing chocolate essence), Scarlet Lady (based on juniper berries), Christmas Pudding Old Ale (including coriander, nutmeg, mace and cinnamon),

Colonel Pepper's Lemon Ale (which sold 750,000 pints in six weeks and featured both lemon and pepper) and Myrrhy Christmas Ale (gold and frankincense were probably too expensive). The brews are available in 2,500 pubs nationally but only for six weeks, unless they prove too popular to be missed. The gloriously hoppy Fuggles Imperial IPA, for instance, now has a permanent place in Whitbread's repertoire. So far, Whitbread is the only major to get seriously involved with speciality ales, but, given its competitors' lemming-like propensity to follow suit, it cannot be long before they do. In the meantime, regionals and micro-breweries are racing to market.

## ——— BLASTS FROM THE PAST ———

Although they are the latest thing, novelty beers aren't – er – new. Before the introduction of hops by the Dutch in the 1500s, beer was flavoured with all manner of herbs and spices. For instance, the recipe for coriander beer dates back to the mid-18th century and traces of heather ale have been identified in a Neolithic shard, which makes it nearly 4,000 years old. Nethergate claims to have been the first modern day UK brewery to use such flavourings when it produced Umbel Magna in 1993. Umbel is the botanical term to describe the inflorescence produced by the family *umbelliferae* of which coriander is a member, says its brewer Ian Hornsey. Similarly Bruce Williams, who spent six years refining an old family recipe for heather ale, sells his brew under the name Fraoch, the Gaelic word for heather. Danish master brewer Stig Andersen, owner of Bunces Brewery, produces Stig Swig flavoured with sweet gale, which he claims was a favourite ingredient of the Vikings, and Sign of Spring, a light green ale, which is a homage to a traditional Danish Whitsun beer.

However, not all the brews have a history. Although the Belgians are adept at producing various fruit beers, Blackmoor Brewery's Banana Madness is simply the result of a slow Sunday afternoon joke. 'I was looking for something new to brew with and I said to myself, as a joke, I wonder if it could be done with bananas,' explains head brewer Graeme Marsh, who claims that the result has attracted lager drinkers and women, which is good, but sounds a warning note for the market. 'Fruit beers that taint the cellar lines they are put through do more harm than good. We have seen cases where the publican has flushed out the line half a dozen times and not been able to get rid of the taste of strawberries,' he says.

At the daft end of the market there are the likes of Desperados, which features a blend of citrus and tequila extracts and – not surprisingly – an 'unbeery' taste, Kentucky Black bourbon beer, and chili beer, which features a chili pepper in every bottle. The less said about that the better.

*Ruth Nicholas, a freelance journalist, specialises in marketing issues.*

# PUBS TO SAVE
## CAMRA'S NATIONAL INVENTORY

*DAVE GAMSTON and JOHN CLARKE introduce the Campaign's list of starred pubs, historic gems which must be preserved.*

T HE 1997 *Good Beer Guide* pub entries feature, for the first time, a symbol for heritage pub interiors. The new symbol, a star, flags up pubs with interiors of outstanding historical interest which have merited a place on CAMRA's National Inventory.

The sole concern of the Inventory is with the internal physical fabric of pubs, not their beer, yet dozens of Inventory pubs are main entries in this year's *Good Beer Guide* because they also serve good cask-conditioned ale. A double blessing indeed! We hope this added information about pubs will not only convey an important campaigning message but will also please the many readers whose enjoyment of traditional beers and traditional pubs goes hand in hand.

What, then, is CAMRA's National Inventory and what is its importance?

The defence of Britain's traditional pubs has always been one of CAMRA's declared concerns. When, in the 1980s, the Campaign set up its national Pub Preservation Group, the forerunner of today's CAMRA Pubs Group, it was already apparent that the future survival of the country's pub heritage, a subject neglected by mainstream preservationists, was very seriously at risk. Ignorance and philistinism were rife among pub owners and operators, there was widespread public apathy, and such official safeguards as existed, in licensing and town planning, seemed largely indifferent to valuable pub interiors or were weakly applied. In particular, the main statutory machinery for protecting historic buildings – listing and listed building control – put very little emphasis on the insides of buildings and showed scant interest in pubs anyway. It was small wonder that Britain's pub heritage had suffered the most terrible depletion in recent decades, mainly through damaging alteration to pub interiors.

## —— VANDALISM ——

Though never denying that pubs need to survive in a real world of commercial pressures, CAMRA also saw that these pressures too often amounted to short-sighted gimmickry or change-for-change's sake which was going unchallenged. No pub, it seemed, was safe. Time and again valuable pubs were being seriously compromised with walls and interior fittings ripped out, sometimes replaced with a reproduction 'historic' interior. Time and again someone's lip-service to pub preservation would leave token fragments, sometimes even an entire room, sitting incongruously amidst the plastic tat or bland open spaces that typify the modern pubfitter's repertoire. Crucially, as CAMRA saw it, there was no evidence of a shared vision – between the different pub owners and operators and the different regulatory authorities – about which pubs should be spared from change. There was simply no guiding philosophy or public statement of any kind about national pub preservation priorities. Even pubs whose interiors cried out to be treated as sacrosanct and recognised as national treasures (no less than many of our historic churches and stately homes) were being left to chance in an uncertain world of market forces and under a wide variety of masters.

The Government's 1989 Beer Supply Orders brought the crisis into urgent focus. The Orders (which followed a major review of the brewing industry by the Monopolies and Mergers Commission) presaged a massive upheaval in the ownership of pubs, including large-scale disposals by the national brewers, and were the spur for CAMRA's Pubs Group to start compiling its own emergency shortlist of the country's most precious pub interiors. This is how the National Inventory began – as an emergency first step towards a structured statement of Britain's pub preservation priorities. The aim was to try to ensure that in the changed world after 1992 (the deadline for implementation of the Beer Orders) there would be no excuses for ignorance among the new players about which are our finest and rarest pub interiors. The same pubs would hopefully be accorded proper respect and given the highest chance to survive intact. Five years on the aim remains the same.

## —— THE FIRST DIVISION ——

As an emergency initiative and first step, all effort was concentrated on identifying the *very best* of the pub heritage – the 'first division', the highest ground of national pub preservation priorities. But it was always strongly in Pubs Group's mind that, by staking out the highest ground first, we would be setting the scene for more detailed stocktaking at regional and local levels. At the end of the day, the whole purpose was to heighten the survival chances of *all* historically-important pubs.

Compilation of the Inventory started in 1991 and with keynote words like 'historic gem and 'national outrage', the search was on for pub interiors of such outstanding importance that their loss or despoliation ought (in an enlightened world!) to provoke a national outcry. The emphasis was on intact survival of historic plan-form and fittings, and it was hoped that complete examples would be found of all pub types – from primitive beerhouses to ornate gin palaces – to reflect the full diversity of the British pub tradition. This hope has been reasonably fulfilled in the emerging listings but with some important qualifications, reflecting present-day realities. For one thing, it was at first imagined that maybe 500 pubs with complete historic interiors would still be found throughout the UK, but less than half that number has come to light so far. For another, some historic pub types have been more susceptible than others to loss or internal change and have become extremely hard to find in intact form.

Surprisingly, perhaps, some of the great Victorian and Edwardian 'gin palaces' of the big cities, with their extravaganzas of decorative tiling, glasswork and mahogany fittings, have been durable survivors and the Inventory has been able to include such famous names as The Bartons Arms, Birmingham, The Crown Liquor Saloon, Belfast, The Princess Louise, London and The Philharmonic, Liverpool – veritable 'cathedrals' among historic pubs. At the opposite end of the scale, in terms both of

*No serious listing of Britain's most important pubs could possibly overlook the Black Friar, London, with its unique and beautifully-preserved Art Nouveau interior of 1905.*

style and survival, are the plain rural beerhouses – time warp establishments which are probably the most 'threatened' species' of our pubs. Typically consisting of just one plain room, sometimes with a bar counter, sometimes without, they are throwbacks to another age but continue to provide a living and way of life for their, often elderly, licensees. Though lacking architectural refinement (and therefore not readily qualifying for the protection of statutory listing), they are, in many ways, the most precious of our pubs because so few of them now remain. Research for the Inventory suggests that perhaps only a dozen or so such establishments may be left in Britain today and a strong point is made of including all known examples in the list.

Also rare are truly unspoilt pub interiors from the period between the wars. Out of step with post-war tastes, and (again) without the protection of statutory listing, they have suffered the pub world's equivalent of ethnic cleansing. Moreover, the very size of the great 'roadhouses' of the city suburbs has made them ideal candidates for internal gutting into themed eateries or nightspots. Against such odds, the survival of original 1920s and 1930s interiors, like those at The Nursery, Stockport and The Three Horseshoes, Boroughbridge, seems increasingly remarkable.

## —— CLOSE CONSULTATION ——

In compiling the National Inventory, Pubs Group was not only able to call on a wealth of knowledge within CAMRA itself but was deliberately outward-looking in its task and the project became a springboard for closer consultation with key statutory and amenity bodies. There was input from all the main national amenity societies and close interest from English Heritage, the Government agency for the historic environment in England

23

(who produced a welcome breakthrough of their own in 1994 with the publication of new statutory listing guidelines for pubs: *Pubs: Understanding Listing*). A consultation draft of the Inventory was sent out three years ago to all local planning authorities and magistrates' offices in the UK and to a range of other parties with a professional interest in conservation. The draft also went to brewers, major pub operators and the pub licensees themselves, most of whom would be hearing about their pub's national significance for the very first time.

*Continuous stewardship through several generations of the same family has been a main reason for the survival, against the odds, of a number of Britain's most remarkable old pubs, such as The Fleece, Bretforton, Worcestershire, whose interior and fittings are still much as they were in the last century.*

Handling feedback from all the consultations and assessing a growing portfolio of recommended pubs has been a major task for CAMRA's small team of volunteer surveyors, drawn mainly, but not entirely, from Pubs Group. Many worthwhile pubs have been flagged up for our attention but relatively few of them have been found, on inspection, to meet our (admittedly demanding) criteria for national ranking. As for the criteria themselves, liaison with local authority planners has led us to consider if these can be more precisely defined and whether some form of 'grading' system might be helpful in the longer term. That such ideas are still at the planning stage reflects that the Inventory itself is seen as an 'organic' document which we expect to keep under constant review and update in the light of comments received and further research. Meanwhile, CAMRA regions are being encouraged to draw up more comprehensive local inventories of pub interiors which may be less intact than those on the national select list but have much of historic merit about them. The National Inventory, as it stands today, is seen as the foundation and precursor of a much larger document. In time we hope to see it grow into a complete inventory of every piece of our surviving pub heritage.

*The National Inventory, as presently constituted, is reproduced in full on the following pages. It is put forward by CAMRA as an evolving concept, open to refinement, and comment on the selections so far is warmly welcomed. Also welcome is any new information on intact or near-intact pub interiors which could be considered for the national selection or for the next tier of regional and local inventories. Please write to: Pubs Group, CAMRA, 230 Hatfield Road, St Albans, Hertfordshire AL1 4LW.*

# THE CAMRA
# NATIONAL INVENTORY

## ENGLAND

**BEDFORDSHIRE**
**Broom:** Cock

**BERKSHIRE**
**Aldworth:** Bell

**CHESHIRE**
**Alpraham:** Travellers Rest
**Gawsworth:**
Harrington Arms
**Macclesfield:** Castle
**Stockton Heath:** Red Lion
**Wheelock:** Commercial

**CORNWALL**
**Falmouth:** Seven Stars

**CUMBRIA**
**Broughton Mills:**
Blacksmiths Arms
**Kendal:** Ring O'Bells

**DERBYSHIRE**
**Brassington:** Gate Inn
**Kirk Ireton:** Barley Mow
**Wardlow Mires:**
Three Stags Heads

**DEVON**
**Drewsteignton:**
Drewe Arms
**Luppitt:** Luppitt Inn
**Topsham:** Bridge
**Widecombe-in-the-Moor:**
Rugglestone Inn

**DORSET**
**Worth Matravers:**
Square & Compass

**DURHAM**
**Durham City:**
Shakespeare, Victoria

**GLOUCESTERSHIRE**
**& BRISTOL**
**Ampney St Peter:**
Red Lion
**Bristol:** Kings Head,
Richmond Springs
**Cheltenham:** Bath Tavern
**Duntisbourne Abbots:**
Five Mile House

**Purton:** Berkeley Hunt Inn
**Willsbridge:** Queens Head

**HAMPSHIRE**
**Steep:** Harrow

**HEREFORDSHIRE**
**Kington:** Olde Tavern
**Leintwardine:** Sun Inn
**Risbury:** Hop Pole

**KENT**
**Snargate:** Red Lion

**LANCASHIRE**
**Brierfield:**
Waggon & Horses
**Great Harwood:** Victoria
**Overton:** Ship Hotel
**Preston:** Black Horse

**GREATER LONDON**
**EC1 Hatton Garden:**
Olde Mitre
**EC4 Blackfriars:**
Black Friar
**WC1 Holborn:**
Cittie of York,
Princess Louise
**WC2 Covent Garden:**
Lamb & Flag, Salisbury
**E1 Stepney:** Hollands
**E14 Poplar:** Grapes
**N2 East Finchley:**
Old White Lion
**N4 Finsbury Park:**
Salisbury
**N6 Highgate:** Flask
**N8 Hornsey:**
Great Northern Railway
**NW3 Hampstead:**
Holly Bush
**NW6 Kilburn:** Black Lion
**NW8 St John's Wood:**
Crockers
**SE1 Southwark:**
George Inn
**SE10 Greenwich:**
Richard I
**SE21 Dulwich:**
Crown & Greyhound
**SE22 Beckenham:**
Jolly Woodman
**Croydon:** Dog & Bull
**SW1 Belgravia:** Antelope,

Nag's Head, Paxton's Head
**SW1 St James's:** Red Lion
**SW18 Wandsworth:**
Spread Eagle
**Kingston upon Thames:**
Druid's Head
**W1 Marylebone:**
Barley Mow
**W1 Soho:** Argyll Arms
**W6 Hammersmith:** Dove
**W9 Maida Vale:**
Prince Alfred,
Warrington Hotel

**GREATER**
**MANCHESTER**
**Altrincham:** Railway
**Bolton:** Howcroft
**Eccles:** Grapes, Lamb,
Royal Oak
**Gorton:** Plough
**Heaton Norris:**
Nursery Inn
**Manchester:** Briton's
Protection, Circus Tavern,
Crown & Kettle,
Peveril of the Peak
**Marple:** Hatters Arms
**Middleton:**
Old Boar's Head
**Mossley:** Colliers Arms
**Rochdale:** Cemetery Hotel
**Stalybridge:** Station Buffet
**Stockport:** Alexandra,
Arden Arms,
Queen's Head,
Swan With Two Necks
**Wigan:** Springfield Hotel

**MERSEYSIDE**
**Liverpool:** Lion,
Philharmonic,
Prince Arthur, Vines
**Lydiate:** Scotch Piper

**NORFOLK**
**Warham:**
Three Horseshoes
**Wymondham:**
Green Dragon

**NORTHUMBERLAND**
**Berwick-upon-Tweed:**
Free Trade
**Netherton:** Star Inn

*The Briton's Protection, Manchester*

## WALES

**GWENT
Abergavenny:**
Hen & Chickens

**MID WALES
Hay-on-Wye:** Three Tuns
**Llanfihangel-yng-
Ngwynfa:** Goat

**WEST WALES
Llandovery:** Red Lion
**Pontfaen:** Dyffryn Arms

## SCOTLAND

**THE BORDERS
Ancrum:** Cross Keys

**FIFE
Kirkcaldy:** Feuars Arms

**GRAMPIAN
Aberdeen:** Grill

**THE LOTHIANS
Dirleton:** Castle
**Edinburgh:** Abbotsford,
Bennets Bar, Café Royal,
Kenilworth

**STRATHCLYDE
Glasgow:** Horseshoe Bar,
Old Toll Bar
**Lochgilphead:** The 'Comm'
**Paisley:** Bull
**Shettleston:** Portland Arms
**Uddingstone:** Rowan Tree

**TAYSIDE
Dundee:** Clep, Speedwell

## OFFSHORE BRITAIN

**NORTHERN IRELAND
Belfast:**
Crown Liquor Saloon
**Cushendun:**
Mary McBride's
**Enniskillen:**
William Blake's

**NOTTINGHAMSHIRE
Nottingham:**
Trip to Jerusalem

**OXFORDSHIRE
Banbury:** Wine Vaults
**Checkendon:** Black Horse
**Steventon:** North Star
**Stoke Lyne:** Peyton Arms
**Stoke Row:** Crooked Billet
**Stoke Talmage:** Red Lion
**Wantage:**
Shoulder of Mutton

**SHROPSHIRE
Halfway House:** Seven
Stars/Halfway House
**Much Wenlock:**
George & Dragon
**Selattyn:** Cross Keys
**Shrewsbury:** Loggerheads

**SOMERSET
Appley:** Globe
**Bath:** Old Green Tree, Star
**Crowcombe:** Carew Arms
**Faulkland:**
Tuckers Grave Inn
**Midsomer Norton:**
White Hart
**Norton St Philip:** George
**Witham Friary:**
Seymour Arms

**STAFFORDSHIRE
High Offley:** Anchor

**SUFFOLK
Brent Eleigh:** Cock
**Bury St Edmunds:**
Nutshell
**Laxfield:** Kings Head
**Pin Mill:** Butt & Oyster
**Rumburgh:** Buck
**Walberswick:** Bell

**SUSSEX (East)
Berwick:** Cricketer's Arms

**TYNE & WEAR
Newcastle upon Tyne:**
Crown Posada

**WARWICKSHIRE
Five Ways:** Case is Altered
**Long Itchington:**
Buck & Bell

**WEST MIDLANDS
Birmingham:** Bartons
Arms, Bellefield,
Black Horse, Red Lion
**Bloxwich:** Turf Tavern
**Sedgley:** Beacon
**Smethwick:**
Waterloo Hotel

**WILTSHIRE
Easton Royal:** Bruce Arms
**Salisbury:**
Haunch of Venison

**WORCESTERSHIRE
Bretforton:** Fleece
**Hanley Castle:** Three Kings

**YORKSHIRE
(East)
Beverley:** White Horse
**Hull:** Olde White Harte
**Skerne:** Eagle Inn
**(North)
Beck Hole:** Birch Hall Inn
**Boroughbridge:**
Three Horseshoes
**Harrogate:** Gardeners Arms
**Saxton:** Greyhound
**York:** Blue Bell
**(West)
Bradford:** Cock & Bottle,
New Beehive
**Heath:** King's Arms

# HOW TO USE THE GOOD BEER GUIDE

THE *GOOD BEER GUIDE* is unique amongst guidebooks. It does not employ professional inspectors who visit pubs only once or twice during the course of the year. Entries, instead, are selected by local CAMRA members, beer enthusiasts who use the pubs in their area week-in, week-out. They decide which pubs should be submitted for the *Guide* at special branch selection meetings where the pros and cons of each pub in the area are weighed up. Some clubs and off-licences are occasionally selected, too, if the branch considers that these establishments make a notable contribution to the good beer scene in its region.

Once pubs have been selected and surveyed for the *Good Beer Guide*, the information is passed to CAMRA head office but CAMRA branches see proofs of their entries and can recommend changes right up to the last possible moment before the *Guide* goes to press. We believe this provides the most up to date research system employed by any guidebook.

## —— SELECTION CRITERIA ——

The primary criterion for inclusion in the *Good Beer Guide* is, of course, good beer – cask-conditioned real ale, traditionally well-kept without the application of life-extending gases. A pub may serve the best food, have the finest family facilities or even the prettiest garden, but, unless the beer is top notch, it will not be selected. This again sets the *Good Beer Guide* apart from other pub guides. Readers' recommendations are extremely useful and sometimes offer another viewpoint which our branches are always keen to bear in mind when considering their selections, but reader recommendation alone does not guarantee entry to the *Guide*, as it does with some other publications.

CAMRA is a consumer organisation, dedicated to raising standards in the pub and brewing world, so, occasionally, other factors enter the selection equation. A pub which indulges in anti-consumer practices, like consistently short-measuring its clients, is unlikely to find favour. The use of deliberately misleading dispense equipment is another important issue. The last few years have seen an increase in the number of pubs which serve keg beer or keg cider through fake handpumps – a crude attempt by the manufacturers to muscle in on the goodwill and respect that traditionally brewed beer and cider enjoy. It's the same ruse that brewers have employed in putting pictures of handpumps on 'draught beers in can' to imply that the processed beer inside is the same as cask beer at a pub. CAMRA is not against the sale of these products – choice for drinkers is foremost amongst the Campaign's objectives – but it has been campaigning against these deceptive dispense methods. The fake pumps look like real handpumps, the beers and ciders are named to sound like real ales and real ciders and it is not until you've paid your money and sampled the drink that you realise that you have been conned. Other dispense methods are available and so CAMRA has been urging publicans to request these and to stop assisting manufacturers in perpetrating this cheap deception. To reinforce the campaign, CAMRA members have decided that pubs which use fake handpumps should no longer feature in the *Good Beer Guide*.

## —— HOW PUBS ARE ARRANGED ——

Pubs are listed in areas which largely following the county system. However, with changes now introduced in the structure of local authorities in most of the UK, the *Good Beer Guide* has had to make some adjustments to its established pattern this year. Gone are the counties of Avon, Cleveland and Humberside; gone, too, are the Welsh counties and the old Scottish regions. Readers will find that the structure for England remains much as before, except that Avon has now been divided between Somerset and Gloucestershire & Bristol, Cleveland has been re-allocated to Durham and Yorkshire, and Humberside has given way to Yorkshire and an enlarged Lincolnshire. Also this year, the two Sussex counties have been combined under one Sussex heading, and the four Yorkshire counties have similarly been grouped together. As before, Greater London and Greater Manchester come under L and M respectively. In Wales and Scotland we have adopted new 'super' regions, as the numerous new local authority areas are too small to sensibly stand alone in the book. To confirm the exact territory covered, the first page of each Welsh and Scottish super region lists the local authority areas featured. In addition, all areas have a location map, pinpointing where all the pubs are situated and also marking the independently-owned breweries and brew pubs. So that readers can identify neighbouring areas, a national map is provided on the inside back cover.

## —— THE PUB ENTRIES ——

An at-a-glance guide to reading pub entries is included on the inside front cover but, basically, each entry provides the following information: name of pub, address, directions and Ordnance Survey reference number (if tricky to find), telephone number (if available), opening hours, a brief description of the pub and its major features and, finally, a row of symbols highlighting its key facilities. For meals and accommodation, no assessment of quality is made, unless mentioned in the pub description. Evening meals are generally assumed to be available until at least 9pm. If a pub finishes serving meals earlier, we say so. Opening hours state the hours in operation most of the week, followed by the hours on days which differ from the norm. Seasonal variations are shown in brackets. For England and Wales, enjoying their first full year of extended Sunday opening, all Sunday hours are clearly stated this year.

Central to each entry is the list of real ales sold. These are arranged alphabetically by brewery and where more than one beer from a brewery is sold its beers are listed in ascending order of strength. Seasonal beers, such as winter ales, are included but are clearly only available at certain times of the year. For further information on all beers, check the breweries section and the beers index at the back of the book.

Finally, this year look out for the star symbol next to a pub's name. This indicates that the pub offers a fine example of an unspoilt, historic interior and is high on the list of CAMRA's pubs to preserve. For further details see Pubs to Save (page 21).

# THE
# GOOD BEER GUIDE

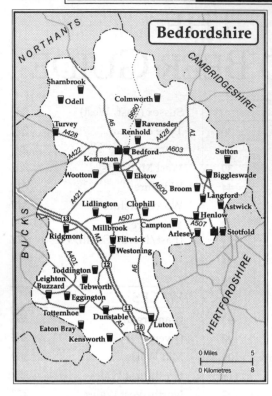

## Bedfordshire

*[Map showing locations including Sharnbrook, Odell, Colmworth, Turvey, Ravensden, Renhold, Kempston, Bedford, Sutton, Wootton, Elstow, Biggleswade, Broom, Langford, Astwick, Lidlington, Clophill, Henlow, Millbrook, Campton, Arlesey, Stotfold, Ridgmont, Flitwick, Westoning, Toddington, Leighton Buzzard, Tebworth, Eggington, Totternhoe, Dunstable, Luton, Eaton Bray, Kensworth]*

0 Miles 5
0 Kilometres 8

---

## Arlesey

### Three Tuns
86 High Street
☎ (01462) 731339
11.30–3, 5.30–11; 12–3, 7–10.30 Sun
**Draught Bass; Morrells Bitter; guest beer** Ⓗ
Picturesque, 15th-century thatched pub in the village centre, featuring low ceilings, lots of beams, a roaring fire and an unusual collection of safe hardware. In CAMRA's *Good Pub Food* guide.
🏚 Q ✿ ◑ ▶ ♣ P

## Astwick

### Tudor Oaks
Taylors Road (A1, midway between Letchworth and Biggleswade)
☎ (01462) 834133
11–11; 12–10.30 Sun
**Boddingtons Bitter; guest beers** Ⓗ
Friendly pub with an oak-beamed bar, five fireplaces and a separate nightclub. Excellent value food. Guest beers change weekly; over 250 different ales sold in 1995. One bitter and one mild are always sold very

cheaply. The cider varies.
🏚 ✿ 🍴 ◑ ▶ ▲ ♣ ⬠ P 🍺

## Bedford

### Fleur de Lis
12 Mill Street (E of A6, High St)
☎ (01234) 211004
10.30–11; 12–10.30 Sun
**Wells Eagle; guest beer** Ⓗ
Very well run, one-bar town-centre pub, featured in every edition of this guide. Parking is difficult lunchtimes. Live music Tue eve. No food Sun.
◑

### Three Cups
45 Newnham Street (down Mill St from High St)
☎ (01234) 352153
11–11; 12–3, 7–10.30 Sun
**Greene King IPA, Abbot, seasonal beers** Ⓗ
Fine, traditional pub near the town centre. The wide range of food at lunchtime includes daily specials and a full breakfast menu. Snacks served 3–7 (no food Sun).
✿ ◑ ▶ 🍺 ♣ P

### Queen's Tavern
120 Queen's Drive (from A428 take Polhill Ave and Haylands Way) ☎ (01234) 358514

11–2.30 (3.30 Sat), 5.30 (6 Sat)–11; 11–11 Fri; 12–3, 7–10.30 Sun
**Greene King XX Mild, IPA, Abbot** Ⓗ
Estate community pub serving home-cooked lunches (eve meals and Sun lunches must be booked). Lively public bar. Quiz Thu.
🏚 Q ✿ ◑ ▶ 🍺 ♣ P

**Try also: Castle,** Newnham St (Greene King)

## Biggleswade

### Golden Pheasant
71 High Street
☎ (01767) 313653
11–11; 11–11 Fri & Sat; 12–3, 7–10.30 Sun
**Wells Eagle, Bombardier; guest beer** Ⓗ
300-year-old pub – a town square local, popular for its games. Good food available every day. As with all Wells pubs, guest beers are served using swan necks and tight sparklers.
Q ✿ ◑ ▶ ⇌ ♣ ♠

**Try also: White Hart,** High St (Greene King)

## Broom

### Cock ☆
23 High Street
☎ (01767) 314411
12–3, 6–11; 12–4, 7–10.30 Sun
**Greene King IPA, Abbot, seasonal beers** Ⓖ
Superb pub where beer is served direct from the cellar. Originally a terrace of houses, it consists of small rooms off a central hallway (children welcome). Well worth visiting.
🏚 🛏 ✿ ◑ ▶ ▲ ♣ P

## Campton

### White Hart
Mill Lane ☎ (01462) 812657 ·
12–3, 6–11; 11–11 Sat; 12–3, 7–10.30 Sun
**Brakspear Bitter; Hook Norton Best Bitter; Theakston Best Bitter; Young's Special; guest beers** Ⓗ
Popular, open-plan village free house with a comfortable lounge and dining area. Games dominate the public bar, which has a flagstone floor and an inglenook. Petanque played.
✿ ◑ ▶ & P

---

🍺 **INDEPENDENT BREWERIES**

**B&T:** Shefford

**Abel Brown's:** Stotfold

**Wells:** Bedford

---

## Clophill

### Stone Jug
Back Street (off A6/A507
roundabout) ☎ (01525) 860526
11–3, 6–11; 12–3, 7–10.30 Sun
**B&T Shefford Bitter; Courage
Directors; John Smith's
Magnet; Theakston Best
Bitter; guest beers** H
Deservedly popular free house
convenient for the Greensand
Ridge Walk. Check before
arriving with children. No food
Sun. ❀ ◖ ♣ P

## Colmworth

### Wheatsheaf
Wilden Road (¾ mile E of B660)
OS101574 ☎ (01234) 376370
11–3, 6.30–11; 12–3, 7–10.30 Sun
**Draught Bass; guest beers** H
17th-century, oak-beamed
country inn to the south of the
village. Mind the low beams!
Guest beers change frequently,
with at least three normally on
sale. Children's play area in the
garden. Good varied bar meals;
franchised restaurant –
bookings (01234) 378990.
🏨 Q ❀ ◖ ▶ ⊞ ♣ P

## Dunstable

### Star & Garter
147 High Street South
☎ (01582) 661044
11–11; 12–10.30 Sun
**Courage Best Bitter, Directors;
guest beer** H
Traditional, two-bar pub with
a comfortable lounge and a
friendly welcome. Courtyard
for families. Meals served 12–5.
❀ ◖ ⊞ ♣

## Eaton Bray

### Hope & Anchor
63 Bower Lane
☎ (01525) 220386
11–3, 5.30–11; 12–4, 7–10.30 Sun
**Greene King IPA; Tetley
Bitter; Vale Wychert Ale;
Wadworth 6X** H
Recently partly rebuilt, this
low-beamed lounge bar and
restaurant offers a homely,
welcoming atmosphere, good
food (late supper licence), and
a large garden.
Q ❀ ◖ ♿ ♣ P

### White Horse
1 Market Square
☎ (01525) 220231
11.30–2.30 (3 Sat), 6 (6.30 Sat)–11;
12–3, 7–10.30 Sun
**Friary Meux BB; Ruddles Best
Bitter** H
Low-beamed historic inn,
dating from the 16th century,
on the village green. The
separate restaurant is guarded
by a full suit of armour. A large
garden includes a children's

play area and offers barbecues
in summer. Good food. No
family room Sat eve.
🏕 ❀ ◖ ♿ ▶ P ✗

## Eggington

### Horseshoes
High Street ☎ (01525) 210282
12–2.30, 6–11; 12–3, 7–10.30 Sun
**Adnams Bitter, Wadworth 6X;
guest beers** H
Picture-postcard village pub
with an upstairs gallery. Good
food (not served Sun eve or
Mon). 🏨 Q 🏕 ❀ ◖ ▶ P

## Elstow

### Swan
High Street (off A6)
☎ (01234) 352066
11.30–3, 6–11; 11–11 Sat; 12–3, 7–11
Sun
**Greene King IPA, Abbot** H
Old village pub near Elstow
Abbey: one L-shaped room,
plus a restaurant. Fresh
produce is always used, so Sun
lunch must be booked (no food
Sun eve). The attractive village
supplies most of the clientele.
🏨 ❀ ◖ ▶ P

## Flitwick

### Wheatsheaf
15 High Street
☎ (01525) 712574
11.30–11; 12–4, 7–10.30 Sun
**Wells Eagle** H, **Bombardier** G,
**Fargo** H
Friendly pub with a games-
oriented public bar and a
plusher lounge.
❀ ◖ ⊞ ⇌ ♣ P

## Henlow

### Engineers Arms
High Street ☎ (01462) 812284
3 (11 Fri & Sat)–11; 12–10.30 Sun
**Hook Norton Best Bitter;
Theakston Old Peculier;
Young's Special; guest beer** H
Locals' pub, catering for all
ages, serving a wide variety of
ales. Although the guest beer is
served via a swan neck, the
sparkler will happily be
removed. Games-oriented:
darts, pool (separate room) and
own football teams.
🏨 ❀ ⊞ ♣ 🍴

## Kempston

### Duke Inn
10 Woburn Road (off A421,
near Saxon shopping centre)
☎ (01234) 854595
11–11; 12–10.30 Sun
**Wells Eagle, Bombardier,
Fargo; guest beer** H
Large pub with a recently
refurbished combined lounge
and bar. The large garden has
attractions for children who are

allowed in the pub daytimes.
The landlord is a *Master
Cellarman.* ❀ ◖ ▶ P

### King William IV
56 High Street (A5134)
☎ (01234) 854533
11.30–3, 5.30–11; 11.30–11 Sat;
12–10.30 Sun
**Wells Eagle, Bombardier,
Fargo; guest beer** H
Attractive, genuine, oak-
beamed building which caters
for a mixed clientele in one bar
and a games room. A nice
landscaped garden includes
children's attractions.
Children's certificate. Eve
meals Tue–Sat. ❀ ◖ ♣ P

## Kensworth

### Farmer's Boy
216 Common Road
☎ (01582) 872207
11–11; 12–10.30 Sun
**Fuller's London Pride, ESB,
seasonal beers** H
Friendly, well-kept village pub
with a small public bar and a
comfortable lounge with a
separate dining area (excellent
home-cooked food). Children's
certificate; play area in the
garden. Note the original
Mann, Crossman & Paulin
leaded windows.
🏨 ❀ ◖ ⊞ ♣ P

## Langford

### Red Cow
60 High Street
☎ (01462) 700642
12–3, 5.30–11 (12–11 summer; may
vary); 12–3, 7–10.30 (12–10.30
summer) Sun
**Greene King IPA, seasonal
beers** H
Unspoilt, one-bar village local.
The landlord is of the old
school – one of a vanishing
breed – and serves the best pint
of Greene King beer in the area.
🏨 ❀ ◖ ♣ P

## Leighton Buzzard

### Black Lion
20 High Street
☎ (01525) 382510
11–2.30, 5.30–11; 12–2.30, 7–10.30 Sun
**Benskins BB; Ind Coope
Burton Ale; Tetley Bitter;
guest beers** H
16th-century building, a pub
since 1891. Crowded at
lunchtime and on weekend
eves. Live music Thu. Venue of
the annual Leighton Buzzard
beer festival. No food Sun.
❀ ◖

### Hunt Hotel
19 Church Road, Linslade
☎ (01525) 374692
11–2.30, 5.30–11; 11–11 Sat; 12–3,
7–10.30 Sun

**Draught Bass; Fuller's London Pride; Tetley Bitter; guest beers** Ⓗ
Modest hotel tucked away in a quiet corner near the station: two bars and a restaurant.
🛏 ◖ ➤

## Stag

1 Heath Road
☎ (01525) 372710
11–2.30 (3 Sat), 6–11; 12–3, 7–10.30 Sun
**Fuller's Chiswick, London Pride, ESB, seasonal beers** Ⓗ
High quality renovation of a one-time basic Allied pub: a wedge-shaped, through bar with an appetising food counter at the end (no food Sun). Tiny car park.
◖ ➤ P

# Lidlington

## Green Man

High Street ☎ (01525) 402869
12–3, 6–11; 12–3, 7–10.30 Sun
**Greene King IPA, Abbot, seasonal beers** Ⓗ
17th-century thatched pub in a quiet village. Traditional games plus petanque are played. The cosy lounge has an attached restaurant area serving a good, varying menu (eve meals Wed–Sat). Handy for ramblers on the Greensand Ridge Path.
🏚 ❀ ◖ ◗ ➤ ➕ P

# Luton

## Bat & Barrel

104–106 Park Street
☎ (01582) 453125
11–11; 12–10.30 Sun
**Wells Eagle, Bombardier, Fargo; guest beers** Ⓗ
Attractive, half-tiled, two-bar town pub, close to the university. Pool and Sky TV in the public; quieter lounge.
❀ ◖

## Bird & Bush

Hancock Drive, Bushmead (off A6 on Bushmead Estate)
☎ (01582) 480723
11.45–3, 5–11; 11.45–11 Fri & Sat; 12–10.30 Sun
**Draught Bass; Hancock's HB; Young's Bitter; guest beer** Ⓗ
Modern estate pub with attractive Yorkshire flagstone and quarry-tiled floors. Good bar food includes vegetarian options (book Sun lunch; no food Sun eve). ❀ ◖ ◗ ⅃ ➕ P

## Bricklayers Arms

16–18 Hightown Road
☎ (01582) 611017
11–2.30, 5–11; 11–11 Fri & Sat; 12–10.30 Sun
**Everards Mild, Beacon, Tiger, Old Original; guest beer** Ⓗ
Friendly, unpretentious town pub with basic furnishings, including a variety of old

wooden casks scattered throughout – the ones above the bar are from the short-lived Mickles micro-brewery.
❀ ⇌ ➕ P

## Mother Redcap

80 Latimer Road
☎ (01582) 30913
11–3, 5–11; 11–11 Fri & Sat; 12–3, 7–10.30 Sun (may vary)
**Greene King IPA, Abbot, seasonal beers** Ⓗ
Well-renovated, one-bar pub with a games area separated from the lounge by a chimney breast. No food Sun.
❀ ◖ ➕ P

## Two Brewers

43 Dumfries Street
☎ (01582) 23777
12–11; 12–10.30 Sun
**B&T Shefford Bitter; guest beers** Ⓗ
Friendly, backstreet local with a good mix of customers. Usually four beers available, including two others from B&T. 🏚 ❀ ➕

## Wigmore Arms

Wigmore Lane
☎ (01582) 417343
11–3, 5.30–11; 11–11 Sat; 12–10.30 Sun
**Ansells Mild; Ind Coope Burton Ale; Tetley Bitter; guest beers** Ⓗ
Modern estate pub next to Asda supermarket: a sports bar and a split-level lounge. Two regularly changing guest beers served. ◖ ◗ ⅃ ➕ P

**Try also: Wheelwrights Arms, Guildford St (Free)**

# Millbrook

## Chequers

1 mile W of B530 OS013387
☎ (01525) 403835
11.30–3, 6–11; 12–3, 7–10.30 Sun
**Adnams Broadside; Banks's Mild; Wadworth 6X; Wells Eagle** Ⓗ
Single-bar country pub and restaurant. Situated above a vehicle proving ground, it offers an elevated view of Marston Vale. No food Sun eve. ❀ ◖ ◗ ✠ ⇌ ➕ P

# Odell

## Bell

Horsefair Lane
☎ (01234) 720254
11–2.30, 6–11 (11–11 Sat in spring and summer); 12–3, 7–10.30 Sun
**Greene King IPA, Rayments Special, Abbot, seasonal beers** Ⓗ
Popular, thatched, multi-roomed village pub serving good food. The large garden running to the River Ouse has a patio and an aviary of unusual birds. A footpath

leads into Harrold Country Park. Sun lunches 12–2; no food Sun eve in winter.
🏚 Q ❀ ◖ ◗ P

# Ravensden

## Blacksmiths Arms

Bedford Road (B660 at crossroads, 3 miles out of Bedford) ☎ (01234) 771496
11–2.30, 6–11.30; 12–3, 7–10.30 Sun
**Boddingtons Bitter; Greene King IPA, Abbot; guest beers** Ⓗ
Rural, family-run public house and restaurant with lounge and public bars. Up to six guest beers, drawn from a range of well over a hundred, are available. Live music occasionally on Sun eve.
Q ❀ ◖ ◗ ⅃ ⅁ & ✠ ➕ P

# Renhold

## Three Horseshoes

42 Top End (1 mile N of A428)
☎ (01234) 870218
11–3, 6–11; 11–11 Sat; 12–3, 7–10.30 Sun
**Greene King XX Mild, IPA, Abbot** Ⓗ**, Winter Ale** Ⓖ**, seasonal beers** Ⓗ
Friendly village pub with a children's play area in the garden. The public bar has traditional pub games and satellite TV. Good value home-cooked food includes fresh steaks and home-made soup. A long-standing outlet for mild. No eve meals Sun or Tue.
🏚 Q ❀ ◖ ◗ ⅃ & ➕ P

# Ridgmont

## Rose & Crown

89 High Street
☎ (01525) 280245
10.30–2.30, 6–11; 12–4, 7–10.30 Sun
**Adnams Broadside; Mansfield Riding Bitter; Wells Eagle, Bombardier** Ⓗ
Popular, welcoming pub with extensive grounds offering camping and caravanning facilities. The lounge bar has a 'Rupert' theme; the public has a separate games area with table football. In every edition of the *Guide*.
🏚 ◖ ◗ ✠ ➕ P

# Sharnbrook

## Swan With Two Nicks

High Street ☎ (01234) 781585
11–3, 5–11; 11–11 Sat; 12–10.30 (12–3, 7–10.30 winter) Sun
**Wells Eagle, Bombardier, Fargo; guest beers** Ⓗ
Friendly village pub with a rear patio. Home-cooked food includes daily specials and a vegetarian choice.
🏚 ❀ ◖ ◗ ⅃ ➕ P

## Stotfold

### Stag
35 Brook Street
☎ (01462) 730261
5.30 (11 Fri & Sat)–11; 12–10.30 Sun
**Abel Brown's Jack of Herts, Little Billy, Pale Ale, seasonal beers; guest beers** Ⓗ
Home of Abel Brown's micro-brewery, founded in 1995. Four guest beers at all times, plus two real ciders. Beers are sometimes served straight from the cellar.
🏚 ✿ ♣ ⌂ P 🍴

## Sutton

### John o'Gaunt
30 High Street
☎ (01767) 260377
12–3, 7–11; 12–3, 7–10.30 Sun
**Greene King IPA, Abbot, seasonal beers** Ⓗ
Attractive pub in a picturesque village, near the golf course. A good range of bar meals includes Sun lunch. Table skittles and a floodlit boules court provide entertainment.
🏚 Q ✿ ◑ ▶ 🕮 ♣ P

## Tebworth

### Queen's Head
The Lane ☎ (01525) 874101
11–3, 6–11; 11–3.30, 7–11 Sat; 12–3, 7–10.30 Sun
**Adnams Broadside** Ⓖ; **Wells Eagle** Ⓗ, **Fargo** Ⓖ
Fine village local with two small bars, popular with locals and visitors alike. Good value food. Local CAMRA *Pub of the Year* 1995. No food Sun.
🏚 ✿ ◑ ▶ 🕮 ♣ P

## Toddington

### Angel
1 Luton Road
☎ (01525) 872380
11–11; 12–10.30 Sun
**Courage Best Bitter; Ruddles Best Bitter; John Smith's Bitter; guest beers** Ⓗ
Dating in part from the 16th century, this is an enterprising and entertaining pub, with live jazz Thu eve and Sun lunch, plus other occasional live events. Cream teas served. Restaurant open Tue–Sat eve.
🏚 ⛬ ✿ ◑ ▶ ♣ P ⚥

### Sow & Pigs
19 Church Square
☎ (01525) 873089
11–11; 12–10.30 Sun
**Greene King IPA, Abbot, seasonal beers** Ⓗ
Unpretentious and unpredictable pub with somewhat haphazard furnishings – the decor is strong on pigs. Visitors may find a sense of humour useful! The upstairs restaurant is a recent addition. In every edition of the *Guide*.
🏚 Q ✿ ◑ ▶ ♣ P

**Try also: Toddington Social & Services Club, High St (CIU)**

## Totternhoe

### Old Farm
16 Church Road
☎ (01582) 661294
12–3, 6–11; 12–4, 7–10.30 Sun
**Fuller's Chiswick, London Pride, ESB, seasonal beers** Ⓗ
Old village pub with a popular public bar, with a low, boarded ceiling, and a quiet, comfortable lounge, with a large inglenook. Good food (not served Sun eve).
🏚 ✿ ◑ ▶ 🕮 ♣ P

## Turvey

### Three Cranes
High Street (just off A428)
☎ (01234) 881305
11–2.30, 6–11; 12–3, 7–10.30 Sun
**Draught Bass; Fuller's London Pride, ESB; Smiles Best Bitter; guest beers** Ⓗ
17th-century coaching inn serving an excellent range of food, including vegetarian dishes, in both the bar and restaurant. 🏚 Q ✿ 🛏 ◑ ▶ P

## Westoning

### Nag's Head
Greenfield Road
☎ (01525) 712630
12–3 (4 Sat), 6–11; 12–3, 7–10.30 Sun
**Wells Eagle, Fargo** Ⓗ
Lively, welcoming, one-bar village local, strong on pub games and competitions. Although meals are served, the emphasis is on 'pub' matters.
✿ ◑ ▶ ♣ P

## Wootton

### Chequers
Hall End Road (½ mile past parish church)
☎ (01234) 768394
11–2.30, 5.30–11; 12–3, 7–10.30 Sun
**Mansfield Riding Mild; Wells Eagle, Fargo** Ⓗ
16th-century coaching inn and restaurant, boasting three real fires, oak beams and brasses. Large garden. No meals Mon eve. 🏚 Q ✿ ◑ ▶ 🕮 ♣ P

---

# NATIONAL BRANDS

National breweries have gained notoriety for the way in which they have taken over and closed breweries, transferring the best brands to other production centres. Wethered's Brewery in Marlow, Buckinghamshire, for instance, was closed by Whitbread in 1988, but Wethered Bitter is still on sale. It was moved first to Flowers in Cheltenham, then to McMullen's of Hertford and is now being produced at Castle Eden Brewery in County Durham!

In the last year, we have witnessed the closure of more major breweries, at Warrington (Tetley Walker), Nottingham (Home) and Halifax (Webster's) by Carlsberg-Tetley and Scottish Courage. Space does not permit us to cover all the changes to production sites when listing the beers in each pub entry (try squeezing in Scottish Courage Webster's Yorkshire Bitter, now brewed by John Smith's but also occasionally produced at Mansfield Brewery), so readers are urged to consult the beers index and the breweries section at the back of the book to discover just who brews what and, indeed, where!

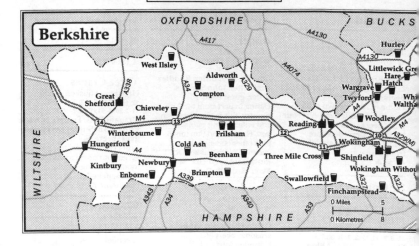

# Aldworth

## Bell Inn ☆
Off B4009 ☎ (01635) 578272
11–3, 6–11; 12–3, 7–10.30 Sun; closed Mon
**Arkell's 3B, Kingsdown; Morrells Bitter, Mild; West Berkshire Good Old Boy** Ⓗ
Ancient, unspoilt village pub with a big garden adjoining the cricket ground, two bars with a central, windowed servery, and an open outside gents'; run by the same family for 200 years. No carpets, fruit machines or piped music, but excellent filled rolls and good fellowship. Good Old Boy is sold as Old Tyler. Near the Ridgeway path.
🏨 Q ✿ ◑ ▶ ⊞ ♣ P

# Ascot

## Stag
63 High Street (A329)
☎ (01344) 21622
11–3, 5.30–11; 11–11 Fri & Sat; 12–3, 7–10.30 Sun
**Greene King IPA, Abbot, seasonal beers** Ⓗ
Comfortable pub near the racecourse. The lounge is extensively ornamented with Victoriana. No lunches Sun.
✿ ◑ ▶ ⌣

# Beenham

## Stocks Inn
☎ (01734) 713127
12–2 (2.30 Sat), 7–11; 12–3, 7–10.30 Sun
**Archers Village; Shepherd Neame Spitfire; Wells Bombardier** Ⓗ
Attractive, brick-built (Flemish bond) country pub dating back to 1720. The comfortable

lounge with a real fire displays interesting artefacts from the landlord's own collection – especially WWII items. Renowned Sun roast lunch; no meals Sun eve or Mon lunch.
🏨 Q ✿ ◑ ▶ ⊞ ♿ ♣ P

# Brimton

## Three Horseshoes
Brimpton Lane
☎ (01734) 712183
11–3 (4 Sat), 6–11; 12–3, 7–10.30 Sun
**Fuller's London Pride, ESB; Wadworth 6X or Adnams Bitter** Ⓗ
Pleasant, Victorian, two-bar village pub, built by Mays of Basingstoke. The panelled lounge, with its fine old clock and old prints, is usually quiet. The larger public bar offers darts, pool and a jukebox. No lunches Sun. Q ✿ ◑ ⊞ ♣ P

# Chieveley

## Olde Red Lion
Green Lane (½ mile NW of M4 jct 13)
☎ (01635) 248379
11–3, 6 (5.30 Fri & Sat)–11; 12–3, 7–10.30 Sun
**Arkell's Bitter, 3B, Kingsdown** Ⓗ
Comfortable, friendly pub rescued by Arkell's. Though popular with passing trade, it remains a village local. Oak beams and a wide range of pub games are features.
🏨 ✿ ◑ ▶ ♣ P

# Cold Ash

## Castle
Cold Ash Hill
☎ (01635) 863232
11.30–3 (4 Sat), 6–11 (11.30–11 summer Sat); 12–4, 7–10.30 Sun

**Courage Best Bitter; Webster's Yorkshire Bitter; guest beers** Ⓗ
Late Victorian village pub with small drinking areas allowing a cosier feel than its one-bar layout would suggest. Good curries; Sun roast. No eve meals Sun or Mon.
🏨 ✿ ◑ ▶ P

Try also: Sun in the Wood, Stoney Lane, Ashmore Green (Wadworth)

# Compton

## Compton Swan Hotel
Cheap Street
☎ (01635) 578269
11–3, 5.30–11; 11–11 Fri & Sat; 12–3, 7.30–10.30 Sun
**Flowers Original; Morland Original, Old Speckled Hen** Ⓗ
Strikingly large pub offering separate lounge and public bars, a pool room and a function room. Tastefully refurbished, with a large, enclosed garden, it offers something for everyone. Children and pets welcome. Good food (snacks only Sun eve – except for residents).
♿ ✿ 🏨 ◑ ▶ ⊞ ♿ P

# Enborne

## Craven Arms
☎ (01635) 253336
11–11; 12–10.30 Sun
**Wadworth IPA, 6X, Farmers Glory, Old Timer, seasonal beers; guest beers** Ⓗ
Attractive, old country pub serving above average food and catering well for families (wonderful, well-equipped garden). One main bar with three smaller areas off. No eve meals Sun. ♿ ✿ ◑ ▶ ♣ P

## Eton

### Watermans Arms

Brocas Street (off High St, near bridge to Windsor)
☎ (01753) 861001
11–2.30 (3 Sat), 6–11; 12–3, 7–10.30 Sun
**Brakspear Bitter; Courage Best Bitter, Directors; Morland Old Speckled Hen; Ushers Best Bitter; Wadworth 6X** Ⓗ
Popular riverside local. The original building dates back to the 16th century. An extensive menu is served in the covered restaurant which was previously the courtyard (families welcome). No food Sun eve. The no-smoking room has a boating theme.
🏾 Q ◑ ▶ ⇌ (Windsor Central/Riverside) ♣ ⌐

## Eton Wick

### Pickwick

32 Eton Wick Road
☎ (01753) 861713
11.30 (12 Sat) 2.30, 5.30 (6 Sat)–11; 12–3, 7–10.30 Sun
**Young's Bitter, Special, seasonal beers** Ⓗ
Comfortable, single-bar pub, known as the Grapes until its name was changed to mean 'Pick of the Wick'. It is well-known today for its Malaysian dishes, prepared with herbs from its recently extended, award-winning patio garden. No eve meals Sun/Mon. Table skittles in the bar. ❀ ◑ ▶ ♣ P

## Finchampstead

### Queens Oak

Church Lane (opp. church)
OS794639 ☎ (01734) 734855
11.30–11, 6 (6.30 Sat)–11 (11.30–4, 6.30–11 summer Sat); 12–3, 7–10.30 Sun

**Brakspear Bitter, Old, Special; Theakston XB** Ⓗ
A winner: an old, two-bar pub, popular with walkers; in this guide since 1981. It features a long-established no-smoking bar and a large garden with a bar and a play area for children. Barbecues in summer; Aunt Sally played. Pizzas are a speciality. Note the key fob collection.
🏾 Q ❀ ◑ ▶ 🚻 ▲ ♣ P ⌐

## Frilsham

### Pot Kiln

On Yattendon–Bucklebury road: ignore signs to Frilsham
OS552731 ☎ (01635) 201366
12–2.30 (not Tue), 6.30–11; 12–3, 7–10.30 Sun
**Arkell's 3B; Morland Original, Old Speckled Hen; West Berkshire Brick Kiln Bitter** Ⓗ
200 years a pub: its four small bars have no other distractions than lively conversation. At the front, meadow, stream and woodlands; at the back, the new West Berks Brewery, whose Brick Kiln Bitter is only found here. Hot filled rolls only Sun and Tue.
🏾 Q ❀ ◑ ▶ 🍴 ♣ P ⌐

## Hare Hatch

### Queen Victoria

Blakes Lane (off A4)
☎ (01734) 402477
11–3, 5.30–11; 12–3, 7–10.30 Sun
**Brakspear Bitter, Old, Special, OBJ** Ⓗ
Oasis of calm civility just yards from the busy main road. The original building is 300 years old. Walkers and well-behaved children welcome. Extensive menu of good food.
❀ ◑ ▶ ♣ P ⌐

## Holyport

### Belgian Arms

Holyport Street (cul-de-sac off village green) ☎ (01628) 34468
11–3, 5.30 (7 winter Sat)–11; 12–3, 7–10.30 Sun
**Brakspear Bitter, Special** Ⓗ
There has been an ale house on this site for over 200 years, and this pub has been owned by Brakspear since 1896. Burnt into the lintel above the entrance is the title 'Registered Hat Maker'. The unspoilt frontage is clad by a 100-year-old wisteria. Popular garden. No meals Sun eve.
🏾 Q ❀ ◑ ▶ P

## Hungerford

### Downgate

Down View, 13 Park Street
☎ (01488) 682708
11–2.30, 6–11; 12–3, 7–10.30 Sun

**Arkell's 3B, Kingsdown** Ⓗ
Quiet pub on the edge of Hungerford Common with a friendly village inn atmosphere and a small, intimate dining area a couple of steps down from the bar. No eve meals Sun or Mon. Pleasant summer drinking.
🏾 Q ❀ ◑ ▶ ⇌ ♣ P

## Hurley

### Black Boy

On A4130
☎ (01628) 824212
11–2.30, 6–11; 12–3, 7–10.30 Sun
**Brakspear Bitter, Old** Ⓗ
Comfortable, one-bar pub dating back to the 16th century with a beamed ceiling and open fires. Once a Royalist safe house, it is named after Charles II who was described as a 'very dark and swarthy child'.
🏾 Q ❀ 🛏 ◑ ▶ P

## Kintbury

### Dundas Arms

Station Road (off A4)
☎ (01488) 658263
11–2.30, 6–11; 12–2.30, 7–10.30 Sun
**Morland Original; Wells Bombardier; guest beers** Ⓗ
Attractive, 18th-century inn by the Kennet & Avon Canal (Lock 78), named after Lord Dundas who opened the canal in 1810. Good outside area from which horse-drawn barges can be seen in summer. Very good home-made bar and restaurant meals (no food Sun/Mon eves).
Q ❀ 🛏 ◑ ▶ ⇌ P

## Littlewick Green

### Cricketers

Coronation Road
☎ (01628) 822888
11–3, 5.30–11; 11–11 Sat; 12–10.30 Sun
**Boddingtons Bitter; Brakspear Bitter; Fuller's London Pride; guest beers** Ⓗ
Charming pub overlooking the green in a picturesque village. Decorated with cricketing memorabilia, it is split into three drinking areas, one with a pool table, one with a large log fire. Small car park.
🏾 ❀ ◑ ▶ ♣ P

| 🔩 INDEPENDENT BREWERIES | |
|---|---|
| **Butts:** Great Shefford | |
| **Greenwood's:** Wokingham | |
| **Reading Lion:** Reading | |
| **West Berkshire:** Frilsham | |

## Maidenhead

### Hand & Flowers

15 Queen Street
☎ (01628) 23800
11–3, 5 (7 Sat)–11; 12–3, 7–10.30 Sun
**Brakspear Bitter, Old, Special** Ⓗ
Small, homely, Victorian pub in the town centre – run by an enthusiastic young couple. Imaginative home cooking; deluxe sandwiches.
🏾 Q ◖ ▶ ≹ ♣

## Moneyrow Green

### White Hart

SE of Holyport Green
☎ (01628) 21460
11–11; 12–3, 7–10.30 Sun
**Morland IPA, Original, Old Speckled Hen** Ⓗ
Originally a hunting lodge in Windsor Royal Forest, this picturesque pub is well supported by locals. Dominoes are played in the public bar, as well as bar billiards and darts. The saloon has an air of class with its wood panelling.
🏾 Q ◖ ◗ ⊞ ⅋ ♣ P

## Newbury

### Coopers Arms

39 Bartholomew Street
☎ (01635) 47469
11–3, 5–11; 11–11 Mon, Fri & Sat; 12–10.30 Sun
**Arkell's 3B, Kingsdown, seasonal beers** Ⓗ
Traditional, down to earth town local with several drinking areas (one no-smoking at lunchtime; children welcome in this room).
◖ ⊞ ⅋ ≹ ♣ P

### Lock, Stock & Barrel

104 Northbrook Street
☎ (01635) 42730
11–11; 12–10.30 Sun
**Fuller's Chiswick, London Pride, ESB, seasonal beers** Ⓗ
Spacious, one-bar pub converted from a coffee shop (open 10am still for this purpose) just off the main shopping street, on the bank of the Kennet & Avon Canal. Pleasant rooftop terrace. Small no-smoking area lunchtimes. Wheelchair WC next to the bar. Meals end at 8pm.
❀ ◖ ▶ ⅋ ≹ ✠

## Old Windsor

### Jolly Gardeners

92–94 St Luke's Road
☎ (01753) 865944
11–11; 12–10.30 (12–5, 8–10.30 winter) Sun
**Courage Best Bitter; Ushers Founders, seasonal beers** Ⓗ

Traditional village pub with one U-shaped bar. No jukebox; games played include shove-ha'penny. Small car park.
❀ ♣ P

### Oxford Blue

Crimp Hill (off A308)
☎ (01753) 861954
11–11; 12–10.30 Sun
**Adnams Bitter; Tetley Bitter; Wadworth 6X** Ⓗ
Pub with a large main room divided to give a separate feel to the bar, lounge and dining areas. The new children's area is also suitable for meetings, conferences, etc. Large collection of civil aircraft models. Ramped access from the car park through the garden to the rear doors.
Q ⅋ ❀ ⋈ ◖ ▶ ♣ P

## Reading

### Bugle

144 Friar Street
☎ (01734) 573514
11–11; closed Sun
**Courage Best Bitter, Directors** Ⓗ
Small, two-bar, town-centre pub holding its own despite huge competition from new theme pubs and café bars. Handy for the shops and cinema. Good value food.
◖ ▶ ⊞ ≹ ♣

### Butler

89–91 Chatham Street (off inner ring road, near swimming pool)
☎ (01734) 391635
11.30–11; 12–11 Sat; 12–10.30 Sun
**Fuller's Chiswick, London Pride, ESB, seasonal beers** Ⓗ
Well-established pub close to the town centre with a good mix of customers and a strong local following. It is named after wine merchants who formerly occupied the premises – Guinness was once bottled on the site. Major alterations are planned. No food Sun. Limited parking.
🏾 ❀ ◖ ▶ ♣ P

### Dove

119 Orts Road (near canal behind the college, E of centre)
☎ (01734) 352556
11–2.30, 5.30–11; 11–11 Sat; 12–3, 7–10.30 Sun
**Brakspear Bitter, Old, Special** Ⓗ
A reminder of a once multi-pubbed area of town: a genuine local which is gaining a reputation for its live music (blues Wed, Irish folk Thu, anything goes Sat). Good community spirit; friendly surroundings. No meals weekends.
◖ ♣ P

### Fisherman's Cottage

224 Kennetside (on canal bank off Orts Road, near college, E of centre) ☎ (01734) 571553
11.30–3, 5.30–11; 11–11 Fri, Sat & summer; 12–3, 7–10.30 Sun
**Fuller's Chiswick, London Pride, ESB, seasonal beers** Ⓗ
A castellated exterior gives way to a pleasant and efficiently-run pub in the Newtown area. Situated by the first/last lock on the Kennet & Avon Canal, it is popular with locals, students and visitors, and offers food in a convivial atmosphere. No eve meals Tue.
🏾 ⅄ ❀ ◖ ▶ ♣ P

### Hobgoblin

2 Broad Street
☎ (01734) 560714
11–11; 12–10.30 Sun
**Wychwood Special, Hobgoblin, Dog's Bollocks; guest beers** Ⓗ
Renowned for its wide selection of guest ales, this small, high street pub is popular with scoopers, gricers, twitchers, fanzines, oglers – and normal customers! Seven beers available, always from independents. It can be pricey but is always worth a visit.
≹ ◔ ✠

### Horse & Jockey

120 Castle Hill (just W of inner ring road, near police station)
☎ (01734) 590172
11–11; 12–10.30 Sun
**Archers Village; guest beers** Ⓗ
Open-plan bar with an enterprising landlord who offers regularly changing guest beers from independents. Excellent food complements the reasonably priced ales. Well worth the walk from the town centre. Food to order Sun. 🏾 ❀ ◖ ▶ ♣

### Retreat

8 St Johns Street (E of centre, near Prudential building)
☎ (01734) 571593
11–11; 12–10.30 Sun
**Boddingtons Bitter; Marston's Pedigree; Wadworth 6X; Wethered Bitter; guest beers** Ⓗ
Even though this pub now has a carpet and a pool table, it's still a genuine backstreet boozer making the best of the Whitbread range (at good prices). Popular with students and locals alike. Live accordion/jam sessions Thu. Parking is very difficult. ♣

### Wallingford Arms

2 Caroline Street/Charles Street (off inner ring road, near swimming pool)
☎ (01734) 575272
12–11; 12–3, 7–10.30 Sun
**Morland Original, seasonal beers** *or* **guest beers** Ⓗ

Good solid local with comfortable bars and a congenial atmosphere. Hard to find but well worth the effort.Many sporting connections. No food Sun.
❀ ◖ ⬤ ♣ P

## Shinfield

### Bell & Bottle

School Green (B3349, off A327)
☎ (01734) 883563
11.30–11; 12–3, 7–10.30 Sun
**Archers Village; Theakston Old Peculier; guest beers** ⒣
Friendly and enthusiastically run, two-bar village pub (ex-Courage) with a superb range of ales for the area – eight guests usually on tap. Real fires in both bars. Food is always available. ⚌ Q ❀ ◖ ⬤ ♣ P

## Slough

### Moon & Spoon

86 High Street
☎ (01753) 531650
11–11; 12–10.30 Sun
**Courage Directors; Matthew Brown Bitter; Theakston Best Bitter, XB; guest beers** ⒣
Large Wetherspoons pub converted from building society premises in early 1995. Good mix of clientele, but it can get crowded weekend eves. Welcoming and safe for lone females.
Q ◖ ⬤ ♿ ⬤ ⟳ ✠

### Red Cow

140 Albert Street
☎ (01753) 522614
11.30–3, 5 (7 Sat)–11; 12–4, 7–11 Sun
**Courage Best Bitter, Directors; Theakston XB; guest beers** ⒣
Oak-beamed ex-farmhouse built in 1547; a finalist for *National Community Pub of the Year*. Quiz night Tue; occasional charity events, including murder mystery nights. No meals Sat eve or Sun. ❀ ◖ ⬤ ♣ P

### Wheatsheaf

15 Albert Street
☎ (01753) 522019
11–11; 12–10.30 Sun
**Fuller's Chiswick, London Pride, ESB, seasonal beers** ⒣
Single-bar pub attracting mainly thirtysomethings. The garden is tented over and heated in winter. A red phone box, plus a pillar box in the garden, are features. Try the pies made with beer. Live music weekend eves. ❀ ◖

## Sunninghill

### Duke's Head

Upper Village Road (off Oriental Rd, off B3020)
☎ (01344) 626949
11–11; 12–10.30 Sun

**Greene King IPA, Rayments Special, Abbot; Marston's Pedigree; guest beers** ⒣
Comfortable, nicely furnished local with a friendly landlord. Extensive menu, but it's still a pub first. No eve meals Sun.
⚌ Q ❀ ◖ ⬤ ♣ P ✠

## Swallowfield

### Crown

The Street (just off B3349, old A33) ☎ (01734) 883260
11–3, 6–11; 12–3, 7–10.30 Sun
**Morland Original, seasonal beers** ⒣
Village pub which has been run by the same family for over 30 years: a large, friendly public bar and a smaller lounge. The hub of local life. Eve meals Thu–Sat.
⚌ ❀ ◖ ⬤ ♣ P

## Three Mile Cross

### Swan

Basingstoke Road (off A33, S of M4 jct 11) ☎ (01734) 883674
11–11; 12–3, 7–10.30 Sun
**Brakspear Bitter; Courage Best Bitter; Fuller's London Pride; Marston's Pedigree; Wadworth 6X** ⒣
17th century coaching inn, complete with oak beams and an inglenook, in a quiet location, now that the village is bypassed. Popular with locals and nearby Reading business people. The small, homely restaurant (open weekday lunch) is renowned for freshly home-cooked food – available in the bar at other times.
⚌ ❀ ◖ ⬤ P

## Twyford

### Duke of Wellington

High Street (100 yds W of traffic lights in village centre)
☎ (01734) 340456
11.30–2.30, 5–11; 12–3, 7–10.30 Sun
**Brakspear Mild, Bitter, Old, Special, OBJ** ⒣
16th-century, two-bar village pub with a quiet, comfortable lounge and a lively public bar. The landlord was *Brakspear Innkeeper of the Year* 1996. No lunches Sun.
Q ❀ ◖ ⬤ ⟳ ♣ P

**Try also: Waggon & Horses** (Scottish Courage)

## Warfield

### Cricketers

Cricketers Lane (off B3022 Binfield–Ascot road)
☎ (01344) 882910
11–3, 6.30–11; 11–11 Fri & Sat; 12–10.30 Sun
**Beer range varies** ⒣

Large, three-bar pub and restaurant set in countryside with a well-appointed family garden. Barbecues in summer. Eight guest beers (brewery of the month policy), plus Gibbs Mew beers. Good food. Meals 12–4 Sun (no meals Sun eve).
❀ ◖ ⬤ ♣ P

## Wargrave

### Bull

High Street (A321 at traffic lights) ☎ (01734) 403120
11–2.30, 6–11; 12–3, 7–10.30 Sun
**Brakspear Bitter, Special** ⒣
Superb, 17th-century pub with oak beams and a huge open fire. Effective air cleaning system. Good reputation for food (no meals Sun eve).
⚌ Q ❀ ◖ ⬤ ♿ ⟳ (not winter Sun)

## West Ilsley

### Harrow

1½ miles from A34
☎ (01635) 281260
11–3, 6–11; 12–4, 7–10.30 Sun
**Draught Bass; Morland Original, Old Speckled Hen, seasonal beers; guest beers** ⒣
Excellent pub, popular with walkers on the nearby Ridgeway, overlooking the cricket ground in an attractive downland village. Food is outstanding, particularly the home-made pies (no meals Sun eve). ⚌ Q ❀ ◖ ⬤ ♣ P

## White Waltham

### Beehive

Waltham Road
☎ (01628) 822877
11–2.30 (3 Sat), 5.30–11; 12–3, 7–10.30 Sun
**Brakspear Bitter; Flowers IPA, Original; guest beers** ⒣
Thriving, friendly local opposite the cricket pitch and near the former WWII airfield. Sympathetically refurbished, it retains two bars. Wide ranging social events include beer and cider festivals and brewery trips. Good value food.
⚌ Q ❀ ◖ ⬤ ♣ ⟳ P

## Windsor

### Prince Christian

11 Kings Road
☎ (01753) 860980
11–3, 5–11; 12–2.30, 7–10.30 Sun
**Brakspear Bitter; Fuller's London Pride; Theakston Best Bitter** ⒣
Free house just off the tourist trail, with a somewhat Irish atmosphere. Popular with staff from nearby council offices. No meals weekends. ◖ ⟳

## Vansittart Arms

105 Vansittart Road
☎ (01753) 865988
11–11; 12–10.30 Sun
**Fuller's Chiswick, London
Pride, ESB** Ⓗ
Comfortable pub with three
separate areas: Fuller's *Pub of
the Year* 1996. It can get very
crowded. No food Sun eve.
🏚 ❀ ◖ ▶ ♣ ✦

## Winterbourne

### Winterbourne Arms

☎ (01635) 248200
11.30–3 (not Mon except bank hols),
6–11; 12–3, 7–10.30 Sun
**Flowers Original; Wadworth
6X; guest beer** Ⓗ
Tastefully refurbished, old
country inn (formerly the New
Inn). Note the rosewood-
cabineted beer engine on static
display. Excellent (but not
cheap), freshly-prepared food
(no meals Sun eve). Peacefully-
set despite standing just ½ mile
S of the M4 (no immediate
access). Cider in summer.
🏚 ❀ ◖ ▶ ⌂ P Ⓤ

## Wokingham

### Duke's Head

56 Denmark Street
☎ (01734) 780316
11.30–3, 5.30 (5 Fri, 6 Sat)–11; 12–3,
7–10.30 Sun
**Boddingtons Bitter; Brakspear
Bitter, Special** Ⓗ

Comfortable town pub popular
with business and passing
trades; originally converted
from three cottages. Archives
mention the Duke's Head as
early as 1791. No food Sun.
Skittle alley for group hire.
❀ ◖ ⇌ ♣ P

### Queen's Head

23 The Terrace (A329, top of
Station Rd) ☎ (01734) 781221
11–3, 5.30–11; 12–3, 7–10.30 Sun
**Morland IPA, Original, Old
Masters, Old Speckled Hen;
guest beer** Ⓗ
Charming, single-bar pub
which retains its traditional
character. The local and
business regulars take an
active role in the many pub
sporting activities. The rear
garden is accessed through the
bar. Aunt Sally played in
summer. Excellent lunches
Mon–Sat. Q ❀ ◖ ⇌ ♣

### Ship

104–108 Peach Street
☎ (01734) 780389
11–3, 6–11; 11–11 Fri & Sat; 12–10.30
Sun
**Fuller's Chiswick, London
Pride, ESB, seasonal beers;
guest beer** Ⓗ
Friendly, two-bar pub, busy on
weekend eves. The small bar is
populated by locals. Covered
patio area for summer eve
drinking; barbecues in
summer. Live music some Sun
eves in the large bar.

Greenwood's beers are
sometimes served.
❀ ◖ ▶ ⊟ ♣ P

## Wokingham
## Without

### Crooked Billet

Honey Hill (off B3430, 2 miles
SE of Wokingham) OS826667
☎ (01734) 780438
11–11
**Brakspear Mild, Bitter, Old,
Special, OBJ** Ⓗ
Gem of a traditional ale house,
well worth seeking out for both
food and drink. The ramp
access and real fire typify the
welcome. Several walks pass
the pub. No eve meals Sun/
Mon. 🏚 Q ❀ ◖ ♣ P

## Woodley

### Inn on the Park

Woodford Park, Haddon Drive
(off Butts Hill Rd from centre)
☎ (01734) 628655
11–2.30, 6–11; 12–3, 7–10.30 Sun
**Brakspear Bitter, Special;
Fuller's London Pride; guest
beers** Ⓗ
Comfortable bar located within
the local sports centre; popular
with a wide cross-section of
residents and visitors. An
unusual, but most welcome
venue for a good real ale
selection (always two guests).
❀ ♿ P

---

# SEEING STARS?

The Bell at Aldworth in Berkshire, CAMRA's *National Pub of the
Year* in 1990, is just one of the pubs in this edition of the *Good Beer
Guide* to boast the new star symbol.

As explained earlier in the book, the star is awarded to pubs which
feature on CAMRA's National Inventory of pubs with rare and
unspoilt interiors of outstanding historic interest. They vary from
brash Victorian gin palaces to basic rural beerhouses and represent
architectural styles which are continually threatened by insensitive
refurbishments.

Not all the pubs on the Inventory feature in the *Good Beer Guide*
(which focuses chiefly on the quality of beer on sale rather than the
pub environment), but all are worth a visit in order to appreciate
their architectural value.

Visit the Bell, enjoy its unchanging atmosphere and the simplicity
and variety of its two-room layout and wonder why brewery
architects and accountants would want to despoil such national
treasures, turning them into characterless, one-bar retail outlets or
replacing their genuine antiquity with fake Tudor beams and clichéd
brassware.

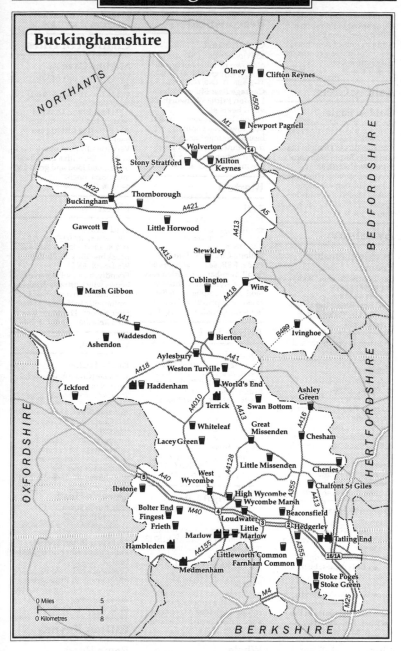

## Buckinghamshire

Olney
Clifton Reynes
Newport Pagnell
Wolverton
Milton Keynes
Stony Stratford
Thornborough
Buckingham
Gawcott
Little Horwood
Stewkley
Cublington
Marsh Gibbon
Wing
Waddesdon
Ashendon
Bierton
Ivinghoe
Aylesbury
Weston Turville
World's End
Ickford
Haddenham
Terrick
Swan Bottom
Ashley Green
Whiteleaf
Great Missenden
Chesham
Lacey Green
Little Missenden
Chenies
West Wycombe
Chalfont St Giles
Ibstone
High Wycombe
Wycombe Marsh
Bolter End
Fingest
Loudwater
Beaconsfield
Frieth
Little Marlow
Hedgerley
Marlow
Tatling End
Hambleden
Littleworth Common
Farnham Common
Medmenham
Stoke Poges
Stoke Green

NORTHANTS
BEDFORDSHIRE
HERTFORDSHIRE
OXFORDSHIRE
BERKSHIRE

0 Miles 5
0 Kilometres 8

---

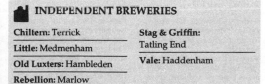

## INDEPENDENT BREWERIES

**Chiltern:** Terrick

**Little:** Medmenham

**Old Luxters:** Hambleden

**Rebellion:** Marlow

**Stag & Griffin:** Tatling End

**Vale:** Haddenham

## Ashendon

### Gatehangers
Lower End (lane by church)
☎ (01296) 651296
12–2.30, 7–11; 12–2.30, 7–10.30 Sun
**Adnams Bitter; Badger Dorset Best; Wadworth IPA, 6X; guest beer** Ⓗ

Formerly the Red Lion, this 400-year-old building, on a hilltop overlooking the northern Vale of Aylesbury, was once used as a courtroom. Imaginative food.
⌂ ❀ ◑ ♣ P

## Ashley Green

### Golden Eagle
On A416 ☎ (01442) 863549
11.30–3.30, 5.30–11; 12–3, 7–11 Sat; 12–3, 7–10.30 Sun
**Adnams Bitter; Draught Bass; Greenalls Bitter, Shipstone's Bitter; Wadworth 6X** Ⓗ
Cosy, welcoming, 17th-century village pub. Superb, home-cooked meals offer value for money (no food Fri/Sat eves or Sun. ❀ ◑ ♣ P

## Aylesbury

### Buckinghamshire Yeoman
Cambourne Avenue, Bedgrove
☎ (01296) 86615
11–11; 12–10.30 Sun
**ABC Best Bitter; Ind Coope Burton Ale; Tetley Bitter; guest beer** Ⓗ
Two-bar estate pub with a large family restaurant and a public bar. ❀ ◑ ⊕ ♿ ♣ P

### Grapes
36 Market Square
☎ (01296) 83735
11–11; 12–10.30 Sun
**Courage Best Bitter, Directors; Vale Notley, Wychert** Ⓗ
Town-centre bar by the civic centre. Wooden floor boards and Victorian decor provide a pleasant atmosphere. Lunches weekdays only; the upstairs restaurant only takes group bookings for eve meals. Regular live music. ◐ ⇌

### Queen's Head
1 Temple Square
☎ (01296) 415484
11–3, 5.30 (7 Sat)–11; 11–11 Fri; 12–3, 8–10.30 Sun
**Greenalls Bitter, Original; Tetley Bitter; guest beer** Ⓗ
Friendly, village-type pub (17th-century) in the old part of town, with two bars and a small dining area. Water jugs hang from the beams in the back bar. Families welcome.
⌂ Q ❀ ⛟ ◐ ⇌ ♣

### Ship
59 Walton Street
☎ (01296) 21888
11–3, 5.30–11; 12–3, 7–10.30 Sun
**Greene King Abbot; Tetley Bitter *or* Vale Notley; *Wadworth 6X*** Ⓗ
Cosmopolitan friendly pub by the basin of the Grand Union Canal opposite the 'Blue Leanie' office block. Disco Thu.
❀ ◐ ⊕ ♿ ⇌ ♣ P

## Beaconsfield

### Greyhound
33 Windsor End (200 yds from old town roundabout on old Slough Rd) ☎ (01494) 673823
11–3, 5.30–11; 12–3, 7–10.30 Sun
**Courage Best Bitter; Fuller's London Pride; Wadworth 6X; guest beers** Ⓗ
Originally a drovers' inn, this pub now has a popular, beamed lounge bar and restaurant area, with a good-size function room upstairs. No eve meals Sun. Q ❀ ◑

## Bierton

### Bell
191 Aylesbury Road
☎ (01296) 436055
11–3, 6–11 (11–11 winter Sat); 12–3, 7–10.30 Sun
**Fuller's Chiswick, London Pride, ESB, seasonal beers** Ⓗ
Small, two-bar pub within easy reach of Aylesbury. Thriving food trade (emphasis on fish; reasonable prices). All food is home-prepared. ❀ ◑ ▲ ♣ P

## Bolter End

### Peacock
On B482 ☎ (01494) 881417
11.45–2.30, 6–11; 12–3, 7–10.30 Sun
**ABC Best Bitter; Brakspear Bitter; Tetley Bitter; Wadworth 6X; guest beers** (occasional) Ⓗ
Pub dating from 1620, located just west of Lane End: one large room with several distinct areas. The emphasis is on freshly prepared, home-cooked bar meals. No food Sun eve. ⌂ Q ❀ ◑ ♣ P ⚡

## Buckingham

### New Inn
18 Bridge Street (over bridge from centre) ☎ (01280) 815713
10–11; 12–3, 7–10.30 Sun (may be all day)
**Greene King IPA, Abbot, seasonal beers** Ⓗ
Enterprising town pub with regular jazz and blues nights (and days), a superbly equipped children's room and a specialisation in Sri Lankan curries. ☋ ❀ ◑

### Whale
14 Market Hill (market square)
☎ (01280) 815537
10–11; 12–10.30 Sun
**Fuller's Chiswick, London Pride, ESB, seasonal beers; Marston's Pedigree; guest beers** Ⓗ
Very welcoming, town-centre local with dark wood panels and a range of drinking areas. Ask for some of the weird pub games. Very pleasant for visitors. ⌂ ❀ ⛟ ◑ ♣ ⚡

## Chalfont St Giles

### Merlins Cave
Village Green (off A413)
☎ (01494) 875101
11–2.30, 5.30–11; 11–11 Fri & Sat; 12–4, 7–10.30 Sun
**ABC Best Bitter; Draught Bass** Ⓗ**; Ind Coope Burton Ale** Ⓖ**; Tetley Bitter; guest beer** Ⓗ
Very friendly pub, dating back to the 1700s, with a good local trade, good food and good jazz music Sun lunch.
⌂ Q ❀ ◐ ⊕ ♿ ♣ P

## Chenies

### Red Lion
Off A404 ☎ (01923) 282722
11–2.30, 5.30–11; 12–3, 7–10.30 Sun
**Benskins BB; Vale Notley; Wadworth 6X** Ⓗ
Friendly, busy, village free house, which attracts drinkers and diners. No machines. Look for the snug to the rear of the dining room. The house beer is from Rebellion. Q ❀ ◑ P ⚡

## Chesham

### Black Horse
The Vale (Cholesbury road, 2 miles N of centre)
☎ (01494) 784656
11–2.30, 6–11; 12–3, 7–10.30 Sun
**Adnams Bitter; Benskins BB; Ind Coope Burton Ale; guest beers** Ⓗ
Comfortable old inn with an enormous garden, popular with diners (sausages and home-made pies are specialities). ⌂ Q ❀ ◑ ⌓ P

### Queen's Head
120 Church Street
☎ (01494) 783773
11–2.30, 5 (6 Sat)–11; 12–3, 7–10.30 Sun
**Brakspear Bitter, Special; Fuller's London Pride; guest beer** Ⓗ
Chesham's only two-bar pub (the lounge has three separate drinking and eating areas). No meals Sun eve.
⌂ Q ❀ ◑ ⊕ ⊖ ♣ P ⚡

## Clifton Reynes

### Robin Hood
OS902512 ☎ (01234) 711574
12–2.30, 6.30–11; 12–2.30, 7–10.30 Sun
**Greene King IPA, Abbot** Ⓗ
Remote, 16th-century pub with two bars and a conservatory, catering for a local clientele. The large garden is ideal on sunny days. Popular with ramblers (but no muddy boots!). No food Mon eve.
⌂ Q ☋ ❀ ◑ ♣ P

## Cublington

### Unicorn
High Street ☎ (01296) 681261
12–3 (not Mon), 5.30–11; 12–3, 7–10.30
Sun
**Beer range varies** Ⓗ
Excellent, low-beamed village
local with open fires at each
end of a long bar. Separate
dining room (no meals Sun
eve). Five changing real ales.
Happy 'hour' 5.30–7pm
🍴 Q ✿ ◖ ▲ P

## Farnham Common

### Yew Tree
Collinswood Road (A355,
N of village) ☎ (01753) 643723
11–11; 12–10.30 Sun
**Morland IPA, Original, Old
Speckled Hen, seasonal beers
or guest beer** Ⓗ
300-year-old country inn with
a small bar and a larger lounge.
Open 8am Mon–Sat for breakfast. 🍴 ✿ ◖ ▶ ⌑ ▲ ♣ P

## Fingest

### Chequers
☎ (01491) 638335
11–3, 6–11; 12–3, 7–10.30 Sun
**Brakspear Bitter, Old,
Special** Ⓗ
Friendly, 15th-century pub
opposite the church. The
emphasis is on food (restaurant
– no meals Sun eve). Large
garden. 🍴 Q ➤ ✿ ◖ ▶ P ✗

## Frieth

### Prince Albert
Moors End (100 yds from Lane
End road) ☎ (01494) 881683
11–3 (2.30 Mon), 5.30 (6 Mon)–11;
12–3, 7–10.30 Sun
**Brakspear Mild, Bitter, Old,
Special** Ⓗ
Pub which has appeared in the
Guide 22 times, offering a
superb atmosphere, location
and hospitality. Joss's platefuls
are a bonus at lunchtime
(Mon–Sat). 🍴 Q ✿ ◖ ▶

## Gawcott

### Cuckoo's Nest
New Inn Lane
☎ (01280) 812092
11–3 (not Mon), 6–11; 12–3, 7–10.30
Sun
**Hook Norton Best Bitter;
Marston's Pedigree; guest
beer** Ⓗ
Traditional, beamed,
welcoming, two-bar village
local. 🍴 Q ✿ ⌑ ♣ P

## Great Missenden

### Cross Keys
High Street ☎ (01494) 865373
11–3, 5–11; 12–3, 7–10.30 Sun

**Fuller's Chiswick, London
Pride, ESB** Ⓗ
400-year-old pub with high-
back settles in the bar area. The
restaurant is the only eating
area in the eve, thus preserving
a good atmosphere in the bar.
🍴 Q ✿ ◖ ▶ ➤ ♣ P

## Haddenham

### Rising Sun
Thame Road ☎ (01844) 291744
11–3, 6–11; 11–11 Fri & Sat; 12–3,
7–10.30 Sun
**Wells Eagle; guest beer** Ⓗ
Small village local usually
serving two interesting guest
beers. Cider in summer.
Occasional mini-beer festivals.
Q ✿ ➤ ♣ ⌂

## Hedgerley

### Brickmould
Village Lane ☎ (01753) 642716
11–11; 12–10.30 Sun
**Theakston Old Peculier; guest
beers** Ⓗ
Comfortable pub in a small
village, offering three drinking
areas and home-cooked food.
Note the aggregation of cats
and dogs. Games include
Carrom, an Asian cross
between shove-ha'penny and
pool. Four guest ales.
🍴 ⛨ ✿ ◖ ▶ ♣ P

### One Pin
One Pin Lane
☎ (01753) 643035
11–3 (4.30 Sat), 5.30 (6 Sat)–11; 12–
10.30 Sun
**Courage Best Bitter,
Directors** Ⓗ
Traditional, two-room pub
with a comfortable lounge.
Games include bar billiards.
Wheelchair access is through
the garden doors. No eve
meals Sun. 🍴 ✿ ◖ ▶ ⌑ ♣ P

### White Horse
Village Lane ☎ (01753) 643225
11–2.30, 5.30 (6 Sat)–11; 12–3, 7–10.30
Sun
**Greene King IPA, Rayments
Special; guest beers** Ⓖ
Picturesque, family-owned free
house with two rooms: a
comfortable lounge and a
wonderful, stone-floored,
rustic bar. All food is home-
cooked (eve meals Fri–Sun). At
least four varying guest beers.
Cider in summer.
🍴 Q ✿ ◖ ▶ ⌑ ♣ ⌂ P

## High Wycombe

### Bell
Frogmoor ☎ (01494) 521317
11–3, 5.30–11; 12–3, 7–10.30 Sun
**Fuller's Chiswick, London
Pride, ESB, seasonal beers** Ⓗ
Cosy pub on the edge of the
town centre. A popular lunch-
time venue (lunches Mon–Sat;

eve meals Mon–Thu). Fish is a
speciality. 🚪 ◖ ▶ ➤

### Rose & Crown
Desborough Road (near bus
station) ☎ (01494) 527982
11.30–3, 5–11; 11–11 Fri & Sat; 12–
10.30 Sun
**Courage Best Bitter; Gale's
HSB; Marston's Pedigree;
Ruddles Best Bitter;
Wadworth 6X; guest beers** Ⓗ
Wycombe's most interesting
selection of beers is served in
an L-shaped, corner pub with a
busy, lunchtime office trade
(no food weekends).
🍴 ◖ ➤ ♣

### Wycombe Wines
20 Crendon Street (near
station) ☎ (01494) 437228
10–10; 12–2, 7–10 Sun
**Adnams Broadside; Fuller's
ESB; Hook Norton Old
Hooky; guest beers** Ⓖ
Popular off-licence with five or
six beers and more at
weekends. Bottled beers
include Belgian. ➤

## Ibstone

### Fox
☎ (01491) 638289
11–3, 6–11; 12–3, 7–10.30 Sun
**Brakspear Bitter; Fuller's
London Pride; Greene King
Abbot; guest beer** Ⓗ
Popular pub, high up in the
Chilterns, offering quality
hotel accommodation and food
in both the bar and restaurant.
Large garden in superb
countryside.
🍴 Q ✿ 🚪 ◖ ▶ ♣ P

## Ickford

### Rising Sun
Worminghall Road
☎ (01844) 339238
12–3, 6–11; 12–3, 7–10.30 Sun
**Draught Bass; Boddingtons
Bitter; Hancock's HB** Ⓗ
Attractive, 15th-century,
timber-framed, thatched
coaching inn. The varied menu
includes an 'eat as much as you
like' buffet lunchtimes.
German food a speciality.
Children's menu and play area.
🍴 ✿ ◖ ▶ ♣ P

## Ivinghoe

### Rose & Crown
Vicarage Lane (turn opp. the
church then 1st right)
☎ (01296) 668472
12–2.30 (3 Sat), 6–11; 12–3, 7–10.30
Sun
**Adnams Bitter; Greene King
IPA; Morrells Mild; guest
beers** Ⓗ
Hard to find, street-corner local
with a comfortable lounge and
a lively public bar on a
different level. A rare outlet for

Morrells Mild. High quality food. ♨ ❀ ◖ ▮ ⊞ ▲ ♣

## Lacey Green

### Pink & Lily

Pink Road, Parslows Hillock
OS828019 ☎ (01494) 488308
11.45–3, 6–11; 12–3, 7–10.30 Sun
**Boddingtons Bitter; Brakspear Bitter, Special; Courage Best Bitter; Wychwood Hobgoblin; guest beers** ℍ
Popular, isolated pub, much extended but retaining its original snug, dedicated to Rupert Brooke. Noted for food (no chips!). No eve meals Sun.
♨ Q ❀ ◖ ♣ P

## Little Horwood

### Shoulder of Mutton

Church Street
☎ (01296) 712514
11–2.30 (not Mon), 6–11; 12–3, 7–10.30 Sun
**ABC Best Bitter; guest beer** ℍ
Grade I, thatched, red brick and whitewashed building dating from the 14th century. The compact, L-shaped bar has an inglenook and low beams. Mind your head!
♨ Q ❀ ◖ ▮ P

## Little Marlow

### King's Head

Church Road (A4155)
☎ (01628) 484407
11–3, 5.30–11; 12–3, 7–10.30 Sun
**Brakspear Bitter; Fuller's London Pride; guest beers** ℍ
One-bar village pub with much character where varied, home-cooked meals are always available. Function room and new separate dining room. Families very welcome.
♨ ❀ ◖ ▮ ♿ P

## Little Missenden

### Crown

Off A413 ☎ (01494) 862571
11–2.30, 6–11; 12–3, 7–10.30 Sun
**Hook Norton Best Bitter; Morrells Varsity** ℍ; **guest beer** ℍ/ⓖ
Fine, traditional pub with a genuine welcome, in the same family for nearly 100 years. Large garden. No lunches Sat–Mon. Cider in summer.
♨ Q ❀ ◖ ♣ ◠ P

## Littleworth Common

### Beech Tree

Dorney Wood Road (2 miles W of A355) ☎ (01628) 661328
11–11; 12–10.30 Sun
**Boddingtons Mild; Flowers IPA; Greenalls Bitter** ℍ
Traditional pub situated in the Burnham Beeches; one of the

few pubs in the area regularly serving mild. No food Sun eve.
♨ Q ❀ ◖ ♣ P

## Loudwater

### Derehams Inn

5 Derehams Lane (N of A40)
OS903907 ☎ (01494) 530965
11–3, 5.30–11; 12–3, 7–10.30 Sun
**Brakspear Bitter; Fuller's London Pride; Taylor Landlord; Wadworth 6X; Young's Bitter; guest beer** ℍ
Cosy pub, formerly the Bricklayers Arms; hard to find, so its custom is mainly local. Small car park. Lunches weekdays only. ♨ ❀ ◖ ♣ P

## Marlow

### Carpenters Arms

15 Spittal Street
☎ (01628) 473649
11–11; 12–3, 7–10.30 Sun
**Morrells Bitter, Varsity** ℍ
Thriving workingman's local of considerable character, acquired by Morrells in 1992. Fresh, home-made sandwiches always available. Small patio at the rear. ♨ Q ❀ ⇌ ♣

### Clayton Arms

16 Oxford Road, Quoiting Square (off A4155)
☎ (01628) 478620
11–3 (3.30 Sat), 5.30 (6 Sat)–11; 12–3.30, 7–10.30 Sun
**Brakspear Mild, Bitter, Old, Special** ℍ
Genuine local unspoilt by recent refurbishment. The public bar's atmosphere has been retained (darts at one end). The function room doubles as a clubs' meeting place and a dining room for small parties. Lit patio at the rear. ♨ Q ❀ ◖ ▮ ⇌ ♣

## Marsh Gibbon

### Greyhound

West Edge ☎ (01869) 277365
12–2.30, 6–11; 12–10.30 Sun
**Fuller's London Pride; Greene King Abbot; Hook Norton Best Bitter** ℍ
Listed building, probably of Tudor origin, with 17th-century brickwork. Rebuilt after a fire in 1740, it still has the fire plaque of Sun Insurance. Popular for Thai cuisine, steaks and quick business lunches.
♨ Q ❀ ◖ ▮ P ⊟

## Milton Keynes

### Foresters

21 Newport Road, New Bradwell ☎ (01908) 312348
10.30–11; 12–3, 7–10.30 Sun
**Wells Eagle** ℍ
Two-bar local on a busy road.

Little has been done to change the down to earth character of this frequently crowded pub.
❀ ⊞ ⇌ (Wolverton) ♣ P

### New Inn

2 Bradwell Road, New Bradwell ☎ (01908) 312094
11–11; 12–10.30 Sun
**Adnams Broadside; Wells Eagle, Bombardier; guest beers** ℍ
Friendly, lively canalside pub offering good value food and a separate restaurant. Enjoy the quiet back garden or sit on the lawn by the canal.
❀ ◖ ▮ ⊞ ♣ P

## Newport Pagnell

### Bull

33 Tickford Street (between Iron Bridge and Aston Martin works) ☎ (01908) 610325
11.30–2.30 (3 Sat), 5.15 (6.30 Sat)–11; 12–3, 6.30–10.30 Sun
**Beer range varies** ℍ
Splendidly unmodernised, reputedly haunted free house with an adventurous variety of eight beers and a large menu of reasonably priced food (no eve meals Sun). Very popular. The house beer, Life's a Bitch, is brewed by Morrells.
Q ❀ ⇌ ◖ ▮ ⊞ ♣

### Cannon

50 High Street
☎ (01908) 211495
11–11; 12–10.30 Sun
**Draught Bass; Fuller's London Pride; Hancock's HB; guest beer** ℍ
18th-century, Grade II listed free house in the centre of town: very much a drinking man's pub. The function room is occasionally opened as a second bar. Snacks weekday lunch. Wheelchair ramp provided. ♨ ♣ P

### Green Man

92 Silver Street (Willen Rd jct, 200 yds off High St)
☎ (01908) 611914
11–11; 12–10.30 Sun
**Banks's Bitter, seasonal beers; Marston's Pedigree; guest beers** ℍ
Family-owned and run, workingman's backstreet boozer where no-one is a stranger for long. Fascinating bric-a-brac in the lounge; old well in the bar. Noisy disco Fri. Cheap beer. ♨ Q ⇌ ⊞ ♣

## Olney

### Swan Inn & Bistro

12 High Street South
☎ (01234) 711111
12–11; 12–3, 7–10.30 Sun
**Fuller's London Pride; Hook Norton Best Bitter; Morrells Bitter; guest beers** ℍ

Late 1700s, stone inn with low ceilings, original beams and wood fires. Excellent value food. 🏨 ❀ ◖▶ ▲ P

## Stewkley

### Swan
High Street North
☎ (01525) 240285
12–3 (not winter Tue), 6–11; 12–3, 7–10.30 Sun
**Courage Best Bitter, Directors; guest beer** ⒣
Village local with a good atmosphere in its cosy, low-beamed lounge and separate dining area. No food Sun eve. ❀ ◖▶ P

## Stoke Green

### Red Lion
Near Wexham Park Hospital
☎ (01753) 521739
11–11; 12–10.30 Sun
**Draught Bass; Fuller's London Pride; guest beers**
(occasional) ⒣
Busy, friendly pub, originally two cottages; you can still see where the old post office used to be. Eve meals Tue–Sat. 🏨 ❀ ◖▶ ♿ ♣ ♉ P ⌀

## Stoke Poges

### Rose & Crown
Hollybush Hill
☎ (01753) 662148
11 (11.30 Sat)–3, 5.30 (7 Sat)–11; 12–4, 7–10.30 Sun
**Adnams Broadside; Morland Original, Old Speckled Hen, seasonal beers** ⒣
Cosy, welcoming pre-war pub with two bar areas, frequented mainly by locals. ❀ ◖ ♣ P

## Stony Stratford

### Vaults (Bull Hotel)
High Street ☎ (01908) 567104
12–11; 12–3, 6.30–10.30 Sun
**Draught Bass; Fuller's London Pride; Hardy Royal Oak; Wadworth 6X; guest beers** ⒣
Narrow, wood and brick, 18th-century bar with a warm welcome. Lots of Victoriana and breweriana. ❀ 🏨 ◖▶ ♿ ♣ P

## Swan Bottom

### Old Swan
OS902055 ☎ (01494) 837239
12–3, 6–11; 11–11 Sat; 12–3, 6–10.30 Sun
**Draught Bass; Butcombe Bitter; Fuller's London Pride; guest beer** ⒣
Old country pub tucked away in the Chilterns in a lovely setting. Large garden; selection of games but no dartboard (low beams!). Eve meals Tue–Sat. 🏨 Q ❀ ◖▶ ♣ P

## Tatling End

### Stag & Griffin
Oxford Road (A40, near A413 jct) ☎ (01753) 883100
11.30–11; 12–10.30 Sun
**Fuller's London Pride; Rebellion IPA** ⒣**; Stiffin Ale; guest beers** ⒢
Pleasant roadside brew pub serving beer by gravity (rare for area). Superb restaurant; pizza delivery service. 🏨 Q ❀ ◖▶ ▲ P

## Thornborough

### Lone Tree
On A421
☎ (01280) 812334
11.30–2.30, 5 (6.30 Sat)–11; 12–3, 7–10.30 Sun
**Black Sheep Best Bitter, Special; Marston's HBC; guest beers** ⒣
Roadside free house offering an outstanding choice. Varied and imaginative food menu, too. 🏨 Q ❀ ◖▶ ⌂ P

## Waddesdon

### Lion
High Street
☎ (01296) 651227
12–2.30, 5.30–11; 12–3, 7–10.30 Sun
**Draught Bass; Fuller's London Pride; guest beer** ⒣
Free house specialising in good quality meals from a daily-changing menu. Ample portions; plenty of elbow room at the large wooden tables (no meals Sun eve). Q ❀ ◖▶ P

## Weston Turville

### Chequers Inn
35 Church Lane (loop road S side of main road)
☎ (01296) 613298
11.30–3 (not Mon), 6–11; 12–3, 7–10.30 Sun
**Adnams Bitter; Brakspear Bitter; Marston's Pedigree; Vale Notley; Wadworth 6X** ⒣
Stone-flagged bar adjoining a popular restaurant offering a high standard of cuisine (no food Sun eve or Mon). Bar meals Tue–Sat. 🏨 ❀ ◖▶ P

## West Wycombe

### George & Dragon
☎ (01494) 464414
11–2.30, 5.30–11; 11–11 Sat; 12–10.30 Sun
**Courage Best Bitter; guest beers** ⒣
18th-century coaching inn with an original timbered bar; noted for its food and garden. 🏨 Q ⛟ ❀ 🏨 ◖▶ P

## Whiteleaf

### Red Lion
Upper Icknield Way (off A4010) ☎ (01844) 344476
11.30–3, 5.30 (6 Sat)–11; 12–3, 7–10.30 Sun
**Brakspear Bitter; Hook Norton Best Bitter; Morland Original; guest beer** ⒣
17th-century, secluded free house, with wooden settles and some interesting antiques. Ask to see the unusual wooden puzzles and games. 🏨 Q ❀ 🏨 ◖▶ P

## Wing

### Cock Inn
High Street ☎ (01296) 688214
11–3, 6–11; 12–3, 7–10.30 Sun
**Beer range varies** ⒣
Former coaching inn comprised of one comfortable bar, a 60-seater restaurant and good facilities for customers with disabilities. Imaginative selection of six ales; seasonal beer festivals. 🏨 Q ❀ ◖▶ ♿ P

## Wolverton

### Craufurd Arms
59 Stratford Road
☎ (01908) 313864
12–11; 12–3, 7–10.30 Sun
**Draught Bass; guest beers** ⒣
Large and imposing, Edwardian pub retaining some original features: one L-shaped, comfortable lounge with a separate restaurant and a function room. No eve meals Sun. 🏨 ◖▶ ≋ P

## World's End

### Marquis of Granby
225 Aylesbury Road (A413, 1 mile N of Wendover)
☎ (01296) 622104
12–11; 12–10.30 Sun
**Adnams Bitter; Marston's Pedigree; Tetley Bitter; Tring Ridgeway; Wadworth 6X; guest beer** ⒣
Refurbished 300-year-old coaching inn with a dining area. Extensive range of meals and snacks served all day. Oak beams and a wood burning stove are features. Weekend barbecues; garden play area. 🏨 ❀ ◖▶ ≋ P

## Wycombe Marsh

### General Havelock
114 Kingsmead Road
OS889915 ☎ (01494) 520391
11–2.30 (3 Fri), 5.30 (5 Fri)–11; 11–11 Sat; 12–4, 7–10.30 Sun
**Fuller's Chiswick, London Pride, ESB, seasonal beers** ⒣
Traditional family pub, smart, friendly and noted for its lunches. 🏨 ❀ ◖ ♣ P

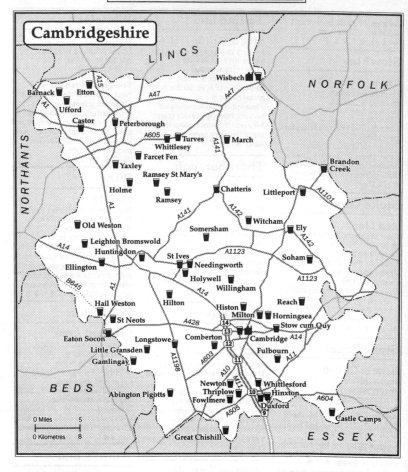

## Cambridgeshire

Abington Pigotts · Barnack · Etton · Ufford · Castor · Wisbech · Peterborough · Turves · Whittlesey · March · Farcet Fen · Yaxley · Ramsey St Mary's · Brandon Creek · Holme · Chatteris · Littleport · Ramsey · Witcham · Old Weston · Somersham · Ely · Leighton Bromswold · Huntingdon · Soham · Ellington · St Ives · Needingworth · Holywell · Willingham · Reach · Hail Weston · Hilton · Histon · Milton · Horningsea · St Neots · Stow cum Quy · Eaton Socon · Longstowe · Comberton · Cambridge · Little Gransden · Fulbourn · Gamlingay · Newton · Whittlesford · Abington Pigotts · Thriplow · Hinxton · Fowlmere · Duxford · Castle Camps · Great Chishill

(LINCS · NORFOLK · NORTHANTS · BEDS · ESSEX)

0 Miles 5
0 Kilometres 8

---

## Abington Pigotts

### Pig & Abbot
Off A505 ☎ (01763) 852273
12–3, 6–11; 12–11 Sat & Sun
**Greene King IPA; Marston's Bitter, Pedigree; guest beer** Ⓗ
Large country pub, off the beaten track. Food-oriented, with country cooking, it caters for local as well as passing trade. Booking essential for the restaurant. ♨ ⊛ ◖ ▶ ♣ P

---

## Barnack

### Millstone
Millstone Lane
☎ (01780) 740296
11–2.30, 6–11; 12–3, 7–10.30 Sun
**Adnams Bitter; Everards Tiger, Old Original; guest beer** Ⓗ
Welcoming, stone-built local with a restaurant offering an extensive menu. Lots of alcoves branch off the small

central bar. In the *Guide* every year since 1976.
Q ⊛ ◖ ▶ ♿ P ⚲

---

## Brandon Creek

### Ship
Off A10 ☎ (01353) 676228
12–2.30, 6.30–11 (11–3, 6–11; 11–11 Sat, summer); 12–3, 7–10.30 (12–10.30 summer) Sun
**Adnams Bitter; Butcombe Bitter; Elgood's Pageant; Hook Norton Old Hooky; guest beer** Ⓗ
Riverside fenland pub; Cambridge CAMRA *Pub of the Year 1996*. It stays open when the sun shines. Cider in summer. ♨ ⊛ ◖ ▶ ◔ P

---

## Cambridge

### Bird in Hand
73 Newmarket Road
☎ (01223) 354034
11–3, 5–11; 11–11 Fri & Sat; 12–3, 7–10.30 Sun

**Greene King XX Mild, IPA, Rayments Special, Abbot, seasonal beers** Ⓗ
Characterful, early 20th-century, one-bar pub. Range of malt whiskies; cheap mild Thu (all day); try the chilli vodka. No food Sat. ♨ ⊛ ◖ ♣ ⊟

### Cambridge Blue
85–87 Gwydir Street (off Mill Rd) ☎ (01223) 361382
12–2.30 (4 Sat), 6–11; 12–3, 7–10.30 Sun
**Nethergate IPA, Bitter, Golden Gate, Old Growler; guest beers** Ⓗ
Characterful terrace pub where a no-smoking bar, a tiny snug and a conservatory complement the extended

---

main bar. The large garden features a model railway. Children's certificate. Note the amazing hat collection. Guest beers always include a mild.
🏃 Q ⛄ ❀ ◖ ▮ ♣ ⌂ ⌿

### Castle
38 Castle Street
☎ (01223) 353194
11.30–2.30, 5–11; 11.30–11 Sat; 12–3, 7–10.30 Sun
**Adnams Mild, Bitter, Broadside; guest beers** Ⓗ
Superbly refurbished, this is Adnams's most westerly pub: five different drinking areas and more upstairs. Suntrap patio. Six guest beers usually on offer. 🏃 ⛄ ❀ ◖ ⌿

### Champion of the Thames
68 King Street
☎ (01223) 352043
11–11; 12–4, 7–10.30 Sun
**Greene King XX Mild, IPA** Ⓗ, **Abbot** Ⓖ
Small pub of immense character. Fine etched windows depict the Champ in action. A rare city-centre outlet for mild. Weekday lunches.
◖

### Cow & Calf
14 Pound Hill
☎ (01223) 576220
12–3.30, 6–11; 12–4, 7–10.30 Sun
**Courage Best Bitter; Elgood's Cambridge Bitter; Nethergate Bitter; Samuel Smith OBB; guest beer** Ⓗ
A traditional pub atmosphere prevails in one of Cambridge's few genuine free houses. Pub cat connoisseurs will not be disappointed. Weekday lunches served. 🏃 ❀ ◖ ♣

### Empress
72 Thoday Street (off Mill Rd)
☎ (01223) 247236
11–2.30, 6.30–11; 12–2.30, 7–10.30 Sun
**Castle Eden Ale; Flowers Original; Marston's Pedigree; Wadworth 6X; guest beer** Ⓗ
Thriving, backstreet pub, heaving in the eve but always friendly and welcoming. Surprisingly large, it has three distinct drinking rooms, plus segregated games areas. A local CAMRA *Pub of the Year* contender yet again. Good value sandwiches. ❀ ♣ ⌂

### Free Press
Prospect Row ☎ (01223) 68337
12–2.30, 6–11; 12–3, 7–10.30 Sun
**Greene King IPA, Abbot, seasonal beers** Ⓗ
Unspoilt, backstreet gem, completely non-smoking. Its features include a small snug and a garden where the rabbits roam. Prints and notices are everywhere with rowing paraphernalia in evidence.

Home-cooked food includes unusual vegetarian options, and a Texan hot chilli. Eve meals until 8.30.
🏃 Q ❀ ◖ ▮ ⌿

### Globe Ale House
21 Hills Road
☎ (01223) 352848
11–11; 12–10.30 Sun
**Boddingtons Bitter; Flowers IPA; Fuller's London Pride; Marston's Pedigree; Morland Old Speckled Hen; guest beers** Ⓗ
There's a curious thrown-together look about this refurbished main street pub. The living room effect of the carpeted upper split-level is off-set by the café-style bare boards and rugs of the lower level. In-house beer festivals and promotions. Food all day Sat and Sun. ❀ ◖ ▮ ⇌ P

### Jug & Firkin (off-licence)
90 Mill Road ☎ (01223) 315034
10.30–1.30, 3–10; 10–10.30 Sat; 12–2.30, 7–9.30 Sun
**Beer range varies** Ⓖ
Over two dozen English bottle-conditioned beers, ten real ciders, and always at least five real ales are available at this off-licence. ⌂

### St Radegund
129 King Street
☎ (01223) 311794
12–2.30, 5.30–11; 12–11 Fri & Sat; 5.30–10.30 Sun, closed Sun lunch
**Bateman XB; Fuller's London Pride; Nethergate Bitter; guest beer** Ⓗ
Pub which more than makes up in character for what it lacks in size. The well-travelled landlord welcomes visitors from near and far. Ask about the Veil Ale. ◖

### Tap & Spile (Mill)
14 Mill Lane (by river)
☎ (01223) 357026
11–11; 12–10.30 Sun
**Adnams Bitter; guest beers** Ⓗ
Still the pick of the ale houses which now abound in the city: a pub with a sturdy interior with oak floors and exposed brickwork, overlooking the mill pond where punts can be hired. Outside drinking on the green. Eight beers.
Q ❀ ◖ ⌂

### Wrestlers
337 Newmarket Road
☎ (01223) 566554
12–3, 5–11; 12–3, 7–10.30 Sun
**Adnams Broadside; Badger Tanglefoot; Mansfield Bitter; Morland Old Speckled Hen; Wells Eagle, Bombardier** Ⓗ
Bustling, buoyant pub, full of life and often noisy, with live music twice a week. Authentic

Thai bar meals and take-aways.
🏃 ◖ ▮ ⌂

## Castle Camps

### Cock
High Street ☎ (01799) 584207
12–3, 7–11; 12–11 Sat; 12–3 (may extend), 7–10.30 Sun
**Greene King IPA, Abbot; Nethergate Bitter; guest beer** Ⓗ
This friendly, two-bar village local goes from strength to strength with its four beers and home-cooked food. Fresh fish and chips Fri eve. No food Sun lunch or Mon eve.
🏃 ❀ ◖ ▮ ⊟ ♣ P

## Castor

### Royal Oak
24 Peterborough Road
☎ (01733) 380217
11–2.30, 6–11; 12–3, 7–10.30 Sun
**Ind Coope Burton Ale; Tetley Bitter; guest beer (weekends)** Ⓗ
A low-beamed ceiling and a maze of passages and bars are features of this thatched, listed building, which has a cosy atmosphere. Popular with passing trade. 🏃 Q ❀ ♣ P

## Chatteris

### Honest John
24A–26 South Park Street
☎ (01354) 692698
11–2.30, 5.30–11; 12–2.30, 5.30–10.30 Sun
**Brakspear Bitter; guest beers** Ⓗ
Former labour exchange, now a very comfortable pub with a large, well-divided main room, a dining room and an upstairs function room. Good value, home-made food.
Q ◖ ▮ & ♣ P

### Walk the Dog
34 Bridge Street
☎ (01354) 693695
12–2.30, 6.30–11; 12–2.30, 7–10.30 Sun
**Adnams Bitter; Draught Bass; Worthington Bitter; guest beer** Ⓗ
Small, friendly pub with a warm atmosphere.
🏃 ❀ ♣ P ▯

## Comberton

### Grapevine
5 Green End ☎ (01223) 263059
12–2.30 (3 Sat; not Wed), 6–11; 12–3, 7–10.30 Sun
**Draught Bass; Greene King IPA; Worthington Bitter; guest beer** Ⓗ
Unpretentious, friendly local whose garden adjoins the village pond. Occasional live entertainment. 🏃 ❀ &

## Duxford

### Plough

St Peters Street
☎ (01223) 833170
11–3, 5.30–11; 12–3, 7–10.30 Sun
**Adnams Bitter; Everards Beacon, Tiger, Old Original; guest beers** Ⓗ
17th-century, thatched house offering a warm welcome and excellent food at reasonable prices (eve meals Tue–Sat). Well situated for the Air Museum. 🏠 ❀ ◖ ▶ P

## Eaton Socon

### Millers Arms

Ackerman Street (off Great North Rd) ☎ (01480) 405965
12–2, 5.30–11; 11–11 Sat
**Greene King XX Mild, IPA, Abbot, seasonal beers** Ⓗ
Small 'village' pub on the larger of Eaton Socon's greens. The spacious garden boasts many children's facilities, and a petanque court. Live jazz and barbecues in the garden in summer. Popular with boat owners from the nearby river. Lunches Tue–Sat.
🏠 ⛟ ❀ ◖ ♣

## Ellington

### Mermaid

High Street (off A14)
☎ (01480) 891450
12–2.30, 7–11; 12–3, 7–10.30 Sun
**Draught Bass** Ⓗ
Single-bar village pub which has changed little in recent years. Warm, friendly atmosphere.
🏠 Q ❀ ◖ ♣ 🍴

## Ely

### Prince Albert

62 Silver Street
☎ (01353) 663494
11.30–3 (3.30 Thu–Sat), 6.30–11; 12–3.30, 7–10.30 Sun
**Greene King XX Mild, IPA, Abbot, seasonal beers** Ⓗ
Classic town local where the emphasis is on good ale and chat. Your own food can be brought into the delightful garden as long as drinks are bought (the pub itself only serves sandwiches). Public car park opposite (entrance from Broad St). Q ❀ ♣

### Royal Standard

24 Forehill ☎ (01353) 662613
11–3, 7–11; 12–4, 7–10.30 Sun
**Greene King IPA, Abbot, seasonal beers** Ⓗ
L-shaped, wood-panelled, one-bar pub with games at one end and a step-down lounge at the other. Handy for the Minster. ❀ ◖ ♣ P 🍴

## West End House

16 West End ☎ (01353) 662907
11–2.30 (3 Sat), 6–11; 12–3, 7–10.30 Sun
**Courage Directors; Marston's Pedigree; Ruddles Best Bitter; Theakston Best Bitter, XB; guest beer** Ⓗ
Pub featuring four drinking areas, low ceilings and a plethora of beams. Friendly welcome from all except the cat. 🏠 ❀ ◖ ♣

## Etton

### Golden Pheasant

1 Main Street ☎ (01733) 252387
11–11; 12–10.30 Sun
**Draught Bass; Woodforde's Wherry;** Ⓗ
19th-century manor house with a large, comfortable lounge, a family room and a restaurant. The big garden houses an aviary. Seven guest beers.
🏠 Q ⛟ ❀ ◖ ▶ ♿ ▲ ♣ P 🍴

## Farcet Fen

### Plough

Milk & Water Drove (B1095)
☎ (01733) 844307
11–4, 6–11; 12–4, 7–10.30 Sun
**Draught Bass; Highgate Dark; John Smith's Bitter; guest beer** Ⓗ
Welcoming, isolated fen pub, featuring a collection of brasses and kettles. Book the restaurant (only fresh produce used). No meals Wed.
🏠 Q ❀ ◖ ▶ ♣ P 🍴

## Fowlmere

### Chequers

High Street ☎ (01763) 208369
11.30–3, 6.30–11; 12–3, 7–10.30 Sun
**Tetley Bitter; Tolly Cobbold Original** Ⓗ
16th-century coaching inn with top class food. The living room drinking area displays wartime aviation photos. The beer range may vary. 🏠 Q ❀ ◖ ▶ P

## Fulbourn

### Baker's Arms

Hinton Road ☎ (01223) 880606
11–11; 12–10.30 Sun
**Greene King XX Mild, IPA, Rayments Special, Abbot, seasonal beers** Ⓗ
Outstanding refurbishment of a village local, retaining considerable drinking space at the bar and keeping food mainly in the dining room. Weekend barbecues; children's play area. ❀ ◖ ▶ ♿ ▲ P

### Six Bells

High Street ☎ (01223) 880244
11.30–2.30 (3 Fri), 6.30 (6 Fri)–11; 12–11 Sat; 12–3, 7–10.30 Sun

**Flowers IPA; Ind Coope Burton Ale; Tolly Cobbold Mild; guest beer** Ⓗ
Thriving village local, the hub of the community. The two bars are both welcoming; the newly refurbished restaurant serves home-cooked meals (eve meals Tue–Sat). Jazz first and third Wed of the month; monthly Sun jazz brunches in the function room.
🏠 ❀ ◖ ▶ ♣ P

## Gamlingay

### Cock

25 Church Street
☎ (01767) 50255
11.30–3, 5.30–11; 11–11 Sat
**Greene King IPA, Rayments Special, Abbot, seasonal beers** Ⓗ
Timber-framed pub of some interest. Both bars have extensive wood panelling and there is a display of 'cocks' in the public bar. The oldest building in Gamlingay. Weekday happy hour 5.30–7.
🏠 ⛟ ❀ ◖ ▶ ♿ ♣ P

## Great Chishill

### Pheasant

24 Heydon Road
☎ (01763) 838535
12–3, 6–11; 12–11 Sat; 12–10.30 Sun
**Adnams Bitter; Marston's Pedigree; Ruddles Best Bitter; guest beers** Ⓗ
Pretty country pub with inglenook, beams, flagstones, a lovely raised garden and a magic cellar – overworked clichés but this is it.
🏠 Q ❀ ◖ ▶ P

## Hail Weston

### Royal Oak

High Street (off B645)
☎ (01480) 472527
11–11
**Wells Eagle, Bombardier; guest beer** Ⓗ
Picturesque, thatched village pub which has a large garden with a children's playground and a pleasant family room with games (video). Eve meals Tue–Sat. 🏠 ⛟ ❀ ◖ ▶ ♣ P

## Hilton

### Prince of Wales

Potton Road (B1040)
☎ (01480) 830257
11–2.30 (not Mon; 12–3 Sat), 6 (7 winter Sat)–11; 12–3, 7–10.30 Sun
**Draught Bass; Highgate Dark; Nethergate IPA; guest beer** (occasional) Ⓗ
Two-bar village pub that offers a warm welcome and a large roaring fire. Friendly atmosphere. No food Mon.
🏠 ❀ 🏠 ◖ ▶ 🏠 ♣ P

## Hinxton

### Red Lion
32 High Street
☎ (01799) 530601
11–2.30, 6–11; 12–2.30, 7–10.30 Sun
**Adnams Bitter; Draught Bass; Boddingtons Bitter; Greene King IPA** Ⓗ
16th-century coaching inn with an award-winning restaurant extension. Lots of beams (old and new). Large garden with animals. ⚏ ❀ ◖ ▶ P

## Histon

### Red Lion
27 High Street
☎ (01223) 564437
11.30–3, 5–11; 11–11 Sat; 12–5, 7–10.30 Sun
**Everards Mild; Home Bitter; Nethergate Golden Gate; Theakston Best Bitter; guest beers** Ⓗ
Enterprising free house offering a choice between a quiet comfy lounge and a boisterous games-oriented public. No food Sun. ⚏ Q ❀ ◖ ✦ P

## Holme

### Admiral Wells
Station Road ☎ (01487) 830730
12–3, 5.30–11; 12–11 Sat; 12–3, 7–10.30 Sun
**Draught Bass; Hancock's HB; Oakham JHB; Shepherd Neame Spitfire; guest beers** Ⓗ
Late 1800s pub with three comfortably furnished rooms and a restaurant. Reopened in early 1995 as a free house after a period of closure. Said to be the lowest pub in England. Petanque played. No food Sun eve. ⚏ Q ❀ ◖ ▶ P

## Holywell

### Ferry Boat Inn
1 mile from Needingworth village, on the river
☎ (01480) 463227
11.30–3, 6–11; 12–3, 7–10.30 Sun
**Draught Bass; Webster's Yorkshire Bitter; guest beers** Ⓗ
Claimed to be the oldest in England, now a sprawling, frequently extended riverside inn with good food and cosy and interesting drinking areas. Moorings and a marina nearby. ⚏ ⛫ ❀ ⌂ ◖ ▶ P ✕

## Horningsea

### Crown & Punchbowl
High Street ☎ (01223) 860643
12–2.30 (not Sat), 6.30–11; 12–3, 7–11 Sun
**Adnams Extra; Elgood's Cambridge Bitter; Greene King IPA** Ⓗ

17th-century inn at the centre of a picturesque village, close to the A14. The cosy, quarry-tiled public bar is perfect for casual conversation; the snug, ideal for pre- or after-dinner drinks, is separated from the meandering dining room by stained-glass screens. ⚏ ⛫ ❀ ⌂ ◖ ▶ ⊞ ✦ P

## Huntingdon

### Old Bridge Hotel
1 High Street (off ring road – just past exit to Godmanchester)
☎ (01480) 452681
11–11; 12–10.30 Sun
**Adnams Bitter; B&T seasonal beers; guest beer** Ⓗ
Smart, 18th-century hotel, overlooking the River Ouse, with a comfortable wood-panelled bar, popular with business people and locals alike. Friendly staff; ever-changing guest beer, which often features new breweries or seasonal beers. ⚏ Q ❀ ⌂ ◖ ▶ P

## Leighton Bromswold

### Green Man
37 The Avenue (off A14)
☎ (01480) 890238
12–3 (not Tue–Thu), 7–11; closed Mon; 12–3, 7–10.30 Sun
**Nethergate IPA; Taylor Landlord; guest beer** Ⓗ
Comfortable rural free house displaying a collection of brewery memorabilia. Wide, and ever-changing, range of guest beers; good value food. Always a warm welcome. CAMRA East Anglia *Pub of the Year* 1992. Hood skittles played. ⛫ ❀ ◖ ⅋ ✦ ⌂ P

## Little Gransden

### Chequers
71 Main Road (off B1040)
☎ (01767) 677348
12–2.30, 7–11; 11–11 Sat; 12–10.30 Sun
**Greene King IPA; guest beer** Ⓗ
Worth searching for, this three-roomed village pub maintains its rustic charm. Recent improvements have only enhanced its qualities. Friendly and welcoming. A different guest ale each week. ⚏ Q ❀ ✦ P

## Littleport

### George & Dragon
13 Station Road
☎ (01353) 862639
11–11; 12–10.30 Sun
**Badger Dorset Best; Wells Eagle, Bombardier; guest beers** Ⓗ

Neatly refurbished, one-bar establishment – an oasis for good real ale in this neck of the woods. Relaxed and comfortable atmosphere. Skittles played. No eve meals Sun. ❀ ◖ ▶ ⌂ P

## Longstowe

### Golden Miller
54 High Street (B1046)
☎ (01954) 719385
12–2.30, 6.30–11
**Adnams Bitter** Ⓗ, **Broadside** Ⓖ; **Bateman XB** Ⓗ
Friendly village pub named after the 1934 Grand National winner, whose photographs adorn the walls. Separate dining room. Oversized glasses for Bateman XB. ⛫ ❀ ◖ ▶ P ⊞

## March

### Rose & Crown
41 St Peters Road
☎ (01354) 52879
11.30–2.30 (not Wed), 7–11
**John Smith's Bitter, guest beers** Ⓗ
150-year-old, traditional, two-roomed pub: the only true free house in March. The guest beer varies to include stouts and porters. Q ✦ ⌂ P

## Milton

### Waggon & Horses
39 High Street
☎ (01223) 860313
12–2.30, 5–11; 12–11 Sat; 12–3, 7–10.30 (12–10.30 summer) Sun
**Bateman XB; Wadworth 6X; guest beers** Ⓗ
Unpretentious and friendly pub where guest beers always include a mild. The dining room is a new addition. ⚏ ❀ ◖ ▶ ⌂ P

## Needingworth

### Queen's Head
30 High Street (off A1123)
☎ (01480) 463946
12–11; 12–3, 7–10.30 Sun
**Smiles Brewery Bitter; Woodforde's Wherry; guest beers** Ⓗ
Two-bar village pub with a strong darts and dominoes following. The handpumps are situated in the bar; four guest beers a week are featured. All food is home-made (eve meals Tue–Sat). ⚏ ❀ ◖ ▶ & ✦ P

## Newton

### Queen's Head
☎ (01223) 870436
11.30 (11 Sat)–2.30, 6–11; 12–2.30, 7–10.30 Sun
**Adnams Bitter, Old, Extra (summer), Broadside** Ⓖ

The landlord celebrated 34 years at this pub and 25 years in sole charge in 1996. Water coolers are used in summer on casks behind the bar.
🏚 Q ➳ ⌸ ♣ ⌂ P

## Old Weston

### Swan

Main Street (B660, off A14)
☎ (01832) 293400
12–3 (not Mon or Tue), 6.30 (7 Sat)–11; 12–3, 7–10.30 Sun

**Adnams Bitter; Greene King Abbot; Morland Old Speckled Hen; Nethergate Old Growler; guest beer** Ⓗ
Characterful village pub with three rooms and plenty of beams. Good atmosphere. Hood skittles played.
🏚 ➳ ❀ ◖ ▶ Å ♣ P

## Peterborough

### Blue Bell

Welland Road, Dogsthorpe (1 mile off A47)
☎ (01733) 54890
11–3, 6.30–11; 12–3, 7–10.30 Sun

**Elgood's Cambridge Bitter, Greyhound, seasonal beers or guest beers** Ⓗ
One of the oldest pubs in Peterborough, converted from a farmhouse in 1665: two large rooms with real fires. The lounge has a separate, oak-panelled snug. Four ales are available. Large patio with a children's play area.
🏚 Q ❀ ◖ ⌸ ♣ P

### Blue Bell

6 The Green, Werrington (½ mile off A15, 1 mile from A47) ☎ (01733) 571264
11–3, 5–11; 12–3, 7–10.30 Sun

**Elgood's Cambridge Bitter, Greyhound, seasonal beers; guest beers** Ⓗ
Attractive white building, circa 1890 (extended in 1985), with a public bar and a very comfortable lounge. Fresh food daily, home-cooked by a friendly landlord who is fiercely proud of the quality of his beer and meals. The best pub in Werrington.
❀ ◖ ▶ ⌸ ♣ P

### Bogarts

17 North Street
☎ (01733) 349995
11–11; closed Sun

**Draught Bass; guest beers** Ⓗ
A traditional atmosphere prevails in this city-centre free house without pool or jukebox, where walls are adorned with old film posters and breweriana. Seven handpumps serve a varying range of beers. Small suntrap beer garden. A must for visitors.
Q ❀ ◖ ⇌ ⌂

### Charters

Town Bridge (steps down from S end of bridge)
☎ (01733) 315700
12–11; 12–10.30 Sun

**Draught Bass; Everards Tiger; Fuller's London Pride; Oakham JHB, Hunky Dory, Old Tosspot; guest beers** Ⓗ
Real ale flagship housed in a large converted Dutch barge, a large, busy venue with a relaxed atmosphere that appeals to all. Spacious restaurant above the bar. 440 different real ales sold in 1995.
❀ ◖ ⇌ ⏚

### Coach & Horses

39–41 High Street, Stanground
☎ (01733) 343400
11.30–2.30, 6–11; 11–11 Sat; 12–3, 7–10.30 Sun

**Marston's Pedigree; John Smith's Bitter; guest beer** Ⓗ
Long-established, friendly local with two contrasting bars, a big garden, a patio and a large function room. No eve meals Wed. Q ❀ ◖ ▶ ⌸ ♿ ♣ P

### Durham Ox

76 Star Road (E out of town along Bishops Rd, left before flyover) ☎ (01733) 66565
12 (11.30 Fri)–3, 5–11; 11.30–4, 6.30–11 Sat; 12–3, 7–10.30 Sun

**Adnams Broadside; Brains SA; Wells Eagle, Bombardier** Ⓗ
Three-roomed local: a basic bar, a lounge and a small dining/lounge area. Q ❀ ⌸ ♣

### Fountain

2 Burghley Road (½ mile N of centre) ☎ (01733) 54533
11–2.30, 7–11; 12–3, 7–10.30 Sun

**Courage Directors; Everards Beacon, Tiger, Old Original; guest beers** Ⓗ
1930s redbrick building on the edge of the city centre: a friendly public bar with a pool table in the centre and a comfortable lounge with a real fire. Frequently changing guest beers. No food Sun.
🏚 ❀ ◖ ⌸ ♣

### Hand & Heart Inn

12 Highbury St (off Lincoln Rd, Millfield) ☎ (01733) 69463
10.30–3, 6–11; 12–3, 7–10.30 Sun

**Courage Directors; Marston's Pedigree; John Smith's Bitter; Wilson's Mild; guest beer** Ⓗ
The finest example in the area of a 1930s backstreet local. Note the original Warwick's windows. Beers at most reasonable prices. The cider varies; often a perry stocked, too. 🏚 ⌸ ♣ ⌂

### Woolpack

29 North Street, Stanground
☎ (01733) 54417
11.30–3, 5.30–11; 11–11 Fri & Sat; 12–3.30, 7–10.30 Sun

**Boddingtons Bitter; Castle Eden Ale; Whitbread seasonal beers; guest beers** Ⓗ
Early 18th-century community pub which also caters for passing boat trade (moorings available). No food Sun. Beer festival May Bank Hol weekend. ❀ ◖ ▶ ♣

## Ramsey

### Jolly Sailor

43 Great Whyte
☎ (01487) 813388
11–3, 5.30 (7 Sat)–11; 12–3, 7–10.30 Sun

**Flowers Original; Ind Coope Burton Ale; Tetley Bitter; guest beer** Ⓗ
Small, cosy and friendly, two-roomed town pub. The Great Whyte River flows through a culvert under the road; pictures of this adorn the walls. Moorings close by on the High Lode. Q ❀ P

## Ramsey St Mary's

### Lion

Hern Road ☎ (01733) 844386
11–11; 12–10.30 Sun

**Draught Bass; Tetley Bitter, Imperial; guest beers** Ⓗ
Excellent fenland pub in one of the longest villages in England. A two-roomed building, the walls are adorned with murals and pictures of brewers and whisky distillers. A revived local due to the efforts of the present licensee. No food Mon eve; meals end at 6 Sun.
🏚 Q ❀ ◖ ▶ ⌸ ♿ ⌂ P

## Reach

### Kings

Fair Green ☎ (01638) 741745
12–3 (not Mon), 7–11; 12–3, 7–10.30 Sun

**Elgood's Cambridge Bitter; Greene King IPA; Old Chimneys Military Mild; guest beers** Ⓗ
Comfortable, split-level, beamed pub handy for the Devil's Dyke and the annual Reach Fair; converted from a farmhouse 21 years ago. Home-made soups are a speciality on the cosmopolitan menu (no food Mon; eve meals Tue–Sat). Home of the Devil's Dyke morris men. Impressive collection of games.
🏚 ❀ ◖ ▶ ♣ P

## St Ives

### Nelson's Head

7 Merryland (off Bridge St)
☎ (01480) 463342
11–3, 6–11; 12–3, 7–10.30 Sun

**Greene King IPA, Abbot, seasonal beers** Ⓗ
Popular, welcoming, town-centre pub tucked away down

a side street and formerly called the Three Tuns. Large front bar with a small rear drinking area. Wheelchair access is via the side gate.
🏾 ⚪ ◗ ⅁ ♣

## St Neots

### Blue Ball
Russell Street (behind car park)
☎ (01480) 386195
11–11; 12–3, 7–10.30 Sun
**Greene King XX Mild ⅁, IPA, Abbot ℍ**
Backstreet, two-bar pub, full of interesting breweriana; always a warm welcome. Converted back to real ale after 18 years of top pressure. Petanque played.
🏾 ⚪ ⅁ ♣ P

## Soham

### Carpenters Arms
76 Brook Street
☎ (01353) 720869
11–11; 12–3, 7–10.30 Sun
**Greene King IPA; guest beers ℍ**
Pleasant, friendly, free house offering a good range of guest beers at the cheapest prices: an L-shaped bar with a lounge beyond featuring aircraft prints and photos, plus a pool room. ⅁ ⚪ ◗ ♣

## Somersham

### Windmill
St Ives Road (B1086, western edge of village)
☎ (01487) 840328
11.30–3, 5–11; 12–3, 7–10.30 Sun
**Greene King IPA, Abbot, seasonal beers ℍ/⅁**
Popular rural pub situated some way out of the main village. Built on the site of a windmill, it offers a cosy bar and a large lounge with a dining area. No food Sun eve.
⅁ ⚪ ◗ ◗ ⅀ Å ♣ P ⅂

## Stow cum Quy

### White Swan
Main Street ☎ (01223) 811821
11–3, 5.30–11; 12–3, 7–10.30 Sun
**Adnams Bitter; Courage Directors; Greene King IPA; John Smith's Bitter; Theakston Best Bitter; guest beer ℍ**
Comfortable local at the centre of a quiet village. Excellent home-cooked meals are served in the bar or adjoining no-smoking restaurant (Tue–Sun). Popular with traditional games teams. ⚪ ◗ ◗ ♣ P

## Thriplow

### Green Man
2 Lower Street
☎ (01763) 208855

12–3, 6–11; 12–3, 7–10.30 Sun
**Fuller's London Pride; Hook Norton Best Bitter; Taylor Landlord; guest beers ℍ**
Ex-Wells pub, saved from closure by a musical director and a military-style campaign by the locals. Now thriving, it stands in a picturesque village famed for its daffodils. Eve meals Mon–Sat. 🏾 ⚪ ◗ ◗ ♣ P

## Turves

### Three Horseshoes
344 March Road
☎ (01733) 840414
12–2.15, 7–11; closed Tue; 12–3, 7–10.30 Sun
**Boddingtons Bitter; Flowers Original; guest beers ℍ**
Pub boasting a wood-panelled bar, decorated with bric-a-brac and a 40-seater restaurant with an extensive menu. The large garden has a play area, patio and barbecue.
🏾 Q ⅀ ⚪ ◗ ◗ ⅁ ♣ P

## Ufford

### Olde White Hart
Main Street ☎ (01780) 740250
11–2.30, 6–11; 12–3, 7–10.30 Sun (may vary)
**Home Bitter; Theakston Best Bitter, Old Peculier, Wadworth 6X; guest beers ℍ/⅁**
17th-century former farmhouse with a homely feel and lots of beams, nooks and crannies. It hosts regular folk nights and serves some 60 guest beers per year plus Inch's cider. Camping in the grounds.
🏾 Q ⚪ ◗ ◗ ⅁ ⅀ Å ♣ ⅂ P ⅂

## Whittlesey

### Bricklayers Arms
Station Road ☎ (01733) 202593
11–3, 6.30–11; 12–3, 7–10.30 Sun
**John Smith's Bitter; Webster's Yorkshire Bitter; guest beer ℍ**
Popular town local with a friendly atmosphere in its large bar and smaller lounge.
🏾 Q ⚪ ⅁ ⅀ ⚪ ♣ P

### Hero of Aliwal
Church Street
☎ (01733) 203736
12–3, 7–11; 12–3, 7–10.30 Sun
**Adnams Bitter; John Smith's Bitter; guest beer ℍ**
Town local with a comfortable bar and a lounge/restaurant; named after local hero Sir Harry Smith who fought in the Punjab.
🏾 Q ⚪ ◗ ◗ ⅁ ⅀ ⅀ ♣ P

## Whittlesford

### Bees in the Wall
36 North Road
☎ (01223) 834289

6–11; 12–2.30, 6–11 Sat (may vary); 12–4, 7–10.30 Sun (may vary)
**Draught Bass; Bateman XB; Hook Norton Best Bitter; Morland Old Speckled Hen; guest beers ℍ**
Early 19th-century listed free house on the north side of a sleepy South Cambs village: a beamed lounge and a traditional public bar. A vintage bee colony is still housed within the north wall.
🏾 ⚪ ⅁ ♣ P

## Willingham

### Three Tuns
Church Street
☎ (01954) 260437
11–2.30, 6–11; 12–3, 7–10.30 Sun
**Greene King XX Mild, IPA, Abbot, seasonal beers ℍ**
Classic, unchanging village local, offering good company. Basic lunchtime snacks.
Q ⚪ ⅁ ♣

## Wisbech

### Rose Tavern
53 North Brink
☎ (01945) 588335
12–2.30, 6 (5.30 Thu & Fri)–11; 12–3, 7–10.30 Sun
**Butterknowle Conciliation Ale; Cains FA; guest beers ℍ**
Cosy, one-roomed pub on the riverside in a listed 200-year-old building, close to Elgood's Brewery. An outbuilding hosts twice-yearly beer festivals.
⚪ ⅀ ♣

## Witcham

### White Horse
7 Silver Street
☎ (01353) 778298
12–3 (not Mon), 6.30–11; 12–3, 7–10.30 Sun
**Boddingtons Bitter; Greene King IPA; Nethergate Bitter; guest beer ℍ**
Run with panache and enthusiasm, this pub has developed an enviable reputation for both its food and ale. No meals Sun eve.
⚪ ◗ ◗ Å ♣ P ⅂

## Yaxley

### Three Horseshoes
179 Main Street
☎ (01733) 242059
11–3, 6–11; 12–3, 7–10.30 Sun
**Courage Directors; John Smith's Bitter; guest beers ℍ**
Early 18th-century, thatched village local with an enormous garden. Sports theme in the bar; traps and old implements in the lounge. Large menu of home-cooked meals.
⚪ ◗ ◗ ⅀ ♣ P

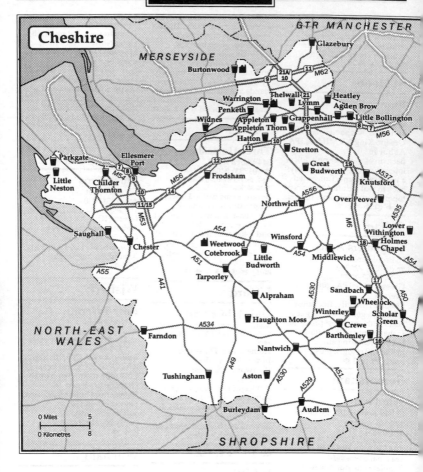

## Agden Brow

### Wheatsheaf
Higher Lane (A56)
☎ (01925) 752567
11.30–3, 5.30–11; 12–3, 7–10.30 Sun
**Hydes' Anvil Mild** Ⓔ, **Bitter**
Ⓔ/Ⓗ, **seasonal beers** Ⓗ
Roadside pub, over 200 years old (extended in the late 1980s), with an open-plan layout and a central bar, plus a games area: a popular eating venue offering a good variety of meals. Eve meals end early (no eve meals Mon–Wed).
🏵 ◑ ♣ P 🚻

## Alpraham

### Traveller's Rest ☆
Chester Road (A51)
☎ (01829) 260523
6–11; 12–3, 6–11 Sat; 12–3, 6–10.30 Sun
**Tetley Mild, Bitter; McEwan 70/-** Ⓗ
Quiet village local, like a private house; unaffected by

change over 30 years. Bowling green to the rear.
🏨 Q 🏵 ♣ P

## Appleton

### Birchdale Hotel
Birchdale Road (signed from A49, by London Bridge)
☎ (01925) 263662
6 (8.30 Sat)–11; 8.30–10.30 Sun
**Boddingtons Bitter; guest beer** Ⓗ
Oasis in the heart of Greenalls land: a quiet hotel in a residential area with a comfortable lounge and a games room. Good value beer in lined glasses. Note: closed lunchtimes. Q 🏨 ♣ P 🚻

## Appleton Thorn

### Appleton Thorn Village Hall
Stretton Road
☎ (01925) 261187
8.30–11; 8.30–10.30 Sun; closed Mon–Wed

**Beer range varies** Ⓗ
This former school houses a true community village hall; CAMRA *Club of the Year* 1995. It features an attractive, comfortably refurbished lounge and bar, plus a maple-floored hall with darts and pool. The six beers change weekly. Boules pitch.
Q 🏵 ♿ ♣ P

## Aston

### Bhurtpore Inn
Wrenbury Road (off A530)
OS610469 ☎ (01270) 780917
12–2.30 (3 Sat), 6.30–11; 12–3, 7–10.30 Sun
**Hanby Drawwell; guest beers** Ⓗ
Former smallholding attracting clientele from miles around with at least six guest beers, plus a huge range of foreign beers in bottle and on draught; various ciders. Good variety of bar meals.
🏨 Q 🏵 ◑ ▣ ♿ ♣ ⌂ P

small, picturesque village. Dated 1614, it displays a list of 18 landlords. The nearby church was the scene of a massacre during the Civil War.
🏠 Q ⭐ 🅿 🍴 ◑ ♣ P

## Bollington

### Church House
Chapel Street
☎ (01625) 574014
12–2.30 (3 Sat), 5.30–11; 12–3, 7–10.30 Sun
**Jennings Bitter; Marston's Pedigree; Tetley Bitter; Theakston Best Bitter** Ⓗ
Popular, busy, corner-terrace pub with a reputation for good food at all times. Renovated church pews make attractive seating in the lounge.
🏠 Q 🚫 ◑ ▶ P

### Lord Clyde
36 Clarke Lane, Kerridge
☎ (01625) 573202
11–11; 12–10.30 Sun
**Draught Bass; Greenalls Mild, Bitter, Original** Ⓗ
Small, one-room country pub, close to the Macclesfield Canal, named after Colin Campbell, a British general in charge at the outbreak of the Indian Mutiny.
Q ⭐ ♣ P

### Queens Arms
40 High Street
☎ (01625) 573068
2 (12 Fri & Sat)–11; 12–3, 7–10.30 Sun
**Robinson's Hatters Mild, Best Bitter** Ⓗ
Solidly built, stone pub, set back slightly from the rest of the terrace, modernised in typical Robinson's style. Very popular. ⭐ ◑ ▶

## Buglawton

### Church House
Buxton Road (A54)
☎ (01260) 272466
11.30–3, 6–11; 12–3, 7–10.30 Sun
**Robinson's Hatters Mild, Best Bitter** Ⓔ, **Frederics** Ⓗ
Classic, between-the-wars-style, roomy pub, catering for local, passing and canal customers. Excellent bar meals and a restaurant (closed Sat eve). Its unusual pub sign is combined with a pigeon cote. Very good outside facilities for children.
🏠 Q 🚫 ⭐ ◑ ▶ ♣ P

## Burleydam

### Combermere Arms
On A525, 3 miles from Audlem
☎ (01948) 871223
11–11; 12–10.30 Sun
**Draught Bass; Worthington Bitter; guest beers** (occasional) Ⓗ
Reputedly haunted, 16th-century free house with a

varied clientele. Several beer festivals each year. 1995 CAMRA South Cheshire *Pub of the Year*. Good food. Occasional cider. Children's indoor adventure play centre.
🏠 🚫 ⭐ ◑ ▶ 👶 ♣ ◑ P

## Burtonwood

### Bridge Inn
Phipps Lane ☎ (01925) 225709
11–11; 12–10.30 Sun
**Burtonwood Mild, Bitter, Buccaneer** Ⓗ
Four-roomed pub oriented towards games and sports; mementos of the licensee's rugby league playing days are displayed. Weekday lunches.
🚫 ⭐ ◑ ▶ ♣ P

## Chester

### Albion Inn
Albion Street ☎ (01244) 340345
11.30–5, 5.30–11; 11–11 Fri; 12–2.30, 7–10.30 Sun
**Cains Bitter; Greenalls Bitter, Original; Stones Bitter** Ⓗ
Small, cosy pub with wartime memorabilia which attracts a mature crowd. Three rooms with a central bar; no gaming machines or jukebox. Good value food served daily lunchtime and Fri/Sat eves (6–8.30). 🏠 Q ◑ ▶ 🍴

### Boathouse Ale Taster Bar
The Groves (on riverfront)
☎ (01244) 328709
11 (Ale Taster Bar 7 Mon–Fri)–11; 12–10.30 Sun
**Marston's Pedigree; Theakston Best Bitter, Old Peculier; guest beers** Ⓗ
Pub with two buildings: the Ale Taster Bar has a comfortable, cosy, traditional atmosphere with low background music and various games available. The family room is in the Riverside Bar.
🏠 🚫 ⭐ ◑ ▶ ♣ P 🚭

### Centurion
Oldfield Drive, Vicars Cross (off A51, 1 mile from centre)
☎ (01244) 347623
11.30 (11 Sat)–11; 12–10.30 Sun
**Jennings Bitter; Tetley Dark Mild, Bitter; guest beers** Ⓗ
Thriving, modern pub holding regular beer festivals and charity fund-raising events. Up to three guest beers always available. Children's play area

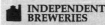

| 🍺 | **INDEPENDENT BREWERIES** |
|---|---|
| **Beartown:** | Congleton |
| **Burtonwood:** | Burtonwood |
| **Coach House:** | Warrington |
| **Weetwood:** | Weetwood |

---

## Audlem

### Bridge Inn
12 Shropshire Street (A529)
☎ (01270) 811267
11–3, 5.30–11; 11–11 Sat & summer; 12–3, 7–10.30 (12–10.30 summer) Sun
**Bateman Mild; Marston's Bitter, Pedigree, HBC** Ⓗ
One of four pubs in a small village, extending a friendly welcome to passers by and canal users as well as locals. Good food. Cider in summer.
🏠 Q 🚫 ⭐ ◑ ▶ 👶 🅰 ♣ ◑ P 🚭

Try also: **Lord Combermere**, The Square (Scottish Courage)

## Barthomley

### White Lion
Audley Road (opp. church)
☎ (01270) 882242
11 (5 Thu)–11; 12–10.30 Sun
**Burtonwood Bitter, Forshaw's, Top Hat, Buccaneer** Ⓗ
Popular, black and white thatched pub at the centre of a

in the garden. Well worth the trip from the city centre.
❀ 🍺 ♣ P

## George & Dragon

Liverpool Road
☎ (01244) 380714
11–3, 5–11; 12–3, 7–10.30 Sun
**Castle Eden Ale; Fuller's London Pride; Morland Old Speckled Hen; Taylor Landlord; Wadworth 6X; guest beers** Ⓗ
Popular, large, open-plan pub with a central bar, frequented by students and locals alike. Up to 12 beers on at any one time. Excellent food.
◁ ▶ ♿ P

## Mill Hotel

Milton Street (just off ring road, behind bingo hall)
☎ (01244) 350035
11–11; 12–10.30 Sun
**Boddingtons Bitter; Weetwood Best Bitter; guest beers** Ⓗ
Busy, popular hotel just outside the city centre. Good selection of guest beers, one of which is always a mild. Sky Sports is usually on TV, but with the volume turned down. The house beer (Mill Premium) is brewed by Coach House. Canalside terrace.
❀ 🛏 ◁ ▶ ≑ P

## Talbot

33 Walter Street, Newtown (behind fire station)
☎ (01244) 317901
11–11; 11–5, 7–11 Sat; 12–5, 7–10.30 Sun
**Burtonwood Mild, Bitter, Forshaw's** Ⓗ
Small, terraced-street local with a convivial atmosphere. Games dominate both rooms.
♿ ≑ ♣

## Union Vaults

44 Egerton Street
☎ (01244) 322170
11–11; 12–10.30 Sun
**Boddingtons Bitter; guest beers** Ⓗ
Much improved, backstreet boozer, just off the city centre, stocking a wide range of independent ales. DIY folk most Sats. ❀ ≑ ♣ ◡

Try also: Faulkener Arms, Faulkener St (Greenalls)

## Childer Thornton

## White Lion

New Road (200 yds off A41)
☎ (0151) 339 3402
11.30–3, 5–11; 11.30–11 Fri & Sat; 12–4, 7–10.30 Sun
**Thwaites Best Mild, Bitter, seasonal beers** Ⓗ
Unspoilt, friendly, two-roomed country pub with a warm welcome for all. The snug is used by families at

lunchtime. No food Sun.
🛏 Q ❀ ◁ P

## Congleton

## Moss Inn

140 Canal Road
☎ (01260) 273583
11–11; 12–10.30 Sun
**Bateman Mild; Marston's Bitter, Pedigree** Ⓗ
Warm, welcoming, cosy pub where the walls are laden with interesting artefacts. A thriving local trade is boosted by cyclists, walkers and 'boaters' from the canal (100 yards). Extensive smoke filter and extraction system. Eve meals 6–8, Tue–Fri.
❀ ◁ ▶ ♿ ≑ ♣ P

## Waggon & Horses

Newcastle Road, West Heath
☎ (01260) 274366
11.30–3, 6–11; 12–3, 7–10.30 Sun
**Marston's Bitter, Pedigree** Ⓗ
Large, well-established inn, on the western edge of town. Tables outside in the summer, with the pub's situation (at the confluence of the A34, A54 and A534), make it somewhat akin to sitting in the middle of a roundabout. No food Sun.
🛏 ◁ Q ♣ P

## Cotebrook

## Alvanley Arms

Forest Road (A49, 1 mile S of A54 jct) ☎ (01829) 760200
11.30–3, 5.30–11; 12–3, 6–10.30 Sun
**Robinson's Hatters Mild, Best Bitter** Ⓗ
Old country pub with attractive décor and furnishings. An imaginative range of quality bar meals predominates. Families welcome. Located on a fast bend so beware! Quiz Sun eve.
🛏 ❀ 🛏 ◁ ▶ P

## Crewe

## Albion

1 Pedley Street (off Mill St)
☎ (01270) 256234
7 (4 Mon, 1 Fri, 12 Sat)–11; 12–3, 7–10.30 Sun
**Tetley Dark Mild, Bitter; guest beer** Ⓗ
Street-corner local with an emphasis on darts and dominoes, plus a pool room. The frequently changing guest beer comes from small breweries. 🍺 ≑ ♣

## British Lion

58 Nantwich Road
☎ (01270) 214379
12–4 (3 Tue & Wed), 7–11; 11–11 Fri; 12–3.30, 7–10.30 Sun
**Ind Coope Burton Ale; Tetley Dark Mild, Bitter; guest beer** Ⓗ

Lively local, known as the Pig, a useful watering hole if changing trains (just 300 yds west of the station).
🛏 ♿ ≑ ♣

## Cross Keys

2 Remer Street, Coppenhall
☎ (01270) 584845
11.30–3, 5.30–11; 11.30–11 Sat; 12–10.30 Sun
**Marston's Pedigree; Tetley Dark Mild, Bitter; guest beer** Ⓗ
Large, brick, multi-roomed pub on the outskirts of Crewe. Good varied food.
◁ ▶ 🍺 ♣ P

## Eaton

## Plough

Macclesfield Road (A536)
☎ (01260) 280207
12–3, 7–11; 12–3, 7–10.30 Sun
**Banks's Bitter; Marston's Pedigree** Ⓗ
Village-centre pub revitalised in recent years by an ex-brewer. Much emphasis is on food and it can get busy as a consequence, but this does not detract from the welcoming atmosphere (a new extension has just been added for food). Motel accommodation.
🛏 ❀ 🛏 ◁ ▶ ♣ P

## Ellesmere Port

## White Swan

Old Chester Road
☎ (0151) 339 9284
11.30–11; 12–10.30 Sun
**Burtonwood Mild, Bitter; guest beers** Ⓗ
Comfortable, two-roomed local, offering an enterprising selection of guest beers in an area not renowned for guests. Good value food. ❀ ◁ ▶ ♣ P

## Farndon

## Farndon Arms

High Street
11–11; 12–10.30 Sun
**Boddingtons Bitter; Burtonwood Forshaw's; Flowers Original; guest beer** Ⓗ
Open-plan, comfortable pub featuring games and a piano, with a restaurant upstairs (children welcome). On the Marches Way, near the River Dee.
🛏 Q ❀ 🛏 ◁ ▶ ♿ ♠ ♣ P ⚲

## Frodsham

## Aston Arms

Mill Lane (off A56, by River Weaver bridge)
☎ (01928) 732333
11–11; 12–10.30 Sun

Burtonwood Mild, Bitter, Top Hat, Buccaneer, seasonal beers Ⓗ
19th-century pub, with several, small, unchanged rooms, close to the River Weaver; great for water sports lovers. At the rear is a bowling green, well used in summer. ⚏ ☣ 🖤 ◑▶ & ♣

## Rowlands's Bar
31 Church Street
☎ (01928) 733361
11–11; 12–10.30 Sun
Boddingtons Bitter; Weetwood Best Bitter; guest beers Ⓗ
Very popular, single-room pub, majoring on guest beers from independent breweries served through four pumps (but they can be pricey). Good food – bar meals and an upstairs bistro. The cider varies. ◑▶ ⇌ ⌂ 🍺

# Glazebury

## Chat Moss
206 Warrington Road
☎ (01925) 762128
12–3, 5.30–11; 12–11 Fri & Sat; 12–10.30 Sun (may vary winter)
Burtonwood Mild, Bitter, Top Hat, Buccaneer, seasonal beers Ⓗ
Rail buffs meet beer buffs in this historic local, situated at the side of the Manchester–Liverpool railway line; plenty of rail photographs are on show. The main lounge is situated away from the bar and games area. ☣ ◑▶ ♣ P

# Grappenhall

## Grappenhall Community Centre
Bellhouse Lane (200 yds from A50) ☎ (01925) 268633
8–11; 12–4, 8–11 Sat; 12–3, 7–10.30 Sun
Ruddles Best Bitter; Webster's Yorkshire Bitter; guest beer Ⓗ
Rambling private club and social centre supporting a wide range of societies and activities. Handy for the Bridgewater Canal. Three widely varying guests per week. A CAMRA membership card allows admission.
Q ☣ & P

# Great Budworth

## George & Dragon
High Street (400 yds off A559)
☎ (01606) 891317
11.30–3.30, 6–11; 11–11 Sat; 12–10.30 Sun
Tetley Bitter; guest beers Ⓗ
Former local CAMRA *Pub of the Year*, set in a picturesque village, opposite the church. Two guest beers. Note: Addlestones Cider is served

under gas pressure.
🖤 ☣ ◑▶ & ♣ P

# Handforth

## Railway
Station Road ☎ (01625) 523472
11–3, 5.30–11; 12–3, 7–10.30 Sun
Robinson's Hatters Mild, Best Bitter Ⓔ
Large, multi-roomed pub facing the station: a thriving local, popular with all. No food Sun. Q ◑ ⊞ ⇌ ♣ P

# Hatton

## Hatton Arms
Hatton Lane ☎ (01925) 730314
11–11; 12–10.30 Sun
Greenalls Mild, Bitter, Original; Tetley Bitter Ⓗ
Traditional, multi-roomed village pub, based on a row of old cottages, now extended to provide a restaurant and letting rooms.
⚏ Q 🖤 ◑▶ ⊞ P

# Haughton Moss

## Nag's Head
Long Lane ☎ (01829) 260265
11–2.30 (3 Sat; not Mon), 6.30–11; 12–3, 7–10.30 Sun
Marston's Bitter, Pedigree; guest beer Ⓗ
Attractive, black and white country pub with a friendly atmosphere and good food. The bowling green provides good viewing in summer.
⚏ Q ☣ ◑▶ P

# Heatley

## Railway
Mill Lane (B5159)
☎ (01925) 752742
12 (11.30 Sat)–11; 12–10.30 Sun
Boddingtons Bitter; Marston's Pedigree; guest beer Ⓗ
Large and still traditional pub, serving as a focal point for the community. Local society meetings are catered for in the many different rooms. Folk club Thu. The large open garden sits alongside the Trans-Pennine Trail. No food Sun. Q ☜ ☣ ◑ ⊞ ♣ P

# Henbury

## Cock Inn
Chelford Road (A537)
☎ (01625) 423186
11–3, 5–11; 12–10.30 Sun
Robinson's Hatters Mild, Best Bitter, Old Tom Ⓗ
Comfortable, main road pub with both local and passing trade, situated just outside Macclesfield. Children welcome in the restaurant. No coaches. Q ☣ ◑▶ ⊞ ♣ P

# Holmes Chapel

## Swan
29 Station Road
☎ (01477) 532259
11–11; 12–10.30 Sun
Samuel Smith OBB Ⓗ
Former coaching inn with good food (very large pizzas a speciality). An interesting old black stove is on display. The car park is reached by driving under the pub.
⚏ ☣ 🖤 ◑▶ ⊞ ⇌ P

# Kettleshulme

## Bull's Head
Macclesfield Road
☎ (01663) 733225
7–11 (12–3, 7–11 summer Sat); 7–10.30 (12–3, 7–10.30 summer) Sun
Boddingtons Bitter; Castle Eden Ale; guest beer Ⓗ
Friendly, stone-terraced pub in the centre of a village within the Peak District National Park. Time has little changed the traditional character of its cosy lounge, public bar and darts area. A guest beer may not be available weekdays.
⚏ ☣ ♣ P

# Knutsford

## Builders Arms
Mobberley Road (off A537)
☎ (01565) 634528
11.30–3, 5.30–11; 12–2, 7–10.30 Sun
Banks's Mild; Marston's Bitter, Pedigree; guest beer (occasional) Ⓗ
Delightful pub in an attractive terrace on the outskirts of the town centre. A former Taylor's Eagle Brewery house, it is a busy pub, with a keen games emphasis. Best approached from the road opposite the Legh Arms. Q ☣ ⊞ ⇌

## Freemasons
Silk Mill Street
☎ (01565) 632368
11–11; 12–3, 7–10.30 Sun
Burtonwood Best Bitter, Buccaneer Ⓗ
Large, white, three-storey building, just off Princess St. Silk Mill St was the birthplace in 1715 of Edward Penny RA, a founding member of, and first professor of painting at, the Royal Academy.
⚏ 🖤 ◑▶ & ⇌ ♣ P

# Little Bollington

## Swan With Two Nicks
Park Lane (off A57 at Stamford Arms, 1 mile from A556)
☎ (0161) 928 2914
11.30–3, 5.30–11 (11–11 summer Sat); 12–10.30 Sun
Boddingtons Bitter; Castle Eden Ale; Coach House Innkeepers; Flowers IPA;

Marston's Pedigree; Morland
Old Speckled Hen Ⓗ
Rural pub, licensed since 1880,
now extended into rear
outbuildings to create a
restaurant. Next to
Bridgewater Canal and
Dunham Hall and Park (NT).
🏚 ❀ ◖ 🍴 P

## Little Budworth

### Shrewsbury Arms

Chester Rd (A54, 3 miles E of
Winsford) ☎ (01829) 760240
11.30–3, 6–11; 12–3, 7–10.30 Sun
Robinson's Old Stockport,
Hartleys XB (summer), Best
Bitter, Frederics Ⓗ
Just 20 minutes from Chester
and five from Oulton Park
motor racing circuit, this neat
pub comprises a snug, a lounge
and a small dining room where
families are welcome. Take
care – located on a fast bend.
No meals Mon eve.
Q ❀ ◖ 🍴 & ♠ P

## Little Neston

### Harp Inn

19 Quayside (from Burton Rd
down Marshlands Rd; left
along Marsh Rd)
☎ (0151) 336 6980
11–11; 12–10.30 Sun
Chester's Mild; Flowers IPA;
Taylor Landlord; Whitbread
Trophy Ⓗ
Delightful, two-roomed, ex-
miners' pub served by one bar.
The superb public bar has a
real fire and low beams. It may
be difficult to get to, but it's a
joy to find. Beware high tides!
Eve meals finish at 8.
🏚 Q ⚓ ❀ ◖ 🍴 P

## Lower Withington

### Red Lion

Trap Street, Dicklow Cob
(B5392) ☎ (01477) 571248
11.45–2.30 (3 Sat), 5.30–11; 12–3,
7–10.30 Sun
Robinson's Dark Mild, Best
Bitter Ⓗ
Large rural pub with a
restaurant, lounge bar and a
tap room for locals; close to
Jodrell Bank Radio Telescope.
Even though the pumpclip
says Robinson's Best Mild, it is
actually a very rare outlet for
Dark Mild.
🏚 ❀ ◖ 🍴 🍴 & ♠ ♣ P

## Lymm

### Spread Eagle

47 Eagle Brow
☎ (01925) 755939
11.30–11; 12–10.30 Sun
Lees GB Mild, Bitter Ⓗ,
Moonraker Ⓔ
Pub located in a picturesque
village, near the Bridgewater

Canal: a split-level lounge, a
cosy snug with a real fire, and a
bar with TV; no piped music.
Friendly welcome and service
from the staff and Rodney, the
pub cat. Good, home-cooked
food. Limited parking.
🏚 Q ◖ 🍴 P

## Macclesfield

### Baths

40 Green Street
6.30–11; 11–4, 6.30–11 Sat; 12–3,
7–10.30 Sun
Banks's Hanson's Mild,
Bitter; Boddingtons Bitter Ⓗ
Small, but thriving local, just
off the A537 Buxton road, a few
minutes' walk uphill from the
station. A local bowling green
inspired its original name
(Bowling Green Tavern), and a
public bath its current name.
The pub has outlived both.
🍴 ≠ ♣

### Chester Road Tavern

18 Chester Road
☎ (01625) 424683
11–3 (4 Fri & Sat), 6–11; 12–3, 7–10.30
Sun
Greenalls Mild, Bitter; Stones
Bitter Ⓗ
Popular pub situated on a
street now quiet after the
opening of the ring road. Keen
dominoes school along with
other pub games. 🍴 ♣

### George & Dragon

Sunderland Street
☎ (01625) 421898
11–3 (4 Thu), 5.30–11; 11–11 Fri; 11–5,
7–11 Sat; 12–3, 7–10.30 Sun
Robinson's Hatters Mild, Best
Bitter Ⓔ
Friendly pub serving good
value food (eve meals Mon–Fri
till 6.45). Pool, darts and
skittles played. Close to both
bus and rail stations.
Q ❀ ◖ 🍴 ≠ ♣

### Queens

5 Albert Place
☎ (01625) 422328
11–11; 12–10.30 Sun
Holt Mild, Bitter Ⓗ
Large Victorian inn opposite
the station. The original
brickwork has been restored by
Holt and it is now an honest
drinking house serving very
cheap beer. 🏚 🍴 ≠ ♣

### Railway View

Byrons Lane ☎ (01625) 423657
12–3, 5–11; 12–3, 7–10.30 Sun
Bateman Mild, XB, XXXB;
guest beer Ⓗ
Pleasant, refurbished pub, 100
yards from the main London
road. Excellent range of beers,
of which the Bateman beers
seem to be permanent. The
house beer is brewed by Coach
House. 🏚 🏚 ♣

## Middlewich

### Big Lock

Webbs Lane (by Lock 76 on
Trent & Mersey Canal, down
Finneys Lane, off A530)
☎ (01606) 833489
11.30–11; 12–3, 7–10.30 Sun
Courage Directors; Ruddles
Best Bitter; Webster's
Yorkshire Bitter; guest beer Ⓗ
Local boosted by canal trade,
and serving real home cooking;
separate family and restaurant
rooms. The house beer is by
Courage. Beer festival Aug
Bank Hol. ❀ ❀ ◖ 🍴 & P

### Cheshire Cheese

Lewin Street (A533, just S of
town) ☎ (01606) 832097
11–4.30, 6.30–11; 12–3, 7–10.30 Sun
Cains Mild, Bitter; John
Smith's Bitter; guest beer
(occasional) Ⓗ
Refreshing outpost of real
choice and quality: a small and
friendly local. Try the mild –
it's the landlord's tipple.
❀ 🍴 & P

## Nantwich

### Frog & Ferret

4 Oatmarket
(opp. Woolworth's)
☎ (01270) 629324
11–11; 12–3, 7–10.30 Sun
Banks's Bitter; Camerons
Strongarm; Marston's
Pedigree; guest beers Ⓗ
Rejuvenated, popular, open-
plan pub, student-oriented, yet
making older customers feel
welcome. The main venue for
Nantwich Folk Festival, early
Sept. A benevolent ghost of
puritan appearance is in
residence. Guest ales from a
varying portfolio. ◖ ≠

### Wilbraham Arms

58 Welsh Row (A534, 500 yds E
of aqueduct) ☎ (01270) 626419
11–11; 12–10.30 Sun
Coach House Coachman's;
John Smith's Bitter; guest
beers Ⓗ
Former Georgian coach house,
now a two-roomed, friendly
pub with a strong local
following and a good cricket
team. Within easy walking
distance of Nantwich moorings
on the Shropshire Union Canal.
Cider in summer.
🏚 🏚 ◖ 🍴 ≠ ♣ ⌂ P

Try also: Oddfellows Arms,
Welshrow (Burtonwood)

## Newbold

### Horseshoe

Fence Lane OS863602
☎ (01260) 272205
11–3, 6–11; 12–3, 7–10.30 Sun

**Robinson's Hatters Mild, Best Bitter** E
Isolated country pub, formerly part of a farmhouse and still enjoying a farming atmosphere; difficult to find but worth the effort. A superb children's play area has swings, a see-saw and climbing frames. Good local trade; welcoming to walkers and canal boaters. No food Mon eve. 🏮 Q 🌣 🛏 ☕ 🛏 ♣ P

## Northwich

### Beehive
44 High Street
☎ (01606) 43704
11–11; 11–5, 7–11 Sat; 12–3, 7–10.30 Sun
**Greenalls Mild, Bitter, Original; Tetley Bitter** H
Town-centre pub with an attractive red brick exterior. The open, split-level interior, friendly welcome and good food at lunchtime make this a popular pub with locals and shoppers alike. No food Sun. 🛏

## Over Peover

### Parkgate Inn
Stocks Lane
☎ (01625) 861455
11–3, 5–11; 11–11 Sat; 12–3, 7–10.30 Sun
**Samuel Smith OBB** H
Very smart, ivy-clad, old pub with several small, wood-panelled rooms, including a tap room. Annual gooseberry competition (Aug) – the winners are in a frame on the wall. Good food.
🏮 Q 🌣 🛏 ☕ 🛏 ♣ P

## Parkgate

### Red Lion
The Parade
☎ (0151) 336 1548
12–11; 12–10.30 Sun
**Ind Coope Burton Ale; Walker Mild, Best Bitter** H
Local CAMRA *Pub of the Year* 1996: a traditional lounge and bar with a superb view of the Welsh hills across the Dee estuary and marsh (famous for birdlife). Local numbers are swelled by many summer visitors. Nelson, the parrot, guards the bar. Q 🛏 ☕ ♣

## Penketh

### Ferry Tavern
Station Road (off A562, follow signs to Yacht Haven)
☎ (01925) 791117
12–3, 6–10.30; 11–11 Sat; 12–10.30 Sun
**Beer range varies** H
Traditional pub on the bank of the River Mersey, with a good

atmosphere. Wide range of bar food for hearty appetites (not served Sun eve); children welcome for meals (children's play area and pets corner). Over 100 whiskies; five guest ales minimum per week.
🏮 🌣 🛏 ☕ P

## Prestbury

### Admiral Rodney
New Road (A538)
☎ (01625) 828078
11–3, 5.30–11; 12–3, 7–10.30 Sun
**Robinson's Hatters Mild, Best Bitter** H
Popular inn in an attractive village terrace; a Grade II listed building. The original front door became the back door when the new road was built through the village.
🏮 Q 🛏 🍽 P

## Rainow

### Highwayman
Whaley Bridge Road (B5470)
☎ (01625) 573245
11–3, 7–11; 12–3, 7–10.30 Sun
**Thwaites Bitter** H
Remote and windswept inn, known as the Blacksmiths Arms until 1949 and locally as 'the Patch': a maze of connecting rooms with a small tap room in the far corner. Three blazing open fires in winter. Breathtaking views from the front door.
🏮 Q 🛏 ☕ 🛏 P

## Sandbach

### Limes
The Limes, 3 Sweetooth Lane (top of Platt Ave, off Middlewich road)
☎ (01270) 763506
11–11; 12–10.30 Sun
**Ind Coope Burton Ale; Robinson's Best Bitter; Tetley Bitter; guest beers** H
Largish estate pub with a bowling green. Guest beers include Carlsberg-Tetley's Tapster's Choice range.
🌣 🛏 ☕ 🛏 ♣ ☕ P ⚲

**Try also: Lower Chequer,** Crosses Sq (Scottish Courage)

## Saughall

### Greyhound Inn
Seahill Road
☎ (01244) 880205
11.30–3, 5–11; 11.30–11 Sat; 12–10.30 Sun
**Boddingtons Bitter; Castle Eden Ale; guest beers** H
Village pub, served from a central bar. Eve meals Mon–Sat till 8.30 (the Mon night 'curry and a pint' deal is especially good value).
Q 🌣 🛏 ♣ P

## Scholar Green

### Rising Sun
112 Station Road
☎ (01782) 776235
12–3, 7–11; 12–3, 7–10.30 Sun
**Marston's Bitter, Pedigree; Thwaites Bitter; guest beer** H
Large, attractive, brick pub on the way out of Scholar Green towards Mow Cop. Good food.
🏮 🛏 ♣ P

## Stretton

### Ring o' Bells
Northwich Road, Lower Stretton (A559, near M56 jct 10)
☎ (01925) 730556
12–3 (3.30 Sat), 5.30 (6 Sat)–11; 12–3.30, 7–10.30 Sun
**Greenalls Mild, Bitter, Original** H
Ever-popular, roadside local. The comfortable bar retains a cosy atmosphere and is warmed by a log fire in winter. The two small snugs are now used by diners (no food Mon). Petanque is popular in summer. 🏮 Q 🌣 🛏 ♣ P

## Tarporley

### Rising Sun
38 High Street
☎ (01829) 732423
11.30–3, 5.30–11; 12–3, 7–10.30 Sun
**Robinson's Hatters Mild, Best Bitter** H
This authentic old pub scores heavily on almost all fronts; a perennial *Guide* entry. The meals in the bar and restaurant are renowned for quality and value. Children welcome at lunchtime (and eves in the restaurant). Q 🛏 P

### Swan Hotel
50 High Street
☎ (01829) 733838
11–11; 12–2, 7–10.30 Sun
**Highgate Saddlers; Marston's Pedigree; Ruddles County; Weetwood Best Bitter; guest beer** H
Elegant, family-run free house, an 18th-century building at the centre of picturesque Tarporley. Two oak-beamed bars boast open fires. Extensive range of English and French cuisine in the dining room and 'brasserie'. Strong connections with the hunt. Belgian beers stocked. 🏮 Q 🌣 🛏 🛏 ♣ P

## Thelwall

### Pickering Arms
Thelwall New Road (via Bell Lane and B5157 from A56)
☎ (01925) 261001
12–11; 12–3.30, 7–10.30 Sun
**Greenalls Mild, Bitter, Original; guest beer** H

Historic, 17th-century, timber-framed village local. Edward the Elder founded the city here in the year 923 (see north gable). Close to the old penny ferry across Manchester Ship Canal. The guest beer is from the Greenalls list. No food Sun eve. ✿ ◑ ▶ P

## Timbersbrook

### Coach & Horses

Dane in Shaw Bank OS890618
☎ (01260) 273019
11–3, 6–11; 12–3, 7–10.30 Sun
**Robinson's Hatters Mild, Best Bitter** Ⓔ
High in the hills above Congleton, this small, brick-built pub with associated farm buildings is half hidden from the main road as it winds upwards from the A537. The interior is mainly a large through-lounge, but there is a tiny tap room.
🏠 ⏁ ✿ ◑ ▶ ⊟ & ♣ P

## Tushingham

### Blue Bell

On A41, 4 miles N of Whitchurch ☎ (01948) 662172
12–3, 6–11; 12–3, 7–10.30 Sun
**Hanby Drawwell, Treacleminer** Ⓗ
Classic, 17th-century pub with an American landlord. It features wooden doors and beams and idiosyncratic decor, including Civil War artefacts and a mummified rat. Children are welcome but may be worried by the immense dog and alleged apparitions.
🏠 Q ⏁ ✿ ◑ ▶ & ♣ P

## Warrington

### Lower Angel

27 Buttermarket Street
☎ (01925) 633299
11–4, 7–11; 12–3, 7–10.30 Sun
**Ind Coope Burton Ale; Walker Mild, Bitter, Best Bitter; guest beer** Ⓗ
Small, popular pub, specialising in beer (not food). A true little gem in a busy town centre; a CAMRA award-winner and a favourite with market traders. Reputedly haunted. Note: Addlestones

Cider is served under gas pressure. ⬌

### Mersey Hotel

Mersey Street (A49, just S of centre) ☎ (01925) 632977
11–11; 12–10.30 Sun
**Vaux Samson, Waggle Dance; guest beer** Ⓗ
Fairly modern, but basic, pub with a bar and a lounge (due for refurbishment). Bar food is always available. Leased from Vaux, it offers their full guest beer list over a six-week cycle; three cask beers are always on sale. 🏠 ◑ ▶ ⊟ ⬌

## Wheelock

### Commercial Hotel ☆

Game Street (off A534, near Bridge 154 of Trent & Mersey Canal) ☎ (01270) 760122
8–11; 12–2, 8–11 Sun
**Boddingtons Bitter; Marston's Pedigree; Thwaites Bitter; guest beer** Ⓗ
This listed Georgian building has been a pub for at least 200 years and was originally known as the New Inn, until taken over by Birkenhead Brewery in 1889; now a lively free house. Live (unplugged) music Thu. Snooker table in the games room. 🏠 Q ♣ ⏁ P

Try also: Cheshire Cheese, Crewe Rd (Banks's)

## Widnes

### Millfield

Millfield Road
☎ (0151) 424 2955
11–11; 11–5, 7–11 Sat; 12–3, 7–10.30 Sun
**Webster's Yorkshire Bitter; Wilson's Mild; guest beer** Ⓗ
Busy, friendly, backstreet pub. ⊟ ♣

## Wilmslow

### Farmers Arms

71 Chapel Lane
☎ (01625) 532443
11–11; 12–10.30 Sun
**Boddingtons Mild, Bitter; guest beer** (occasional) Ⓗ
Traditional, Victorian town pub: several rooms replete with brasses and antiques. Very busy at times due to its good atmosphere, it features

some eye-catching finery around the etched lounge windows. The garden is kept in beautiful condition. No food Sun. 🏠 ⏁ ✿ ◑ ⊟ P

### New Inn

Alderley Road
☎ (01625) 523123
11.30–3 (3.30 Fri & Sat), 5.30–11; 12–3, 7–10.30 Sun
**Hydes' Anvil Light, Bitter** Ⓔ, **seasonal beers** Ⓗ
Extensive modernisation of a much smaller pub, designed almost exclusively to cater for shoppers trooping from Sainsbury's supermarket next door. Eve meals Tue–Sat.
◑ ▶ ⬌ ♣ P

## Wincle

### Wild Boar

On A54 ☎ (01260) 227219
12–3, 7–11; 12–3, 7–10.30 Sun
**Robinson's Hatters Mild, Best Bitter** Ⓗ
Traditional, welcoming, stone-built pub high on the moors with warming open fires in cold weather. Fortnightly clay-pigeon shoots can make Sun lunchtime very busy. A popular venue for sledging and skiing when snowy.
🏠 Q ✿ ◑ ▶ P

## Winsford

### Princes Feathers

Station Road (off A54)
☎ (01606) 594191
11–3, 6–11; 12–3, 7.30–10.30 Sun
**Chester's Mild; Flowers IPA; guest beers** Ⓗ
Local CAMRA *Pub of the Year* 1995: a two-roomed town pub with boxing memorabilia in the bar. Cask ale nights Tue feature a cheap beer promotion. Sat lunches served.
🏠 ✿ ⬌ ♣ P

## Winterley

### Foresters

Crewe Road ☎ (01270) 762642
12–11; 12–10.30 Sun
**Marston's Pedigree; Tetley Dark Mild, Bitter** Ⓗ
Friendly, beamed, roadside village local with some interesting wood carvings.
🏠 ✿ ◑

---

# TETLEY WALKER (1852–1996) RIP

At a stroke of the accountant's pen, Britain lost another chunk of its brewing heritage in 1996. Desperate for economies, Carlsberg-Tetley drew a line under 140 years of brewing in Warrington and closed the Tetley Walker brewery. The casualties, once again, are jobs and consumer choice.

# THE NEW BREWERIES

The 1997 *Good Beer Guide* introduces a remarkable 68 new independent breweries and brew pubs. Full details can be found in the breweries section, beginning on page 418, but here is an area by area checklist of the new producers.

## ENGLAND

**BERKSHIRE**
West Berkshire: Frilsham

**BUCKINGHAMSHIRE**
Little: Medmenham
Stag & Griffin:
Tatling End

**CUMBRIA**
Bitter End: Cockermouth
Coniston: Coniston
Old Cottage: New Hutton

**DORSET**
Cranborne: Cranborne
Quay: Weymouth

**DURHAM**
High Force:
Forest-in-Teesdale
Middleton:
Barnard Castle

**HAMPSHIRE**
Wingfields: Portsmouth

**HEREFORDSHIRE**
Dunn Plowman: Kington
Ledbury: Ledbury
SP Sporting Ales:
Stoke Prior

**HERTFORDSHIRE**
Original: Watford

**KENT**
Swale: Milton Regis
Viking: Broadstairs

**LEICESTERSHIRE &
RUTLAND**
Fulbeck: Twyford
Grainstore: Oakham
Original: Braunstone

**GREATER LONDON**
Hedgehog & Hogshead:
Highbury
Hedgehog & Hogshead:
Sutton
O'Hanlon's: Clerkenwell
Original: North Finchley

Pitfield: Hoxton
Scanlon's: Yiewsley

**GREATER
MANCHESTER**
Bank Top: Bolton
Cobden's: Stockport

**NORFOLK**
Wolf: Attleborough
York Tavern: Norwich

**NORTHAMPTONSHIRE**
Hop House:
Northampton
Leyland: Wellingborough

**NORTHUMBERLAND**
Northumberland:
Ashington

**NOTTINGHAMSHIRE**
Bramcote: Bramcote
Mallard: Carlton

**SHROPSHIRE**
Salopian: Shrewsbury

**SOMERSET**
Bath: Henstridge
Moor: Ashcott

**SUFFOLK**
Blue Boar: Oulton
St Peter's: South Elmham

**SURREY**
North Downs: Capel
Planets: Woking

**SUSSEX**
Baynards: Baynards
Rectory: Plumpton Green

**WARWICKSHIRE**
Feldon: Shipston-on-Stour
Warwickshire:
Kenilworth

**WILTSHIRE**
Wylye Valley: Corton

**WORCESTERSHIRE**
Brandy Cask: Pershore

**YORKSHIRE**
Black Horse:
Hebden Bridge
Easingwold: Easingwold
Glentworth: Skellow
Kitchen: Huddersfield
Riverhead: Marsden
Tigertops: Flanshaw
York: York

## WALES

**GLAMORGAN**
Swansea: Bishopston

**MID WALES**
Red Lion: Llanidloes

**NORTH-WEST WALES**
Cambrian: Dolgellau

**WEST WALES**
Nag's Head: Abercych
Tynllidiart Arms:
Capel Bangor
Watkin: Llandeilo

## SCOTLAND

**FIFE**
Backdykes: Thornton
Burntisland: Burntisland

**THE HIGHLANDS
& ISLANDS**
Isle of Skye: Uig

**STRATHCLYDE**
Lugton: Lugton

**TAYSIDE**
Aldchlappie: Kirkmichael
Moulin: Moulin

## NORTHERN IRELAND

**CO. DOWN**
Whitewater: Kilkeel

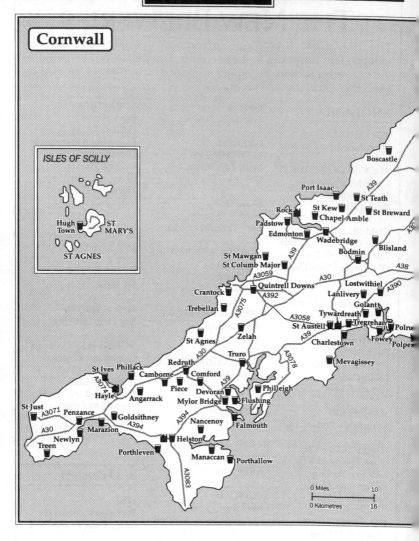

## Cornwall

*ISLES OF SCILLY*

Hugh Town
ST MARY'S
ST AGNES

Boscastle
Port Isaac
St Teath
Rock
St Kew
St Breward
Chapel Amble
Padstow
Edmonton
Wadebridge
Bodmin
Blisland
St Mawgan
St Columb Major
A3059
Quintrell Downs
Lostwithiel
Crantock
Lanlivery
Trebellan
Golant
Tywardreath
Tregrehan
St Austell
Polru
St Agnes
Zelah
Charlestown
Fowey
Polper
Truro
Mevagissey
Redruth
St Ives
Phillack
Camborne
Comford
Piece
Devoran
Philleigh
Hayle
Angarrack
Mylor Bridge
Flushing
St Just
Penzance
Nancenoy
Falmouth
Newlyn
Goldsithney
Treen
Marazion
Helston
Porthleven
Manaccan
Porthallow

0 Miles 10
0 Kilometres 16

---

## Altarnun

### Rising Sun
☎ (01566) 86332
11–3, 5.30–11; 12–3, 7–10.30 Sun
**Draught Bass; Boddingtons Bitter; Flowers Original; guest beers** Ⓗ
Fine, 16th-century pub on the edge of Bodmin Moor, unspoilt by time. A lively local with a friendly welcome.
🏚 Q ⛄ ❀ 🛏 🍴 ▶ 🅰 ♣ P

## Angarrack

### Angarrack Inn
32 Steamers Hill (off A30)
☎ (01736) 752380
11–3, 6–11; 12–3, 7–10.30 Sun

**St Austell Bosun's, XXXX Mild, HSD** Ⓗ
Attractive, welcoming and comfortable village pub, offering an extensive and good value menu of home-cooking (no food Mon eve in winter).
🏚 ❀ 🍴 ▶ 🅰 P

## Blisland

### Royal Oak
The Green ☎ (01208) 850739
12–3, 6–11 (11–11 summer); 12–3, 7–10.30 Sun
**Draught Bass; Flowers IPA; guest beers** Ⓗ
Set on the only village green in Cornwall, in the heart of *Poldark* country, this fine granite free house features a collection of barometers in the

public bar. Lizards are housed in the family/games room. A mild is usually served. Friendly atmosphere; home-cooked local produce.
🏚 Q ⛄ ❀ 🍴 ▶ 🍺 ♣ ⌂ P

## Bodmin

### Masons Arms
5–9 Higher Bore Street
☎ (01208) 72607
11–3, 5–11; 11–11 Fri & Sat; 12–3, 7–10.30 Sun
**Draught Bass; Fuller's London Pride; Wadworth 6X; Worthington Bitter; guest beers** Ⓗ
Historic town pub, built before the Napoleonic Wars and reputed to hold the oldest continuous licence in

Cornwall. Good value food.
Friendly atmosphere; the
lounge is quiet.
Q ☎ ⛲ 🏨 ◑ ▶ 🍺 ♣ P

## Boscastle

### Cobweb
☎ (01840) 250278
11–3 (2.30 Mon), 6–11; 11–11 Fri;
11–midnight Sat; 12–3, 7–10.30 Sun
**Draught Bass; St Austell
Tinners, Trelawny's Pride;
Shepherd Neame Spitfire;
guest beers** H
Thriving village pub with live
music Sat eves. Close to the
harbour, this is a very popular
meeting place.
🚶 Q ☎ ⛲ ◑ ▶ 🍺 ♣ P

### Napoleon
High Street ☎ (01840) 250204
11–3, 6–11; 12–3, 7–10.30 Sun

**Draught Bass; St Austell
Tinners, Trelawny's Pride,
HSD** G
Comfortable, small, 16th-
century pub, made up of
several rooms on different
levels, giving a relaxed
ambience. Unscheduled
evening sing-songs.
🚶 Q ☎ ⛲ 🏨 ◑ ▶ 🍺 ♣ P

## Botus Fleming

### Rising Sun
Off A388
☎ (01752) 842792
7–11; 12–4.30, 7–11 Sat; 12–4.30,
7–10.30 Sun
**Draught Bass; Worthington
Bitter; guest beers** H
Unspoilt, unpretentious pub,
tucked away in a quiet village
on the outskirts of Saltash; now
in the third generation of
family ownership. Good value
Inch's cider. Rarely open
weekday lunchtimes. A classic.
🚶 Q ⛲ 🍺 ▲ ♣ ◔ P

## Callington

### Coachmaker's Arms
Newport Square
☎ (01579) 382567
11–3, 6.30–11; 12–3, 7–10.30 Sun
**Draught Bass; Greene King
Abbot; guest beer** H
300-year-old coaching inn with
a warm atmosphere and a
popular small bar. Good food.
En suite accommodation.
Q 🏨 ◑ ▶ ♣ P

## Camborne

### Waggoners Arms
Trelowarren Street
☎ (01209) 718605
11–11; 12–3, 7–10.30 Sun
**Draught Bass; Flowers
Original; guest beer** H
Busy, town-centre, one-
roomed pub. The guest ale is
constantly changing. Very
quiet Sun when no food is
served. 🚶 ◑ ▶ ⇌ ♣ P

Try also: Tyacks Hotel,
Commercial St (St Austell)

## Chapel Amble

### Maltster's Arms
☎ (01208) 812473
11–3, 5.30–11; 12–2.30, 7–10.30 Sun
**Draught Bass; Ruddles
County; Sharp's Cornish
Coaster; guest beer** H
17th-century, olde-worlde pub
with low beams, wood
panelling and a slate floor in
the bar. Excellent menu – fish is
a speciality. The house beer is
brewed by Sharp's. The family
room is upstairs. Cider in
summer.
🚶 Q ☎ ⛲ ◑ ▶ ♣ ◔

## Charlestown

### Rashleigh Arms
☎ (01726) 73635
11–11; 12–10.30 Sun
**Draught Bass; Ruddles
County; St Austell Tinners,
Trelawny's Pride; Sharp's
Own; Tetley Bitter; Wadworth
6X; guest beers** H
Large, friendly inn overlooking
the famous port, comprising
two large bars, a restaurant
and a family room. Cornish
Tourist Board commended
accommodation.
Q ☎ ⛲ 🏨 ◑ ▶ 🍺 ⚓ ▲ ♣ P

## Comford

### Fox & Hounds
On A393 ☎ (01209) 820251
11–3, 6–11 (varies summer); 12–3,
7–10.30 Sun
**Draught Bass; St Austell
XXXX Mild (winter), Tinners,
HSD, Winter Warmer** G
Comfortable country pub with
a restaurant specialising in
home cooking. Look for the old
frieze in the snug. The pub and
garden are a blaze of colour in
summer. 🚶 ⛲ ◑ ▶ 🍺 ▲ ♣ P

## Crantock

### Old Albion
Langurroc Road
☎ (01637) 830243
11–11; 12–10.30 Sun
**Courage Best Bitter; John
Smith's Bitter; guest beers** H
Picture-postcard, thatched pub
with a smuggling history,
popular with holidaymakers
visiting the superb sandy
beach. A wide-ranging menu
caters for most tastes – Sun
lunches a speciality. Fine range
of malt whiskies.
🚶 Q ☎ ⛲ ◑ ▶ ▲ ♣ ◔ P

## Devoran

### Old Quay Inn
St John's Terrace (off A39)
☎ (01872) 863142
11–3 (2.30 winter), 6 (7 winter)–11;
12–3 (2.30 winter), 7–10.30 Sun
**Draught Bass; Flowers IPA;
guest beers** H
Welcoming pub, home to
thriving village teams. Fine
views over Devoran quay and
creek. Limited parking.
🚶 ⛲ 🏨 ◑ ▶ ♣ P

| **INDEPENDENT BREWERIES** | |
| --- | --- |
| **Bird in Hand:** Hayle | |
| **Blue Anchor:** Helston | |
| **St Austell:** St Austell | |
| **Sharp's:** Rock | |

## Edmonton

### Quarryman Inn
Off A39, S of Wadebridge
☎ (01208) 816444
11–11; 12–10.30 Sun
Draught Bass; guest beers Ⓗ
Pub built in the mid 18th century as a school house for quarry workers' families. Their houses are now part of a holiday and sports complex, with a bistro. Keen sports following. The beer range includes four guests, plus a Sharp's beer in summer.
🏰 Q ✿ ⇔ ◑ ▶ 👤 ♣ P ⚓

## Falmouth

### Quayside Inn
Arwenack Street
☎ (01326) 312113
11–11 (upstairs bar); 11–3, 7–11 (downstairs bar); 12–10.30 Sun
Draught Bass Ⓖ; Courage Directors; Flowers Original; Fuller's London Pride; Ruddles County; Tetley Bitter Ⓗ; guest beers Ⓖ
Large, two-bar pub, overlooking the customs house, quay and harbour. The upstairs bar boasts over 200 whiskies; the downstairs bar has a wide range of ever-rotating guest beers. Live music Fri and Sat eves. No food Sun eve.
✿ ◑ ▶ ⇌ (The Dell) ⚓

### Seven Stars                      ☆
The Moor ☎ (01326) 312111
11–3, 6–11; 12–3, 7–10.30 Sun
Draught Bass Ⓖ; Ruddles County Ⓗ; Sharp's Own; guest beers Ⓖ
Unspoilt by 'progress', a pub in the same family for five generations. The present landlord is an ordained priest. The lively tap room has casks on display; quiet snug to the rear. Q ✿ ⚐

## Five Lanes

### King's Head
Off A30 ☎ (01566) 86241
11–11; 12–4, 7–10.30 Sun
Butcombe Bitter; Sharp's Cornish Coaster Ⓗ; guest beers Ⓗ/Ⓖ
16th-century coaching inn, now bypassed. A flagstoned floor graces the public bar and restaurant. Five beers and excellent food; good value B&B. Happy hour 3–6 Mon–Sat.
🏰 ✿ ⇔ ◑ ▶ ⚐ 👤 ♣ ⚓ P

## Flushing

### Royal Standard
St Peter's Hill (off A393; also via passenger ferry from Falmouth) ☎ (01326) 374250
11–2.30 (3 Fri & Sat), 6.30–11; 12–3, 7–10.30 Sun (varies winter)
Draught Bass; Flowers IPA; Sharp's Doom Bar Ⓗ
Friendly local, run by the present landlord for 30 years. Home-made pasties and apple pies are specialities (take-away available). Fine views of the Penryn River from the front patio, but beware of swans in the road and high spring tides.
🏰 ✿ ◑ ▶ ♣

## Fowey

### Galleon
12 Fore Street
☎ (01726) 833014
11–11; 12–10.30 Sun
Draught Bass; Flowers IPA; Sharp's Cornish Coaster Ⓗ
400-year-old pub on the river, refurbished but still keeping its Cornish character. Fine views from the lounge area and the patio. Wide range of bar meals (fish a speciality). Trad jazz Sun lunch; live music Fri eve.
✿ ⇔ ◑ ▶ 👤 ▲ ♣ ⚓

## Golant

### Fisherman's Arms
Fore Street ☎ (01726) 832453
11–3, 6–11; 12–3, 7–10.30 Sun
Courage Best Bitter; Ushers Best Bitter, Founders Ⓗ
Charming village pub in a delightful waterside setting with views across the River Fowey. Try the home-cooked food. Extra riverside parking at low tide, but beware of being cut off. 🏰 Q ✿ ◑ ▶ ♣ P

## Goldsithney

### Crown
Fore Street ☎ (01736) 710494
11–3, 6–11; 12–10.30 Sun
St Austell XXXX Mild, Trelawny's Pride, HSD Ⓗ
Attractive, comfortable, village pub with a very popular restaurant (booking advisable); excellent home-cooked bar meals, too. 🏰 ✿ ⇔ ◑ ▶

## Gunnislake

### Rising Sun Inn
Calstock Road
☎ (01822) 832201
11–3, 5–11; 11–11 Sat; 12–3, 7–10.30 Sun
Draught Bass; Dartmoor Best Bitter; Juwards Bitter, Premium (occasional); St Austell HSD; Sharp's Cornish Coaster Ⓗ
Friendly pub with pleasing decor, serving an excellent beer choice and superb quality and value food. Exceptionally helpful and attentive bar staff. Views over the Tamar Valley.
🏰 Q ✿ ⇔ ◑ ▶ ▲ ♣ ⚓ P ⚓

## Helston

### Blue Anchor
Coinagehall Street
☎ (01326) 562821
10.30–11; 12–10.30 Sun
Blue Anchor Middle, Best, Special or Extra Special Ⓗ
The flagship of pub-breweries: a rambling, unspoilt, 15th-century, granite building, with a thatched roof and its own brewery at the rear (famous for its 'Spingo' beers). No jukebox or bandits, only good chat in its two bars. Occasional cider.
🏰 Q ☜ ◑ ▶ ▲ ⚓

## Isles of Scilly: St Mary's

### Bishop & Wolf
Main Street, Hugh Town
☎ (01720) 422790
11–11; 12–10.30 Sun
St Austell XXXX Mild, Tinners, Trelawny's Pride, HSD Ⓗ
Named after the two famous local lighthouses, this lively pub features marine decor in its large bar, pool room and upstairs restaurant. The beer is fined at the pub, after its sometimes arduous sea crossing. ☜ ◑ ▶ ▲ ♣

Try also: Turks Head, St Agnes (Carlsberg-Tetley)

## Kilkhampton

### New Inn
☎ (01288) 321488
11–2.30, 6–11; 12–3, 7–10.30 Sun
Draught Bass; Sharp's Own; guest beer Ⓗ
Spacious, 15th-century village pub which once had its own brewery: a quiet front bar and a family room with a skittle alley. Good, home-cooked meals. 🏰 Q ☜ ✿ ◑ ▶ ♣ P

## Kingsand

### Rising Sun
The Green ☎ (01752) 822840
11–11; 12–10.30 Sun
Draught Bass; Courage Best Bitter; guest beer Ⓗ
Former customs house, a Grade II listed building in a village of narrow streets. Popular, yet quiet, it stands on the Coastal Path. Friendly host. Parking for four cars. Excellent food (meals served all day Sat–Sun).
🏰 Q ✿ ⇔ ◑ ▶ ▲ ♣ P

## Lanlivery

### Crown Inn
Off A390, 2 miles W of St Austell ☎ (01208) 872707
11–3, 6–11; 12–3, 7–10.30 Sun

Draught Bass; Sharp's Own; Worthington Bitter Ⓗ
Comfortable, old-fashioned pub – a listed building. The restaurant has an inglenook and a low, beamed ceiling. Accommodation in pleasant country surroundings.
🏾 Q ♨ ✿ ⛂ ◖ ▶ ⊟ ⅙ ▲ ♣ P

## Launceston

### Baker's Arms
Southgate Street
☎ (01566) 772510
11–3, 7–11; 11–11 Sat; 12–3, 7–10.30 Sun
Courage Directors; John Smith's Bitter; Wadworth 6X; guest beer Ⓗ
Popular town pub next to the historic Southgate Arch: a cosy, wood-panelled lounge bar and a games-oriented public. Good value meals.
🏾 Q ♨ ◖ ▶ ⊟ ♣

## Lostwithiel

### Royal Oak
King Street (off A390)
☎ (01208) 872552
11–11; 12–10.30 Sun
Draught Bass; Fuller's London Pride; Marston's Pedigree; St Austell Trelawny's Pride; guest beers Ⓗ
Busy, 13th-century inn, renowned for good food. A stone-floored bar contrasts with a comfortable lounge and restaurant. Guest beers come from small independent breweries. Many unusual bottled beers available. Families welcome.
Q ✿ ♨ ◖ ▶ ⊟ ▲ ➿ ♣ P

## Manaccan

### New Inn
☎ (01326) 231323
11–3, 6–11; 12–3, 7–10.30 Sun
Castle Eden Ale; Flowers IPA; guest beers (summer) Ⓖ
Very traditional, thatched village pub, serving good, home-cooked food. No jukebox or fruit machines. Limited parking. 🏾 Q ✿ ◖ ▶ P

## Marazion

### Station House
½ mile from A30
☎ (01736) 50459
11–11; 12–10.30 Sun
Courage Best Bitter, Directors; John Smith's Bitter; guest beers Ⓗ
Large, one-room pub/ restaurant overlooking the beach and St Michael's Mount. Live music Thu; no jukebox. Good value, home-cooked food. Families welcome.
✿ ◖ ▶ ⅙ P

## Mevagissey

### Fountain
St George's Square
☎ (01726) 842320
11–3, 6–11; 11–11 Sat & summer; 12–10.30 Sun
St Austell Tinners, Trelawny's Pride, Winter Warmer Ⓖ
Traditional, olde-worlde, harbourside inn, licensed for 500 years. The two bars, with slate floors and beams, display historic photos. The restaurant is open March–Oct. Accommodation is now en suite, with central heating.
🏾 Q ♨ ◖ ▶ ▲ ♣

## Mylor Bridge

### Lemon Arms
Off A393 at Penryn
☎ (01326) 373666
11–3, 6–11; 12–3, 7–10.30 Sun
St Austell Tinners, HSD, Winter Warmer Ⓖ
Friendly, one-bar village-centre pub, popular with local sports teams. Good food.
🏾 ✿ ◖ ▲ ♣ P

## Nancenoy

### Trengilly Wartha
Off B3291 OS731282
☎ (01326) 40332
11–3, 6.30–11 (may vary summer); 12–3, 7–10.30 Sun
Dartmoor Best Bitter; Sharp's Cornish Coaster Ⓖ; guest beers Ⓖ/Ⓗ
Delightful remote pub/hotel with owners who like to ring the changes with guest beers. Excellent, ever-changing menu. Wonderful country walks nearby.
🏾 Q ♨ ✿ ♨ ◖ ▶ ⅙ ♣ ⊙ P

## Newlyn

### Fisherman's Arms
Fore Street ☎ (01736) 63399
10.30–3, 5.30–11; 12–3, 7.30–10.30 Sun
St Austell Bosun's, Trelawny's Pride, HSD Ⓗ
Popular old local with superb views over the busy fishing harbour and St Michael's Mount. Note the inglenook and intriguing ceiling display of memorabilia. Good, simple food. Very limited parking.
🏾 ✿ ◖ ▶ ▲ ♣ P

## Padstow

### London Inn
6–8 Lanadwell Street
☎ (01841) 532554
11–11; 12–10.30 Sun
St Austell Bosun's, XXXX Mild (summer), Tinners, Trelawny's Pride, HSD Ⓗ
Friendly pub, frequented by locals, with a wide range of

whiskies. Knocked together from three cottages in the early 1800s, it is small and decorated with a nautical theme.
🏾 Q ♨ ◖ ▶ ♣

### Old Ship Hotel
Mill Square ☎ (01841) 532357
11–3, 6–11 (11–11 summer); 12–3, 7–10.30 (12–10.30 summer) Sun
Boddingtons Bitter; Brains SA; Flowers Original; guest beers Ⓗ
Pleasing, family hotel, just off the harbour: the only free house in the town, with a sheltered outdoor drinking area and a restaurant. Live music Sat eve (more often in summer).
Q ♨ ✿ ♨ ◖ ▶ ⊟ ♣ P

## Penzance

### Mount's Bay Inn
The Promenade, Wherrytown
☎ (01736) 63027
11–2.30, 6.30–11; 12–2.30, 7–10.30 Sun
Draught Bass; Worthington Bitter; guest beers Ⓗ
Small, friendly, free house on the seafront towards Newlyn, serving a varying choice of guest beers. Dining area in the bar (no meals Sun or Tue eves in winter). 🏾 Q ◖ ▶ ⅙

### Turk's Head
48 Chapel Street
☎ (01736) 63093
11–11; 12–3, 7–10.30 Sun
Boddingtons Bitter; Flowers Original; Marston's Pedigree Ⓗ
The oldest pub in Penzance – a very friendly local with an attractive bar. Varied, good value food. Q ♨ ◖ ▶ ➿

## Phillack

### Bucket of Blood
☎ (01736) 752378
11–2.30, 6–11; 12–3, 7–10.30 Sun
St Austell XXXX Mild, Trelawny's Pride, HSD Ⓗ
Historic, friendly pub close to Hayle beaches. The name is derived from a gory legend! Meals in summer.
🏾 Q ♨ ✿ ◖ ▶ ▲ ♣ ⊙ P

## Philleigh

### Roseland Inn
On King Harry Ferry Road
☎ (01872) 580254
11.30 (11 summer)–3, 6.30 (6 summer)–11; 12–3, 7–10.30 (12–10.30 summer) Sun
Draught Bass; Greenalls Bitter; Marston's Pedigree; guest beer (occasional) Ⓗ
Classic, 17th-century country pub at the heart of the Roseland Peninsula, with slate floors and beams, a restaurant, a bar and a locals' snug. Good menu of home-cooked food. Cider in summer.
🏾 Q ♨ ✿ ◖ ▶ ⊙ P

## Piece

### Countryman

On Four Lanes–Pool road
☎ (01209) 215960
11–11; 12–3, 7–10.30 Sun
**Courage Best Bitter, Directors;
Morland Old Speckled Hen;
Sharp's Own; John Smith's
Bitter; Wadworth 6X** H
Former count-house for the
local tin-mining community: a
welcoming, popular country
pub, said to be haunted by
three maidens. Entertainment
and good food provided.
🏠 🌣 ◑ ▮ ♿ ♠ ♣ P 🍽

## Polperro

### Blue Peter

The Quay ☎ (01503) 272743
11–11; 12–10.30 Sun
**St Austell Tinners, HSD;
guest beer** H
The smallest pub in Polperro,
reached by a flight of steps at
the harbour. Convivial
atmosphere. Live music 2–5
Sun. 🏠 ♣

### Crumplehorn Inn

The Old Mill ☎ (01503) 272348
11–11; 12–10.30 Sun
**Dartmoor Best Bitter; St
Austell XXXX Mild, HSD;
guest beer** H
Haunted inn, converted from
an old mill – mentioned in the
*Domesday Book*. Self-contained
chalets and B&B available.
🏠 Q 🌣 🛏 ◑ ▮ ♿ ♠ ♣ P

## Polruan

### Lugger Inn

The Quay ☎ (01726) 870007
11–3, 6–11 (11–11 summer); 12–3,
7–10.30 (12–10.30 summer) Sun
**St Austell Bosun's, XXXX
Mild, Tinners, Trelawny's
Pride, HSD** H
Friendly pub near the quay,
served by the Fowey River
passenger ferry.
🏠 ◑ ▮ ♿ ♠ ♣

## Porthallow

### Five Pilchards

☎ (01326) 280256
11–3, 6–11 (closed eve & Mon in
winter); 12–3, 7–10.30 Sun
**Greene King Abbot; guest
beers** H
Attractive, rural pub, only
yards from the beach, with
views across to Falmouth. Fine
collection of ship's lamps,
model ships and wreck
histories. Self-contained flat
available. 🏠 🌣 ◑

## Porthleven

### Atlantic Inn

Peverell Terrace
☎ (01326) 562439

12–11; 12–10.30 Sun
**Boddingtons Bitter; Brakspear
Bitter; Flowers Original;
Wadworth 6X; guest beer** H
Friendly, strong community
local overlooking the harbour.
Live music.
🏠 🌣 🛏 ◑ ▮ ♠ ♣ P

## Port Isaac

### Shipwrights Inn

The Terrace ☎ (01208) 880305
12–2.30 (3.30 Sat), 7–11; 12–3, 7–10.30
Sun
**Draught Bass; Flowers IPA;
guest beers** H
Pleasant, family-run pub and
bistro decorated with old
shipwright's tools and flags. A
friendly place to enjoy sea
views. 🏠 🌣 🛏 ◑ ▮ 🍴 ♣

## Quintrell Downs

### Two Clomes

East Road (A392)
☎ (01637) 871163
12–3, 7 (6 summer)–11; 12–3, 7–10.30
Sun
**Otter Bitter; Sharp's Doom
Bar; guest beers** H
18th-century free house which
takes its name from the old
clome ovens either side of the
open log fire. Set on the
outskirts of Newquay, it has
camping and caravan sites
nearby.
🏠 Q 🛏 🌣 ◑ ▮ ♿ ♠ ♣ ➔ P

## Redruth

### Tricky Dickie's

Tolgus Mount (off old Redruth
bypass) ☎ (01209) 219292
11–3, 6–11 (midnight Tue & Thu); 12–3,
7–10.30 Sun
**Greene King Abbot; Sharp's
Own; Tetley Bitter; Wadworth
6X; guest beer** H
Renovated old tin mine smithy
offering squash and exercise
facilities, plus some live music.
The emphasis is on the
restaurant and bar meals.
Children welcome.
🌣 ◑ ▮ ♿ ♣ P 🍽

## Rilla Mill

### Manor House Hotel

☎ (01579) 62354
12–3, 7 (6.45 Sat)–11; 12–3, 7–10.30
Sun
**Draught Bass; guest beers** H
Very busy, comfortable,
17th-century inn and
restaurant in the Lynher
Valley. Excellent food. Self-
catering cottages to let.
Q 🌣 🛏 ◑ ▮ ♿ P

## St Agnes

### Driftwood Spars

Trevaunance Cove
☎ (01872) 552428

11–11 (midnight Fri & Sat); 12–10.30
Sun
**Draught Bass; Ind Coope
Burton Ale; St Austell HSD;
Sharp's Own; Tetley Bitter;
guest beers** H
Rambling, 17th-century hotel
with a nautical theme, close to
the beach and popular all year
round. Extensive menu and
comfortable accommodation.
Live entertainment at
weekends. Over 80 single malt
whiskies. Note: Addlestones
Cider is served under gas.
🏠 🛏 🌣 🛏 ◑ ▮ P

## St Austell

### Carlyon Arms

Sandy Hill (1 mile E of town on
Bethel road) ☎ (01726) 72129
11–3, 5–11; 11–11 Sat; 12–10.30 Sun
**St Austell XXXX Mild,
Tinners, Trelawny's Pride,
HSD** H
Friendly local serving good,
home-cooked food (eve meals
Tue–Sat). Live music Wed and
Fri eve. 🏠 🌣 🛏 ◑ ▮ ♣ P

## St Breward

### Old Inn

☎ (01208) 850711
12–3, 6–11; 12–3, 7–10.30 Sun
**Draught Bass; John Smith's
Bitter; guest beers** H
Fine, solid, moorland pub
dating from the 11th century,
with slate flagstoned floors and
thick granite walls; next to the
highest church in Cornwall.
Selection of malts.
Comfortable, lived-in
atmosphere.
🏠 Q 🛏 🌣 ◑ ▮ ♿ ♣ P

## St Cleer

### Stag Inn

Fore Street ☎ (01579) 342305
12–3, 7–11; 11–11 Sat; 12–3, 7–10.30
(12–10.30 summer) Sun
**Draught Bass; Brains SA;
Greene King Abbot; Sharp's
Cornish Coaster; Smiles Best
Bitter; guest beers** H
Welcoming inn on the edge of
Bodmin Moor offering a good
range of beers and regular
events. Beer festival last
weekend in June. Family room
available when not too busy.
🏠 Q 🛏 🌣 ◑ ▮ ♿ ♣ P

## St Columb Major

### Ring o' Bells

3 Bank Street ☎ (01637) 880259
12–3, 5–11; 12–11 Fri & Sat; 12–4,
7–10.30 Sun
**Draught Bass** G**; Sharp's
Cornish Coaster, Own** H**;
guest beers** G
The small frontage of this pub
hides a long, narrow interior of
three different bars, catering
for all tastes. Good value meals

(supper licence till 12). Varying guest beers.
🏚 🍽 ❀ ◖ ▮ ▲ P

## St Ives

### Sloop Inn

The Wharf ☎ (01736) 796584
11–11; 12–10.30 Sun
**Boddingtons Bitter; Courage Best Bitter; Morland Old Speckled Hen; Ruddles County; John Smith's Bitter** Ⓗ
Old harbourside inn with three bars – two without music. Seafood a speciality.
Q 🍽 ❀ 🍴 ◖ ▮ ᕵ 🐾 ♣

## St Just

### Star Inn

Fore Street ☎ (01736) 788767
11–3, 5–11 (11–11 summer); 12–10.30 Sun
**St Austell XXXX Mild** Ⓗ, **Tinners, Trelawny's Pride, HSD** Ⓖ
Fine old granite pub in an old tin-mining area, a typical Cornish local with friendly staff. Cider in summer.
🏚 🍽 🍴 ◖ ▮ ᗉ

## St Kew

### St Kew Inn

Churchtown ☎ (01208) 841259
11–2.30, 6–11; 12–2.30, 7–10.30 Sun
**St Austell XXXX Mild** (summer) Ⓗ, **Tinners, HSD** Ⓖ
Popular, 15th-century pub next to the church, with a worn slate floor and an open range in the public bar, complemented by a comfortable lounge and dining rooms. Excellent food. Large garden. 🏚 Q ❀ ◖ ▮ 🍷 P

## St Mawgan

### Falcon Inn

☎ (01637) 860225
11–11; 12–3, 7–10.30 Sun
**St Austell Tinners, Trelawny's Pride, HSD** Ⓗ
Creeper-clad, stone-built inn at the centre of a delightful village, just down the hill from Newquay airport. Good food. The garden is a picture in spring and summer.
🏚 Q ❀ 🍽 ◖ ▮ P

## St Teath

### White Hart Hotel

☎ (01208) 850281
11–2.30, 6–11; 12–3, 7–10.30 Sun
**Draught Bass; Ruddles County; Ushers Best Bitter** Ⓗ
Dating from the 1700s, this village-centre pub was partly rebuilt in 1884. Its quiet snug and noisy public bar (satellite TV) suit most tastes. Good food. Small play area in the garden.
🏚 Q 🍽 ❀ 🍽 ◖ ▮ 🍷 🐾 P

## Stratton

### King's Arms

Howells Road (A3092)
☎ (01288) 352396
12–3, 6.30–11; 12–3, 7–10.30 Sun
**Boddingtons Bitter; Exmoor Ale; Sharp's Own; guest beers** Ⓗ
Delightful, popular, 17th-century village pub with two bars and slate flag flooring. Changing range of guest beers. Limited parking (free car park close by).
🏚 🍽 ❀ 🍽 ◖ ▮ 🐾 🍷 P

Try also: **Tree**, Fore St (Free)

## Trebellan

### Smugglers Den Inn

Take Cubert road off A3075, left to Trebellan
☎ (01637) 830209
11–3 (12–2 winter), 6–11; 12–3, 7–10.30 Sun
**Boddingtons Bitter; Flowers IPA; guest beers** Ⓗ/Ⓖ
Tucked down a narrow lane, it is a joy to find this old thatched pub. Extensive, good value menu. Camping and caravan site across the lane. Deservedly popular. 🏚 Q ❀ ◖ ▮ ▲ P

## Treen

### Logan Rock Inn

☎ (01736) 810495
10.30–11; 12–10.30 Sun
**St Austell Bosun's, Tinners, Trelawny's Pride, HSD** Ⓗ
Outstanding small pub near superb coastal scenery and the Minack Open Air Theatre. The bar is full of character and offers good food. Try a stiff walk to the 'moving' Logan stone. 🏚 🍽 ❀ ◖ ▮ P

## Tregrehan

### Britannia Inn

On A390 ☎ (01726) 812889
11–11; 12–10.30 Sun
**Draught Bass; Morland Old Speckled Hen; St Austell Tinners; Sharp's Own; Worthington Bitter; guest beer** Ⓗ
Large, 16th-century inn and restaurant, open all day for food and drink. Safe garden and play area.
Q 🍽 ❀ ◖ ▮ 🍷 ᗉ ▲ P

## Truro

### City Inn

Pydar Street (B3284, Perranporth road)
☎ (01872) 72623
11–11; 12–3, 7–10.30 Sun
**Draught Bass; Courage Best Bitter, Directors; John Smith's Bitter; Wadworth 6X; guest beer** Ⓗ

Popular local with a friendly atmosphere and a fine collection of pub jugs and memorabilia. Large garden with a covered area. Good value food. ❀ 🍽 ◖ ▮ 🐾

### Old Ale House

7 Quay Street ☎ (01872) 71122
11–11; 11–3, 7–10.30 Sun
**Draught Bass; Boddingtons Bitter; Sharp's Cornish Coaster, Doom Bar, Own** Ⓗ; **guest beers** Ⓖ
Old, 'ale house' theme pub with a sawdust floor: a popular meeting place with a friendly atmosphere and good food. Live (loud) music Thu and Sat. At least five, changing guest beers. ◖ ▮

## Tywardreath

### New Inn

Fore Street ☎ (01726) 813901
11.30–3, 6–11; 11–11 Sat; 12–5, 7–10.30 Sun
**Draught Bass** Ⓖ; **St Austell XXXX Mild, Trelawny's Pride** Ⓗ, **Winter Warmer** Ⓖ
Popular village local, near the coast, with a large, secluded garden; in the *Guide* since 1974. A classic. Limited parking.
Q ❀ ◖ ▮ ▲ 🍷 (Par) 🐾 🍷 P

## Upton Cross

### Caradon Inn

On B3254 ☎ (01579) 362391
11.30–4, 5.30–11; 12–3, 7–10.30 Sun
**Flowers Original; St Austell HSD; guest beers** Ⓗ/Ⓖ
Friendly, 17th-century, slate-clad country inn. Pool and jukebox in the public bar; quieter lounge. Good value food. Near Sterts Open Air Theatre and a clay pigeon range. Cider in summer.
🏚 Q ❀ ◖ ▮ 🍷 🍷 P

## Wadebridge

### Ship Inn

Gonvena Hill
☎ (01208) 812839
11–11; 12–10.30 Sun
**Flowers IPA; Marston's Pedigree** Ⓗ
Friendly, cosy, 16th-century coaching inn with beamed ceilings and a fine leaded window. 🏚 🍽 ◖ ▮ 🐾 P

## Zelah

### Hawkins Arms

High Street ☎ (01872) 540339
11–3, 6–11; 12–4, 7–10.30 Sun
**Tetley Bitter; guest beers** Ⓗ
Handy pub, off the busy A30, offering four changing guest beers, home-cooked meals and good value B&B. Garden for children; no-smoking area for diners.
🏚 Q 🍽 ❀ 🍽 ◖ ▮ ᗉ 🐾 🍷 P

# Cumbria

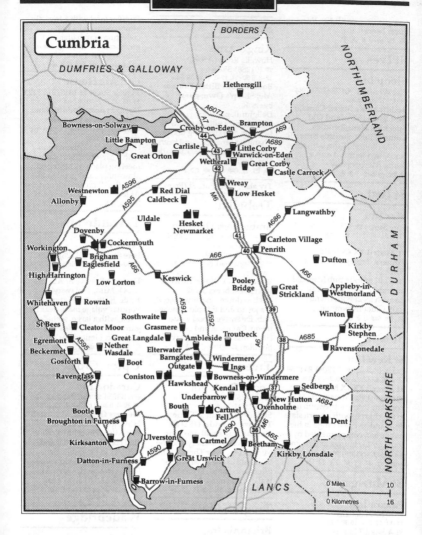

## Cumbria

BORDERS
DUMFRIES & GALLOWAY
NORTHUMBERLAND

Hethersgill

Bowness-on-Solway
Little Bampton
Great Orton
Carlisle
Crosby-on-Eden
Brampton
Little Corby
Warwick-on-Eden
Great Corby
Wetheral
Castle Carrock
Wreay
Low Hesket
Westnewton
Red Dial
Caldbeck
Langwathby
Allonby
Uldale
Hesket Newmarket
Carleton Village
Dovenby
Cockermouth
Penrith
Workington
Brigham
Eaglesfield
Dufton
High Harrington
Low Lorton
Keswick
Pooley Bridge
Great Strickland
Appleby-in-Westmorland
Whitehaven
Rowrah
Rosthwaite
Winton
St Bees
Cleator Moor
Grasmere
Kirkby Stephen
Egremont
Great Langdale
Ambleside
Troutbeck
Ravenstonedale
Beckermet
Nether Wasdale
Elterwater
Gosforth
Boot
Barngates
Outgate
Windermere
Ings
Ravenglass
Coniston
Hawkshead
Bowness-on-Windermere
Kendal
Bootle
Underbarrow
New Hutton
Sedbergh
Broughton in Furness
Bouth
Cartmel Fell
Oxenholme
Dent
Kirksanton
Ulverston
Cartmel
Beetham
Datton-in-Furness
Great Urswick
Kirkby Lonsdale
Barrow-in-Furness
LANCS
DURHAM
NORTH YORKSHIRE

0 Miles 10
0 Kilometres 16

## Allonby

### Ship
☎ (01900) 881017
11–3, 7–11; 12–3, 7–10.30 Sun
**Yates Bitter, Premium; guest beer** H
Refurbished hotel in a quiet seaside village on the beautiful Solway coast, with stunning views of Scotland across the Firth. Quiet, pleasant surroundings; good food.
🏨 Q 🍴 ◑ ▲ P

## Ambleside

### Golden Rule
Smithy Brow (100 yds off A591, towards Kirkstone)
☎ (0153 94) 32257
11–11; 12–10.30 Sun

**Robinson's Hatters Mild, Old Stockport, Hartleys XB, Best Bitter** H
Traditional drinking pub, popular with locals, students and visitors. No jukebox, piped noise or meals; conversation and well-filled rolls/pork pies offered instead. 🏨 Q ✿ ♣

### Queen's Hotel
Market Place
☎ (0153 94) 32206
11–11; 12–10.30 Sun
**Jennings Bitter; Tetley Bitter; Theakston XB; guest beer** H
Village-centre hotel which has a ground-floor lounge bar, a dining room and Victoria's Restaurant (set eve meals). The cellar bar opens at 6.45pm offering pool, a jukebox and pizzas. 🏨 ✿ 🍴 ◑ ▶ ♣

# Appleby-in-Westmorland

## Golden Ball
High Weind ☎ (0176 83) 51493
12–3, 7–11; 12–3, 7–10.30 Sun
**Jennings Bitter, Cumberland Ale** Ⓗ
Friendly, honest, no-frills, town-centre pub. Sandwiches and snacks available. Children's certificate.
🍴 ≋ ♣

## Royal Oak Inn
Bongate ☎ (0176 83) 51463
11–3, 6–11; 12–10.30 Sun
**Black Sheep Best Bitter; Theakston Best Bitter; Yates Bitter; Younger Scotch; guest beers** Ⓗ
Well-appointed inn, south of the town centre. The left hand entrance is to a splendid tap room, the right to a lounge and dining room. Up to four guests, plus a house beer brewed by Hesket Newmarket.
🏰 Q ❀ 🛏 ◖❐ 🍴 ♣

# Barngates

## Drunken Duck Inn
Between Skelwith Bridge and Hawkshead OS351012
☎ (0153 94) 36347
11.30–3, 6–11; 12–3, 6–10.30 Sun
**Boddingtons Bitter; Jennings Bitter; Mitchell's Lancaster Bomber; Theakston Old Peculier; Yates Bitter** Ⓗ
Isolated, but very popular, inn with mountain views. No jukebox, machines or TV. Good quality meals include vegetarian choices. A house beer is brewed by Yates. Arrive early for seats and food.
🏰 Q ☜ ❀ 🛏 ◖❐ ▲ P ✂

# Barrow-in-Furness

## Albion Hotel
29 Dalton Road
☎ (01229) 820089
11–3, 5.30–11; 11–11 Fri & Sat; 12–3, 7–10.30 Sun
**Matthew Brown Bitter; Theakston Best Bitter; guest beer** Ⓗ
Warm, friendly, town-centre local, popular with all ages, with two distinctive rooms. Good quality lunches, Mon–Fri, 12–2. ❀ 🛏 ◖ 🍴 ≋ ♣

# Beckermet

## Royal Oak
☎ (01946) 841551
11–3, 6–11; 11–11 Sat; 12–10.30 Sun
**Jennings Bitter, Cumberland Ale; guest beer** Ⓗ
Low-ceilinged, multi-roomed country pub with warming fires and a welcome to match. Panelled games room; cosy, intimate, central bar offering

friendly conversation. Excellent food (with unusual choices on a specials board) at fair prices. Children's certificate.
🏰 Q ☜ ❀ 🛏 ◖❐ P

# Beetham

## Wheatsheaf Hotel
☎ (0153 95) 62123
11–3, 6–11; 12–3, 7–10.30 Sun
**Boddingtons Bitter** Ⓗ
Unspoilt, village hotel with three bars, including a stone-flagged tap room. Good value food (home-made pies a speciality). The beer range varies. Families welcome until 8.30. 🏰 Q ◖❐ 🍴 ▲ ♣ P

# Boot

## Burnmoor Inn
Off Hardknott Pass road, through Eskdale Valley
☎ (0194 67) 23224
11–3, 5–11; 12–3, 5–10.30 Sun
**Jennings Bitter, Cumberland Ale** Ⓗ
Charming inn, set in a fold of the hills near the foot of Scafell, close to the terminus of La'al Ratty narrow gauge steam railway. Surrounded by beautiful scenery, with masses of things to do, it is perennially popular. The food has an Austrian flavour. Families welcome.
🏰 Q ❀ 🛏 ◖❐ ▲ ♣ P

# Bootle

## King's Head Hotel
Main Street ☎ (01229) 718239
11–3, 6–11; 11–11 Sat; hours vary Sun
**Younger Scotch** Ⓗ
If you've never been to a really traditional public house, try this. No bar, only a serving doorway. 🏰 Q ❀ ▲ ♣ P

# Bouth

## White Hart Inn
☎ (01229) 861229
12–3.30 (4 Sat; not Mon), 6–11; 12–3.30, 6–10.30 Sun
**Boddingtons Bitter; Castle Eden Ale; Tetley Bitter; guest beer** (summer) Ⓗ
Pub with an unspoiled gem of a main bar leading on to a games room and a dining area. The walls of this bar echo traditional local hunting themes, with mounted birds and fox and deer masks.
🏰 ❀ 🛏 ◖❐ ▲ ♣ P

# Bowness-on-Solway

## King's Arms
☎ (0169 73) 51426
7–11; 1–3, 7–11 Sat; 1–3, 7–10.30 Sun

**Jennings Bitter, Cumberland Ale, Cocker Hoop** Ⓗ
Traditional, basic, village pub at the western end of Hadrian's Wall, featuring old photographs and a real fire.
🏰 Q ☜ ▲ ♣

# Bowness-on-Windermere

## Westmorland Arms
Lake Road
☎ (0153 94) 45678
11–11; 12–10.30 Sun
**Jennings Bitter, Cumberland Ale, Sneck Lifter; guest beer** Ⓗ
Cosy pub which has had various names as a free house and is now the first in South Lakeland to be owned by Jennings. Guest beers in the ground floor bar; live music in the cellar bar (open 10pm–1am Fri–Sat).
🛏 ◖❐ ♣

# Brampton

## White Lion Hotel
High Cross Street
☎ (0169 77) 2338
11–11; 12–3, 7–10.30 Sun
**Boddingtons Bitter; Theakston Best Bitter; guest beers** Ⓗ
Busy, two-roomed, town-centre pub with a lounge and a bar. Wide choice of good food.
🏰 🛏 ◖❐ ♿ ♣ P

# Brigham

## Lime Kiln
Low Road
☎ (01900) 825375
12–3, 6.30–11; 12–3, 7–10.30 Sun
**Robinson's Hartleys XB** Ⓗ
Pleasant, two-roomed village local, popular for meals, especially curries. No food Mon except bank hols. Children welcome.
Q ❀ 🛏 ◖❐ ▲ ♣ P

# Broughton in Furness

## Manor Arms
The Square
☎ (01229) 716286
12–11; 12–10.30 Sun
**Draught Bass; Butterknowle Banner Bitter; Old Ebenezer; Yates Bitter; guest beer** (winter) Ⓗ
18th-century, family-run free house in a quiet village square. Local CAMRA *Pub of the Year* for the last six years. Food all day. Accommodation discounts for CAMRA members. Cider in winter.
🏰 Q ❀ 🛏 ♣ ○ 🍺

## Caldbeck

### Oddfellows Arms
☎ (0169 74) 78227
12–3, 6.30–11; 12–3, 7–10.30 Sun
**Jennings Bitter, Cumberland Ale; guest beers** Ⓗ
Large pub in one of North Cumbria's most picturesque villages. Fine food served in the restaurant or bar.
✿ ✎ ⑴ ▷ & P

## Carleton Village

### Cross Keys
On A686 ☎ (01768) 866233
11–3, 6–11; 12–3, 7–10.30 Sun (may vary)
**Ward's Best Bitter; guest beer** Ⓗ
17th-century inn on the outskirts of Penrith; rumoured to be haunted.
♨ Q ✿ ⑴ ▷ Å ♣ P ⊟

## Carlisle

### Caledonian Cask House
17 Botchergate
☎ (01228) 30460
11–11; 12–10.30 Sun
**Boddingtons Bitter; guest beers** Ⓗ
Large, city-centre pub with up to five guest beers, changed regularly. Good value, home-cooked food. ⑴ ⇌ ⌂

### Carlisle Rugby Club
Warwick Road
☎ (01228) 21300
7 (5.30 Fri, 6 Sat)–11 (12.30–11 Sat during football season); 12–3, 7–10.30 Sun
**Tetley Bitter; Yates Bitter; guest beer** Ⓗ
Welcoming, friendly club with a cosy lounge and a large bar, often crowded when Carlisle Utd are at home. Show this guide or CAMRA membership to be signed in. ♨ ⏃ ✿ ♣ P

### Howard Arms
107 Lowther Street
☎ (01228) 32926
11–11; 12–10.30 Sun
**Theakston Best Bitter, XB** Ⓗ
Multi-roomed, city-centre pub, usually crowded. Evidence of its former owners, the State Management scheme, can be seen in the collection of old bottles. Unusual tiled frontage.
✿ ⑴ ⇌

### Maltsters' Arms
John Street (A595/B5299 jct, near castle) ☎ (01228) 20499
5.30 (12 Sat)–11; 12–3, 7–10.30 Sun
**Jennings Cumberland Ale; guest beer** Ⓗ
Refurbished, one-roomed pub, opposite the former State Management Brewery. Good value bar meals. ⑴ ▷ ♣

## Cartmel

### Cavendish Arms
Off the square
☎ (0153 95) 36240
11.30–11; 12–10.30 Sun
**Cartmel Buttermere Bitter, Lakeland Gold, Thoroughbred; guest beer** Ⓗ
14th/15th-century coaching inn whose landlord gives guided fell walks. The main outlet for Cartmel Brewery, with low beams and a friendly atmosphere. Selection of bottled foreign beers; sometimes an additional guest beer.
♨ Q ✿ ⇌ ⑴ ▷ & ♣ P

## Cartmel Fell

### Masons Arms
Strawberry Bank (between Fell foot and Bowland Bridge)
OS413895 ☎ (0153 95) 68486
11.30–3, 6–11 (11.30–11 high summer); 12–3, 7–10.30 Sun
**Lakeland Amazon, Great Northern, Big Six; guest beers** Ⓗ
Secluded, yet busy, four-roomed, fellside pub offering a legendary range of bottled beers. The outlet for Lakeland Brewing Co. (range may vary). Fine views over Winster Valley. A real gem (albeit expensive).
♨ Q ✿ ⑴ ▷ ⌂ P ⊟

## Castle Carrock

### Weary Sportsman
On B6431, 4 miles S of Brampton ☎ (01228) 70230
12–3, 7–11; 12–3, 7–10.30 Sun
**Draught Bass; guest beers** Ⓗ
Cosy village local with a collection of sporting pictures and brasses. Excellent food.
Q ✿ ⇌ ⑴ ▷ ♣ P

## Cleator Moor

### New Victoria
Ennerdale Road
☎ (01946) 811345
11–11; 12–10.30 Sun
**Boddingtons Bitter; Jennings Bitter, Cumberland Ale; guest beer** Ⓗ
Comfortable, friendly, refurbished pub on the main street. Strong community atmosphere. ✿ ♣

## Cockermouth

### Bitter End
15 Kirkgate ☎ (01900) 828993
11.30–3, 5.30–11 (11–11 summer); 12–3, 7–10.30 (12–10.30 summer) Sun
**Bitter End Cocker Snoot, Skinners Old Strong; Ind Coope Burton Ale; Jennings Bitter; Tetley Bitter, Imperial; Yates Bitter; guest beers** Ⓗ
Interesting brew pub created out of a derelict shell by licensees with a proven commitment to real ales and superb food (not served Sun eve). Brewing takes place in a small room, visible through glass from the lounge. Clear labelling explains the process. Children welcome for meals.
♨ ⑴ ▷ Å

### Bush Hotel
Main Street ☎ (01900) 822064
11–11; 12–10.30 Sun
**Jennings Mild, Bitter, Cumberland Ale, Cocker Hoop, Sneck Lifter; guest beers** Ⓗ
Refurbished town-centre pub, a showcase for Jennings Brewery and a local CAMRA award-winner. Less common guest beers. ♨ ⑴ ▷

### Swan Inn
Kirkgate ☎ (01900) 822425
11–3, 7–11; 12–3, 7.30–10.30 Sun
**Jennings Bitter, Cocker Hoop** Ⓗ
Popular pub on a cobbled Georgian square, near the Kirkgate Centre (roadside parking nearby). Beers from the Jennings range may vary; large choice of whiskies. Bustling and friendly.
Q ♣

## Coniston

### Black Bull
Yewdale Road
☎ (0153 94) 41668
11–11; 12–10.30 Sun
**Coniston Bluebird, Old Man Ale; Theakston Old Peculier; guest beer** Ⓗ
16th-century coaching inn with oak beams and Donald Campbell memorabilia. The Coniston beers are a treat, brewed in the micro-brewery on the premises. Meals served 11–9. ♨ Q ✿ ⇌ ⑴ ▷ P ⌿ ⊟

## Crosby-on-Eden

### Stag Inn
☎ (01228) 573210
11.30–3, 6–11; 12–3, 7–10.30 Sun
**Jennings Mild, Bitter, Cumberland Ale** Ⓗ
Village local with low, beamed ceilings which benefits from a recently opened village bypass.
♨ Q ✿ ⑴ ▷ ♣ P

## Dalton-in-Furness

### Golden Ball Inn
15 Tudor Square
☎ (01229) 467757
11–11; 12–10.30 Sun
**Robinson's Old Stockport, Hartleys XB, Best Bitter** Ⓗ
Comfortable town-centre hostelry, popular with locals

and visitors. Regular, varied live music. ♨ ✿ ◗ ⇌ ♣

## Dent

### Sun Inn
Main Street ☎ (0153 96) 25208
11–2.30, 7–11 (may vary); 11–11 Sat & summer; 12–10.30 Sun
**Dent Bitter, Ramsbottom, T'Owd Tup; Younger Scotch** Ⓗ
Traditional pub in a charming village. The bar area is music-free and has a no-smoking section. The games room has pool and a jukebox. Good value meals. The George & Dragon, almost next door, is also owned by Dent Brewery and is recommended.
♨ Q ✿ 🍴 ◗ ▲ ♣ P ⚅

## Dovenby

### Ship Inn
Main Street ☎ (01900) 828097
11–3, 5.30–11; 11–11 Sat; 12–10.30 Sun
**Jennings Bitter** Ⓗ
Cosy, friendly country pub where families are welcome and children under ten eat free (Mon–Fri). A second Jennings beer is available in summer.
♨ Q ✿ 🍴 ◗ ♣ P

## Dufton

### Stag Inn
☎ (0176 83) 51608
12–3 (not winter Mon), 6–11 (11–11 summer); 12–3, 7–10.30 (12–10.30 summer) Sun
**Boddingtons Bitter; guest beers** Ⓗ
Unspoilt local in an attractive village on the Pennine Way. Popular with locals and visitors alike, it has a superb antique kitchen range in the front bar. Self-catering holiday cottage available.
♨ ✿ ◗ ▲ ♣ P

## Eaglesfield

### Black Cock
☎ (01900) 822989
11–3, 6–11; 12–4, 7–10.30 Sun
**Jennings Bitter** Ⓗ
Gem of a pub run by a gem of a landlady; well worth a detour. Unspoilt and unaltered, it stands in a delightful village with a history. ♨ Q ✿ ♣

## Egremont

### Blue Bell
Market Place ☎ (01946) 820581
12–3, 6–11; 12–2, 7–10.30 Sun
**Robinson's Hartleys XB, Best Bitter** Ⓗ
Light and airy modernisation of an historic pub. The long, enclosed garden at the back is safe for children. Ruins of a castle across the road.
♨ ✿ ♣

## Elterwater

### Britannia Inn
☎ (0153 94) 37210
11–11; 12–10.30 Sun
**Boddingtons Bitter; Jennings Bitter, Cumberland Ale; guest beers** Ⓗ
Very popular pub in probably the most visited valley in the Lake District. There is a front bar, with entrance hall and a dining room, a small back bar and a large patio. If all these are full, the village green acts as an overspill. No jukebox, pool, TV or machines.
♨ Q ✿ 🍴 ◗ ▶ ⊞ ▲ ♣

## Gosforth

### Globe Hotel
The Square ☎ (0194 67) 25235
12–3, 5.30 (7 Fri)–11; 12–3, 7–10.30 Sun
**Theakston Best Bitter, XB, Old Peculier; Younger No. 3** Ⓗ
Unpretentious local at the heart of the village. Hearty home-cooked meals (no food Fri and Sat eves). Interesting old buildings, craft shops, a pottery and four other real ale pubs make Gosforth enjoyable to visit. ♨ ✿ Q 🍴 ◗ ▶ ⅙ ♣ P

## Grasmere

### Traveller's Rest Inn
On A591, ½ mile N of village
☎ (0153 94) 35604
11–11; 12–10.30 Sun
**Jennings Mild, Bitter, Cumberland Ale, Sneck Lifter; guest beer** Ⓗ
Roadside pub, popular for good value meals: a small bar next to a big log fire, a family/ games room up steps, a dining area and a (no-smoking) dining room. Meals all day in summer. The King's Head at Thirlspot (6 miles N) is in the same ownership and is also recommended.
♨ ✿ 🍴 ◗ ▶ ▲ ♣ P

## Great Corby

### Queen Inn
☎ (01228) 560731
12–2.30, 5.30 (7 Sat)–11; 12–3, 7–10.30 Sun (may vary winter)
**Beer range varies** Ⓗ
Excellent, welcoming village free house within easy walking distance of Wetheral station (across the viaduct). CAMRA Cumbria *Pub of the Year* 1995.
♨ Q ✿ ♣ P

## Great Langdale

### Old Dungeon Ghyll
☎ (0153 94) 37272
11–11; 12–10.30 Sun
**Jennings Cumberland Ale; Theakston XB, Old Peculier; Yates Bitter; guest beers** Ⓗ

The bar at the 'ODG' has a special place in the hearts of vast numbers of climbers, walkers and campers, for the beer and the informal atmosphere. A more formal bar in the hotel is for diners/ residents.
♨ Q ✿ 🍴 ◗ ▶ ⊞ ▲ ♣ ◔ P

## Great Orton

### Wellington Inn
☎ (01228) 710775
12–2.30, 7–11; 11.30–11 Sat; 12–3, 7–10.30 Sun
**Robinson's Hartleys XB, Best Bitter** Ⓗ
Traditional, multi-roomed village local serving good value bar meals (not Tue eve).
♨ ✿ ◗ ▶ ▲ ♣ P

## Great Strickland

### Strickland Arms
Off A6, between M6 jcts 39 and 40 ☎ (01931) 712238
12–3 (not Wed), 6–11; 12–3, 7–10.30 Sun
**Ind Coope Burton Ale; Jennings Bitter; Tetley Bitter; Worthington Bitter** Ⓗ
Welcoming, two-roomed pub with no jukebox or machines; pool in the separate games area. Children's certificate; play area in the garden.
♨ Q ✿ 🍴 ◗ ▶ ⅙ ▲ ♣ P ⊟

## Great Urswick

### Derby Arms
☎ (01229) 586348
12–3, 5.30–11; 12–3, 7–10.30 Sun
**Robinson's Hatters Mild, Old Stockport, Hartleys XB, Frederics** Ⓗ
Comfortable village local. The 'crack' is good and the ale is better. ♨ ♨ ♣ P

## Hawkshead

### King's Arms
The Square ☎ (0153 94) 36372
11–11; 12–10.30 Sun
**Greenalls Original; Tetley Bitter; Theakston Best Bitter; guest beer** Ⓗ
Village-centre pub with a dining room. The beer range may vary in summer; occasional cider; Handy for the Beatrix Potter Museum (NT). Self-catering cottage to let.
♨ Q ✿ 🍴 ◗ ▶ ▲ ♣ ◔

## Hesket Newmarket

### Old Crown
1 mile SE of Caldbeck
OS341386 ☎ (0169 74) 78288
12–3 (not Mon–Fri except school hols), 5.30–11; 12–3, 7–10.30 Sun
**Hesket Newmarket Great Cockup, Blencathra, Skiddaw Special, Doris's 90th Birthday**

Ale, Catbells Pale Ale, Old
Carrock Ⓗ
Superb fellside village pub,
offering fine food. Hesket
Newmarket Brewery is in the
converted barn at the back. Eve
meals finish at 8.30 (no eve
meals Sun or Mon, except bank
hols). 🏚 Q ❀ ◖ ◗ ▲ ♣

## Hethersgill

### Black Lion
Off A6071 ☎ (01228) 75318
11–11; 12–10.30 Sun
Draught Bass; guest beer Ⓗ
Hub of village activity which
doubles as the local post office;
recently refurbished to provide
more bar area. Good value
toasties. 🏚 ❀ ♣ P

## High Harrington

### Galloping Horse
Main Road ☎ (01900) 830083
11–3, 5.30–11; 12–3, 7–10.30 Sun
Jennings Mild, Bitter Ⓗ
Large, comfortable pub of
several rooms. Tasty,
reasonably priced meals
include a renowned steak pie,
runner-up in a Jennings pub
meal competition. Large games
room; children's certificate
(until 9.30).
Q ☎ ❀ ◖ ◗ ♣ P ⅄

## Ings

### Watermill Inn
Off A591
☎ (01539) 821309
12–2.30, 6–11; 12–3, 6–10.30 Sun
Black Sheep Special; Lees
Moonraker; Theakston Best
Bitter, XB, Old Peculier; guest
beers Ⓗ
Family-run free house, a
frequent Westmorland
CAMRA *Pub of the Year*: no
jukebox, piped noise, pool or
machines. It majors on guest
beers and unusual bottles from
home and abroad. Good value
meals. Storytelling club 8pm
on the first Tue of the month.
Dogs welcome. Good B&B.
🏚 Q ❀ 🍴 ◖ ◗ ♿ ♣ ⌂ P ⅄

## Kendal

### Brewery Arts Centre
122A Highgate
☎ (01539) 723166
12–2.30, 6–11; 12–3 Sun (closed winter
Sun)
Beer range varies Ⓗ
Former Whitwell Mark
Brewery, now a thriving arts
centre. The Vats Bar upstairs
has two unusual alcove seats.
The Malt Room is used for gigs
and the Westmorland Beer
Festival (Oct). The Theatre Bar
is open 7–11, Mon–Sat. Beers
come from Vaux/Ward's,
except for the guest ale.
❀ ◖ ◗

### Ring O'Bells ☆
39 Kirkland
☎ (01539) 720326
12–3 (may extend summer), 6–11;
12–10.30 Sun
Vaux Lorimer's Best Scotch,
Samson; Ward's Best Bitter Ⓗ
Unspoilt, two-bar local in the
consecrated grounds of the
parish church. The snug 'twixt
the bars is a gem, complete
with a laying out (coffin) table.
No jukebox or machines just
friendly chatter.
🏚 Q ❀ 🍴 ◖ ◗ ♣

## Keswick

### Bank Tavern
47 Main Street
☎ (0176 87) 72663
11–11; 12–10.30 Sun
Jennings Mild, Bitter,
Cumberland Ale, Sneck
Lifter Ⓗ
Popular local, maintaining a
community spirit and a
welcome for visitors in this
tourist-oriented town.
Q ☎ ❀ 🍴 ◖ ◗ ▲ ♣

### Lake Road Inn
Lake Road ☎ (0176 87) 72404
11–3, 6–11 (11–11 summer); 12–10.30
Sun
Jennings Bitter, Cumberland
Ale, Cocker Hoop; guest
beers Ⓗ
Cosy, attractive, refurbished
town pub, popular with
visitors and locals alike.
Winner of *Keswick in Bloom*
pubs' competition. It stocks the
full range of Jennings beers in
summer. Children's certificate.
Eve meals finish at 8.30 (not
served winter Wed).
🏚 ❀ ◖ ◗ ▲ ♣

## Kirkby Lonsdale

### Snooty Fox Tavern
Main Street ☎ (0152 42) 71308
11–11; 12–10.30 Sun
Taylor Landlord; Theakston
Best Bitter; guest beer Ⓗ
Two pubs in one! The front bar
with marble top tables, pew
seating and adjoining dining
areas, is noted for its wide-
ranging menu and interesting
bric-a-brac. The back bar has a
part-stone flag floor, a jukebox
and is home to the more liquid
diner!
🏚 Q ❀ 🍴 ◖ ◗ ♿ ▲ P 🛏

## Kirkby Stephen

### White Lion
4 Market Street
☎ (0176 83) 71481
11–3, 6–11 (11–11 summer); 12–3,
7–10.30 Sun (may vary)
Jennings Bitter, Cumberland
Ale, Cocker Hoop; guest
beer Ⓗ
Friendly, two-roomed local at

an important 'staging post' on
the Wainwright Coast to Coast
Walk. Strong on darts and
dominoes. ◖ ◗ ▲ ♣

## Kirksanton

### King William IV Hotel
☎ (01229) 772009
12–3, 7 (6.30 summer)–11; 12–3,
7–10.30 Sun
Jennings Bitter, Cumberland
Ale; Mitchell's Original; guest
beers Ⓗ
Popular community local with
a friendly atmosphere. The
walls are adorned with photos
of old Millom and the RAF
base. Child portions on the
menu.
🏚 ❀ 🍴 ◖ ◗ ♿ ▲ ♣ P

## Langwathby

### Shepherds Inn
☎ (01768) 881335
11–3, 6.30–11 (may vary summer);
12–3, 7–10.30 (12–10.30 summer) Sun
Boddingtons Bitter; Castle
Eden Ale Ⓗ
Good stopping off point in this
part of the Eden Valley, also
close to the Settle–Carlisle
steam railway: a split-level pub
by the village green.
🏚 ❀ ◖ ◗ ⇟ ♣ P

## Little Bampton

### Tam O'Shanter Inn
☎ (0169 73) 51566
7–11; 12–3, 7–1am Fri & Sat; 12–10.30
Sun
Jennings Bitter; guest beers Ⓗ
Large, welcoming village pub
with a bar and a lounge.
Excellent food.
Q ❀ ◖ ◗ ♿ ▲ ♣ P

## Little Corby

### Haywain
Off A69 ☎ (01228) 560598
12–3, 7 (6.30 Fri)–11; 11–11 Sat;
12–10.30 Sun
Robinson's Old Stockport,
Best Bitter Ⓗ
Two-roomed village local
offering good value food and
regular live entertainment. A
third Robinson's beer is
stocked (varies). ❀ ◖ ◗ ♣ P

## Low Hesket

### Rose & Crown
On A6, 3 miles S of M6 jct 42
☎ (0169 74) 73346
11.30–3, 6–11; 12–3, 7–10.30 Sun
Jennings Mild, Bitter,
Cumberland Ale Ⓗ
Excellent roadside inn where a
friendly welcome is assured in
the cosy lounge (no-smoking)
and the comfortable bar. Good
value bar meals (not served
Mon eve except bank hols).
One of few mild outlets in the
area.
🏚 ❀ ◖ ◗ P ⅄

## Low Lorton

### Wheatsheaf Inn
☎ (01900) 85268
12–3, 6–11 (11–11 summer); 12–3, 7–10.30 (12–10.30 summer) Sun
**Broughton Oatmeal Stout; Jennings Bitter, Cumberland Ale, Cocker Hoop, Sneck Lifter** Ⓗ
Pleasant country pub with superb food (restaurant or bar meals), a children's certificate and an enclosed garden. Lots of interesting artefacts and books on display, plus an extensive collection of teddies!
⌂ ✿ ◑ ▶ ▲ ♣ P

## Nether Wasdale

### Screes Hotel
☎ (0194 67) 26262
12–3, 6–11; 12–3, 6–10.30 Sun
**Jennings Bitter; Theakston Best Bitter; Yates Bitter; guest beers** Ⓗ
Homely hotel with split-level bars, set in a delightful hamlet, a mile west of beautiful Wastwater; much loved by walkers, climbers and campers. Regular live music and guest ales nights. The garden boasts superb views.
🏘 Q ⌂ ✿ ✿ ⇔ ◑ ▶ ▲ ♣ P

## Outgate

### Outgate Inn
On B5286, between Hawkshead and Clappersgate
☎ (0153 94) 36413
12–3, 6–11 (11–11 summer); 12–3, 7–10.30 (12–10.30 summer) Sun
**Robinson's Hartleys XB, Best Bitter, Frederics** Ⓗ
Spacious, two-roomed country pub with ample parking, well away from it all. An alcove in the bar houses a collection of old local bottles. It can be busy summer weekends.
🏘 Q ⌂ ✿ ⇔ ◑ ▶ ▲ P ⅍

## Oxenholme

### Station Inn
☎ (01539) 724094
11–3, 6–11 (11–11 summer Sat); 12–10.30 Sun
**Boddingtons Bitter; Flowers Original; Theakston Best Bitter; guest beer** Ⓗ
Friendly, two-roomed pub, an easy walk up from the station. The large garden has a play area. The guest beer comes from Whitbread's Cask Collection.
🏘 ✿ ⇔ ◑ ▶ ▲ ⇌ ♣ P

## Penrith

### Agricultural
Castlegate (opp. station)
☎ (01768) 862622
11–11; 12–10.30 Sun

### Jennings Mild, Bitter, Cumberland Ale, Sneck Lifter; guest beer (occasional) Ⓗ
Gem of a pub; the meeting place for a host of local societies, including mountain rescue.
🏘 Q ✿ ⇔ ◑ ▶ ⇌ ♣ P

### Tap & Spile
27 Southend Road
☎ (01768) 862832
12–3, 5–11; 11.30–11 Sat; 12–3, 7–10.30 Sun
**Tap & Spile Premium; guest beers** Ⓗ
Recent conversion to a Tap & Spile, offering up to seven guest beers, plus a guest cider or perry: a friendly, two-roomed pub displaying pictures of old Penrith. Well worth a detour. ◑ ⇌ ♣ ⌂

## Pooley Bridge

### Sun Inn
☎ (0176 84) 86205
11–11; 12–10.30 Sun
**Jennings Bitter, Cumberland Ale, Sneck Lifter** Ⓗ
Comfortable inn with a cosy, wood-panelled lounge, popular with diners. Pool (winter) and TV in the lower bar; separate dining room. One of the bedrooms is reputedly haunted. Cycle hire available to explore this not too hilly, but interesting, area.
🏘 ✿ ⇔ ◑ ▶ ⇌ ▲ ♣ P

## Ravenglass

### Ratty Arms
W side of Ravenglass main line station ☎ (01229) 717676
11–3, 6–11 (11–11 summer); 12–3, 7.30–10.30 Sun
**Jennings Bitter; Ruddles Best Bitter; Theakston Best Bitter; Webster's Yorkshire Bitter** Ⓗ
Cheerful, friendly local, converted from a station, with much railway memorabilia. It stands next to the main line and the narrow gauge station (La'al Ratty) stations. Also nearby are Muncaster Castle, a Roman bathhouse and a water mill. Superb food (all day Sun and in summer); good vegetarian menu.
🏘 Q ⌂ ✿ ◑ ▶ ▲ ♣ P

## Ravenstonedale

### Black Swan
☎ (0153 96) 23204
11.30–3, 6–11; 12–3, 7–10.30 Sun
**Jennings Bitter; Younger Scotch; guest beers** Ⓗ
Traditional, stone-built Victorian hotel, well-modernised and retaining a locals' bar, a comfortable lounge and a dining room. Up

to three guest beers. Overnight accommodation for guests with disabilities. The King's Head down the road, in the same ownership, is also good.
🏘 Q ✿ ⇔ ◑ ▶ ⊟ ▲ ♣ P

## Red Dial

### Sun Inn
On A595, halfway between Carlisle and Cockermouth
☎ (0169 73) 42167
11–3, 6–11; 12–3, 6–10.30 Sun
**Hesket Newmarket Doris's 90th Birthday Ale; Jennings Cumberland Ale; Theakston Best Bitter** Ⓗ
Extended roadside inn where food is served in the bar or no-smoking restaurant. Games room. Q ✿ ⇔ ◑ ▶ ⇌ ♣ P

## Rosthwaite

### Riverside Bar, Scafell Hotel
☎ (0176 87) 77208
11–11; 12–10.30 Sun
**Jennings Cumberland Ale; Theakston Best Bitter, XB, Old Peculier** Ⓗ
Refurbished real ale bar at the rear of a country hotel in a beautiful valley, popular for outdoor pursuits. Children (well-behaved), walkers and climbers (boots and all) welcome. Enquire about campers' breakfasts and flask-filling. 🏘 Q ⌂ ✿ ⇔ ◑ ▶ ▲ P

## Rowrah

### Stork Hotel
On A5086 ☎ (01946) 861213
11–3, 6–11; 12–5, 7–10.30 Sun
**Boddingtons Bitter; Jennings Bitter** Ⓗ
Family-run local, near a karting track and the Coast to Coast Walk/Cycleway.
🏘 Q ⌂ ✿ ⇔ ♣ P

## St Bees

### Manor House Hotel
11–12 Main Street
☎ (01946) 822425
11–11; 12–10.30 Sun
**John Smith's Bitter; Theakston Best Bitter** Ⓗ
Historic building at the heart of a quiet seaside village, with much of interest architecturally. Good home cooking; popular for Sun lunches. Large games area. Children's certificate.
Q ⌂ ✿ ⇔ ◑ ▶ ⊟ ▲ ⇌ ♣ P

## Sedbergh

### Red Lion
Finkle Street ☎ (0153 96) 20433
11–11; 12–10.30 Sun

Jennings Mild, Bitter,
Cumberland Ale, Sneck Lifter
(summer); guest beer
(occasional) ⊞
Good example of a largely
unspoilt, small town local. An
L-shaped bar has bench seats
and tables at one end, with
pool and a jukebox at the other.
Covered patio at the rear.
Parking nearby.
🏘 ✿ ◖ ▶ ♣

## Troutbeck

### Queen's Head Hotel
Townhead ☎ (0153 94) 32174
11–11; 12–10.30 Sun
Boddingtons Bitter; Mitchell's
Lancaster Bomber; Tetley
Bitter; guest beers ⊞
Award-winning, roadside pub,
noted for its high quality
meals, its four-poster bed-
frame bar and Mayor's Parlour.
Several nooks and crannies on
different levels; no jukebox,
pool, TV or machines. Fine
views. It usually has a local
micro's beer as one of the
guests. 🏘 ✿ 🛏 ◖ ▶ ♣ P

## Uldale

### Snooty Fox
☎ (0169 73) 71479
12–3, 6.30–11; 12–11 Sat; 12–10.30 Sun
Theakston Best Bitter ⊞
Charming inn, nestling in a
peaceful village in the northern
fells, within the Lake District
National Park, offering views
of Skiddaw. It supports
Hearing Dogs for the Deaf. The
Uld Ale comes from Hesket
Newmarket Brewery.
Q ✿ 🛏 ◖ ▶ ♿ ♣ P

## Ulverston

### King's Head Hotel
Queen Street ☎ (01229) 582892
10.30–11; 12–10.30 Sun
Boddingtons Bitter; Morland
Old Speckled Hen; Theakston
Best Bitter, XB; guest beers ⊞
Cosy, old, town-centre local,
offering regularly changing
guest beers, a bowling green
and a garden at the rear. Very
friendly, but it can get busy at
weekends. 🏘 ✿ 🛏 ≕

### Stan Laurel Inn
The Ellers ☎ (01229) 582814
12–3, 7–11; 11–11 Sat; 12–3, 7–10.30
Sun
Jennings Cumberland Ale;
Tetley Bitter, Imperial; guest
beer ⊞
Friendly local near the old
Hartleys Brewery, featuring
Stan Laurel memorabilia;
within walking distance of the
Stan Laurel Museum (he was
born in the town). B&B
planned. Q ✿ ◖ ▶ ⊟ ♣ P

## Underbarrow

### Punchbowl Inn
☎ (0153 95) 68234
12–3.30, 6–11; 12–3.30, 7–10.30 Sun
(may vary)
Draught Bass; Boddingtons
Bitter; guest beer ⊞
Pleasant village inn dating
from 1540 and modernised in
the 18th century! The remains
of a priest hole can be seen
behind the bar. Function/
games/family room up some
steps. Good value meals (last
orders 8.30) in the spacious bar
or a room off. No lunches Tue.
🏘 ✿ ◖ ▶ ▲ P

## Warwick-on-Eden

### Queen's Arms Inn and Motel
Off A69, 4 miles E of Carlisle
☎ (01228) 560699
11–3, 5.30–11; 12–4, 7–10.30 Sun
Tetley Bitter, Imperial ⊞
Excellent, 18th-century free
house and restaurant offering a
good choice of meals, a large
garden and an adventure
playground. Guest beers
planned.
🏘 Q ✿ 🛏 ◖ ▶ ♿ ♣ P

## Wetheral

### Wheatsheaf
☎ (01228) 560686
11–3 (may vary winter), 6–11; 11–11
Sat; 12–10.30 Sun
Greenalls Bitter, Original ⊞
Good food is on offer at this
one-roomed village local. The
village is on the bank of the
River Eden and there is
excellent local walking and
fishing. 🏘 ✿ ◖ ▶ ≕ ♣ P

## Whitehaven

### Central
Duke Street ☎ (01946) 692796
11–11; 12–10.30 Sun
Theakston Mild, Best Bitter,
XB; guest beers ⊞
Busy, two-roomed, town-
centre pub, popular with all.
The lounge has a railway
theme; the back bar is popular
with sporting types. Lunches
Thu–Sun. ◖ ⊟ ≕ ♣

### Golden Fleece
Chapel Street
☎ (01946) 63194
11–11; 12–10.30 Sun
Jennings Bitter, Sneck Lifter;
guest beer ⊞
Lively drinkers' pub with loyal
regulars and a 'party'
atmosphere much of the time.
Paintings of seasoned regulars
adorn the walls. ✿ ≕ ♣

### Royal Standard
West Strand (harbourside)
☎ (01946) 691130

11–11; 12–10.30 Sun
Jennings Bitter ⊞
Large, open-plan pub boasting
a fine view of the harbour.
Popular with fishermen and
nautically themed. ≕ ♣

## Windermere

### Greys Inn
Elleray Road
☎ (0153 94) 43741
11–11; 12–10.30 Sun
Theakston Mild, Best Bitter,
XB, Old Peculier; guest
beers ⊞
Lively pub with a strong local
following, noted for two well-
chosen guest beers, attentive,
courteous staff and good value
meals (all day Sun). A raised
area is no-smoking until 9.30.
Pool and TV in the games area;
TV also in the small family
room with access to a safe
patio. 🏘 ☎ ✿ 🛏 ◖ ▶ ≕ ♣ P

## Winton

### Bay Horse
☎ (0176 83) 71451
12–3 (not Mon in winter, or Tue), 7 (6
summer)–11; 12–3, 7–10.30 Sun
Jennings Bitter; Theakston
Best Bitter; Younger Scotch;
guest beer ⊞
Traditional village local
overlooking the green, with a
stone-flagged bar (dogs
admitted) and a raised games
area. Separate lounge.
🏘 Q ✿ 🛏 ◖ ▶ ⊟ ♣ P

## Workington

### Commercial
5 Market Place
☎ (01900) 603981
12–5, 6.30–11; 12–4, 7–10.30 Sun
Jennings Bitter ⊞
Popular, well-run pub, close to
the lively town centre. ♣ ✄

### George IV
Stanley Street
☎ (01900) 602266
11–3, 7–11; 12–2, 7–10.30 Sun
Jennings Bitter ⊞
Cosy, end of terrace, quiet,
friendly local, on probably the
oldest street in town.
Convenient for RL, football
and greyhound stadia and next
to an attractive harbour
development. 🏘 Q ☎ ≕ ♣

## Wreay

### Plough Inn
☎ (0169 74) 73504
12–2 (3 Sat), 7 (6.30 Fri & Sat)–11;
12–3, 7–10.30 Sun
Black Sheep Best Bitter;
Tetley Bitter ⊞
Two-roomed village local
serving good value bar meals
(no lunches in winter).
✿ ◖ ▶ ♿ ♣ P

# Derbyshire

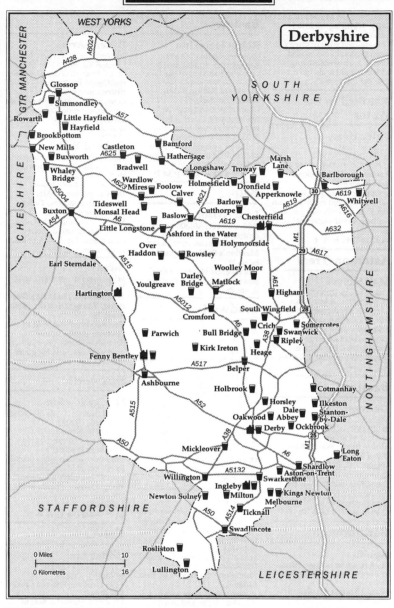

## Apperknowle

**Yellow Lion**
High Street ☎ (01246) 413181

12–3, 5–11; 12–3, 7–10.30 Sun
**Draught Bass; Greene King Abbot; Stones Bitter; guest beers** Ⓗ
Busy, stone-built village free house, with a large lounge and a no-smoking restaurant. Winner of several local CAMRA awards.
Q ✿ ⌂ ◑ ◗ ♣ P

 **INDEPENDENT BREWERIES**

**Black Bull:** Fenny Bentley

**Brunswick:** Derby

**John Thompson Inn/ Lloyds:** Ingleby

**Leatherbritches:** Fenny Bentley

**Townes:** Chesterfield

**Whim:** Hartington

## Ashbourne

**Bowling Green**
North Avenue (A515 towards Buxton)
☎ (01335) 342511
11–3, 5.30–11; 11–11 Thu & Sat; 12–10.30 Sun

71

Draught Bass; Mansfield Old
Baily; Worthington Bitter;
guest beer (occasional) H
Two-roomed edge of town pub
serving good home-cooked
food. A restaurant is being
added. A mild is also sold.
Q 🏠 🚪 ◖ ▲ ♣ P

## Ashford in the Water

### Bull's Head
Church Street
☎ (01629) 812931
11.30–3, 6.30–11; 12–3, 7–10.30 Sun
Robinson's Old Stockport,
Best Bitter H
Unspoilt country pub with an
oak-beamed ceiling in the main
bar. Popular with villagers and
walkers. Good variety of bar
lunches.
🏚 Q 🏠 ◖ 🏠 ⅄ ▲ ♣ P

## Aston-on-Trent

### Malt Shovel
The Green ☎ (01332) 792256
11.30–4, 6–11; 12–4, 6–10.30 Sun
Marston's Pedigree; Tetley
Bitter; guest beers H
Friendly village local in a quiet
location with a lounge and a
panelled bar. Bar billiards
played. Eve meals Fri and Sat.
🏠 ◖ ▶ ♣ P

## Bamford

### Derwent
Main Road
☎ (01433) 651395
11–11; 12–10.30 Sun
Stones Bitter; Ward's Best
Bitter H
Unspoilt, Peak District hotel
dating from 1890, with a tap
room, two lounge areas and a
dining room serving good,
home-cooked food.
Q 🛏 🏠 🚪 ◖ ▶ 🏠 ▲ 🚶 ♣ P

## Barlborough

### Apollo
High Street ☎ (01246) 810346
12–11; 12–4, 7–11 Sat; 12–3, 7–10.30
Sun
Ward's Thorne BB, Best
Bitter H
Popular, main road local
consisting of a maze of small
rooms and alcoves.
🛏 🏠 ♣ P

## Barlow

### Hare & Hounds
32 Commonside Road
☎ (0114) 289 0464
11–4, 7–11; 12–4, 7–10.30 Sun
Draught Bass, Stones Bitter H
Friendly, multi-roomed, cosy
local. The rear lounge has
views across the valley.
🏚 Q 🛏 🏠 ⅄ ♣ P

## Baslow

### Robin Hood Inn
Chesterfield Road (A619/
B6050 jct) ☎ (01246) 583186
11.30–3.30, 6.30–11; 11–11 Sat; 12–3,
7–10.30 (12–10.30 summer) Sun
Mansfield Riding Bitter,
Bitter, Old Baily H
Country pub in a popular
walking area, catering for
motorists as well as hikers
(hikers' bar at the rear).
Children's playground. Note:
Riding Mild is kept under gas
in winter.
🏚 🏠 ◖ ▶ 🏠 ▲ ♣ P ⅄ 🍴

## Belper

### Lord Nelson
Bridge Street (A6, 300 yds N of
centre) ☎ (01773)
2.30 (11.30 Fri & Sat)–11; 12–10.30 Sun
Marston's Pedigree; guest
beers H
Town-centre tavern serving
two rooms from a central bar.
🏠 ⛽ ♣

## Bradwell

### Valley Lodge
Church Street
☎ (01433) 620427
12–4 (not winter Mon–Fri), 7–11; 12–3,
7–10.30 Sun
Coachhouse Coachman's;
Stones Bitter; Vaux Waggle
Dance; guest beers H
Large, lively, three-roomed
pub in a scenic Peak District
village. The tap room has a
pool table and is separated
from the comfortable lounge
by a small foyer bar.
🏚 Q 🏠 ◖ ▶ 🏠 ▲ ♣ P

## Brookbottom

### Fox Inn
Brookbottom Road (access on
foot from Strines station along
the Goyt Way, or by a narrow
road from New Mills)
☎ (0161) 427 1634
11.30–3, 7 (5.30 summer)–11; 12–3,
7–10.30 Sun
Robinson's Hatters Mild, Best
Bitter H
Whitewashed stone pub in a
quiet hamlet tucked in a dip,
with a low-slung, relaxing
lounge and a basic games
room. Family room till early
eve. 🏚 🛏 🏠 ◖ ▲ ♣ P

## Bull Bridge

### Lord Nelson
Off A610 ☎ (01773) 852037
11–3, 6–11; 12–3, 7–10.30 Sun
Mansfield Riding Mild, Bitter,
Old Baily H
Popular, two-roomed local in a
hamlet near Crich/Ambergate.
Busy lunchtime for its food.
🏠 ◖ ♣ P 🍴

## Buxton

### Baker's Arms
26 West Road (off High St by
London Rd) ☎ (01298) 24404
12–3, 6 (7 Sat)–11; 12–3, 7–10.30 Sun
Ind Coope Burton Ale; Tetley
Bitter; guest beer H
Cosy, two-roomed pub with an
ivy-clad exterior. Tapster's
Choice guest beers.
🏠 ⅄ ▲ ♣ P

### Duke of York
123 St John's Road (main road
in Burbage area, towards Leek)
☎ (01298) 24006
11–3, 6–11; 12–3, 7–10.30 Sun
Ind Coope Burton Ale;
Marston's Pedigree; Tetley
Bitter; guest beers H
Very comfortable pub with a
large interior and a good pub
food menu. Tapster's Choice
guest beers. Q ◖ ▶ P

### Swan
High Street ☎ (01298) 23278
11–11; 12–10.30 Sun
Tetley Bitter; Theakston Best
Bitter; Younger Scotch; guest
beers H
Three-roomed pub with an
interesting collection of
Scottish militaria. Over 100
malt whiskies; varying guest
beers. Q ◖ P

## Buxworth

### Navigation Inn
Canal Basin (100 yds off B6062)
☎ (01663) 732072
11–11; 12–10.30 Sun
Marston's Pedigree; Taylor
Landlord; Webster's
Yorkshire Bitter; guest beer H
Excellent, multi-roomed pub
with an extensive restaurant,
alongside the only remaining
UK canal tramway
interchange.
🏚 🛏 🏠 🚪 ◖ ▶ 🏠 ⅄ ♣ P

## Calver

### Bridge Inn
Calver Bridge (A623)
☎ (01433) 630415
11.30–3 (4.30 Sat), 5.30–11; 12–4.30,
7–10.30 Sun
Hardys & Hansons Best Bitter,
Classic; Stones Bitter; guest
beer (occasional) H
Unspoilt, village local. The
spacious tap room has a games
area. Eve meals end at 8.30; no
eve meals Mon or winter Sun.
🏚 Q 🏠 ◖ ▶ 🏠 ⅄ ▲ ♣ P ⅄

## Castleton

### Bull's Head
Cross Street ☎ (01433) 620256
12–3, 6–11 (12–11 summer); 12–3,
7–10.30 Sun
Robinson's Best Bitter, Old
Tom H

Friendly local in a major tourist village: a lounge, a pool room and a restaurant (eve meals by arrangement). 🏨 ⊨ ◑ ▶ ♣ P

# Chesterfield

## Chesterfield Bowl

Storforth Lane, Birdholme (near A61) ☎ (01246) 550092
11–11; 12–10.30 Sun
**Hardys & Hansons Best Bitter, Classic** Ⓗ
Modern, 16-lane bowling alley with a large bar overlooking the action. 🏨 ◑ ▶ & P ⊬ 🖥

## Derby Tup

387 Sheffield Road, Whittington Moor ☎ (01246) 454316
11.30–3, 5 (6 Sat)–11; 12–3, 7–10.30 Sun
**Bateman XXXB; Kelham Island Fat Cat PA; Marston's Pedigree; Taylor Landlord; guest beers** Ⓗ
Superb, unspoilt, corner free house with three rooms, offering 15 guest beers a week (always one mild). Eve meals end at 7.30. Q ◑ ▶ & ♣

## Market Hotel

95 New Square (smaller market square) ☎ (01246) 273641
11–11; 12–2.30, 7–10.30 Sun
**Ind Coope Burton Ale; Marston's Pedigree; Tetley Bitter; guest beers** Ⓗ
Open-plan pub with a stone and wood floor, exposed brick and wood panelling. Many guest beers. No meals Sun.
◑

## Royal Oak

43 Chatsworth Road, Brampton (A617, opp. B&Q) ☎ (01246) 277854
11.30–11; 12–10.30 Sun
**Bateman XB; Everards Tiger; Theakston Best Bitter, XB, Old Peculier; Townes Best Lockoford, seasonal beers; guest beers** Ⓗ
Friendly local hosting beer festivals and live music, and serving nine ales, 30 bottle-conditioned continental beers, fruit wines and 140 single malts. 🏨 🏨 ⊕ ♣ ⊖ P

## Rutland Arms

Stevenson Place (near crooked spire) ☎ (01246) 205857
11–11; 12–10.30 Sun
**Boddingtons Bitter; Castle Eden Ale; Marston's Pedigree; guest beers** Ⓗ
Very popular, refurbished, historic town-centre pub. Excellent food.
🏨 Q ◑ ▶ & ⇌ ♣

# Cotmanhay

## Bridge Inn

Bridge Street (off Church St, straight over island) OS439468

☎ (0115) 932 2589
11–11; 12–10.30 Sun
**Hardys & Hansons Best Mild, Best Bitter** Ⓗ
Traditional local by the Erewash Canal, frequented by boaters.
Q ⊕ ⊕ & ♣ P 🖥

# Crich

## Cliff Inn

Town End, Cromford Road ☎ (01773) 852444
11–3, 6–11; 11–11 Sat; 12–3, 6–10.30 Sun
**Hardys & Hansons Best Mild, Best Bitter, Classic** Ⓗ
Cosy, friendly two-roomed stone pub, popular with locals and visitors to the Tramway Museum.
Q ⓑ ◑ ▶ ▲ P

# Cromford

## Boat Inn

Scarthin (off Market Place) ☎ (01629) 823282
10–3, 6.30–11; 11–11 Sat; 12–3.30, 6.30–10.30 Sun
**Draught Bass; Morland Old Speckled Hen; Townes Muffin Ale; guest beers** Ⓗ
18th-century, traditional local in a quaint village. Open fires, stone walls and candlelight are features. Inventive food. The house beer is supplied by Townes.
🏨 Q ⊕ ◑ ▶ &

# Cutthorpe

## Gate Inn

Overgreen ☎ (01246) 276923
11.30–3, 6 (6.30 Mon & Tue)–11; 12–3, 7–10.30 Sun
**Boddingtons Bitter; Flowers Original; Mansfield Riding Bitter; guest beer** Ⓗ
Well preserved village pub. Popular for food and drink.
🏨 Q ⓑ ⊕ ◑ ▶ & ▲ P ⊬ 🖥

# Dale Abbey

## Carpenter's Arms

Off A6096 ☎ (0115) 932 5277
12–3, 7–11; 12–4, 7–10.30 Sun
**Ind Coope Burton Ale; Mallard Bitter; guest beers** Ⓗ
Popular, food-oriented pub, off the beaten track in a pretty hamlet. Guest beers are mostly from micro-brewers. In the same family for 64 years.
🏨 ⓑ ⊕ ◑ ▶ ⊕ & ▲ P

# Darley Bridge

## Three Stags' Heads

Main Road ☎ (01629) 732358
12–3, 6–11; 12–11 Sat; 12–3, 7–10.30 Sun
**Hardys & Hansons Best Mild, Best Bitter** Ⓗ

250-year-old village pub with a smart lounge, plus a bar and pool room. 🏨 Q ⊕ ◑ ♣ P

# Derby

## Alexandra Hotel

203 Siddals Road ☎ (01332) 293993
11–11; 12–10.30 Sun
**Draught Bass; Bateman Mild, XB; Marston's Pedigree; Younger No. 3** Ⓗ**; guest beers** Ⓗ/Ⓖ
Friendly pub with two rooms, featuring wooden floors, a bottled beer collection and photos of trains. At least five guest beers.
Q ⊕ ⇌ ⊖ P

## Brunswick Inn

1 Railway Terrace ☎ (01332) 290677
11–11; 12–10.30 Sun
**Brunswick Recession, First Brew, Second Brew; Taylor Landlord; guest beers** Ⓗ
The oldest purpose-built railwaymen's pub, with its own, on-site brewery. Beers from all over the country are served as well. Several rooms with stone-flagged floors.
Q ⓑ ⊕ ◑ & ⇌ ♣ ⊖ ⊬

## Drill Hall Vaults

1 Newlands Street ☎ (01332) 298073
12–2.30, 7–11; 11–11 Fri; 12–2.30, 7–11 Sat; 12–10.30 Sun
**Marston's Pedigree** Ⓗ
Friendly, multi-sectioned, comfortable, one-roomed pub with brass items on the walls and a pool table.
🏨 ◑ ♣

## Flowerpot

25 King Street ☎ (01332) 204955
11–11 (midnight Thu–Sat); 12–10.30 Sun
**Draught Bass; Taylor Landlord** Ⓗ**; guest beers** Ⓗ/Ⓖ
Lively, extended pub offering ten beers and brewery theme weekends. Large function room with live music. The bar has a novel 'viewing cellar'. Meals finish early.
Q ⊕ ◑ ▶ & ♣

## Furnace Inn

Duke Street ☎ (01332) 331563
11–11; 12–10.30 Sun
**Hardys & Hansons Best Mild, Best Bitter, Classic** Ⓗ
Traditional local with an open-plan interior, near St Mary's Bridge.
⊕ ⊕ ♣

## New Zealand Arms

2 Langley Street ☎ (01332) 370387
12–11; 12–10.30 Sun

**Ind Coope Burton Ale; Marston's Pedigree; Tetley Bitter; guest beer** H
Lively backstreet local retaining a traditional style in its open-plan layout. Eve meals Fri only (steak night). ◖ ◻ ♣

### Olde Spa Inn
204 Abbey Street
☎ (01332) 343474
11–3, 6–11; 12–3, 7–10.30 Sun
**Ind Coope Burton Ale; Marston's Pedigree** H
Grade II listed building (1773). The open-plan interior retains many original features, including a Minton-style tiled floor. Q ❀ ◖ ♣ P

### Peacock Inn
87 Nottingham Road
☎ (01332) 340712
12–3, 5.30–11; 11–11 Fri; 11–3, 6.30–11 Sat; 12–3, 7–10.30 Sun
**Marston's Pedigree** H
Stone-built coaching inn, now a lively local featuring a long front bar with a lower room at the rear. ♨ ❀ ⊞ ♣

### York Tavern
23 York Street (off Vernon St, off Friargate) ☎ (01332) 362849
12–3, 6–11; 12–11 Fri; 11–11 Sat; 12–10.30 Sun
**Marston's Pedigree; guest beers** H
Busy, friendly, backstreet local, near the old greyhound stadium: a U-shaped pub with a pool table and a darts area. Varying guest beers. ❀ ♣

## Dronfield

### Victoria
Stubley Lane ☎ (01246) 412117
12–11; 12–10.30 Sun
**Banks's Mild, Bitter; Marston's Pedigree; guest beer** H
Genuine local with a comfortable, L-shaped lounge and a darts area. ❀ ◖ ♣

## Earl Sterndale

### Quiet Woman
Off B5053 ☎ (01289) 83211
11–3, 6–11; 12–3, 7–10.30 Sun
**Bateman Mild; Marston's Bitter, Pedigree, Owd Rodger** H
Village green pub untainted by progress, in the heart of the Peak District National Park; in every edition of this guide.
♨ Q ⌂ ❀ ◻ ♣ ♠ P

## Fenny Bentley

### Coach & Horses
☎ (01335) 350246
11.30–2.30, 6.30–11; 12–3, 6.30–10.30 Sun
**Draught Bass; Black Bull Dovedale, Best Bitter, seasonal beers** H
Charming pub featuring low

ceilings and panelled walls. A restaurant is adjacent to the bar. Q ❀ ◖ ◻ ◻ ♠ P ✚

## Foolow

### Bull's Head
☎ (01433) 630873
12–3 (not winter Mon), 6.30–11; 12–3, 7–10.30 Sun
**Draught Bass** (weekends); **Black Sheep Best Bitter; Ward's Best Bitter** H
Local by the village pond, a successful combination of a pub and restaurant.
♨ Q ⌂ ◖ ◻ ♠ P ⎔

## Glossop

### Bull's Head
102 Church Street
☎ (01457) 853291
12–11; 12–10.30 Sun
**Robinson's Old Stockport, Best Bitter, Old Tom** H
Listed, 16th-century, roadside inn, at the foot of the Pennines. Renowned for its Indian/Balti cuisine. ⌂ ❀ ◻ ♠ ◻ ♣

### Crown Inn
142 Victoria Street
☎ (01457) 865426
11.30–11; 12–10.30 Sun
**Samuel Smith OBB** H
Ever-friendly local, with two small, comfortable snugs, a lively games room and an attractive central bar, serving the cheapest pub pint in town.
♨ Q ❀ ◻ ◻ ♠ ✚

### Friendship
3 Arundel Street
☎ (01457) 855277
12.30–3, 5–11; 12–4, 7–11 Sat; 12–3, 7–10.30 Sun
**Robinson's Hatters Mild, Best Bitter** H
Typical street-corner local with an old engraved lamp over the door and an attractive, wood-panelled interior, with a semi-circular bar. The lounge is open-plan, and the tap room is served by a hatch. Families welcomed. ♨ Q ❀ ◻ ◻ ◻ ♠ ♣

### Nag's Head
19 Charlesrow Road
☎ (01457) 853163
12–11; 12–10.30 Sun
**Boddingtons Bitter; Chester's Best Mild; Flowers IPA; Marston's Pedigree; guest beer** H
Detached stone pub showing great commitment to the community and, in particular, to customers with disabilities: a lively tap room and a large lounge. Live music weekends.
♨ ❀ ◖ ◻ ⊞ ◻ ◻ ♠ P

### Star Inn Ale House
2 Howard Street
☎ (01457) 853072
12–11; 12–10.30 Sun

**Boddingtons Bitter; Lees Bitter; guest beers** H
Central ale house with polished wooden floors and knowledgeable staff. Five guest beers; beers from Phoenix and Taylor feature regularly.
⊞ ◻ ⇌ ♠ ◔ P

## Hathersage

### Scotsman's Pack
School Lane ☎ (01433) 650253
12–3, 6–11; 12–11 Sat; 12–10.30 Sun
**Burtonwood Mild, Bitter, Forshaw's, Top Hat** (weekends) H
Comfortable village pub with three lounge areas served by a central bar. A feature is 'Little John's Chair', made for a giant, but perhaps not the one buried in the nearby churchyard.
Q ⌂ ❀ ◻ ◖ ◻ ♠ ♣ P

## Hayfield

### Kinder Lodge
10 New Mills Road
☎ (01663) 743613
12–3, 7–11 (12–11 summer); 12–10.30 Sun
**Ind Coope Burton Ale; Tetley Bitter** H
Stone-built, three-storey pub close to the site of the old station. Good games room and accommodation. Hikers and cyclists welcome.
Q ❀ ◻ ◖ ♣ P

### Royal
Market Place
☎ (01663) 742721
12–11; 12–10.30 Sun
**Marston's Pedigree; John Smith's Bitter; guest beers** H
Centrally located former vicarage, next to the River Sett and the cricket ground. Original oak panels and pews are features. Regular live music. ♨ Q ❀ ◻ ◖ ◻ ♠ P

## Heage

### Black Boy
Old Road (set back off B6013)
☎ (01773) 856799
12–3, 6.30–11; 12–4, 7–10.30 Sun
**Mansfield Riding Mild, Bitter, Old Baily, seasonal beers** H
Large, homely, open-plan stone building with a restaurant above.
♨ ❀ ◖ ♠ ♣ P ⎔

### White Hart
2 Church Street (B6013/B6374 jct) ☎ (01773) 852302
11.30–3.30, 6–11; 12–2.30, 7–10.30 Sun
**Draught Bass; Marston's Pedigree** H
Large, attractive, unspoilt 17th-century building with cosy rooms. Good food; no meals Sun. ♨ ❀ ◖ ◻ ♠ P ⎔

## Higham

### Crown Inn

Belper Road, Old Higham
(B6013) ☎ (01773) 832310
12–3, 6.30–11; 12–10.30 Sun
**Mansfield Riding Bitter,
seasonal beers; Wells
Bombardier** 🄷
15th-century, Grade II listed
free house with an exciting
menu. 🏚 ❀ 🍴 🌓 ▶ 🄰 ♣ P

## Holbrook

### Wheel Inn

Chapel Street (2nd left from
village on Kilburn road)
☎ (01332) 880006
11.30–3, 6.30–11; 11.30–11 Sat; 12–3,
7–10.30 Sun
**Bateman XXXB; Mansfield
Riding Mild; Taylor Landlord;
Vaux Waggle Dance; Ward's
Thorne BB; guest beer** 🄷
Friendly, multi-roomed pub.
Good food is served in a
separate dining area. Large
garden. 🏚 ⛄ ❀ 🌓 ▶ ♣

## Holmesfield

### Travellers Rest

Main Road ☎ (0114) 289 0446
12–11; 12–4, 7–10.30 Sun
**John Smith's Bitter; Stones
Bitter; Younger No. 3** 🄷
Pleasant pub with a pool table
in the tap room and a spacious
lounge. ❀ 🄰 🄰 ♣ P

## Holymoorside

### Lamb

Loads Road ☎ (01246) 566167
12–3 (not Mon–Thu), 7–11; 12–3,
7–10.30 Sun
**Draught Bass; Home Bitter;
Theakston XB; guest beers** 🄷
Cosy village pub offering up to
four guest ales. Local CAMRA
*Pub of the Year 1994.*
🏚 Q ❀ 🌓 ▶ 🄰 🄰 ♣ P

## Horsley

### Coach & Horses

47 Church Street (just off A609)
☎ (01332) 880581
11.30–3 (4 Sat), 6–11; 12–4, 7–10.30
Sun
**Banks's Mild; Marston's
Bitter, Pedigree, HBC** 🄷
Homely, open-plan village pub
with a feature beamed ceiling,
a garden, a conservatory and
home-cooked food (eve meals
end at 8; no eve meals Sun).
🏚 Q ⛄ ❀ 🌓 ▶ 🄰 🄰 ♣ P

## Ilkeston

### Anchor

Market Street (off Market
Place) ☎ (0115) 944 4385

11–4 (5 Sat), 6 (7 Sat)–11; 11–11 Mon &
Fri; 12–3, 7–10.30 Sun
**Mansfield Riding Mild,
Riding Bitter; guest beer** 🄷
Busy, two-room local with a
comfortable family room. The
garden has a play area and a
bouncy castle. Function
room. Wheelchair ramp at the
rear.
⛄ ❀ 🄰 🄰 ♣ 🄰

### Dewdrop Inn

Station Street (off A6096)
☎ (0115) 932 9684
11.30–3 (not Sat), 7–11; 12–3, 7–10.30
Sun
**Black Bull Best Bitter; Kelham
Island Pale Rider; Springhead
Roaring Meg; Vaux Waggle
Dance; Ward's Best Bitter** 🄷;
**guest beers** 🄶 & 🄷
Old, unchanged Victorian
boozer: a small bar with TV
and pool, a passageway, a snug
and a high-ceilinged lounge
hosting impromptu pianists.
Occasional cider.
🏚 Q ⛄ ❀ 🍴 🌓 🌓

## Ingleby

### John Thompson Inn

☎ (01332) 862469
12–2.30, 7–11; 12–2.30, 7–10.30 Sun
**Draught Bass; JTS XXX** 🄷
Classy brew pub: a converted
15th-century farmhouse
displaying many antiques and
paintings.
🏚 ⛄ ❀ 🌓 🄰 ♣ P

## Kings Newton

### Pack Horse Inn

Packhorse Road
☎ (01332) 862767
11.30–2.30, 6–11; 12.30–2.30, 7–10.30
Sun
**Burtonwood Forshaw's, Top
Hat, Buccaneer** 🄷
Renovated old pub with
a split-level lounge and a
top bar. It caters mainly for
diners.
🏚 ❀ 🌓 ▶ 🄰 P

## Kirk Ireton

### Barley Mow ☆

Main Street ☎ (01335) 370306
12–2, 7–11; 12–2, 7–10.30 Sun
**Hook Norton Best Bitter, Old
Hooky; Marston's Pedigree;
guest beers** 🄶
Tall, gabled, Jacobean-period
building. Its many rooms
feature low-beamed ceilings,
slate tables and well-worn
woodwork. A gem.
🏚 Q ❀ 🍴 🄰 ♣ ↺ P ✕ 🄰

## Little Hayfield

### Lantern Pike

Glossop Road
☎ (01663) 747590
12–3, 7–11 (may vary); 12–10.30
Sun

**Boddingtons Bitter; Flowers
IPA; Taylor Landlord** 🄷
Picturesque pub in a hamlet
surrounded by walking
country.
🏚 Q ❀ 🍴 🌓 ▶ P

## Little Longstone

### Packhorse

Main Street
☎ (01629) 640471
11–3, 5 (6 Sat)–11; 12–3, 7–10.30 Sun
**Marston's Bitter, Pedigree** 🄷
Unspoilt village local, a pub
since 1787, with three rooms.
Ramblers are welcome in the
tap room. Excellent meals.
🏚 Q ❀ 🌓 ▶ 🄰 🄰 ♣

## Long Eaton

### Hole in the Wall

Regent Street (off Market
Place) ☎ (0115) 973 4920
11–3, 6–11; 11–11 Fri & Sat; 12–4,
7–10.30 Sun
**Draught Bass; Worthington
Bitter; guest beers** 🄷
Excellent, two-roomed local: a
bar with TV and pool, a
lounge, plus an off-sales hatch.
The garden has a skittle alley
and barbecue. Guest beers are
changed weekly.
❀ 🌓 🄰 ♣ ↺

## Longshaw

### Grouse Inn

☎ (01433) 630423
12–3, 6–11; 12–3, 7–10.30 Sun
**Vaux Waggle Dance; Ward's
Best Bitter; guest beer** 🄷
Pub originally built as a
farmhouse in 1804; the hayloft,
barn doors and stone trough
still survive. A lounge at the
front leads to a conservatory
and an adjoining tap room. No
eve meals Mon/Tue.
🏚 Q ⛄ ❀ 🌓 ▶ 🄰 ♣ P

## Lullington

### Colville Arms

Main Street ☎ (01827) 373212
7–11; 12–3, 7–11 Sat; 12–3, 7–10.30
Sun
**Draught Bass; Marston's
Pedigree; guest beers
(weekends)** 🄷
Busy, 18th-century free house:
a basic, wood-panelled bar, a
smart lounge, plus a second
lounge/function room.
Bowling green.
🏚 ❀ 🄰 ♣ P

## Marsh Lane

### George Inn

Lightwood Road (off B6056,
right at paper shop)
☎ (01246) 433178

12–4, 7–11; 12–3, 7–10.30 Sun
**Boddingtons Bitter; Stones Bitter; Ward's Best Bitter; guest beer** H
Very popular pub on the edge of the village with views over the Rother Valley, retaining traditional style and values.
🏚 Q ❀ & ♣ P

## Matlock

### Boathouse
Dale Road ☎ (01629) 583776
12–3, 6–11; 12–11 Fri & Sat; 12–10.30 Sun
**Hardys & Hansons Best Mild, Best Bitter, Classic** H
Basic, friendly, three-roomed local by the River Derwent.
🏚 ≿ ❀ 🛏 ◑ ▶ & ⇌ ♣ P

### Gate
72 Smedley Street
☎ (01629) 580818
12–2 (3 Fri), 7 (6.30 Fri)–11; 12–11 Sat
**Home Bitter; Marston's Pedigree; Theakston XB, guest beer** H
Local with a comfortable lounge and a public bar. Good value food. 🏚 ❀ ◑ ▶ ♣ P

### Thorn Tree
48 Jackson Road (on hillside N of town, behind County Hall)
☎ (01629) 582923
11.30–3 (3.30 Sat; not Mon or Tue), 7–11; 12–3.30, 7–11 Sun
**Draught Bass; Mansfield Bitter, Old Baily; guest beer** H
Welcoming, 18th-century local with two cosy rooms. Views across the valley. ❀ ◑ ♣

## Melbourne

### Lamb Inn
High Street ☎ (01332) 862779
12–3, 5–11; 11–11 Fri & Sat; 12–10.30 Sun
**Draught Bass; Theakston XB; guest beer** H
Attractive, mock-Tudor pub with a cheerful, comfortable interior. 🏚 Q ❀ ◑ ☒ ♣

## Mickleover

### Honeycomb
Ladybank Road
☎ (01332) 515600
11.30–2.30, 6.30–11; 11.30–2.30, 7–10.30 Sun
**Everards Beacon, Tiger, Old Original** H
Honeycomb-shaped pub on two levels; popular with all ages. ❀ ◑ ☒ ♣ P

## Milton

### Swan Inn
Main Street ☎ (01283) 703188
12–2.30 (3.30 Sat), 7–11; 12–3.30, 7–10.30 Sun
**Marston's Pedigree** H
Popular, friendly village local with a lounge and a bar, close to Foremark Reservoir. No

meals Mon except bank hols.
🏚 ❀ ◑ ▶ ☒ ♣ P

## Monsal Head

### Monsal Head Hotel
☎ (01629) 640250
11–11; 12–10.30 Sun
**Marston's Pedigree; John Smith's Bitter; Theakston Old Peculier; guest beers** H
150-year-old country hotel with an elegant lounge. Most ales are in the rear stable bar, which retains stall seating and an inglenook. Lloyds house beer.
🏚 Q ❀ 🛏 ◑ ▶ ▲ ♣ P

## New Mills

### Beehive
Albion Road
11–3, 5.30–11; 12–3, 7–10.30 Sun
**Boddingtons Bitter; Flowers IPA; guest beer** H
Unusual, triangular local with a small lounge and a larger vault, plus a small restaurant. Near the Peak Forest Canal.
◑ ▶ ☒ ⇌ (Newtown) ♣

## Newton Solney

### Unicorn
Repton Road ☎ (01283) 703324
11.30–3, 5–11; 11.30–11 Sat; 12–3, 7–10.30 Sun
**Draught Bass; Marston's Pedigree; guest beer** H
Lively village pub with a good following for games. No food Sun. One guest beer per week, normally high gravity.
🏚 ❀ 🛏 ◑ ▶ ☒ & ♣ P

## Oakwood

### King's Corner
Morley Road, Chaddesden
☎ (01332) 678410
11.30–11; 12–3, 7–10.30 (12–10.30 summer) Sun
**Camerons Strongarm; Marston's Pedigree** H
Modern pub, in traditional style, featuring stained-glass panels and Victoriana. Families welcome. No eve meals Sun.
◑ ▶ & ♣ P ☒ 🗄

## Ockbrook

### Royal Oak
Green Lane ☎ (01332) 662378
11.30–2.30, 7–11; 12–3, 7–10.30 Sun
**Draught Bass; guest beer** H
Friendly village meeting place with small and cosy rooms, a cobbled yard and a cottage garden. 🏚 Q ❀ ♣ P

## Over Haddon

### Lathkil Hotel
½ mile S of B5055

☎ (01629) 812501
11.30–3, 6.30–11; 12–3, 7–10.30 Sun
**Ward's Mild, Thorne BB, Best Bitter** H
Free house in an idyllic setting (view of Lathkil Dale), with a fine oak-panelled bar. Excellent food (not served Sun eve).
🏚 Q ≿ 🛏 ◑ ▶ ▲ P ☒ 🗄

## Parwich

### Sycamore Inn
☎ (01335) 390212
12–2 (11.30–3 Sat), 7–11 (closed Mon Nov–Feb); 12–3, 7–10.30 Sun
**Robinson's Hatters Mild, Old Stockport, Best Bitter, Frederics** H
Traditional country pub in an unspoilt village location. Good food; no eve meals Sun or Tue.
🏚 Q ≿ ❀ ◑ ▶ ▲ ♣ P

## Ripley

### Prince of Wales
Butterly Hill ☎ (01773) 743499
12–3, 7–11; 12–3, 7–10.30 Sun
**Marston's Bitter, Pedigree; guest beer** H
Popular, friendly local offering changing guest beers. ♣ P

## Rosliston

### Bull's Head
Main Street ☎ (01283) 761705
12–3, 7–11; 12–3, 7–10.30 Sun
**Draught Bass; Marston's Pedigree** H
Early 1900s village pub featuring a homely lounge and a public bar. 🏚 Q ◑ & ♣ P

## Rowarth

### Little Mill Inn
Off Siloh Road
☎ (01633) 743178
11–11; 12–10.30 Sun
**Banks's Bitter; Camerons Strongarm; Marston's Pedigree; guest beer** H
Large, multi-roomed pub of character, boasting log fires and a working waterwheel. Adventure playground. Good food. 🏚 Q ❀ 🛏 ◑ ▶ & ▲ P

## Rowsley

### Grouse & Claret
Main Road ☎ (01629) 733233
11–11; 12–10.30 Sun
**Mansfield Riding Bitter, Bitter, Old Baily, seasonal beers** H
Over 100-year-old, imposing, stone pub, comfortably refurbished but retaining a tap room (hikers welcome). Home-cooked meals. Family room in summer and on winter eves.
🏚 ≿ ❀ 🛏 ◑ ▶ ☒ & ▲ ♣ P ☒

## Shardlow

### Malt Shovel
The Wharf
☎ (01332) 799763
11–11; 12–3, 7–10.30 (may be 12–10.30 summer) Sun
**Marston's Bitter, Pedigree; guest beers** Ⓗ
Multi-roomed, canalside tavern converted from an old maltings. Full of character, it is popular with boaters. No food Sun.
⌂ Q ✿ ◖ Å ♣ P

## Simmondley

### Hare & Hounds
High Lane ☎ (01457) 852028
12–3, 5–11; 11–11 Sat; 12–10.30 Sun
**Ind Coope Burton Ale; Marston's Pedigree; Tetley Mild, Bitter; guest beer** Ⓗ
Former 19th-century textile mill with extensive views of Glossopdale. Good choice of food and an ever-changing guest beer.
Q ⌂ ✿ ◖ ▶ & ♣ P

## Somercotes

### Horse & Jockey
Leabrooks Road
☎ (01773) 602179
11–3, 7–11; 12–3, 7–10.30 Sun
**Home Mild, Bitter; Theakston Mild; guest beer** Ⓗ
Busy, multi-roomed local. One of the oldest pubs in the area, it remains unspoilt.
✿ ⊞ ♣

## South Wingfield

### Old Yew Tree Inn
Manor Road (B5035)
☎ (01773) 833763
12–2 (3 Sat), 7–11; 12–10.30 Sun
**Marston's Pedigree; guest beers** Ⓗ
Popular pub near Wingfield Manor. Up to three guest ales. Oak panelling in the main room.
⌂ Q ✿ ◖ ▶ Å ♣ P

## Stanton-by-Dale

### Chequers
Dale Road
☎ (0115) 932 0946
11–2.30 (3 Thu–Sat), 6 (7 Sat)–11; 12–3, 7–10.30 Sun
**Draught Bass** Ⓔ
Bustling local featuring an old water pump in its single bar. No meals Sun. Q ✿ ◖ ♣ P

## Swadlincote

### Springfield
25 North Street (Springfield road) ☎ (01283) 221546
11–11; 12–4, 7–10.30 Sun
**Draught Bass; Marston's Pedigree** Ⓗ
Pleasing, two-roomed popular local. ⌂ ✿ ◖ & ♣ P

## Swanwick

### Boot & Slipper
The Green ☎ (01773) 606052
12–3, 7–11; 11–11 Sat; 12–3, 7–10.30 Sun
**Mansfield Riding Bitter, Old Baily, seasonal beers** Ⓗ
One-roomed local with skittles outside, a TV room upstairs and a pool table. ⌂ ✿ ♣ P ⊟

## Swarkestone

### Crewe & Harpur Arms
Swarkestone Road
☎ (01332) 700641
11–11; 12–10.30 Sun
**Marston's Bitter, Pedigree, HBC** Ⓗ
200-year-old coaching inn by the River Trent, displaying Bonnie Prince Charlie memorabilia. ⌂ ✿ ◖ ▶ & P

## Ticknall

### Chequers
High Street ☎ (01332) 864392
12–2.30, 6–11; 12–3, 7–10.30 Sun
**Marston's Pedigree; Ruddles Best Bitter, County** Ⓗ
Small, friendly, two-roomed local with an inglenook. Many games. ⌂ Q ✿ ♣ P

## Tideswell

### George
Commercial Road
☎ (01298) 871382
11–3, 7–11; 12–3, 7–10.30 Sun
**Hardys & Hansons Best Mild (summer), Best Bitter, Classic** Ⓗ
Substantial stone hotel next to the church ('the Cathedral of the Peak'): a large L-shaped lounge, a snug and a tap room. ⌂ Q ✿ ⨳ ◖ ▶ Å ♣ P

## Troway

### Gate Inn
Main Road ☎ (01246) 413280
12–3, 7–11; 12–3, 7–10.30 Sun
**Burtonwood Bitter, Forshaw's, Top Hat** Ⓗ
Well-preserved, family-run pub on the side of the beautiful Moss Valley: a cosy village local. ⌂ Q ⌂ ✿ ⊞ & ♣ P ⊟

## Wardlow Mires

### Three Stags Heads ☆
At A623/B6465 jct
☎ (01298) 872268
7 (12 Sat, summer & bank hols)–11; 12–10.30 Sun
**Hoskins & Oldfield Old Navigation; Kelham Island**
Fat Cat PA, Pale Rider; Springhead Bitter; guest beer (occasional) Ⓗ
Carefully restored, two-roomed, 17th-century farmhouse pub. The stone-flagged bar is heated by an ancient range.
⌂ Q ✿ ◖ ▶ Å P

## Whaley Bridge

### Shepherds Arms
Old Road
☎ (01663) 732384
11–3, 5.30–11; 12–3, 7–10.30 Sun
**Banks's Mild; Marston's Bitter, Pedigree** Ⓗ
Ageless local overlooking the main street. The lounge is quiet and softly lit, contrasting with an excellent, lively, flagstoned vault.
⌂ Q ✿ ⊞ ⇌ ♣ P

## Whitwell

### Jug & Glass
Portland Street
☎ (01909) 720289
11–3, 6.30–11; 12–3, 6.30–10.30 Sun
**John Smith's Bitter, Magnet** Ⓗ
Unspoilt, two-roomed local with a wooden bar and open fires; a listed building in an ex-mining community.
⌂ Q ⊞ & ♣ P ⊟

## Willington

### Green Dragon
The Green
☎ (01283) 702327
11–5, 7–11; 12–5, 7–10.30 Sun
**Marston's Pedigree; Tetley Bitter; guest beer** Ⓗ
Cosy, village pub in a quiet location close to the Trent and Mersey Canal. Popular with diners.
✿ ◖ ▶ ⇌ P

## Woolley Moor

### White Horse Inn
Off B6014 ☎ (01246) 590319
11.30–2.30 (3.30 Sat), 6–11; 12–3.30, 5–10.30 Sun
**Draught Bass; Bateman Mild; guest beers** Ⓗ
Village pub with a view of Amber Valley and a 17th-century tap room, extended to form an award-winning restaurant. Extensive menu.
Q ✿ ◖ ▶ ⊞ Å ♣ P

## Youlgreave

### George Inn
Church Street
☎ (01629) 636292
11–3, 6.30–11; 11–11 Sat; 12–10.30 Sun
**Home Bitter; Theakston Mild, Best Bitter; guest beer** Ⓗ
Large, lively local opposite a very fine church.
Q ✿ ⨳ ◖ ▶ ⊞ & Å ♣ P

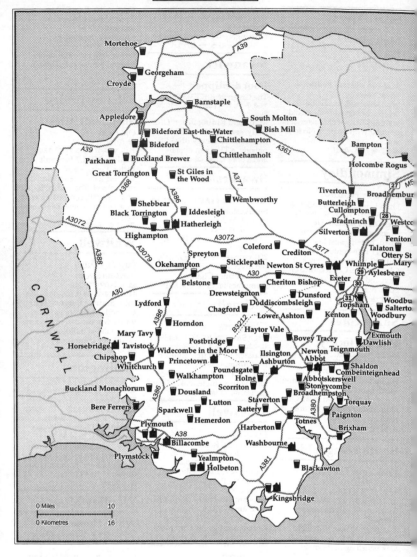

## Abbotskerswell

### Two Mile Oak
Totnes Road (A381)
☎ (01803) 812411
11–3, 5–11; 11–11 Sat; 12–10.30 Sun
**Draught Bass** G**; Flowers IPA;
guest beers** H
15th-century coaching house,
with two bars and a
restaurant.
🏚 Q ❀ ◑ ▷ 🍴 ⅃ ♣ P

## Appledore

### Coach & Horses
5 Market Street (behind quay)
☎ (01237) 474470

12–3, 7–11; 12–11 Thu–Sat; 12–3,
7–10.30 (12–10.30 summer) Sun
**Courage Directors; guest
beers** H
Convivial local hosting jazz
and blues Wed. Lunchtime
snacks. 🏚 Q ☙ ▲

## Axminster

### Axminster Inn
Silver Street
☎ (01297) 34947
11–11; 12–10.30 Sun
**Palmers BB, IPA, Tally Ho!,
200 (occasional)** H
Originally a farmers' local; a
lively town pub, just behind
the church. Unpretentious and

friendly.
🏚 ☙ ❀ ⅃ ≽ ♣ ◔

## Axmouth

### Ship Inn
Church Street
☎ (01297) 21838
11–2, 6–11; 12–2.30, 7–10.30 Sun
**Flowers IPA; Greenalls Royal
Wessex** H
Well known pub offering
excellent food in a large dining
room. Convalescing owls make
unusual drinking companions.
One of only three pubs in
Devon in every edition of the
*Guide*. Family room and cider
in summer.
🏚 Q ☙ ❀ ◑ ▷ ⅃ ▲ ♣ ◔ P

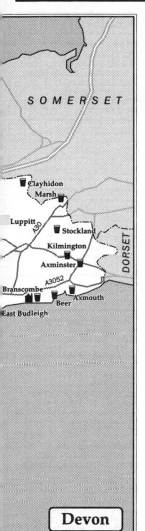

**S O M E R S E T**

Clayhidon
Marsh

Luppitt
Stockland

Kilmington

Axminster

A3052

Branscombe
Beer Axmouth

East Budleigh

**DORSET**

**Devon**

11–3, 6–11; 12–3.30, 7–10.30 Sun
**Draught Bass; Boddingtons Bitter; Exmoor Ale; Marston's Pedigree** Ⓗ
15th-century 'Devon longhouse' inn, serving good food in a friendly local atmosphere. No-smoking family room. Guest cider in summer. 🚫 Q 🛏 ⚘ 🍴 ◖▮ ⚓
♣ ⌂ P ⚐

## Barnstaple

### Corner House
108 Boutport Street
☎ (01271) 43528
11–3, 5–11; 11–11 Fri & Sat; 12–3, 7–10.30 Sun
**Draught Bass; M&B Brew XI; guest beer** Ⓗ
Unpretentious purveyor of good beers at realistic prices.
Q ⇌ ♣

### Rolle Quay
Rolle Quay ☎ (01271) 45182
11–11; 12–10.30 Sun
**Cotleigh Barn Owl; Ushers Best Bitter; guest beers** Ⓗ
Pub near the end of the main shopping area. Good range of ales; good food from an extensive menu. Summer beer festival.
Q ⚘ ◖▮ 🍴 ⚓ ▲ ♣ ⌂

## Beer

### Barrel of Beer
Fore Street ☎ (01297) 20099
11.30–2.30, 5–11 (11.30–11 summer); 12–10.30 Sun
**Flowers Original; Fuller's London Pride; guest beer** Ⓗ
One-bar local in a picturesque village, well known for its good food. Q 🛏 ◖▮ 🍴 ▲ ⌂

## Belstone

### Tors Hotel
Off A30, between Exeter and Okehampton ☎ (01837) 840689
11–2.30, 6–11; 12–3, 7–10.30 Sun
**Butcombe Bitter; Otter Ale; guest beer** Ⓗ

Large granite building on the edge of Dartmoor, ideal for walkers.
🚫 Q ⚘ ⚓ ◖▮ 🍴 ♣

## Bere Ferrers

### Old Plough
☎ (01822) 840358
12–3, 7–11; 12–3, 7–10.30 Sun
**Boddingtons Bitter; Flowers IPA; Marston's Pedigree** Ⓗ; **guest beer** Ⓖ
16th-century village inn, by the River Tavy in an area of outstanding beauty. Cider in summer.
🚫 ⚘ ◖▮ ⇌

## Bideford

### Joiners Arms
Market Square
☎ (01237) 472675
11–3, 7–11; 12–10.30 Sun
**Draught Bass** Ⓗ; **Jollyboat Mainbrace** Ⓖ; **St Austell Trelawny's Pride; guest beers** Ⓖ / Ⓗ
Well-run friendly, popular local hosting regular quiz and folk nights.
🚫 🛏 ⚘ ⚓ ◖▮ ♣

### King's Arms
The Quay
☎ (01237) 475196
11–11; 12–10.30 Sun
**Draught Bass; Flowers Original; guest beers** Ⓗ
Quayside pub: open-plan, but still with some quiet corners. Open 9am for breakfasts.
🚫 🛏 ⚓ ◖▮ ♣

### Portobello
Market Square
☎ (01237) 472991
11 (6 Mon)–11; 12–10.30 Sun
**Ushers Best Bitter, Founders** Ⓗ
Rambling old local in the market square, named after a naval battle on the Spanish Main. Live music Fri.
🛏 ♣

## Aylesbeare

### Halfway Inn
At A3052/B3180 jct
☎ (01395) 232273
11.30–3, 5.30–11 (11.30–11 summer); 12–10.30 Sun
**Draught Bass; Flowers Original; guest beer** Ⓗ
Two-bar country pub and restaurant, situated at a busy crossroads. Good value food; friendly staff.
Q ⚘ ◖▮ 🍴 ▲ ♣ P

## Bampton

### Exeter Inn
Tiverton Road (1 mile from Bampton) ☎ (01398) 331345

---

### 🏭 INDEPENDENT BREWERIES

| | |
|---|---|
| **Beer Engine:** Newton St Cyres | **Otter:** Luppitt |
| **Blackawton:** Washbourne | **Princetown:** Princetown |
| **Blewitts:** Kingsbridge | **Royal Inn:** Horsebridge |
| **Branscombe Vale:** Branscombe | **Summerskills:** Billacombe |
| **Exe Valley:** Silverton | **Sutton:** Plymouth |
| **Jollyboat:** Bideford | **Tally Ho!:** Hatherleigh |
| **King's Head:** Plymouth | **Teignworthy:** Newton Abbot |
| **Mildmay:** Holbeton | **Thompson's:** Ashburton |
| **Mill:** Newton Abbot | |

## Bideford East-the-Water

### Ship on Launch
14 Barnstaple Street
☎ (01237) 472426
11–11; 12–4, 7–10.30 Sun
**Beer range varies** H
Three-bar pub dating from 1791, a legacy of Bideford's seafaring past, featuring old ships' timbers. Handy for walkers on the Tarka Trail.
Q ☎ ❀ ◑ ▶ ♣ ⇔ P

## Bish Mill

### Mill Inn
From S Molton, take B3137 towards Tiverton
☎ (01769) 550944
11.30–3, 6.30–11 (11–11 summer); 12–3, 7–10.30 (12–10.30 summer) Sun
**Draught Bass; Cotleigh Tawny; guest beer** H
Traditional 17th-century wayside inn and restaurant with a settle next to a log fire. Skittle alley. Open 7.30 in summer for breakfast.
🚶 ❀ 🛏 ◑ ▶ ▲ ♣ ⇔ P

## Blackawton

### George Inn
Main Street ☎ (01803) 712342
12–2.30, 7–11 (11–11 summer); 12–10.30 Sun
**Palmers IPA** H**; guest beers** H/G
Recently revived village pub where the beer range changes constantly. Good selection of foreign bottled beers. Churchwards cider, plus a perry in summer. 🚶 Q ☎ ❀ 🛏 ◑ ▶ ❷ ▲ ♣ ⇔ P 🍴

## Black Torrington

### Torridge Inn
Take A3072 from Hatherleigh towards Holsworthy
☎ (01409) 231243
11–3, 6–11; 12–4, 7–10.30 Sun (may vary)
**Brakspear Bitter; Fuller's London Pride** H
Large, open-plan, L-shaped bar with some original beams and a village atmosphere. No food Tue–Wed lunch, or Sun.
☎ ❀ 🛏 ◑ ▶ P

## Bovey Tracey

### Old Thatched Inn
Station Road ☎ (01626) 833421
11.30–3, 5.30–11; 11–11 Sat; 12–10.30 Sun
**Dartmoor Best Bitter; Teignworthy Reel Ale; Tetley Bitter, Imperial; Wadworth 6X** H
16th-century, thatched ex-coaching house at the gateway to Dartmoor. Good value food.
☎ ❀ ◑ ▲ ⇔ P

## Bradninch

### Castle Inn
1 Fore Street ☎ (01392) 881378
11.30–2.30, 6.30–11; 12–3, 7–10.30 Sun
**Cotleigh Tawny; Dartmoor Best Bitter; Oakhill Best Bitter; guest beer** H
Old coaching inn, recently renovated, offering a warm, friendly atmosphere and comfortable surroundings. Good value, home-cooked meals. Families welcome.
❀ ◑ ▶ ዿ ♣ P

## Branscombe

### Fountain Head
☎ (01297) 680359
11–2.30, 7 (6 summer)–11; 12–2.30, 7–10.30 Sun
**Branscombe Vale Branoc, Olde Stoker** H
14th-century pub with huge log fires, wood-panelled walls and a stone-flagged floor. The lounge bar was formerly the village blacksmith's – the forge now forms the central fireplace. Main outlet for the local brewery which also brews the house beer.
🚶 Q 🛏 ◑ ▶ ❷ ▲ ♣ P

## Brixham

### Blue Anchor
83 Fore Street
☎ (01803) 859373
11–11; 12–10.30 Sun
**Blackawton Headstrong; Dartmoor Strong; guest beer** H
Historic, 16th-century harbourside pub, a former sail loft, where the food is very reasonably priced. Live music; popular with tourists and locals. 🚶 Q ▶ ♣

### Maritime Inn
King Street ☎ (01803) 853535
11–11; 12–10.30 Sun
**Beer range varies** H
One for those who like maritime memorabilia; overlooking Brixham quay.
🚶 Q ◑ ▶

## Broadhembury

### Drewe Arms
☎ (01404) 841267
11–2.30, 6–11; 12–2.30, 7–10.30 Sun
**Otter Bitter, Ale, Head** G**; guest beer** (occasional) H
A picturesque exterior and a relatively unspoilt, old-fashioned interior are features of this thatched, Grade II listed inn which is full of character; a village pub set amongst thatched, whitewashed cottages. Children allowed in the dining areas (no food Sun eve). 🚶 Q ❀ ◑ ▶ ♣ ⇔ P

## Broadhempston

### Monk's Retreat
The Square ☎ (01803) 812203
12–3, 6.30–11; 12–3, 6.30–10.30 Sun
**Draught Bass; Teignworthy Reel Ale; guest beers** H
Cosy pub with a warm atmosphere, in a quiet village.
🚶 Q 🛏 ◑ ▶

## Buckland Brewer

### Coach & Horses
Take A386, then A388 from Bideford ☎ (01237) 451395
11.30–3, 6–11; 12–3, 7–10.30 Sun
**Flowers Original; Fuller's London Pride; Jollyboat Mainbrace; guest beer** (occasional) H
Friendly, unspoilt, thatched, village pub retaining many original features in two bars, plus a children's room.
🚶 Q ❀ 🛏 ◑ ▶ ♣ P

## Buckland Monachorum

### Drake Manor Inn
☎ (01822) 853892
11.30–2.30 (3 Sat), 6.30–11; 12–3, 7–10.30 Sun
**John Smith's Bitter; Ushers Best Bitter, Founders, seasonal beers** H
16th-century local in a picturesque village. Over 50 whiskies. 🚶 Q ❀ ◑ ▶ ❷ P

## Butterleigh

### Butterleigh Inn
☎ (01884) 855407
12–2.30, 6 (5 Fri)–11; 12–2.30, 7–10.30 Sun
**Cotleigh Barn Owl, Tawny, Old Buzzard; guest beer** (occasional) H
Friendly village inn with a stained-glass porch; popular for food and accommodation.
🚶 Q ❀ 🛏 ◑ ▶ ዿ ♣ P

## Chagford

### Globe Inn
High Street ☎ (01647) 433485
11–3, 7–11; 11–11 Sat; 12–3, 7–10.30 Sun
**Courage Best Bitter, Directors; guest beers** H
Friendly, 16th-century, two-bar coaching inn in the centre of a delightful country town. Cider in summer.
🚶 Q 🛏 ◑ ▶ ❷ ዿ ▲ 🍴

## Cheriton Bishop

### Old Thatch Inn
☎ (01647) 24204
11–3, 6–11; 12–3, 7–10.30 Sun
**Badger Tanglefoot; Cotleigh Tawny; Wadworth 6X** H

Comfortable, Grade II listed, olde-worlde, thatched village pub, now more food-oriented, though still popular with local drinkers. ▲ ➤ ◁ ▶ ▲ P

## Chipshop

### Chipshop Inn

Off A384, 3 miles W of Tavistock OS437751
☎ (01822) 832322
12–2.30, 5–11; 12–11 Sat; 12–10.30 Sun
**Draught Bass; Exmoor Ale; Sharp's Own; guest beers** H
Welcoming, one-bar pub on a remote crossroads. Collection of mirrors; free, popular skittle alley. ▲ Q ◁ ▶ ▲ ♣ P

## Chittlehamholt

### Exeter Inn

☎ (01769) 540281
11.30–2.30, 6–11; 12–3, 7–10.30 Sun
**Dartmoor Best Bitter** G; **Tetley Bitter, Imperial** H
16th-century, thatched inn on the edge of Exmoor. A friendly pub, popular with fishermen, which fields its own cricket team.
▲ ➤ ❀ ➤ ◁ ▶ ▲ ♣ ◐ P

## Chittlehampton

### Bell Inn

The Square ☎ (01769) 540368
11–3, 7–11; 11–11 Sat; 12–3, 7–10.30
(may extend) Sun
**Draught Bass; guest beers** H
Pub in an attractive village square, opposite the church. Note the jug and bottle etched on the hallway window. 100 whiskies in the bar; cider in summer. ❀ ◁ ▶ ♣ ◐

## Clayhidon

### Half Moon Inn

☎ (01823) 680291
12–2.30, 7–11; 12–10.30, 7–10.30 Sun
**Draught Bass; Cotleigh Tawny, Old Buzzard; guest beer** (occasional) H
Old, but well cared-for, village local with nice views across the Culm Valley. Bolhayes cider.
▲ Q ➤ ❀ ◁ ▶ ▲ ▲ ♣ ◐ P

## Coleford

### New Inn

☎ (01363) 84242
12–2.30, 6–11; 12–2.30, 7–10.30 Sun
**Badger Dorset Best; Otter Ale; Wadworth 6X** H
Large, well-appointed, pub/ restaurant with one bar; a 13th-century, Grade II listed, building with a splendid thatched roof. Friendly atmosphere. Rather expensive, but worth a visit.
▲ ❀ ➤ ◁ ▶ ▲ P

## Combeinteignhead

### Wild Goose

☎ (01626) 872241
11.30–2.30, 6.30–11; 12–3, 6.30–10.30
Sun
**Wadworth 6X; guest beers** H
17th-century farmhouse in a quiet village near the River Teign. Jazz Mon. Good food. Cider in summer.
▲ Q ❀ ◁ ▶ ▲ ▲ ◐ P

## Crediton

### Crediton Inn

28A Mill Street
☎ (01363) 772882
11–11; 12–2, 7–10.30 Sun
**Draught Bass; guest beer** H
Lively town-centre local built in 1852. The inn sign depicts St Boniface. Skittle alley.
◁ ▶ ➤ ♣

## Croyde

### Billy Buds

12 Hobbs Hill
☎ (01271) 890606
11–3, 6–11 (11–11 summer); 12–3,
7–10.30 (12–10.30 summer) Sun
**Flowers Original; guest beers** H
Previously the Carpenters, this pub was sensitively refurbished in 1995. Candle lighting and a wonderful open log fire make it very cosy and welcoming. Good food.
▲ ❀ ➤ ◁ ▶ ▲ P ⊬

### Thatched Barn Inn

Hobbs Hill ☎ (01271) 890349
10–11; 12–10.30 Sun
**Draught Bass; St Austell Trelawny's Pride, HSD; Tetley Bitter** H
Spectacularly popular pub in season, offering superb food: a converted thatched barn which still manages to be attractively intimate. ❀ ➤ ◁ ▶ ▲ P

## Cullompton

### White Hart

19 Fore Street ☎ (01884) 33260
11–11; 12–10.30 Sun
**Courage Best Bitter, Directors; John Smith's Bitter** H
Recently modernised, town-centre pub with good value food. ▲ ➤ ◁ ▶ ♣ P

## Dawlish

### Marine Hotel

Marine Parade
☎ (01626) 865245
11–11; 12–10.30 Sun
**Draught Bass; Dartmoor Best Bitter, Strong; guest beer** (occasional) H
Pleasant, seafront, hotel bar close to the town centre and station. Food served all day.
➤ ◁ ▶ ➤

## Doddiscombsleigh

### Nobody Inn

☎ (01647) 252394
12–2.30 (3 winter Sat), 7 (6 summer
Sat)–11; 12–3, 7–10.30 Sun
**Draught Bass** G; **guest beer** (occasional) H
16th-century inn with many original features, including beams and a fireplace; well-known for its food and immense range of wines (700), whiskies (240) and over 40 local cheeses. The house beer is not brewed here.
▲ Q ➤ ◁ ▶ ▲ ◐ P

## Dousland

### Burrator Inn

☎ (01822) 853121
11–11; 12–10.30 Sun
**Draught Bass; Flowers Original; St Austell HSD; Wadworth 6X; guest beers** H
Victorian country inn, near Burrator Reservoir in Dartmoor National Park; ideally situated for walking the moors. Large restaurant.
▲ ➤ ❀ ➤ ◁ ▶ ▲ ♣ P

## Drewsteignton

### Drewe Arms            ☆

The Square OS736908
☎ (01647) 21224
11–2.30, 6–11; 12–3, 7–10.30 Sun
**Flowers IPA** G
Thatched, traditional village pub, untouched for a century, home of the longest serving landlady in the country until her retirement aged 99 in 1994. There has been much concern about proposed changes. However Whitbread have stated that none will occur. The pub remains high on CAMRA's 'at risk' list.
▲ Q ➤ ▲ ♣ ◐

## Dunsford

### Royal Oak

☎ (01647) 252256
11.30–2.30 (3 Fri & Sat), 6.30 (6 Fri &
Sat)–11; 12–3, 7–10.30 Sun
**Draught Bass; Fuller's London Pride; Greene King Abbot; guest beer** H
Popular local in a small village with a well-decorated, Victorian interior. Various eve entertainments. Reasonably priced, extensive, food menu.
▲ Q ❀ ➤ ◁ ▶ ▲ ♣ ◐ P

## East Budleigh

### Rolle Arms

Exmouth Road
☎ (01395) 442012
11–2.30, 6–11; 12–2.30, 7–10.30 Sun
**Boddingtons Bitter; Flowers IPA, Original** H

Pleasant one-bar, village pub, with a dining room serving excellent, home-cooked food. Popular with nearby agricultural college students.
🚪 🍽 ⌖ ♿ ▲ ♣ ⌚ P

## Exeter

### Brook Green Tavern
31 Well Street
☎ (01392) 496370
11–2.30 (3 Sat), 6–11; 12–3, 7–10.30 Sun
**Otter Ale; guest beer** Ⓗ
Friendly, one-bar, pub near the football ground, with up to eight cask ales available. Whitbread-supplied beers are kept under nitrogen, but local independent and unusual guest beers are served traditionally.
🍽 ▶ ≢ (St James's Pk) ♣ P

### Butlers
Mary Arches Street
☎ (01392) 71586
8–11; 8–10.30 Sun
**Draught Bass; Boddingtons Bitter; guest beer** Ⓗ
Refurbished pub with generally four guest ales available at very competitive prices. Don't be put off by the door attendants. 🍽 ⌖ ≢ (Central)

### Double Locks Hotel
Canal Banks, Marsh Barton (follow lane next to incinerator, over canal) OS932900
☎ (01392) 56947
11–11; 12–10.30 Sun
**Adnams Broadside** Ⓖ;
**Everards Old Original;
Greene King Abbot** Ⓗ; **Smiles Brewery Bitter** Ⓖ, **Best Bitter, Exhibition** Ⓗ; **guest beers** Ⓖ
Highly successful, slightly eccentric, canalside pub with a huge outdoor area and two rooms suitable for families, plus an atmospheric old bar. Good value food; barbecues in summer. Frequent live music. Generally up to 12 ales. Wheelchair WC.
🚪 🛏 ⊛ 🍽 🍽 ⌖ ▲ ♣ ⌚ P

### Fizgig & Firkin
St Ann's Well, 18A Lower North Street ☎ (01392) 53284
11–11; 12–10.30 Sun
**Firkin St Ann's Best, Fizgig, Floosy, Dogbolter; guest beer** (occasional) Ⓗ
Large, single-bar pub, in part of a former brewery, now a successful member of the Firkin group. The brewery under the pub supplies other Firkin pubs in the region. Tours available. Frequent live bands. Wheelchair WC.
🍽 ▶ ⌖ ≢ (Central/St David's)

### Great Western Hotel
Red Cow Village, St David's
☎ (01392) 74039

11–11; 12–10.30 Sun
**Draught Bass; Smiles Best Bitter; Stones Bitter; guest beer** Ⓗ
Busy railway hotel with two comfortable bars and a restaurant; popular with travellers. Generally three guest ales; good value food. Wheelchair WC. Q 🚪 🍽 ▶ ⊞ ⌖
≢ (St David's) P

### Jolly Porter
St David's Hill
☎ (01392) 54848
11–11; 12–10.30 Sun
**Courage Best Bitter, Directors; John Smith's Bitter; guest beer** Ⓗ
Long, narrow pub on several levels, popular with students. Good value food. Jazz club Wed eve. Two-week autumn beer festival.
🍽 ▶ ≢ (St David's) ♣

### Well House
Cathedral Yard
☎ (01392) 58464
11–11; 7–10.30 Sun, closed Sun lunch
**Draught Bass; guest beer** Ⓗ
Popular pub, with independent beers (mainly local), next to the Cathedral Green. The house beer is from Bass.
🍽 ≢ (Central)

## Exmouth

### Country House Inn
Withycombe Village Road
☎ (01395) 263444
11–2.30, 5–11; 11–11 Sat; 12–4, 7–10.30 Sun
**Boddingtons Bitter; Flowers Original; Greenalls Royal Wessex** Ⓗ
Village-style local hosting barbecues beside the stream in summer; formerly a blacksmith's. Excellent food, especially Sat eve (book); no food other eves or Sat–Sun lunch. ⊛ 🍽 ♣ ⌚

### Grove
The Esplanade
☎ (01395) 272101
11–3, 5–11 (11–11 summer); 12–10.30 Sun
**Boddingtons Bitter; Brakspear Special; Flowers Original; Greene King Abbot; guest beers** Ⓗ
Warm, friendly, seafront pub near the docks. Good home-cooked food includes locally-caught seafood. Live music Fri. Monthly mini-beer festival (Oct–May: last Sat). Wheelchair WC. 🛏 ⊛ 🍽 ⌖ P

## Feniton

### Nog Inn
Ottery Road
☎ (01404) 850210
11–3, 6–11; 12–3, 7–10.30 Sun

**Cotleigh Tawny; guest beer** Ⓗ
Genuine village local, with a friendly landlord, good food, plus a squash court. Inch's cider in summer.
🚶 ⊛ 🚪 ≢ ♣ ⌚ P

## Georgeham

### King's Arms
33 Chapel Street
☎ (01271) 890240
12.30–3.30, 7–11 (midnight Fri & Sat); 12–3, 7–10.30 Sun
**Draught Bass; Marston's Pedigree; Morland Old Speckled Hen; St Austell HSD; guest beers** Ⓖ
Wonderful local, drawing a friendly lunchtime crowd. Excellent food. Euchre, skittles and tiddlywinks played.
🚶 ⊛ 🚪 🍽 ▶ ▲ ♣

### Rock Inn
Rock Hill
☎ (01271) 890322
11–11; 12–10.30 Sun
**Draught Bass; Marston's Pedigree; Morland Old Speckled Hen; Ruddles Best Bitter; Tetley Bitter; Ushers Best Bitter, Founders; Wadworth 6X** Ⓗ
Tardis-like pub offering eight ales and a superb choice of food on an ever-changing menu. North Devon CAMRA *Pub of the Year* 1994 and 1995. Any of the above ales could give way to a guest beer. Cider in summer.
🚶 🛏 ⊛ 🚪 🍽 ▶ ⌖ ♣ ⌚ P

## Great Torrington

### Black Horse Inn
High Street
☎ (01805) 622121
11–3, 6–11; 11–11 Sat; 12–10.30 Sun
**John Smith's Bitter; Ushers Best Bitter, Founders; guest beers** Ⓗ
16th-century coaching inn, with some parts 12th-century, famous for its Civil War history as the office of Gen. Fairfax during the Battle of Torrington. Children welcome in a delicensed lounge. No food Sun eve.
🚶 Q 🚪 🍽 ▶ ♣

## Harberton

### Church House Inn
☎ (01803) 863707
12–3, 6–11; 12–10.30 Sun
**Draught Bass; Courage Best Bitter; guest beers** Ⓗ
12th-century pub with a friendly atmosphere; a one-roomed bar with a small family room hidden behind a medieval oak screen.
🚶 Q 🛏 ⊛ 🍽 ▶ ▲ ♣ ⌚ P

## Hatherleigh

### Tally Ho! Country Inn and Brewery

14 Market Street (A386, near Okehampton)
☎ (01837) 810306
11–2.30 (may vary), 6–11; 12–2.30, 7–10.30 Sun
**Tally Ho! Potboiler's Brew, Master Jack's Mild, Tarka's Tipple, Nutters, Thurgia, Jollop** Ⓗ
15th-century market town inn with a wood block floor at one end, an oak-beamed ceiling and an intimate restaurant. Good food.
🏚 Q ✿ 🛏 ◑ ▶ ♣ P

## Haytor Vale

### Rock Inn

☎ (01364) 661305
11–3, 6.30–11; 12–3, 6–10.30 Sun
**Draught Bass; Dartmoor Best Bitter; Hardy Country, Royal Oak** Ⓗ
200-year-old village inn serving excellent food in a pleasant atmosphere.
🏚 Q ╅ ✿ 🛏 ◑ ▶ ᕦ ᕤ P ⊬

## Hemerdon

### Miners Arms

☎ (01752) 336040
11–2.30, 5.30–11; 12–3, 7–10.30 Sun
**Draught Bass** Ⓗ/Ⓖ**; Boddingtons Bitter; Sutton XSB; Ushers Best Bitter; guest beers** Ⓗ
Former tin miners' pub on the hill overlooking Plympton. Good facilities for children.
🏚 Q ╅ ✿ ♣ ᕦ P

## Highampton

### Golden Inn

On A3072
☎ (01409) 231200
11.30–2.30, 6.30–11; 12–2, 7–10.30 Sun
**Butcombe Bitter; St Austell HSD** Ⓗ
16th-century, thatched inn with a low, beamed ceiling and a D-shaped bar. Hops decorate the open fireplace and the restaurant area.
🏚 Q ✿ ◑ ▶ ♣ P

## Holbeton

### Dartmoor Union

Fore Street
☎ (01782) 830288
11.30–3, 6–11.30; 12–3, 6–10.30 Sun
**Summerskills Best Bitter; Wadworth 6X** Ⓗ
Former workhouse and cider press which celebrated its 200th birthday in 1993. Good family room.
🏚 ╅ ✿ ◑ ▶ ᕤ ᕦ P

## Holcombe Rogus

### Prince of Wales

☎ (01823) 672070
11.30–3 (not Tue), 6.30–11; 12–3.30, 7–10.30 Sun
**Cotleigh Tawny; Otter Bitter; Wadworth 6X; guest beer** Ⓗ
Pleasant country pub with interesting, cash register handpumps. Sheppy's cider in summer. Beer festivals some bank hol weekends.
╅ ✿ ◑ ▶ ᕦ ᕤ ♣ ᕦ P ⊬

## Holne

### Church House Inn

3½ miles from Buckfast
☎ (01364) 631208
12–2.30, 7–10.30 (11 Fri & Sat); 12–3, 6.30–10.30 Sun
**Blackawton Bitter; Dartmoor Best Bitter; Morland Old Speckled Hen; Wadworth 6X** Ⓗ
14th-century inn within the Dartmoor National Park. Good food. Bar skittles played.
🏚 Q ╅ ✿ ♣ ◑ ▶ ᕦ ᕤ ᕦ P

## Horndon

### Elephant's Nest Inn

Off A386, 1½ miles E of Mary Tavy
☎ (01822) 810273
11.30–2.30, 6.30–11; 12–2.30, 7–10.30 Sun
**Boddingtons Bitter; Palmers IPA; St Austell HSD; guest beer** Ⓗ
Picturesque, 16th-century moorland pub with a relaxed atmosphere. Good value, varied menu.
🏚 Q ╅ ✿ ◑ ▶ ᕤ ᕦ P

## Iddesleigh

### Duke of York

On B3217
☎ (01837) 810253
11.30–3 (not winter Mon–Wed), 7–11 (11.30–11 summer); 12–3, 7–10.30 Sun
**Adnams Extra; Cotleigh Tawny; guest beers** Ⓖ
12th-century inn of unspoilt character featuring rocking chairs next to a large log fire; a quiet pub where conversation is enjoyed. Attractive garden; magnificent views of Dartmoor. No food Mon.
🏚 Q ╅ ✿ 🛏 ◑ ▶ ♣

## Ilsington

### Carpenter's Arms

☎ (01364) 661215
11–3, 6–11; 12–10.30 Sun
**Flowers IPA; guest beers** Ⓗ
Farmers' and villagers' local, in a small village on the edge of Dartmoor.
🏚 Q ✿ ◑ ▶ ᕦ

## Kenton

### Devon Arms Hotel

Fore Street
☎ (01626) 890213
11–3, 5–11; 12–3, 7–10.30 Sun
**Draught Bass; Fuller's London Pride; Wadworth 6X; guest beer** (occasional) Ⓗ
Large, friendly, village pub with a good food menu. Built in the 16th century, it only became a pub in 1822. Family room in summer.
Q ╅ ✿ 🛏 ◑ ▶ ᕤ ♣ ᕦ P

## Kilmington

### New Inn

The Hill
☎ (01297) 33376
11–3, 6–11 (11–11 summer); 12–3, 6–10.30 Sun
**Palmers BB, IPA** Ⓗ
Palmers Brewery's western outpost is a fine, friendly village inn just off the A35. Superb views from the garden.
🏚 Q ╅ ✿ ◑ ▶ ᕤ ᕦ ᕤ ♣ P

## Kingsbridge

### Ship & Plough

The Quay ☎ (01548) 852485
11–11; 12–10.30 Sun
**Blewitts Best, Nose, Head Off; guest beer** Ⓗ
Splendid, oak-beamed brew pub with friendly locals.
╅ ✿ ◑ ▶

## Lower Ashton

### Manor Inn

Off B3193 ☎ (01647) 252304
12–2.30, 6 (7 Sat)–11; 12–2.30, 7–10.30 Sun
**Shepherd Neame Spitfire; Teignworthy Reel Ale; Theakston XB** Ⓗ**; Wadworth 6X; guest beer** Ⓖ
Typical, unspoilt country pub. The public bar is simply furnished with a few tables and chairs, a dartboard, an open fire and a small bar area. The lounge is more comfortable. Well-deserved reputation for home-cooking.
🏚 Q ✿ ◑ ▶ ᕤ ᕦ ♣ ᕦ P

## Lutton

### Mountain Inn

Old Church Lane
☎ (01752) 837247
11–2.30, 7 (6 Thu–Sat & summer)–11; 12.30–3.30, 7 (6 summer)–10.30 Sun
**Dartmoor Best Bitter; Tetley Imperial; guest beer** Ⓗ
Cob walls and a big fireplace make this pub worth visiting. Families are very welcome (high chair provided). Ciders in summer.
🏚 Q ╅ ✿ ◑ ▶ ♣ ᕦ P

## Lydford

### Castle Inn
☎ (01822) 820241
11.30–3, 6–11; 12–3, 7–10.30 Sun
**Blackawton Bitter** G; **Fuller's London Pride** H; **guest beers** G
Cosy, 16th-century inn, next to the castle. The Tinners Bar and Foresters Restaurant feature low ceilings, slate floors, large stone fireplaces and curios. Award-winning food.
🏠 Q ✤ 🛏 ◖ ▶ P

### Mucky Duck Inn
Next to Whitelady Falls entrance of Lydford Gorge
☎ (01822) 820208
12–2.30 (3 summer), 6–11; 12–3, 7–10.30 Sun
**Sharp's Own; guest beers** H
Accommodating inn, with slate floors, exposed stone walls and two large family rooms, plus pool and function rooms.
🏠 Q ✿ ✤ 🛏 ◖ ▶ P

## Marsh

### Cottage Inn
☎ (01460) 234339
11–3, 6–11; 12–3, 7–10.30 Sun
**Otter Ale; John Smith's Bitter** H
Small, friendly, village pub on the Somerset border, just off the A303.
🏠 ✿ ✤ ◖ ▶ 🛏 ▲ ♣ ♻ P

## Mary Tavy

### Mary Tavy Inn
Lane Head (A386)
☎ (01822) 810326
11.45–3, 6–11; 12–3, 7–10.30 Sun
**Draught Bass; St Austell XXXX Mild, HSD; guest beers** H
Welcoming, 16th-century inn on the western edge of Dartmoor, serving good value food.
🏠 Q ✿ ✤ 🛏 ◖ ▶ ▲ ♣ P

## Mortehoe

### Ship Aground
The Square ☎ (01271) 870856
12–3.30, 6–11; 12–3, 7–10.30 Sun
**Cotleigh seasonal beers; guest beers** H
Enchanting village pub, once two cottages; warm and inviting, with top notch food.
🏠 ✿ ✿ ◖ ▶ ▲ ♣ ♻

## Newton Abbot

### Golden Lion
4 Market Street
☎ (01626) 67062
11–2.30, 5.30–11; 12–3, 7–10.30 Sun
**Ind Coope Burton Ale; Teignworthy Reel Ale, seasonal beers** H

Popular local, the only one in town to regularly sell beers from the local Teignworthy Brewery. Games room.
✿ 🛏 ◖ ▶

### Highweek Inn
Highweek Village
☎ (01626) 56490
11–11; 12–10.30 Sun
**Draught Bass; Worthington Bitter; guest beer** H
One-bar pub with a dining area. 🏠 ✿ ◖ ▶ P

### Old Rydon Inn
Rydon Road, Kingsteignton
☎ (01626) 54626
11–3, 6–11; 12–2.30, 7–10.30 Sun
**Draught Bass; Wadworth 6X; guest beer** H
Very old, friendly pub/restaurant with a conservatory. Excellent food. 🏠 Q ✿ ◖ ▶ P

## Newton St Cyres

### Beer Engine
☎ (01392) 851282
11.30–2.30, 6–11; 11–11 Sat; 12–3, 7–10.30 Sun
**Beer Engine Rail Ale, Piston Bitter, Sleeper Heavy** H
Friendly and deservedly popular brew pub near the station. At weekends the downstairs bar is open and the brewery may be viewed. Good value food includes locally-made sausages and cheeses. Live entertainment every weekend.
🏠 Q ✿ ◖ ▶ ▲ 🚆 ♣ P

## Okehampton

### Plymouth Inn
26 West Street ☎ (01837) 53633
12–3, 7–11; 12–11 Sat; 12–10.30 Sun
**Sharp's Cornish Coaster** G; **guest beers** G / H
Old coaching inn with a cosy bar, a good restaurant and a continually changing list of beers. Fine family room.
Q 🛏 ✿ ◖ ▶ 🛒 ♣

## Ottery St Mary

### Masons Arms
Sandhill Street
☎ (01404) 812300
11–2 (12–3 Sat), 6–11; 12–2.30, 7–10.30 Sun
**Teignworthy Reel Ale** H
Comfortable town local with a small frontage, but very roomy and cosy inside. ▲ ♣ ♻

## Paignton

### Devonport Arms
42 Elmbank Road
☎ (01803) 558322
11–11; 12–10.30 Sun
**Courage Best Bitter; Morland Old Speckled Hen; John Smith's Bitter** H; **guest beers** H/G

Backstreet local, near the zoo. Well worth finding.
🏠 Q 🛏 ✿ ◖ 🛒 ▲ ♣

### Polsham Arms
35 Lower Polsham Road
☎ (01803) 558360
11–11; 12–10.30 Sun
**Boddingtons Bitter; Gale's HSB; Wadworth 6X; guest beer** H
Two-bar pub: pool, skittles and music in one bar; quiet lounge. Bikers welcome.
✿ ◖ ▶ 🛒 🚆 ♣ P

## Parkham

### Bell Inn
Off A39 ☎ (01237) 451201
12–2.30, 6.30–11; 12–3, 7–10.30 Sun
**Draught Bass** G; **Flowers IPA** H; **guest beer** H/G
13th-century, thatched cottages with a modernised bar divided into three areas. Varied food; good atmosphere. The pool room becomes a family room in summer. Q ✿ 🛏 ◖ ▶ ♣ P

## Plymouth

### Clifton
35 Clifton Street, Greenbank (off North Hill)
☎ (01752) 266563
5 (11 Fri & Sat)–11; 12–10.30 Sun
**Badger Tanglefoot** H/G; **Draught Bass; Flowers IPA** H; **Summerskills Indiana's Bones; guest beers** G
Warm, friendly pub. The guest beers are unusual for Plymouth. Summerskills house beer. 🛒 🚆 ♣

### Dolphin Hotel
14 Barbican ☎ (01752) 660876
10–11; 12–10.30 Sun
**Draught Bass; guest beer** (occasional) G
Traditional fisherman's pub widely considered to serve the best Bass in Plymouth. 🏠 Q

### London Inn
8 Church Road, Plympton St Maurice ☎ (01752) 337025
11–11; 12–10.30 Sun
**Courage Best Bitter; Ruddles County; guest beers** H
17th-century coaching inn, reputedly haunted by Roundheads and Cavaliers who died here after a Civil War battle. 🏠 ◖ ▶ ▲ ♣ P

### Masonic Inn
65 Devonport Road, Stoke
☎ (01752) 607257
10–11; 12–10.30 Sun
**Courage Best Bitter; guest beers** H
Popular, single-bar free house that has been rebuilt by its own locals. The guest beers are chosen by CAMRA members. Ten mins' walk from Plymouth Argyle FC.
🛒 🚆 (Devonport) ♣

### Millbridge Inn

23 Molesworth Road, Stoke
☎ (01752) 563056
11–11; 12–10.30 Sun
**Draught Bass; Boddingtons Bitter; Courage Best Bitter; Marston's Pedigree; Wadworth 6X; guest beers** H
Den for discerning drinkers in a desert; well-known for its beer festivals. Friendly and catering for all ages; popular with rugby fans.
🏚 Q ☎ ⚴ ◑ ▶ ♿ ⌂ P

### Notte Inn

60 Notte Street, Barbican
☎ (01752) 254883
11–11; 7–10.30 Sun, closed Sun lunch
**Draught Bass; Boddingtons Bitter; Morland Old Speckled Hen; Wadworth 6X; guest beer** H
Pub dating back to the early 1800s, with many former uses, including a paint factory and a private club. Very good food.
◑ ▶

### Prince Maurice

3 Church Hill, Eggbuckland
☎ (01752) 771515
11–3, 7 (6 Fri)–11; 11–11 Sat; 12–3, 7–10.30 Sun
**Badger Tanglefoot; Draught Bass; John Smith's Magnet; Summerskills Best Bitter; Indiana's Bones; Theakston Mild; guest beers** H
Cosy, two-bar pub in a village swallowed up by residential expansion. Plymouth CAMRA *Pub of the Year* 1994 and '95. The house beer is brewed by Summerskills. 🏚 ⚴ ♣ P ⛉

### Royal Albert Bridge Inn

930 Wolseley Road, Saltash Passage ☎ (01752) 361108
10.30–11; 12–10.30 Sun
**Draught Bass; Courage Best Bitter** H
Friendly, riverside local in the shadow of Brunel's bridge, with picturesque views across the River Tamar to Cornwall.
⚴ ◑ ▶ ⬚ ⇄ (St Budeaux/Ferry Rd) ♣

### Shipwright's Arms

13 Sutton Road, Coxside
☎ (01752) 665804
11–3, 6 (5.30 Fri)–11; 12–3, 7–10.30 Sun
**Courage Best Bitter, Directors** H
Cosy, friendly, one-room pub with many loyal regulars.
🏚 Q ⚴ ◑ ♿ ♣ P

### Thistle Park Tavern

32 Commercial Road, Coxside
☎ (01752) 667677
11–11; 12–10.30 Sun
**St Austell HSD; Sutton Dartmoor Pride, XSB, Gold, Plymouth Porter; guest beers** H

Basic, but comfortable, pub with a convivial atmosphere, next door to Sutton Brewery. Popular with locals and students. ◑ ♣ ⌂

## Plymstock

### Boringdon Arms

Boringdon Terrace, Turnchapel
☎ (01752) 402053
11–11; 12–10.30 Sun
**Draught Bass; Butcombe Bitter; RCH Pitchfork; Summerskills Best Bitter; guest beers** H
Friendly neighbourhood pub which stages a bi-monthly beer festival. Good value food. A diary of events is displayed on a blackboard. The waterside village lies near the coastal path. Cider in summer.
🏚 Q ☎ ⚴ ⬚ ◑ ▶ ⬚ ♣ ⌂

### New Inn

Boringdon Road, Turnchapel
☎ (01752) 402765
12–3 (not Mon–Thu), 6–11 (12–11 Mon–Sat April–Sept); 12–3, 6–10.30 (12–10.30 summer) Sun
**Draught Bass; Flowers Original; Fuller's Chiswick; Shepherd Neame Spitfire; guest beers** H
Recently refurbished village local with a very welcoming atmosphere. Fine view over the Cattewater; opposite the yachting marina and water taxi (when running). 🏚 ◑ ▶ ♣

## Postbridge

### Warren House Inn

On B3212 ☎ (01822) 880208
11–3, 5.30–11 (11–11 summer); 12–10.30 Sun
**Gibbs Mew Bishop's Tipple; guest beers** H
The third highest inn in England stands isolated on the moor. A log fire has been burning continuously since 1845. Hikers and families welcome.
🏚 Q ☎ ⚴ ◑ ▶ ▲ ♣ ⌂ P

## Poundsgate

### Tavistock Inn

☎ (01364) 631251
11–2.30, 6–11; 12–2.30, 7–10.30 Sun
**Courage Best Bitter; Ushers Best Bitter, Founders** H
700-year-old pub in a small Dartmoor village, with a cosy front bar.
🏚 Q ☎ ⚴ ◑ ▶ ⌂ P

## Rattery

### Church House Inn

☎ (01364) 642220
11–3, 6–11; 12–10.30 Sun
**Dartmoor Best Bitter, Strong; guest beers** H
One of England's most historic inns, dating from 1028. A large

fireplace and a grandfather clock enhance the bar area. Good range of food.
🏚 Q ⚴ ◑ ▶ ▲ P

## St Giles in the Wood

### Cranford Inn

On B3227 ☎ (01805) 623309
11–2.30, 6–11; 12–3, 7–10.30 Sun
**Draught Bass; Marston's Pedigree; Morland Old Speckled Hen; Wadworth 6X; guest beer** H
Converted farmhouse offering many outdoor attractions in summer and convivial company in winter. A second guest beer is stocked in summer. 🏚 Q ⚴ ⬚ ◑ ▶ P

## Scorriton

### Tradesman's Arms

OS704685 ☎ (01364) 631206
12–2, 7–11; 12–10.30 Sun
**Draught Bass; Worthington Bitter** H**; guest beers** G
Quiet, 300-year-old pub, built to serve tin miners from the moor. Good atmosphere. No meals Mon eve. 🏚 Q ☎ ⚴ ⬚ ◑ ▶ ▲ ♣ ⌂ P ⛉

## Shaldon

### Clifford Arms

34 Fore Street
☎ (01626) 872311
11–2.30, 5–11; 11–11 Sat; 12–10.30 Sun
**Draught Bass; guest beers** H
One of Devon's prettiest pubs, much photographed for its fabulous summer floral displays. 18th-century, olde worlde pub atmosphere.
⚴ ◑ ▶ ▲ ⌂

## Shebbear

### Devil's Stone Inn

On B3072 ☎ (01409) 281210
11–2.30, 6–11; 11–11 Sat; 12–3, 7–10.30 Sun
**Boddingtons Bitter; Brakspear Bitter; Flowers IPA** H
Reputedly haunted, 16th-century pub in a village dating back to pagan times, taking its name from the nearby Devil's Stone. Welcoming bar with a real fire and games room.
🏚 ⚴ ⬚ ◑ ▶ ♿ ▲ ♣ ⌂ P

## Silverton

### Silverton Inn

Fore Street ☎ (01392) 860196
11.30–3, 6–11; 11.30–11 Sat; 12–10.30 Sun
**Beer range varies** H
One-bar village local, with no silly frills. Recommended restaurant upstairs (Thu and Sat eves and Sun lunch; booking advisable). Local Exe

Valley beers are always available. 🏮 ◖ ▶ ⓑ

## South Molton

### George Hotel
Broad Street
☎ (01769) 572514
11–3, 6–11; 12–3, 7–10.30 Sun
**Draught Bass; Ind Coope Burton Ale; Tetley Bitter** Ⓗ
Family-run, 16th-century posting inn with a comfortable, friendly atmosphere, log fires and home cooking. It hosts jazz, film shows, etc.
🏮 Q ⌂ 🛏 ◖ ▶ ⓑ ▲ P

## Sparkwell

### Treby Arms
☎ (01752) 837363
11–3, 6–11; 12–3.30, 7–10.30 Sun
**Draught Bass; Mildmay Colours Best; guest beers** Ⓗ
Pub dating from 1750, next to Dartmoor Wildlife Park. Compact and cosy, it has a separate dining area. Mildmay Colours is sold as Treby Best.
🏮 ❀ ◖ ▶ ⓑ ♣ P ⓣ

## Spreyton

### Tom Cobley Tavern
☎ (01647) 231314
12–2.30, 7–11; closed Mon; 12–2.30, 7–10.30 Sun
**Butcombe Bitter; Cotleigh Tawny; guest beer** Ⓗ
Quiet, mildly eccentric, thatched, village local. A superb function/family room has an indoor barbecue available for party bookings. All food is home-cooked. Table tennis played.
🏮 Q ❀ ⌂ ◖ ▶ ♣ P

## Staverton

### Sea Trout
☎ (01803) 762274
11–3, 6–11; 12–10.30 Sun
**Draught Bass; Dartmoor Best Bitter; Wadworth 6X** Ⓗ**; guest beers** Ⓖ
16th-century cottages have been converted to form this warm pub.
🏮 Q ❀ ◖ ▶ ⓑ ⓑ ⥮ ♣ ⌂ P

## Sticklepath

### Devonshire
Off A30 ☎ (01837) 840626
11–11; 12–3, 7–10.30 Sun
**Draught Bass; St Austell Tinners; guest beers** Ⓖ
Low beams and a granite floor, dating back to 1640, give a nice, cosy feel to this pub. The casks are stillaged against the back wall and cooled by a mill leat. Lunchtime snacks. Cider in summer.
🏮 Q 🛏 ❀ ▶ ⓑ ▲ ♣ ⌂ P

## Stockland

### King's Arms
☎ (01404) 881361
12–3, 6.30–11; 12–3, 7–10.30 Sun
**Exmoor Ale; Otter Ale; Ruddles County; John Smith's Bitter** Ⓗ
Carefully enlarged and modernised, Grade II listed free house with a friendly atmosphere. Excellent menu. No food Sun.
Q ⌂ ◖ ▶ ⓑ ⓑ ⓑ ▲ ♣ ⌂ P

## Stoneycombe

### Bickleigh Mill
☎ (01626) 873201
11–3, 7–11; 12–3, 7–10.30 Sun
**Draught Bass; guest beers** Ⓗ
Large, single-bar pub serving very good food in a quiet, happy atmosphere.
🏮 Q ◖ ▶ P

## Talaton

### Talaton Inn
☎ (01404) 822214
12–3, 7–11; 12–3, 7–10.30 Sun
**Otter Bitter; Wadworth 6X; guest beer** Ⓗ
Popular, friendly, village pub with a restaurant (good value, home-cooked food).
🏮 🛏 ❀ ◖ ▶ ⓑ ♣ P

## Tavistock

### Tavistock Inn
Brook Street
☎ (01822) 612661
11.30–3, 5.30–11; 11.30–11 Fri & Sat; 12–6 (12–3, 7–10.30 bank hol weekends) Sun
**Courage Best Bitter; Ushers Best Bitter, Founders, seasonal beers** Ⓗ
Friendly town local; a single bar with pool and dining areas.
🏮 ◖ ▶

## Teignmouth

### Blue Anchor
Teign Street ☎ (01626) 772741
11–11; 12–10.30 Sun
**Adnams Broadside; Boddingtons Bitter; Marston's Pedigree; Theakston Old Peculier** Ⓗ**; guest beers** Ⓖ
One-bar, quayside pub dominated by a pool table and a jukebox. Seven ales available.
🏮 ❀ ◖ ▶ ⥮ ♣ ⌂

### Golden Lion
85 Bitton Park Road
☎ (01626) 776442
12–4, 6–11; 11–11 Sat; 12–10.30 Sun
**Beer range varies** Ⓗ
Two-bar free house, offering two or three constantly changing ales.
❀ ⓑ ⥮ ♣ ⌂ P

## Tiverton

### Racehorse
Wellbrook Street
☎ (01884) 252606
11–11; 12–10.30 Sun
**Morland Old Speckled Hen; Ushers Best Bitter; Webster's Yorkshire Bitter** Ⓗ
Popular, friendly local with a large function room-cum-skittle alley. The children's garden has play equipment and a pets corner. Food available all day (until 7.30 Sun).
🏮 🛏 ❀ ◖ ⓑ ♣ ⌂ P

### White Horse
12 Gold Street
☎ (01884) 252022
11–11; 12–10.30 Sun
**Draught Bass; Boddingtons Bitter** Ⓗ
Small, split-level, friendly, town-centre pub, serving good value food. 🛏 ◖ ⓑ ♣

## Topsham

### Bridge Inn ☆
Bridge Hill ☎ (01392) 873862
12–2, 6–10.30 (11 Fri & Sat); 12–2, 7–10.30 Sun
**Adnams Broadside; Branscombe Vale Branoc, Olde Stoker; Exe Valley Devon Glory; Gibbs Mew Bishop's Tipple; guest beer** Ⓖ
Well-known, 18th-century, Grade II listed pub, unchanged for many years and kept by the same family for generations. The old barn at the rear was once a brewery. Up to 12 ales.
🏮 Q ⥮ P

### Globe Hotel
34 Fore Street
☎ (01392) 873471
11–11; 12–3, 7–10.30 Sun
**Draught Bass; Hancock's HB; Worthington Bitter; guest beer** Ⓗ
16th-century coaching house, Grade II listed, with many original beams. Excellent food.
Q 🛏 ◖ ▶ ⓑ ⥮ ♣ ⌂ P

## Torquay

### Crown & Sceptre
2 Petitor Road, St Marychurch
☎ (01803) 328290
11–3, 5.30–11; 11–11 Sat; 12–3, 6–10.30 Sun
**Courage Best Bitter, Directors; Marston's Pedigree; Morland Old Speckled Hen; Ruddles County; John Smith's Bitter; guest beers** Ⓗ
200-year-old stone coaching inn with a friendly atmosphere.
🏮 Q 🛏 ❀ ◖ ⓑ ⓑ ♣ P

### Devon Dumpling
108 Shiphay Lane (near Torbay Hospital) ☎ (01803) 613465

11–3, 5.30–11; 11–11 Sat; 12–10.30 Sun
**Courage Best Bitter; Morland Old Speckled Hen; Ruddles County; John Smith's Bitter; Wadworth 6X** H
16th-century, converted farmhouse, reputedly haunted. The family room is upstairs. Popular with locals.
🏠 Q ⏃ 🏮 ◑ ▶ ♿ ▲ ♣ P

### Drum Inn
Cockington Village
☎ (01803) 605143
11–3, 6–11; 11–11 Sat; 12–10.30 Sun
**Dartmoor Best Bitter, Strong** H
Large, friendly, family pub with extensive gardens, in a picturesque, thatched village. Skittles played. Cider in summer. 🏠 Q ⏃ 🏮 ◑ ▶ ♿ ▲ ♣ ⏏ ⚥

### Pig in Black
168–170 Union Street
☎ (01803) 213848
11–11; 12–10.30 Sun
**Courage Best Bitter, Directors; Morland Old Speckled Hen; John Smith's Bitter; guest beers** H
Busy, town-centre pub, popular with the business community lunchtimes and a young clientele eves.
◑ ⇌ (Torre) ♣

## Totnes

### Kingsbridge Inn
9 Leechwell Street
☎ (01803) 863324
11–2.30, 5.30–11; 12–10.30 Sun
**Draught Bass; Courage Best Bitter; Dartmoor Best Bitter; guest beers** H
Friendly pub: a comfortable, subtly lit bar with many alcoves and a low ceiling, plus a dining area.
Q ⏃ 🏮 ◑ ▶ ▲ ♣ ⏏ ⚥

### Rumours
30 High Street
☎ (01803) 864632
10–11; 12–10.30 Sun
**Draught Bass; Dartmoor Best Bitter; guest beers** H
Bare-floorboarded, café-style pub with a Continental atmosphere. Q ◑ ▶ ▲ ⇌ ⏏

## Walkhampton

### Walkhampton Inn
☎ (01822) 855556
11.30–3, 6–11; 12–3, 7–10.30 Sun

**Dartmoor Best Bitter; Princetown Jail Ale; guest beers** H
Village-centre pub with a main bar area surrounded by three other rooms, including a restaurant (formerly neighbouring cottages), with low beams and exposed walls. Limited parking.
🏠 ✿ 🛏 ◑ ▶ ⏏ P

## Wembworthy

### Lymington Arms
Lama Cross ☎ (01837) 83572
12–3 (not winter Tue), 6–11; 12–4, 7–10.30 Sun
**Flowers Original; Wadworth 6X; guest beers** H
Large coaching house built by Lord Portsmouth for entertaining his friends. Ideally situated for the Tarka Trail.
🏠 ✿ 🛏 ◑ ▶ ♣ ⏏ P

## Westcott

### Merry Harriers
On B3181 ☎ (01392) 881254
12–2.30, 7–11; 12–2, 7–10.30 Sun
**Draught Bass** H
Friendly roadside inn whose restaurant enjoys a reputation for high quality, home-cooked food (not served Sun lunch).
🏠 Q ✿ ◑ ▶ ♿ ▲ P

## Whimple

### New Fountain Inn
Church Road
☎ (01404) 822350
11–3, 6–11; 12–3, 7–10.30 Sun
**Oakhill Bitter; Shepherd Neame Spitfire; Teignworthy Reel Ale; guest beer** H
Family-run local, with a warm, friendly atmosphere. Varied menu of good value, home-cooked food in the restaurant (where children are welcome).
🏠 ✿ ◑ ▶ 🍴 ⇌ ♣ ⏏ P

## Whitchurch

### Whitchurch Inn
Church Hill ☎ (01822) 615383
11–3, 5 (6 Tue & Thu)–11; 11–11 Sat; 12–4, 6–10.30 Sun
**Draught Bass; Worthington Bitter; guest beer** H
Village pub near the moor: a single bar with exposed beams and a large fireplace with a built-in bread oven. The restaurant is in the Tithe Room.

Parking for four cars.
◑ ▶ P

## Widecombe in the Moor

### Rugglestone Inn ☆
¼ mile S of village OS721766
☎ (01364) 621327
11.30–2.30 (3 Sat), 7 (6 summer, 5 Sat)–11; 12–3, 7–10.30 Sun
**Butcombe Bitter; Flowers IPA** G
Unspoilt, cosy, little pub in a splendid Dartmoor setting.
🏠 Q ✿ ◑ ▶ ♿ ▲ ♣ ⏏ P

## Woodbury

### White Hart
Church Stile Lane
☎ (01395) 23221
11–3, 6–11; 11–11 Sat; 12–3, 7–10.30 Sun
**Draught Bass; Otter Ale** H
Formerly housing for builders of the church: a pub over 500 years old, well-known for its home-cooked food. Large games and function rooms.
🏠 Q ⏃ ✿ ◑ ▶ 🎱 ♿ ▲ ♣ P

## Woodbury Salterton

### Diggers Rest
☎ (01395) 32375
11–2.30, 6.30–11; 12–2.30, 7–10.30 Sun
**Draught Bass; Dartmoor Best Bitter** H
14th-century, Grade II listed, thatched pub, noted for its food. Unusual handpumps. The skittle alley doubles as a family room in summer.
🏠 Q ⏃ ◑ ▶ 🎱 ♿ ▲ ♣ ⏏ P

## Yealmpton

### Volunteer
Fore Street
☎ (01752) 880463
11–3, 5–11; 11–11 Fri, Sat & summer; 12–10.30 Sun
**Courage Best Bitter; Directors; John Smith's Bitter; Summerskills Best Bitter** H
200-year-old pub: a comfortable lounge, and a public bar with a collection of nearly 500 naval crests on the beams. Large garden, safe for children.
🏠 ✿ ◑ ▶ 🎱 ♣

---

# THE OTHER REAL THING

More and more pubs are now serving real cider, as well as real ale. For further information about this neglected traditional British drink, pick up a copy of *The CAMRA Guide to Real Cider*, priced £7.99, from bookshops or direct from CAMRA.

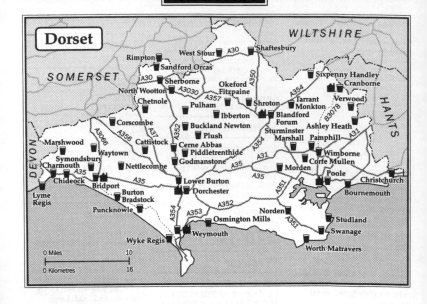

## Dorset

River Stour. One large, comfortable room. 🏠 🅰 ♣

## Ashley Heath

### Struan Hotel
Horton Road (½ mile N of A31/A338 jct)
☎ (01425) 473553
11–3, 6–11; 12–3, 7–10.30 Sun
**Badger Dorset Best, Tanglefoot; Wells Eagle** Ⓗ
1920s manor house with a restaurant serving excellent meals, but also a relaxed lounge bar for casual callers. Jazz Thu eves. 🏠 ◑ ▶ ⌂ P

## Blandford Forum

### Damory Oak Inn
Damory Court Street
☎ (01258) 452791
11–11; 12–3, 7–10.30 Sun
**Badger Dorset Best** Ⓗ
Set on the fringe of the town centre, this pub features a two-roomed bar and a friendly local atmosphere. 🏠 ❀

### King's Arms
Whitecliff Mill Street
☎ (01258) 452163
11–11; 12–10.30 Sun
**Draught Bass; Ringwood Best Bitter; Worthington Bitter** Ⓗ
Historic Georgian hotel on the former site of JL Marsh Brewery and the starting place of the great fire of Blandford.
🏠 ❀ 🏠 ♣

### Stour Inn
Blandford St Mary (S of town)
☎ (01258) 451276
11–2.30, 6–11; 12–3, 7–10.30 Sun
**Badger Dorset Best** Ⓗ
The Badger Brewery tap, situated on the banks of the

## Bournemouth

### Cottonwood Hotel
Grove Road ☎ (01202) 553183
11–3, 5–11; 11–11 Sat & summer Fri; 12–10.30 Sun
**Draught Bass; Ringwood Best Bitter; guest beer** (occasional) Ⓗ
Hotel bar, open to non-residents, on the east clifftop, with views to the Purbeck Hills. Pianist Thu, jazz Fri.
❀ 🏠 ♿ ⇌ P

### Dean Court Supporters' Club
King's Park (adjoins AFC Bournemouth football ground)
☎ (01202) 398313
11–3, 7–11; 12–3, 7–10.30 Sun
**Wadworth 6X; Worthington Bitter; guest beer** Ⓗ
Large, two-roomed club serving interesting guest beers. Show the *Guide* or CAMRA membership to enter (no admittance on match days to non-club members). ♿ ♣ P

### Jug of Ale
134 Old Christchurch Road
☎ (01202) 780260
11–11; 12–10.30 Sun
**Boddingtons Bitter; Flowers Original; Fuller's London Pride; Marston's Pedigree** Ⓗ; **guest beers** Ⓖ
Large Hogshead ale house opposite Horseshoe Common. Busy and popular with the young, especially at weekends. Always three guest beers. Eve meals until 8. ◑ ▶ ⌂

### Moon in the Square
4–8 Exeter Road (between the Square and the beach)
☎ (01202) 314940
11–11; 12–10.30 Sun
**Theakston Best Bitter, XB; Wadworth 6X; Younger Scotch; guest beers** Ⓗ
Very popular Wetherspoon pub close to the beach but amongst the big stores. Twice-yearly beer festivals; good value food.
❀ ◑ ▶ ⌂ ⌘

### Porterhouse
113 Poole Road, Westbourne
☎ (01202) 768586
11–11; 12–3, 7–10.30 Sun
**Ringwood Best Bitter, XXXX Porter, Fortyniner, Old Thumper; guest beers** Ⓗ
The best example of a proper pub in Bournemouth. Former local CAMRA *Pub of the Year*. Reasonable prices; friendly staff. ◑ ♣

### Punch & Judy
31 Poole Hill ☎ (01202) 290016
11–3, 5–11; 11–11 Sat; 12–3, 7–10.30 Sun

---

### INDEPENDENT BREWERIES

| | |
|---|---|
| **Badger:** | Blandford Forum |
| **Cranborne:** | Cranborne |
| **Goldfinch:** | Dorchester |
| **Hardy:** | Dorchester |
| **Palmers:** | Bridport |
| **Poole:** | Poole |
| **Quay:** | Weymouth |

**Marston's Bitter, Pedigree,
HBC** Ⓗ
Five minutes' walk from the
town centre: a friendly and
popular pub with all ages.
Good value food. ◖ ♿

## Bridport

### Bull Hotel
34 East Street ☎ (01308) 422878
10–11; 12–3, 7–10.30 Sun
**Draught Bass; Flowers IPA,
Original; Teignworthy Reel
Ale** Ⓗ
Comfy bar at the back of a high
street hotel. Its first recorded
innkeeper was in 1586.
🏨 ❀ 🛏 ◖ ▶ ♠ P

### Crown Inn
West Bay Road (A35)
☎ (01308) 422037
11.30–3, 6.30–11; 12–3, 7–10.30 Sun
**Palmers BB, IPA, 200** Ⓗ
Spacious pub on the A35
roundabout, allegedly haunted
by a previous tenant. Minicom
system for hard of hearing
customers.
❀ ◖ ▶ ♿ ♠ ♣ ○ P

### Woodman
South Street ☎ (01308) 456455
11–3, 7–11; 12–3, 7–10.30 Sun
**Draught Bass; guest beers** Ⓗ
Recently extended free house
on the south side of town. The
carvery Sun is popular. Eve
meals Fri–Sun. Two beer
festivals a year (June and Nov).
Large public car park at the
rear. ❀ ◖ ▶ ♿ ♣

## Buckland Newton

### Gaggle of Geese
☎ (01300) 345249
12–2.30, 6.30–11; 12–3, 7–10.30 Sun
**Badger Dorset Best; Draught
Bass** Ⓗ**; Butcombe Bitter;
Flowers Original; Fuller's
London Pride** Ⓖ**; Wadworth
6X** Ⓗ
Large friendly village pub
hosting a goose fair in May and
September. Wheelchair access
is via the kitchen.
🏨 ❀ ◖ ▶ ♿ ♣ P

## Burton Bradstock

### Anchor
Mill Street ☎ (01308) 897228
11–2.30, 7–11; 12–3, 7–10.30 Sun
**Ushers Best Bitter, Founders,
seasonal beers; guest beer** Ⓗ
Well-maintained pub at the
village centre. ◖ ▶ ♠ ♣ ○ P

### Dove Inn
Southover ☎ (01308) 897897
11–2.30, 6.30–11; 12–3.30, 7–10.30 Sun
**Beer range varies** Ⓗ
Welcoming, three-bar local
offering up to three ales and
three ciders; good food.
Teignworthy house beer.
🏨 Q ⚲ ❀ ◖ ▶ ♠ ▲ ○ P

## Cattistock

### Fox & Hounds
Duck Street
☎ (01300) 320444
12–3 (not Mon), 7–11; 12–3, 7–10.30
Sun
**Fuller's London Pride; Otter
Bitter; guest beers** Ⓗ
Attractive village inn, featuring
15th-century oak beams, open
fires and flagstone floors.
Sizeable portions on the bar
menu; also an à la carte
restaurant. Children welcome –
play area opposite. Cider in
summer.
🏨 Q ❀ ▦ ◖ ▶ ♠ ♣ ○ P

## Cerne Abbas

### Red Lion
Long Street ☎ (01300) 341441
11.30–2.30, 6.30–11; 12–3, 7–10.30 Sun
**Wadworth IPA, 6X; guest
beers** Ⓗ
Pub with a striking Victorian
frontage, at the centre of a
picturesque village, near the
famous Cerne Giant. Good
menu of traditional dishes.
🏨 Q ❀ ◖ ▶ ▲ ♣

### Royal Oak
Long Street ☎ (01300) 341797
11–3, 5.30–11; 12–3, 6.30–10.30 Sun
**Flowers IPA, Original;
Morland Old Speckled Hen;
guest beers** Ⓗ
500-year-old pub with three,
cosy, adjoining rooms.
Interesting food; good Sun
lunches. 🏨 Q ◖ ▶ ♿ ▲ ♣

## Charmouth

### George
The Street ☎ (01297) 560280
11–3, 7–11; 12–3, 7–10.30 Sun
**Otter Bitter; Ruddles Best
Bitter; John Smith's Bitter** Ⓗ
Busy, single-bar local in a
one-street village, drawing a
mainly young clientele.
🏨 ◖ ▶ ♿ ♣

## Chetnole

### Chetnole Inn
☎ (01935) 872337
11–2.30 (4 Sat), 6.30–11; 12–3, 7–10.30
Sun
**Otter Ale; Palmers IPA; guest
beers** Ⓗ
A warm welcome, good food
and three guest ales await at
this village pub set in tranquil
countryside. Mini-beer festival
Easter. Cider in summer.
🏨 Q ◖ ▶ ♠ ▲ ♠ ♣ ○ P

## Chideock

### George
Main Street ☎ (01297) 89419
11–3, 7–11; 12–3, 7–10.30 Sun
**Palmers BB, IPA, Tally Ho!,
200** Ⓗ

Cosy, roadside pub in a small
village near the coast. The bar
ceiling is covered in foreign
money. 🏨 Q ◖ ▶ ▲ P

## Christchurch

### Olde George Inn
2A Castle Street
☎ (01202) 479383
10.30–2.30 (3 Sat), 6 (7 Sat)–11; 12–3,
7–10.30 Sun
**Flowers Original; Ringwood
Fortyniner; Strong Country
Bitter; guest beer** Ⓗ
Centrally-located, Tudor
coaching inn with two, low-
ceilinged bars and a pleasant
courtyard. The music room
hosts a folk and blues night
Wed and jazz Thu. Friendly
welcome. ❀ ◖ ⇌ P

### Ship Inn
☎ (01202) 484308
11–11; 12–10.30 Sun
**Boddingtons Bitter; Flowers
Original; Marston's Pedigree;
Whitbread Fuggles IPA** Ⓗ**;
guest beers** Ⓗ/Ⓖ
Small Whitbread Hogshead ale
house in the centre of town –
one of the oldest pubs in
Christchurch. Real solid fuel
stove. ◖ ⇌ ♣

## Corfe Mullen

### Coventry Arms
Mill Street (A31, 2 miles W of
Wimborne) ☎ (01258) 857284
11–2.30 (3 Sat), 5.30–11; 12–3, 5.30–
10.30 Sun
**Draught Bass; Courage
Directors; Hampshire King
Alfred's; Ringwood Best
Bitter, Old Thumper** Ⓖ
Pub dating back to 1426, built
on a site mentioned in the
*Domesday Book*; famous for its
500-year-old mummified cat.
Excellent food. Folk music Tue.
Large riverside garden.
Q ❀ ◖ ▶ ♿ ▲ ♣ P

### Dorset Soldier
Wareham Road
☎ (01202) 694403
10–2.30, 5–11; 10–11 Sat; 12–10.30 Sun
**Badger Dorset Best,
Tanglefoot** Ⓗ
Friendly village pub with
lounge and public bars, plus a
55-seater restaurant. Excellent
range of food. Various games
teams. 🏨 ❀ ◖ ▶ ♠ ♿ ♣ P

### Lambs Green Inn
Lambs Green Lane (150 yds
from Wimborne bypass)
☎ (01202) 880000
11–2.30, 6–11; 12–3, 7–10.30 Sun
**Draught Bass; guest beer** Ⓔ
Lounge bar with a separate
thatched restaurant offering a
glorious view across
Wimborne. A large garden has
children's play equipment.
❀ ◖ ▶ ♿ ▲ P ✂

## Corscombe

### Fox Inn
Church end of village
☎ (01935) 891330
12–2.30, 7–11; 12–4, 7–11 Sat & Sun
Exmoor Ale G; Fuller's
London Pride; Smiles
Brewery Bitter H
Superb, two-bar village inn in
ramblers' countryside,
featuring a stone-flagged floor
and a slate bar top. Excellent
food.
🏚 Q ✿ ◑ ▶ ▲ ♣ ⌂ P

## Cranborne

### Sheaf of Arrows
The Square ☎ (01725) 517456
11.30–2.30 (3.30 Sat), 6–11; 12–3,
7–10.30 Sun
Cranborne Quiver; Ringwood
Best Bitter H
Traditional local with a new
brewhouse at the rear. Two
main bars: a public, plus a
small, quiet lounge; also a
skittle alley. Q ✿ ◑ ▶ ▲

## Dorchester

### Tom Brown's
47 High East Street
☎ (01305) 264020
11–3, 6–11; 11–11 Fri; 12–3, 7–10.30
Sun
Goldfinch Tom Brown's,
Flashman's Clout, Midnight
Blinder H
Wooden-floored home of the
Goldfinch Brewery, selling
award-winning ales.
◑ ⇌ (South/West) ♣

## Godmanstone

### Smiths Arms
☎ (01300) 341236
11–3, 6–11; 12–3, 7–10.30 Sun
Ringwood Best Bitter G
The smallest pub in England
with a very cosy, friendly
atmosphere in winter and a
pleasant riverside garden for
summer. 🏚 Q ✿ ◑ ▶ ♣ P

## Ibberton

### Crown
OS785071 ☎ (01258) 817448
11–2.30, 7–11; 12–2.30, 7–10.30 Sun
Draught Bass; guest beers H
Set at the heart of the
Blackmore Vale, this beautiful
country pub serves three
changing ales in a two-roomed
bar. Local cider.
🏚 Q ✿ ◑ ▶ ▲ ⌂ P

## Lower Burton

### Sun
1 mile N of Dorchester on old
Sherborne road
☎ (01305) 250445
11–3, 5.30–11 (11–11 summer Sat);
12–3, 6.30–10.30 Sun

Draught Bass; Fuller's London
Pride; Smiles Brewery Bitter;
guest beers H
Attractive, old-fashioned pub,
popular for food and its varied
beers. Some of the best toilets
in Dorset! Cider in summer.
🏚 Q ✿ ◑ ▶ ▲ ⌂ P

## Lyme Regis

### Angel
Mill Green, Monmouth Street
(off High St) ☎ (01297) 443267
11–2.30, 7–11; 12–2.30, 7–10.30 Sun
Palmers BB, IPA G
Unspoilt, backstreet local with
a 1950s feel. The beers are
stillaged behind the bar.
Q ☎ ⇌ ♣ P

### Volunteer
31 Broad Street
☎ (01297) 442214
11–3 (extends summer), 7–11; 12–3,
7–10.30 Sun
Draught Bass H; Branscombe
Vale Branoc G; Fuller's
London Pride H
Welcoming single bar at the
top end of the main street.
Children are welcome in the
restaurant. A house beer,
Donegal Ale, is brewed by
Branscombe Vale.
Q ⇌ ◑ ▶ ▲ ♣

## Marshwood

### Bottle Inn
☎ (01297) 678254
11–2.30, 6–11; 12–2.30, 7–10.30 Sun
Otter Bitter; Wadworth 6X H
Excellent, 400-year-old
roadside inn, with low ceilings
and wooden pews. Popular
with walkers (maps available
from the bar).
🏚 Q ✿ ⇌ ◑ ▶ ▲ ♣ P

## Morden

### Cock & Bottle
On B3075 ☎ (01929) 459238
11–2.30, 6–11; 12–3, 7–10.30 Sun
Badger Dorset Best,
Tanglefoot; Wells Eagle H
Friendly, village pub in a rural
setting. A restaurant has been
built on, but is in keeping with
the character of this 400-year-
old inn. 🏚 ✿ ◑ ▶ ▲ ♣ P

## Nettlecombe

### Marquis of Lorne
OS956517 ☎ (01308) 485236
11–2.30, 6.30 (6 summer)–11; 12–2.30,
7–10.30 Sun
Palmers BB, IPA, Tally Ho! or
200 H
Excellent, wood-panelled,
multi-roomed, 16th-century
inn with a central bar; a
welcome stop after walking
round Eggardon Hill.
Extensive range of good value
food. CAMRA regional Pub of

the Year 1996.
🏚 Q ☎ ✿ ⇌ ◑ ▶ ♣ P

## Norden

### Halfway Inn
Wareham Road (A351, Corfe
road) ☎ (01929) 480402
11–3, 6–11; 12–3, 7–10.30 Sun
Flowers Original H; Ringwood
Fortyniner G; Strong Country
Bitter H; guest beer G
Ancient Purbeck, multi-
roomed house which
specialises in Greek-Cypriot
and English food. Near the
Blue Pool and the Swanage
steam railway. 🏚 ✿ ◑ ▶ P

## North Wootton

### Three Elms
☎ (01935) 812881
11–2.30, 6.30 (6 Fri & Sat)–11; 12–3,
7–10.30 Sun
Boddingtons Bitter; Butcombe
Bitter; Fuller's London Pride;
RCH East St Cream; Shepherd
Neame Spitfire; guest beers H
Deservedly popular pub,
serving nine real ales
(including a house beer) and a
wide range of good food
(especially vegetarian). 1100
model vehicles on show.
Q ✿ ⇌ ◑ ▶ ♣ ⌂ P

## Okeford Fitzpaine

### Royal Oak
Lower Street (A357)
☎ (01258) 860308
12–2.30, 5.30 (6.30 Sat)–11; 12–2.30,
7–10.30 Sun
Ringwood Best Bitter; Tisbury
Old Wardour; Wadworth 6X H
Situated in a picturesque
village, this popular games
local offers a comfortable
lounge and a public bar.
Upstairs skittle alley; bar
billiards played. Good value,
home-cooked food.
🏚 Q ✿ ◑ ▶ ⌂

## Osmington Mills

### Smugglers Inn
Off A353 ☎ (01305) 833125
11–2.30 (3 Sat), 6.30 (6 Sat)–11 (11–11
summer); 12–3, 7–10.30 Sun
Courage Best Bitter, Directors;
Ruddles County; guest beer H
Spacious clifftop pub on the
Dorset Coast Path. A stream
and a playground are features
of the garden. Crowded in
summer.
🏚 ✿ ⇌ ◑ ▶ ▲ ♣ P

## Pamphill

### Vine Inn
Vine Hill (off B3082)
☎ (01202) 882259
11–2.30, 7–11; 12–3, 7–10.30 Sun
Strong Country Bitter H;
guest beer G

E Dorset CAMRA *Pub of the Year* 1995: a friendly, split-level pub in a rural area with two small bars. Close to the NT's Kingston Lacy house, the pub is also a National Trust property. Limited parking.
Q ❀ ❶ ♣ ○ P ⎕

## Piddletrenthide

### Piddle Inn
☎ (01300) 348468
11.30–2.30, 6.30–11; 11.30–11 Sat; 12–3, 7–10.30 Sun
**Draught Bass; Ringwood Best Bitter; Wadworth 6X** Ⓗ
Licensed since the 1770s, this traditional village pub boasts 160 chamber pots. The garden is on the bank of the Piddle. Good food.
♨ ☎ ❀ ❶ ⏸ ♣ ○ P

### Poachers Inn
☎ (01300) 348358
11–3, 6.30–11 (12–11 summer); 12–3, 7–10.30 Sun
**Ruddles Best Bitter; John Smith's Bitter; guest beer** (summer) Ⓗ
Well-modernised village pub with its own swimming pool.
❀ ⛵ ❶ ⏸ ♣ P ⎕

## Plush

### Brace of Pheasants
2 miles off B3143, above Piddle Valley ☎ (01300) 348357
12 (11.30 summer)–2.30, 7–11; 12–3, 7–10.30 Sun
**Butcombe Bitter; Wadworth 6X; guest beers** Ⓗ
Traditional, warm village pub in pretty countryside, below Dorsetshire Gap. Popular for good food. ♨ Q ❀ ❶ ⏸ ♣ P

## Poole

### Albion Hotel
470 Ringwood Road, Parkstone
☎ (01202) 732197
11–3, 5–11; 11–11 Sat; 12–3, 7–10.30 Sun
**Badger Dorset Best, Tanglefoot** Ⓗ
Large, two-bar pub on the main road into Poole: a comfortable lounge bar and a more basic public bar with a pool table. No eve meals Sun.
❶ ♣ P

### Bermuda Triangle
10 Parr Street, Lower Parkstone
☎ (01202) 748087
11–3, 5.30–11; 12–10.30 Sun
**Beer range varies** Ⓗ
Small, but popular, true free house, offering three or four constantly changing ales, plus over 30 bottled beers. Various artefacts on the Bermuda Triangle theme are displayed.
⛽ (Parkstone)

### Blue Boar
Market Close
☎ (01202) 682247
11–3, 5–11; 12–5, 7–10.30 Sun
**Draught Bass; Courage Best Bitter, Directors; John Smith's Bitter; guest beers** Ⓗ
Former merchant's house in old Poole town, converted to a high standard and featuring nautical artefacts in its large, comfortable, upper-floor lounge and more basic cellar bar, which serves as a children's room Mon–Sat lunch. No food Sun.
⛵ ❶ ❶ ⛽ ♣

### Branksome Railway Hotel
429 Poole Road, Parkstone (opp. station)
☎ (01202) 769555
11–11; 12–10.30 Sun
**Fuller's London Pride; Hampshire Pendragon** Ⓗ
Large, Victorian, one-bar pub, featuring high ceilings, railway pictures and a large family-cum-meeting room. The beers may vary.
⛵ ⛽ (Branksome) ♣ P

### Brewhouse
68 High Street
☎ (01202) 685288
11–11; 11–5, 7–11 Sat; 12–10.30 Sun
**Poole Best Bitter, Holes Bay Hog, Bosun, Double Barrel** Ⓗ
Long, narrow pub with a bare-boarded floor. Popular with locals, it has possibly the best ale prices in Dorset. Poole Brewery is at the rear. ⛽

### Inn in the Park
26 Pinewood Road, Branksome Park ☎ (01202) 761318
11–2.30 (3 Sat), 5.30 (6 Sat)–11; 12–3, 7–10.30 Sun
**Draught Bass; Wadworth IPA, 6X** Ⓗ
Plush, comfortable inn in an exclusive residential area near Branksome beach. The dining area welcomes children lunchtime. ♨ ❀ ⛵ ❶ P

### Parkstone Hotel
58 Station Road, Parkstone
☎ (01202) 740210
11–2.30 (3.30 Sat), 6–11; 12–3, 7–10.30 Sun
**Hardy Pope's Traditional, Country, Royal Oak** Ⓗ
Pub next to the station, with a pleasant lounge bar with a rail theme decor and a public bar with a jukebox and a pool table. ❶ ❶ ⛽ (Parkstone) P

### Tudor Bars
3 Banks Road, Sandbanks (1½ miles from ferry)
☎ (01202) 707244
11–3, 6–11; 12–3, 7–10.30 Sun
**Poole Bosun; Ringwood Best Bitter; Wadworth 6X; guest beer** Ⓗ
Spacious, long bar with pool tables and a TV room, 100

yards from the Shore Road beach with a view towards Brownsea Island. ⛵ ❶ ❶ ♣ P

## Pulham

### Halsey Arms
☎ (01258) 817344
11.30–2.30 (not Wed), 6–11; 12–3, 7–10.30 Sun
**Exmoor Ale; Hardy Country; guest beers** Ⓗ
Welcoming, traditional village pub with a log fire and an excellent selection of changing guest beers. A children's play area is separate from the garden. Good food.
♨ Q ⛵ ❀ ❶ ♣ ○ P ⎕

## Puncknowle

### Crown
Church Street (1 mile from B3157) ☎ (01308) 897711
11–3, 7–11; 12–3, 7–10.30 Sun
**Palmers BB, IPA, Tally Ho!, 200** Ⓗ
Sizeable pub in a beautiful village. Paintings for sale.
♨ Q ⛵ ⛵ ❶ ⏸ Å ♣ ○ P

## Rimpton

### White Post Inn
☎ (01935) 850717
12–3, 6.30–11; 12–3, 7–10.30 Sun
**Draught Bass; Butcombe Bitter; Oakhill Best Bitter; guest beer** Ⓗ
Free house straddling the Somerset border, with pleasant views. Excellent value food.
Q ❀ ❶ ♣ ○ P ⚲

## Sandford Orcas

### Mitre Inn
☎ (01963) 220271
11.30–3, 7–11; 12–3, 7–10.30 Sun
**Morland Old Speckled Hen; guest beers** Ⓗ
Flagstone-floored, rural, 18th-century village pub. No meals Mon eve.
♨ ❀ ⛵ ❶ ⏸ Å ♣ ○ P

## Shaftesbury

### Fountain Inn
Breach Lane, Enmore Green
☎ (01747) 852062
11–2, 7–11; 11–11 Sat; 12–10.30 Sun
**Fuller's London Pride; Smiles Best Bitter; Wadworth 6X; guest beer** Ⓗ
Comfortable, split-level pub, popular with young people and Sky Sports viewers.
❶ ❶ ○ P

## Sherborne

### Digby Tap
Cooks Lane ☎ (01935) 813148
11–2.30, 5.30–11; 12–3, 7–10.30 Sun

**Beer range varies** H
Basic, traditional town
drinking house; stone-flagged
floors, panelling and old
photos add to the atmosphere.
No food Sun. ♨ ◖ ⬆ ♣ ☼

## Skippers

Horsecastles ☎ (01935) 812753
11–2.30, 5.30–11; 12–3, 7–10.30 Sun
**Adnams Bitter; Draught Bass;
Wadworth IPA, 6X** H
End of terrace, former cider
house, now one of only three
Wadworth tied houses in
Dorset. Regular food events.
⚜ ◖ ▶ ⬆ ♣ P

## Shroton

### Cricketers

☎ (01258) 860421
11–2.30, 7–11; 12–3, 7–10.30 Sun
**Smiles Best Bitter; guest
beers** H
Unpopular village inn with an
excellent restaurant, opposite
the village cricket square.
Lovely walks around the
nearby iron age fort at
Hambledon Hill.
♨ Q ⚜ ◖ ▶ P

## Sixpenny Handley

### Roebuck

High Street ☎ (01725) 552002
11–2.30, 6–11 (closed Mon eve in
winter); 12–3, 7–10.30 Sun
**Ringwood Best Bitter,
Fortyniner, XXXX Porter;
guest beers** (occasional) H
Upmarket, L-shaped bar with a
cosy fireplace. No food Mon.
♨ Q ⚜ ◖ ▶ ♣ ☼

## Studland

### Bankes Arms

Manor Road ☎ (01929) 450225
11–11 (closed Mon–Thu eves in
winter); 12–10.30 Sun
**Castle Eden Ale; Fremlins
Bitter; Strong Country Bitter;
guest beers** H
Picturesque village pub, very
popular in summer. Owned by
the National Trust, it retains
real character. A large garden
overlooks the sea. Food is
served all day in summer.
♨ ⛺ ⚜ 🏠 ◖ ▶ ♣ ☼

## Sturminster Marshall

### Red Lion

Church Street (1 mile E of
A350) ☎ (01258) 857319
11–2.30, 6–11; 12–3, 6–10.30 Sun
**Badger Dorset Best,
Tanglefoot** H
Large village pub with a skittle
alley doubling as a family
room and a no-smoking area.
Popular for food.
♨ ⛺ ⚜ ◖ ▶ ♣ P ✘

## Swanage

### Red Lion

High Street
☎ (01929) 423533
10.30–11; 12–10.30 Sun
**Flowers Original; Ringwood
Fortyniner; Strong Country
Bitter** G
Popular, down-to-earth, two-
bar pub. The public bar adjoins
the ground floor cellar from
where the beers are dispensed.
A lounge bar leads to the
garden and children's room.
Eve meals Fri and Sat (steak
night). ⛺ ⚜ ◖ ▶ 🏠 ♣ ☼ P

## Symondsbury

### Ilchester Arms

☎ (01308) 422600
11–2.30, 7–11; 12–3, 7–10.30 Sun
**Palmers BB, IPA, 200** H
Unspoilt village local in a
beautiful part of W Dorset.
Impressive inglenook.
♨ ⚜ 🏠 ◖ ▶ ♿ ▲ ♣ ☼ P

## Tarrant Monkton

### Langton Arms

On A354 ☎ (01258) 830225
11.30–3, 6–11; 11.30–11 Sat; 12–3,
7–10.30 Sun
**Smiles Best Bitter; Wadworth
6X; guest beers** H
17th-century country pub with
four frequently changing ales
in the lounge and on request in
the public bar. Children's play
areas, a skittle alley and a local,
varied menu.
♨ Q ⛺ ⚜ 🏠 ◖ ▶ 🏠 P

## Verwood

### Albion

Station Road ☎ (01202) 825267
11–2.30, 5 (6 Sat)–11; 12–2.30, 7–10.30
Sun
**Gibbs Mew Salisbury, Wake
Ale, Bishop's Tipple** H
Lovely, cosy pub on the edge
of town, built in 1866 as
Verwood's railway station.
Good value food. ⚜ ◖ ▶ P

## Waytown

### Hare & Hounds

☎ (01308) 488203
12–2.30, 7–11; 11.30–3, 6.30–11 Sat;
12–3, 7–10.30 Sun
**Palmers BB, IPA, 200**
(occasional) G
Friendly village local.
Wonderful views from the
garden. No meals Mon lunch
or Sun–Mon eves in winter.
♨ Q ⛺ ⚜ ◖ ▶ 🏠 ▲ ♣ ☼ P

## West Stour

### Ship

☎ (01747) 838640
11–3, 6–11; 12–3, 7–10.30 Sun

**Draught Bass; guest beers** H
18th-century coaching inn on a
bend of the A30 at the edge of
the village. Unspoilt, with
snugs, it serves good food.
♨ Q ⚜ 🏠 ◖ ▶ ♣ P

## Weymouth

### Kingswood

55 Rodwell Road (Portland
road) ☎ (01305) 784926
11–11; 12–10.30 Sun
**Beer range varies** H
Small hotel on the main road
out of town, with a friendly
locals' bar. A house beer is
sometimes served. Meals all
day Sun (late supper licence).
⛺ ⚜ 🏠 ◖ ▶ ♣ P

### Weatherbury Hotel

7 Carlton Road (off Dorchester
road) ☎ (01305) 786040
11–2.30, 5.30–11; 11–11 Fri & Sat;
12–10.30 Sun
**Draught Bass; guest beers** H
Comfortable pub in a
residential area. Four guest
beers.
⛺ ⚜ 🏠 ◖ ▶ P ✘

## Wimborne

### Crown & Anchor

Wimborne Road, Walford
(B3078, N of town)
☎ (01202) 841405
10.30–2.30, 6–11; 12–3, 7–10.30 Sun
**Badger Dorset Best** H
Pleasant, friendly, out-of-town
local by the River Allen, handy
for the craft centre at Walford
Mill and the walk to High Hall.
♨ Q ⚜ ◖ ▲ ♣ P

## Worth Matravers

### Square & Compass ☆

Off B3069 OS097777
11–3, 6–11; 11–11 Sat; 12–3, 7–10.30
Sun
**Ringwood Fortyniner; Strong
Country Bitter; guest beers** G
Centuries-old, this terrific pub
has flagstoned floors, low
ceilings and a serving hatch
and is decorated with
sculpture, beachcombing finds
and fossils. Superb sea views.
Run by the Newman family
since 1907. Phone to camp.
♨ Q ⚜ ▲ ☼ ♣

## Wyke Regis

### Wyke Smugglers

76 Portland Road
☎ (01305) 760010
11–2.30, 6–11; 12–3, 7–10.30 Sun
**Boddingtons Bitter; Flowers
Original; Ringwood Old
Thumper; guest beers** H
Very popular local, home to
many teams especially darts
(three boards). Guest beers
come from micro- and regional
brewers. ⚜ ♿ ♣ P

# Durham

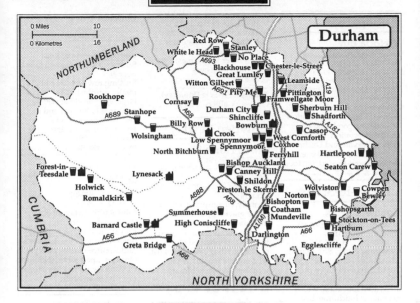

## Barnard Castle

### King's Head
14 Market Place
☎ (01833) 690333
11–11; 12–10.30 Sun
**Butterknowle Conciliation Ale; John Smith's Bitter** Ⓗ
Wood-panelled, town-centre pub comprising two rooms: one large front room and a spacious side room. Secluded beer garden.
☒ ❀ ⋈ ⊲ ▲

Try also: Three Horseshoes, Galgate (Bass)

## Billy Row

### Dun Cow (Cow's Tail)
Old White Lea (down lane by Royal George PH)
☎ (01388) 762714
7.30–11; 12–2, 7.30–11 Sat; 12–2, 7–10.30 Sun
**Butterknowle Banner Bitter, Conciliation Ale** Ⓗ
Off the beaten track but well worth a visit; an unspoilt, two-roomed pub with an open fire and a cooking range. One of few original inns left in the county, owned by the same family since 1830. Note: closed weekday lunchtimes.
🏘 Q ❀ ♣ P ⊬

## Bishop Auckland

### Tap & Spile
13 Cockton Hill Road (opp. hospital) ☎ (01388) 602550
12–3, 6–11; 12–11 Sat; 12–3, 7–10.30 Sun
Camerons Strongarm; Tap & Spile Premium; Theakston Best Bitter, Old Peculier; guest beers Ⓗ
Typical Tap & Spile, offering many pub games. Food is served Thu–Sun. Up to four varied guest beers.
🏘 ❀ ⊲ ⇌ ♣ ⊙ P ⊬

## Bishopsgarth

### Mitre
Harrowgate Lane
☎ (01642) 580238
11–11; 12–10.30 Sun
**Boddingtons Bitter; Castle Eden Ale; guest beers** Ⓗ
Beefeater restaurant which the management regards as a pub with a restaurant, not vice versa! The decor is based on a tithe barn theme, with old Stockton artefacts – look out for the half monk! ❀ ⊲ ▶ P

## Bishopton

### Talbot
The Green ☎ (01740) 630371
11–3, 6–11; 12–3, 7–10.30 Sun
**Camerons Strongarm; Ind Coope Burton Ale; Tetley Imperial** Ⓗ
Pleasant village local with a growing emphasis on meals. In the *Guide* for 23 consecutive editions, under the same landlord. 🏘 Q ❀ ⊲ ▶ P

## Blackhouse

### Charlaw Inn
On B6532 ☎ (01207) 232085
11–3, 6.30–11; 12–3, 7–10.30 Sun
**Boddingtons Bitter; Theakston Best Bitter; guest beer** (occasional) Ⓗ
A restaurant and conservatory are included in this large five-roomed establishment, as well as a lively bar which features soccer memorabilia. A popular pub for its varied meal selection. Outdoor play area for children.
Q ☒ ❀ ⊲ ▶ ⊟ ♣ P ⊟

## Canney Hill

### Sportsman
4 Canney Hill (200 yds from Canney Hill roundabout, off A689) ☎ (01388) 603847
11–3, 7–11; 11–11 Sat; 12–3, 7–10.30 Sun
**Camerons Bitter, Strongarm; Everards Tiger** Ⓗ
Bright and lively roadside inn with a lounge bar and a snug. The decor reflects its earlier horse racing connections.
🏘 ▶ P ⊟

 **INDEPENDENT BREWERIES**

| | |
|---|---|
| **Butterknowle:** | Lynesack |
| **Camerons:** | Hartlepool |
| **Durham:** | Bowburn |
| **High Force:** | Forest-in-Teesdale |
| **Hodges:** | Crook |
| **Middleton:** | Barnard Castle |

## Cassop

### Victoria Inn

Front Street, North Cassop
☎ (01429) 821410
11–2 (not Tue–Wed), 6.30–11; 11–4,
6.30–11 Sat; 12–4, 6.30–10.30 Sun
**Worthington Bitter; guest beers** H
250-year-old, friendly village pub, with an attractive central bar, offering good food and good conversation. Panoramic view of the vale and Durham Cathedral. Darts, domino, and football teams fielded. No food Sun. ⚒ ✿ ◖ ♣ ☐

## Chester-le-Street

### Butchers Arms

Middle Chare (off Front St)
☎ (0191) 388 3605
11–3, 6.30–11; 12–3, 7–10.30 Sun
**Camerons Bitter, Strongarm; Marston's Pedigree** H
Popular, friendly town pub. The single U-shaped bar has areas used for eating, which get busy at lunchtime. Eve meals in summer.
⚒ Q ⊨ ◖ ▶

### Smiths Arms

Brecon Hill, Castle Dene
☎ (0191) 385 6915
4 (12 Fri & Sat)–11; 12–3, 7–10.30 Sun
**Draught Bass; Stones Bitter; Theakston XB; guest beer** H
Miles from anywhere, minutes from everywhere, this old country-style pub under the A1(M) has an average size bar and a larger lounge with a games room at the rear for pool, darts, dominoes and games machines. Comfortably furnished. ⚒ Q ✿ ♣ P

**Try also:** Market Tavern, Market Place (Whitbread)

## Coatham Mundeville

### Foresters Arms

On A167, ¼ mile S of A1(M) jct
☎ (01325) 320565
11–3, 4.45–11; 11–11 Fri & Sat; 12–3,
7–10.30 Sun
**John Smith's Bitter, Magnet** H
Welcoming pub with a strong Irish flavour, serving well-prepared food (no meals Sun eve). Happy 'hour' 5–7 during the week. See the Vietnamese pot-bellied pig in the garden.
⚒ ✿ ◖ ▶ P ☐

## Cornsay

### Blackhorse Inn

Old Cornsay Village (2 miles W of B6301) ☎ (0191) 373 4211
7–11; 12–3, 7–10.30 Sun
**Stones Bitter; guest beer** H
Neat village inn in remote West Durham with a picturesque view of Gladdow Valley: a single bar and a larger restaurant room, with outside drinking on the village green. Lunchtime meals Sun (pub closed other lunchtimes). No food Sun/Mon eves.
Q ✿ ▶ ♣ P

**Try also:** Fir Tree (Monkey), Cornsay Colliery (Free)

## Cowpen Bewley

### Three Horse Shoes

☎ (01642) 561541
11–3, 5.30 (7 Sat)–11; 12–3, 7–10.30
Sun
**Camerons Strongarm; guest beer** H
Homely village pub at one end of the green. A pub has been on this site for 550 years; the present building was opened in 1955 and inherited the earlier building's helpful ghost, who cools the cellar in hot weather! Wheelchair ramps available.
⚒ Q ✿ ◖ ▶ ⊞ & ♣ P ☐

## Coxhoe

### Cricketers

Victoria Terrace, Cornforth Lane ☎ (0191) 377 0510
12–2, 7–11; 12–10.30 Sun
**Vaux Lorimer's Best Scotch, Samson; guest beers** H
Attractive, one-bar village local. Well upholstered during a recent refurbishment, it boasts a beamed ceiling and plenty of bric-a-brac. Separate lounge and bar areas.
Q ✿ ◖ ▶

## Darlington

### Binns Department Store (Off-Licence)

1–7 High Row
☎ (01325) 462606
9–5.30 (6 Sat); closed Sun
House of Fraser department store with a small but well-stocked beer section in the basement. Some 200 quality beers to take away, including dozens of British and Belgian bottle-conditioned ales. Good selection of special glasses.

### Britannia

Archer Street ☎ (01325) 463787
11.30–3 (may extend), 5.30–11; 12–3,
7–10.30 Sun
**Camerons Strongarm; Tetley Bitter, Imperial** H
Relaxed, uncomplicated old local, on the fringe of the town centre, but a million miles from the hectic weekend 'circuit'. A bastion of cask beer for 130 years, it is still recognisable as the private house it originally was. Q ♣ P

### Golden Cock

13 Tubwell Row
☎ (01325) 468843
11–11; 12–10.30 Sun
**Courage Directors; John Smith's Bitter, Magnet; guest beer** H
Bustling town-centre pub, totally refurbished in 1995: a large, split-level bar with a pool area to the rear and a small snug to one side. Function room upstairs. Eve meals Fri and Sat.
✿ ✿ ◖ ▶ ⇌ ♣

### Grey Horse

39 Haughton Green, Haughton Village
☎ (01325) 465402
11–11; 12–10.30 Sun
**John Smith's Magnet** H
A village local atmosphere prevails in this pub which is often full due to the licensee's radical price-cutting policy. One U-shaped room. (Not to be confused with the Grey Horse near the town centre.)
✿ ◖ ♣ P ☐

### Number Twenty-2

22 Coniscliffe Road (W edge of town centre)
☎ (01325) 354590
11–11; closed Sun
**Hambleton Nightmare; Village White Boar, Bull, Old Raby; guest beers** H
Very popular, classy new pub in a former restaurant. Huge curved windows and a high ceiling give it an airy spaciousness even when packed. Catering for 'thirtysomethings', it turns over 15-plus independent ales per week. Good range of food and wines, but no spirit licence. No food Mon eve.
◖ ▶ ⌂ ☐

### Pennyweight

Bakehouse Hill, Market Place
☎ (01325) 464244
11–11; 12–10.30 Sun
**Vaux Double Maxim, Waggle Dance; Ward's Best Bitter; guest beers** H
Busy, one-roomed market place pub with a modern layout but traditional furnishings. It can be noisy (and pricey) Fri and Sat eve, but offers an adventurous range of beers for a Vaux tied house. Pavement tables in summer. ✿ ◖ ⇌ ⌂

### Railway Tavern

8 High Northgate (A167, ½ mile N of centre)
☎ (01325) 464963
11–11; 12–10.30 Sun
**Boddingtons Bitter; Wadworth 6X; Whitbread Fuggles IPA; guest beers** H
Possibly the first 'Railway' pub in the world, taking its name from the nearby 1825 Stockton

& Darlington line. A buoyant, well-run, two-roomer with usually six cask ales, it offers good value (and varied) meals and an equally expansive 'menu' of board games. Small patio.

🏾 ❀ ◖ ▶ ◱ ≈ (North Rd) ♣

## Tap & Spile

99 Bondgate ☎ (01325) 381679
11.30–11; 12–10.30 Sun
**Beer range varies** H
Popular, town-centre pub, after the style of a Victorian ale house. A function room upstairs stages live music most weekends. Up to eight real ales and regular farmhouse ciders. No food Sun. ◖ ≈ ♣ ◔ ⊬

# Durham City

## Brewer & Firkin

58 Saddler Street
☎ (0191) 386 4134
11–11; 12–10.30 Sun
**Boddingtons Bitter; Castle Eden Ale; guest beers** H
Pub which perseveres with a varied cask selection in the face of the 'Bottle and Hooch' brigade at weekends: a one-room bar in fake traditional style with walls adorned with bull horns, old phones, etc. plus a downstairs disco room. Live music in the bar weekdays. Occasional cider.
◖ ≈ ◔

## Dun Cow

37 Old Elvet ☎ (0191) 386 9219
11–11; 12–10.30 Sun
**Boddingtons Bitter; Castle Eden Ale; guest beers** H
One of Durham's little gems – a two-roomed pub near the prison. The bar, as small as a snug, is popular with the locals. The larger lounge has a mixed clientele and is often busy at weekends. Q ◖ ◱ ♿

## Half Moon

New Elvet (opp. County Hotel)
☎ (0191) 386 4528
11–11; 12–3, 7–10.30 Sun
**Draught Bass; Worthington Bitter** H
Unspoilt old inn, 20 years in the *Guide*. A split-level, crescent-shaped bar gives the pub its name. Q

## Old Elm Tree

12 Crossgate
☎ (0191) 386 4621
12–3, 6–11; 12–11 Sat; 12–3, 7–10.30 Sun
**Vaux Samson; guest beer** H
A recently altered interior has not deprived this pub of its character. The split bar and comfortable lounge are popular with all ages.
Q ❀ 🛏 ≈ P

**Try also: Colpitts Hotel**, Hawthorn Tce, **Victoria Hotel**☆ , Hallgarth St (Free)

# Egglescliffe

## Pot & Glass

Church Road (off A135)
☎ (01642) 651009
12–3, 5.30–11; 12–4.30, 7–10.30 Sun
**Draught Bass; Worthington Bitter** H
Superb village local beside the parish church, in whose graveyard lies a previous licensee who carved the ornate bar fronts from old furniture. Resident ghostly nuns.
Q 🛏 ❀ ◖ ◱ ≈ ♣ P

# Ferryhill

## Black Bull

2–3 Main Street
☎ (01740) 651325
11–11; 12–10.30 Sun
**McEwan 80/-; Theakston Black Bull** H
Friendly, four-roomed pub and restaurant (open Thu–Sun). Quiz night (Thu); live entertainment weekends. All day breakfasts available. Note the collection of terrible ties in the bar.
Q 🛏 ❀ ◖ ▶ ♣ P 🖥

**Try also: Post Boy**, Market Place (Whitbread)

# Forest-in-Teesdale

## High Force Hotel

☎ (01833) 622222
11–5, 7–11 (hours may be reduced in winter); 12–10.30 Sun
**High Force Low Force, Teesdale Bitter, Forest XB; Theakston Best Bitter** H
Small, unpretentious, stone-built old hotel (one of the highest in England) next to the spectacular falls. The public bar has two linked rooms, serving beers from the hotel's own brewery. The landlord is happy to show visitors the brewhouse.
🏾 Q 🛏 ❀ 🛏 ◖ ▶ ♣ P

# Framwellgate Moor

## Tap & Spile

27 Front Street (½ mile from A167 bypass)
☎ (0191) 386 5451
11.30–3, 6 (5 Fri)–11; 12–3, 7–10.30 Sun
**Hambleton White Boar; Tap & Spile Premium; guest beers** H
Pub featuring bare walls and wooden floors in typical Tap & Spile style. Three rooms, including one no-smoking and a partitioned family room, attract clientele from a wide area. Up to seven guest beers.
Q 🛏 ♣ ◔ ⊬

**Try also: Marquis of Granby**, Front St (Samuel Smith)

# Great Lumley

## Old England

Front Street
☎ (0191) 388 5257
11–11; 12–10.30 Sun
**Worthington Bitter; guest beers** H
Pub with a large, noisy, lively bar, popular with youngsters and some older clientele, plus a quiet, comfortable lounge with a friendly atmosphere, popular with locals. Food Mon–Sat eves and Fri–Sun lunch.
Q ◖ ▶ ◱ ♣ P

# Greta Bridge

## Morritt Arms Hotel

Signed off A66
☎ (01833) 627232
11–11; 12–10.30 Sun (Sir Walter Scott bar opens 8.30)
**Butterknowle Conciliation Ale; Taylor Landlord; Tetley Bitter; Theakston Best Bitter** H
Two very different hostelries exist here, in a fine setting, secluded from the nearby A66. The main bar, in the magnificently traditional country house hotel, has bow-tied barmen and hotel prices; the detached Sir Walter Scott bar serves the local trade with a smaller beer range at lower prices.
🏾 Q ❀ 🛏 ◖ ▶ ◱ ♣ P

# Hartburn

## Masham Hotel

87 Hartburn Village
☎ (01642) 580414
11–11; 12–3, 7–10.30 Sun
**Draught Bass; Black Sheep Special; guest beer** H
Unspoilt village pub. Its several small drinking areas are warm and welcoming to all. Q ❀ 🛏 ♣ P 🖥

# Hartlepool

## Brewer & Firkin

2 Whitby Street
☎ (01429) 273564
11–11 (may vary midweek); 12–10.30 Sun
**Boddingtons Bitter; Castle Eden Ale; guest beers** H
Large, one-room pub on various levels. Handy for the museum and art gallery complex and the town centre. The Cask and Curry Club is popular Fri. Up to eight cask ales available.
🏾 🛏 ◖ ≈ ♣

## Causeway

Elwick Road, Stranton (near Camerons Brewery)
☎ (01429) 273954
11–11; 12–10.30 Sun

**Banks's Bitter; Camerons Bitter, Strongarm; guest beers** [H]
Victorian-style pub: a large bar plus two cosy rooms where beer is served from a hatchway. Folk club Sun eve. Cleveland CAMRA *Pub of the Year* 1995, offering four guest ales.
Q ♘ ❀ ◐ ⊟ ♣ P ⊡

## Jacksons Arms
Tower Street
☎ (01429) 862413
11–11; 12–10.30 Sun
**Draught Bass; Boddingtons Bitter; Theakston XB; guest beers** [H]
Traditional, two-room, street-corner pub with an upstairs bar, located near the new art gallery and museums complex, and close to the college and town centre.
Q ◐ ◗ ⊟ ⇌ ♣

## Touchdown
245 West View Road
☎ (01429) 266320
7 (12 Sat)–11; 12–4, 7–10.30 Sun
**Camerons Strongarm** [H]
Three-roomed, 1950s estate pub on the northern edge of town, near two rugby clubs. Note: closed weekday lunchtimes. ⊟ P ⊡

# High Coniscliffe

## Duke of Wellington
On A167 ☎ (01325) 374283
11–3, 6–11; 12–3, 7–10.30 Sun
**Camerons Strongarm; Ind Coope Burton Ale; Theakston Best Bitter** [H]
Friendly, cosy, traditional rural village pub with a warm welcome plus a garden and a safe children's play area.
♛ ❀ ◐ ♣ P ⊡

# Holwick

## Strathmore Arms
Off B6277 OS909268
☎ (01833) 640362
12–11; 12–10.30 Sun
**Ruddles Best Bitter; Tetley Bitter; guest beers** [H]
Isolated, but welcoming, stone-built hostelry, three miles along a cul-de-sac near the south bank of the Tees, a stroll away from the Pennine Way – well worth the journey. The cosy bar is arranged around an open hearth. The camping field lies in the shadow of magnificent Holwick Scar. No food Mon.
♛ Q ❀ ⛟ ◐ ◗ ▲ ♣ P

# Leamside

## Three Horse Shoes
Pithouse Lane (off A690)
☎ (0191) 584 2394
12–3 (not Mon–Wed), 7–11; 12–3, 7–10.30 Sun
**Theakston Best Bitter; guest beers** [H]
Friendly country inn comprising a large bar with a lounge at one end and a family room off the other. A meeting place for local clubs. Up to four guest beers – mostly from independent breweries.
♘ ❀ ◐ ◗ ▲ ♣ P

# Low Spennymoor

## Frog & Ferret
Coulson Street (between town centre and A167)
☎ (01388) 818312
11–11; 11–4.30, 7–11 Sat; 12–3, 7–10.30 Sun
**Boddingtons Bitter; Courage Directors; Samuel Smith OBB; Theakston XB; guest beers** [H]
Small, clean, comfortable, street-corner local catering for all tastes. Friendly bar staff and the absence of electronic machines ensure a popular drinking place with a steady turnover of guest beers. Note the original pub sign above the entrance. Q ⊡

# No Place

## Beamish Mary Inn
600 yds off A693
☎ (0191) 370 0237
12–3, 6–11; 12–11 Fri & Sat; 12–10.30 Sun
**Black Sheep Best Bitter; Jennings Cumberland Ale; McEwan 80/-; Theakston Best Bitter, XB, Old Peculier; guest beers** [H]
Situated in an ex-mining village, close to the local museum: customers travel from all over the region to this popular pub, replete with memorabilia. Rock and blues in converted stables Thu and Sat; folk club Wed; annual beer fest (Jan). The house beer is brewed by Big Lamp.
♛ ❀ ⛟ ◐ ◗ ⊟ ♿ ▲ ♣ ⌓ P

# North Bitchburn

## Red Lion
☎ (01388) 763561
12–3, 7–11; 12–3, 7–10.30 Sun
**Courage Directors; Marston's Pedigree; John Smith's Bitter; guest beer** [H]
Friendly, traditional village pub with a bar, pool room and dining area. Very popular for its excellent meals and wide range of guest beers. A regular guest is the pub's own Mane Brew, brewed by Hambleton. Regional CAMRA *Pub of the Year* 1995.
♛ Q ❀ ◐ ◗ ♣ P ⊡

# Norton

## Red Lion
Harland Place (A193, at roundabout) ☎ (01642) 554858
11.30–11; 12–3, 7–10.30 Sun
**John Smith's Bitter, Magnet; guest beer** [H]
Large corner pub comprising a lounge, bar, buffet, games/pool room and an upstairs function room decorated in Victorian style. Parts of the pub date back 300 years. Strong local patronage. Q ◐ ⊟ ♣ P

## Unicorn
147 High Street
☎ (01642) 553888
11.30–3.30, 5.30–11; 11–11 Sat; 12–3.30, 7–10.30 Sun
**John Smith's Magnet** [H]
Friendly local with several rooms off a small bar. It stands next to the old Norton green and the duckpond. Lunchtime sandwiches. Q ❀ ⊟ ♿ ♣

# Pittington

## Hallgarth Manor Village Tavern
High Pittington (1 mile SW of Pittington on unclassified road to Sherburn) OS328438
☎ (0191) 372 1188
6.30–11; 6.30–10.30 Sun
**Boddingtons Bitter; Tetley Bitter** [H]
Listed, Grade II, 18th-century manor house, converted to an hotel with a pub in an extension to the main building. Beautiful mature gardens. An oasis in a real ale desert. Note: the pub is closed lunchtimes.
Q ❀ ⛟ ◐ ◗ ⊟ ♣ P

# Pity Me

## Lambton Hounds
62 Front Street (A167)
☎ (0191) 386 4742
11–11; 12–4, 7–10.30 Sun
**Vaux Lorimer's Best Scotch; Ward's Best Bitter; guest beer** [H]
18th-century coaching inn on the old Great North Road, featuring a village bar, a snug with bell-push service, a lounge with a coal fire and good food. No meals Sun eve. Quoits played in summer. Good B&B. Families well catered for.
♛ Q ♘ ❀ ⛟ ◐ ◗ ⊟ ♣ P

# Preston le Skerne

## Blacksmith's Arms
¾ mile E of A167
☎ (01325) 314873
12–3, 6 (7 winter)–11; 12–3 Sun, closed Sun eve
**Black Sheep Best Bitter; John Smith's Magnet** [H]

The 'Hammers' stands isolated but welcoming on the road to Great Stainton: a large comfortable lounge and a smaller bar. ❀ ◖ ▷ ⛺ ♣ P

## Red Row

### Black Horse
Off A6076 ☎ (01207) 232569
12 (11 Sat)–3, 7 (6 Sat)–11; 12–3, 7–10.30 Sun
**Ward's Best Bitter; guest beer** Ⓗ
Traditional alehouse, dating from 1642, hidden away but convenient for Beamish Open Air Museum. ♨ Q ⛺ ❀ P

## Romaldkirk

### Kirk Inn
The Green ☎ (01833) 650260
12–2.30, 6–11; 12–3, 7–10.30 Sun
**Black Sheep Best Bitter; Boddingtons Bitter; Butterknowle Bitter; Castle Eden Ale; guest beer** Ⓗ
Charming, single-room pub, with a warm and welcoming atmosphere. Situated on the village green, it doubles as a part-time post office. Excellent meals are produced by the landlord. ♨ Q ❀ ◖ ▷ ♣

## Rookhope

### Rookhope Inn
☎ (01388) 517215
12–3 (not Mon–Fri), 7–11 (11–11 summer); 12–3, 7–10.30 (12–10.30 summer) Sun
**Hexhamshire Devil's Water; Tetley Bitter; guest beer** Ⓗ
Pleasant country pub on the Coast-to-Coast walk in Weardale. Friendly licensees offer good food and always at least one local beer.
♨ Q ♒ ❀ ⇌ ◖ ▷ ⛫ ♣ P

## Seaton Carew

### Seaton Hotel
Church Street
☎ (01429) 266212
12–11; 12–10.30 Sun
**Boddingtons Bitter; Castle Eden Ale; Flowers Original; Marston's Pedigree; Morland Old Speckled Hen** Ⓗ
Seafront pub, dating from 1792, displaying old pictures of Seaton in the lounge. Reputed to be haunted. Meals available in the bar and restaurant.
Q ♒ ❀ ⇌ ◖ ▷ ♣ P

## Shadforth

### Plough Inn
South Side (B1283)
☎ (0191) 372 0375
6.30–11; 2–5, 6.30–11 Fri; 12–11 Sat; 12–4, 7–10.30 Sun
**Draught Bass; Stones Bitter; guest beers** Ⓗ

Traditional, two-bar country pub, popular with all. The beer range is changed weekly. Durham CAMRA 1996 *Pub of the Year* ♨ Q ❀ ♣ P

## Sherburn Hill

### Burley Lodge
19 Front Street
☎ (0191) 372 2334
11–2 (4 Sat), 7–11; 12–3, 7–10.30 Sun
**Theakston Best Bitter, XB; guest beers** Ⓗ
Two-room village pub, catering for all ages, with facilities for darts, dominoes, pool and shove-ha'penny. Basic bar snacks. All beers come from Scottish Courage.
❀ ♣ P ⛫

### Moor Edge
Front Street ☎ (0191) 372 1618
12–4, 7–11; 12–3, 7–10.30 Sun
**Vaux Lorimer's Best Scotch; Ward's Best Bitter; guest beers** Ⓗ
18th-century village inn, where the bar and lounge boast coal fires reflecting its warm and friendly atmosphere. A haven for the dominoes enthusiast, quoits played in the garden in summer. ♨ Q ❀ ⛫ ♣ P ⛫

## Shildon

### Timothy Hackworth
107 Main Street (B6282)
☎ (01388) 772525
12–11; 12–10.30 Sun
**Camerons Bitter, Strongarm** Ⓗ
Friendly village local named after a famous steam engine builder, opposite the world's first railway passenger station. The decor features pictures of old Shildon and steam engines built by Hackworth at the nearby Soho Works, now a museum. Q ♣ P ⛫

## Shincliffe

### Seven Stars
On A177 ☎ (0191) 384 8454
12–2.30, 6.30–11; 12–3, 7–10.30 Sun
**Vaux Samson, Waggle Dance; Ward's Best Bitter** Ⓗ
Former coaching inn, now a stylish, upmarket pub in a smart city suburb. The bar is decorated with old red embossed wallpaper; very comfortable, small lounge with a side restaurant room.
Q ❀ ⇌ ◖ ▷ ⛫

Try also: Avenue, High Shincliffe (Vaux)

## Stanhope

### Grey Bull
17 West Terrace
☎ (01388) 528177
11.30 (2.30 Mon–Fri, Christmas–Easter)–11; 12–10.30 Sun

**Newcastle Exhibition; Theakston Best Bitter** Ⓗ
Friendly, down-to-earth local with one large room, built in the 1780s as a combined pub and violin maker's.
♨ Q ❀ ♣ P

### Queen's Head
89 Front Street (A689)
☎ (01388) 528160
12–3, 7–11; varies Sun
**Newcastle Exhibition; Theakston Best Bitter, XB; guest beers** Ⓗ
Comfortable, friendly, two-roomed pub near the market place, with a pool table in one room. Bar snacks served.
⇌ ≷ (limited service)

## Stanley

### Blue Boar Tavern
Front Street (off A693, top end of town) ☎ (01207) 231167
11–3, 7–11; 11–11 Thu–Sat; 12–10.30 Sun
**Draught Bass; Stones Bitter; guest beers** Ⓗ
Original coaching inn at the top of a busy street, popular lunchtimes and weekends. The guest ales usually change three times a week. Live music in the main lounge Sat eve.
♨ ❀ ◖ ▷ ♣ P

### Ox Inn
Oxhill (visible from A693)
☎ (01207) 233626
7 (12 Fri & Sat)–11; 12–3, 7–10.30 Sun
**Draught Bass; guest beer** Ⓗ
Pub with a large U-shaped room with a very high ceiling, recently extended using existing buildings. The conservatory overlooks the garden/play area. A lively crowd enjoys music Sat eve.
♨ ❀ ◖ ▷ ♣ P

## Stockton-on-Tees

### Fitzgerald's
9–10 High Street
☎ (01642) 678220
11.30–3 (3.30 Fri, 4 Sat), 6.30–11; 7–10.30 Sun, closed Sun lunch
**Draught Bass; Taylor Landlord; Theakston Old Peculier; Younger IPA; guest beers** Ⓗ
Pub whose superb stone facade features Shap granite pillars and opens on to a split-level, open-plan interior. Regular beer festivals. ◖ ≷ ♣

### Sun Inn
Knowles Street
☎ (01642) 615676
11–4, 5.30–11; 11–11 Wed, Fri & Sat; 12–4, 7–10.30 Sun
**Draught Bass** Ⓗ
Classic, town-centre pub, reckoned to sell more Draught Bass than any other pub in Britain. Folk club Mon.
⛫ ≷ ♣

### Theatre

Yarm Lane (near Swallow
Hotel) ☎ (01642) 674478
11–11; 7–10.30 Sun, closed Sun lunch
**Theakston Best Bitter, XB,
Old Peculier** H
Victorian-style town pub. Bar
snacks available, except Fri and
Sat. Pool played. ♣

## Summerhouse

### Raby Hunt

On B6279 ☎ (01325) 374604
11.30–3, 6.30–11; 12–3, 7–10.30 Sun
**Newcastle Exhibition;
Theakston Black Bull; guest
beer** H
Neat, welcoming old stone free
house, in a pretty white-
washed hamlet with a homely
lounge and a busy locals' bar.
Good home-cooked lunches
(not served Sun).
🍴 Q ✿ ◖ ▣ ♣ P

## West Cornforth

### Square & Compass

7 The Green ☎ (01740) 650975
12–2 (3 Sat), 7–11; 12–3, 7–10.30 Sun
**Draught Bass; Stones Bitter;
guest beers** H
Cosy pub with views over the
village green and surrounding
countryside. The decor
includes historic photographs
of the village and green. Quiz
Thu; quoits played. No food
Sun eve. 🍴 Q ✿ ◖ ▶ ♣ P

## White le Head

### Highlander Inn

Front Street (B6311)
☎ (01207) 232416
7.30–11; 12–4, 7–11 Sat; 12–3, 7–10.30
Sun

**Beer range varies** H
Pub situated at the top of a
hillside village, featuring an
intimate lounge with a small
dining area. The lively bar
hosts varied music/
entertainment. Note: closed
weekday lunchtimes.
Q ✿ ✿ ▶ ▣ ♣ P ✕

## Witton Gilbert

### Glendenning Arms

Front Street ☎ (0191) 371 0316
12–4, 7–11; 12–4, 7–10.30 Sun
**Vaux Samson** H
Twenty-one years in the *Guide*,
this friendly local, thankfully,
never changes. The two rooms
include a comfortable lounge.
Racing mementoes decorate
the bar. Outside seating is in
the large car park.
🍴 Q ✿ ♣ P

### Travellers Rest

Front Street (A691)
☎ (0191) 371 0458
11–3, 6–11; 12–3, 7–10.30 Sun
**McEwan 80/-; Theakston Best
Bitter, XB, Old Peculier;
Younger Scotch, No. 3** H
Popular village pub with
attractive, traditional decor,
featuring a split-level, no-
smoking room and a
conservatory, ideal for
children. Boules played. Wide
variety of meals in the
restaurant, plus bar snacks.
🍴 Q ✿ ✿ ◖ ▶ ♣ P ✕

**Try also: Centurion,** Langley
Park (Vaux)

## Wolsingham

### Bay Horse Hotel

Upper Town (B6296, ½ mile
N of centre)

☎ (01388) 527220
11–11; 12–10.30 Sun
**Ruddles County; Tetley
Bitter** H
19th-century pub with later
extensions, serving good food
in an attractive rural setting.
The bar has two linked
rooms; separate restaurant
and lounge bar. Children
welcome.
Q ✿ ⊨ ◖ ▶ ▣ ♣ P ⊟

### Mill Race

West End
☎ (01388) 526551
11–11; 12–10.30 Sun
**Vaux Lorimer's Best Scotch,
Bitter, Samson, Double
Maxim, Waggle Dance; guest
beers** H
Warm, friendly, family pub
offering the complete range
of Vaux cask ales and
serving food all day. Family
certificate and
accommodation.
🍴 Q ✿ ✿ ⊨ ◖ ▶ ♠ ♣ P

## Wolviston

### Wellington

31–33 High Street
☎ (01740) 644439
12–11; 12–10.30 Sun
**Draught Bass; Worthington
Bitter; guest beers** H
Traditional village pub with
lots of character: a tiny basic
bar with two larger rooms, one
boasting a fine collection of
chamber pots. Upstairs
function room available
except Thu, when the local
folk club meets. Popular
lunchtimes for meals.
Wheelchair access is from the
rear car park.
Q ✿ ◖ ▶ ♿ ♣ P

---

# BREW IT YOURSELF

Beer enthusiasts who enjoy making, as well as drinking, good ales
should look out for three comprehensive brewing manuals
which reveal how home-brew needn't taste of sterilising fluid and
plastic. *The CAMRA Guide to Home Brewing* (priced £6.99), by
Graham Wheeler, provides all the information you need to make a
start, plus tips for more experienced home-producers. *Brew Your
Own Real Ale at Home* (also priced £6.99), by Graham Wheeler and
Roger Protz, takes readers a step further and reveals how they can
recreate over 100 famous British commercial brands. And for fans of
Continental beers like wheat beers, Guezes, Pilsners and Trappist
ales, *Brew Classic European Beers at Home*, at £8.99, by the same
authors, is a must. Copies are available from all good bookshops, or
direct (and post-free) from CAMRA, 230 Hatfield Road, St Albans,
Hertfordshire AL1 4LW. Discounts are available for CAMRA
members.

# BEERS OF THE YEAR

Chosen by CAMRA tasting panels, by votes from the general public at beer festivals and by a poll of CAMRA members, these are the *Good Beer Guide Beers of the Year*. Each was found to be consistently outstanding in its category and took its place in the *Champion Beer of Britain* contest at the Great British Beer Festival at Olympia in August 1996. These beers have also been awarded a tankard symbol in the breweries section of this book. The categories for Old Ales and Strong Milds, Barley Wines, and Porters and Stouts are not included this year. These are to be judged at a winter beer festival and the results will be featured in *Good Beer Guide 1998*. A new category for Speciality Beers (beers brewed with non-standard ingredients) has been introduced, and the number of beers in the Bitters and Best Bitters categories has been doubled, to reflect their prominence in pubs compared with that of beers in other categories.

## DARK AND LIGHT MILDS

Bateman Dark Mild
Belhaven 60/- Ale
Brains Dark
Guernsey Braye Ale
Harveys XX Mild Ale
Highgate Dark
Tomlinson's Hermitage Mild

## BITTERS

Adnams Bitter
Big Lamp Bitter
Border Special Bitter
Butcombe Bitter
Caledonian Deuchars IPA
Caledonian Murrays Pale
    Summer Ale
Dyffryn Clwyd Dr Johnson's
    Draught
Everards Beacon
Hardys & Hansons Best Bitter
Harveys Sussex Pale Ale
Oakham JHB
Otter Bitter
Pilgrim Surrey Bitter
Woodforde's Wherry Best Bitter

## SPECIALITY BEERS

Brewery on Sea Spinnaker Buzz
Harviestoun Schiehallion
Heather Fraoch Heather Ale
Nethergate Umbel Ale
Passageway St Arnold
Steam Packet Ginger Minge

## BEST BITTERS

Adnams Extra
Batham Best Bitter
Brains SA
Butterknowle Banner Bitter
Caledonian 80/- Ale
Camerons Strongarm
Crouch Vale Millennium Gold
Fuller's London Pride
Harveys Sussex Best Bitter
Mansfield Old Baily
North Downs Old Cocky
Otter Ale
Parish Somerby Premium
Plassey Bitter

## STRONG BITTERS

Bullmastiff Son of a Bitch
Cheriton Diggers Gold
Greene King Abbot Ale
Hop Back Summer Lightning
Maypole Mayday
Plassey Dragon's Breath
Tomlinson's Deceitful Rose

## BOTTLE-CONDITIONED BEERS

Bass Worthington White Shield
Gale's Prize Old Ale
Hardy Thomas Hardy's Ale
King & Barnes Festive
Marston's Oyster Stout
Scottish Courage Imperial
    Russian Stout
Shepherd Neame Spitfire

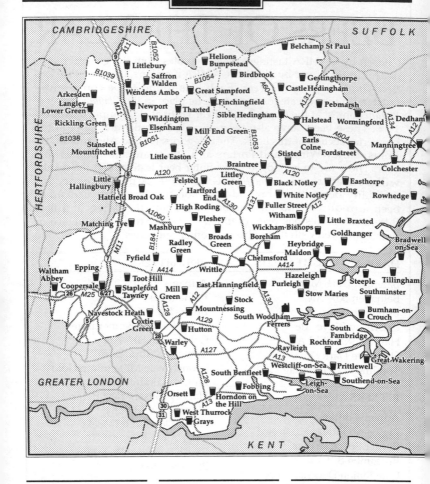

## Aingers Green

### Royal Fusilier
Weeley Road (1 mile S of Gt
Bentley Green) OS119204
☎ (01206) 250001
11–3, 6.30–11; 12–3, 7–10.30 Sun
**Beer range varies** Ⓗ/Ⓖ
Friendly free house, run by
the same couple since 1958.
Extended in 1990 to
accommodate a pool table
and inside toilets, it has a
good local following.
🏡 ✿ ♣ P

## Arkesden

### Axe & Compasses
☎ (01799) 550272
11.30–2.30, 6–11; 12–3, 7–10.30 Sun
**Greene King IPA, Abbot** Ⓗ
Superb, 17th-century,
friendly, traditional village
local with a thriving food
trade.
🏡 Q ✿ ◑ ▶ ♣ P

## Belchamp St Paul

### Cherry Tree Inn
Knowl GreenOS784413
☎ (01787) 237263
12–3, 7–11; 12–11 Sat; 12–3, 7–10.30
Sun; closed Tue
**Adnams Bitter; Greene King
IPA; guest beer** Ⓗ
Cosy, friendly, isolated pub,
comfortably refurbished.
Excellent value beer and food
(cooked on the premises).
Good play area for children.
Popular with local morris men.
🏡 Q ✿ ◑ ▶ ♣ P

## Birdbrook

### Plough
The Street (1 mile off B1054)
☎ (01440) 785336
11–2.30, 6–11; 12–3, 7–10.30 Sun
**Adnams Bitter; Greene King
IPA; guest beer** Ⓗ
Friendly village local. No food
Sun eve; good value snacks.
🏡 Q ✿ ◑ ▶ ⊞ ♣ P

## Black Notley

### Vine
105 The Street, Witham Road
☎ (01376) 324269
12–2.30 (4 Sat), 6–11; 12–4, 6–10.30
Sun
**Ridleys IPA; guest beers** Ⓗ
Small country pub now
extended into an adjoining
barn which provides seating
for diners. Ever changing range
of guest beers (approx. 150 in
the last year), plus a house
beer. Good, reasonably priced,
home-cooked food. Cressing
station is nearby (¾ mile).
Q ◑ ▶ ⊞ ⇔ P

## Boreham

### Queen's Head
Church Road
☎ (01245) 467298
10–3, 5–11; 12–3, 7–10.30 Sun
**Greene King IPA, Abbot** Ⓗ
Excellent, friendly village local
with two contrasting bars.

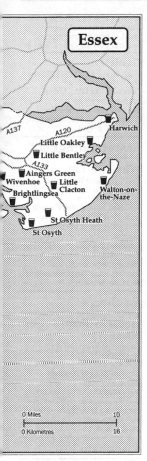

Essex

Harwich

Little Oakley

Little Bentley

Aingers Green

Wivenhoe · Little
Clacton

Brightlingsea

Walton-on-
the-Naze

St Osyth Heath

St Osyth

0 Miles 10

0 Kilometres 16

Good value in every way. No
food Sun eve. Q ❀ ◑ ▶ ⊞ ♣ P

## Bradwell-on-Sea

### Green Man

The Street, Waterside
☎ (01621) 776226
12–3, 7–11 (11–11 summer Sat); 12–3,
7–10.30 (12–10.30 summer) Sun
**Adnams Bitter, Extra; Ridleys
IPA; guest beer** Ⓗ
Traditional, 15th-century inn
near the river and marina,
formerly used by smugglers. A
superb fireplace graces the
unspoilt public bar. Sit at the
undertaker's table and try to
work out the meaning of the
sign above the fireplace.
🏚 Q ❀ ◑ ▶ ⊞ ♣ P

## Braintree

### King William IV

114 London Road (near B1053/
A120 jct) ☎ (01376) 330088
11–3, 6–11; 11–11 Sat; 12–3, 7–10.30
Sun
**Ridleys IPA** Ⓖ
Cosy, two-bar local with a very

friendly atmosphere. Darts and
quizzes are popular.
Lunchtime snacks. Award-
winning flower displays in
summer. 🏚 ❀ ⊞ ♣ P

### Wagon & Horses

53 South Street (B1256)
☎ (01376) 553356
11–3 (4 Sat), 5.30 (6 Sat)–11; 12–3,
7–10.30 Sun
**Greene King IPA, Abbot,
seasonal beers** Ⓗ
Comfortable pub with a large
lounge, a raised dining area
and a friendly snug. Look for
the well. ❀ ◑ ▶ ⇌ ♣ P

## Brightlingsea

### Railway Tavern

58 Station Road (near B1029)
☎ (01206) 302581
5 (12 Fri & Sat)–11; 12–3, 7–10.30 Sun
**Beer range varies** Ⓗ
Two-bar pub popular with
locals in the early eve. No food
apart from crisps, etc. Variety
of games. Five ales always on
sale. Close to the promenade.
🏚 Q ➳ ❀ ⊞ ♿ ▲ ♣ ▭

## Broads Green

### Walnut Tree

1 mile W of B1008
☎ (01245) 360222
11.30–2.30, 6.30–11; 12–2.30, 7–10.30
Sun
**Ridleys IPA** Ⓖ/Ⓗ**, seasonal
beers** Ⓖ
Well-preserved, Victorian
agricultural community pub
overlooking an attractive
village green, with an unspoilt
public bar and a snug. A later
extension accommodates the
lounge bar. Flo's home-made
pickled eggs are a must.
🏚 Q ❀ ◑ ▶ ⊞ ♣ P

## Burnham-on-
Crouch

### Olde White Harte
Hotel

The Quay/Shore Road (near
B1010) ☎ (01621) 782106
11–11; 12–10.30 Sun
**Adnams Bitter; Hancock's
IPA; Tolly Cobbold Bitter** Ⓗ
Fine, traditional riverside pub,
frequented by locals and
yatchsmen; bustling on
summer eves, particularly at
weekends. Enjoy a pint on the
jetty. 🏚 Q ➽ ◑ ▶ ⊞ P

## Castle Hedingham

### Bell Inn

10 St James Street (B1058)
☎ (01787) 460350
11.30–3, 6–11; 12–3, 7–10.30 Sun
**Greene King IPA, Abbot;
Shepherd Neame Master
Brew Bitter** Ⓖ

Excellent, genuine-timbered,
many-roomed pub with casks
behind the bar. Occasional live
music; good value food (not
served Mon eve except bank
hols). Comfortable family
room.
🏚 Q ➳ ❀ ◑ ▶ ⊞ ▲ ♣ P ⌿

## Chelmsford

### Bird in Hand

New Writtle Street
☎ (01245) 600002
11–3, 6–11; 11–11 Fri & Sat; 12–10.30
Sun
**Ridleys IPA, Rumpus** Ⓗ
Two-roomed, backstreet local
near the football and cricket
grounds. Friendly, welcoming
landlord. ❀ ◑ ▶ P

### Endeavour

351 Springfield Road (B1137)
☎ (01245) 257717
11–11; 12–2.30, 7–10.30 Sun
**Greene King XX Mild, IPA,
Abbot; Shepherd Neame
Master Brew Bitter; guest
beer** Ⓗ
Quiet, three-roomed pub
popular with people who enjoy
a convivial atmosphere and
beer at some of the cheapest
prices in an expensive area.
Interesting pub sign.
🏚 Q ◑ ▶ ⊞ ♣

### Original Plough

28 Duke Street
☎ (01245) 250145
11–11; 12–3, 7–10.30 Sun
**Ind Coope Burton Ale; Tetley
Bitter; guest beers** Ⓗ
Beamed ale house close to the
rail station offering six guest
beers and occasional live jazz/
blues. The landlord is a *Master
Cellarman*. ❀ ◑ ⇌ ♣ P

### White Horse

25 Townfield Street (behind
station) ☎ (01245) 269556
11–3, 5.30 (7 Sat)–11; 12–10.30 Sun
**Beer range varies** Ⓗ
Friendly, backstreet free house
serving a wide, changing range
of ales, most from small
breweries. No pool table or
jukebox. Essex CAMRA *Pub of
the Year* 1992. Due for
refurbishment. No meals Sat/
Sun. ◑ ⇌ ♣

## Colchester

### Beer House

126 Magdalen Street (A134)
☎ (01206) 792642
12–2.30, 5.30–11; 12–11 Fri & Sat;
12–4, 7–10.30 Sun

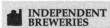

### INDEPENDENT
BREWERIES

**Crouch Vale:**
South Woodham Ferrers

**Ridleys:** Hartford End

Greene King IPA, Abbot, seasonal beers; guest beers Ⓗ
Pleasant, single-bar pub (formerly the Bakers Arms) with keen and friendly hosts. Pool is popular; buskers play Tue. It can be smoky when packed. Eve meals end at 7.
❀ ◖ ▮ ≢ (Town) ✦ ☗

### British Grenadier

67 Military Road (left from station; take right fork)
☎ (01206) 791647
11–2.30 (3 Fri & Sat), 7–11; 12–3, 7–10.30 Sun
Adnams Mild (summer), Bitter Ⓗ, Old Ⓖ; guest beer (occasional) Ⓗ
Friendly, two-bar local with a strong darts and pool following. The highest pub in town. ⊞ ≢ (Town) ✦

### King's Arms/ Hogshead

61–63 Crouch Street
☎ (01206) 572886
11–11; 12–10.30 Sun
Boddingtons Bitter Ⓗ; Castle Eden Ale Ⓖ; Flowers IPA Ⓗ; Fuller's London Pride Ⓖ; guest beers Ⓗ/Ⓖ
Large, open-plan pub, tastefully refurbished. Very popular with all ages; good atmosphere. Occasional beer festivals.
♨ ❀ ◖ ▮ ⅋ ☗ P

### Odd One Out

28 Mersea Road (B1025, near St Botolph's) ☎ (01206) 578140
4.30 (11 Fri & Sat)–11; 12–10.30 Sun
Archers Best Bitter; Ridleys IPA; guest beers Ⓗ
Excellent, friendly pub, drawing customers from all walks of life: a basic public bar and a cosy lounge. Always five guest beers on sale, one a mild.
♨ Q ❀ ≢ (Town) ✦ ☗ ⌇

### Rose & Crown

51 East Street, East Gates
☎ (01206) 866677
11–3, 6.30–11; 12–3, 7–10.30 Sun
Adnams Broadside; Tetley Bitter; Tolly Cobbold IPA Ⓗ
The oldest recorded inn in Colchester, a former coaching house with an old prison cell downstairs. Its very comfortable, single bar has a beamed interior. The house beer is brewed by Tolly Cobbold. Q ⇔ ◖ ▮ ⅋ P

### Stockwell Arms

18 West Stockwell Street
☎ (01206) 575560
10.30–11; 10.30–3.30, 6.30–11 Sat; 12–3, 7–10.30 Sun
Marston's Pedigree; Morland Old Speckled Hen; Nethergate Bitter; Ruddles Best Bitter, County; Webster's Green Label, Yorkshire Bitter Ⓗ

Historic, friendly, family pub in the ancient Dutch quarter. The enthusiastic landlord has been here 17 years. Full Sun lunch (best to book). Eve meals on request.
Q ❀ ◖ ▮ ≢ (North) ✦ ⊟

### Tap & Spile

123–125 Crouch Street
☎ (01206) 573572
11–2.30, 5.30–11; 11–11 Sat; 12–3, 7–10.30 Sun
Adnams Bitter; Nethergate Bitter; Tap & Spile Premium; Theakston Best Bitter; guest beers Ⓗ
Popular, friendly pub, pleasing to the eye, with strong sporting connections. Five guest beers (over 800 different ales to date); a sparkler-free zone! Good value food. ♨ ❀ ◖ ☗

## Coopersale

### Garnon Bushes

13 Coopersale Common (off B181) ☎ (01992) 573096
11–11; 12–10.30 Sun
Badger Tanglefoot; Fuller's London Pride; Greene King IPA; Young's Bitter Ⓗ
One-bar pub in a 17th-century building; formerly four workers' cottages, it still retains a cottage atmosphere. Very popular for food (restaurant). One of the beers is occasionally replaced by a beer from another large independent. Q ❀ ◖ ▮ ✦ P

## Coxtie Green

### White Horse

173 Coxtie Green Road (1 mile W of A128 at Mores Cane jct)
OS564959 ☎ (01277) 372410
11.30–3, 5.30–11; 12–4, 7–11 Sat; 12–3, 7–10.30 Sun
Wadworth 6X; guest beers Ⓗ
Small, cosy country pub with a very large garden featuring a children's play area. Usually six real ales; beer festival second weekend in July. No meals Sun. ❀ ◖ ▮ ⊞ ✦ P

## Dedham

### Sun Hotel

High Street ☎ (01206) 323351
11–11; 12–3, 7–10.30 Sun
Adnams Bitter; Courage Directors; guest beers Ⓗ
15th-century, large pub/hotel in a picturesque village. Spacious garden and car park. Barbecues in summer.
♨ ⛺ ❀ ◖ ▮ ⅋ ✦ P

## Earls Colne

### Bird in Hand

Coggeshall Road (B1024)
☎ (01787) 222557
12–2.30, 6–11; 12–2.30, 7–10.30 Sun

Ridleys IPA Ⓗ, Mild Ⓖ, ESX, Rumpus, seasonal beers Ⓖ/Ⓗ
Pearl of a quiet, traditional, two-bar pub. ♨ Q ❀ ◖ ▮ ⊞ P

### Castle

High Street ☎ (01787) 222694
12–11; 12–4, 7–10.30 Sun
Greene King IPA, Abbot, seasonal beers Ⓗ
Beamed pub with log fires. Good food; no eve meals Sun.
♨ Q ❀ ◖ ▮ ⊞ ⅋ ▲ ✦ P

## East Hanningfield

### Windmill Tavern

The Tye, Main Road
☎ (01245) 400315
11–11; 12–10.30 Sun
Boddingtons Bitter; Crouch Vale Best Bitter; Marston's Pedigree; guest beer Ⓗ
Friendly, original free house opposite the village green. The guest beer changes weekly. Home-made food (roast lunches Sun). No eve meals Mon. ♨ ❀ ◖ ▮ P

## Easthorpe

### House Without a Name

Easthorpe Road (off A12)
☎ (01206) 213070
12–3, 6.30–11; 11 Sat; 12–10.30 Sun
Greene King IPA; guest beers Ⓗ
Very old, attractive pub with a double-sided large fire at its centre. Separate restaurant/ function room.
♨ ❀ ◖ ▮ ✦ P

## Elsenham

### Crown

High Street ☎ (01279) 812827
11–2.30, 6–11; 12–2.30, 7–10.30 Sun
Crouch Vale SAS; King & Barnes Sussex; Marston's Pedigree Ⓗ
Deservedly popular, friendly village pub with a pargetted exterior and a good reputation for food. No food Sun.
♨ ❀ ◖ ▮ ✦ P

## Epping

### Forest Gate

Bell Common (off B1393)
OS451011 ☎ (01992) 572312
10–3, 5.30–11; 12–3, 7–10.30 Sun
Adnams Bitter Ⓗ, Broadside Ⓖ; Ridleys IPA Ⓗ; guest beers Ⓖ
On the edge of Epping Forest: a single-bar, traditional pub which has been in existence since the 17th century and run by the same family for many years. Spacious green to the front. The two guest beers usually come from local independent brewers.
♨ Q ❀ ◖ ✦ ☗ P

## Feering

### Sun Inn
3 Feering Hill (B1024)
☎ (01376) 570442
11–3, 6–11; 12–3, 6–10.30 Sun
**Courage Directors; guest beers** ⊞
Heavily timbered former mansion, richly decorated with carved beams. Log fires; interesting history; large garden. Beer festivals May and August bank hol. Phone first to camp.
🏠 ❀ ◑ ▮ ⅘ Å ⇌ (Kelvedon) P

## Felsted

### Chequers
Braintree Road (B1417)
☎ (01371) 820226
11–2.30, 6–11; 11–11 Fri, Sat & summer; 12–10.30 Sun
**Ridleys IPA** ⊞
Solid Victorian pub in a quiet village. A sporty atmosphere spills over from the nearby public school. The landlady has presided now for over 40 years. Good value food; weekend barbecues in summer.
Q ⅌ ❀ ◑ ▮ 🍺 ⅘ ♣ P

## Finchingfield

### Red Lion
Church Hill (B1053)
☎ (01371) 810400
12–3, 7 (6 Fri)–11; 12–10.30 Sun (may vary in summer)
**Ridleys IPA, Rumpus** ⊞
Friendly local in one of the most picturesque villages in Essex. Separate restaurant.
🏠 ❀ ◑ ▮ ♣ P

## Fobbing

### White Lion
Lion Hill (B1420, 1 mile S of A13) ☎ (01375) 673281
11–2.30 (4 Sat), 5 (6.30 Sat)–11; 12–3.30, 7–10.30 Sun
**Benskins BB; Ind Coope Burton Ale; Tetley Bitter; guest beers** ⊞
Pleasant coaching inn on the brow of a hill. Interesting collection of beer glasses. Fortnightly guest beer. No meals Sun, or Sat eve.
Q ❀ ◑ ▮ 🍺 P

## Fordstreet

### Coopers Arms
On A604 ☎ (01206) 241177
12–3 (may extend), 7–11; 12–3, 7–10.30 Sun
**Greene King IPA; guest beers** ⊞
Friendly pub in a nice village setting with a good collection of porcelain spirit bottles behind the bar. Fishing club

and a golf society; games night Mon. ❀ ◑ ▮ ♣ P

## Fuller Street

### Square & Compasses
1½m E of A131 OS748161
☎ (01245) 361477
11.30–3.30, 6–11; 11–11 Sat (11.30–11 winter Sat); 12–4, 7–10.30 Sun
**Ridleys IPA** Ⓖ
Cosy, little timber-framed pub in a tiny hamlet: three small rooms, one has an old pitch-penny bench. Good, home-prepared food at all times.
🏠 Q ❀ ◑ ▮ 🍺 Å ♣ P

## Fyfield

### Queen's Head
Queen's Street (just off B184)
☎ (01277) 899231
11–3, 6–11; 11–11 Sat; 12–3, 7–10.30 Sun
**Adnams Bitter; Greene King IPA; Mansfield Bitter; guest beers** ⊞
Genuine free house, the focal point of the village; popular with all ages. Its long bar has spacious alcoves and offers regularly changing guest beers (at least two), from independents. The garden looks onto the River Roding. Essex Huffers are on sale. No food Sat eve.
🏠 ❀ ◑ ▮ ♣ P

## Gestingthorpe

### Pheasant
Audley End
☎ (01787) 461196
12–3, 6–11; 12–3, 7–10.30 Sun
**Adnams Bitter, Broadside; Draught Bass; Greene King IPA** ⊞
Multi-roomed pub traditionally furnished, with a friendly atmosphere. No eve meals Sun. 🏠 ❀ ◑ ▮ ♣ P

## Goldhanger

### Cricketers
33 Church Street (near B1026)
☎ (01621) 788250
11.30–2.45, 7–11; 12–3, 7–10.30 Sun
**Greene King IPA; guest beers** ⊞
Cosy village pub with a sitting room atmosphere. Two beer festivals a year. 🏠 🍺 Å P

## Grays

### Theobald Arms
141 Argent Street,/Kings Walk (near riverside and A126)
☎ (01375) 372253
10.30–3, 5.30–11; 10.30–11 Fri & Sat; 12–10.30 Sun
**Courage Best Bitter; guest beers** ⊞
Traditional family-run, two-bar pub near the Thames. Good value food (no meals

Sat/Sun). Two guest beers: one from Crouch Vale and one from the Scottish Courage portfolio.
❀ ◑ 🍺 ⇌ ♣ P

## Great Sampford

### Red Lion Inn
Finchingfield Road (B1053)
☎ (01799) 586325
11–11; 12–10.30 Sun
**Ridleys IPA, ESX, Rumpus** ⊞
Friendly local with a games room and a no-smoking restaurant.
🏠 ❀ 🏮 ◑ ▮ P

## Great Wakering

### Anchor
High Street
☎ (01702) 219265
11–11; 12–10.30 Sun
**Badger Tanglefoot; Draught Bass; Porters Suffolk Bitter** ⊞
Friendly, family-run pub with three bars. The food is excellent. Note the collection of walking sticks.
🏠 Q ❀ ◑ ▮ ♣ P

## Halstead

### Dog Inn
37 Hedingham Road (A604)
☎ (01787) 477774
12–3, 6–11; 12–3, 7–10.30 Sun
**Adnams Bitter; Nethergate Bitter; guest beer** ⊞
Friendly, 18th-century local, offering reasonably priced, en-suite accommodation close to the town centre. Over 300 different guest ales to date.
🏠 ⅌ ❀ 🏮 ◑ ▮ ♣ P

## Harwich

### Alma
25 King's Head Street (near the quay)
☎ (01255) 503474
11.30–3, 7–11; 12–10.30 Sun
**Flowers Original; Greene King IPA; Tolly Cobbold Mild** ⊞
Pub boasting one large bar and a small 'corridor' bar, classic wood-effect graining, etched glass and a collection of bottled ships. House beer from Tolly Cobbold.
🏠 Q ❀ ◑ ♣

### Hanover Inn
65 Church Street
☎ (01255) 502927
10.30–3, 6–11; 12–3, 7–10.30 Sun (may vary)
**Tolly Cobbold Mild; guest beers** ⊞
Cosy, timbered pub displaying Admiralty charts and Giles cartoons. The back bar is a games room. The house bitter is brewed by Tolly Cobbold.
🏠 🏮 ⇌ ♻ ♣

## Hatfield Broad Oak

### Cock

High Street ☎ (01279) 718273
12–3, 6–11; 12–3, 7–10.30 Sun
**Adnams Bitter; Fuller's London Pride; Greene King IPA; guest beers** H
Unique surviving example of an Essex rural pub boasting uncompromising traditionalism and a friendly atmosphere. Good value, tasty food. 1996 local CAMRA *Pub of the Year*. ♨ Q ⌚ ✿ ◁ ▷ ♣ P

## Hazeleigh

### Royal Oak

Fambridge Road (B1018, 1 mile S of Maldon) ☎ (01621) 853249
11–11 (11–4, 6–11 winter); 12–10.30 (12–4, 7–10.30 winter) Sun
**Greene King IPA** G**; Shepherd Neame Master Brew Bitter** H
Simple Gray's pub with a good reputation.
♨ Q ✿ ◁ ▷ ⊟ Å P

## Helions Bumpstead

### Three Horseshoes

Water Lane OS650414
☎ (01440) 730298
11.45–2.30, 7–11; 12–2.30, 7–10.30 Sun
**Greene King IPA, Abbot, seasonal beers** H
Fine, friendly, remote pub boasting superb award-winning gardens. No food Mon/Tue eves, or Sun.
♨ Q ✿ ◁ ▷ ⊟ Å ♣ P

## Heybridge

### Maltsters Arms

Hall Road (near B1022)
☎ (01621) 853880
11–11; 12–4, 6–10.30 Sun
**Greene King IPA, Abbot** G
Intimate local, enjoying a good lunchtime trade. Q ♣

## High Roding

### Black Lion

The Street ☎ (01371) 872847
11–3, 6–11; 12–3, 7–10.30 Sun
**Ridleys IPA, ESX, seasonal beers** G
15th-century, timber-framed pub with no loud music. Home-grown vegetables feature in the excellent cuisine; small restaurant.
♨ Q ⌚ ✿ ◁ ▷ ⊟ Å ♣ P

## Horndon on the Hill

### Bell

High Road ☎ (01375) 672451
11–2.30 (3 Sat), 6–11; 12–3, 7–10.30 Sun
**Draught Bass** G**; Fuller's London Pride** H**; guest beers** G/H

Popular, 15th-century coaching inn now bypassed by traffic. Quality food in the bar and restaurant. Nice views from the outside patio. Mini-beer festival Aug.
♨ Q ✿ ✿ ◁ ▷ P

## Hutton

### Chequers

213 Rayleigh Road (A129)
☎ (01277) 224980
12 (11 Sat)–11; 12–10.30 Sun
**Draught Bass; Harveys BB; guest beer** H
Small, cosy pub with beams. The guest beer is usually from an independent brewery not available locally (including Crouch Vale). Weekend meals to order.
✿ ◁ ⊟ ♣ P

## Langley Lower Green

### Bull

OS436345 ☎ (01279) 777307
12–2.30, 6–11; 12–3, 7–10.30 Sun
**Greene King IPA, Abbot** H
Classic, rural, Victorian pub in one of the smallest Essex villages. A pitch-penny game is hidden under a bench cushion in the saloon bar. Snacks/sandwiches served on request.
♨ Q ✿ ⊟ ♣ P

## Leigh-on-Sea

### Broker

213–217 Leigh Road
☎ (01702) 471932
11–2.30, 6–11; 12–3, 7–10.30 Sun
**Shepherd Neame Spitfire; Tolly Cobbold Original; guest beers** H
Friendly, family-run local serving good, traditional food in the restaurant and bar (restaurant open Thu–Sat eves and Sun lunch). Children's certificate. ✿ ◁ ⍾

### Crooked Billet

51 High Street, Old Leigh
☎ (01702) 714854
11–11; 12–10.30 Sun
**Adnams Bitter; Ind Coope Burton Ale; Tetley Bitter** H**; guest beers** H/G
Friendly, listed, 16th-century pub with estuary views, formerly used by smugglers, in an old fishing town. This Taylor Walker Heritage pub offers an extensive fish menu and home-made pub fare (no meals Sun). At least three guest beers. ♨ Q ✿ ◁ ⊟ ⇌

### Elms

1060 London Road
☎ (01702) 74687
10–11; 12–10.30 Sun
**Courage Directors; Theakston Best Bitter; Younger Scotch; guest beers** H

Wetherspoon pub with friendly staff and a guest ale all week. The large single bar is popular with young and old alike and is busy at weekends. Occasional beer festivals with low prices. Q ✿ ◁ ▷ & P ⍾

## Little Bentley

### Bricklayers Arms

Rectory Road (just off A120)
☎ (01205) 250405
12–3.30, 6–11; 12–3, 7–10.30 Sun
**Greene King IPA** H**; Mauldons Squires** G
Small, homely, two-room pub, justly proud of its food. A regular rendezvous for country folk. Try the German ice cream.
Q ◁ ▷ P

## Little Braxted

### Green Man

Kelvedon Road (1½ miles SE of village) OS849130
☎ (01621) 891659
11–3, 5–11; 12–3, 7–10.30 Sun
**Ridleys IPA, Witchfinder, Rumpus** H
Traditional pub in an idyllic setting, with a pleasant garden. It can be rather expensive, particularly for half-pints (prices rounded up).
♨ Q ✿ ◁ ▷ ⊟ P

## Littlebury

### Queen's Head

High Street ☎ (01799) 522251
12–11; 12–3, 7–10.30 Sun
**Draught Bass; Courage Directors; John Smith's Bitter; Younger IPA; guest beers** H
600-year-old village local with traditional features and good accommodation. The landlord is an accomplished chef. No food Sun eve. Easter beer festival. ♨ ✿ ✿ ◁ ▷ & ♣ P

## Little Clacton

### Apple Tree

The Street ☎ (01255) 861026
11–11 (midnight Sat); 12–3, 7–10.30 Sun
**Wells Eagle; guest beers** H
Friendly village pub hosting live music Fri/Sat. Three guest beers. Q ✿ ◁ ▷ P

## Little Easton

### Stag

Duck Street (1 mile W of B184)
☎ (01371) 870214
11–2.30 (extends if busy), 6–11; 12–3, 7–10.30 Sun
**Ridleys IPA** H
Friendly, refurbished village local enjoying fine views over the Chelmer Valley from its large garden (excellent children's play area).
♨ ✿ ◁ ▷ ⊟ Å ♣ P

## Little Hallingbury

### Sutton Arms
Bishop's Stortford Road, Hall
Green (off A1060)
☎ (01279) 730460
11–2.30, 6–11; 11–11 Sat; 12–10.30 Sun
**B&T Shefford Bitter; Ind
Coope Burton Ale; Tetley
Bitter; guest beer** H
Two-roomed pub, popular for
its range of food. The smaller
snug bar retains a village local
atmosphere. It can get very
busy at weekends. Book to
camp. ♨ ❀ ◑ ▶ ⊞ ▲ ♣ P

## Little Oakley

### Olde Cherry Tree
Clacton Road (B1414)
☎ (01255) 880333
11–2.30, 5–11; 12–3, 7–10.30 Sun
**Adnams Bitter, Broadside;
Wells Eagle; guest beer** H
Historic pub on a *Domesday
Book* site. Despite its country
location, its popularity has
risen, thanks to the 100%
increase in beer choice and
value for money meals.
♨ Q ❀ ◑ ▶ ♣ P

## Littley Green

### Compasses
Off B1417 opp. Ridleys
Brewery OS699172
☎ (01245) 362308
11.30–3, 6–11; 12–3, 7–10.30 Sun
**Ridleys IPA, Mild, ESX,
Witchfinder, Rumpus, Winter
Ale** G
Victorian, cottage-style pub,
difficult to find. Local CAMRA
*Pub of the Year* 1995 (for the
fifth time). The bar food
speciality is the Essex Huffer (a
very large bap). Good range of
whiskies. A real gem.
♨ Q ☎ ❀ ◑ ▶ ♣ P

## Maldon

### Blue Boar
Silver Street/12 Coach Lane
☎ (01621) 852681
11–2.30 (3 Fri & Sat), 6–11; 12–3,
7–10.30 Sun
**Adnams Bitter; guest beer** G
Friendly, old coaching inn in
the town centre, full of
character, with a wealth of
exposed beams. A classic.
♨ Q ☎ ❀ ⇔ ◑ ▶ ⊞ P

### Queen's Head
Hythe Quay ☎ (01621) 854112
10.30–11; 12–10.30 Sun
**Greene King IPA, Abbot;
Shepherd Neame Master
Brew Bitter** H
Three-bar pub with a strong
nautical atmosphere,
overlooking the busy quayside.
♨ ❀ ◑ ⊞ P

## Manningtree

### Crown Hotel
High Street ☎ (01206) 396333
11–11; 12–10.30 Sun
**Greene King XX Mild, IPA,
Abbot; guest beer**
(occasional) H
Spacious, low-ceilinged pub
and separate restaurant
overlooking the River Stour.
Many genuine nautical
artefacts donated by locals,
adorn the walls. Function/
games room. No eve meals
Mon. ❀ ◑ ▶ ♣ P

## Mashbury

### Fox
Fox Road (2 miles from Gt
Waltham) OS650127
☎ (01245) 231573
12–2 (not Mon or Tue), 6.30–11
(7–10.30 Tue); 12–3, 7–10.30 Sun
**Ridleys IPA, Rumpus** G
Friendly, traditional,
350-year-old country pub
renowned for its home-cooked
food. No meals Tue eve; meals
other eves till 8.45. Book Sun
lunch. Casks are on stillage
behind the bar. Hard to find.
♨ ❀ ◑ ▶ ⊞ ♣ P

## Matching Tye

### Fox Inn
The Green/Newmans End (2
miles E of Churchgate St, Old
Harlow) OS515113
☎ (01279) 731335
12–3, 7–11; 12–10.30 Sun
**Draught Bass; Ridleys
seasonal beers; Shepherd
Neame Spitfire; guest beer** H
Large old pub with three
rooms, one used as a dining
area. Food is served during all
opening hours. Extensive
garden with a petanque piste.
Q ❀ ◑ ▶ ⊞ ⅃ ♣ P

## Mill End Green

### Green Man
1m E of B184 OS619260
☎ (01371) 870286
11.30–3, 6–11; 12–3, 7–10.30 Sun
**Adnams Bitter; Greene King
IPA; Ridleys IPA** H**; guest
beer** G
Friendly, 15th-century, oak-
studded, low-beamed country
pub, featured in TV's *Lovejoy*.
Superb gardens; outdoor area
for families. Good value food
(not served Sun eve).
♨ Q ❀ ⇔ ◑ ▶ ▲ ♣ P

## Mill Green

### Viper
Mill Green Road OS641018
☎ (01277) 352010
11–2.30 (3 Sat), 6–11; 12–3, 7–10.30
Sun
**Beer range varies** H

Quaint country pub in a
woodland setting. The public
bar (tap room) is a rare
survivor of its type. Cider in
summer. ♨ Q ❀ ◑ ⊞ ♣ ⇔ P

## Mountnessing

### Prince of Wales
199 Roman Road (B1002)
☎ (01277) 353445
11–3, 6–11; 12–3, 7–10.30 Sun
**Ridleys IPA, Mild, ESX,
Witchfinder, Rumpus** H,
**Winter Ale** G
Fine, old, beamed pub near the
windmill. Superb Sun lunches.
Local CAMRA *Pub of the Year*
1996. ♨ ❀ ◑ ▶ ♣ P

## Navestock Heath

### Plough
Sabines Road OS538970
☎ (01277) 372296
11–11; 12–10.30 Sun
**Butcombe Bitter; Castle Eden
Ale; Flowers IPA; Fuller's
London Pride; Marston's
Pedigree; Nethergate Bitter;
guest beers** H
Excellent, free house offering
six to eight ales; recently
redecorated. Local CAMRA
*Pub of the Year* 1992–1995. Good
value food and beer. No meals
Sun/Mon eves in winter.
♨ ❀ ◑ ▶ ⅃ ♣ ⇔ P ⊬

## Newport

### Coach & Horses
Cambridge Road (B1383)
☎ (01799) 540292
11–3, 6–11; 12–10.30 Sun
**Flowers Original; Whitbread
Fuggles IPA; guest beers** H
Warm, welcoming,
16th-century coaching inn.
Excellent restaurant and bar
food. ♨ ❀ ◑ ▶ ⇌ P ⊬

## Orsett

### Foxhound
18 High Road (B188, near
hospital) ☎ (01375) 891295
11–3.30, 6–11; 11–11 Sat; 12–3, 7–10.30
Sun
**Courage Best Bitter, Directors;
Crouch Vale IPA; Webster's
Yorkshire Bitter** H
Traditional village local: the
public bar has a rustic feel
while the saloon displays
foxhound memorabilia. The
Fox's Den restaurant has a
good reputation. Ask about the
pub sign! Q ❀ ◑ ▶ ⊞ ♣ P

## Pebmarsh

### King's Head
The Street ☎ (01787) 269306
12–2, 7 (5 Fri)–11; 12–3, 7–10.30 Sun
**Greene King IPA; guest
beers** H

Real ale drinkers' paradise with a 1470, oak-beam interior and a constantly changing line-up of at least four beers. Skittle alley in a barn.
🏾 Q ♒ ❀ ◑ ▶ ♿ ▲ ♣ P

## Pleshey

### White Horse
The Street ☎ (01245) 237281
11–3, 7–11; 12–4, 7–10.30 Sun
**Beer range varies** Ⓗ
Attractive, many-beamed country pub, combining good beer and food in an acceptable manner. A new drinkers' bar is under construction. Families welcome in the restaurant area.
🏾 Q ◑ ▶ ⊟ ♿ ▲ ♁ P

## Prittlewell

### Spread Eagle
267 Victoria Avenue (1 mile N of Southend centre)
☎ (01702) 348383
11.30–3, 5–11; 11.30–11 Thu & Fri; 11–4 (3 match days), 7–11 Sat; 12–4, 7–10.30 Sun
**Fuller's London Pride; Hancock's HB; Wadworth 6X; guest beers** Ⓗ
Traditional, but pricey, ale house, handy for Southend FC (visiting supporters not allowed). No car park in summer. Q ❀ ◑ ▶ ⇌ P

## Purleigh

### Bell
The Street (by the church)
☎ (01621) 828348
11–3, 6–11; 12–3, 7–10.30 Sun
**Adnams Bitter; Benskins BB; Greene King IPA; guest beer** Ⓗ
Spacious traditional country pub with an inglenook, on a 13th-century site. Very friendly; no music. No meals Tue eve. 🏾 Q ❀ ◑ ▶ ♿ ♁ P

## Radley Green

### Cuckoo
500 yds from A414, between Writtle and Norton Heath OS622054 ☎ (01245) 248356
12–2.30, 6–11; 12–4, 7–10.30 Sun
**Ridleys IPA, seasonal beers** Ⓗ
Remote country pub (formerly the Thatcher's Arms), surrounded by farmland; popular with caravanners. Lots of safe outdoor drinking areas for children.
🏾 Q ❀ ◑ ▶ ▲ ♁ P

## Rayleigh

### Spread Eagle
High Street ☎ (01268) 775717
10–11; 12–10.30 Sun
**Adnams Bitter; Crouch Vale IPA; Tetley Bitter; Tolly Cobbold Bitter; guest beers** Ⓗ

Attractive, two-bar, 17th-century, town pub popular with shoppers. Sports-oriented, its three TV screens cover events. Excellent food (Mon–Sat); breakfasts from 8am. ❀ ◑ ♿ ⇌ ⇌

## Rickling Green

### Cricketers Arms
½ mile W of B1383 near Quendon OS511298
☎ (01799) 543210
12–3, 6–11; 12–10.30 (12–3, 7–10.30 winter) Sun
**Flowers IPA; guest beers** Ⓖ
Enlarged old pub in an idyllic setting overlooking the cricket green. Guest beers always include a mild or a dark beer and a strong ale. Excellent, imaginative food.
🏾 Q ♒ ❀ ⊟ ◑ ▶ ⊟ ♁ P

## Rochford

### Golden Lion
35 North Street
☎ (01702) 545487
12–11; 12–10.30 Sun
**Fuller's London Pride; Greene King Abbot; Hancock's HB; guest beers** Ⓗ
Small and basic, no frills drinkers' pub with a changing range of guest beers, often including a mild. The bar has been slightly extended; new toilets and a patio are under construction. Local *Pub of the Year* plaques are on display.
◑ ⇌ ♁ ⇌

## Rowhedge

### Walnut Tree
Fingringhoe Road
☎ (01206) 728149
7.30–11; 12–3, 7–11 Sat; 12–3, 7–10.30 Sun; closed Mon & Wed
**Beer range varies** Ⓗ
Friendly, lively rural pub on the outskirts of Colchester, with a real vinyl jukebox! Cheese club Fri eve from 9pm; good reasonably-priced food always available. ❀ ◑ ▶ ♁ P

## Saffron Walden

### Cross Keys
High Street ☎ (01799) 522207
10.30–11; 12–10.30 Sun
**Benskins BB; Ind Coope Burton Ale; Tetley Bitter** Ⓗ
Dating from 1450, this single-bar (plus pool room and restaurant) pub has a good lunchtime trade and can be busy in the eve and at weekends. The landlord is a *Master Cellarman*.
❀ ⊟ ◑ ▶ ♁ P

### Eight Bells
18 Bridge Street (B184)
☎ (01799) 522790
11–3, 6–11; 12–10.30 Sun

**Adnams Bitter; Friary Meux BB; Ind Coope Burton Ale; Tetley Bitter; guest beers** Ⓗ
16th-century, oak-beamed inn. The single bar has a family room off; the rest of the pub is given over to food (wide range of good, reasonably-priced meals).
♒ ❀ ◑ ▶ ⇌ P

## St Osyth

### White Hart
71 Mill Street (W of village)
☎ (01255) 820318
12–3, 7–11; 12–10.30 Sun
**Adnams Bitter; guest beers** Ⓗ
The second generation now runs this family pub and the selection of beers remains excellent. The 20th-century building adjoins a 16th-century clapboarded room with an inglenook. Fri nights can be funky!
🏾 Q ♒ ❀ ◑ ▶ ▲ ♁ P

## St Osyth Heath

### Beehive
Heath Road, Chisbon Heath
☎ (01255) 830396
11–3, 7–11; 12–4, 7–10.30 Sun
**Adnams Bitter; Tetley Bitter** Ⓗ
Central bar in a spacious modern pub with a period feel. Popular with young farmers.
🏾 ♒ ❀ ◑ ▶ ♿ ♁ P

## Sible Hedingham

### Sugar Loaves
175 Swan Street (A604)
☎ (01787) 462720
12–11; 12–10.30 Sun
**Flowers IPA; Fuller's ESB; Greene King IPA; guest beers** Ⓗ
Restored, 15th-century, oak-beamed inn; a friendly local with two bars. Live music weekly. Thai food is a speciality. Bought by Adnams in summer 1996 and the beer range may change.
🏾 ♒ ❀ ◑ ▶ ⊟ ♿ ♁ P

## South Benfleet

### Half Crown
27 High Street (B1014, 150 yds from station)
☎ (01268) 792027
12–11; 12–10.30 Sun
**Draught Bass; Fuller's London Pride; Hancock's HB; guest beers** Ⓗ
Open-plan tavern with beamed ceilings. Good selection of food (extremely good value); no eve meals Fri–Sun. Good service. Regular beer festivals. No jukebox or pool table but satellite TV is available.
❀ ◑ ▶ ♿ ⇌ (Benfleet) ♁ P

## Southend-on-Sea

### Baker's Bar

15–17 Alexandra Street (off
High St near the Royals
shopping centre)
☎ (01702) 390403
10.30–midnight (2am Fri & Sat);
7–10.30 Sun, closed Sun lunch
**Courage Directors; Shepherd
Neame Master Brew Bitter;
guest beers** [G]
Cellar bar, formerly a Victorian
bakehouse, usually serving six
ales. Popular with the younger
set (prices are high). Meals all
day. ❀ ◖ ▶ ⇌ (Central)

### Cork & Cheese

10 Talza Way, Victoria Circus
(in Victoria Plaza shopping
centre) ☎ (01702) 616914
11–11; closed Sun
**Beer range varies** [H]
1994–1995 local CAMRA *Pub of
the Year*, with over 800 different
ales sold since Feb 1992.
Entrance is via Talza Way only
after 6pm.
❀ ◖ ⇌ (Victoria) ♣ ⌂ P

### Last Post

5 Weston Road/8–10 Clifftown
Road (opp. Central station)
☎ (01702) 431682
10–11; 12–10.30 Sun
**Courage Directors; Greene
King Abbot; Marston's
Pedigree; Theakston Best
Bitter; Younger Scotch; guest
beers** [H]
Vast, welcome Wetherspoon
oasis straddling two streets.
One side is a former post office
(counter signs intact). Popular
with all ages.
Q ❀ ◖ ▶ ॑ ⇌ (Central) ⧖

### Liberty Belle

10–12 Marine Parade
☎ (01702) 466936
10–11; 12–10.30 Sun
**Courage Best Bitter, Directors;
guest beers** [H]
Recently refurbished pub
standing out from the rest of
the seafront hostelries: a
deservedly regular *Guide* entry.
Check the chalkboards for
guest beers and cider. Pool and
darts played.
ॐ ❀ ﹅ ◖ ⇌ (Central) ♣ ⌂

### Sun Rooms

20–21 Market Place (off
Alexandra St)
☎ (01702) 436661
12–midnight (1am Fri & Sat); 1–10.30
Sun
**Beer range varies** [H]
Friendly, relaxed bar-
restaurant with an unusual,
colourful interior. The live
music most eves attracts a
younger clientele. Selection of
draught foreign beers; home-
cooked traditional and foreign
dishes. ❀ ◖ ⇌ (Central) ♣

## South Fambridge

### Anchor Hotel

South Fambridge Road
☎ (01702) 203535
11–3, 6–11; 11–11 Sat; 12–3, 7–10.30
(12–10.30 summer) Sun
**Crouch Vale IPA; Greene
King Abbot; Tetley Imperial;
guest beers** [H]
Riverside free house offering a
good range of beers.
Occasional beer festivals. The
restaurant and garden are
popular at weekends. Upstairs
room for pool and darts. Good
food at reasonable prices.
Q ॐ ❀ ◖ ▶ ॑ ♣ ⌂ P ⧖

## Southminster

### Station Arms

39 Station Road (near B1020/
B1021) ☎ (01621) 772225
12–3, 5.30–11; 12–11 Sat; 12–4, 7–10.30
Sun
**Crouch Vale Best Bitter; guest
beers** [H]
Friendly and informal,
weatherboarded pub, to the
east of the town centre,
offering varied guest beers.
Regular beer festivals – the
main event is in July, during
Flower Show weekend (held
nearby). No eve meals Sun or
Wed. ❀ Q ॐ ❀ ◖ ▶ ⇌ ♣ ⌂

## Stansted Mountfitchet

### Queen's Head

3 Lower Street (B1351)
☎ (01279) 812458
11–3 (4 Sat), 5.30 (7 Sat)–11; 12–2.30,
7–10.30 Sun
**Draught Bass; Flowers IPA;
Morland Old Speckled Hen;
Tolly Cobbold Original** [H]
Bright and friendly village
pub, mostly 17th-century. No
food Sun. ❀ ◖ ⇌ ♣

## Stapleford Tawney

### Moletrap

Tawney Common (single track
road 1 mile W of Toot Hill)
OS501015 ☎ (01992) 522394
12–3, 6 (7 winter)–11; 12–4, 6 (7
winter)–10.30 Sun
**Crouch Vale IPA; McMullen
AK, Country** [H]
Isolated free house, popular
with all ages. It is 400 years old
and was once owned by the
inventor of a moletrap.
Difficult to find.
❀ Q ❀ ◖ ♣ P

## Steeple

### Star

Main Street ☎ (01621) 772646
12–3, 7–11 (11–11 summer); 12–3,
7–10.30 (12–10.30 summer) Sun

**Adnams Bitter; guest beers** [H]
Friendly pub attracting a
sailing crowd in summer and
locals in winter. Families
welcome. ❀ Q ❀ ﹅ ◖ ▶ ▲ P

## Stisted

### Dolphin

Coggeshall Road (A120)
☎ (01376) 321143
11–3, 6–11; 12–3, 7–10.30 Sun
**Ridleys IPA, Mild, ESX** [G]
Two-bar, beamed pub with
welcoming real fires and a
family atmosphere. No eve
meals Tue/Sun.
❀ ❀ ◖ ▶ P

## Stock

### Hoop

High Street ☎ (01277) 841137
11–11; 12–10.30 Sun
**Adnams Mild, Bitter;
Boddingtons Bitter** [H]**;
Wadworth 6X; guest beers** [G]
16th-century pub with a very
popular small bar. A good
range of hot food is always
available, together with at least
six guest ales. The large garden
hosts an annual beer festival
(May). Q ❀ ◖ ▶ ॑ ♣ ⌂

## Stow Maries

### Prince of Wales

Woodham Road OS830993
☎ (01621) 828971
11–11; 12–10.30 Sun
**Fuller's Chiswick; guest
beers** [H]
Beautifully restored rural gem
with a working Victorian
bakery and a changing range of
five or six esoteric ales (always
a mild and a stout or porter):
the flagship of the Big Ears beer
agency. Runner-up for national
CAMRA *Pub of the Year* 1996.
Excellent food. ❀ Q ॐ ❀ ◖ ▶
⊟ ▲ ♣ ⌂ P ⊟

## Thaxted

### Rose & Crown Inn

31 Mill End (near B184)
☎ (01371) 831152
11–3, 5–11 (12–2.30, 6–11 winter);
12–3, 7–10.30 Sun
**Ridleys IPA; guest beer** [H]
Friendly, well-run local in an
historic town with a
magnificent church, Guildhall
and windmill. It is believed to
have been built on the site of a
monks' hostelry. The cosy
dining area offers excellent
food. ❀ ﹅ ◖ ▶ ⊟ ▲ ♣ P

### Star

Mill End (B184)
☎ (01371) 830368
11–11; 12–4, 7–10.30 Sun
**Adnams Mild, Bitter,
Broadside, Old; guest beer** [H]
Popular local with a keen darts

following. Exposed beams and vast brick fireplaces feature in both bars. Safe children's play area. Popular with local morris men. Good value food.
🏕 ❀ ◖❯ 🍴 ♣ P

## Tillingham

### Cap & Feathers
8 South Street (B1021)
☎ (01621) 779212
11.30–3, 6–11; 12–3, 7–10.30 Sun
**Crouch Vale Dark, IPA, Best Bitter; guest beers** Ⓗ
Unspoilt, 15th-century, award-winning pub in a small village, offering home-cooked food, traditional games, and a welcoming atmosphere. No eve meals Wed.
🏕 Q ⛵ ❀ 🍴 ◖❯ ♣ ⌂ P ⚲

## Toot Hill

### Green Man
☎ (01992) 522255
11–3, 6–11; 12–3, 7–10.30 Sun
**Crouch Vale Best Bitter; guest beers** Ⓗ
19th-century inn offering guest beers from independents. Popular, home-cooked food (separate French restaurant). Floral courtyard in summer.
🏕 Q ❀ ◖❯ ♣ P

## Waltham Abbey

### Old Spotted Cow
Fountain Place (near market square) ☎ (01992) 711345
10–11; 12.30–3, 7–10.30 Sun
**McMullen AK, Gladstone** (summer), **Stronghart** Ⓗ
Basic, friendly, backstreet local with a small public bar, close to the historic abbey. No lunches Sun. ❀ ◖ 🍴 ♣ P

## Walton-on-the-Naze

### Royal Marine
5–7 Old Pier Street (near B1034)
☎ (01255) 674000
10–11; 12–10.30 Sun
**Adnams Bitter; Boddingtons Bitter; Marston's Pedigree; guest beer** Ⓗ
Large leaded windows dominate the lounge bar of this mellow and unusual pub which has a beer cellar in the loft! Friendly local clientele. Check meals availability out of season. 🏕 Q ◖❯ 🍴 ⇌ ♣ P

## Warley

### Brave Nelson
138 Woodman Road (off B186)
☎ (01277) 211690
12–3, 5.30–11; 12–11 Sat; 12–10.30 Sun
**Nethergate Bitter; Ruddles Best Bitter; Webster's Yorkshire Bitter; guest beer** Ⓗ

Comfortable, pleasant local displaying wood panelling in both bar areas and many nautical artefacts. A rare, but regular, outlet for Nethergate in this area. ❀ ◖ ♣ P

## Wendens Ambo

### Bell
Royston Road (B1039)
☎ (01799) 540382
11.30–2.30, 6–11 (may vary in summer); 12–3, 7–10.30 Sun
**Adnams Bitter; Ansells Mild; guest beers** Ⓗ
Welcoming, cosy, traditional village pub, a focal point for many village events. Children welcome in the separate dining room and the extensive gardens. No food Mon eve. Petanque played. 🏕 ❀ ◖❯ ⇌ (Audley End) ♣ P

## Westcliff-on-Sea

### Palace Bar
Palace Theatre, London Road (A13) ☎ (01702) 342564
12–2.30, 6–11; 7–10.30 Sun, closed Sun lunch
**Courage Directors; Greene King IPA; guest beers** Ⓗ
Modern foyer bar in a Georgian theatre: a live music venue Sun night. Q ❀ ⛅

## West Thurrock

### Fox & Goose
584 London Road (near A126 and Lakeside shopping centre)
☎ (01708) 866026
11.30–11; 12–5, 7–10.30 Sun
**Greene King IPA; Ridleys Mild; Tetley Bitter; guest beer** Ⓗ
Friendly, family local hosting regular entertainment. The extensive menu includes Balti meals. Fortnightly guest beer. ❀ ◖❯ P

## White Notley

### Cross Keys
The Street ☎ (01376) 583297
11–3, 6.30–11; 12–10.30 Sun
**Ridleys IPA, Mild, Rumpus** Ⓗ
Attractive village local dating back to the 14th century and formerly owned by Chappell's Brewery. It retains its large public bar whilst the saloon is now shared with an eating area. Eve meals Fri/Sat only; no lunches Tue.
🏕 ❀ ◖❯ 🍴 ⇌ ♣ P

## Wickham Bishops

### Mitre
The Street
☎ (01621) 891378
11.30–3.30, 5.30–11; 11.30–11 Sat; 12–10.30 Sun
**Ridleys IPA, Rumpus, seasonal beers** Ⓗ

Lively village local, staging regular social events. Busy restaurant. 🏕 Q ❀ ◖❯ 🍴 P

## Widdington

### Fleur de Lys
High Street ☎ (01799) 540659
12–3, 6–11; 12–3, 7–10.30 Sun
**Adnams Bitter; Draught Bass; Flowers Original; Wadworth IPA, 6X; guest beers** Ⓗ
Friendly, well-run village local offering a good choice of ales and an extensive range of good value food. Live folk music Fri eve. Comfortable family room.
🏕 Q ⛵ ❀ ◖❯ 🍴 ⅙ A ♣ P

## Witham

### George
36 Newland Street (B1389/ B1018 jct) ☎ (01376) 511098
10–11; 12–10.30 Sun
**Ridleys IPA** Ⓗ
Friendly, two-bar pub with a comfortable lounge. Meeting room available. No meals Sun.
Q ◖ 🍴 ⇌ ♣ P

## Wivenhoe

### Horse & Groom
55 The Cross (B1028)
☎ (01206) 824928
10.30–3, 5.30 (6 Sat)–11; 12–3, 7–10.30 Sun
**Adnams Mild, Bitter, Old, seasonal beers; guest beer** Ⓗ
Adnams house just outside a pretty sailing village. Good value, home-cooked food at lunchtime, Mon–Sat.
Q ❀ ◖ 🍴 ⅙ ♣ P

## Wormingford

### Crown Inn
Main Road
☎ (01787) 227405
11.30–3, 6–11; 12–3, 7–10.30 Sun
**Greene King IPA** Ⓗ, **Abbot** Ⓖ
Former coaching inn, 310 years old, opposite an airfield. A comfortable lounge bar, with a separate dining area, contrasts with a basic public bar. Popular with walkers.
Q ❀ ⛺ ◖❯ 🍴 ⅙ A ♣ P 🛏

## Writtle

### Wheatsheaf
The Green ☎ (01245) 420695
11–2.30, 5.30–11; 11–11 Sat; 12–10.30 Sun
**Greene King XX Mild, IPA, Abbot; Shepherd Neame Master Brew Bitter** Ⓗ
Unspoilt village local with a busy public bar and a cosy lounge. It is often full (including the outside front porch drinking area in good weather). Q ❀ 🍴 ♣ P

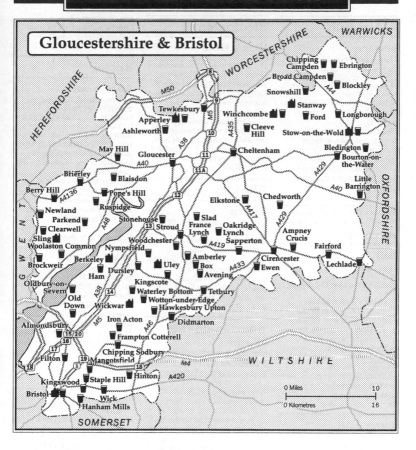

Gloucestershire & Bristol

## Almondsbury

### Bowl Inn
Church Road, Lower
Almondsbury
☎ (01454) 612757
11–3, 5 (6 Sat)–11; 12–3, 7–10.30 Sun
**Courage Best Bitter, Directors;
Wadworth 6X; guest beers** Ⓗ
Pleasant, 17th-century inn,
next to the village church, with
a good reputation for food in
the bar and restaurant.
Accommodation includes a
small cottage.
🏠 ✿ 🛏 🕻 ▶ P

## Amberley

### Black Horse
OS849016 ☎ (01453) 872556
12–3, 6–11; 12–3, 6–10.30 Sun
**Archers Best Bitter; Dartmoor
Best Bitter; Tetley Bitter; guest
beers** Ⓗ
Lively local on the edge of
Minchinhampton Common,
enjoying a valley view from the
conservatory bar extension.
Venue for SW England
Spoofing finals.
🏠 Q ✿ 🕻 ▶ ♣ ✀

## Ampney Crucis

### Butcher's Arms
☎ (01285) 851486
11.30–3, 6–11; 11.30–11 Sat; 12–3,
7–10.30 Sun
**Dartmoor Best Bitter;
Wadworth 6X** Ⓗ **guest
beer** Ⓖ
Popular village local with a
friendly atmosphere. High
standard of food; changing
guest beer.
🏠 Q ✿ 🛏 🕻 ▶ ♣ ⌂ P

## Apperley

### Coal House Inn
Gabb Lane (off B4213)
OS854283 ☎ (01452) 780211
11.30–3, 6–11; 12–3, 7–10.30 Sun
**Wadworth 6X; Wickwar
Coopers' WPA; guest beers** Ⓗ
Originally a coal wharf, now a
welcoming local on the banks
of the River Severn (mooring
available). The approach road
is liable to flooding in winter.
🏠 Q ✿ 🕻 ▶ ⛺ ♣ P

### 🍺 INDEPENDENT BREWERIES

| | |
|---|---|
| **Berkeley:** Berkeley | **Ross:** Bristol |
| **Donnington:** Stow-on-the-Wold | **Smiles:** Bristol |
| **Farmers Arms:** Apperley | **Stanway:** Stanway |
| **Freeminer:** Sling | **Uley:** Uley |
| **Goff's:** Winchcombe | **Wickwar:** Wickwar |
| **Hardington:** Bristol | |

## Ashleworth

### Boat Inn

The Quay (beyond Tithe Barn on road to 'The Quay')
OS819251 ☎ (01452) 700272
11 (12 winter)–2.30, 6 (7 winter)–11;
12–3, 7–10.30 Sun
**Arkell's 3B; Oakhill Yeoman; Smiles Best Bitter; guest beers** G
Delightful old pub beside the Severn: a small miracle of survival. Owned by the same family for over 400 years, its interior has hardly changed in a century. Lunchtime snacks. Quoits played. Moorings available. Q ❀ ♣ ⇔ P

**Try also: Queens Arms** (Free)

## Avening

### Bell

High Street (B4014)
☎ (01453) 836422
12–3, 6–11; 12–11 Sat; 12–3, 7–10.30 Sun
**Marston's Bitter; Taylor Landlord; Wickwar Brand Oak; guest beers** H
Traditional village pub serving an extensive range of guest beers and good food. Unusual pub games; quiz night Thu; live music Sat. The entertainments and guest beers are all advertised in the pub's own newsletter.
🏨 Q ❀ 🍴 ◖ ▶ ♣ P

## Berry Hill

### Kings Head

28 Grove Road (B4228)
☎ (01594) 810550
12–3, 7 (6 summer)–11; 12–3, 7–10.30 Sun
**Greene King Abbot; Marston's Bitter; Wadworth 6X; guest beer** (summer) H
Friendly free house, used by locals and visitors alike. Food available till 10.30 every day.
❀ ◖ ▶ ▲ ♣ P ⅄

## Blaisdon

### Red Hart

2 miles off A48/A40
☎ (01452) 830477
12–3, 7 (6 Fri & Sat)–11; 12–2.30, 7–10.30 Sun
**Hardy Dorchester; Tetley Bitter; Theakston Best Bitter; guest beers** H
Attractive, stone-flagged, one bar pub at the heart of the village, with an adventurous guest beer policy. Children's certificate – well-behaved children welcome. Large outdoor area. Cider in summer. Good, home-cooked food. Twice Gloucestershire CAMRA *Pub of the Year*.
🏨 Q ❀ ◖ ▶ ▲ ♣ ⇔ P

## Bledington

### King's Head

On B4450 ☎ (01608) 658365
11–2.30, 6–11; 12–2.30; 7–10.30 Sun
**Hook Norton Best Bitter; Wadworth 6X; guest beers** H
Delightful, 16th-century, stone-built inn overlooking the village green with a heavy accent on food (booking essential at weekends) and a monthly changing guest beer; cider in summer. Aunt Sally played. Good B&B. 🏨 ❀ 🍴 ◖
▶ ⇌ (Kingham) ♣ ⇔ P

## Blockley

### Crown

High Street ☎ (01386) 700245
11–11; 12–10.30 Sun
**Beer range varies** H
Stylishly refurbished upmarket, Elizabethan inn in a quiet Cotswold village; popular with locals and tourists alike. The four beers are changed regularly.
🏨 Q ❀ 🍴 ◖ ▶ P

## Bourton-on-the-Water

### Parrot & Alligator

Riverside ☎ (01451) 820371
11–11; 12–10.30 Sun
**Beer range varies** H
A year-round beer festival: eight beers in winter and up to 21 in summer. The house beer (Parrot Dropping) comes from Wychwood. The pub's name derives from the landlord's time in the East Indies. Occasional cider (Dunkertons). Children's certificate and adventure playground.
🍴 ❀ 🍴 ◖ ▶ ▲ ⇔ ⅄ 🍴

## Box

### Halfway House

OS857003 ☎ (01453) 832631
11.30–3, 6 (5.30 Fri & Sat)–11; 12–3, 7–10.30 Sun
**Adnams Bitter; Marston's Bitter, Pedigree; Taylor Landlord; guest beers** H
Pleasant, comfortable pub on the edge of a common, offering an enterprising range of guest beers. Restaurant closed Sun eve and Mon.
🍴 ❀ 🍴 ◖ ▶ ▲ ♣ P

## Brierley

### Swan

On A4136 ☎ (01594) 860460
11–3, 7–11; 12–2.30, 7–10.30 Sun
**Boddingtons Bitter; Morland Old Speckled Hen; Tetley Bitter** H
Welcoming Forest pub in the village centre. Its basic interior has a lively public bar. Lunchtime snacks. Children welcome – play area in the garden. 🏨 ❀ 🍴 ♣ ⇔ P 🍴

## Bristol

### Annexe Inn

Seymour Road, Bishopston
☎ (0117) 949 3931
11.30–2.30, 6–11; 11.30–11 Sat; 12–3, 7–10.30 Sun
**Courage Georges BA, Best Bitter; Marston's Pedigree; Smiles Best Bitter; Ushers seasonal beers; Wadworth 6X; guest beer** H
Recently refurbished and improved pub with a no-smoking conservatory/family area opening on to a pleasant, safe garden. Good beer range for the area. Bar skittles played.
Q ♿ ❀ ◖ ▶ ♣ ⅄ 🍴

### Beaufort Arms

23 High Street, Clifton
☎ (0117) 973 5906
12–11; 12–10.30 Sun
**Banks's Mild, Bitter; Camerons Bitter, Strongarm; guest beers** H
Recently refurbished as a Tap House, this friendly backstreet pub has a young clientele and is popular with students. Separate darts area; bar billiards in the bar.
🏨 ◖ ▶ ♣ 🍴

### Bell

16–18 Hillgrove Street, Stokes Croft (off A38, near Jamaica St)
☎ (0117) 924 3373
11.30–2.30, 6–11; 12–3, 7–10.30 Sun
**Butcombe Bitter; Fuller's London Pride; guest beer** H
Attractive, late 18th-century pub with a bay-fronted, tiled exterior and two well-restored, wood-panelled bars. Home-cooked food served till 8.30; pinball and Sky TV.
❀ ◖ ▶

### Bell

21–23 Alfred Place, Kingsdown
☎ (0117) 921 5398
12–3, 5.30–11; 12–11 Sat; 12.30–4, 7–10.30 Sun
**Wickwar Brand Oak, Olde Merryford** H
Cosy, friendly, candlelit local on the edge of Kingsdown Estate. Wickwar Coopers' WPA is sold as Kingsdown Bitter. ❀ ◖

### Bridge Inn

16 Passage Street
☎ (0117) 949 9967
11.30–11; 12–3, 7–10.30 Sun
**Draught Bass; Bath Gem; Courage Best Bitter** H
Tiny, street-corner local close to Countership Bridge. Bright and comfortable, it is arguably Bristol's smallest pub.
◖

## Cadbury House

68 Richmond Road, Montpelier
☎ (0117) 924 7874
12–11; 12–3, 7–10.30 Sun
**Courage Best Bitter; Wickwar Brand Oak** H
Busy, cosmopolitan pub. The large garden at the rear is popular in summer. Old one-armed bandits are a feature. Alternative beers from Wickwar may be stocked.
🚲 ⬤ ◗ ≠ (Montpelier) ♿

## Commercial Rooms

43–45 Corn Street
☎ (0117) 927 9681
11–11; 12–10.30 Sun
**Matthew Brown Bitter; Butcombe Bitter; Courage Directors; Theakston Best Bitter; guest beers** H
Wetherspoons' stunning conversion of a business club from 1810, still popular with business people. Its austere Greek Revival-style architecture resembles the Bank of England. Ornate gas lights and a tall bar counter feature in the palatial 'Grand Room'; galleried eating area. Wheelchair WC.
Q ◗ ◐ ♿ ⬤ ✆

## Hope & Anchor

38 Jacobs Wells Road, Hotwells
☎ (0117) 929 2987
12–11; 12–10.30 Sun
**Beer range varies** H
Popular, friendly, genuine free house with four regularly changing real ales from far and wide. Interesting and sensibly priced food available all day. Children welcome in the secluded, terraced garden.
⬤ ◗ ▶

## Kellaway Arms

140 Kellaway Avenue, Horfield
☎ (0117) 949 7548
11.30–2.30 (3 Fri), 6–11; 11–11 Sat; 12–10.30 Sun
**Courage Georges BA, Best Bitter; Marston's Pedigree; Smiles Best Bitter** H
Comfortable, friendly, two-bar local near Horfield Common: a deceptively large public bar and a smaller lounge. Sizeable garden. Q ⬤ ◗ ◐ ♣

## King's Head ☆

60 Victoria Street
☎ (0117) 927 7860
11–3, 5.30 (7.30 Sat)–11; 11–11 Fri; 12–3, 7.30–10.30 Sun
**Draught Bass; Courage Georges BA, Best Bitter** H
Small, unspoilt Victorian pub, boasting a superb bar back and a tramcar bar. Excellent lunchtime snacks. Within easy walk of Temple Meads station.
Q ≠ (T Meads)

## Lamb

69 West Street, Bedminster
☎ (0117) 966 7759

11–4 (5 Sat), 5.30 (7 Sat)–11; 12–4, 7–10.30 Sun
**Butcombe Bitter** G**; Courage Best Bitter; Ruddles County** H
Friendly local with a strong darts following. Crossword aficionados number among the regulars. Large china plate collection. Tiny car park.
⬤ ♣ P

## Lion Tavern

19 Church Lane, Clifton Wood (up steps from Hotwell Rd, opp. Plume of Feathers)
☎ (0117) 926 8492
12–2.30 (3 Sat), 6–11; 12–3, 6–10.30 Sun
**Butcombe Bitter; Courage Best Bitter, Directors; Marston's Pedigree; Smiles Best Bitter** H
Traditional, two-bar local, off the beaten track, popular with locals and students. Eve meals 6–8 (not Sun). ◗ ▶ ◐ ♣

## Orchard

Hanover Place (off Cumberland Rd)
12–3, 5–11; 12–3, 7–10.30 Sun
**Draught Bass; Courage Best Bitter; Hardington Best Bitter** H
Popular, single-bar pub close to Brunel's *SS Great Britain*. Three ciders. ⬤ ◗ ♿

## Phoenix

15 Wellington Road, St Judes
☎ (0117) 955 8327
11.30–11; 12–3, 7–10.30 Sun
**Draught Bass** G/H**; Oakhill Best Bitter; Otter Bitter** H**; Wadworth 6X** G**; Wickwar Coopers' WPA, Brand Oak** H**; guest beers** G/H
Basic, no-frills, street-corner pub with up to ten real ales on sale. A warm and friendly welcome is guaranteed.
♣

## Post Office Tavern

17 Westbury Hill, Westbury-on-Trym ☎ (0117) 940 1233
11–11; 12–3, 7–10.30 Sun
**Draught Bass** G**; Fuller's London Pride; Otter Bitter; Shepherd Neame Spitfire; Smiles Brewery Bitter** H**; guest beers** G/H
Interesting pub featuring lots of old GPO memorabilia. The good menu includes substantial home-made pizzas (only pizzas available eves).
Q ◗ ▶ ✆

## Prince of Wales

5 Gloucester Road, Bishopston
☎ (0117) 924 5552
11–2.30, 5.30–11; 11–11 Sat; 12–10.30 Sun
**Butcombe Bitter; Courage Georges BA, Directors** H
Busy, two-bar town pub, with a courtyard; popular with locals and students.
⬤ ◗ ≠ (Montpelier) ♣

## Prince of Wales

84 Stoke Lane, Westbury-on-Trym ☎ (0117) 962 3715
11–3, 5.30–11; 11–11 Sat; 12–3.30, 7–10.30 Sun
**Courage Georges BA, Best Bitter; Smiles Best Bitter; Ushers Best Bitter; Young's Special** H
Friendly pub in a residential area, displaying royal memorabilia and sporting items. Popular in summer for its large garden (barbecues and boules). No-smoking area lunchtime. Extensive wine list.
⬤ ◗ ♣ ✆

## Princess of Wales

1 Westbourne Grove, Bedminster ☎ (0117) 949 3008
11–3, 5.30–11; 11–11 Fri & Sat; 12–3, 7–10.30 Sun
**Draught Bass; Courage Best Bitter; Flowers Original; guest beer** H
Tidy, friendly local with a central bar and a nice patio area at the front. The entertainment is oriented towards an older clientele.
⬤ ♣

## Quinton House

2 Park Place, Clifton
11–3, 5.30–11; 11–11 Fri & Sat; 12–3, 7–10.30 Sun
**Courage Best Bitter; Ushers Best Bitter, Founders, seasonal beers** H
Small pub with a single L-shaped bar, behind Queens Road shops. ◗

## Railway Tavern

Station Road, Fishponds
☎ (0117) 965 8774
12–11; 12–3, 5.30–11 Mon; 12–10.30 Sun
**Ind Coope Burton Ale; Smiles Best Bitter; Tetley Bitter; guest beer** H
Large, one-bar, friendly local with a skittle alley. The publican is a *Master Cellarman* for Burton Ale. Families very welcome. Handy for the Bristol–Bath Cycle Track.
⬤ ◗ ♿ ♣

## Robin Hood

56 St Michael's Hill, Kingsdown ☎ (0117) 929 1334
11–11; 11–2.30, 7–11 Mon; 12–2.30, 5–10.30 Sun
**Badger Dorset Best, Tanglefoot; Smiles Best Bitter; Wadworth IPA, 6X; guest beer** H
Sympathetically refurbished, wood-panelled pub, attracting a 25+ age group who crowd the narrow drinking area. Irish folk music Wed. The guest beer changes every two weeks.
⬤ ◗ ▶ ♣

## Seven Ways

23 New Street, St Judes
☎ (0117) 955 6862

11.30–3, 6.30 (7 Sat)–11; 12–3, 7–10.30 Sun

**Courage Best Bitter; Ushers Best Bitter; seasonal beers** H
Friendly, two-bar local in the Old Market drinking area. Busy lunchtimes; quiet eves. Stonehouse cider.
Q ◑ ⊟ ♿ ♣ ⌂

## Victoria

20 Chock Lane, Westbury-on-Trym ☎ (0117) 950 0441
12–3, 5–11; 12–4, 7–10.30 Sun

**Adnams Broadside; Badger Tanglefoot; Draught Bass; Wadworth IPA, 6X** H, **seasonal beers** G/H
Built in the 1700s and once used as a court house, this comfortably furnished pub is out of the way down a quiet lane. Boules played. Pizzas only eves and weekends.
❀ ◑ ▶ ♣

## Broad Campden

### Bakers Arms

Off B4081 ☎ (01386) 840515
11.30–2.30, 6–11; 12–3, 7–10.30 Sun

**Donnington BB; Hook Norton Best Bitter; Stanway Stanney Bitter; Wickwar Brand Oak; guest beers** H
Fine old country pub, boasting exposed Cotswold stone walls and oak beams. Note the framed handwoven rug depicting the inn on the bar wall. ᨺ Q ❀ ◑ ▶ ♣ ⌂ P

## Brockweir

### Brockweir Country Inn

Off A466 over bridge
☎ (01291) 689548
12–2.30 (3 Sat), 6–11; 12–3, 7–10.30 Sun

**Freeminer Bitter; Hook Norton Best Bitter; guest beers** H
Unspoilt village pub on the banks of the River Wye. Beams come from a ship built in Brockweir many years ago. Tintern Abbey and Offa's Dyke are nearby. Good B&B and good value food. ᨺ Q ❄ ❀ ❤ ◑ ⊟ ♠ ♣ ⌂ P

## Chedworth

### Hare & Hounds

Fosse Cross (A429)
☎ (01285) 720288
11–3, 6–11; 12–3, 7–10.30 Sun

**Hook Norton Best Bitter; Shepherd Neame Spitfire; Wadworth 6X; guest beers** (summer) H
Comfortable, 400-year-old, stone-built pub with an L-shaped bar, licensed since at least 1772. Snacks and good value meals (including vegetarian) in the bar and restaurant. Morris dancers in summer. Book the adjacent

caravan site. Children's certificate.
ᨺ Q ❀ ◑ ▶ ♿ ♠ ⌂ P

## Cheltenham

### Adam & Eve

8 Townsend Street
☎ (01242) 690030
10–3, 5–11; 11–11 Sat; 12–3, 7–10.30 Sun

**Arkell's Bitter, 3B, seasonal beers** H
Small, friendly terrace-fronted, two-bar local. Lunchtime snacks (not served Sun).
Q ❀ ⊟ ❤ ♣

### Bayshill Inn

85 St Georges Place
☎ (01242) 524388
11–3, 5–11; 11–11 Sat; 12–3, 7–10.30 Sun

**Badger Tanglefoot; Wadworth IPA, 6X** H, **Old Timer** G; **guest beer** H
Very popular, town-centre pub without frills, serving good value lunches (Mon–Sat). Near the bus station. The guest beer changes fortnightly.
❀ ◑ ⌂

### Beaufort Arms

184 London Road (A40)
☎ (01242) 526038
11–2.30, 6 (7 Sat)–11; 12–3, 7–10.30 Sun

**Badger Tanglefoot; Wadworth IPA, 6X, Farmers Glory, Old Timer; guest beer** H
Excellent local on the main road. The decor features pictures of horses at Cheltenham Races. Try the curries or chef's daily special. Limited parking.
Q ❄ ❀ ◑ ⊟ ♿ ♣ ⌂ P

### Hewlett Arms

Harp Hill ☎ (01242) 228600
11–2.30 (3 Thu & Fri, 5 Sat), 6–11; 12–5, 7–10.30 Sun

**Boddingtons Bitter; Goff's Jouster; Wadworth 6X; guest beers** H
Pub at the foot of Harp Hill, popular with local office-workers. Varied, home-cooked meals. Large garden.
ᨺ ❀ ◑ ⊟ ♣ P

### Kemble Brewery Inn

27 Fairview Street
☎ (01242) 243446
11.30–3, 5.30–11; 11–11 Sat; 12–4, 7–10.30 Sun

**Archers Village, Best Bitter, Golden; guest beer** H
Popular, backstreet local which can get crowded. Good value food. ❀ ◑ ▶ ♣

### Suffolk Arms

Suffolk Road ☎ (01242) 524713
11–11; 12–10.30 Sun

**Draught Bass; Boddingtons Bitter; Brakspear Bitter; Flowers Original; Whitbread WCPA; Wickwar Brand Oak** H

Traditional local with a skittle alley-cum-function room. Good food available seven days a week. ◑ ▶ ♣ ⌂

### Tailor's

Cambray Place
☎ (01242) 255453
11–3, 5–11; 11–11 Sat; 12–2, 7.30–10.30 Sun

**Badger Tanglefoot; Smiles Best Bitter; Wadworth IPA, 6X, Farmers Glory, Old Timer; guest beer** H
Creeper-clad pub on two levels: entrance steps lead to a large horseshoe-shaped bar with armchairs and settees. The basement bar, open Thu–Sat, is popular with students.
❀ ◑

## Chipping Campden

### Volunteer

Lower High Street
☎ (01386) 840688
11–3, 6.30–11; 12–3, 7–10.30 Sun

**Draught Bass; Stanway Stanney Bitter; Theakston XB; guest beers** H
Stone-built pub, slightly away from the village centre. The name dates from the 1840s, but the pub from 1709. Special food nights monthly. Four guest beers. ᨺ Q ❀ ❤ ◑ ▶ ♣ ⌂

## Chipping Sodbury

### Beaufort Hunt

72 Broad Street
☎ (01454) 312871
10.30–3, 5–11; 12–3, 7–10.30 Sun

**Draught Bass; Tetley Bitter; guest beers** H
Homely, two-bar high street local in a pleasant market town. Ornately decorated, it has an attractive outdoor drinking area. The guest beer changes weekly; a house beer, Dave's Tipple, is also available. Good food. ◑ ♣

## Cirencester

### Corinium Court Hotel

12 Gloucester Street
☎ (01285) 659711
11–3, 6–11; 12–2.30, 7–10.30 Sun

**Hook Norton Best Bitter** H, **Old Hooky, seasonal beers** G; **Wadworth 6X** H
Upmarket hotel in a 16th-century building with a charming courtyard entrance and a superb, small, flagstoned bar opening on to a smart, comfortable lounge. Attractive walled garden. Separate restaurant.
ᨺ Q ❀ ❤ ◑ ♿ ♠ A P

### Golden Cross

20 Blackjack Street
☎ (01285) 652137
11–3, 6–11; 11–11 Sat; 12–10.30 Sun

**Arkell's Bitter, 3B, seasonal beers** H
Gimmick-free pub relying on friendly and efficient service and good company to appeal to all ages. Full-sized snooker table. Families welcome in the skittle alley when it is not in use. ▲ ❀ 🛏 ◖▶ ▲ ♣

### Oddfellows' Arms

10–14 Chester Street
☎ (01285) 641540
11–3, 5.30–11; 12–5, 7–10.30 Sun
**Ruddles County; Wadworth 6X; guest beers** H
Many make the effort to find this sensitively refurbished, backstreet pub which serves a good range of home-cooked food (not Sun eve) and two frequently changing guest beers. Large garden at the rear; good family room. Live Irish music most Fri.
▲ ☞ ❀ ◖▶ ▲

Try also: Waggon & Horses, London Rd (Free)

## Clearwell

### Lamb

The Cross, High Street
(Redbrook road out of centre)
☎ (01594) 835441
12–3 (not Mon–Thu), 6–11; 12–3, 7–10.30 Sun
**Freeminer Bitter** G; **guest beers** H
Pub with a small, cosy bar and a larger lounge, hosted by a friendly landlord. Always at least one guest beer. Eve meals until closing time.
▲ Q ◖▶ 🛏 ❀ ▲ ⌂ P

## Cleeve Hill

### High Roost

On B4632 ☎ (01242) 672010
11.30–2.30 (3 Sat), 7–11; 12–3.30, 7–10.30 Sun
**Hook Norton Best Bitter, Old Hooky; Theakston XB** H
Pub set on the highest hill in the county, with expansive views through large bay windows across the Vale of Severn. Children allowed in for meals until 8 (no food Tue eve). Jukebox. Note: the pub is reached by a flight of steps.
❀ 🛏 ◖▶ ♣ P

## Didmarton

### King's Arms

The Street
☎ (01454) 238245
11.30–3, 6–11; 12–3, 7–10.30 Sun
**Marston's Pedigree; Smiles Best Bitter; John Smith's Bitter; Uley Bitter** H
17th-century, former coaching inn, undergoing renovation. It was leased in 1745, for 1000

years, from Beaufort Estate at six pence per year! Boules pitch. Restaurant closed Sun eve and Mon (bar meals available).
▲ Q ❀ 🛏 ◖▶ ▣ ▲ ♣ P

## Dursley

### Old Spot Inn

Hill Road
☎ (01453) 542870
11–11; 12–3, 7–10.30 Sun
**Draught Bass; Uley Old Ric, Old Spot; Worthington Bitter; guest beers** H
18th-century farm cottage that became a school and then a pub late last century. Now lovingly refurbished, it is a superb watering hole for Cotswold Way walkers. Substantial snacks available most times, except Fri/Sat eve. Occasional folk and blues. Public car park opposite.
▲ Q ❀ ⚒ ♣ ✄

## Ebrington

### Ebrington Arms

☎ (01386) 593223
11–2.30, 6–11; 12–3, 7–10.30 Sun
**Donnington SBA; Hook Norton Best Bitter; guest beers** H
Stone-built village pub with a lovely old entrance door and a superb inglenook in the dining room. No food Sun eve.
▲ Q ☞ ❀ 🛏 ◖▶ ♣ ⌂ P

## Elkstone

### Highwayman Inn

Beech Pike (A417)
☎ (01285) 821221
11–2.30, 6–11; 12–3, 7–10.30 Sun
**Arkell's Bitter, 3B, Kingsdown** H
Old coaching inn, complete with a stage coach in the car park. Welcoming log fires at each end of the main bar. Good selection of food.
▲ Q ❀ ◖▶ P

## Ewen

### Wild Duck Inn

Drakes IslandOS007977
☎ (01285) 770310
11–11; 12–10.30 Sun
**Smiles Best Bitter; Theakston Best Bitter, XB, Old Peculier; Wadworth 6X** H
Three-star country hotel with a beautiful exterior and gardens. Built in 1563, the pub retains a slightly rustic feel with panelling, settles, old paintings and an imposing Elizabethan fireplace. Excellent menu, specialising in fish. Wild Duck house beer.
▲ ❀ 🛏 ◖▶ 🚆 (Kemble)
♣ P

## Fairford

### Plough

London Street
☎ (01285) 712409
11–3, 6.30–11; 11–11 Fri & Sat; 12–10.30 Sun
**Arkell's Bitter, 3B, seasonal beers** H
Pleasant town pub to suit all tastes, with two contrasting bars – a charming, small lounge and a lively public bar with a pool table. Skittle alley. No lunches Tue.
▲ Q 🛏 ◖▶ ▣ ▲ ♣ P

## Filton

### Filton Recreation Centre

Elm Park ☎ (0117) 979 1988
12–2 (2.30 Thu & Fri), 6.30–11; 12–2, 4–11.30 Sat; 12–3, 7–10.30 Sun
**Butcombe Bitter; Ind Coope Burton Ale; Smiles Best Bitter; Tetley Bitter; guest beer (occasional)** H
Comfortable, well-laid-out single bar, part of the recreation centre complex but open to the public. The landlord is a Burton Ale *Master Cellarman.* Q & P

## Ford

### Plough Inn

On B4077 ☎ (01386) 584215
11–11; 12–10.30 Sun
**Donnington BB, SBA** H
Splendid, unspoilt, country pub where the cellar used to be a jail. Note the rhyme on the front wall. A racing theme is in evidence. Wooden fort in the children's area. No food Sun eve. ▲ ❀ 🛏 ◖▶ ▣ ♣ ⌂ P

## Frampton Cotterell

### Rising Sun

43 Ryecroft Road
☎ (01454) 772330
11.30–2.30, 7–11; 12–3, 7–10.30 Sun
**Draught Bass; Butcombe Bitter; Smiles Best Bitter; Wadworth 6X; Wickwar Coopers' WPA; guest beer** H
Popular, nicely decorated, single-bar pub; a genuine free house with good support for local brews. Avon CAMRA *Pub of the Year* 1995.
Q ❀ ◖▶ & ♣ P

## France Lynch

### King's Head

☎ (01453) 882225
11–3, 5.30–11; 11–11 Sat; 12–4, 7–10.30 Sun
**Archers Best Bitter; Tetley Bitter; Wye Valley Bitter** H
Single-bar village free house. The village name reflects its Huguenot connections.
Q ❀ ◖▶ ▲ ♣ P

## Gloucester

### Linden Tree
73–75 Bristol Road (A430,
¾ mile S of centre)
☎ (01452) 527869
11–2.30, 5–11; 11–11 Fri & Sat;
12–10.30 Sun
**Badger Tanglefoot; Hook
Norton Best Bitter; Wadworth
IPA, 6X, seasonal beers; guest
beers** H
Country-style pub in a Grade II
listed building. Good,
inexpensive food (not served
Sun eve) and excellent
accommodation. Occasional
beer festivals. Tiny car park.
🏚 🏠 ◖ ♣ P

### Whitesmith's Arms
81 Southgate Street
☎ (01452) 414770
11–11; 12–10.30 Sun
**Arkell's Bitter, 3B,
Kingsdown, seasonal beers** H
Named after maritime metal-
workers, this pub stands
opposite the historic city docks
and was recently extended into
the medieval, timber-framed
building next door. Large
garden. 🏚 ❀ ◖ ♦ ♣

## Ham

### Salutation
OS680983 ☎ (01453) 810284
11 (10 Sat)–2.30, 6–11; 12–3, 7–10.30
Sun
**Draught Bass; Berkeley Old
Friend** H
Much improved country pub
with a recently added skittle
alley. Large attractive garden;
separate children's play area.
Close to Berkeley Castle.
Q ❀ ◖ ♦ ♣ ⟲ P

## Hanham Mills

### Old Lock & Weir
From Hanham go to foot of
Abbots Road, turn right
☎ (0117) 967 3793
11–11; 12–4, 7–10.30 Sun
**Draught Bass; Exmoor Gold;
Marston's Pedigree; Morland
Old Speckled Hen** H
300-year-old, welcoming,
single-bar, multi-roomed
riverside pub, mentioned in
Conan Doyle's *Micah Clark*.
Much stone and wood are in
evidence. Friendly staff;
families welcome. Collection of
malt whiskies. Excellent Sun
lunch. Good games selection.
❀ ◖ ♦ ♣ P

## Hawkesbury Upton

### Beaufort Arms
High Street (500 yds from A46)
☎ (01454) 238217
12–3, 5.30–11; 12–11 Sat; 12–10.30 Sun

**Wadworth 6X; Wickwar Brand
Oak; guest beers** H
18th-century free house with
Victorian modifications and a
stable converted to a dining
area (good quality food). A
friendly two-bar local, close to
the Cotswold Way. Well-
behaved families, walkers and
cyclists welcome. Cider in
summer.
🏚 Q ❀ ◖ ♦ 🏠 ♣ ⟲ P

## Hinton

### Bull
1½ miles SW of M4 jct 18
OS735768 ☎ (0117) 937 2332
11–3 (not Mon), 7–11; 12–3, 7–10.30
Sun
**Draught Bass; Wadworth IPA,
6X** H**, Old Timer** G**, seasonal
beers** H
Mature, unspoilt country local
with a large garden for
children and an attractive bar
and lounge. Full meals are
served in the restaurant.
🏚 Q ⟲ ❀ ◖ ♦ ♣ P ✂

## Iron Acton

### Rose & Crown
High Street ☎ (01454) 228423
5–11; 12–2.30, 6–11 Sat; 12–3, 7–10.30
Sun
**Draught Bass; Marston's
Pedigree; Uley Pig's Ear;
Whitbread WCPA; guest
beer** H
Friendly, traditional,
17th-century village pub with
two bars. Good B&B. Closed
weekday lunchtimes.
🏚 ❀ 🏠 ♣

## Kingscote

### Hunters Hall
On A4135 ☎ (01453) 860393
11–11; 12–10.30 Sun
**Draught Bass; Hook Norton
Best Bitter; Marston's
Pedigree; Uley Old Spot** H
16th-century coaching inn:
several small, separate bars
with stone-flagged floors, oak
settles and open fireplaces;
welcoming for families. The
no-smoking area is on the first
floor. 🏚 ❀ 🏠 ◖ ♦ 🍴 ♣ P ✂

## Kingswood

### Prince Albert
130 Two Mile Hill Road
☎ (0117) 961 0239
12–2, 5–11; 12–11 Fri & Sat; 12–3,
7–10.30 Sun
**Hardington Bitter, Best Bitter,
Moonshine, Jubilee; guest
beer** H
Wood-panelled, four-roomed
local hosting live music Tue
and Sat eves, and karaoke Thu
eve. Separate games room.
Quiet at lunchtime; lively
weekend eves. Watch your bad

language or you'll get the stick!
Sky TV. Q 🏠 ♣

## Lechlade

### Trout Inn
St John's Bridge (A417)
☎ (01307) 252313
11–3, 6–11; 12–3, 7–10.30 Sun
**Courage Best Bitter, Directors;
guest beer** H
Attractive, 13th-century inn on
the Thames, originally the
almshouse of a priory, with a
flagstoned floor and low
ceiling. Comfortable family
room off the lounge. Very
original menu. Jazz nights in
the public bar.
🏚 Q ⟲ ❀ ◖ ♦ 🏠 ♿ ♣ P

## Little Barrington

### Inn for all Seasons
OS205121 ☎ (01451) 844324
11–2.30, 6–11; 12–2.30, 7–10.30 Sun
**Draught Bass; Wadworth
6X** H**; guest beers** G
14th-century former coaching
inn, now an hotel with a
comfortable lounge. The
emphasis is on food. Sixty
different whiskies. The guest
beers are from the Wychwood
range. 🏚 ❀ 🏠 ◖ ♦ P

## Longborough

### Coach & Horses
Off A424 ☎ (01451) 830325
11–2.30, 7–11; 12–3, 7–10.30 Sun
**Donnington XXX, BB, SBA** H
Friendly, one-bar pub in a
quiet village with morris
dancing connections. Food
summer lunchtimes only.
Parking can be difficult.
🏚 Q ❀ ◖ ♣

## Mangotsfield

### Folly Inn
Folly Bridge, Westerleigh Road
(off A4174) ☎ (0117) 956 1590
11–3, 6–11; 12–4, 7–10.30 Sun
**Draught Bass; Butcombe
Bitter** G**; Courage Georges
BA, Best Bitter** H**; Smiles Best
Bitter; Wadworth 6X** G
Enormous isolated pub with a
well furnished lounge and a
separate public bar. Restaurant
closed Sun eve (bar meals
served).
🏚 Q ❀ ◖ ♦ ♣ P ✂

## May Hill

### Glasshouse Inn
N of A40, W of Huntley
OS710213 ☎ (01452) 830529
11.30–2.30, 6–11; 12–2.30, 7–10.30 Sun
**Butcombe Bitter; Whitbread
WCPA; guest beers** G
Unspoilt, family-run country
pub with an original quarry-
tiled floor. The outdoor
drinking area has an old cider

press and a bench canopied by a yew bridge. No children allowed inside the pub. Quoits played.

🏚 Q 🏵 ♠ ✿ 🖰 P

## Newland

### Ostrich

On B4231
☎ (01594) 833260
12–2.30 (3 Sat), 6.30–11; 12–3, 6.30–10.30 Sun
**Beer range varies** Ⓗ
Charming and unspoilt, traditional English pub. Eight real ales are usually available. Interesting menu of good food.

🏚 Q 🏵 ◑ ▶ ♠ ✿

## Nympsfield

### Rose & Crown

The Cross
☎ (01453) 860240
11.45–2.45, 5.30–11; 11.45–11 Sat; 12–10.30 Sun
**Draught Bass; Boddingtons Bitter; Uley Old Spot; Wadworth 6X; Wickwar Brand Oak; guest beers** Ⓗ
300-year-old, stone-built pub in the village centre. An open fire and a stove at either end of the main bar ensure a cosy atmosphere. The bar and attached restaurant serve good value food. Floral display in summer.

🏚 Q 🏵 🚐 ◑ ▶ ♠ ✿ P

## Oakridge Lynch

### Butcher's Arms

N edge of village
☎ (01285) 760371
11–3, 6–11; 12–3, 7–10.30 Sun
**Archers Best Bitter; Draught Bass; Goff's Jouster; Hook Norton Old Hooky; Tetley Bitter; Theakston Best Bitter** Ⓗ
18th-century former butcher's shop, now a popular village free house. Food is available in all three bars and the restaurant (eve meals Wed–Sat).

🏚 Q 🐌 🏵 ◑ ▶ ♠ ✿ P

## Oldbury-on-Severn

### Anchor Inn

Church Road
☎ (01454) 413331
11.30–2.30 (3 Sat), 6.30 (6 Sat)–11; 12–3, 7–10.30 Sun
**Draught Bass** Ⓖ; **Black Sheep Best Bitter; Butcombe Bitter; Theakston Best Bitter** Ⓗ, **Old Peculier** Ⓖ; **Worthington Bitter** Ⓗ
Very popular, friendly village local: a converted mill with a well-used garden in summer. Excellent, good value, home-cooked food in both the bar and dining room. Boules pitch.

🏚 Q 🏵 ◑ ▶ 🍴 ♠ P

## Old Down

### Fox Inn

Inner Down ☎ (01454) 412507
12–3, 6–11; 12–3, 6–10.30 (12–10.30 summer) Sun
**Draught Bass; Flowers IPA, Original** Ⓗ
Picturesque old village pub, built from local stone; cosy yet spacious. A vined terrace, with colourful hanging baskets, and a children's play area are in the garden. Bar snacks. Boules played. Taunton Traditional cider on gravity dispense.

🏚 Q 🏵 ✿ P

## Parkend

### Fountain

Off B4234 ☎ (01594) 562189
12–3, 6–11; 12–midnight Sat; 12–3, 7–10.30 Sun
**Draught Bass; Freeminer Bitter; guest beers** Ⓗ
One-bar pub at the heart of the Forest of Dean, near Forest of Dean Railway. Old tools and implements hang from the beams. Good food includes take-away curries. Self-catering lodge available for groups (book).

🏚 🏵 🚐 ◑ ▶ 🍴 ♠ P

## Pope's Hill

### Greyhound

On A4151, Elton–Littledean road ☎ (01452) 760344
12 (11 Sat)–3, 5.30–11; 12–3, 7–10.30 Sun
**Beer range varies** Ⓗ
Welcoming pub with a good local trade. Note the montages made out of clock/watch parts: some are for sale. Good value, basic pub food. No children in the bar (use the family room).

🏚 🐌 🏵 ◑ ▶ 🍴 ♠ ✿ P

## Ruspidge

### New Inn

Ruspidge Road (B4227)
☎ (01594) 824508
7 (11 Sat)–11; 12–4, 7–10.30 Sun
**Wye Valley Bitter; guest beers** Ⓗ
Comfortable village pub open in the eve only during the week. The separate games room has a good selection, including table skittles.

🏚 🏵 🍴 ♠ P

## Sapperton

### Daneway Inn

Daneway OS939034
☎ (01285) 760297
11–2.30 (3 Sat), 6.30–11; 12–3, 7–10.30 Sun
**Archers Best Bitter** Ⓔ/Ⓗ; **Draught Bass** Ⓗ; **Wadworth 6X** Ⓖ
Superb old inn set in an idyllic

position near the western end of the now disused Sapperton canal tunnel. Note the magnificent Dutch-carved fireplace in the lounge. Large garden. Occasional cider. The house beer is brewed by Archers.

🏚 Q 🐌 🏵 ◑ ▶ 🍴 ♠ ✿ P ⌿

## Slad

### Woolpack

On B4070 ☎ (01452) 813429
11 (12 winter)–3, 6–11; 12–3, 6 (7 winter)–10.30 Sun
**Draught Bass; Boddingtons Bitter; Uley Old Spot, Pig's Ear; Wadworth 6X** Ⓗ
Authentic, 16th-century pub, clinging to the side of the Slad Valley, offering splendid views. It was made famous by author Laurie Lee, who still occasionally visits. Quoits played.

🏚 Q 🐌 🏵 ◑ ▶ 🍴 ♠ ✿ ⌿

## Snowshill

### Snowshill Arms

☎ (01386) 852653
11 (11.30 winter)–2.30, 6 (6.30 winter)–11; 12–2.30, 7–10.30 Sun
**Donnington BB, SBA** Ⓗ
Typical Cotswold country pub, catering for both locals and tourists. The adjacent manor house (NT) should not be missed. The pub garden has a play area.

🏚 Q 🏵 ◑ ▶ 🍴 ♠ ✿ P

## Staple Hill

### Humpers Off-Licence

26 Soundwell Road
☎ (0117) 956 5525
12–2, 4.30–10.30; 12–10.30 Sat & Sun
**Draught Bass; Smiles Best Bitter; Wickwar Brand Oak, Olde Merryford** Ⓗ; **guest beers** Ⓖ
Excellent, street-corner off-licence, offering the widest beer range and lowest prices for miles (up to three guest beers available, often strong brews). Popular local Richards cider is also sold. Generous range of polypins at Christmas.

✿

## Stonehouse

### Spa Inn

Oldends Lane
☎ (01453) 822327
11–3, 6.30 (7 winter)–11; 12–3, 7–10.30 Sun
**Wadworth IPA, 6X; guest beers** Ⓗ
Cosy, welcoming Wadworth pub adjoining a factory estate. Popular at lunchtime. Skittles and quoits played in the garden. Excellent blackboard food menu.

🏵 ◑ ▶ 🍴 🏚 ⥥ ♠ ✿ P

## Stow-on-the-Wold

### Talbot
The Square ☎ (01451) 830631
11–3, 7–11; 11–11 Sat; 12–3, 7–10.30
Sun
**Wadworth IPA, 6X** Ⓗ
Refurbished, large open bar
with a separate games room.
Popular with younger
clientele.
🏰 🝙 ♣

## Stroud

### Duke of York
22 Nelson Street
☎ (01453) 758715
12–3, 7–11; 11.30–3, 6–11 Fri; 11.30–11
Sat; 12–10.30 Sun
**Draught Bass; Butcombe
Bitter; Wells Eagle; guest
beers** Ⓗ
Comfortable town pub, next to
a public car park. No food Sun.
🝙 ⇌

## Tetbury

### Crown Inn
Gumstool Hill
☎ (01666) 502469
11–3, 5.30–11; 11–11 Sat; 12–10.30 Sun
**Boddingtons Bitter; Flowers
IPA, Original; guest beers** Ⓗ
Resplendent Cotswold stone
pub at the top of Gumstool
Hill: a comfortable lounge bar
with a conservatory at the rear.
Information about guest beers
is displayed in the bar. Public
car park adjacent.
🏰 Q 🝙 🛏 🝙 ▶ 🝙

**Try also: Royal Oak,**
Cirencester Rd (Free)

## Tewkesbury

### Old Black Bear
High Street (near river bridge)
☎ (01684) 292202
11–11; 12–3, 7–10.30 Sun
**Greenalls Bitter, Original;
Wadworth 6X; Worthington
Bitter** Ⓗ**; guest beers** Ⓖ
The oldest inn in the county,
with rambling bar areas and a
pleasant terrace overlooking
the River Avon (mooring
available). Table skittles.
🝙 🝙 ▶ ▲ ♣ 🝙

### White Bear
Bredon Road ☎ (01684) 296614
11–3, 6–11; 11–11 Fri & Sat; 12–10.30
Sun
**Wye Valley Bitter, HPA; guest
beers** Ⓗ
One-bar, basic pub, off the end
of the high street. Thatcher's
cider. Skittle alley.
🝙 ▲ 🝙 🝙 P

**Try also: Albion,** Oldbury Rd
(Ansells)

## Waterley Bottom

### New Inn
Follow signs from N Nibley
OS758964 ☎ (01453) 543659
12–2.30, 7–11; 12–2.30, 7–10.30 Sun
**Cotleigh Tawny; Greene King
Abbot; Smiles Best Bitter** Ⓗ**;
Theakston Old Peculier** Ⓖ**;
guest beers** Ⓗ
Large, friendly free house in a
beautiful setting, surrounded
by steep hills, a couple of miles
from two golf courses. The
house beer (WB) is produced
by Cotleigh. Good B&B and
home-cooked food.
🏰 Q 🝙 🛏 🝙 ▶ 🝙 🝙 🝙 P

## Wick

### Rose & Crown
High Street ☎ (0117) 937 2198
11.30–2.30, 5.30 (6 Sat)–11 (11–11
Tue–Sat in summer); 12–10.30 Sun
**Courage Best Bitter, Directors;
John Smith's Bitter;
Wadworth 6X** Ⓗ
Comfortable and spacious old
inn dating from 1640; the birth
place of John Gully, champion
prizefighter. The restaurant has
a no-smoking area. Boules
played. 🏰 Q 🝙 🝙 ▶ ♣ P

## Winchcombe

### Bell Inn
Gretton Road
☎ (01242) 602205
11–3, 6 (7 winter)–11; 12–3, 7–10.30
Sun
**Draught Bass; Brains Dark;
Donnington BB, SBA;
Shepherd Neame Spitfire;
Wickwar Coopers' WPA** Ⓗ
Comfortable and welcoming
local. 🏰 🝙 🛏 ♣ 🝙 P

### Plaisterers Arms
Abbey Terrace (B4632)
☎ (01242) 602358
11–3, 6–11; 11–11 Sat; 12–10.30 Sun
**Goff's Jouster, White Knight;
Tetley Bitter; Wadworth 6X** Ⓗ
Two-bar, multi-level pub in the
centre of an ancient Saxon
town. Large garden. Good
choice of home-cooked food.
🏰 🝙 🛏 🝙 ▶ ♣

## Woodchester

### Ram
Station Road (off A46)
☎ (01453) 873329
11.30–3, 5.30–11; 11.30–11 Sat;
12–10.30 Sun
**Boddingtons Bitter; John
Smith's Bitter; Uley Old Spot;
guest beers** Ⓗ
Comfortable, stone-built, oak-
beamed free house with an
L-shaped bar looking across
Nailsworth Valley. Blackboard
menu. 🏰 🝙 🝙 ▶ ♣ P

## Woolaston
## Common

### Rising Sun
The Common (1 mile off A48)
OS590009 ☎ (01594) 529282
12–2.30 (not Wed), 6.30–11; 12–3,
7–10.30 Sun
**Fuller's London Pride; Hook
Norton Best Bitter; Theakston
Best Bitter; guest beers**
(summer) Ⓗ
Lovely country pub with
excellent views. Authentic
Indian curries to eat in or take
away. Swings in the garden;
children allowed in lunchtime.
🏰 Q 🝙 🝙 🝙 ▲ ♣ P

## Wotton-under-
## Edge

### Star
21 Market Street
☎ (01453) 844651
12–3, 5.30–11; 12–11 Fri & Sat; 12–3,
7–10.30 Sun
**Draught Bass; Wickwar
Coopers' WPA; guest beers** Ⓗ
Town local with two bars and a
games room. Simple meals at
lunchtime. Occasional cider.
Public car park nearby.
Q 🝙 🝙 🝙 ♣ 🝙

---

# WHO'S WHO?

Remember to check the breweries section and the beers index at
the back of this book to discover who brews the beers listed in the
pub entries. Boddingtons and Flowers may sound like independent
breweries but, in fact, are only brands owned by Whitbread. Just as
Ansells is owned by Carlsberg-Tetley and Theakston by Scottish
Courage.

*Just champion! Chris Norman, proprietor of Somerset's
Cottage Brewery, delivers a cask of Norman's Conquest,
CAMRA's* **Champion Beer of Britain 1995,** *to exclusive grocer
Fortnum & Mason's (photograph: Mike Benner)*

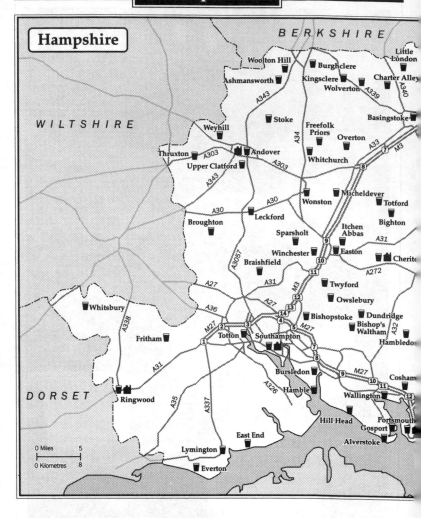

## Hampshire

*(map of Hampshire showing towns including Woolton Hill, Burghclere, Ashmansworth, Kingsclere, Wolverton, Charter Alley, Little London, Basingstoke, Stoke, Weyhill, Freefolk Priors, Overton, Thruxton, Andover, Whitchurch, Upper Clatford, Micheldever, Wonston, Totford, Bighton, Leckford, Broughton, Sparsholt, Itchen Abbas, Easton, Winchester, Cherite, Braishfield, Twyford, Owslebury, Whitsbury, Bishopstoke, Dundridge, Bishop's Waltham, Fritham, Totton, Southampton, Hambledo, Ringwood, Bursledon, Hamble, Cosham, Wallington, Hill Head, Portsmouth, Gosport, Alverstoke, East End, Lymington, Everton; bordered by Berkshire, Wiltshire and Dorset)*

---

## Aldershot

### Albion

28 Waterloo Road
☎ (01252) 408010
10.30–2.30, 5.30–11; 10.30–11 Sat;
12–4, 7–10.30 Sun
**Gale's Best Bitter, HSB,
Festival Mild, seasonal beers;
guest beers** Ⓗ
Good backstreet local, with a
lively and comfortable public
bar and a cosy snug. A small
garden is accessed through the
public bar. No meals Sun.
🏔 ❀ ◖ ▶ ◖ ≈ ♣

### Crimea

1 Crimea Road
☎ (01252) 343163
11–3, 5.30–11; 11–11 Sat; 12–10.30 Sun
**Ushers Best Bitter, Founders,
seasonal beers** Ⓗ
Friendly, Tudor-style,
Victorian pub opposite the
football ground: a good local.
❀ ◖ ≈ ♣ P

### Red Lion

Ash Road ☎ (01252) 23050
11–11; 12–3, 7–10.30 Sun
**Courage Best Bitter; guest
beers** Ⓗ
Large, welcoming, one-bar
pub, with a mixed clientele
usually engaged in lively (not
loud) debate. Guest beers
change regularly. Occasional
folk music. 🏔 ❀ ◖ ▶ ≈ P

### Royal Staff

37A Mount Pleasant Road (off
High St, top of Waterloo Rd)
☎ (01252) 22932
12–3 (2 Tue), 5 (5.30 Mon)–11; 12–11
Sat; 12–10.30 Sun
**Fuller's Chiswick, London
Pride, ESB, seasonal beers** Ⓗ
Beautifully refurbished in the
best Victorian style, this
backstreet local has a very
comfortable and lively single
bar with a strong community
atmosphere. Good children's
garden. ❀ ◖ ♣

---

## Alton

### Railway Hotel

Anstey Road ☎ (01420) 84208
10.30–2.30, 5–11; 12–3, 7–10.30 Sun
**Courage Best Bitter; Ushers
Best Bitter, Founders *or*
seasonal beer** Ⓗ
Excellent, basic, one-bar local,
serving no cooked meals.
Charity events are regularly
held. The jukebox is very
occasionally loud. The first
stop from the station.
≈ 🖱

**Try also: Eight Bells,** Church
St (Free)

**Fuller's London Pride; Marston's Bitter; guest beers** Ⓗ
Traditional, two-bar town pub offering occasional live music. Interesting collection of anniversary beer bottles.
🏚 ✿ 🍺 ♣ P

## Lamb

21 Winchester Street (just off town centre, near police station) ☎ (01264) 323961
11–3, 6 (5 Fri, 7 Sat)–11; 12–3, 7–10.30 Sun
**Wadworth 6X, Old Timer; guest beer** Ⓗ
Late 16th-century town pub with three rooms, low beams and a collection of horsebrasses. One other Wadworth beer is also sold. Cheaper beer weekday lunchtimes and early eves. Wheelchair WC.
🏚 Q ✿ 🍺 🚹 🚻 ♣

## Lardicake

Adelaide Road (200 yds from East St) ☎ (01264) 323447
11–3, 5–11; 11–11 Fri & Sat; 12–4, 7–10.30 Sun
**Draught Bass; Gibbs Mew Salisbury, Wake Ale, Bishop's Tipple; Tetley Bitter; Theakston Best Bitter** Ⓗ
Unpretentious, one-bar pub next to a housing estate east of the town centre. Parking eves only. 🏚 ✿ 🍺 ♣ P

## Ashmansworth

### Plough

Off A343 ☎ (01635) 253047
12–2.30 (not Mon or Tue), 6–11; 12–3, 7–10.30 Sun
**Archers Village, Best Bitter, Golden; guest beers** Ⓗ
Hampshire's highest pub (700 ft above sea level): a completely unspoilt rural pub with casks on stillage behind the bar. Friendly and popular with locals and visitors.
🏚 Q ✿ 🍺 ♣

## Basingstoke

### Bounty Inn

81 Bounty Road ☎ (01256) 20071
11–11; 12–10.30 Sun
**Courage Best Bitter; Ushers Best Bitter, Founders, seasonal beers** Ⓗ
Two-bar local near Mays Bounty cricket ground with character and a friendly welcome. The public bar features Sky TV and sporting memorabilia; separate, small dining/family room.
🏚 Q 🚼 ✿ 🍺 🍺 P

### Queen's Arms

Bunnian Place (by station car park) ☎ (01256) 465488
11–3, 5–11; 11–11 Fri & Sat; 12–3, 7–10.30 Sun

**Courage Best Bitter, Directors; John Smith's Bitter; guest beers** Ⓗ
Surviving Victorian pub enjoying trade from office tower blocks nearby as well as regulars. An ideal refreshment stop for rail passengers who can view trains thundering overhead. 🍺 ♣ ≢ ♣

## Bentworth

### Sun Inn

Sun Hill (off A339 down narrow lane) OS661401
☎ (01420) 562338
12–3, 6–11; 12–3, 7–10.30 Sun (closed winter Sun eve)
**Cheriton Diggers Gold; Courage Best Bitter; Marston's Pedigree; Ringwood Best Bitter** Ⓗ
Pub dating from the 17th century, much altered in recent years but retaining lots of charm and character. The house beer is brewed by Hampshire Brewery. Cider in summer.
🏚 Q 🚼 ✿ 🍺 🚹 🖐 P

## Bighton

### Three Horseshoes

Off A31/B3047 OS616344
☎ (01962) 732859
11–2.30, 6–11; 12–3, 7–10.30 Sun
**Gale's Butser, Winter Brew, HSB** Ⓗ
Superb rural local where the art of conversation is still practised. A pub since 1615, it has a quiet, relaxing lounge, whilst the public bar houses a country crafts collection and the old pub sign. No food Mon.
🏚 Q ✿ 🍺 🚹 🚻 ▲ ♣ P

## Bishopstoke

### Foresters Arms

1 Stoke Common Road
☎ (01703) 620287
12–3, 7–11; 12–3, 7–10.30 Sun

---

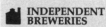

### ⬛ INDEPENDENT BREWERIES

**Cheriton:** Cheriton

**Gale's:** Horndean

**Hampshire:** Andover

**Hedgehog & Hogshead:** Southampton

**Newale:** Andover

**Ringwood:** Ringwood

**Spikes:** Portsmouth

**Wingfields:** Portsmouth

**Worldham:** East Worldham

---

## Alverstoke

### Alverbank Hotel

Stokes Bay Road
☎ (01705) 510005
11–11; 12–10.30 Sun
**Ringwood Best Bitter; guest beers** Ⓗ
Originally a Victorian country house on the bank of the River Alver, overlooking Stokes Bay, with some magnificent wood panelling inside: a quiet, relaxing pub which can get busy at holiday times.
🏚 Q ✿ 🍺 🍺 ▲ P

## Andover

### Blacksmith's Arms

New Street
☎ (01264) 352881
11–2 (not Tue), 5–11; 11–11 Sat; 12–3, 7–10.30 Sun

Gibbs Mew Overlord,
Salisbury, Deacon, Wake Ale;
Theakston Best Bitter Ⓗ
Warm, friendly pub fielding
numerous games teams. The
public bar has a pool annexe;
the lounge has a log fire in
winter. Reputedly haunted.
Lunches by arrangement.
🏚 Q 🌣 🛏 ♣ ⌂ P 🍺

## Bishop's Waltham

### Bunch of Grapes
St Peter's Street
☎ (01489) 892935
10–2, 6–11; 12–2, 7–10.30 Sun
Courage Best Bitter Ⓖ; Ushers
seasonal beers Ⓗ
Situated in a narrow street
leading to the parish church,
this small pub has been
unaltered for many years and
is of a type increasingly rare in
these economic times. Strong
golf society. Q 🌣 ♣

## Braishfield

### Newport Inn
Newport Lane (lane opp.
phone box) ☎ (01794) 368225
10–2.30, 6–11; 12–2.30, 7–10.30 Sun
Gale's Butser, Best Bitter,
Winter Brew, HSB Ⓗ
A gem in a time warp, worth a
detour. The doorstep
sandwiches and giant
ploughmans are famous
throughout the county.
Communal singing around the
piano Sun eve (be prepared to
join in). Large, rambling
garden. Q 🌣 ⊞ ♣ P

## Broughton

### Tally Ho!
High Street ☎ (01794) 301280
12–2.30 (3 Sat), 6–11; 12–3, 7–10.30
Sun
Cheriton Pots Ale, Best Bitter,
Diggers Gold Ⓖ
Real conversationalists' pub,
with no electronic distractions
but lots of flagstones and
polished wood. This Georgian
house is Cheriton's second pub
and offers the usual value for
money. No eve meals Tue. On
the Clarendon Way long
distance path.
🏚 Q 🌣 ◑ ▶ ⊞ ♣ ⌂

## Burghclere

### Carpenters Arms
Harts Lane (just E of A34)
☎ (01635) 278251
11–3, 6–11; 12–5, 7–10.30 Sun
Arkell's Bitter, 3B,
Kingsdown, seasonal beers Ⓗ
Large, one-bar friendly pub
with an attractive conservatory
at the rear. The garden has
extensive views to the south.
🏚 Q 🌣 ◑ ▶ ♿ P

### Queen
Harts Lane (just E of A34)
☎ (01635) 278350
11–3, 6–11; 12–3, 7–10.30 Sun
Adnams Bitter, Broadside;
Arkell's 3B Ⓗ
No-nonsense, one-bar pub
with a friendly atmosphere.
Strong racing following. No
food Sun. Q 🌣 ◑ ♿ ♣ P

## Buriton

### Five Bells
48 High Street
☎ (01730) 263584
11–2.30 (3 Fri & Sat), 5.30–11; 12–3,
7–10.30 Sun
Ballard's Best Bitter; Friary
Meux BB; Ind Coope Burton
Ale; Ringwood XXXX Porter,
Old Thumper; Tetley Bitter Ⓗ
Very popular, traditional
village pub with two beamed
bars, each with an imposing
fireplace. Well known for its
good quality food. Self-
catering accommodation.
🏚 Q 🌣 🛏 ◑ ▶ ⊞ ▲ ♣ P

## Bursledon

### Jolly Sailor
Land's End Road, Old
Bursledon
☎ (01703) 405557
11–2.30, 6–11; 11–11 Sat; 12–10.30 Sun
Badger Dorset Best,
Tanglefoot; Wadworth 6X Ⓗ
16th-century riverside inn of
Howards' Way fame, with a
beamed ceiling, flagstone floor
and a restaurant area offering
an extensive menu. Bursledon
station car park is nearby.
Access is difficult – beer arrives
by its own cliff railway!
Moorings on the River
Hamble. 🏚 🌣 ◑ ▶ ⊞ 🚆

### Linden Tree
School Road (off A27 / A3025)
☎ (01703) 402356
11–2.30 (3 Sat), 6 (5 Fri)–11; 12–3,
7–10.30 Sun
Draught Bass; Wadworth IPA,
6X, Farmers Glory (summer),
Old Timer Ⓗ
Excellent, comfortable, one-bar
pub with no obtrusive music
machines. A children's play
area and pergola make it ideal
for summer; a blazing log fire
extends a warm welcome in
winter. High quality, home-
cooked meals (not served Sun
or Sat eve; till 8 other eves).
🏚 🌣 ◑ ▶ ♣ P

## Catherington

### Farmer Inn
300 Catherington Lane
☎ (01705) 592402
12–3, 6–11; 12–11 Sat; 12–3, 7–10.30
Sun
Gale's Best Bitter, HSB Ⓔ

Friendly, two-bar village local
with a thriving social scene,
used by walkers (very handy
for Catherington Down). The
handpumps operate electric
pumps. 🏚 Q 🌣 ◑ ⊞ ▲ ♣ P

## Chalton

### Red Lion
☎ (01705) 592246
11–3, 6–11; 12–3, 7–10.30 Sun
Gale's Butser, Best Bitter,
HSB, seasonal beers; guest
beers Ⓗ
Reputedly the oldest pub in
Hampshire, originally the
residence and workshop for
craftsmen building the village
church. It is a delightful
building with a thatched roof
and white daub and wood
construction. Large inglenook
in the public bar. No eve meals
Sun. 🏚 ➵ 🌣 ◑ ▶ ⊞ ♿ P

## Charter Alley

### White Hart
White Hart Lane (1 mile W off
A340) ☎ (01256) 850048
12–2.30 (3 Sat), 7–11; 12–3, 7–10.30
Sun
Fuller's London Pride; Greene
King Abbot; Harveys BB;
guest beers Ⓗ
Multi-purpose village pub
with a restaurant, skittle alley
and a strong local following for
its beer range. A wood burning
stove features in the front bar.
No food Mon eve. Cider in
summer. 🏚 🌣 ◑ ▶ ♣ ⌂ P

## Cheriton

### Flower Pots
W of B3046 at S end of village
☎ (01962) 771318
12–2.30, 6–11; 12–3, 7–10.30 Sun
Cheriton Pots Ale, Best Bitter,
Diggers Gold Ⓖ
Quiet, yet busy, village inn
with its own brewery at one
side and an accommodation
block at the other. The bars are
cosy and cottagey. Very good
value beer; simple, wholesome
food (no meals Sun eve). Many
good walks and the Watercress
Line are nearby. 🏚 Q ➵ 🌣 🛏
◑ ▶ ⊞ ♿ ▲ ♣ ⌂ P

## Cosham

### Salisbury
Lonsdale Avenue
☎ (01705) 362346
11–11; 12–10.30 Sun
Wadworth IPA, 6X, Farmers
Glory Ⓗ, seasonal beers; guest
beers Ⓖ
Friendly, two-bar pub in the
backstreets; one of a few
Wadworth pubs in the area.
Quiz Wed. No food Sun.
🌣 ◑ ⊞ ♿ 🚆 ♣ P

## Cove

### Thatched Cottage
122 Prospect Road
☎ (01252) 543118
11–11; 12–10.30 Sun
**Courage Best Bitter, Directors;
Ruddles County; Theakston
Best Bitter, Old Peculier;
Wadworth 6X** Ⓗ
Low-beamed, quaint, thatched
building set back from the
road; a managed house but it
still manages to offer six beers.
Extensive garden at the rear.
One bar is quiet and cosy; the
other is large and noisy.
🏚 ❀ ◖ ▶ P

## Denmead

### Fox & Hounds
School Lane (1½ miles W of
centre)
☎ (01705) 255421
12–2.30 (3 Sat), 6–11; 12–4, 7–10.30
Sun
**Marston's Bitter, Owd
Rodger, HBC; Taylor
Landlord; guest beers** Ⓗ
Traditional, friendly country
pub now a free house, with
good views towards
Portsdown Hill. Difficult to
find but worth trying. No eve
meals Sun. Q ❀ ◖ ▶ ♿ ▲ P

## Dundridge

### Hampshire Bowman
Dundridge Lane (1½ miles off
B3035) OS578185
☎ (01489) 892940
11 (12 Mon)–2.30 (3 Sat), 6–11; 12–3,
7–10.30 Sun (extends in summer)
**Archers Village, Golden;
Ringwood XXXX Porter,
Fortyniner; guest beers** Ⓖ
Excellent country pub along a
winding country lane, where
all sorts of people meet. One
traditional, brick-floored bar
with a small serving counter
(once an abattoir). Quiz night
Mon. No meals Sun eve or
Mon. 🏚 Q ❀ ◖ ▶ ▲ ♣ P

## East End

### East End Arms
Lymington Road (3 miles E of
IOW ferry) OS362968
☎ (01590) 626223
11.30–3, 6.30–11; 12–3, 7–10.30 Sun
**Adnams Broadside** Ⓖ**;
Draught Bass; Ringwood Best
Bitter** Ⓗ**, Fortyniner, Old
Thumper; guest beers** Ⓖ
Popular country pub used
mainly by locals; rather remote
but worth finding. A basic
public contrasts with a
comfortable lounge.
Traditional country game pies
are served. Busy at weekends.
🏚 Q ❀ ◖ ▶ 🍴 ♿ ▲ ♣ P

## Easton

### Cricketers Inn
Off B3047
☎ (01962) 779353
11.30–2.30 (3.30 Sat), 6–11; 12–3.30,
7–10.30 Sun
**Ballard's Best Bitter; Cheriton
Pots Ale; Ringwood Best
Bitter, Old Thumper; guest
beers** Ⓗ
Comfortable pub in a
picturesque village with an
L-shaped bar well decorated
with various knick-knacks and
old pictures of the pub. Ever-
changing selection of guest
beers from small brewers; good
range of home-cooked foods
(separate restaurant).
🏚 ❀ 🛏 ◖ ▶ ♣ ⌂ P

## Emsworth

### Lord Raglan
35 Queen Street
☎ (01243) 372587
11–3, 6 (5 Fri)–11; 12–3, 7–10.30
(12–10.30 summer) Sun
**Gale's Butser, HSB; guest
beer** Ⓗ
Grade II-listed, flint-faced,
friendly, traditional pub with
an attractive waterside garden.
Children's certificate. Live
music Sun.
🏚 Q ❀ ◖ ▶ ▲ ⇌ ⌂

## Everton

### Crown
4 Old Christchurch Road (off
A337, look for board)
☎ (01590) 642655
11–2.30 (3 Sat), 6–11; 12–3, 7–10.30
Sun
**Flowers Original; Fuller's
London Pride; Strong Country
Bitter; guest beers** Ⓗ
19th-century, traditional
village inn with two bars,
offering a good selection of
home-cooked fare. The lively
and friendly public bar has an
excellent jukebox. Prize-
winning floral displays in
summer. No food Sun eve
Oct–March.
🏚 Q ❀ ◖ ▶ 🍴 ♿ ▲ ♣ ⌂ P

## Farnborough

### Prince of Wales
184 Rectory Road
☎ (01252) 545578
11.30–2.30, 5.30–11; 12–3.30, 7–10.30
Sun
**Badger Dorset Best,
Tanglefoot; Fuller's London
Pride; Hogs Back TEA;
Ringwood Fortyniner; guest
beers** Ⓗ
True bastion of real ale, always
busy with those who know
their beers. Welcoming and
friendly.
Q ❀ ◖ ⇌ (North) P

## Farringdon

### Rose & Crown
Crows Lane (off A32)
☎ (01420) 588231
11–3, 6–11; 12–3, 7–10.30 Sun
**Draught Bass; Fuller's London
Pride; guest beers** Ⓗ
Friendly village free house
with a separate eating area.
Ringwood and Hampshire
beers are sold regularly. No
eve meals Sun. 🏚 Q ❀ ◖ ▶ P

## Fleet

### Flying Goose
Faulkeners Close, Ancells
Farm ☎ (01252) 811479
11–3, 5–11; 11–11 Fri & Sat; 12–10.30
Sun
**Draught Bass; guest beers** Ⓗ
Modern estate pub which
attracts a varied clientele.
Features include a flagstone
floor, no-smoking family room
and a separate darts area. Live
music; summer barbecues.
🎵 ❀ ◖ ▶ ⇌ ♣ P ✄

## Freefolk Priors

### Watership Down
Priory Lane (off B3400 ½ mile E
of Whitchurch)
☎ (01256) 892254
11–3, 6–11; 12–3, 7–10.30 Sun
**Archers Best Bitter; Brakspear
Bitter; guest beers** Ⓗ
Victorian pub renamed after
the novel by Richard Adams:
one large room divided into
two different areas. Attractive
garden with views of the River
Test. The three guests always
include a mild.
🏚 ❀ ◖ ▶ ♣ P 🚬

## Fritham

### Royal Oak
1 mile S of B3078 OS232141
☎ (01703) 812606
11–2.30 (3 summer), 6–11; 12–3,
7–10.30 Sun
**Ringwood Best Bitter;
Wadworth IPA, 6X** Ⓖ
In a class of its own – a tiny
unspoilt, thatched pub at the
end of a New Forest track with
a small front bar and a tiny
snug. The focus for all the
country activities in the area. A
pint straight from the cask,
drunk before the log fire, is a
winter life-saver.
🏚 Q ❀ ▲ ♣

## Golden Pot

### Golden Pot
Old Odiham Road (B3349)
☎ (01420) 84130
11–3, 5.30–11; 12–3.30, 5.30–10.30
Sun
**Draught Bass; Flowers
Original; Morland Original,**

**Old Speckled Hen, seasonal beers** H

Built in 1901, this former drovers' lodge is now a friendly rural pub with a family welcome. Former stables are now the skittle alley. The emphasis is on children's facilities and special eves. Food is recommended.
🏾 ❀ ◑ ♠ P

## Gosport

### Queen's Hotel

143 Queens Road
☎ (01705) 525518
11.30–2.30, 7–11; 11.30–11 Sat; 12–3, 7–10.30 Sun

**Archers Village; Ringwood Fortyniner; Smiles Best Bitter; guest beers** H

Award-winning pub which sets the standard for the area; hidden away in the backstreets but well worth seeking out. There are three drinking areas, the focal point being an old open fire with an elegant, carved wood surround. 🏾 ♠

### Wheatsheaf

225 Brockhurst Road (A32)
☎ (01705) 581546
12–2, 5.30–11; 11–11 Fri & Sat; 12–10.30 Sun

**Flowers Original** G

Basic local with two separate bars; situated near the historic Fort Brockhurst. No meals Sun.
❀ ◑ ♠ P

### Windsor Castle

33 St Thomas Road
☎ (01705) 355136
11–3, 6–11; 11–11 Fri & Sat; 12–10.30 Sun

**Gale's HSB** G

Basic local comprised of one open-plan bar with a traditional bare-board floor and a separate games room. Other Gale's beers are occasionally on offer. Extensive range of whiskies. ❀ ♠ P

## Greatham

### Silver Birch

Petersfield Road
☎ (01420) 538262
11–3, 6–11; 12–4, 7–10.30 Sun

**Ringwood Best Bitter; guest beers** H

Two-bar local with a separate eating area, run by a friendly couple who are keen supporters of nearby micros. Large etched-glass doors and unusual 'parrotphenalia' feature. No eve meals winter Sun. 🏾 Q ❀ 🛏 ◑ ◐ ⊞ & P

## Hamble

### King & Queen

High Street ☎ (01703) 454247
11–11; 12–10.30 Sun

**Boddingtons Bitter; Fuller's London Pride; Strong Country Bitter; Wadworth 6X; guest beer** H

Single-bar pub with a separate bistro (open Tue–Sat eves), used by locals and the yachting community (laundry facilities). Bar billiards table. Book Sun lunch. Strong Country Bitter is sold as 'Totally Pissed'.
🏾 ❀ ◑ ♠ P

## Hambledon

### New Inn

West Street ☎ (01705) 632466
12–2.30, 7–11; 12–2.30, 7–10.30 Sun

**Ballard's Trotton; Ringwood Best Bitter, Fortyniner, Old Thumper** H

Friendly village pub where the art of conversation has not been lost: a genuine free house selling beer at some of the lowest prices in the south of England. 🏾 Q ❀ ⊞ & ♠ P

## Hartley Wintney

### Waggon & Horses

High Street ☎ (01252) 842119
11–11; 12–3, 7–10.30 Sun

**Courage Best Bitter, Directors; Gale's HSB; Wadworth 6X; guest beer** H

Friendly, traditional pub in the centre of the village with a cosy, small lounge and a livelier public bar.
🏾 Q ❀ ◑ ⊞ ♠

## Havant

### Old House at Home

2 South Street
☎ (01705) 483464
11–11; 12–10.30 Sun

**Gale's Butser, Best Bitter, HSB, seasonal beers; guest beers** H

Popular pub in a quiet corner of town, built in the 17th century (despite the 1339 date outside) as five cottages. Some original wood beams in both bars. Live music Sat eve. Home to several sports clubs; special events arranged.
🏾 ❀ ◑ ⊞ ≉ ♠

## Hawkley

### Hawkley Inn

Pococks Lane OS747292
☎ (01730) 827205
12–2.30 (3 Sat), 6–11; 12–2.30, 7–10.30 Sun

**Ballard's Trotton, Best Bitter; Cheriton Pots Ale; Pilgrim Talisman; Ringwood Fortyniner; guest beers** H

Popular free house in a village well off the beaten track, attracting a varied clientele, including walkers, and furnished in an individual style (note the moose head).

The range of beers occasionally changes. Two beer festivals a year. No eve meals Sun.
🏾 Q ❀ ◑ ▶ & ✂

## Hill Head

### Crofton

48 Crofton Lane
☎ (01329) 314222
11–2.30, 5–11; 11–11 Fri & Sat; 12–5, 7–10.30 Sun

**John Smith's Bitter; Ushers Best Bitter, Founders, seasonal beers** H

Large, modern pub in a residential area. Despite extensive renovation, two bars have been retained, plus a separate dining area and a function room with a skittle alley. No eve meals Sun.
❀ ◑ ▶ ⊞ ♠ ⌣ P

### Osborne View

67 Hill Head Road
☎ (01329) 664623
11–11; 12–10.30 Sun

**Badger Dorset Best, Tanglefoot** H

Appropriately named pub with extensive views over the Solent: a popular village local with a large, open-plan bar and plenty of room for drinkers and diners. Beers from the Gribble Inn are also available.
🏾 ❀ ◑ ▶ P ✂

## Horndean

### Brewer's Arms

1 Five Heads Road (100 yds off old A3) ☎ (01705) 591325
12–2 (3.30 Fri, 4 Sat; not Mon), 5 (6 Sat)–11; 12–4, 7–10.30 Sun

**Flowers Original; Worthington Bitter; guest beers** H

Friendly two-bar local, formerly a Gale's house, hence the exterior design. Plans of earlier alterations are displayed in the lounge.
Q ❀ ⊞ ♠ P

### Ship & Bell

6 London Road (next to brewery) ☎ (01705) 592107
11–11; 12–3.30, 7–10.30 Sun

**Gale's Butser, Best Bitter, HSB, Festival Mild, seasonal beers** H

The Gale's brewery tap, built on the site of the original brewhouse: a spacious 300-year-old building with two contrasting bars. Six beers always on sale. Sun eve meals may only be available to residents. No-smoking area lunchtime in the lounge.
🏾 Q ⌂ 🛏 ◑ ▶ ⊞ ♠ P ✂

## Itchen Abbas

### Trout Inn

Main Road (B3047)
☎ (01962) 779537

11–3, 6 (5.30 summer)–11; 12–3 (4 summer), 7 (6 summer)–10.30 Sun
**Marston's Bitter, Pedigree** Ⓗ
Smart, lively country inn in the lovely Itchen Valley. The two bars are adorned with breweriana and local views. The lounge bar forms part of the restaurant, whilst the bar has a separate games area. Jovial atmosphere; good banter. Quality accommodation. 🏠 Q 🛏 ◑ ▷ 🍴 ₲ 🌳 P

## Kingsclere

### Swan Hotel
Swan Street (B3051)
☎ (01635) 298314
11–3, 5.30–11; 12–3, 7–10.30 Sun
**Greene King Abbot; Hampshire King Alfred's; Tetley Bitter; guest beers** Ⓗ
Listed hotel in the centre of a village at the southern end of Watership Down, on the Berkshire border (good walking country). Excellent food. 🏠 Q 🛏 ◑ ▷ 🌳 P

## Langstone

### Ship Inn
Langstone Road (A3023)
☎ (01705) 471719
11–11; 12–10.30 Sun
**Gale's Butser, Best Bitter, HSB; guest beer** Ⓗ
Large pub on the only road to Hayling Island, busy with office workers from nearby Havant lunchtimes. The emphasis is on food, especially local fish. The large outdoor drinking area offers yachting views in summer. Gale's No. 1 pub in 1995. 🏠 Q ◑ ▷ ₲ P

## Lasham

### Royal Oak
Off A339 ☎ (01256) 381213
11–2.30 (3 Sat), 6–11; 12–3, 7–10.30 Sun
**Hampshire King Alfred's; Ringwood Best Bitter; guest beers** Ⓗ
Welcoming country pub adjacent to the church. The attractive garden is perfect for viewing gliders from the local airfield. Unusual selection of guest beers. The good value food is recommended. 🏠 Q 🌳 ◑ ▷ 🍴 🌳 ➔ ◔ P

## Leckford

### Leckford Hutt
London Road (A30)
☎ (01264) 810738
11–3, 5–11; 12–10.30 Sun
**Marston's Bitter, Pedigree, HBC** Ⓗ
Traditional, multi-roomed, drovers' pub built in the 18th century, with its own 250-feet deep well. The function room

can be used by families. Look for the three brass handpumps reputed to be as old as the pub. Camping is in a field at the side. 🏠 Q 🛏 🌳 ◑ ◀ ▷ ₲ 🌺 ➔ ◔ P

## Little London

### Plough
Silchester Road (1 mile E of A340) ☎ (01256) 850628
12–3, 6–11; 12–3, 7–10.30 Sun
**Greene King Abbot; Ringwood Best Bitter; Wethered Bitter; guest beer** Ⓗ
Small village local with a quarry tiled floor and a large open fire in its bar area; small lounge with TV for sporting use. No food Sun. Cider in summer.
🏠 Q 🌺 ◑ ▷ ₲ ➔ ◔ P

## Lower Froyle

### Prince of Wales
☎ (01420) 23102
11–2.30, 6–11; 12–3, 7–10.30 Sun
**Fuller's London Pride; Greene King Abbot; Taylor Landlord; guest beers** Ⓗ
Family-run country pub in a scenic village, boasting five handpumps. Popular with diners, with food served in a separate eating area (no food Sun eve). 🏠 🌺 ◑ ▷ ₲ ➔ P

## Lymington (Pennington)

### Musketeer
26 North Street
☎ (01590) 676527
11.30–3, 5.30–11; 12–4, 7–10.30 Sun
**Brakspear Bitter; Ringwood Best Bitter, Fortyniner; guest beer** Ⓗ
Traditional, friendly, village-centre local. The lunchtime menu includes unusual home-made specials; eve menu Sat only (book). No food Sun.
🏠 Q 🛏 🌺 ◑ ▷ P

## Medstead

### Castle of Comfort
Castle Street (2 miles N from A31 at Four Marks)
☎ (01420) 562112
11–3, 6–11; 12–3, 7–10.30 Sun
**Courage Best Bitter; Ushers Best Bitter, Founders, seasonal beers** Ⓗ
Low-beamed, unspoilt village pub with shining brasses. Steam trains run nearby on the Watercress Line.
🏠 Q 🌺 ◑ ▷ ₲ ➔ P 🍺

## Micheldever

### Dever Arms
Winchester Road (off A33)
☎ (01962) 774339
11.30–3, 6–11; 12–3, 7–10.30 Sun

**Badger Dorset Best, Tanglefoot; Cheriton Pots Ale; Hop Back Summer Lightning; Pilgrim Talisman; Ringwood Best Bitter** Ⓗ
Popular village pub with a friendly atmosphere. One large bar with two open fires, plus a separate no-smoking restaurant area. Food is better quality than normally found in pubs and more unusual. No food Sun eve. Jazz Thu eve.
🏠 Q 🛏 🌺 ◑ ▷ 🌳 ◔ P

## North Camp

### Old Ford
Lynchford Road
☎ (01252) 544840
11–11; 12–4, 7–10.30 (12–10.30 summer) Sun
**Courage Best Bitter; Hogs Back TEA; guest beers** Ⓗ
Pub where a superbly designed facade fronts a long bar in natural wood. The extensive riverside garden has an enclosed children's play area and a pets corner. Bookable skittle alley. Good value Sun roasts.
🛏 🌺 ◑ ▷ ⇌ ➔ P

## Oakhanger

### Red Lion
☎ (01420) 472232
11–3, 6–11; 12–3, 7–10.30 Sun
**Courage Best Bitter, Directors; Ringwood Fortyniner** Ⓗ
An established landlord with a caustic sense of humour presides over this unspoilt country pub which has a first class restaurant. It occasionally sells Worldham beers. A gem.
🏠 Q ◑ ▷ P

## Overton

### Old House at Home
Station Road (100 yds N of B3400) ☎ (01256) 770335
11–3, 5.30–11, 11–11 Fri & Sat; 12–3, 7–10.30 Sun
**Courage Best Bitter; Ushers Founders, seasonal beers** Ⓗ
Single-bar village local just out of the centre. Games old and new are enthusiastically played. Good family garden with children's playthings.
🏠 🛏 🌺 ◑ ▷ ⇌ ➔

## Owslebury

### Ship Inn
Off B2177, 1½ miles N of Marwell Zoo ☎ (01962) 777358
11–3, 6–11; 11–11 Sat; 12–10.30 Sun
**Bateman Mild; Marston's Bitter, Pedigree, HBC** Ⓗ
Lively, 300-year-old village pub. The comfortable main bar has nautical and cricket memorabilia and a large open fireplace. A recently enlarged second bar has a family area.

123

Large garden with children's play area, marquee, pond and animals. Good food.
♛ Q ❀ ⛟ ◐ ◑ ♣ P

## Petersfield

### Good Intent
46 College Street (near old A3/A272 jct)
☎ (01730) 263838
11–3, 6–11; 12–3, 7–10.30 Sun
**Gale's Butser, Best Bitter, IPA, HSB, Festival Mild, seasonal beers; guest beers** Ⓗ
Friendly, traditional, 16th-century local hosting live music Sun nights. Excellent food including theme nights; no eve meals Sun.
♛ ♘ ❀ ◐ ◑ ♿ ⇌ ♣

## Portsmouth

### Apsley House
13 Auckland Road West, Southsea (set back from Clarence Parade)
☎ (01705) 821294
12–3, 6–11; 12–11 Sat & summer; 12–10.30 Sun
**Archers Golden; Greene King Abbot; Ind Coope Burton Ale; Marston's Pedigree; Tetley Bitter** Ⓗ
Backstreet pub hidden away near Southsea shopping centre; named after the Duke of Wellington's London home (hence the No. 1 Portsmouth on the pub sign). A house beer, Carnival, is brewed by Brewery-on-Sea. ❀ ◐ ♣ ⌓

### Artillery Arms
Hester Road, Milton, Southsea
☎ (01705) 733610
11–3, 6–11; 12–4, 7–10.30 Sun
**Gale's Best Bitter; Ind Coope Burton Ale; guest beers** Ⓗ
Backstreet free house, run by the same family for 25 years, with two distinct bars, one with pool and darts, the other more relaxed. Very much a locals' pub but always friendly. Try the penny one-arm bandit in the family room.
♘ ⊟ ♣ P

### Connaught Arms
117 Guildford Road, Fratton
☎ (01705) 646455
11.30–2.30, 6–11; 11.30–11 Fri & Sat; 12–10.30 Sun
**Draught Bass; Brakspear Bitter; Fuller's London Pride; King & Barnes Sussex; guest beer** Ⓗ
Attractive brewers' Tudor corner pub, renowned as Portsmouth's pasty pub: local CAMRA *Pub of the Year* 1995. Constantly changing guest beer from independent brewers; much used patio in summer. A gem.
❀ ◐ ◑ ⇌ (Fratton) ♣ ⌓

### Diamond
70 King Street, Southsea
☎ (01705) 822071
11.30–5, 7–11; 12–3, 7–10.30 Sun
**Wadworth IPA, 6X, seasonal beers; guest beers** Ⓗ
Friendly local recently given a sympathetic internal refurbishment, leaving a quiet area to one side of the bar.
◐ ⇌ ♣

### Dolphin Hotel
41 High Street, Old Portsmouth (opp. Anglican Cathedral lawns)
☎ (01705) 823595
11–11; 12–10.30 Sun
**Brakspear Bitter; Flowers Original; Gibbs Mew Bishop's Tipple** Ⓖ**; Marston's Pedigree; Whitbread Abroad Cooper, Fuggles IPA** Ⓗ**; guest beers** Ⓖ **&** Ⓗ
17th-century coaching inn with two distinct areas; now a popular Hogshead pub serving up to 14 beers (guests mainly from independents). Selection of Belgian beers. Food is good value for the area (served till 8). Close to the historic sights of old Portsmouth. Function room.
♛ ❀ ◐ ◑ ⇌ (Harbour) ♣ ⌓

### Eldon Arms
15–17 Eldon Street, Southsea
☎ (01705) 851778
11–2.30 (3 Sat), 5 (5.30 Sat)–11; 12–3, 7–10.30 Sun
**Hardy Dorchester, Country, Royal Oak; guest beers** Ⓗ
Tile-fronted ale house serving three guest beers, changing weekly. An interesting selection of traditional games, including shove-ha'penny, together with good food, make this a pub for all.
♘ ❀ ◐ ◑ ⇌ ♣ ⌓

### Fifth Hampshire Volunteer Arms
74 Albert Road, Southsea (200 yds from King's Theatre)
☎ (01705) 827161
12–11; 12–10.30 Sun
**Gale's Butser, Best Bitter, Winter Brew, HSB, seasonal beers** Ⓗ
Street-corner local which still has two contrasting bars: a lively public with darts, rock music and TV, plus a comfortable lounge with military memorabilia. Possibly the best ladies' WC in Southsea. A plaque commemorates the birthplace of the local CAMRA branch in 1974. Lunches Sat and Sun.
Q ◐ ⊟ ♣

### Florist
324 Fratton Road, Fratton
☎ (01705) 820289
11–3, 6–11 (12–10.30 bank hols); 11–11 Sat; 12–10.30 Sun
**Wadworth IPA, 6X, Farmers Glory, Old Timer *or* seasonal beers** Ⓗ
Attractive, two-bar, Grade II-listed corner local with a brewers' Tudor exterior and a witch's hat tower. The lounge at the rear is quiet. The public bar has darts, pool table, a jukebox and a TV. Run by the same family for 35 years.
Q ⊟ ⇌ (Fratton)

### Leopold Tavern
154 Albert Road, Southsea
☎ (01705) 829748
11–11; 12–10.30 Sun
**Burts VPA; Whitbread Pompey Royal** Ⓗ
Pub whose exterior offers a classic example of the former United Brewery's glazed tilework. Inside is much larger than expected. An unusual porcine clock sits on original carved wood bar fittings. Photos of old Portsmouth are on show. Yes, the bar is crooked. ♣

### Old Oyster House
291 Locksway Road, Milton, Southsea (off A288 Milton Rd, near university Langstone site)
☎ (01705) 827456
12–11; 12–10.30 Sun
**Brains Dark; Fuller's London Pride; Hardington Bitter; guest beers** Ⓗ
Large, thriving pub near the only remaining section of the Portsea Canal, drawing a varied clientele. Reduced prices on selected beer during the week. Two ciders and a mild are usually available. Ring for food details.
♘ ❀ ◐ ◑ ♣ ⌓ P

### Red White & Blue
150 Fawcett Road, Southsea
☎ (01705) 780013
11–11; 12–10.30 Sun
**Gale's Butser, Best Bitter, IPA, Winter Brew, HSB** Ⓗ
Compact corner local patriotic to two nations. Unusual collection of board games, but, if you are bored, count the gnomes and the horses, or play with the spare handpumps!
◐ ⇌ (Fratton) ♣

### Rose in June
102 Milton Road, Copnor (by Kingston prison)
☎ (01705) 824191
12–3 (not Tue), 5.30–11; 11–11 Fri & Sat; 12–10.30 Sun
**Draught Bass; Gale's Best Bitter, HSB; Greene King Abbot; Tetley Imperial; guest beers** Ⓗ
Friendly, two-bar local with a large garden and children's play area. Summer barbecues; occasional live music. Pool and darts played. Gale's Best is sold as Rose Bitter. ❀ ⊟ ♣

### Royal Marine Artillery Tavern (RMA)

58 Cromwell Road, Eastney, Southsea (opp. old Royal Marines barracks)
☎ (01705) 820896
11–11; 12–10.30 Sun
**Gale's Butser, HSB, seasonal beers _or_ guest beers** Ⓗ
Surprisingly large, corner local with a quiet saloon bar and a function room. It has the only permanent skittle alley in the city. No keg beers. Curried and chilli eggs are the landlord's speciality (a bit warm though – be warned!). Numerous games played. Q ⊞ ▲ ♣ ○

### Sir Loyne of Beefe

152 Highland Road, Eastney, Southsea (opp. new police station) ☎ (01705) 820115
11–11; 12–5, 7.30–10.30 Sun
**Draught Bass; Courage Best Bitter, Directors; Highgate Dark; Hop Back Summer Lightning; Ringwood Old Thumper; guest beers** Ⓗ
Genuine free house, handy for the Royal Marines Museum and the seafront. As well as the main bar, there is a snug and a no-smoking room. Eight ales, plus a cider. Live music occasionally.
⊞ ○ ✠

### Sir Robert Peel

Astley Street, Southsea (take Norfolk St from King's Rd, then left into Sackville St)
☎ (01705) 345708
11.45–3.30 (4.30 Sat), 7–11; 12–4.30, 7–10.30 Sun
**Bateman XB; Ringwood Best Bitter, Old Thumper; guest beers** Ⓗ
1960s estate pub, originally built for Ind Coope, with two large bars. The landlord, ex-licensee of the Wig & Pen, has introduced six reasonably priced beers from independents. Good value lunches.
◖ ⊞ ⇌ ♣ ○ P

## Priors Dean

### White Horse (Pub With No Name)

400 yds off main road, signed E Tisted OS714290
☎ (01420) 588387
11–2.30 (3 Sat), 6–11; 12–3, 7–10.30 Sun
**Ballard's Best Bitter; Gale's Butser, HSB, Festival Mild; Ringwood Fortyniner; Theakston Old Peculier; guest beers** Ⓗ
Famous old pub hidden down a gravel track in a field (second track from the main road), with no pub sign (it fell down years ago), hence the nickname. Ten

beers are on offer, two of which are house beers, the stronger brewed by Ringwood, the other by Gale's.
♨ Q ❀ ◖ ♣ ▲ P

## Ringwood

### Inn on the Furlong

12 Meeting House Lane
☎ (01425) 475139
11–3, 5–11; 11–11 Fri & Sat; 12–10.30 Sun
**Ringwood Best Bitter, True Glory, XXXX Porter, Fortyniner, Old Thumper; guest beer** Ⓗ
Situated next to a large car park, this is one of only two tied Ringwood pubs; popular with locals and tourists alike. It is single-bar but multi-roomed, with a no-smoking conservatory. Live blues Tue; Easter beer festival. Indian specials on the menu.
♨ ❀ ◖ ♣ ✠

### London Tavern

Linford Road, Poulner
☎ (01425) 473819
11.30–4, 5.30–11; 11–11 Fri & Sat; 12–3.30, 7.30–10.30 Sun
**Fuller's London Pride; Ringwood Best Bitter; Whitbread Pompey Royal; guest beer** Ⓗ
Nice-looking pub on the eastern fringe of town, with a diamond brick pattern. Inside is one large homely bar with a fireplace and a log-burner, plus a conservatory. A locals' pub where conversation rules. Whitbread guest beer.
♨ ❀ ◖ ♣ P

## Selborne

### Queen's Hotel

High Street
☎ (01420) 511454
11–11; 12–10.30 Sun
**Courage Best Bitter; Ushers Best Bitter, Founders, seasonal beers** Ⓗ
Village pub offering live jazz and, in summer, horse-drawn rides. The public bar has a pool table while the smaller saloon has an adjacent eating area. Children's certificate.
♨ Q ㈓ ◖ ▶ ⊞ P

### Selborne Arms

High Street
☎ (01420) 511247
11–3, 5.30–11; 11–11 Sat; 12–4, 7–10.30 (12–10.30 summer) Sun
**Courage Best Bitter, Directors; Wadworth 6X; guest beers** Ⓗ
Popular with locals and ramblers, this pub usually features a guest beer from Hampshire Brewery, but occasionally has others. Very busy in summer.
♨ Q ❀ ㈓ ◖ ▶ ⊞ P

## Southampton

### Bosun's Locker

Castle Square, Upper Bugle Street ☎ (01703) 333364
11–3, 6 (7 Sat)–11; 11–11 Fri; 12–3, 7–10.30 Sun
**Draught Bass; Boddingtons Bitter; Fuller's London Pride; guest beer** Ⓗ
Welcoming, nautically-themed pub, a stone's throw from the city centre, serving a variety of home-cooked fare. Inspired choice of guest beer, usually from small independent breweries. Tall people risk being caught in fishnets!
㈓ ◖ ▶ ♣ ○

### Crown

9 Highcrown Street, Highfield (off Highfield Lane, near university) ☎ (01703) 315033
11.30–2.30, 6–11; 11.30–11 Fri & Sat; 12–3, 7–10.30 Sun
**Flowers Original; Fuller's London Pride; Hampshire King Alfred's; Marston's Pedigree; Wadworth 6X** Ⓗ
Busy, comfortable, one-bar pub close to Southampton Common, popular with students and locals. The beer range may vary. ❀ ◖ ▶ P

### Freemantle Arms

33 Albany Road, Freemantle
☎ (01703) 320759
10.30–3, 6–11; 10.30–11 Fri & Sat; 12–3, 7–10.30 Sun
**Banks's Mild; Marston's Bitter, Pedigree, HBC** Ⓗ
Friendly, two-bar local in a quiet cul-de-sac, featuring a popular, colourful garden and a patio. Venue for an annual leek and vegetable show (first Sat in Sept). ❀ ⊞ ♣ ⊟

### Gate

138–140 Burgess Road, Bassett
☎ (01703) 678250
11–3.30 (4 Fri & Sat), 7–11; 12–3, 7–10.30 Sun
**Hardy Pope's Traditional, Country, Royal Oak, seasonal beers; guest beers** Ⓗ
Large, single-bar pub near the university, dating from the early 1840s. It was a brewery for many years. Sky TV, pool and darts are popular at night. No lunches Sun. Two changing guest beers. ❀ ◖ ♣ P

### Guide Dog

38 Earls Road, Bevois Valley (off Bevois Valley Rd)
11.30–3 (4 Sat), 6–11; 12–4, 7–10.30 Sun
**Wadworth IPA, 6X; guest beer** Ⓗ
Small, but comfortable, sidestreet local with a pleasant homely feel. The name derives from the fundraising efforts of a former landlady. Good value ales. ◖ ▶ ♣

### Hobbit

134 Bevois Valley Road
☎ (01703) 232591
6–11 (midnight Thu); 5–1am Fri;
6–1am Sat; 12–3, 7–10.30 Sun
**Boddingtons Bitter; Flowers
Original; Hop Back Special,
Thunderstorm; Marston's
Pedigree; Whitbread Best
Bitter; guest beer** ⓗ
Popular students' pub with a
lively, friendly atmosphere.
Local bands play in the lower
bar. Large, pleasant, multi-
levelled garden.
🅰 ≢ (St Denys) ♣

### Miller's Pond

2 Middle Road, Sholing
(Station Rd jct)
☎ (01703) 444755
11–11; 12–10.30 Sun
**Wadworth IPA, 6X, seasonal
beers or guest beer** ⓗ
Much altered and extended,
corner local in a mature
residential area. Named after a
now drained pond, it has been
run by the same family since
1972. Book Sun lunch.
🅰 ◖ ≢ (Sholing) P

### New Inn

16 Bevois Valley Road
☎ (01703) 228437
12–3, 6.45–11; 12–3, 7–10.30 Sun
**Gale's Butser, Best Bitter,
Winter Brew, HSB, seasonal
beers or guest beers** ⓗ
One-bar corner pub with a
cosmopolitan clientele and a
relaxed atmosphere. Excellent
lunchtime food, 120 malt
whiskies and foreign bottled
beers add to the appeal. Etched
windows confirm its past
ownership by Strongs.
◖ ♣

### Park Inn

37 Carlisle Road, Shirley (off
Romsey Rd, near precinct)
☎ (01703) 787835
11–3 (3.30 Sat), 5 (6.30 Sat)–11; 12–3,
7–10.30 Sun
**Badger Tanglefoot; Wadworth
IPA, 6X, Old Timer; guest
beer** ⓗ
Friendly, one-bar local near
shops, maintaining the feel of a
two-bar pub. Note the
interesting mirrors.
🅰 ◖ ♣

### Richmond Inn

108 Portswood Road,
Portswood
☎ (01703) 554523
11–11; 12–10.30 Sun
**Banks's Mild; Marston's
Bitter, Pedigree, HBC** ⓗ
Popular, two-bar pub in a busy
suburb. Dating from the 1870s,
it was once owned by
Winchester Brewery. The
public bar has Sky TV, and live
Irish music Thu; the lounge has
an old LSD cash register. Good
whisky selection. 🅰 🍺 ♣

### Salisbury Arms

126 Shirley High Street, Shirley
(opp. shopping precinct)
☎ (01703) 774624
10–11; 12–3, 7–10.30 Sun
**Banks's Mild; Marston's
Bitter, Pedigree, HBC** ⓗ
Friendly, refurbished pub on a
street corner. One bar, centrally
situated, allows all-round
access. Sparklers are used only
when requested. ◖

### Waterloo Arms

101 Waterloo Road, Freemantle
☎ (01703) 220022
12–11; 12–10.30 Sun
**Hop Back GFB, Special, Entire
Stout, Thunderstorm,
Powerhouse, Summer
Lightning** ⓗ
Popular, one-bar local with a
mixed clientele. The walls are
festooned with awards for Hop
Back beers. One-off brews are
occasionally available. Ten
mins' walk from Central
station. No food Sun.
🅰 ◖ ≢ (Millbrook) ♣

## Sparsholt

### Plough

☎ (01962) 776353
11–2.30 (3 Fri & Sat), 6.30–10.30 (11 Fri
& Sat); 12–3, 7.30–10.30 Sun
**Wadworth IPA, 6X; guest
beer** ⓗ
Pleasant, 18th-century pub in
the downs west of Winchester.
Though popular for its high
quality food (not served Sun
eve), it is still pleasant for a
drink. No fruit machines;
impromptu live music.
Wheelchair WC.
🅰 🅰 ◖ 🅑 Å ♣ P

## Standford

### Robin Hood

Standford Lane (B3004)
☎ (01428) 751508
11–11; 12–3, 7–10.30 Sun
**Draught Bass; Gibbs Mew
Overlord, Salisbury, Bishop's
Tipple** ⓗ
From the outside this pub
resembles a railway station! It
features fine etched windows
and has an interesting blend of
furniture styles within. Live
music Wed and Fri. Mexican-
style food is a speciality.
🅰 ◖ 🅑 P

## Stoke

### White Hart

Off B3048
☎ (01264) 738355
12–3 (11.30–4 Sat), 6.30–11; 12–3,
7–10.30 Sun
**Brakspear Bitter** ⓖ**; Fuller's
London Pride; Hampshire
King Alfred's, Lionheart,
Pendragon; Strong Country
Bitter** ⓗ

Traditional, friendly village
local with a skittle alley.
Unusual and interesting menu.
🅰 🅰 🅰 ◖ 🅑 & ♣ P 🍺

## Thruxton

### White Horse

Off A303 westbound, between
Thruxton and E Cholderton
☎ (01264) 772401
11.30–3, 6.30–11; 12–3, 7–10.30 Sun
**Fuller's London Pride; Smiles
Brewery Bitter, seasonal
beers** ⓗ
Charming old thatched pub
with a beamed ceiling. Carving
above the fireplace dates it
from 1451. No food Sun/Mon
eves. Quiz Sun; folk Thu. It is
situated below the A303 dual
carriageway but, once inside,
you'd never know. The family
room is the pool room.
🅰 Q 🅰 🅑 ◖ 🅑 & ♣ ⌂ P

## Totford

### Woolpack Inn

On B3046, S of Brown
Candover
☎ (01962) 732101
11.30–3, 6–11; 12–3, 7–10.30 Sun
**Cheriton Pots Ale; Gale's
HSB; Hardy Country; Palmers
IPA** ⓗ
16th-century, flint and stone
country inn and restaurant.
The large, pleasant garden has
a duck pond.
🅰 Q 🅰 🍴 ◖ 🅑 ♣ P

## Totton

### Swan Inn

High Street
☎ (01703) 862185
11–11; 12–3, 7–10.30 Sun
**Flowers Original; Strong
Country Bitter; Whitbread
Pompey Royal; guest beer**
(occasional) ⓗ
Friendly pub in the older part
of Totton. The nautically-
themed lounge tends to attract
locals whereas the larger
public bar is popular with
younger drinkers. The
walled garden is very
pleasant on summer eves.
🅰 ◖ 🍺 ≢ ♣

## Twyford

### Phoenix

High Street (B3335, 1 mile from
M3 jct 11) ☎ (01962) 713322
11.30–3, 6–11; 12–3, 7–10.30 Sun
**Marston's Bitter, Pedigree** ⓗ
Busy, friendly inn serving a
good range of value for money
food. The skittle alley/function
room becomes a family room
lunchtime. The pub can
arrange accommodation in
village houses.
🅰 🅰 🅰 ◖ 🅑 ♣ P

## Upper Clatford

### Crook & Shears
Off A343
☎ (01264) 361543
11.30–3.30, 6–11; 12–3.30, 7–10.30 Sun
**Flowers Original; Fuller's Chiswick, London Pride; guest beers** H
Two-bar, thatched, 17th-century village inn with a strong local trade. Real pub food includes 12 different sausages (no eve meals Sun). Famous for its skittle alley and barbecues.
🏚 Q ❀ ◑ ▶ ⊞ ♣

## Upton Grey

### Hoddington Arms
Bidden Road (off A32)
☎ (01256) 862371
11.30–2.30 (3 Sat), 6.30 (7 Sat)–11; 12–2.30, 7–10.30 Sun
**Marston's Pedigree** G; **Morland IPA, Original, Tanner's Jack, Old Speckled Hen** H
18th-century listed building in a pretty village, serving good quality food: a main bar, a dining room and a good-sized family room. No food Sun eve.
🏚 ☖ ❀ ◑ ▶ ♣ P

## Wallington

### White Horse
44 North Wallington (¾ mile off A27 at Delme roundabout)
☎ (01329) 235197
11–2.30, 5 (6 Sat)–11; 12–2.30, 7–10.30 Sun
**Draught Bass** H & G; **M&B Brew XI** H; **guest beers** H/G
Small village local next to the River Wallington, with a patio garden. Well renovated, its two bars each have a different character, with fresh flowers on the tables. Its situation, on the fringe of Fareham, makes parking difficult – use the council car park at night (opposite Sainsbury). No meals Sun, or Mon eve; booking advised other eves.
🏚 ❀ ◑ ▶ ♣

## Weyhill

### Weyhill Fair
Weyhill Road (A342)
☎ (01264) 773631
11–3, 6 (5 Fri)–11; 12–3, 7–10.30 Sun
**Morrells Bitter, Varsity, Graduate; guest beers** H
300-year-old, chalk-walled pub offering daily changing guest beers (printed menu). Interesting, freshly cooked food. Near Thruxton circuit.
🏚 ☖ ❀ ◑ ▶ ▲ P ⊬ 🍺

## Whitchurch

### Prince Regent
104 London Road (B3400, ½ mile from centre)
☎ (01256) 892179
11–11; 12–10.30 Sun
**Archers Best Bitter; Hop Back GFB, Summer Lightning** H
Friendly, unpretentious village local overlooking the Test Valley, well worth the walk up from the village. Food available all day. Cellar bar for functions. 🏚 ❀ ◑ ▶ ♣ ⌂ P

## Whitsbury

### Cartwheel
Whitsbury Road (signed from A338) ☎ (01725) 518362
11–2.30 (3 Sat), 6–11; 12–3, 7–10.30 Sun
**Beer range varies** H
Remote, but thriving, free house with a games area and a dining room. Six ales are usually available, offering an excellent selection. An imaginative and varied menu features some local produce. No food Tue eve in winter. Formerly a barn, bakery and wheelwright's, hence the name. 🏚 Q ❀ ◑ ▶ ▲ ♣ P

## Winchester

### Foresters Arms
71 North Walls
☎ (01962) 861539
12–11; 12–10.30 Sun
**Marston's Bitter, Pedigree** H
Boisterous, busy, sidestreet local, close to the sports centre. Comfortable and friendly, it has active darts and pool teams. ≢ ♣

### Hyde Tavern
57 Hyde Street (400 yds N of Theatre Royal)
☎ (01962) 862592
11–2.30 (3 Sat), 5 (6 Sat)–11; 12–3, 7–10.30 Sun
**Marston's Bitter, Pedigree, HBC** H
Delightful, 15th-century, two-bar local with low ceilings and a bizarrely sloping floor. The ever-encroaching tide of swan-neck dispense has thankfully avoided this pub. Definitely worth finding. Q ⊞ ≢

### Wykeham Arms
75 Kingsgate Street
☎ (01962) 853834
11–11; 12–10.30 Sun
**Hardy Dorchester, Country, Royal Oak** H
Large, busy and attractive, corner backstreet pub near the cathedral and college, striving to provide old-fashioned qualities in separate drinking and eating areas. Cosy rooms and old school desks are features. No food Sun.
🏚 Q ☖ ◑ ▶ P ⊬

## Winchfield

### Woodys
Station Hill ☎ (01252) 842129
12–2.30, 5.30–11; 12–3, 7–10.30 Sun
**Ringwood Best Bitter; guest beers** H
Free house in extensive grounds, comprised of a public bar, a saloon and a third (no-smoking) bar, which is used as an eating area. Up to four beers available, plus occasional cider. Function room (with handpumps).
❀ ☖ ◑ ▶ ♿ ≢ ⌂ P ⊬

## Wolverton

### George & Dragon
Townsend (1 mile off A339)
☎ (01635) 298292
12–3, 5.30–11; 12–3, 7–10.30 Sun
**Brakspear Special; Fuller's London Pride; Hampshire King Alfred's; Wadworth IPA, 6X** H
Characterful, large, relaxed country pub with a wealth of beams and a big log fire. The selection of good food includes vegetarian options. Separate skittle alley/function room.
🏚 Q ❀ ◑ ▶ ⊞ P

## Wonston

### Wonston Arms
Stoke Charity Road (off A30 at Sutton Scotney)
☎ (01962) 760289
11–3, 6.30–11; 12–3, 7–10.30 Sun
**Palmers IPA; guest beers** H
Unspoilt basic local with one large room; popular with a cricket team. A genuine no-nonsense pub serving three changing guest beers.
🏚 Q ❀ ♿ ♣ P

## Woolton Hill

### Rampant Cat
Broad Layings (off A343 then road opp. 'The Stores' in village centre)
☎ (01635) 253474
12–3 (not Mon), 7–11; 12–3, 7–10.30 Sun
**Archers Best Bitter; Arkell's 3B, Kingsdown; guest beer** H
Pleasant, welcoming country pub with a large L-shaped bar, friendly locals and a resident alsatian dog. A separate restaurant leads to a patio and large garden. Popular with ramblers (near NT woodlands). No meals Mon.
🏚 Q ❀ ◑ ▶ ♣ P

**Try also: Coopers Arms** (Ushers)

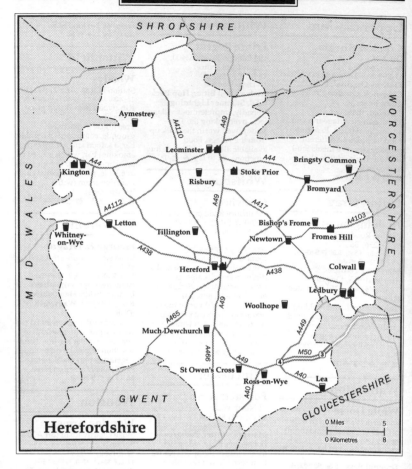

Herefordshire

## Aymestrey

### Riverside Inn
☎ (01568) 708440
12–3, 6.30–11; 12–3, 7–10.30 Sun
**Morland Old Speckled Hen;
Otter Bitter, Ale; Wadworth
6X; guest beers** Ⓗ
Friendly, 16th-century,
riverside inn where the bar
area leads through to a lounge
with plenty of seating. Good
menu; unusual ales for the
area.
🏨 Q ✿ 🛏 ◑ ▶ ▲ ♣ P

## Bishop's Frome

### Chase Inn
On B4214
☎ (01885) 490234
12 (11.30 Sat)–3.30, 6–11; 12–3.30,
7–10.30 Sun
**Hook Norton Best Bitter; Wye
Valley Bitter** Ⓗ
Uncomplicated, relaxing and
friendly pub opposite the
village green. Two bar areas
and a restaurant cater for all

and are run with enthusiasm.
Sun lunches are particularly
good value. An ideal B&B stop.
Buxom Bitter is a house beer
from Wye Valley. Children's
choices on the menu.
🏨 ✿ 🛏 ◑ ▶ 🍴 ♣ P

## Bringsty Common

### Live & Let Live
Off A44; at pub sign follow
right-hand track onto common
OS699547
☎ (01886) 821462
12–3 (Wed & Fri), 6–11; 11–11 Sat &
summer; 12–10.30 Sun
**Draught Bass; Wye Valley
HPA; guest beer** Ⓗ
One of the last of a breed: an
inn-cum-cottage with
marvellous views towards the
Malverns, a superb landlady
and many original features,
including a large fireplace and
low beams. Snuff available. A
must! No road access means a
drive across the common is
necessary.
🏨 Q ✿ 🍴 ▲ ♣ ➪

## Bromyard

### Rose & Lion
5 New Road
☎ (01885) 482381
11–3, 6–11; 11–11 Sat; 12–3, 7–10.30
Sun
**Wye Valley Bitter, HPA,
Supreme; guest beer** Ⓗ
Friendly, unpretentious pub
with two bars: a public bar
populated by people who
enjoy games and a cosy, laid-
back lounge. A games room at

the rear has a pool table. Unashamedly a drinkers' pub – Wye Valley's latest acquisition. Q ❀ ⊞ ♣ P

# Colwall

## Chase Inn

Chase Road, Upper Colwall (200 yds off B4218, Walwyn Rd, signed 'British Camp')
☎ (01684) 540276
12–2.30 (not Tue), 6–11; 12–2.30, 7–10.30 Sun
**Donnington BB, SBA; Wye Valley HPA, seasonal beers** Ⓗ
Delightfully discrete, two-bar free house tucked away in a wooded backwater of the Malvern Hills. Very limited, but very wholesome, lunchtime menu (not served Sun); probably the finest pub garden in the county. Worth the 25-min walk from Colwall station. Q ❀ ◑ ⊞ ♣ P

# Hereford

## Barrels

69 St Owen Street
☎ (01432) 274968
11–11; 12–10.30 Sun
**Wye Valley Bitter, HPA, Supreme, Brew 69, seasonal beers; guest beer** Ⓗ
One of the last multi-roomed pubs in Hereford: brash, lively and home of Wye Valley Brewery. Good mix of locals; popular with students at weekends. Charity beer festival Aug Bank Hol. No food served.
❀ ⊞ ♣ ▱

## Lichfield Vaults

11 Church Street
☎ (01432) 267994
11–11; 12–10.30 Sun
**Ansells Mild; Marston's Pedigree; Tetley Bitter; guest beers** Ⓗ
Refurbished town-centre pub, a Festival Ale House with one large bar, located near the cathedral. Popular at weekends with the more discerning city-centre drinkers.
❀ ◑ & ⇌ ♣

## Spread Eagle

King Street ☎ (01432) 272205
11–3, 6–11; 11–11 Sat; 12–10.30 Sun
**Draught Bass; Boddingtons Bitter; Fuller's London Pride; Greene King Abbot; Wadworth 6X; guest beer** Ⓗ
Wooden floors and oak beams lend character to the main bar areas, but this pub feels metropolitan with its young and lively clientele at weekends. Annual beer festival. Restaurant available.
❀ ◑ ▶

## Three Elms Inn

1 Canon Pyon Road
☎ (01432) 273338

11–11; 12–10.30 Sun
**Boddingtons Bitter; Flowers Original; Marston's Pedigree; guest beers** Ⓗ
At first glance a standard Whitbread house; step inside this one-bar refurbished pub to discover an enthusiastic landlord ensuring quality and variety. Six beers; excellent family facilities. An oasis in an area of Hereford devoid of good beer. Berni Inn menu. Wheelchair WC.
♿ ❀ ◑ ▶ & ♣ P

## Treacle Mine

83–85 St Martin's Street
☎ (01432) 266022
11–3.30 (12–3 Mon), 6–11; 11–11 Fri & Sat; 12–10.30 Sun
**Banks's Mild, Bitter; guest beers** Ⓗ
Deservedly popular, stylishly refurbished, small, one-bar pub on the south side of the Wye. Old and new meet in an unorthodox mix of beams, bare brickwork and satellite TV. Lively locals guarantee a buzz at all times. Parking can be a problem. Cider in summer.
♣ ▱

## Victory

88 St Owen Street
☎ (01432) 274998
11–11; 12–10.30 Sun
**Wye Valley Bitter, HPA, Supreme, seasonal beers; guest beer** Ⓗ
Very successful part of the Wye Valley estate: the long single bar area of this busy, but friendly, pub has a galleon theme, a good, balanced clientele and the best variety of beers in Hereford. Good value food; live music. Herefordshire CAMRA *Town Pub of the Year* 1995. ♿ ❀ ◑ ▶ & ♣ ▱

**Try also: Castle Pool Hotel,** Castle St (Free)

# Kington

## Olde Tavern ☆

22 Victoria Road
☎ (01544) 231384
7.30–11; 12–3, 7–11 Sat; 12–3, 7.30–10.30 Sun
**Ansells Bitter** Ⓗ
An outstanding relic of old Kington, a must for all connoisseurs of the English pub: two bars complete with settles, benches and curios hide behind an ornate Victorian facade. A previous winner of *Best Pub* awards. Q ⊞ ♣

## Old Fogey

37 High Street
☎ (01544) 230685
5.30 (11 Sat)–11; 12–10.30 Sun
**Wood Special; Wye Valley Bitter; guest beers** Ⓗ
One-bar pub with a wonderfully snug and unspoilt

interior and interesting bar furniture. The friendly locals and cracking atmosphere make a visit a treat. There are too few pubs of this standard around! Q ♣

# Lea

## Crown Inn

Gloucester Road (A40)
☎ (01989) 750407
12–3, 6.30–11; 12–3, 7–10.30 Sun
**John Smith's Bitter; RCH Pitchfork, East St Cream; guest beer** Ⓗ
15th-century pub with a half-timbered room which has recently been opened without disturbing the resident ghost or spoiling the pub atmosphere. Enterprising menu, well-cooked and presented (no eve meals Sun); good value. Herefordshire CAMRA *Country Pub of the Year* 1995.
♿ ❀ ◑ ▶ ♣ P

# Ledbury

## Horseshoe Inn

Homend ☎ (01531) 632770
12–11; 12–3, 7–10.30 Sun
**Ansells Bitter; Wye Valley Bitter; guest beers** Ⓗ
A flight of stone steps leads into this single-bar pub that, although fitted out in contemporary fashion, still retains much character. The most adventurous guest beers for Ledbury area are served.
♿ ❀ ◑ ▶ ⇌ ♣

## Prince of Wales

Church Lane ☎ (01531) 632250
11–3 (4 Sat), 7–11; 12–3, 7–10.30 Sun
**Banks's Hanson's Mild, Bitter** Ⓗ
16th-century, black and white timbered pub located in famously picturesque Church Lane, a recently recobbled alley that appears on many chocolate boxes. Two bars mix comfort and character. The landlord is keen on pub games. Guest cider in summer.
◑ ♣ ▱

## Royal Oak Hotel

Southend (just S of crossroads in town centre)
☎ (01531) 632110
11–3, 6–11; 12–3, 6–10.30 Sun
**Ledbury Doghill, SB, Best** Ⓗ
Home of Ledbury Brewing Co., which operates from an old brewhouse, last used in 1921. The hotel has a ground floor bar, with dining chairs and tables, and a cellar bar that caters for the drinking trade, with live entertainment from time to time.
♿ ⌂ ◑ ▶ ♣ P ✄

**Try also: Brewery Inn,** Bye St (Marston's)

## Leominster

### Black Horse
South Street
☎ (01568) 611946
11–2.30, 6–11; 11–11 Sat; 12–3, 7–10.30 Sun
**Courage Directors; Wadworth 6X; guest beers** [H]
Outstanding free house which has the best selection of real ales for miles. A lively public contrasts with a smaller lounge and restaurant. No eve meals Sun. The 'tap' for Marches Ales, which include a house beer. ❀ ◖ ◗ ⊞ ♿ ⇌ ♣ P

### Grapes Vaults
Broad Street
☎ (01568) 611404
11–3 (3.30 Sat), 5 (6 Sat)–11; 12–3.30, 6–10.30 Sun
**Banks's Mild; Marston's Bitter, Pedigree; guest beers** [H]
A plain facade conceals a brilliantly restored town pub: wood screens, etched-glass and settles make it a must. Adventurous guest beers. Good value food. Parking is a problem. ♨ Q ◖ ◗

**Try also: Hop Pole**, Bridge St (Free)

## Letton

### Swan Inn
On A438 ☎ (01544) 327304
11–3, 6–11; 11–11 Wed–Sat; 12–3, 7–10.30 Sun
**Fuller's London Pride; guest beer** (summer) [H]
Pleasant roadside inn convenient for Wye Valley walks. The main bar caters well for diners and locals alike (food is always available). Separate restaurant. Old Swan Bitter is brewed by Wye Valley.
♨ Q ❀ 🛏 ◖ ◗ ⊞ ▲ P

## Much Dewchurch

### Black Swan
On B4348, 2 miles W of A49
☎ (01981) 540295
12–3 (11.30–3 Sat), 6–11; 12–3, 7–10.30 Sun
**Draught Bass; Fuller's London Pride; Taylor Landlord; guest beers** [H]
14th-century building modernised in the 17th century, with a very appealing interior. Wide range of ales, including a house beer; decent food.
♨ Q ❀ 🛏 ◖ ◗ ⊞ ▲ ♣ P

## Newtown

### Newtown Inn
Newtown Cross (A4103/A417 jct) ☎ (01531) 670423
11–3, 7 (6.30 Sat)–11; 12–3, 7–10.30 Sun
**Banks's Bitter; Draught Bass; guest beer** (summer) [H]
Small, standard roadside pub. An unpretentious, two-bar interior includes a small dining area and a conventional public bar. Dining can be popular – booking advised. No eve meals Sun. Late supper licence Mon–Sat. Q ❀ 🛏 ◖ ◗ ⊞ ♣ P

## Risbury

### Hop Pole Inn (Bert's) ☆
On Pencombe road, ½ mile E of village OS554549
11–5, 6–11; 12–3, 7–10.30 Sun
**Wood Parish *or* Special** [G]
200-year-old, isolated pub that time has forgotten. The landlord has been here since 1929 and has not been swayed by the vagaries of fashion – no keg beers; no gimmicks. The single bar has bus seats. Beer is served straight from the cellar.
♨ Q ❀ ⊞ ♣ P

## Ross-on-Wye

### Crown & Sceptre
Market Place ☎ (01989) 562765
11–11; 12–10.30 Sun
**Archers Best Bitter; Draught Bass; Greene King Abbot; Morland Old Speckled Hen; guest beers** [H]
*The* real ale pub in Ross: this comfortable, town-centre pub is very popular, especially at weekends. Good food (no eve meals in winter). Beer festival Easter. Herefordshire CAMRA *Pub of the Year* 1994.
♨ ❀ ◖ ◗ ♣ ⌓

**Try also: Geezers Bar**, 14B Henry St (Free)

## St Owen's Cross

### New Inn
☎ (01989) 730274
12–2.30 (3 Sat), 6–11; 12–3, 7–10.30 Sun
**Draught Bass; Tetley Bitter; Wadworth 6X; guest beers** [H]
18th-century gem covered with hanging baskets in summer. The interior boasts fine fireplaces and furnishings going back to the 16th century. Good balance between ale and food (try the doorstop sandwiches).
♨ ❀ 🛏 ◖ ◗ ▲ ♣ P

## Tillington

### Bell Inn
Tillington Road
☎ (01432) 760395
11–3, 6–11; 12–3, 7–10.30 Sun
**Boddingtons Bitter; Fuller's London Pride; Whitbread WCPA; guest beer** [H]
Neat and tidy inn and restaurant at the heart of the village. A lively public bar, with a jukebox, contrasts with a mellow lounge, which divides into bar and patio-styled areas. Good for families at weekends.
♨ ❀ ◖ ⊞ ▲ ♣ ⌓ P

## Whitney-on-Wye

### Rhydspence Inn
On A438, 1 mile W of village
☎ (01497) 831262
11–2.30, 7–11; 12–2.30, 7–10.30 Sun
**Draught Bass; Felinfoel Double Dragon; Robinson's Best Bitter** [H]
Plush, refined, 14th-century inn that straddles the Welsh border. It retains many fine original features plus a public bar. Good food; extensive wine list; à la carte restaurant. ♨ Q
♘ ❀ 🛏 ◖ ◗ ⊞ ▲ ♣ ⌓ P

## Woolhope

### Crown Inn
☎ (01432) 860468
12–2.30, 6.30–11; 12–3, 7–10.30 Sun
**Hook Norton Best Bitter; Smiles Best Bitter; Tetley Bitter** [H]
Unashamedly successful pub that specialises in food. Very popular with out-of-town diners, it also encourages a discerning beer trade – an area of the bar being set aside. Very welcoming.
Q ❀ 🛏 ◖ ◗ ⌓ P

## BOOMING AHEAD

The micro-brewery boom continues apace, with well over 60 new breweries featured in this edition of the *Good Beer Guide.* A full list of new producers can be found on page 57, with complete details of their beers in the breweries section at the back of the book.

# WHO OWNS WHOM?

Lack of space in the pub entries prohibits the *Good Beer Guide* from outlining exactly who brews which beer brands. The national brewers make little effort to stamp their names on all their products, preferring in many cases to allow drinkers to believe that the beers on sale come from small, craft breweries. The fact is most of them did, at one time, come from such local producers but these were bought up and closed by the big brewers, with the beer brands transferred elsewhere.

Full details of all beers brewed by the nationals can be found in the beers index and the breweries section at the back of this book, but here is a quick checklist of who owns which real ale brands.

## BASS

Hancock's
M&B
Stones
Worthington

## CARLSBERG-TETLEY

ABC/Aylesbury
Allsopp's
Ansells
Arrol's
Benskins
Dartmoor
Firkin
Friary Meux
HP&D (Holt, Plant & Deakin)
Ind Coope
Nicholson's
Tetley
Peter Walker

## GREENALLS (PUB GROUP)

Davenports
Devenish
Shipstone's

## SCOTTISH COURAGE

Matthew Brown
Courage
Home
McEwan
Newcastle
John Smith's
Theakston
Webster's
Wilson's
Younger

## WHITBREAD

Bentley's
Boddingtons
Castle Eden
Chester's
Flowers
Fremlins
Higsons
Oldham
Strong
Wethered

Some regional brewers also own and use the brand names from closed breweries: Banks's (Hanson's), Federation (Buchanan's), Greene King (Rayments), Robinson's (Hartleys) and Ward's (Darley) are the most prominent.

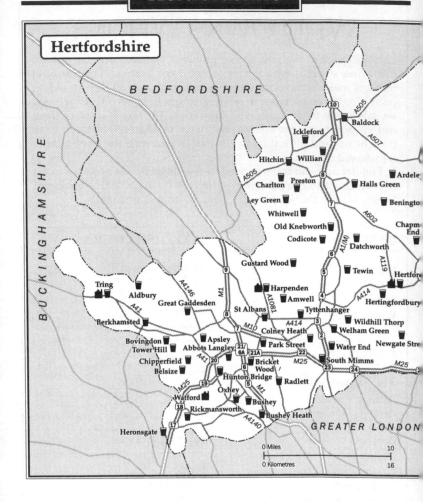

**Hertfordshire**

*BEDFORDSHIRE*

*BUCKINGHAMSHIRE*

Baldock
Ickleford
Hitchin · Willian
Charlton · Preston · Halls Green · Ardele
Ley Green · Beningto
Whitwell
Old Knebworth · Chapm End
Codicote · Datchworth
Gustard Wood · Tewin · Hertfor
Tring · Harpenden
Aldbury · Amwell
Great Gaddesden · Hertingfordbury
St Albans · Tyttenhanger
Berkhamsted · Wildhill Thorp
Apsley · Colney Heath · Welham Green
Bovingdon · Abbots Langley · Water End · Newgate Stre
Tower Hill · Park Street
Chipperfield · Bricket · South Mimms
Belsize · Wood
Hunton Bridge
Oxhey · Radlett
Watford
Rickmansworth · Bushey
Bushey Heath
Heronsgate · *GREATER LONDON*

0 Miles 10
0 Kilometres 16

---

## Abbots Langley

### Compasses
95 Tibbs Hill Road
☎ (01923) 262870
11–11; 12–4, 7–10.30 Sun
**Courage Best Bitter, Directors;
Fuller's London Pride;
Ruddles County** H
A strong food emphasis has
not spoiled this pub which is
still popular with locals. Over
100 whiskies available.
❀ ◑ ♿ ♣ P

## Aldbury

### Greyhound
19 Stocks Road
☎ (01442) 851228
10.30–11; 12–10.30 Sun
**Tring Ridgeway; guest
beers** H
Attractive village pub with a
traditional, unspoilt front bar
dominated by a huge fireplace.

Good food menu. The house
beer comes from the local Tring
Brewery. Cider in summer.
🏚 ❀ 🛏 ◑ ▶ 🍴 ♿ ▲ ♣ ○

**Try also: Valiant Trooper,
Trooper Rd (Free)**

## Amwell

### Elephant & Castle
Amwell Lane (1 mile W of B651
in Wheathampstead) OS167133
☎ (01582) 832175
11–3, 5.30–11; 11–11 Sat; 12–10.30 Sun
**Beer range varies** H
18th-century pub made from
three cottages with a glass-
covered, 200ft well in the bar
area. The two bars are at
different levels. Large gardens
in a peaceful setting. The one
regular house ale, Amwell
(ABV 3.7%), comes from
Carlsberg-Tetley. Seven guest
beers.
🏚 Q ❀ ◑ ▶ P

## Apsley

### White Lion
44 London Road
☎ (01442) 68948
11–3, 5.30–11; 11–11 Fri & Sat; 12–
10.30 Sun
**Fuller's London Pride, ESB,
seasonal beers** H
Street-corner local, usually
noisy (darts, quiz and football
teams), situated on the old A41
London Road. London pub-
type atmosphere. No food Sat;
book Sun lunch. Limited
parking. 🏚 ❀ ◑ ⇌ ♣ P

## Ardeley

### Jolly Waggoner
Off B1037, 1½ miles E of
Cromer OS310272
☎ (01438) 861350
12–2 (3 Sat; not Mon), 6.30–11; 12–3,
7–10.30 Sun
**Greene King IPA** G**, Abbot** H

## White Hart

21 Hitchin Street
☎ (01462) 893247
11–11; 11–4, 6.30–11 Sat; 12–3, 7–10.30 Sun
**Greene King XX Mild, IPA, Abbot** H
Popular, one-bar, town pub with a large Simpson's Brewery sign in the bar. Concessions for pensioners on real ales weekday lunchtimes. Customers may bring their own sandwiches to this 'pub with no grub'; a genuine drinkers' pub. ✿ ⧓ ♣

## Barley

### Chequers

London Road
☎ (01763) 848378
11–2.30, 5.30–11; 12–3, 7–10.30 Sun
**Greene King IPA, Abbot** H
Friendly village pub.
🏨 ✿ ◑ ▶ ♣ P

## Belsize

### Plough

Dunny Lane (Sarratt Chipperfield road) OS034008
☎ (01923) 262800
11–3, 5.30–11; 12–3, 7–10.30 Sun
**Greene King IPA; Tetley Imperial** H
Friendly, cosy country pub worth trying to find. Good food; steaks are a speciality. Children's certificate.
🏨 ✿ ◑ ▶ ♣ P

## Benington

### Lordship Arms

42 Whempstead Road (3 miles E of Stevenage via B1037)
☎ (01438) 869665
12–3, 6–11; 12–3, 7–10.30 Sun
**Fuller's ESB; McMullen AK; Young's Special; guest beers** H
Smartly renovated country local at the top end of the village, serving a changing range of interesting guest beers and home-cooked food. Telephone memorabilia includes a working red phone box in the garden. The cider varies. 🏨 ✿ ◑ ▶ ♣ ⌂ P

Try also: **Bell** (Greene King)

## Berkhamsted

### Boat

Gravel Path, Ravens Lane (off old A41 by Baptist church, by canal bridge) ☎ (01442) 877152
11–3, 5.30–11; 11–11 Fri & Sat; 12–10.30 Sun
**Fuller's Chiswick, London Pride, ESB, seasonal beers** H
Smart pub with an excellent food menu. The patio overlooks the canal. Eve meals Mon and Tue only.
✿ ◑ ▶ ♿ ⧓ ♣ P

## Bishop's Stortford

### Tap & Spile

31 North Street
☎ (01279) 654978
11–3, 5.30–11; 11–11 Fri & Sat; 12–3, 7–10.30 Sun
**Beer range varies** H
17th-century inn: three rooms on split levels plus a function room offering live music at weekends. Eight handpumps (one with cider) offer an ever-changing range of beers. Relaxed atmosphere; pleasant garden. Good food.
🏨 ✿ ◑ ♣ ⌂ P

## Bovingdon

### Wheatsheaf

High Street
☎ (01442) 832196
11–2.30 (3 Sat), 6–11; 12–3, 7–10.30 Sun
**Boddingtons Bitter; guest beer** H
Fine example of a traditional village pub – friendly, cosy and unspoilt. Dating back to the 15th century, it features lots of brass, plus old photographs of the village, old sewing machine tables and matching stools which provide a nostalgic atmosphere. Fresh food. Good choice of board games. Q ✿ ◑ ♣ P

## Bricket Wood

### Gate

Station Road
☎ (01923) 672470
12–3 (not Mon), 5.30–11; 12–4, 7–10.30 Sun
**Fuller's London Pride, ESB; Marston's Owd Rodger; Morland Old Speckled Hen; Scanlon's Spike; Tring Ridgeway; guest beers** H
Village pub offering up to nine changing beers, fruit wines, Liefmans cherry beer and occasional ciders and perries. Eve meals finish at 7.30.
✿ ◑ ▶ ⧓ P

### Moor Mill

Smug Oak Lane (off A5183 by M25 bridge) OS152024
☎ (01727) 875557
11–11; 12–10.30 Sun

---

Picturesque, 16th-century, pink-washed former cottages in a charming village setting. Friendly service in a simply furnished bar and restaurant. Good quality food from a varied menu (booking essential for Sun lunch). Large, well-tended garden. Q ✿ ◑ ▶ ♣ P

## Baldock

### Old White Horse

1 Station Road (A507/A505 jct)
☎ (01462) 893198
11–3, 5.30–11; 11–11 Sat; 12–3, 7–10.30 Sun
**Boddingtons Bitter; Fuller's London Pride; Taylor Landlord; guest beers** G/H
Former coaching inn on the old Great North Road. Recently extended, it serves usually 12 beers, some on gravity dispense. Mini-beer festivals held periodically. Jamaican cuisine available.
🏨 ✿ ◑ ▶ ⧓ ♣ P

| 🍺 INDEPENDENT BREWERIES | |
|---|---|
| **Dark Horse:** | Hertford |
| **Fox & Hounds:** | Barley |
| **Harpenden:** | Harpenden |
| **McMullen:** | Hertford |
| **Original:** | Watford |
| **Tring:** | Tring |

**Draught Bass; Courage Directors; Gale's seasonal beers; Young's Special; guest beers** H
Restored Anglo-Saxon mill on the River Ver, mentioned in the *Domesday Book*. Book for meals in the Granary dining room. All beer is dispensed through quarter-pint pull swan necks – ask if you want the light sparkler removed. The house beer comes from Bass.
🏰 Q ❀ ◖ ▮ P

## Buntingford

### Crown
17 High Street
☎ (01763) 271422
12–3, 6–11; 12–11 Sat; 12–3.30, 7–10.30 Sun
**Courage Best Bitter, Directors; Mauldons Bitter; guest beer** H
Popular, friendly pub hosting folk music Mon eve.
🏰 Q 🐾 ❀ ◖ ▮ ♣

## Bushey

### Swan
25 Park Road (off A411)
☎ (0181) 950 2256
11–11; 12–10.30 Sun
**Benskins BB; Ind Coope Burton Ale** H
Unspoilt, traditional, back-street pub. Visit it while you still can. 🏰 ♣

## Bushey Heath

### Black Boy
19 Windmill Street (off Windmill Lane)
☎ (0181) 950 2230
11.30–3 (4 Sat), 5.30–11; 11.30–11 Fri; 12–4, 7–10.30 Sun
**Adnams Bitter; Benskins BB; Chiltern Beechwood; guest beers** H
Friendly, backstreet pub well worth finding. Up to five beers available; real cider occasionally. Good quality food. ❀ ◖ ▮ ⏝ P

## Chapmore End

### Woodman
30 Chapmore End (off B158, near A602 jct) OS328164
☎ (01920) 463143
12–3, 6–11; 12–3, 7–10.30 Sun
**Greene King IPA, Abbot, seasonal beers** G
Recently extended without losing any of its character, this rural gem still dispenses its beer by gravity from the cellar in the traditional way. Large garden with a mini zoo. The varied menu includes Baltis and pizzas. No food Sat eve or Sun.
🏰 Q ❀ ◖ ▮ ▯ P

## Charlton

### Windmill
Charlton Road
☎ (01462) 432096
11–3, 5.30–11; 12–3, 7–10.30 Sun
**Adnams Broadside; Mansfield Riding Mild; Wells Eagle, Bombardier** H
Pleasant village pub serving home-cooked food daily. Ducks are resident on the stream by the garden.
❀ ◖ ▮ P

## Chipperfield

### Royal Oak
1 The Street ☎ (01923) 266537
12–3, 6–11; 12–3, 7–10.30 Sun
**Draught Bass; Flowers Original; Ind Coope Burton Ale; Worthington Bitter; guest beer** (occasional) H
Smart, friendly pub celebrating 16 years in the *Guide*. Highly polished wood and brass abound. Good food (sandwiches only Sun); book eve meals. 🏰 Q ❀ ◖ ▮ P

## Codicote

### Goat
77 High Street (B656)
☎ (01438) 820475
12–11; 12–10.30 Sun
**Adnams Bitter; Benskins BB; Greene King IPA** H
Traditional, oak-beamed, timber-framed building built in 1590, with a 17th-century barn now used as a function room. The focus of the village harvest festival. No meals Sun eve.
Q ❀ ◖ ▮ ♣ P

## Colney Heath

### Crooked Billet
High Street ☎ (01727) 822128
11–2.30, 5.30–11; 11–11 Sat; 12–10.30 (12–4, 7–10.30 winter) Sun
**Fuller's London Pride; Greene King Abbot; Theakston Best Bitter; guest beers** H
300-year-old, cottage-style pub with two bars, offering good, home-cooked food (eve meals Fri and Sat, plus Thu in summer). The large garden has a children's adventure play area. 🏰 ❀ ◖ ▮ P

## Datchworth

### Plough
5 Datchworth Green (1 mile from B197 at Woolmer Green)
☎ (01438) 813000
11.30–3, 6–11; 12–4, 7–10.30 Sun
**Greene King IPA, Abbot, seasonal beers** H
Small, welcoming local just off the village green: one room with a large, central, open wood fire. A secluded garden stands to the rear of this former Simpson's (Baldock) house built in 1840. Home-cooked food (not served Sun).
🏰 ❀ ◖ ▮ ▲ P

## Tilbury
1 Watton Road (1 mile from B197 at Woolmer Green)
☎ (01438) 812496
11–3, 5–11; 11–11 Thu–Sat; 12–10.30 Sun
**Draught Bass; Palmers IPA; guest beers** H
Large, friendly two-room pub with a dining room (no-smoking) and a large garden. A changing range of nine beers includes a mild: unusual beers and ales from small independents are a speciality. Wide range of home-cooked food. The cider varies.
Q ❀ ◖ ▮ ▯ ▲ ♣ ⏝ P

## Great Gaddesden

### Cock & Bottle
Off A4146 ☎ (01442) 255381
11.30–3, 5.30–11; 12–3, 7–10.30 Sun
**Fuller's ESB; Greene King Abbot; Hop Back Summer Lightning; Taylor Landlord; guest beers** H
Set in the Gade Valley close to Hemel Hempstead, an ever improving pub which welcomes drinkers, diners and families. Very reasonable prices; usually busy. Book for Sun lunch. Cider in summer. No-smoking area at mealtimes.
🏰 Q 🐾 ❀ ◖ ♣ ⏝ P ⚥

## Green Tye

### Prince of Wales
Off B1004 ☎ (01279) 842517
11.30–3, 5.30–11; 11–11 Sat; 12–3, 7–10.30 Sun
**Flowers IPA; McMullen AK; guest beers** H
Traditional country pub in a picturesque village in ideal rambling country. A good halt, it is mentioned in several rambling guides. Monthly guest beer. Occasional beer festivals and other events are held in a marquee in the garden. 🏰 ❀ ♣ P

## Gustard Wood

### Cross Keys
Ballslough Hill (off B651, 1 mile N of Wheathampstead) OS174165 ☎ (01582) 832165
11.15–3.30, 5.30–11; 11.15–11 Sat; 12–10.30 Sun
**Fuller's London Pride; Greene King IPA; Taylor Landlord; guest beers** H
17th-century country pub, full of clocks and toy cars. Good, reasonably priced meals (eve meals in summer only). Large garden. 🏰 Q ◖ ▮ P

# Halls Green

## Rising Sun

Weston Road (minor road from Weston to Cromer) OS275287
☎ (01462) 790487
11–2.30, 6–11; 12–3, 7–10.30 Sun
**Draught Bass; Courage Directors; McMullen AK, Country, Gladstone** Ⓗ
Beautiful, one-bar pub in the country. The enormous garden has children's play equipment. The conservatory acts as a restaurant (excellent food). Families are most welcome. Unusual range of Polish flavoured vodkas.
🏤 🍺 ❄ ◖ ▶ ♣ P

# Harpenden

## Carpenters Arms

14 Cravells Road, Southdown (off A1081) ☎ (01582) 460311
11–3, 5.30–11; 12–3, 7–10.30 Sun
**Courage Best Bitter; Ruddles County; Webster's Yorkshire Bitter; guest beers** Ⓗ
Most congenial old local – snug, homely and friendly. Devotees of classic cars will appreciate the memorabilia. No meals Sun. 🏤 Q ❄ ◖ ▶

## Harpenden Arms

30 High Street (A1081/Station Rd jct) ☎ (01582) 712095
11.30–11; 12–3, 7–10.30 Sun
**Fuller's Chiswick, London Pride, ESB, seasonal beers** *or* **guest beer** Ⓗ
A good mixture of locals and passing trade helps create a pleasant atmosphere in this popular, town-centre pub which can get very busy at weekends. Thai food restaurant attached.
❄ ◖ ▶ ⇌ ♣

## Red Cow

171 Westfield Road
☎ (01582) 621058
11–11; 12–10.30 Sun
**Harpenden Special; Marston's Pedigree; Ruddles County; Webster's Yorkshire Bitter** Ⓗ
Friendly pub housing a small brewery. Watch out for the low beams and the numerous plaques carrying drink related quotations. Efficient staff.
🏤 ❄ ◖ ▶ P 🍴

# Heronsgate

## Land of Liberty, Peace & Plenty

Long Lane (off M25 jct 17) OS023949 ☎ (01923) 282226
12–11; 12–10.30 Sun
**Courage Best Bitter; Young's Special; guest beers** Ⓗ
Isolated pub with a welcome for all, serving three guest beers from independent breweries; the choice changes

regularly as does the real cider. Up to six draught beers from Belgium, too. Occasional beer festivals. ❄ ◖ ▶ ♣ ⌂ P 🍴

# Hertford

## Sportsman

117 Fore Street
☎ (01992) 551621
12–3, 5.30–11; 12–11 Fri & Sat; 12–3, 7–10.30 Sun
**Adnams Bitter; Everards Tiger; Marston's Pedigree; Ruddles Best Bitter; Wadworth 6X** Ⓗ
Busy, town-centre pub, decorated with sporting artefacts. Formerly known as the Blue Coat Boy, after the local school, it was once the brewery tap for Young's of Hertford. No food Sun eve; the former restaurant is now a lounge. ◖ ▶ ⇌ (East)

## White Horse

33 Castle Street
☎ (01992) 501950
12–2.30, 5.30–11; 12–3, 7–11 Sat; 12–3.30, 7–10.30 Sun
**Dark Horse Ale, Sunrunner; Fuller's London Pride; Hook Norton Best Bitter** Ⓗ**; guest beers** Ⓗ/Ⓖ
Hertford's leading free house, specialising in guest beers from all leading micros and small brewers; also the 'tap' for the Dark Horse brewery. The upper floor is a no-smoking area where children are welcome. No canned music; live folk alternate Sun lunch. No meals Sat. 🏤 Q 🍺 ❄ ◖ 🍴 ⇌ (East/North) ⌂ ⊁

# Hertingfordbury

## Prince of Wales

244 Hertingfordbury Road (400 yds from A414)
☎ (01992) 581149
11–3, 5.30 (6 Sat)–11; 12–4, 7–10.30 Sun
**Fuller's London Pride; McMullen AK; Wadworth 6X; Younger IPA; guest beers** Ⓗ
Popular, one-bar village local which always offers a warm welcome. Good value varied menu (no food Sun eve).
🏤 ❄ 🍴 ◖ ▶ ♣ P

# High Wych

## Rising Sun

1 mile W of Sawbridgeworth
☎ (01279) 724099
12–2.30 (3 Fri & Sat), 5–11; 12–3, 7–10.30 Sun
**Courage Best Bitter, Directors; guest beers** (weekends) Ⓖ
A *Guide* regular for over 20 years – affectionately known as 'Sid's'. Lager in bottles only. Join in the conversation at the bar. 🏤 Q 🍺 ❄ ♣ P

# Hitchin

## Victoria

1 Ickleford Road
☎ (01462) 432682
12–3, 6–11; 12–3, 7.30–10.30 Sun
**Greene King IPA, Abbot** Ⓗ
Welcoming corner local between the station and the town centre, with a split-level interior. Home-cooked food. Limited parking.
❄ ◖ ▶ ⇌ ♣ P

# Hunton Bridge

## Kings Head

Bridge Road (off A41, S of M25 jct 20) OS082005
☎ (01923) 262307
11–4, 5–11; 12–4, 7–10.30 Sun (may vary in summer)
**Benskins BB; Ind Coope Burton Ale; Tetley Bitter; guest beers** Ⓗ
Friendly pub where the large garden has children's entertainments. The family room and skittle alley are in the old canal stables (can be cold in winter). Guest beers are from the Carlsberg-Tetley range.
🍺 ❄ ◖ ▶ ♣ P

# Ickleford

## Cricketers

107 Arlesey Road (off A600)
☎ (01462) 432629
11–3, 6–11; 11–11 Sat & summer Fri; 12–10.30 Sun
**Draught Bass; Fuller's London Pride; Ruddles Best Bitter; Shepherd Neame Master Brew Bitter; Wadworth 6X; Woodforde's Wherry; guest beers** Ⓗ
Very friendly village free house which attracts custom from near and far. Usually at least ten beers at any one time. Local CAMRA *Pub of the Year* 1994. Home-cooked food and good accommodation.
Q ❄ 🛏 ◖ ▶ ♣ ⌂ P 🍴

# Ley Green

## Plough

Plough Lane ☎ (01438) 871394
11–11; 12–4, 7–11 Sun
**Greene King IPA, Abbot** Ⓗ
Country pub overlooking farmland and woods, with a garden and paddock for children.
🏤 Q 🍺 ❄ ◖ ▶ ♠ ♣ P

# Newgate Street

## Coach & Horses

☎ (01707) 872326
11–3, 5.30–11; 12–3, 7–10.30 Sun (may vary in summer)
**ABC Best Bitter; Ansells Bitter; Draught Bass; Dartmoor Best Bitter; Tetley Bitter** Ⓗ

Genuine, old, ivy-covered pub next to the church. Many different clubs meet here. The family room doubles as a function room.
🏚 Q ☎ ⚑ P

## Old Knebworth

### Lytton Arms
Park Lane
☎ (01438) 812312
11–3, 5–11; 11–11 Fri & Sat; 12–3, 7–10.30 Sun
**Draught Bass; Fuller's London Pride; Theakston Best Bitter; Woodforde's Wherry; guest beers** Ⓗ
Large, 19th-century Lutyens building on the edge of Knebworth Park with a conservatory at the rear. The 12 beers always available usually include a mild; large selection of bottled foreign beers, plus cider and perry, and 50-plus malt whiskies. Children's certificate.
🏚 Q ☎ ⚘ ◖ ♦ ♣ ⌂ P ⚲

## Oxhey

### Victoria
39 Chalk Hill (A411, 200 yds SE of Bushey Arches)
☎ (01923) 227993
11–3, 5.30–11; 12–4.30, 7–10.30 Sun
**Benskins BB; guest beer** Ⓗ
Nice, little two-bar pub in a busy area with unusual, split-level bars and a hidden room. Ask for the guest beer if it is not obvious.
⚘ ◖ ⊟ ⇌ (Bushey)

## Park Street

### Overdraught
86 Watling Street (A5183)
☎ (01727) 874280
11–11; 12–3, 7–10.30 Sun
**Marston's Bitter, Pedigree; guest beers** Ⓗ
Friendly village local with two bar areas, plus an outside bar with a barbecue for summer. The two guest beers come from micro-breweries. Children's certificate. Good value lunches; eve meals finish early.
🏚 Q ⚘ ◖ ⇌ ⌂ P

## Preston

### Red Lion
The Green
☎ (01462) 459585
12–3, 5.30–11; 12–11 Sat; 12–3, 7–10.30 Sun
**Adnams Bitter; Badger Tanglefoot; Greene King IPA; guest beers** Ⓗ
Village-owned, Georgian-style pub. Good home-cooked food is served daily.
🏚 ☎ ⚘ ◖ ♦ ♣ P

## Pye Corner

### Plume of Feathers
On High Wych road between Harlow and Sawbridgeworth
☎ (01279) 424154
11.30–3, 5.30 (7 Sat)–11; 12–4, 7–10.30 Sun
**Courage Best Bitter; Marston's Pedigree; Theakston XB; guest beers** Ⓗ/Ⓖ
Former court house and coaching inn boasting a ghost and fast gaining a reputation for good food. Three regularly changing guest beers (one on gravity). Children's certificate applied for; family-oriented. Ten mins' walk from Harlow Town station. 🏚 ◖ ♦ ⊟ ♣ P

## Radlett

### Cat & Fiddle
14 Watling Street (A5183)
☎ (01923) 469523
11–11; 12–10.30 Sun
**Courage Best Bitter, Directors; Morland Old Speckled Hen; guest beers** Ⓗ
18th-century pub comprised of many oak-panelled bars, with the feel of a country inn; replete with china cats and bric-a-brac.
🏚 Q ⚘ ◖ ⇌ ♣ P

## Rickmansworth

### Fox & Hounds
183 High Street
☎ (01923) 441119
11–11; 12–10.30 Sun
**Courage Best Bitter, Directors; guest beer** Ⓗ
Recently refurbished pub, retaining separate public and lounge bars and a popular meeting room. Friendly local atmosphere. Note the unusual pub sign.
🏚 ⚘ ◖ ⇌ ⊖ ♣ P

## St Albans

### Farriers Arms
35 Lower Dagnall Street (off A5183) ☎ (01727) 851015
12–2.30, 5.30–11; 12–11 Sun (may vary)
**McMullen AK, Country, Gladstone; guest beer** Ⓗ
Lively backstreet local, where there's always sporting activity. A perennial entry in the *Guide*. Parking can be tricky. ◖ ♣

### Garibaldi
61 Albert Street (off Holywell Hill) ☎ (01727) 855046
11–11; 12–10.30 Sun
**Fuller's Chiswick, London Pride, ESB, seasonal beers** Ⓗ
Friendly, popular, backstreet local. Good food served all day until 9, except Sun eve.
⚘ ◖ ♦ ⇌ (Abbey) ♣ ⚲

## Lower Red Lion
34–36 Fishpool Street
☎ (01727) 855669
12–2.30 (3 Sat), 5.30–11; 12–3, 7–10.30 Sun
**Adnams Bitter; Fuller's London Pride; Greene King Abbot; guest beers** Ⓗ
17th-century, small coaching inn, local CAMRA *Pub of the Year* 1995. Four guest beers from micro-brewers; beer festivals May Day and August Bank Hol weekends. The Roaring Success house beer comes from Tring Brewery. No food Sun.
🏚 Q ⚘ ⚑ ◖ P

## Sawbridgeworth

### Gate Inn
81 London Road (100 yds Harlow side of double mini-roundabouts)
☎ (01279) 722313
11.30–2.30, 5.30 (5 Fri & Sat)–11; 12–3, 7–10.30 Sun
**Adnams Bitter; Brakspear Special; Castle Eden Ale; Fuller's London Pride; Whitbread Pompey Royal** Ⓗ
Pub dating back to Napoleonic times, on the site of the town's Parsonage Gate. Run by a very friendly family, it suits people of all ages. Guest beers, including a mild, (from all over UK) are regularly changed – the total now tops 750. No food Sun.
Q ◖ ⚛ ⇌ ♣ ⌂ P

## South Mimms

### Black Horse
65 Blackhorse Lane (200 yds from B556) ☎ (01707) 642174
11–3, 5.30–11; 11–11 Fri & Sat; 12–3, 7–10.30 Sun
**Greene King XX Mild, IPA, Abbot** Ⓗ
Lively local with a genuinely friendly welcome. Darts in one bar and a comfortable lounge.
🏚 ⚘ ◖ ⊟ ♣ P

## Tewin

### Plume of Feathers
57 Upper Green Road
☎ (01438) 717265
11–2.30 (3 Sat), 6–11; 12–3, 7–10.30 Sun
**Adnams Bitter; Draught Bass; Boddingtons Bitter; guest beers** Ⓗ
One of the county's oldest licence-holders: a timber-framed building which has one bar and several separate areas. Popular with both diners and drinkers, it offers up to four guest beers (sparklers are used on most beers; the staff will happily remove them if asked).
🏚 Q ⚘ ◖ ♦ P

## Tower Hill

### Boot
On Bovingdon–Chipperfield road ☎ (01442) 833155
11–11; 12–10.30 Sun
**Adnams Bitter; Draught Bass; Benskins BB; Tetley Bitter; guest beers** H
Idyllic country pub with various outdoor drinking areas, including a children's play area and a working chieftain tank! Excellent, home-cooked food (not served Sun eve). Cider in summer (gravity dispensed).
🏠 Q ⊛ ◑ ▯ 🏵 ⚲ ♣ ⌂ P ⚥

## Tring

### King's Arms
King Street (near Natural History Museum)
☎ (01442) 823318
11.30–2.30 (11–3 Sat), 7–11; 12–4, 7–10.30 Sun
**Brakspear Special; Wadworth 6X; guest beers** H
Backstreet local, very busy at all times. Hard to find, but impossible to miss, it serves a constantly changing and varied range of ales. No-smoking area lunchtime. The cider varies.
🏠 Q ⊛ ◑ ♣ ⌂ ⚥

### Robin Hood
1 Brook Street
☎ (01442) 824912
11.30–2.30, 5.30–11; 11–3, 6.30–11 Sat; 12–3, 7–10.30 Sun
**Fuller's Chiswick, London Pride, ESB, seasonal beers** H
Superb, olde-worlde pub, always gleaming. The excellent and varied food menu specialises in seafood dishes (all fresh fish). The licensee has a Fuller's cellarmanship award. Well worth a visit.
🏠 ⊛ ◑ ▯ ⚲ ♣

## Tyttenhanger

### Barley Mow
Barley Mow Lane (off A414)
OS190060 ☎ (01727) 827777
11–3, 6.30 (5 Fri)–11 (11–11 summer); 12–3, 7–10.30 (12–10.30 summer) Sun
**Adnams Bitter; Draught Bass; Courage Directors; Fuller's London Pride, ESB; guest beers** H
Pub restored to its original state after years in the wilderness. Popular with the rugby fraternity; Sky TV for sports fans. Eve meals Thu–Sat.
🏠 Q ⊛ ▯ ⚲ P

## Ware

### Albion
12 Crib Street (behind St Mary's church)
☎ (01920) 463599
11–11; 12–3, 7–10.30 Sun
**Adnams Bitter; Boddingtons Bitter; Flowers IPA** H
Oak-beamed bar in a 16/17th-century, half-timbered building which features wonderful floral displays outside in summer. The superb snug is very popular with locals. 🏠 ◑ ⚲ ♨

### Angel (Tap & Spile)
54 Star Street ☎ (01920) 463288
12–3, 5.30 (6 Sat)–11; 12–3, 7–10.30 Sun
**Beer range varies** H
A new landlord has transformed this pub into Ware's premier place for guest ales from micro-breweries. It is due to be converted to a Tap & Spile. Three different drinking areas make for a very friendly and cosmopolitan atmosphere.
🏠 ⊛ ◑ ▯ ⚲ ♣ ⌂ P

### Worppell
35 Watton Road
☎ (01920) 462572
11.30–2.30, 5–11; 11–11 Fri & Sat; 12–3, 7–10.30 Sun
**Greene King IPA, Abbot, seasonal beers** H
Formerly the New Rose & Crown: the new name is that of a builder who bought and re-built the pub in the 1800s. Having recently been altered, it maintains its very friendly and popular atmosphere.
◑ ♨ ♣ P

### Water End (North Mymms)

### Old Maypole
43 Warrengate Road (off B197)
☎ (01707) 642119
11–2.30, 5.30–11; 12–3, 7–10.30 Sun
**Greene King IPA, Abbot, seasonal beers** H
Warm and friendly, 16th-century, split-level pub. Supervised children are welcome in the no-smoking room. No food Sun.
🏠 Q ⚥ ⊛ ◑ P ⚥

### Woodman
Warrengate Road (off Swanland Road, old A1, by Water End Café)
☎ (01707) 650502
11–3, 5.30–11; 12–3, 7–10.30 Sun (all day Sun if busy)
**Courage Directors; Marston's Pedigree; Wadworth 6X** H

250-year-old, two-bar pub with brass and beams. The back garden is quiet. Note: Woodman's Best Bitter is Courage Best. 🏠 Q ⊛ ◑ P

## Welham Green

### Hope & Anchor
2 Station Road
☎ (01707) 262935
11–2.30, 5–11; 11–11 Sat; 12–10.30 Sun
**Courage Best Bitter, Directors; John Smith's Bitter** H
18th-century village local with two contrasting bars and well-kept gardens. John Smith's is on swan neck and tight sparkler as recommended by the brewery. No food Sun.
⊛ ◑ ▯ ⚲ ♨ ♣ P

## Whitwell

### Maiden's Head
67 High Street
☎ (01438) 871392
11.30–2.30, 5–11; 12–3, 7–11 Sun
**Draught Bass; McMullen AK, Country** H
Characterful, timbered pub with friendly locals and bar staff. The landlord is a four-times winner of McMullen's *Cellarman of the Year* award.
🏠 ⊛ ◑ ♣ P

## Wildhill Thorp

### Woodman
45 Wildhill Lane (between A1000 and B158, near Essendon) OS265068
☎ (01707) 642618
11.30–2.30, 5.30–11; 12–2.30, 7–10.30 Sun
**Greene King IPA, Abbot, seasonal beers; McMullen AK; guest beers** H
Genuine, friendly local where *Wildhill Whistler*, a fortnightly journal, keeps customers up to date on local goings on. Lowish prices; good, chip-free lunches (not served Sun). Sky television available in the snug/music room. 🏠 Q ⊛ ◑ P

## Willian

### Three Horseshoes
Baldock Lane (tiny lane opp. church, 1 mile off A1(M) jct 9, towards Letchworth)
☎ (01462) 685713
11–11; 12–10.30 Sun
**Greene King IPA, Abbot, seasonal beers** H
Comfortable, single-bar pub with a friendly atmosphere. The newly opened function room hosts bridge, darts and pool players alike.
🏠 ⊛ ◑ ♣

# Isle of Wight

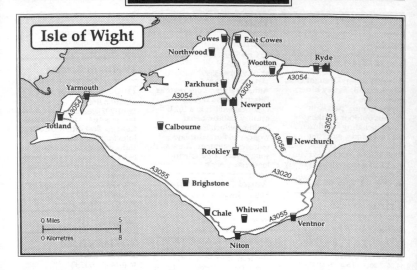

## Brighstone

### Countryman
Limerstone Road (B3399)
☎ (01983) 740616
11–3, 7–11 (11–11 summer); 12–3,
7–10.30 Sun (extends in summer)
**Badger Dorset Best,
Tanglefoot; Wells Eagle; guest
beers** Ⓗ
Spacious and friendly,
single-bar pub serving very
good food. Near many
holiday attractions but
unspoilt.
🏰 Q ☎ 🕯 ◑ ◗ ♣ P ⚲

## Calbourne

### Blacksmith's Arms
Calbourne Road (2 miles
W of Newport)
☎ (01983) 529263
11–3, 6–11 (11–11 summer); 12–10.30
Sun
**Beer range varies** Ⓗ
Delightful country pub with a
friendly atmosphere, a good
selection of German bottled
beers and three to four real
ales. Good food.
🏰 Q ☎ ◑ ◗ P 🍺

## Chale

### Wight Mouse
Newport Road (B3399)
☎ (01983) 730431
11–11; 12–10.30 Sun
**Boddingtons Bitter; Marston's
Pedigree; Morland Old
Speckled Hen; Strong
Country Bitter; Wadworth 6X;
guest beer** Ⓗ
Very busy, old stone pub with
an adjoining hotel, near
Blackgang Chine theme park.
An award-winning family and
whisky pub, it has a garden

play area and three family
rooms. Food all day. Live
music every night (hence high
beer prices).
🏰 ☎ ❀ ☎ ◑ ◗ ▲ P

## Cowes

### Anchor
1 High Street
☎ (01983) 292823
11–11; 12–3, 7–10.30 Sun
**Badger Tanglefoot** Ⓖ;
**Flowers Original; Fuller's
London Pride** Ⓗ; **Goddards
Fuggle-Dee-Dum** Ⓖ; **Greene
King Abbot; Wadworth
6X** Ⓗ
Good locals' and visitors' pub,
catering for all needs. The
stables have been converted to
a restaurant. Live
entertainment makes the beer
expensive. 🏰 ❀ ◑ ◗

## East Cowes

### Ship & Castle
21 Castle Street
☎ (01983) 290522
11–11; 12–10.30 Sun
**Badger Dorset Best; guest
beers** Ⓗ
Pleasant, one-bar town pub
(formerly the Robin Hood),
which serves some interesting
beers. ◑ ◗ ♣

### Victoria Tavern
62 Clarence Road
☎ (01983) 295961
11–4, 7–11; 12–3, 7–10.30 Sun
**Goddards Special; Marston's
Pedigree; John Smith's
Bitter** Ⓗ
Modernised, early Victorian
town pub with an unusual
clinker-built boat bar. Loud
and bright.
◑ ◗ ♣ 🍺

## Newchurch

### Pointer Inn
High Street (N of A3056, 2
miles W of Sandown)
☎ (01983) 865202
11–4, 6–11 (11–11 summer); 12–4,
7–10.30 (12–10.30 summer) Sun
**Gale's Best Bitter, HSB,
Festival, seasonal beers; guest
beer** Ⓗ
Thriving drinkers' pub which
also offers good, home-cooked
food in large portions, a small
menagerie in the garden and
limited free camping for card-
carrying CAMRA members.
Cider in summer. Definitely no
swan necks!
🏰 Q ❀ ◑ ◗ ⊟ ▲ ♣ ⌂ P 🍺

## Newport

### Castle Inn
91 High Street
☎ (01983) 522528
10.30–11; 12–10.30 Sun
**Draught Bass; Boddingtons
Bitter; Fuller's London Pride;
Greene King Abbot** Ⓗ
Popular, 16th-century,
flagstone-floored pub with a
warm welcome. Good value,
home-cooked food. Separate
function/family room.
🏰 ☎ ◑ ◗ ♣

### Prince of Wales
36 South Street (opp. bus
station) ☎ (01983) 525026
10.30–11; 12–3, 7–10.30 Sun

---

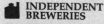
**INDEPENDENT
BREWERIES**

**Burts:** Newport

**Goddards:** Ryde

**Ushers Best Bitter, Founders, seasonal beers** Ⓗ
Town-centre pub attracting a cross-section of drinkers. Food includes home-cooked specials made with real ale.
⚒ ◖ ▮ ⅋ ♣ ⟳ ▯

### Railway Medina
1 Sea Street (Holyrood St jct)
☎ (01983) 528303
11–3, 6–11; 11–11 Thu–Sat & summer; 12–4.30, 7–10.30 Sun
**Gale's HSB; Goddards Special; guest beer** Ⓗ
Delightful, street-corner local opposite the old local brewery. Plentiful railway memorabilia.
⚒ Q ✿ ◖ ▮ ♣

## Niton

### Buddle
St Catherine's Road (follow signs for St Catherine's Lighthouse) ☎ (01983) 730243
11–3, 6–11 (11–11 Fri & Sat in summer); 12–3, 7–10.30 (12–10.30 summer) Sun
**Draught Bass; Flowers Original; Hampshire Ironside; Whitbread Best Bitter; guest beers** Ⓗ
Ancient, stone-built pub facing the sea; once a smuggler's haunt. It specialises in seafood and home-cooked pies. Note: the beer can be expensive.
⚒ ☎ ✿ ◖ ▮ ▲ ♣ P

### White Lion Inn
High Street ☎ (01983) 730293
11–3.30, 7–11; 12–3, 7–10.30 Sun
**Castle Eden Ale; Fuller's London Pride; Strong Country Bitter** Ⓗ
Beautiful, old inn at the village centre, reputedly haunted and now famous for its home-made steak and kidney pies. The beers may vary. ☎ ✿ ◖ ▮ P

## Northwood

### Travellers Joy
Pallance Road (follow signs for Porchfield off A3020)
☎ (01983) 298024
11–2.30, 5–11; 11–11 Fri & Sat; 12–3, 7–10.30 Sun
**Ansells Mild; Goddards Special; Ringwood Old Thumper; Ruddles County; Theakston Old Peculier; guest beers** Ⓗ
Well-renovated country inn offering a fine choice of ales (at least nine, including a mild and a porter). Local CAMRA *Pub of the Year* for many years. The large garden has a children's play area.
☎ ✿ ◖ ▮ ▲ ♣ ⟳ P ⚥ ▯

## Parkhurst

### Cask & Custard Pot
2 Cowes Road (A3020)
☎ (01983) 522709
10.30–3, 6–11 (11–11 summer); 12–3, 7–10.30 (12–10.30 summer) Sun
**Burts Nipper, Newport Nobbler, VPA, Vectis Venom, seasonal beers** Ⓗ
Former Whitbread, then Gale's, pub now brought to life under Burts. Very good beer prices; interesting, good value food. ☎ ✿ ◖ ▮ ⊟ ♣ ⟳ P

## Rookley

### Chequers
Niton Road (off A3020)
☎ (01983) 840314
11–11; 12–10.30 Sun
**Draught Bass; Courage Best Bitter, Directors; Morland Old Speckled Hen; John Smith's Bitter; Wadworth 6X** Ⓗ
Character country pub at the heart of the island: a lounge bar and a large restaurant with a flagstoned public bar. Large children's play area inside and out. Extensive menu of home-cooked food; fresh fish always available.
⚒ Q ☜ ✿ ◖ ▮ ⊟ ▮ ▲ ♣ P ▯

## Ryde

### Lake Superior
Marlborough Road, Elmfield (A3055, 1 mile from seafront)
☎ (01983) 563519
12–2.30, 5.30–11; 12–11 Fri & Sat; 12–3, 7–10.30 Sun
**Badger Dorset Best, Tanglefoot; Ind Coope Burton Ale; guest beers** Ⓗ
Excellent, Victorian corner local, surrounded by rural housing: two separate bars, a rear patio and a games room. Beer festival Easter. Family room in summer. ⚒ ☜ ✿ ▮
≄ (St Johns) ♣ P ▯

## Totland

### Highdown Inn
Highdown Lane (1½ miles E of Alum Bay, on Alum Bay old road) OS324858
☎ (01983) 752450
11–3, 7–11 (11–11 summer); 12–10.30 Sun
**Ushers Best Bitter, Founders** Ⓗ
Country pub adjacent to downland and fine walks, once a notorious smuggling den, now an excellent stopping-off point during a bracing visit to Tennyson Down. Good food.
⚒ Q ✿ ⛵ ◖ ▮ ⊟ ▮ ♣ P ▯

## Ventnor

### Bonchurch Inn
Bonchurch Chute (just off Sandown road)
☎ (01983) 852611
11–2.30, 6–11; 12–3, 7–10.30 Sun
**Courage Best Bitter, Directors** Ⓖ
Superbly preserved, stone pub, tucked away in a courtyard; formerly the stables of the adjacent manor house. Floors from a ship's deck; chairs from a liner. Authentic Italian food. Accommodation in summer.
Q ⛵ ◖ ▮ ⊟ ♣ P

### Volunteer
30 Victoria Street (near bus station) ☎ (01983) 852537
11–11; 12–3, 7–10.30 Sun
**Badger Dorset Best; guest beers** Ⓗ
Former Burts house: a superb town local offering a fine selection of ales, priced to sell.
Q ♣

## Whitwell

### White Horse Inn
High Street ☎ (01983) 730375
11–3, 6.30–11; 12–3, 6.30–10.30 Sun
**Gale's Butser, Best Bitter, HSB; guest beer** Ⓗ
Reputed to be the oldest pub on the island: a quiet, thatched village inn with a large garden. Good food.
⚒ Q ☜ ✿ ◖ ▮ ⊟ ♣ P

## Wootton

### Woodman Arms
119 Station Road, Wootton Common ☎ (01983) 882785
11–3, 6–11; 12–3, 7–10.30 Sun
**Draught Bass; Flowers Original; Fuller's London Pride; Strong Country Bitter; guest beers** Ⓗ
Friendly country pub, very popular with locals; near the steam railway. Good value food. ✿ ◖ ▮ ▮ ▲ ≄ ♣ P

## Yarmouth

### Wheatsheaf
Bridge Road (by ferry terminal)
☎ (01983) 760456
11–3, 6–11 (11–11 summer); 12–3, 7–10.30 (12–10.30 summer) Sun
**Boddingtons Bitter; Flowers Original; Gale's HSB; Goddards Special** Ⓗ
Old coaching house, now, with additional rooms, a spacious, comfortable pub for families. Attractive and interesting surroundings. Cheap food in winter. ⚒ Q ✿ ◖ ▮ ▮ ♣

---

Protect your pleasure – Join CAMRA now!

# Kent

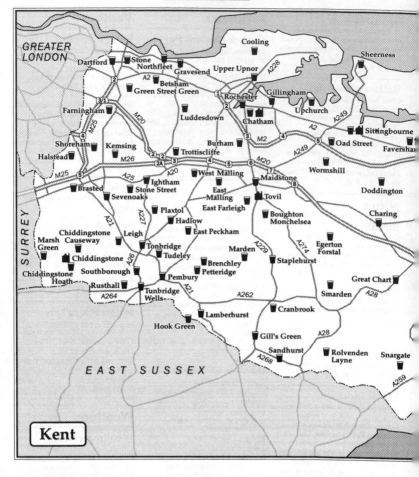

Kent

## Badlesmere

### Red Lion
Ashford Road (A251)
☎ (01233) 740320
11.30–3, 6–11; 11.30–11 Fri & Sat;
12–10.30 Sun
**Fuller's London Pride; Greene King XX Mild, Abbot; Shepherd Neame Master Brew Bitter; guest beers** Ⓗ
16th-century village pub with gas lights in the bar. A rare outlet for cask mild and cider. Eve meals Thu–Sat.
🏠 ⊛ ◑ ▶ ♣ ⌂ P

## Barfreston

### Yew Tree Inn
☎ (01304) 831619
11–3, 6–11; 11–11 Fri & Sat; 12–10.30 Sun
**Black Sheep Best Bitter; Fuller's ESB; Greene King XX Mild, IPA; Mauldons Black Adder; Taylor Landlord; guest beers** Ⓗ

Lively, traditional, village-centre pub, alongside the famous Norman church (1½ miles from Shepherd's Well station).
🏠 ⊛ ◑ ▶ ♣ ⌂ P

## Betsham

### Colyer Arms
Station Road (B262, 1 mile S of A2) ☎ (01474) 832392
11.30–11; 11.30–4.30, 7–11 Sat; 12–4, 7–10.30 (12–10.30 summer) Sun
**Burtonwood Bitter; Courage Best Bitter; Ruddles County; Shepherd Neame Master Brew Bitter; Wadworth 6X; guest beer** Ⓗ
Village pub named after a WWI VC hero: a popular convivial local with Bat and Trap and petanque teams. Good food in the restaurant or conservatory (not served Sun or Mon eves). The large garden has a children's play area.
⊛ ◑ ▶ ⊞ ♣ P

## Birchington

### Sea View
96 Station Road
☎ (01843) 841702
11–11; 12–3, 7–10.30 Sun
**Shepherd Neame Master Brew Bitter, Best Bitter, Spitfire, Bishops Finger** Ⓗ
Built in 1865 to cater for travellers on the newly-built London, Chatham and Dover Railway; a one-bar pub boasting a friendly atmosphere. Function room.
⊛ 🏠 ◑ ⅏ ▲ ⇌ ♣ P

## Bishopsbourne

### Mermaid
400 yds from A2
☎ (01227) 830581
11.30–3, 6–11; 12–3, 7–10.30 Sun
**Shepherd Neame Master Brew Bitter** Ⓗ
Attractive, unpretentious pub in a typically Kentish village,

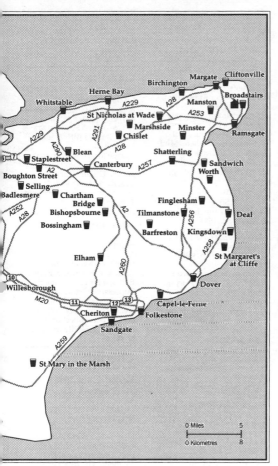

0 Miles 5
0 Kilometres 8

the former home of author
Joseph Conrad. 🏰 Q ❀ ◑ ♣

## Blean

### Royal Oak
140 Blean Common (A290)
☎ (01227) 471247
11–11; 12–10.30 Sun
**Mitchell's Lancaster Bomber;
Shepherd Neame Master
Brew Bitter; guest beers** Ⓗ
Victorian pub with a
conservatory restaurant, bar
billiards and a large screen TV
for sporting events. Popular
with locals and visitors alike.
❀ ◑ ♣ P 🍴

## Bossingham

### Hop Pocket
The Street ☎ (01227) 709866
12–3, 7–11; 12–3, 7–10.30 Sun (may
open all day)
**Shepherd Neame Best Bitter;
Taylor Landlord; guest
beers** Ⓗ

19th-century, candlelit pub. Its
ceiling is thatched with hop
bines in the Kentish style.
Popular for food. Annual beer
festival, with camping in the
grounds. 🏰 ❀ ◑ ♣ 🅰 ♣ P

## Boughton
## Monchelsea

### Red House
Hermitage Lane (S off B2169,
down Wierton Rd and East
Hall Hill) OS783488
☎ (01622) 743986
12–3 (not Tue), 7–11; 12–11 Sat;
12–10.30 Sun
**Fuller's London Pride; Greene
King Abbot; Hampshire
Lionheart; Hop Back Summer
Lightning; Otter Bitter; guest
beers** Ⓗ
Welcoming, country free
house, with a good selection of
guest beers, plus an extensive
range of imported bottled
beers and fruit wines. May beer
festival.
🏰 🍷 ❀ ◑ 🅰 ♣ ○ P

## Boughton Street

### Queen's Head
111 The Street
☎ (01227) 751369
11–3, 6–11; 11–11 Sat; 12–4, 7–10.30
Sun
**Shepherd Neame Master
Brew Bitter, Spitfire** Ⓗ
Unpretentious, 16th-century
inn with good value food and
accommodation: a lively public
bar and a wood-panelled
saloon. Wheelchair WC. Note:
there is a price premium on
halves.
🏰 Q ❀ 🛏 ◑ ♣ 🔗 🅰 ♣ P

## Brasted

### Bull Inn
High Street (A25)
☎ (01959) 562551
10–2.30, 5.30–11; 11–11 Sat; 12–3,
7–10.30 Sun
**Shepherd Neame Master
Brew Bitter, Spitfire, Bishops
Finger** Ⓗ
Very friendly pub on the edge
of the village, catering for both
local and passing trades. Fairly
close to Chartwell.
❀ ◑ ♣ P

## Brenchley

### Bull Inn
High Street ☎ (01892) 722701
11–3, 5–11; 12–4, 7–10.30 Sun
**Greene King IPA, Abbot;
Shepherd Neame Master
Brew Bitter; guest beer** Ⓗ
19th-century village pub with
two separate drinking/eating
areas either side of a long bar.
A pictorial history of Brenchley
village life is on show. Beer
festivals held in the barn/
function room.
🏰 ❀ 🛏 ◑ ♣ ♣ P

## Bridge

### Plough & Harrow
86 High Street
☎ (01227) 830455
12–3, 6–11; 11–11 Sat; 12–3, 7–10.30
Sun
**Shepherd Neame Master
Brew Bitter** Ⓗ
Friendly local, good for games,
originally a maltings and a

### 📍 INDEPENDENT BREWERIES

**Flagship:** Chatham

**Goacher's:** Tovil

**Larkins:** Chiddingstone

**Shepherd Neame:**
Faversham

**Swale:** Sittingbourne

**Viking:** Broadstairs

brewery. The landlord was Shepherd Neame *Cellar Master of the Year* 1995. Highly commended in a national *Clean Loo* competition. 🏠 ◖ ♣ P

## Broadstairs

### Bradstow Bar (Albion Hotel)

6–12 Albion Street
☎ (01843) 868071
11–3, 6–11; 12–3, 7–10.30 Sun
**Courage Directors; Shepherd Neame Master Brew Bitter; Webster's Yorkshire Bitter** Ⓗ
Small, friendly hotel bar which boasts a large garden with superb views over Viking Bay, the town's main beach. Handy for all seafront attractions.
❀ 🚃 ≈

### Neptune's Hall

1–3 Harbour Street
☎ (01843) 861400
11–11; 12–4, 7–10.30 Sun
**Shepherd Neame Master Brew Bitter, Spitfire, Porter** Ⓗ
Welcoming, three-bar, Victorian ale house, a short walk from the picturesque harbour; often packed. A venue for music during the town's annual folk week (Aug). 🏠 Q ❀ ◖ 🍴 ♣

## Burham

### Windmill

292 Rochester Road
☎ (01634) 861919
11.30–3, 6.30–11; 12–3, 7–10.30 Sun
**Fuller's London Pride; Worthington Bitter; guest beer** Ⓗ
Friendly village local with two bars and a restaurant.
❀ ◖ 🍴 ♣ P

**Try also: Toastmasters Inn,** Church St (Free)

## Canterbury

### Bishop's Finger

13 St Dunstan's Street (between Westgate and West station)
☎ (01227) 768915
11–11; 12–3, 7–10.30 Sun
**Shepherd Neame Master Brew Bitter, Spitfire, Bishops Finger** Ⓗ
Friendly, welcoming, two-bar pub with a pleasant patio with children's toys.
❀ ◖ 🍴 ≈ (West)

### Canterbury Beer Shop

83 Northgate (by the King's School) ☎ (01227) 472288
11–1, 5.30–10; 11–10 Sat; closed Sun & bank hols
**Adnams Broadside; Fuller's ESB; Harveys BB; guest beers** Ⓗ
Off-licence serving a range of cask beers and a large selection

of Belgian and other bottle-conditioned beers.
≋ (West)

### Canterbury Tales

12 The Friars (opp. Marlowe Theatre) ☎ (01227) 768594
11–11; 12–10.30 Sun
**Goacher's Light; Shepherd Neame Master Brew Bitter; guest beers** Ⓗ
Busy and enterprising pub specialising in Kent beers but also with a wide range of guests from elsewhere. Mini-festivals and theme nights; live music, including jazz Sun afternoons. ◖ 🍴 (West)

### New Inn

Havelock Street (off ring road near Christ Church College)
☎ (01227) 464584
11.30–3 (4 Wed & Fri), 6 (5 Wed & Fri)–11 (may be 11–11 Sat); 12–4, 7–10.30 Sun
**Greene King IPA; guest beers** Ⓗ
Victorian, terraced, two-bar pub with a conservatory and a small garden. Relaxed and friendly; popular with students and locals. Up to five guest beers. 🐾 ❀ ◖ 🍴 ≋ (East)

### Tap & Spile

76 St Dunstan's Street (near Westgate) ☎ (01227) 463583
11–11; 12–3, 7–10.30 (sometimes 12–10.30) Sun
**Tap & Spile Premium; guest beers** Ⓗ
The Rose & Crown until 1995, this ancient pub has stripped wood floors and tables. Third of a pint sampler glasses available. Seven guest beers.
❀ ◖ ≋ (West) ♣ ⌂

**Try also: Dolphin,** St Radigunds; **Flying Horse,** Dover St; **Jolly Sailor,** Northgate (all Whitbread)

## Capel-le-Ferne

### Royal Oak

New Dover Road (B2011, near A20) ☎ (01303) 244787
11.30–3 (4 Sat), 6 (7 Sat)–11; 12–4, 8 (7 in summer)–10.30 Sun
**Shepherd Neame Master Brew Bitter; guest beers** Ⓗ
Old split-level pub on the famous white cliffs with fine Channel views. Traditional snug at the front; games in the back bar. Note the weather photos! No eve meals Wed.
🏠 Q ❀ ◖ 🍴 ▲ ♣ P

## Charing

### Bowl Inn

Egg Hill Road
☎ (01233) 712256
5 (12 Fri & Sat)–11; 12–10.30 Sun
**King & Barnes Sussex; guest beers** Ⓗ

Remote, 16th-century inn with a large inglenook. CAMRA Kent (joint) *Pub of the Year* 1994, serving three constantly changing guest beers.
🏠 ❀ ▲ 🍴 ♣ P

## Chartham

### Cross Keys

Bolts Hill (left from station, up hill) ☎ (01227) 738216
12–3, 6–11; 11–11 Sat; 12–10.30 Sun
**John Smith's Bitter; guest beers** Ⓗ
Village local dating from the 18th century; popular for games. Usually three guest ales. 🏠 ❀ ▲ ≋ ♣ P 🍴

## Chatham

### Alexandra

43 Railway Street
☎ (01634) 843959
11–11; 12–3, 7–10.30 Sun
**Shepherd Neame Master Brew Bitter, Spitfire, Porter, Bishops Finger** (summer) Ⓗ
Impressive Victorian building near the station, a haven for weary commuters. A good bottled beer collection adorns the walls. Friendly welcome.
❀ ≋ ♣

## Cheriton

### Royal Cheriton

339 Cheriton Road
☎ (01303) 277007
11–11; 12–10.30 Sun
**Beer range varies** Ⓗ
Old bakery reincarnated as a biker café, a night club and, eight and a half years ago, a pub. Comfortable and frequented by locals of all ages. Three or four guest beers.
❀ ◖ 🍴 ≋ (Folkestone W) ♣

## Chiddingstone Causeway

### Little Brown Jug

On B2027, opp. Penshurst station ☎ (01892) 870318
11.30–3, 6–11; 12–3, 7–10.30 Sun
**Harveys BB; guest beers** Ⓗ
Busy, friendly, family-run free house offering three ever-changing guest beers – many unusual. Excellent range of good food. Spacious garden.
🏠 Q ❀ 🚃 ◖ 🍴 ♿ ≋ (Penshurst) P ✦

## Chiddingstone Hoath

### Rock

Between Chiddingstone and Penshurst ☎ (01892) 870296
11.30–3, 6–11; 12–3, 7–10.30 Sun
**Larkins Bitter, Porter; Shepherd Neame Master Brew Bitter** Ⓗ

16th-century rural pub in an isolated setting. A worn red-brick floor features in the main bar, which is heated by a wood-burning stove. The unusual wooden pump handles dispense Larkins ales brewed just down the road. Ring the Bull played.
🏛 Q 🏵 ◑ ▶ ♣ P

## Chislet

### Six Bells
Church Lane (off A28/A299)
☎ (01227) 860373
12–2.30, 6.30–11; 12–4, 7–10.30 Sun
**Adnams Mild, Bitter, Extra, Broadside; Draught Bass; guest beers** Ⓗ
Traditional, friendly free house with a log fire and a large garden. Beer festival Aug. Bat and Trap and boules played.
🏛 Q 🏵 ◑ ▶ ♠ ♣ P

## Cliftonville

### Olde Charles
382 Northdown Road
☎ (01843) 221817
11–11; 12–10.30 Sun
**Draught Bass; Flowers Original; Ind Coope Burton Ale; Shepherd Neame Master Brew Bitter; guest beers** Ⓗ
Large, mock Tudor roadside tavern built in the 1920s. Spacious, but cosy, its furniture includes sofas. Large garden; good value food. Old Hazy cider. 🏛 🏵 ◑ ▶ ♣ ⬭ P

## Cooling

### Horseshoe & Castle
Main Road ☎ (01634) 221691
11.30–3, 7 (5 Fri)–11; 12–10.30 Sun
**Adnams Bitter; Draught Bass; Flagship Ensign** Ⓗ
Nestled in a sleepy village with Dickensian connections, this pub reputedly has a haunted cellar. Note: the Addlestones Cider is on a cask breather.
🏛 🏵 ◑ ▶ ♣ P⅄

## Cranbrook

### Prince of Wales
High Street ☎ (01580) 713058
11.30–2.30, 6.30–11; 12–4, 7–10.30 Sun
**Harveys BB; guest beers** Ⓗ
Vibrant town-centre free house with two bars: one has a jukebox, pool, etc., the other is split-level and simply furnished. Both can get very busy. 🏛 ⅃ 🏵 ◑ ▶

## Dartford

### Paper Moon
55 High Street
☎ (01322) 281127
10–11; 12–10.30 Sun

**Courage Directors; Theakston Best Bitter, XB; Younger Scotch; guest beer** Ⓗ
Town-centre pub, formerly a bank, tastefully decorated in the typical Wetherspoons format, with interesting photographs of, and information on, old Dartford. Enterprising range of guest beers. Popular with all ages.
Q ◑ ▶ ♿ ≠ ⅄

### Tiger
28 St Albans Rd (off A226)
☎ (01322) 293688
11–11; 12–10.30 Sun
**Courage Best Bitter; John Smith's Bitter; Shepherd Neame Master Brew Bitter; guest beer** Ⓗ
Sports-oriented, sidestreet corner local fielding darts, pool and football teams. Its reverse L-shaped bar has a pool table at one end and is quiet at the other. No meals Sat/Sun.
🏵 ◑ ≠ ♣

### Wat Tyler
80 High Street
☎ (01322) 272546
10–11; 12–10.30 Sun
**Courage Best Bitter; Theakston Old Peculier; Young's Special; guest beer** Ⓗ
Long, narrow, historic town-centre free house named after the 14th-century leader of the Peasants' Revolt. Good value regular beers and an ever-changing guest. A convivial meeting place. ◑ ≠ ⌂

## Deal

### Saracen's Head
11 Alfred Square
10.30–11; 12–10.30 Sun (may vary)
**Shepherd Neame Master Brew Bitter, Spitfire, Bishops Finger** Ⓗ
Large, single-bar, corner pub in an historic part of town.
🏛 🍴 ◑ ≠ ♣

### Ship Inn
141 Middle Street (parallel to seafront) ☎ (01304) 372222
11–11; 12–10.30 Sun
**Draught Bass; Fuller's ESB; Greene King Abbot; Shepherd Neame Master Brew Bitter; Worthington Bitter** Ⓗ
Cosy pub in a conservation area. Naval prints in the back bar; piano and occasional live music in the front. 🏛 ◑

Try also: **Admiral Penn**, Beach St (Free)

## Doddington

### Chequers
The Street
11–4, 7–11; 11–11 Fri & Sat; 12–3, 7–10.30 Sun

**Shepherd Neame Master Brew Bitter, Spitfire, Bishops Finger** Ⓗ
Excellent village local with two contrasting bars. CAMRA regional *Pub of the Year* 1995. Note the Kentish dartboard.
🏛 Q ⅃ 🏵 ◑ ▣ ♣ P

## Dover

### Blakes
52 Castle Street (off Market Sq)
☎ (01304) 202194
11–3, 7–11; 12–3 Sun, closed Sun eve
**Beer range varies** Ⓗ
Smart downstairs wine bar with a large upstairs bar for functions – busy lunchtimes; quieter eves. Topical photos on display. Usually three beers.
🏵 ◑ ▶ ≠ (Priory)

### Boar's Head
46–48 Eaton Road
☎ (01304) 204490
11–3, 6–11; 11–11 Sat; 12–3, 7–10.30 Sun
**Beer range varies** Ⓗ
Vibrant community local which provides a welcome break from theme pubs. Two beers from Greene King or Whitbread, with occasional guests and beer festivals. Skittle alley; live music.
🏛 ⅃ ≠ (Priory) ♣

### Crown & Sceptre
25 Elms Vale Road
☎ (01304) 201971
11.30–4 (3 Mon), 7–11; 12–3, 7–10.30 Sun
**Shepherd Neame Master Brew Bitter, Spitfire** Ⓗ
Friendly, two-bar, backstreet local hosting occasional events – live music, games nights, etc. Extensive collection of ferry prints. 🏵 ≠ (Priory) ♣

### Old Endeavour
124 London Road
☎ (01304) 204417
11–11; 12–10.30 Sun
**Shepherd Neame Master Brew Bitter** Ⓗ
Lively town pub, home of regular live music and in-pub events, with a verandah overlooking the River Dour. Mixed and friendly clientele. Large games/meeting room. Other Shepherd Neame beers are sold as guests. 🏵 ◑ ▶ ♣

## East Farleigh

### Victory
Farleigh Bridge (by station)
☎ (01622) 726591
11–11; 12–10.30 Sun
**Goacher's Mild, Dark; Tetley Bitter** Ⓗ
Friendly pub with an eating area at one end (varied menu). Very popular Sun lunches; recommended summer barbecues. Families welcome;

the large garden has a play area. ⊛ ◖◗ ▲ ⇌ ♣ P

## East Malling

### Rising Sun
125 Mill Street
☎ (01732) 843284
12–11; 12–10.30 Sun
**Goacher's Light; Harveys BB; Morland Old Speckled Hen; Shepherd Neame Master Brew Bitter** Ⓗ
Sensibly-priced beer and food in simple surroundings draw regular custom from discerning drinkers and local and visiting societies to this deservedly-popular, family-run village pub. No meals Sat/Sun. ⊛ ◖ ⇌

## East Peckham

### Harp
Hale Street (A228, near B2015 jct) ☎ (01622) 872334
11–11; 12–10.30 Sun
**Fuller's London Pride; Harveys BB; guest beers** Ⓗ
Well-kept, comfortable, low-ceilinged pub with every imaginable kind of china ornament plus brassware and musical instruments. Newspapers to read. Children welcomed. Good range of food. Note: Addlestones Cider is under gas pressure.
ӎ ⊛ ◖◗ ▲ P ⊟

## Egerton Forstal

### Queen's Arms
OS894466 ☎ (01233) 756386
11–3, 6–11; 12–3, 7–10.30 Sun
**Harveys BB; Rother Valley Level Best; Wells Bombardier; guest beers** Ⓖ
Dating back some 150 years, this quiet village local with beamed ceilings offers beers from independents and micros from all over the country. Wells Bombardier was named after the landlady's father, Bombardier Billy Wells. All day breakfasts; no meals Tue.
ӎ Q ⊛ ◖◗ ⊞ ♣ ⇦ P

## Elham

### Rose & Crown
High Street
☎ (01303) 840226
11–3, 6–11; 12–3, 7–10.30 Sun
**Home Bitter; Theakston Mild; guest beers** Ⓗ
Traditional free house serving two guest beers: a rare outlet for mild. Excellent range of food. Children allowed in the eating areas.
ӎ Q ⊛ ◖◗ ♣ P

**Try also: King's Arms**, The Square (Whitbread)

## Farningham

### Chequers
High Street ☎ (01322) 865222
11–11; 12–10.30 Sun
**Fuller's London Pride, ESB; Morland Old Speckled Hen; Taylor Landlord; guest beers** Ⓗ
Welcoming and comfortable, corner local in a picturesque village. Up to five guest beers available. Recommended home-made food (not served Sun). ◖ ♣

## Faversham

### Chimney Boy
59 Preston Street
☎ (01795) 532007
11–3, 6–11; 12–3, 7–10.30 Sun
**Shepherd Neame Master Brew Bitter** Ⓗ
Busy pub by the station with a games room. The menu features dishes including Shepherd Neame Porter. A comfortable cosmopolitan house typical of a market town.
⊛ ◖◗ ⇌ ♣ P

### Crown & Anchor
41 The Mall (100 yds from rear exit of station)
☎ (01795) 532812
10.30–3 (4 Sat), 5.30 (6 Sat)–11; 12–3, 7–10.30 Sun
**Shepherd Neame Master Brew Bitter** Ⓗ
Welcoming pub on the outskirts of town.
Q ⌖ ◖◗ ⇌ ♣ ⊟

### Mechanic's Arms
44 West Street (W of centre)
☎ (01795) 532693
11–3, 6.30–11; 12–4, 7–10.30 Sun
**Shepherd Neame Master Brew Bitter** Ⓗ
Friendly, local drinkers' pub in an old part of town. Snacks lunchtime. Q ⊛ ⊞ ⇌ ♣

## Finglesham

### Crown
The Street ☎ (01304) 612555
11–3, 6–11; 12–3, 7–10.30 Sun
**Morland Old Speckled Hen; Ruddles County; Shepherd Neame Master Brew Bitter; Webster's Yorkshire Bitter** Ⓗ
Award-winning, welcoming and popular village local with a separate restaurant (excellent food). Caravan Club site behind. ӎ ⊛ ◖◗ ▲ P

## Folkestone

### Harvey's Wine Bar
10 Langhorne Gardens (Sandgate road)
☎ (01303) 253758
11.30–11; 12–10.30 Sun
**Draught Bass; Worthington Bitter** Ⓗ; **guest beers** Ⓖ/Ⓗ

Long-standing *Guide* entry in the basement of Langhorne Gardens Hotel. Interesting range of guest beers, including from local breweries.
ӎ ⊛ ⊭ ◖ ⇌ (Central) ♣ ⇦

### Lifeboat
42 North Street (down Tram Rd, 1st left under railway, left again)
11–3 (4 Fri), 6–11; 11–11 Sat; 12–4.30, 7–10.30 Sun
**Draught Bass; Fuller's London Pride; guest beers** Ⓗ
Classic backstreet pub serving up to six beers (interesting and varied range of guests). Regular quiz nights; crib is also popular.
⊛ ◖◗ ⇌ (Central) ♣

## Gillingham

### Barge
63 Layfield Road
☎ (01634) 850485
12–3, 7–11; 12–11 Sat; 12–10.30 Sun
**Wadworth 6X; guest beers** Ⓗ
Candlelit pub serving four guest beers. Excellent views of the River Medway; sailing artefacts are on show. Folk Club Mon. ♣ ◖◗

### Falcon
95 Marlborough Road
☎ (01634) 850614
12–3, 5.30–11; 12–11 Sat; 12–5, 7–10.30 Sun
**Ruddles Best Bitter; John Smith's Bitter; guest beers** Ⓗ
Small, single-bar townhouse just off the high street. The two guest handpumps offer a fine selection. Occasional barbecues. Bat and Trap pitch.
⊛ ⇌ ♣

### King George V
1 Prospect Row, Brompton (off end of Brompton High St)
☎ (01634) 842418
11.30–11; 12–4, 7–11 Sat; 12–4, 7–10.30 Sun
**Draught Bass; guest beers** Ⓗ
Formerly the King of Prussia, this one-bar local maintains a strong link with the old Chatham Dockyard through its many naval artefacts. No food Sun. ⊛ ⊭ ◖ ♣

### Prince of Guinea
49 Medway Road
☎ (01634) 851534
11–11; 12–4, 7–10.30 (12–10.30 summer) Sun
**Harveys Pale Ale, BB, Armada, seasonal beers** Ⓗ
Recent Harveys acquisition with no keg bitter in its one bar. A good venue for improving your foreign language skills (it attracts juggernaut drivers from the local docks). Good value food. Function room.
⊛ ◖◗ ♣

### Roseneath

79 Arden Street
☎ (01634) 852553
11.30–11; 12–10.30 Sun
**Beer range varies** Ⓗ
Friendly, busy, one-bar pub
where five guest pumps
dispense changing beers
mostly from micro-brewers.
The house ale, Snakehound, is
brewed by Goacher's. Charity
beer festival June.
✤ ◖ ▶ ≉ ♣

### Will Adams

73 Saxton Street
☎ (01634) 575902
12–3, 7–11 (12–11 Sat football match
days); 12–3, 7–10.30 Sun
**Fuller's London Pride; guest
beers** Ⓗ
Friendly, one-bar local named
after a famed shipbuilder and
adventurer. The landlord
sponsors and follows the local
professional soccer club (hence
the very bright exterior!).
Excellent value food. Three
ever-changing guest ales.
✤ ◖ ≉ ♣

## Gill's Green

### Wellington Arms

Just off A229, N of Hawkhurst
☎ (01580) 753119
12–3, 0–11 (12–11 summer); 12–3,
7–10.30 (12–10.30 summer) Sun
**Harveys BB; Wadworth 6X;
guest beers** Ⓗ
Hidden away pub popular
with ramblers and those
seeking wholesome lunchtime
and eve refreshment in
friendly surroundings. The
premises date back to
Elizabethan times (an inn has
been licensed here since 1615).
🏚 ✤ ◖ ▶ P

## Gravesend

### Jolly Drayman

1 Love Lane, Wellington Street
☎ (01474) 352355
11.30 (12 Sat)–3, 6 (7 Sat)–11; 12–3,
7–10.30 Sun
**Draught Bass; Fuller's London
Pride; guest beers** Ⓗ
Part of the old Wellington
brewery: a comfortable,
lounge-style pub, tastefully
decorated (very low beams –
mind your head!). In all
editions of the *Guide* and
known locally as the Coke
Oven. Lunches Tue–Fri.
✤ ◖ ≉ ♣ P

### Prince Albert

26 Wrotham Road (by police
station) ☎ (01474) 352432
12 (11 Fri & Sat)–11; 12–10.30 Sun
**Shepherd Neame Master
Brew Bitter, Spitfire, Porter** Ⓗ
Very friendly, two-bar local
which is pleasantly different.
Visitors are soon part of the
family. 🏚 ✤ ⊞ ≉ ♣ P

### Somerset Arms

10 Darnley Road
☎ (01474) 533837
11–11 (midnight Thu–Sat); 12–4,
7.30–10.30 Sun
**Beer range varies** Ⓗ
Town-centre pub with
country-style decor, wooden
church pews and lots of pots
and brass, serving six changing
ales from all over Britain,
including many not normally
seen in this area. Discos Thu–
Sun eves. Eve meals Mon–
Wed. ◖ ▶ ≉

### Windmill Tavern

45 Shrubbery Road
☎ (01474) 352242
11–11; 12–10.30 Sun
**Harveys BB; Ruddles Best
Bitter; Shepherd Neame
Master Brew Bitter;
Wadworth 6X; Webster's
Yorkshire Bitter; guest beer** Ⓗ
Just out of the town centre: a
three-bar, country-style pub in
a conservation area with a
large, picturesque garden.
Active quiz and darts teams.
Eve meals to order.
✤ ◖ ▶ ⊞ ▲ ♣ P

## Great Chart

### Hooden Horse

The Street ☎ (01233) 625583
11.30–2.30, 6–11; 12–3, 7–10.30 Sun
**Goacher's Light; Hook Norton
Old Hooky; Hop Back
Summer Lightning;
Theakston Old Peculier; guest
beers** Ⓗ
Hop-strewn ceilings and
candlelit tables feature in this
tiled and timber-floored pub.
An extensive range of home-
cooked food is served up to
half an hour before closing.
The original pub in the Hooden
Horse chain. ✤ ◖ ▶ ⌂

## Green Street Green (Darenth)

### Ship

Green Street Green Road (B260,
1½ miles E of Longfield)
☎ (01474) 702279
11–2.30, 6–11 (11–11 summer Sat);
12–3, 7–10.30 (12–10.30 summer) Sun
**Courage Best Bitter; Young's
Bitter; guest beers** Ⓗ
Imposing 17th-century pub
overlooking the village green.
Excellent value lunches;
regular gourmet eves. Try the
back bar but beware of the
ghost! 🏚 ⚲ ✤ ◖ ♣ P

## Hadlow

### Fiddling Monkey

Maidstone Road (A26)
☎ (01732) 850267
11–3, 6–11; 11–11 Fri & Sat; 12–10.30
Sun

**Boddingtons Bitter; Harveys
BB; Larkins Bitter; Young's
Special; guest beer**
(summer) Ⓗ
Spacious, single-bar local with
separate areas. The large rear
garden features Bat and Trap.
Parking is rather limited.
🏚 ✤ ⚲ ◖ ♣ P ⛉

## Halstead

### Rose & Crown

Otford Lane (off A224 opp.
Polhill Arms)
☎ (01959) 533120
11.30–2.30, 4.30–11; 11–11 Sat;
12–10.30 Sun
**Courage Best Bitter; guest
beers** Ⓗ
200-year-old, flint two-bar pub,
with an open fire and no music
or machines in the quiet bar. A
Larkins and a Harveys beer are
regulars, plus three guest
beers. No meals Sun. Pleasant
and safe garden for children
who can also use the pool
room. 🏚 ⚲ ⚲ ✤ ◖ ◔ ♣ P

## Herne Bay

### Share & Coulter

Thornden Wood Road, West
End (1 mile from Thanet Way,
A299, off Greenhill
roundabout) ☎ (01227) 374877
11–3, 6–11; 12–3, 7–10.30 Sun
**Shepherd Neame Master
Brew Bitter, Spitfire** Ⓗ
400-year-old traditional
country pub offering many
local activities: a popular
meeting place for local clubs.
No meals Sun.
🏚 ⚲ ⚲ ✤ ◖ ▶ ⊞ ▲ ♣ P

## Hook Green

### Elephant's Head

Furnace Lane (B2169)
☎ (01892) 890279
11 (12 Sat)–3, 6–11 (11–11 summer
Sat); 12–3, 7–10.30 Sun
**Harveys XX Mild, Pale Ale,
BB, Old, Armada, seasonal
beers** Ⓗ
Popular, 15th-century pub on
the Sussex border with ample
parking and a large garden on
three sides. Good, home-made
food; barbecues and spit-roasts
in summer on the covered
patio. Caravan site; one flat to
let. 🏚 Q ✤ ⍾ ◖ ▶ ▲ P

## Ightham

### Old House

Redwell Lane (½ mile SE of
village, between A25 and
A227) OS590559
☎ (01732) 882383
7–11 (9 Tue); 12–3, 7–11 Sat; 12–3,
7–10.30 Sun
**Brakspear Bitter** Ⓖ**; Flowers
IPA** Ⓗ**; guest beer** Ⓖ
Difficult to find pub with no
sign. Partly 16th-century, it has

two unspoilt bars and a large open fireplace, and is a haven from the bustling 20th century.
🏠 Q ♠ ✦

## Kemsing

### Rising Sun

Cotmans Ash Lane OS563599
☎ (01959) 522683
11–3, 6–11; 12–3, 7–10.30 Sun
**Boddingtons Mild; Flowers Original; Fremlins Bitter; Morland Old Speckled Hen; guest beers** Ⓗ
Isolated country pub with a lovely outdoor drinking area, popular with families and hikers in summer. The main bar area is a converted hunting lodge. Food is good quality. Occasional beer festivals in a marquee.
🏠 Q ⛄ ⊛ ◖▮ ♣ ⊖ P

## Kingsdown

### King's Head

Upper Street ☎ (01304) 373915
11–2.30, 7–11; 12–2.30, 7–10.30 Sun
**Draught Bass; Hancock's HB; Worthington Bitter** Ⓗ
Village local at the eastern end of the white cliffs. Families welcome in the back bar. Booking advised for eve meals (served Wed–Sat).
⊛ ◖▮ ♣

Try also: Zetland Arms, Wellington Parade (Free)

## Lamberhurst

### Chequers

The Broadway
☎ (01892) 890260
11–3, 6–11; 12–3, 7–10.30 Sun
**Shepherd Neame Master Brew Bitter, Spitfire** Ⓗ
Situated in the village centre, where the River Teise crosses under the A21, this period, two-bar pub caters for locals and visitors. Village history pictures adorn the saloon bar.
🏠 ⊛ ♠ ◖▮ ⊟ P

## Leigh

### Fleur de Lis

High Street ☎ (01732) 832235
12–3, 6–11; hours vary Sun
**Greene King IPA, Rayments Special** Ⓗ
Friendly village pub with distinct bar, lounge and dining areas. ◖▮ ⇌ ♣ P

## Luddesdown

### Cock Inn

Henley StreetOS664672
☎ (01474) 814208
12–11; 12–10.30 Sun
**Adnams Mild, Bitter; Ind Coope Burton Ale** Ⓗ**; guest beers** Ⓗ/Ⓖ
Superb, two-bar free house offering up to eight ales, a house beer and two ciders. Small breweries are well represented. Classic car memorabilia features in the public bar. Accessible by public footpath from Sole Street station. Well worth finding. 🏠 Q ⊛ ◖▮ ♣ ⊖ P

Try also: Golden Lion, Luddesdown Rd (Free)

## Maidstone

### Greyhound

77 Wheeler Street (just N of centre) ☎ (01622) 754032
11–3, 6–11; 12–3, 7–10.30 Sun
**Shepherd Neame Master Brew Bitter** Ⓗ
Friendly, traditional, street-corner pub near the prison. A second Shepherd Neame cask ale is stocked. Live jazz Sun lunch. Eve meals served Thu, or other eves if booked; no lunches Sun.
Q ⊛ ◖▮ ⇌ (East) ♣ P

### Hare & Hounds

45–47 Lower Boxley Road
☎ (01622) 678388
11–3 (3.30 Fri), 5.30–11; 12–5, 7–11 Sat, 12–3, 7–10.30 Sun
**Flowers IPA; Fuller's London Pride; guest beer** Ⓗ
Welcoming, often busy, town pub near the prison. The patio at the rear hosts occasional barbecues. Eve meals end at 7 (no eve meals Sat/Sun; no lunches Sun).
⊛ ◖▮ ⇌ (East) ♣

### Pilot

23–25 Upper Stone Street
☎ (01622) 691162
11–3, 6 (7 Sat)–11; 12–3, 7–10.30 Sun
**Harveys XX Mild, BB, Old, Armada, seasonal beers** Ⓗ
Grade II listed building on a busy road out of town: the only Harveys pub in the area. Note the growing collection of headgear. Petanque and cribbage teams. No food Sun lunch. 🏠 Q ⊛ ◖▮ ♣

### Wheelers Arms

1 Perry Street (near Springfield, off old A229) ☎ (01622) 752229
12–11; 12–10.30 Sun
**Shepherd Neame Master Brew Bitter** Ⓗ
Genuine, popular local for all tastes. Food is always available and musical eves are held. One other Shepherd Neame beer is also sold.
⊛ ◖▮ ⇌ (East) ♣

## Manston

### Jolly Farmer

High Street ☎ (01843) 823208
10.30–3, 5.30–11; 10.30–11 Sat; 12–10.30 Sun
**Boddingtons Bitter; Flowers Original; Fremlins Bitter** Ⓗ**; guest beers** Ⓗ/Ⓖ
Busy village pub serving the local community and the expanding Kent International Airport; extensively decorated with flying memorabilia. Good value food. The large garden has Bat and Trap. Children's certificate.
🏠 ⊛ ◖▮ ⅃ ⅍ ♣ P

## Marden

### Stilebridge Inn

Staplehurst Road (A229)
☎ (01622) 831236
11–3, 6–11; 12–10.30 Sun
**Beer range varies** Ⓗ
Stylish and comfortable pub with a very friendly welcome in its several bar areas and separate beamed restaurant. Constantly changing range of five ales (250–300 a year). Excellent food from one of the most varied bar and restaurant menus in the area.
Q ⊛ ◖▮ P ⅊

## Margate

### Spread Eagle

25 Victoria Road
☎ (01843) 293396
11.30–3, 5.30–11; 11.30–11 Fri & Sat; 12–10.30 Sun
**Fuller's London Pride; Greene King IPA; Viking Ale, Thor's Thunder; guest beers** Ⓗ
Excellent, backstreet, corner local with a busy and friendly atmosphere – well worth the walk up from the seafront. Good value food – pizzas a speciality (not served Sun). Local CAMRA *Pub of the Year* 1995. ⊛ ◖▮ ♣

## Marsh Green

### Wheatsheaf Inn

On B2028 ☎ (01732) 864091
11–3, 5.30–11; 11–11 Sat; 12–3, 7–10.30 Sun
**Adnams Bitter; Harveys BB; Larkins Bitter; Taylor Landlord; guest beers** Ⓗ
Popular, friendly, multi-bar pub with a conservatory at the rear. Nine real ales, many changing weekly. Excellent value, good quality food.
🏠 Q ⛄ ⊛ ◖▮ ⅍ ♣ ⊖ P ⅊

## Marshside

### Gate Inn

Boyden Gate (Chislet turn off A28 in Upstreet)
☎ (01227) 860498
11–2.30 (3 Sat), 6–11; 12–3, 6–10.30 Sun
**Shepherd Neame Master Brew Bitter, Spitfire, Porter** Ⓖ
Splendid country pub, now 20 times in the *Guide*. It features apple trees, duck-racing,

cricket, rugby and food theme eves. Beer festival Aug. Excellent food. No-smoking area lunchtime.
🏾 Q ᗒ 🌣 ⏪ ◖ ⬥ & ♠ ♣ P ⌇

## Minster (Thanet)

### New Inn
2 Tothill Street
☎ (01843) 821294
11–3, 6–11; 11–11 Fri & Sat; 12–10.30 Sun
**Boddingtons Bitter; Wadworth 6X; guest beers** Ⓗ
Large, cosy, one-bar, corner inn in an attractive village. The spacious garden is all that remains of a Victorian landscaped 'pleasure complex' and 'tea garden'. Eve meals Wed–Sat.
🏾 🌣 ᒣ ◖ ⬥ ♠ ⇌ ♣ P

### Saddler
7 Monkton Road
☎ (01843) 821331
10.30–3, 6–11; 11–11 Sat; 12–10.30 Sun
**Shepherd Neame Master Brew Bitter, Spitfire** *or* **Bishops Finger** Ⓗ
Popular, two-bar Victorian pub which extends a welcome to locals and casual visitors. The large garden, suitable for kids of all ages, includes a Bat and Trap pitch. Good value food (not served Tue/Sun).
🏾 Q 🌣 ◖ 🍴 ♠ ⇌ ♣

## Northfleet

### Rose
Rose Street (small estate by station) ☎ (01474) 365791
11–11; 12–3, 7–10.30 Sun
**Shepherd Neame Master Brew Bitter, Spitfire** Ⓗ
Very friendly, one-bar local with a lively atmosphere. Occasional live music. Well kept outside drinking area.
🌣 & ⇌ ♣ P

## Oad Street

### Plough & Harrow
☎ (01795) 843351
11–11; 12–10.30 Sun
**Greene King IPA; Shepherd Neame Master Brew Bitter; Swale Copperwinkle; guest beers** Ⓗ
Pub selling an ever-changing range of ales: twice local CAMRA *Pub of the Year*. Eve meals Thu–Sat.
🏾 Q 🌣 ◖ ◖ 🍴 P

## Pembury

### Black Horse
High Street ☎ (01892) 822141
11–11; 12–3, 7–10.30 Sun
**King & Barnes Sussex; Morland Old Speckled Hen; Wadworth 6X; Young's Special** Ⓗ

Old village pub with an open fire and a central bar which divides the room into two areas. Popular seafood restaurant in the grounds. A house beer is also sold.
🏾 🌣 ◖ ◖

## Petteridge

### Hopbine
Petteridge Lane OS662421
☎ (01892) 722561
12 (11 Sat)–2.30, 6–11; 12–3, 7–10.30 Sun
**King & Barnes Mild, Sussex, Broadwood, Festive, seasonal beers** Ⓗ
Warm and friendly, unspoilt, one-bar pub with a varied clientele, hosting a midsummer drama festival. No meals Wed.
🏾 Q 🌣 ◖ ◖ 🍴 & ⟲ P

## Plaxtol

### Golding Hop
Sheet Hill
11–3, 6–11; 12–4, 7–10.30 (12–10.30 summer) Sun
**Adnams Bitter, Broadside; Arundel Best Bitter; Young's Bitter** Ⓖ
Attractive, 15th-century inn with an open fire and three separate areas with one bar; originally a cider house.
🏾 Q 🌣 ◖ ◖ ♠ ⟲ P

## Ramsgate

### Artillery Arms
36 Westcliffe Road (next to hospital) ☎ (01843) 853282
11–11; 12–10.30 Sun
**Beer range varies** Ⓗ
Superb, small, corner local said to have been a brothel in Victorian times, offering an adventurous and ever-changing roster of beers. It can get busy and boisterous at times. ◖ ♠ ♣

### Churchill Tavern
19–22 The Paragon
☎ (01843) 587862
11.30–11; 12–10.30 Sun
**Fuller's London Pride; Ringwood Old Thumper; Taylor Landlord; Theakston Old Peculier; guest beers** Ⓗ
Outstanding cliff-top bar which can get very busy with locals, visitors and foreign students. It serves up to 12 ales and was rebuilt in the late 1980s to resemble a country pub, using old timbers and church pews. Good value food. Folk club Sun/jazz Wed.
🏾 ◖ ♠ ♣

### Honeysuckle Inn
31 Honeysuckle Road
☎ (01843) 597532
11–2.30 (3 Sat), 5.30–11; 12–3, 7–10.30 Sun

**Beer range varies** Ⓗ
Small and charming, 18th-century inn built as a farm dwelling in 1693, granted an ale licence in 1789 and gaining its present name by 1800. No food Sun. Beers come from a list of over 15 products.
ᗒ 🌣 ◖ ♣ P

## Rochester

### Granville Arms
83 Maidstone Road
☎ (01634) 845243
11.30–11; 12–10.30 Sun
**Greene King IPA, Abbot, seasonal beers** Ⓗ
Attractive, award-winning, square-bar pub only a few minutes' walk from local historic monuments.
🏾 🌣 ◖ ♣ P

### Greyhound
68 Rochester Avenue
☎ (01634) 844120
10–3, 6–11; 10–11 Sat; 12–10.30 Sun
**Shepherd Neame Master Brew Bitter** Ⓗ
Two-bar, backstreet local in which a kitchen range and chaises-longues feature in the lounge: a town pub with a country feel. Bottled-conditioned Shepherd Neame Spitfire is also on sale.
🏾 🌣 ◖ ◖ 🍴 ♣

### Man of Kent
6–8 John Street
☎ (01634) 818771
12–11; 12–10.30 Sun
**Beer range varies** Ⓗ
A must: a pub dealing solely in Kent micro-breweries' beer; very friendly, particularly to bikers. Excellent range of games. 🏾 🌣 ⇌ ♣ ⟲

### Star
Star Hill
☎ (01634) 826811
11–11; 12–10.30 Sun (closed winter Sun eve)
**Beer range varies** Ⓗ
Seven ales are on offer at this busy, one-bar town house. Good value food. A fine collection of bottled beers is on show. ◖ ⇌

Try also: **Ship**, High St (Free)

## Rolvenden Layne

### Another Hooden Horse
26 Maytham Road (turn at Rolvenden church)
☎ (01580) 241837
12–2.30 (not Mon & Tue), 6.30 (6 Mon)–11; 12–10.30 Sun
**Goacher's Light; Hook Norton Old Hooky; Hop Back Summer Lightning; Theakston Old Peculier; guest beer** Ⓗ
Out of the way village pub

consisting of one candlelit, open-beamed, hop-strewn bar and an intimate meeting room, featuring pew seats and stuffed ducks. Extensive range of home-cooked food served up to half an hour before closing.
🛏 ◖ ▶ ⌂

## Rusthall

### Toad Rock Retreat
1 Harmony Street (off A264, 1 mile W of Tunbridge Wells)
☎ (01892) 520818
11–3, 6–11; 11–11 Sat; 12–3, 7–10.30 Sun
**Adnams Bitter; Fuller's London Pride; Harveys BB; guest beers** Ⓗ
Friendly, two-bar pub dating from the 16th century, opposite the local landmark Toad Rock. Good value food (including vegetarian and a specialist sausage menu). Ever-changing selection of guest ales.
🛏 Q ❀ ◖ ▶ ♣ P

## St Margaret's at Cliffe

### Cliffe
High Street
☎ (01304) 852400
11–4, 6–11; 12–4, 7–10.30 Sun
**Adnams Extra; Shepherd Neame Master Brew Bitter, Spitfire, Bishops Finger; guest beers** Ⓗ
Smart hotel where relaxation and conversation take precedence over life's other pressures. Tourists welcomed.
🛏 ❀ 🛏 ◖ ▶ ▲ P

### Hope Inn
High Street
☎ (01304) 852444
11–11; 12–3, 7–10.30 Sun
**Shepherd Neame Master Brew Bitter, Spitfire** Ⓗ
True village local which welcomes visitors. Shep's hospitality at its best. Skittle alley.
🛏 ❀ ◖ ▶ ▲ ♣ P

## St Mary in the Marsh

### Star
Opp. church OS064279
☎ (01797) 362139
11–3, 7–11; 12–3, 7–10.30 Sun
**Shepherd Neame Master Brew Bitter; Wadworth 6X; guest beer** Ⓗ
Attractive village pub on the wild and windy Romney Marsh. Close to Romney, Hythe and Dymchurch Railway, it attracts families in summer and locals in winter. Interesting guest beers.
🛏 Q ❀ ❀ 🛏 ◖ ▶ ▲ ♣ P

## St Nicholas at Wade

### Bell Inn
The Street ☎ (01843) 847250
11–3, 6–11; 12–3, 7–10.30 Sun
**Draught Bass; Flowers IPA; Wadworth 6X; guest beers** Ⓗ
Country pub, dating from Tudor times, with a post-war extension to the rear. The large number of small rooms helps preserve an intimate atmosphere. Good food (not served Sun eve).
🛏 Q ❀ ❀ ◖ ▶ 🛏 ⌂

## Sandgate

### Clarenden
Brewer's Hill (up steps at the side of Sandgate Hotel, on Hythe road) ☎ (01303) 268684
11.30–3, 6 (7 Sat)–11; 12–3, 7–10.30 Sun
**Shepherd Neame Master Brew Bitter, Best Bitter, Spitfire** Ⓗ
Pleasant hillside pub overlooking the Channel. Please park on the main road, but beware stormy weather – your car may get pebble-dashed! Good value food (no eve meals Thu/Sun).
🛏 ❀ ◖ ▶

### Ship Inn
65 Sandgate High Street
☎ (01303) 248525
11–11; 12–10.30 Sun
**Courage Directors; Fuller's London Pride; Greene King IPA, Abbot; Whitbread Fuggles IPA; guest beers** Ⓖ
Welcoming, classic pub where the food is excellent value (many local specialities). The pub backs onto the sea, ideal for summer. ❀ ◖ ▶ 🛏 ⌂

## Sandhurst

### New Swan
Queen Street ☎ (01580) 850260
11–3, 5 (6 Sat)–11; 12–3, 7–10.30 Sun
**Greene King IPA; Harveys BB; guest beers** Ⓗ
Don't be put off by the plain 1950s exterior: a warm welcome awaits at this pub which has found a new lease of life – the village has its local again. One large room has a central bar, a pool table at one end and simple furnishings at the other. Children welcome. No eve meals Wed.
🛏 ❀ ◖ ▶ ♣ P

## Sandwich

### Crispin
High Street ☎ (01304) 617365
11–11; 12–10.30 Sun
**Draught Bass; Mansfield Old Baily** Ⓗ

Ancient low-ceilinged house next to the Barbican (tollgate). The town, although now inland, retains much of its original Cinque Ports heritage. No meals Sun.
🛏 Q ◖ ▲ ➤ ♣

## Selling

### Sondes Arms
Station Road ☎ (01227) 752246
12–3 (5 summer Sat), 7–11; 12–3, 7–10.30 Sun
**Shepherd Neame Master Brew Bitter** Ⓗ
Delightful local, one minute from the station. The extensive garden, with goats and birds, is an attraction for drinkers and families alike. Meals in summer. 🛏 ❀ ◖ ➤ ♣ P

## Sevenoaks

### Halfway House
London Road (left from station) ☎ (01732) 457198
11–2.30, 6 (7 Sat)–11; 12–3, 7–10.30 Sun
**Greene King IPA, Rayments Special, Abbot, seasonal beers** Ⓗ
Friendly, inviting pub with two bars. Good range of food, if slightly expensive. Quiz Mon. 🛏 ❀ ◖ ▶ ➤ ♣ P

## Shatterling

### Green Man
Pedding Hill (A257)
☎ (01304) 812525
11.15–2.30 (3 Sat), 6.30–11; 12–3 Sun, closed Sun eve
**Shepherd Neame Master Brew Bitter; Young's Bitter; guest beer** Ⓗ
Isolated pub in an attractive rural setting with local, passing and tourist trade. Pub games' histories are displayed in the bar. Good food; eve meals end at 8.45 (Sun eve meals only for residents). ❀ 🛏 ◖ ▲ ♣ P

## Sheerness

### Halfway House
Queenborough Road, Halfway
☎ (01795) 662917
10–3, 6–11; 12–3, 7–10.30 Sun
**Courage Best Bitter; guest beers** Ⓗ
Refurbished, large one-bar pub: a regular outlet for Goacher's beers including Mild. Thai food is a speciality (à la carte restaurant). Frequent quizzes; pool and darts.
❀ 🛏 ◖ ▶ 🍺

### Red Lion
61 High Street, Bluetown
☎ (01795) 663165
12–3, 6 (8 Sat)–11; 12–3, 8–10.30 Sun
**Beer range varies** Ⓗ
Classic, two-bar free house with three ever-changing guest

ales and excellent value food. Beware of the clock in the public bar! Q ◖ ⊞ ⇌

## Shoreham

### Royal Oak

High Street ☎ (01959) 522319
10.30–3, 6–11; 12–3, 7–10.30 Sun
**Adnams Mild, Bitter, Broadside; Brakspear Bitter; Fremlins Bitter; guest beers** Ⓗ
Highly recommended pub in the middle of an attractive Darent Valley village: the hub of local life and welcoming to strangers (good stopping point for ramblers). Good value food. Unusual games.
♨ Q ❀ ◖ ▶ ⊞ ⇌ ♣ ⌂

## Sittingbourne

### Old Oak

68 East Street ☎ (01795) 472685
10.30–2.30, 7–11; 12–2.30, 7–10.30 Sun
**Flowers IPA; guest beers** Ⓗ
Traditional local offering a friendly welcome and an ever-changing guest ale.
Q ❀ ◖ ▶ ♣

### Park Tavern

Park Road ☎ (01795) 472486
11–3, 7–11; 11–11 Fri & Sat; 12–3, 7–10.30 Sun
**Shepherd Neame Master Brew Bitter, Best Bitter** Ⓗ
Traditional, street-corner local still retaining its tap room. Many games played.
❀ ⊞ ⇌ ♣

### Ship Inn

22 East Street ☎ (01795) 425087
11–3 (4 Fri & Sat), 6–11; 12–3, 7–10.30 Sun
**Courage Best Bitter; Ruddles Best Bitter; guest beer** Ⓗ
Popular town local retaining two bars. The guest ale is usually sold at an attractive lower price. A steady outlet for the new Swale Brewery.
▱ ◖ ⊞ ⇌ P

## Smarden

### Bell

Bell Lane (Headcorn road, 1 mile from centre)
☎ (01233) 770283
11.30–2.30, 6–11; 12–3, 7–10.30 Sun
**Fuller's London Pride; Goacher's Light; Harveys Pale Ale; Marston's Pedigree; Morland Old Speckled Hen** Ⓗ; **guest beers** Ⓖ
Large, 16th-century country pub with three bars and a children's room. The interior is a delight, with low, dark-beamed ceilings. Tables in the no-smoking bar are reservable and so are mainly used by diners. Classic car rally second Sun lunch each month. ♨ Q ▱
❀ ♨ ◖ ▶ ⊞ Ⓐ ♣ P ⌿

## Snargate

### Red Lion ☆

On B2080 between Brenzett and Appledore
☎ (01797) 344648
11–3, 7–11; 12–3, 7–10.30 Sun
**Beer range varies** Ⓖ
Take a step back in time at this unspoilt country pub with bare timber floors, a marble bar top, real fires in every bar and three-five independents' beers. Try your hand at Toad in the Hole! A must!
♨ Q ▱ ❀ ⊞ ♣ ⌂ P

## Southborough

### Bat & Ball

141 London Road
☎ (01892) 518085
10–11; 12–10.30 Sun
**Exmoor Beast; guest beer** Ⓗ
Small, comfortable, single-bar pub on the main road, featuring a range of beers not normally seen in the area. Occasional live music at weekends. ♨ ❀ ♣

## Staplehurst

### Lord Raglan

Chart Hill Road (½ mile N of A229 at Cross at Hand)
OS786472 ☎ (01622) 843747
12–3, 6–11; 12–4, 7–10.30 Sun (closed winter Sun eve)
**Fremlins Bitter; Goacher's Light; Harveys BB; guest beers** Ⓗ
Popular, unspoilt country pub with a large garden set amongst orchards. The bar area is adorned with local hops and guest beer clips. The guest ale is usually strong and the range may extend in summer. Excellent value and quality food. Children welcome.
♨ Q ❀ ◖ ▶ Ⓐ P

## Staplestreet

### Three Horseshoes

☎ (01227) 750842
11–3 (4.30 Sat), 5 (6 Sat)–11; 11–11 Fri; 12–3, 7–10.30 Sun
**Shepherd Neame Master Brew Bitter, Porter** Ⓖ
Bare-floored, classic Kentish country pub, unusually serving Shepherd Neame by gravity. Nice collection of bottles. No electronic games. Dogs welcome. No lunches Sun/Mon. ♨ Q ❀ ◖ ▶ ♣ P

## Stone (Dartford)

### Bricklayer's Arms

62 London Road (A226, 1 mile E of Dartford)
☎ (01322) 284552

11–11; 12–10.30 Sun
**Courage Best Bitter; guest beers** Ⓗ
Small, welcoming, terraced pub serving two regularly changing beers from small breweries (from Kent when available). Live music often Sat eve. ❀ ♣

## Stone Street

### Padwell Arms

1 mile S of A25, between Seal and Ightham OS569551
☎ (01732) 761532
12–3, 6–11; 12–3, 7–10.30 Sun
**Badger Dorset Best; Harveys BB; Hook Norton Old Hooky; guest beers** Ⓗ
Welcoming, award-winning old pub overlooking an apple orchard and serving four guest beers at all times. An impressive display of pump clips from stocked ales is mounted above the bar. Convenient for Ightham Mote.
♨ ❀ ◖ ♣ ⌂ P

## Tilmanstone

### Ravens

Upper Street ☎ (01304) 617337
11–2.30, 7–11; 12–3, 7–10.30 Sun
**Hancock's HB; Worthington Bitter; guest beer** Ⓗ
Refurbished and extended village local, popular with the farming community. Good food (book eve meals).
♨ ❀ ◖ ▶ ♣ P

Try also: **Plough & Harrow**, Dover Rd (Free)

## Tonbridge

### New Drum

54 Lavender Hill
☎ (01732) 365044
11–11; 12–4, 7–10.30 Sun
**Courage Best Bitter; Harveys BB; guest beers** Ⓗ
Formerly known as Uncle Tom's Cabin, this small, backstreet free house has been refurbished and enlarged but is still a friendly family-run local.
❀ ◖ ⇌ ♣

### Stag's Head

9 Stafford Road
☎ (01732) 352017
12–3, 6–11; 11–11 Sat; 12–3, 7–10.30 Sun
**Boddingtons Bitter; Taylor Best Bitter; guest beers** Ⓗ
One-bar pub of Victorian origin with a lounge area in front of the bar and a games area at the end. The loud jukebox may put off some visitors. ❀ Ⓐ ♣ P

Try also: **Primrose**, Pembury Rd (Whitbread); **Priory Wine Cellars**, Priory St (Off-Licence)

## Trottiscliffe

### Plough

Taylors Lane ☎ (01732) 822233
11.30–3, 6–11; 12–4, 7–10.30 Sun
**Fremlins Bitter; Wadworth 6X;
guest beer** Ⓗ
Cosy, two-bar, 15th-century
village pub in popular walking
country. Trosley Country Park
and Coldrum Longbarrow are
local attractions. Diners can
outnumber drinkers at times
but the guest ale is usually an
interesting beer. No eve meals
Sun. ♨ ❀ ◑ ▶ ⊕ ♣ P

## Tudeley

### George & Dragon

Five Oak Green Road (B2161)
☎ (01892) 832521
11–2.30, 6 (7 Mon)–11 (10.30 Wed);
12–2.30, 7–10.30 Sun
**Greene King IPA, Rayments
Special, Abbot** Ⓗ
Attractive, two-bar, part-
weatherboarded country pub
overlooking hop gardens. It
dates back to the 16th century
and has plenty of old beams
and polished wood, especially
in the cosy saloon. Renowned
for its food. Bat and Trap
played. ♨ ❀ ◑ ▶ ⊕ ♣ P

## Tunbridge Wells

### Bedford Hotel

2 High Street (opp. station)
☎ (01892) 526580
11–11; 12–7 Sun
**Greene King XX Mild, IPA,
Rayments Special, Abbot,
seasonal beers** Ⓗ
Single-bar, corner pub, close to
the Pantiles. Popular with
office workers and shoppers
during the day and commuters
and regulars eves.
◑ ▶ ❀ ⇌ ♣

### Crystal Palace

69 Camden Road
☎ (01892) 548412
11–3, 7–11; 11–11 Sat; 12–10.30 Sun
**Harveys Mild, Pale Ale, BB,
Old** Ⓗ
The only Harveys tied house in
Tunbridge Wells, this Victorian
pub is popular with office
workers at lunchtimes and
regulars eves. No food Sun.
♨ ☎ ❀ ◑ ⇌ ♣

**Try also: Bitter End**, Camden
Rd (Off-Licence); **Greyhound**,
Upper Grosvenor Rd (Bass)

## Upchurch

### Brown Jug

76 Horsham Lane
☎ (01634) 235287
11–2.30 (3 Sat), 6–11; 12–3, 7–10.30 Sun
**Shepherd Neame Master
Brew Bitter** Ⓗ
Two-bar village local offering a
warm and friendly welcome.
♨ Q ☎ ❀ ⊕ ♣ P

## Upper Upnor

### Tudor Rose

29 High Street
☎ (01634) 715305
11.30–3.30, 7–11; 12–3.30, 7–10.30 Sun
**Young's Bitter, Special; guest
beers** Ⓗ
Friendly, multi-roomed pub
near Upnor Castle and
overlooking the River
Medway. Six guest beers
served; beer festival May.
Morris men events in summer.
Good food (no meals Sun).
♨ ☎ ❀ ◑ ▶ ﯼ

## West Malling

### Joiner's Arms

64 High Street
☎ (01732) 840723
11–3, 5–11; 11–11 Fri & Sat; 12–3,
7–10.30 Sun
**Shepherd Neame Master
Brew Bitter, Bishops Finger** Ⓗ
Friendly, two-bar local offering
good value lunches. No food
Sun. Bar billiards played.
♨ ❀ ◑ ﯼ ⇌ ♣

## Whitstable

### Alberres

Sea Street ☎ (01227) 273400
11.30–4, 7–11; 11.30–11 Fri & Sat;
12–10.30 Sun
**Ind Coope Burton Ale; Tetley
Bitter; guest beer** Ⓗ
Former Tomson & Wotton pub
– note the windows. A sign in
the bar shows the 1953 flood
level. ◑ ♣

### East Kent

72 Oxford Street (B2205)
☎ (01227) 272018
10–11; 12–10.30 Sun
**Shepherd Neame Master
Brew Bitter, Spitfire, Porter** Ⓗ
Traditional, three-bar town
pub with a spacious bar area.
Games and local events are
hosted. Family welcome. Live
music Fri eve. No food Sun.
☎ ❀ ◑ ⇌ ♣ P

## Noah's Ark

83 Canterbury Road
☎ (01227) 272332
11–3, 6–11; 12–3, 7–10.30 Sun
**Shepherd Neame Master
Brew Bitter** Ⓗ
Basic, two-bar local with the
longest serving landlord in the
area. ⊕ ⇌ ♣

## Willesborough

### Hooden on the Hill

Silver Hill Road (off A20)
☎ (01233) 662226
12–2.30, 6–11; 12–10.30 Sun
**Goacher's Light; Hook Norton
Old Hooky; Hop Back
Summer Lightning;
Theakston Old Peculier; guest
beer** Ⓗ
Basically furnished, stone-
floored, candlelit pub with
several areas, all featuring
hop-decorated ceilings.
Extensive range of home-
cooked food served up to half
an hour before closing. Large
garden. ❀ ◑ ▶ ⌣

## Wormshill

### Blacksmith's Arms

The Street (take B2163 from
Sittingbourne)
☎ (01622) 884386
12–2.30, 7 (6 Fri & Sat)–11; 12–3,
7–10.30 Sun
**Everards Tiger; Shepherd
Neame Master Brew Bitter;
guest beers** Ⓗ
16th-century free house with a
real fire, beams, tiled floor and
a Watneys Red Barrel
illuminated sign above the bar.
Good food (no eve meals Sun).
Not so quiet Fri eve.
♨ Q ❀ ◑ ▶ ⊕ ▲ P

## Worth

### St Crispin Inn

The Street
☎ (01304) 612081
11–2.30, 6–11; 12–4.30, 7–10.30 Sun
**Boddingtons Mild; Gale's
HSB; Marston's Pedigree;
Shepherd Neame Master
Brew Bitter** Ⓗ**; guest
beers** Ⓖ
Popular old village local,
carefully refurbished and
extended. The restaurant is
popular. Two ever-changing
guest beers. Chalet
accommodation.
♨ ❀ ﯼ ◑ ▶ ♣ P

---

# LOOK NEXT DOOR

Don't forget to check neighbouring counties for more excellent
pubs. Good beer does not end at county boundaries!

# BEER FESTIVAL CALENDAR 1997

CAMRA beer festivals provide wonderful opportunities for sampling beers not normally found in the locality. Festivals are staffed by CAMRA members on a voluntary basis and offer a wide range of interesting real ales from breweries all over the country, plus live entertainment and much more. The biggest event is the Great British Beer Festival in August, where over 400 different beers can be enjoyed. For further details of this and the major regional events outlined below, together with precise dates and venues, contact CAMRA on (01727) 867201, or see your local press.

**JANUARY**
Atherton
Exeter
Merseyside
York

**FEBRUARY**
Basingstoke
Battersea
Bradford
Burton upon Trent
Dorchester
Dover
Durham
Fleetwood
Plymouth
Sussex
Truro

**MARCH**
Camden (London Drinker)
Darlington
Dukeries (N Notts)
Ealing
Eastleigh
Gosport
Leeds
Rugby
Walsall
Wigan

**APRIL**
Castle Point
Chippenham
Coventry
Dunstable
Farnham
Grappenhall
Mansfield
Newcastle upon Tyne
Oldham
Perth
Swansea

**MAY**
Alloa
Cambridge
Chester
Cleethorpes
Colchester

Dewsbury
Doncaster
Dudley
Lincoln
Milton Keynes
Northampton
Ongar
Ripon
Sudbury
Wolverhampton
Woodchurch
Yapton

**JUNE**
Barnsley
Bury St Edmunds
Catford
Exeter
Leighton Buzzard
Salisbury
Stockport
Surrey
Thurrock (Grays)

**JULY**
Ardingly
Canterbury
Chelmsford
Clacton
Cotswolds
Derby
Grantham
Larling
Southampton
Tameside Canals
Woodcote

**AUGUST**
**Great British Beer Festival**
Birmingham
Peterborough
Portsmouth
Truro

**SEPTEMBER**
Belfast
Burton upon Trent
Carmarthen
Chappel (Essex)
Chichester

Durham
Feltham
Glasgow
Harbury
Ipswich
Maidstone
Newton Abbot
Northampton
Northwich
St Ives (Cambs)
Sheffield
Shrewsbury
Tamworth

**OCTOBER**
Alloa
Bath
Bedford
Cardiff
Darlington
East Lancs
Edinburgh
Guernsey
Holmfirth
Keighley
Letchworth
Loughborough
Middlesbrough
Norwich
Nottingham
Overton
Scunthorpe
Severn Valley Railway
Stoke-on-Trent
Swindon
Wakefield

**NOVEMBER**
Aberdeen
Bury
Dudley
Jersey
Luton
Mid Wales
Rochford
Woking

**DECEMBER**
London (Pig's Ear)

151

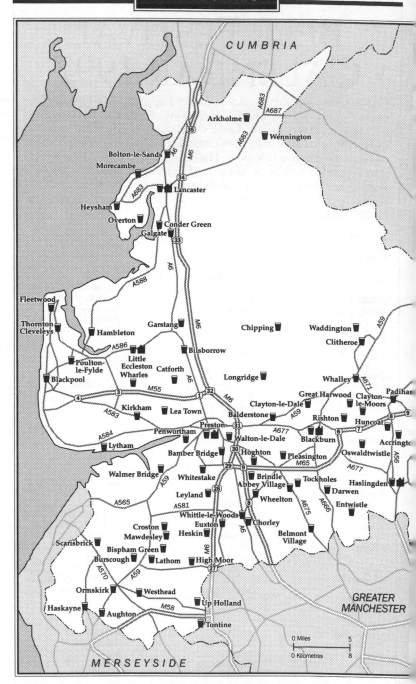

## Abbey Village

### Hare & Hounds
129 Bolton Road (A675/Dole
Lane jct)
☎ (01254) 830534

12–2.30, 5–11; 12–11 Sat; 12–10.30
Sun
**Boddingtons Bitter; Flowers
Original; Taylor Landlord;
guest beers** Ⓗ
Popular country inn: one large
main room with a central bar

and a games room at the back.
Handy for walks. Food
served all day Sat/Sun
until 8.30.
🏚 🛏 ⊛ ◑ ♣ P

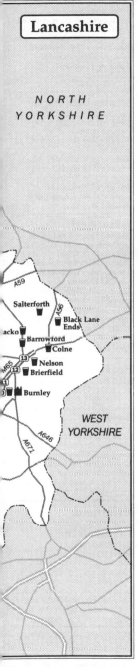

## Lancashire

*NORTH YORKSHIRE*

Salterforth

Black Lane Ends

acko

Barrowford

Colne

13 Nelson

12 Brierfield

Burnley

*WEST YORKSHIRE*

---

## Accrington

### King's Arms
Lee Street ☎ (01254) 234030
11–11; 12–10.30 Sun
**John Smith's Bitter; guest beer** Ⓗ

---

Modernised, friendly, one-roomed, town-centre pub.
✿ ⇌ ♣

## Arkholme

### Bay Horse
☎ (0152 42) 71425
11.30–3 (not winter Mon), 6–11; 12–3, 7–10.30 Sun
**Mitchell's Original, seasonal beers** Ⓗ
Small, old-fashioned country inn dating back to 1705, in a tourist-free village. The last keg-only Mitchell's pub to go real (1995), it has a small bar with two dining areas and a games room. No muddy boots.
✿ ◑▶ ♣ P

## Aughton

### Dog & Gun
223 Long Lane
☎ (01695) 423303
5–11; 12–3, 5–11 Sat; 12–2, 7–10.30 Sun
**Burtonwood Mild, Bitter, Forshaw's** Ⓗ
Excellent village local, ideal for a quiet pint. A central bar serves two lounges. Bowling green. ✿ Q ✿ ⇌ (Aughton Pk) ♣ P

### Royal Oak
134 Liverpool Road (A59)
☎ (01695) 422121
11.30–11; 12–10.30 Sun
**Ind Coope Burton Ale; guest beer** Ⓗ
Attractive, popular local where comfortable drinking areas surround a central bar. Bowling green. Good lunchtime menu: the guest beer is usually a 'Tapster's Choice' ale. ✿ ◑ ⊞ & ⇌ (Aughton Pk) ♣ P

## Balderstone

### Myerscough
Whalley Road (A59)
☎ (01254) 812222
11.30–3, 5.30–11; 12–3, 7–10.30 Sun
**Robinson's Hatters Mild, Best Bitter** Ⓗ
Pleasant country inn, close to the aerodrome, with a cosy, wood-panelled lounge and a small room with a real fire. Quality meals (finish at 8.30).
✿ Q ✿ ⇔ ◑▶ P

## Bamber Bridge

### Olde Original Withy Trees
157 Station Road
☎ (01772) 30396
11–11; 12–10.30 Sun
**Burtonwood Bitter; guest beer** Ⓗ
Locals' pub which can get busy; a refurbished former

---

farmhouse. Strong darts following. Q ⅗ ✿ ◑ ⇌ P

## Barrowford

### Old Bridge Inn
146 Gisburn Road
☎ (01282) 613983
3 (7 Tue, 2 Fri, 11 Sat)–11; 12–10.30 Sun
**Robinson's Old Stockport, Best Bitter** Ⓗ
Warm, inviting, local, retaining a Hartley and Bells brewery window.
♨ ✿ ♣ P

## Belmont Village

### Black Dog Inn
2 Church Street (A675)
☎ (01204) 811218
12–4 (3 Mon–Wed), 7–11; 12–4, 6.30–10.30 Sun
**Holt Mild, Bitter** Ⓗ
Popular, homely, moorland village pub, multi-roomed and well-decorated with antiques (no jukebox). Eve meals for residents only Mon–Tue.
♨ Q ⅗ ✿ ⇔ ◑▶

## Bilsborrow

### White Bull
Garstang Road (A6)
☎ (01995) 640324
3 (11 summer)–11; 12–10.30 Sun
**Theakston Mild, Best Bitter; guest beer** Ⓗ
Unspoilt pub on the main road by the Lancaster Canal. The guest beer is from the Scottish Courage list.
♨ Q ♣ P

## Bispham Green

### Eagle & Child
Malt Kiln Lane
☎ (01257) 462297
12–3, 5.30–11; 12–10.30 Sun
**Boddingtons Bitter; Coach House Gunpowder Mild; Theakston Best Bitter; Thwaites Bitter; guest beers** Ⓗ
Outstanding, 16th-century village local with antique furniture and stone-flagged floors. Renowned for its food; own bowling green.
♨ Q ✿ ◑▶ ⊖ P ⅍

---

**INDEPENDENT BREWERIES**

| | |
|---|---|
| **Hart:** | Little Eccleston |
| **Little Avenham:** | Preston |
| **Mitchell's:** | Lancaster |
| **Moorhouse's:** | Burnley |
| **Porter:** | Haslingden |
| **Thwaites:** | Blackburn |

## Blackburn

### Navigation Inn
Canal Street, Mill Hill
☎ (01254) 53230
10.30–11; 12–10.30 Sun
**Thwaites Best Mild, Bitter** Ⓗ
Consistently busy pub selling
well-priced beer.
❀ ⊕ ≢ (Mill Hill) ♣ P

### Shamus O'Donnell's
200 Bolton Road, Ewood
(A666/ Albion Rd jct)
☎ (01254) 665952
11–11; 12–10.30 Sun
**Boddingtons Bitter; Flowers
Original; Marston's Pedigree;
Morland Old Speckled Hen;
Tetley Bitter; guest beers** Ⓗ
Friendly community pub with
an Irish flavour, popular with
all ages. Live music four times
a week; pleasant garden;
freshly cooked food.
❀ ◖ ▶ ᵭ ♣

### Wellington Inn
362 Livesey Branch Road
☎ (01254) 201436
2 (12 Sat)–11; 12–4, 7–10.30 Sun (may
open all day Sun for football)
**Boddingtons Bitter; Flowers
IPA; Mansfield Old Baily** or
**Morland Old Speckled Hen** Ⓗ
Comfortable community pub
with the emphasis on free and
easy sing-alongs. Popular with
all ages. ᴹ ❀ ⊕ ♣

## Black Lane Ends

### Hare & Hounds
Skipton Old Road (3 miles
from Colne centre, past golf
club) ☎ (01282) 863070
12–3 (not Tue or Thu), 7–11 (11–11
summer Sat); 12–3, 7–10.30 Sun
**Taylor Mild, Golden Best,
Landlord** Ⓗ
Remote country pub on the
Pennine moors. Camping by
arrangement. Good value
traditional food (not served
Tue eve).
ᴹ Q ⛺ ❀ ◖ ▶ ♣ P

## Blacko

### Cross Gaits
Beverley Road (down side of
school) ☎ (01282) 616312
12–3 (not Mon–Wed), 5.30 (6 Sat)–11;
12–4 (12–10.30 summer) Sun
**Burtonwood Mild, Bitter, Top
Hat** Ⓗ
Popular, welcoming, cosy
country pub with a children's
play area in the garden.
Lunches Fri–Sun; eve meals
Wed–Sat. ᴹ Q ❀ ◖ ▶ ♣ P

## Blackpool

### Bispham Hotel
Red Bank Road (by
Sainsbury's) ☎ (01253) 351752
11–11; 12–10.30 Sun

**Samuel Smith OBB** Ⓗ
Distinctively designed, old-
fashioned, busy local. Live
entertainment some nights. No
food Sun/Mon.
Q ◖ ⊕ ⊖ (Red Bank Rd)

### Counting House
10 Talbot Square (opp. North
Pier) ☎ (01253) 290979
10.30–11; 12–10.30 Sun
**Boddingtons Bitter; Cains
Bitter; guest beers** Ⓗ
Converted bank; a very busy
pub at weekends. Food served
until 7.45 daily and all day Sun.
The family room closes at 8.
ᴼ ◖ ▶ ᵭ ≢ (North) ⊖
(North Pier) ♣

### Criterion
83 Topping Street (off Talbot
Rd, near bus station)
☎ (01253) 22036
10.30–11; 12–10.30 Sun
**Tetley Bitter** Ⓗ
Old-fashioned, traditionally
decorated, 1940s pub; a
backstreet local. ◖ ≢ (North)

### Empress Hotel
59 Exchange Street (off Dickson
Rd) ☎ (01253) 751347
11–11 (12.30am summer Fri & Sat);
12–10.30 Sun
**Thwaites Best Mild, Bitter** Ⓗ
Spacious, Victorian, old-
fashioned, basic hotel with a
large games room, a dance
floor and a Wurlitzer organ.
Lancashire's only ever-present
*Guide* entry.
ᴼ 🛏 ⊕ ≢ (North) ♣

### Pump & Truncheon
13 Bonny Street
☎ (01253) 21869
11–11; 12–10.30 Sun
**Boddingtons Mild, Bitter;
Whitbread Abroad Cooper;
guest beers** Ⓗ
An oasis near the central pier
where tourists are welcomed
as locals. Wide range of beers
and fruit wines. Free supper
Sun eve. Blackpool's premier
cask ale house.
ᴹ Q ◖ ⊖ (Central Pier) ♣ ᵭ

### Raikes Hall
16 Liverpool Road (off Church
St) ☎ (01253) 294372
11–11; 12–10.30 Sun
**Bass Mild; Draught Bass;
Stones Bitter; Worthington
Bitter; guest beers** Ⓗ
Built in 1750 as part of the
Raikes Hall estate, and once a
Catholic convent: a large,
elegantly furnished pub.
Popular games room; resident
jazz club. Meals till 7.30;
children welcome in a
designated area. Limited
parking. Q ❀ ◖ ▶ ⊕ ♣ P

### Saddle Inn
286 Whitegate Drive (A583/
Preston Old Rd jct)
☎ (01253) 798900
12 (11.30 Sat)–11; 12–10.30 Sun

**Draught Bass; Worthington
Bitter; guest beers** Ⓗ
Small, but cosy, three-roomed,
popular local; the oldest
continuously licensed house in
Blackpool (1776). Excellent
value cheese dishes; ever-
changing guest beers.
Children's play area.
ᴹ Q ❀ ◖ P ↯

### Stanley Beer Engine
139 Church Street (near Winter
Gardens) ☎ (01253) 26582
11–11; 12–10.30 Sun
**Boddingtons Bitter; guest
beers** Ⓗ
Basic, popular, Whitbread ale
house, full of Blackpool FC
memorabilia. Wholesome food
and up to 13 beers. Difficult
parking. ◖ ≢ (North) ⊖
(Tower) ♣ ᵭ

### Wheatsheaf
194–196 Talbot Road (A586,
opp. station) ☎ (01253) 25062
10.30–11; 12–10.30 Sun
**Morland Old Speckled Hen;
Theakston Mild, Best Bitter,
XB, Old Peculier** Ⓗ
Traditional, lively, corner local
offering a good selection of
single malts and wines. A
meeting point for many clubs.
ᴹ ≢ (North) ♣

## Bolton-le-Sands

### Royal
Main Road (A6)
☎ (01524) 732057
11–11; 12–10.30 Sun
**Mitchell's Original, Lancaster
Bomber** Ⓗ
1902 building knocked through
in the 1980s but retaining
dining, lounge and games
areas around a central bar. A
local most of the year, with an
influx from caravan sites in
summer. Access from the canal
towpath. ❀ ◖ ♣ P

## Brierfield

### Lane Ends Inn
1 High Reedley
☎ (01282) 612072
12–2, 7–11; 11–11 Sat; 12–10.30 Sun
**Vaux Samson; guest beers** Ⓗ
Welcoming, semi-open-plan,
roadside local at the top end of
town with a fancy collection of
brasses and coppers. See the
'tap' room! ◖ ᵭ ♣ P

### Poultry Fanciers WMC
39 Railway View
☎ (01282) 612404
8–11; 8–10.30 Sun
**Moorhouse's Premier;
Thwaites Bitter** Ⓗ
Well-run workingmen's club
(CIU); show this guide or a
CAMRA membership card to
gain entry (at least 30 mins
before closing). Thwaites guest
beers. ᵭ ≢ ♣ P ⍄

## Brindle

### Cavendish Arms
Sandy Lane (B5256)
☎ (01254) 852912
11–2.30, 5.30–11; 12–3, 7–10.30 Sun
**Burtonwood Bitter, seasonal
beers** Ⓗ
Outstanding, traditional,
village pub displaying 1930s
stained-glass and wood
carvings. Close to Hoghton
Towers. Children welcome at
mealtimes.
🏚 Q ☎ ❀ ◑ ▶ ⊟ ♣ P

## Burnley

### Coal Clough
41 Coal Clough Lane (200 yds
E of M65 jct 10)
☎ (01282) 423226
11–4, 5.30–11; 12–3, 7–10.30 Sun
**Draught Bass; Boddingtons
Bitter; Worthington Bitter** Ⓗ
Friendly, end-of-terrace, busy,
community local with a
popular games room.
⊟ ⇌ (Barracks) ♣

### Garden Bar
131–133 St James Street
☎ (01282) 414895
11–11; 12–10.30 Sun
**Lees GB Mild, Bitter** Ⓗ
Large, open-plan pub where
the decor reflects the pub's
name. Discos at weekends.
Wheelchair WC.
◑ ♿ ⇌ (Central)

### George IV
Padiham Road
☎ (01282) 771426
11–11; 12–10.30 Sun
**Boddingtons Bitter; Chester's
Mild; Flowers Original;
Marston's Pedigree;
Whitbread Trophy; guest beer**
(occasional) Ⓗ
Large, main road pub which
gets lively. Regular events,
plus live entertainment Sun
eve. Lunches 12–2, Mon–Fri.
◑ ♣ P

### Sparrow Hawk Hotel
Church Street
☎ (01282) 421551
11–3, 6–11; 11–11 Sat; 12–3, 7–10.30
Sun
**Moorhouse's Premier, Pendle
Witches Brew; Theakston Best
Bitter; guest beers** Ⓗ
Spectacular, friendly Victorian
hotel, thought to be Burnley's
oldest pub. Cabaret eves at
weekends. Good range of
beers; occasional cider
🛏 ◑ ▶ ⇌ (Central) ♣ ⊖ P

### Tim Bobbin Hotel
319 Padiham Road
☎ (01282) 424165
11–11; 12–10.30 Sun
**Samuel Smith OBB** Ⓗ
Lively, main road pub with a
games room, named after a
local character. ❀ ⊟ ♣ P

## Burscough

### Martin Inn
Martin Lane, Drummersdale
(off B5242 near Bescar)
☎ (01704) 892302
11.30–3, 5.30–11; 12–4, 7–10.30 Sun
**Draught Bass; Boddingtons
Bitter; Tetley Dark Mild,
Bitter; Walker Best Bitter;
guest beers** Ⓗ
Welcoming inn, close to the
Leeds–Liverpool Canal, and
not far from Martin Mere
Wildfowl Trust. A central bar
serves a large, stone-floored
bar area. Good choice of food.
🏚 ❀ 🛏 ◑ ▶ ▲ P

## Catforth

### Bay Horse Hotel
Catforth Road (off B5269)
☎ (01772) 690389
11–11; 12–10.30 Sun
**Boddingtons Bitter;
Burtonwood Bitter,
Buccaneer** Ⓗ
Good, homely, village local
boasting 'good food, good
drink, good humour'. Children
have a play area and are
welcome in a designated area.
🏚 Q ☎ ❀ ◑ ▶ ⊟ ♿ ▲ ♣ P

### Running Pump
Catforth Road (off B5269)
☎ (01772) 690265
11–3, 5–11; 11–11 Sat; 12–10.30 Sun
**Robinson's Hatters Mild,
Hartleys XB, Best Bitter** Ⓗ**,
Old Tom** (winter) Ⓖ
Charming country pub of
character, one of the oldest in
rural Fylde. Excellent, home-
cooked food (restaurant closed
Mon). 🏚 Q ❀ ◑ ▶ ♿ ♣ P

## Chipping

### Sun Inn
2 Windy Street
☎ (01995) 61206
11–11; 12–10.30 Sun
**Boddingtons Mild, Bitter** Ⓗ
Refurbished, stone pub in a
pretty tourist village. Several
drinking areas. Food served all
day until late.
🏚 Q ❀ ◑ ▶ ▲ ♣

## Chorley

### Jacksons Arms
67 Cunliffe Street
☎ (01257) 275605
6.30 (12 Fri & Sat)–11; 12–10.30 Sun
**Thwaites Best Mild, Bitter,
Craftsman** Ⓗ
Traditional, terraced pub, close
to the town centre: a small
public bar and a larger lounge.
Biker-friendly. 🛏 ⊟ ♣

### Malt 'n' Hops
50–52 Friday Street
☎ (01257) 260967
12–11; 12–10.30 Sun

**Boddingtons Bitter;
Moorhouse's Black Cat Mild;
Taylor Landlord; Webster's
Yorkshire Bitter; guest
beers** Ⓗ
Single-bar pub of character,
furnished with finds from
antique dealers. The exterior is
unusual (converted from a
corner shop eight years ago).
Four guest beers. ⇌

### Railway
20–22 Steeley Lane (behind
station) ☎ (01257) 411449
12–11; 12–10.30 Sun
**Draught Bass; Stones Bitter;
Theakston Mild, Best Bitter;
guest beers** Ⓗ
Lively local, decorated in mock
Edwardian style, with a single
bar, large alcoves and a display
of model vehicles. A local
CAMRA award-winner.
🏚 ❀ ⇌ ♣

### Shepherd's Arms
38 Eaves Lane (1 mile E of
centre) ☎ (01257) 410549
12–11; 12–10.30 Sun
**Matthew Brown Mild, Bitter;
Theakston Best Bitter; guest
beer** Ⓗ
Impressive, red-brick local
with a main bar and alcoves,
close to Leeds–Liverpool Canal
Bridge 66. ♣

### Tut 'n' Shive
Market Street (A6)
☎ (01257) 262858
11–11; 12–10.30 Sun
**Boddingtons Bitter; Castle
Eden Ale; guest beers** Ⓗ
Formerly the Royal Oak; the
name of the original owners,
Chester's, can be seen in the
tilework. Split-level bar, with a
downstairs bar open at
weekends. Six guests, often
including unusual
independents' beers.
◑ ⇌ ⊖

## Clayton-le-Dale

### Royal Oak
Longsight Road (A59)
☎ (01254) 812453
12–3, 6–11; 12–11 Sat; 12–10.30 Sun
**Vaux Samson; Ward's Best
Bitter; guest beers** Ⓗ
Friendly, 19th-century inn: a
games room, a comfortable
lounge with a log fire and a
40-seat restaurant offering
bargain three-course Sun
lunches. Large garden (play
area).
🏚 Q ☎ ❀ 🛏 ◑ ▶ ♿ ▲ ♣ P

## Clayton-le-Moors

### Albion
243 Whalley Road
☎ (01254) 238585
12–11; 12–10.30 Sun

**Porter Mild, Bitter,
Rossendale Ale, Porter,
Sunshine** H
Open-plan pub next to the
canal. Porter Brewery's second
pub. ❀ ◖ ♣ P

## Wellington Hotel

Barnes Square
☎ (01254) 235762
2–11 (midnight Sat); 12–10.30 Sun
**Thwaites Best Mild, Bitter,
seasonal beers** H
Large, multi-roomed local;
semi-open-plan, with a tap
room. ♣

## Clitheroe

### New Inn

Parson Lane
☎ (01200) 23312
11–11; 12–10.30 Sun
**Moorhouse's Black Cat Mild,
Premier; OB Bitter; guest
beers** H
Friendly local, opposite the
castle with a very traditional
interior of four rooms. Folk
music Fri eve.
🏚 Q ♿ ⊟ & ⇌ ♣ P

## Colne

### Golden Ball Inn

Burnley Road
☎ (01282) 861862
11–4, 7–11; 11–11 Thu–Sat; 12–10.30
Sun
**Tetley Mild, Bitter; guest
beers** H
Popular roadside inn, popular
with trippers to the mill shop
(behind the pub) at lunchtimes.
Splendid, home-cooked food.
Children welcome lunchtime
in the conservatory, which
leads to a well-maintained
garden. ♿ ❀ ◖ & P

## Conder Green

### Stork

On A588
☎ (01524) 751234
11–11; 12–10.30 Sun
**Boddingtons Bitter; guest
beers** H
Long, panelled, beamed
building with a large
restaurant, a snug (children
welcome), a plush lounge and
a pool room. Handy for the
Lune Estuary Path. Three guest
beers. 🏚 ❀ 🛏 ◖ ▶ ♠ ♣ P

## Croston

### Black Horse

Westhead Road (A581,
Southport road)
☎ (01772) 600338
11–11; 12–10.30 Sun
**Theakston Mild, Best Bitter;
guest beers** H
True free house; a children-
friendly, real ale haven,
offering six guest beers, superb
value food and a bowling

green to the rear. Occasional
cider.
Q ♿ ❀ ◖ ▶ & ⇌ ♣ ♻ P

## Darwen

### Greenfield

Lower Barn Street
☎ (01254) 703945
12–3, 5.30–11; 12–11 Fri & Sat; 12–
10.30 Sun
**Boddingtons Bitter; Taylor
Landlord; Thwaites Best Mild,
Bitter; guest beers** H
Open-plan pub next to the
Sough tunnel, serving good
value food (all day Sun until 7;
no eve meals Tue). Three guest
beers usually include a porter.
Q ❀ ◖ ▶

### Park Hotel

1 Cemetery Road (A666, S end
of town)
☎ (01254) 760357
11.30–11; 12–10.30 Sun
**Vaux Mild, Samson; guest
beers** H
Friendly, semi-open-plan,
corner local. Lively at
weekends ♣

### Punch Hotel

Chaples
☎ (01254) 702510
12–11; 12–10.30 Sun
**Chester's Mild; Whitbread
Trophy; guest beer** H
Large, multi-roomed, friendly,
games pub. The only outlet for
cider (and occasionally perry)
in town.
❀ 🛏 ◖ ▶ & ♣ ♻ P

## Entwistle

### Strawbury Duck

Overshores Road (signed on
the Edgworth–Darwen Roman
road) OS727178
☎ (01204) 852013
12–3 (not Mon), 7–11; 12–11 Sat;
12–10.30 Sun
**Boddingtons Bitter; Marston's
Pedigree; Moorhouse's Pendle
Witches Brew; Taylor
Landlord; guest beers** H
Old, isolated but busy country
pub next to the station. A good
base for walks in the hill
country. Children welcome till
8.30, but no motorcyclists.
🏚 Q ♿ ❀ 🛏 ◖ ▶ ⇌ P

## Euxton

### Euxton Mills

Wigan Road (A49 / A581 jct)
☎ (01257) 264002
11.30–3 (4 Sat), 5.30 (6.15 Sat)–11;
12–10.30 Sun
**Burtonwood Mild, Bitter,
Forshaw's** H
Welcoming, splendid, 18th-
century pub with excellent
value food. Children welcome
in the dining area. No food
Mon eve in winter.
Q ❀ ◖ ▶ ⊟ & ♣ P ⚲

## Fleetwood

### Mount

The Esplanade (near Marine
Hall complex)
☎ (01253) 874619
11–11; 12–10.30 Sun
**Boddingtons Bitter;
Theakston Best Bitter; guest
beers** (summer) H
Large, modernised, Victorian
building close to the beach. It
has a pool and darts room, a
large family room and a public
bar. ♿ ❀ ◖ ⊟ & ♣

### North Euston Hotel

The Esplanade
☎ (01253) 876525
11–11; 12–10.30 Sun
**Ruddles County;
Webster's Yorkshire Bitter;
Wilson's Mild, Bitter; guest
beers** H
Large, Victorian, stone-fronted
building overlooking
Morecambe Bay and the River
Wyre, and near the bus and
tram termini. Spacious rooms;
the family room closes at 7.
House beer from Moorhouse's.
Q ♿ 🛏 ◖ & ⊖ (Ferry) P ⚲

### Ship

24–26 Warren Street (off Lord
St by council offices)
☎ (01253) 778415
11–11; 12–10.30 Sun
**Boddingtons Bitter; guest
beers** H
Busy, friendly pub with a
central bar, a comfortable
lounge, a pool table and darts.
Excellent pizzas.
🏚 ❀ ◖ & ⊖ (Lord St) ♣

### Wyre Lounge Bar

Marine Hall, The Esplanade
☎ (01253) 771141
12–4, 7–11; 12–4, 7–10.30 Sun
**Courage Directors;
Moorhouse's Premier,
Pendle Witches Brew; guest
beers** H
Part of the attractive Marine
Hall and Gardens complex;
twice local CAMRA *Pub of the
Year*, famous for its choice of
guest beers. Home of the
Fleetwood beer festival.
Q ❀ & P

## Galgate

### Plough

Main Street
☎ (01524) 751337
11–11; 12–10.30 Sun
**Boddingtons Bitter; guest
beers** H
Modernised and open-plan
pub with a distinct, cosy
'lounge' end. A robust
masculine atmosphere is
augmented on Sat by sports
teams. Handy for the canal.
🏚 ❀ ◖ P

# Garstang

## Royal Oak

Market Place ☎ (01995) 603318
11–3 (4 Thu), 7–11; 11–11 Fri & Sat;
12–10.30 Sun
**Robinson's Hatters Mild,
Hartleys XB, Best Bitter,
Frederics** H
Some parts date from a 1480
farmhouse, but this is mostly a
1670 coaching inn,
thoughtfully renovated, with
intimate drinking areas.
❀ ⌂ ◗ ♣ P

# Great Harwood

## Dog & Otter

Cliffe Lane ☎ (01254) 885760
11.30–3, 6–11; 12–10.30 Sun
**Jennings Mild, Bitter,
Cumberland Ale, Sneck
Lifter; guest beer** H
On the outskirts of town,
Jennings' first tied pub in E
Lancs offers ale and home-
cooked food at realistic prices.
Families welcome.
▲ Q ◖◗ ▲ P

## Royal Hotel

Station Road ☎ (01254) 883541
12–1.30 (3 Sat; not Mon & Tue), 7–11;
12–3, 7–10.30 Sun
**Burtonwood Bitter; guest
beers** H
Cosy, open-plan pub, free from
loud music. Four guest beers
plus a wide selection of
continental bottles. A CAMRA
regional *Pub of the Year*.
❀ ⌂ ◗ ▲ ♣ ☗

# Hambleton

## Shard Bridge Inn

Old Bridge Lane (by new
Shard bridge)
☎ (01253) 700208
12–3, 6–11 (11–11 summer); 12–10.30
Sun
**Robinson's Best Bitter;
Walker Best Bitter; guest
beers** H
Originally the Ferry Boat Inn,
dating back to 1786,
overlooking the River Wyre: a
comfortable, relaxing lounge,
and a games room; families
welcome. Good home-made
meals (served all day Sun,
12–9).
❀ ◗ ⊟ ♿ ▲ ♣ ⌆ P ⏦

# Haskayne

## Ship Inn

6 Rosemary Lane (300 yds from
A5147 at Downholland)
☎ (01704) 840572
12–3, 6–11 (12–11 summer); 12–3,
6–10.30 (12–10.30 summer) Sun
**Tetley Imperial; Walker Mild,
Bitter** H
Rural canalside pub with a
reputation for good food, plus
a children's playground and

garden. Local CAMRA *Summer
Pub of the Year 1994.*
▲ ⏦ ❀ ◖◗ ♣ P ⏦

# Haslingden

## Griffin Inn

86 Hud Rake ☎ (01706) 214021
12–11; 12–3, 7–10.30 Sun
**Porter Mild, Bitter,
Rossendale Ale, Porter,
Sunshine** H
Open-plan pub with views
over the valley; great for
conversation. Award-winning
ales brewed by landlord David
Porter. No food Mon.
▲ Q ◖ ♣

# Heskin

## Farmers Arms

85 Wood Lane (B5250
☎ (01257) 451276
12–11; 12–10.30 Sun
**Boddingtons Bitter; Castle
Eden Ale; Flowers IPA;
Morland Old Speckled Hen;
Taylor Landlord; guest beers**
(occasional) H
Country pub with a food-
oriented, split-level lounge and
a comfortable public bar for
drinkers. Families welcome
(large garden play area). Close
to Camelot Theme Park.
▲ Q ❀ ◖◗ ⊟ ▲ ♣ P

# Heysham

## Old Hall

Heysham Road
☎ (01524) 851209
11–11; 12–10.30 Sun
**Mitchell's Original, Lancaster
Bomber, seasonal beers** H
Actually an old hall, dated
1584, rescued from dereliction
in 1958 and fitted out in
Mitchell's usual style: a single
large bar with the counter at
one end. Note the stained-
glass. ❀ ◖◗ P

## Royal

7 Main Street
11–3, 5.45–11; 11–11 Thu–Sat; 12–4.30,
7–10.30 Sun
**Mitchell's Original, Lancaster
Bomber** H
Old, four-roomed, low-
ceilinged pub near St Patrick's
Chapel and rock-hewn graves.
Busy local trade; packed with
holidaymakers in the season.
Children admitted to the
games room until 7.30.
▲ ❀ ◖ ⊟ ♣

# High Moor

## Rigbye Arms

2 Whittle Lane
☎ (01257) 462354
12–3, 5.30–11 (12–11 Thu–Sat in
summer); 12–10.30 Sun
**Ind Coope Burton Ale; Tetley
Dark Mild, Mild, Bitter; guest
beers** H

Remote, homely, rural pub,
popular with ramblers.
Deserved reputation for food
(restaurant open Fri/Sat; meals
all day Sun); own bowling
green.
▲ ❀ ◖◗ ⊟ P

# Hoghton

## Black Horse

Gregson Lane (off A675 at
Higher Walton)
☎ (01254) 852541
12–11; 12–10.30 Sun
**Matthew Brown Bitter;
Theakston Mild, Best Bitter,
XB; guest beer** H
Large, friendly open-plan
village pub with a games area,
catering mainly for drinkers,
with few gimmicks. Children
allowed in for food. Scottish
Courage guest beers.
▲ ❀ ◖ ♣ P

# Huncoat

## Griffin Head Hotel

Burnley Road (400 yds W of
A679/A56 jct)
☎ (01254) 231577
12–2.30 (3 Fri & Sat), 5 (7 Sat)–11;
12–3, 7–10.30 Sun
**Thwaites Best Mild, Bitter,
seasonal beers** H
Homely, friendly local with a
family room and a games area
(pool). The home-cooked food
is second to none (not served
Mon). ☞ ❀ ◖ P

# Kirkham

## Queen's Arms

7 Poulton Street (opp. Market
Place) ☎ (01772) 686705
11–11; 12–10.30 Sun
**Theakston Best Bitter, XB;
guest beer** (occasional) H
Well-run, lively, town-centre
local, full of character.
Children welcome in a
designated area. Excellent
garden (summer barbecues);
pool room; wheelchair WC.
❀ ♿ ♣

## Swan Hotel

115 Poulton Street
☎ (01772) 682078
12–11; 12–10.30 Sun
**Matthew Brown Mild, Bitter;
Theakston Best Bitter; Wells
Bombardier; guest beers** H
Popular, friendly, two-bar local
with a large screen TV and
entertainment at weekends.
❀ ⏦ ⊟ ♣ P

# Lancaster

## Fibber McGee's

2 James Street (in maze of
alleys, near market)
☎ (01524) 63720
11–11; 12–10.30 Sun
**Mitchell's Original, Lancaster
Bomber, seasonal beers** H

**157**

The facade is all that remains of the old Ship Inn; the inside was totally revamped in 1995 and given the theme of a fictitious Irish fish-poacher. Irish music played. Children's certificate. No-smoking area lunchtime. ◁ & ≠ ♣ ½

## Golden Lion

Moor Lane ☎ (01524) 63198
12–3, 7–11; 12–3, 7–10.30 Sun
**Theakston Best Bitter, Black Bull, XB, Old Peculier** ℍ
A pub since at least 1612: an L-shaped bar and adjoining games room (bar billiards and skittles) plus a no-smoking 'Heritage' room. ﬦ ♣ ½

## Gregson

Moorgate ☎ (01524) 849959
7–11 (midnight Fri & Sat); 7–10.30 Sun
**Thwaites Bitter, Craftsman, seasonal beers** ℍ
Originally the product of Victorian philanthropy, now owned by a residents' association. The bar is cosy; the hall hosts entertainment. Pizzas available.
ﬦ & ♣

## John O'Gaunt

35 Market Street
☎ (01524) 65356
11–3 (5 Sat), 6 (7 Sat)–11; 11–11 Fri;
12–3, 7–10.30 Sun
**Boddingtons Bitter; Ind Coope Burton Ale; Jennings Bitter; Tetley Bitter; guest beers** ℍ
Small pub, often packed, with a handsome original frontage. Live music often; the landlord is a jazz enthusiast. Snacks only Sun lunch. ⊛ ◁ ≠

## Keystones

92 Penny Street
☎ (01524) 65533
11–11; 12–10.30 Sun
**Draught Bass; Highgate Dark; Stones Bitter; Worthington Bitter; guest beers** ℍ
Single-room pub revamped in 1995 with plenty of brown wood and plaster, divided by pillars into games and drinking areas. Three guest beers, some from Bass. No food Sun eve.
⊛ ◁ ▶ ≠ ♣

## Priory

36 Cable Street (next to bus station)
11–3, 6–11; 11–11 Fri & Sat; 6–10.30 Sun, closed Sun lunch
**Mitchell's Original, Lancaster Bomber, seasonal beers** ℍ
Large, unprepossessing pub, but improvements are promised. Popular with students. ⌂

## Royal

Thurnham Street
☎ (01524) 65007
11.30–3, 7–11; 7–10.30 Sun, closed Sun lunch

**Thwaites Best Mild, Bitter, Craftsman, seasonal beers** ℍ
Pub knocked into a single large bar with comfortable seating. Daytime trade comes from the nearby civic buildings.
⊛ ◁ P

## Wagon & Horses

27 St George's Quay
☎ (01524) 615602
11–11; 12–10.30 Sun
**Robinson's Hatters Mild, Old Stockport** (occasional), **Hartleys XB, Best Bitter, Old Tom** ℍ
Two houses knocked together – one fitted out in vault style, the other as a lounge. Close to the Maritime Museum.
ﬦ ⊛ ⇔ ◁ ≠ ♣

# Lathom

## Railway Tavern

Hoscar Moss Road
☎ (01704) 892369
12–3, 5–11; 12–11 Sat; 12–3, 7–10.30 Sun
**Jennings Bitter; guest beers** ℍ
Refurbished, but unspoilt, friendly village local next to Hoscar station. Excellent home-cooked food (not served Mon lunch). Popular with cyclists. ﬦ Q ⊛ ◁ ▶ ⇔ ≠ (Hoscar) ♣ P

## Ship Inn

Wheat Lane (off B5209, near Burscough, over canal swing bridge) ☎ (01704) 893117
12–3, 5.30 (7 Sat)–11; 12–3, 7–10.30 Sun
**Moorhouse's Pendle Witches Brew; Theakston Mild, Best Bitter, XB, Old Peculier; guest beers** ℍ
Rural canalside pub, winner of CAMRA awards, an excellent family-run, free house with nine handpumps and up to five changing guests. Good value lunches (not served Sun).
Q ⛵ ⊛ ◁ P ½

# Lea Town

## Smith's Arms (Slip Inn)

Lea Lane ☎ (01772) 726906
12–3, 6.30–11; 12–10.30 Sun
**Thwaites Best Mild, Bitter** ℍ
Country gem with lunchtime trade from the nearby BNFL factory; a drinkers' pub but offering food – ruthless chilli a speciality (no eve meals Tue or Sun). Don't miss.
ﬦ Q ⊛ ◁ ▶ ♣ P

# Leyland

## Dunkirk Hall

Dunkirk Lane (B5248/B5253 jct) ☎ (01772) 422102
11–3, 5–11; 11–11 Fri & Sat; 12–10.30 Sun

**Courage Directors; John Smith's Bitter; Webster's Green Label** ℍ
17th-century converted farmhouse, west of the town centre: a listed building with flagged floors, panelled walls and beams. No food Mon.
Q ⊛ ◁ ▶ P

## Eagle & Child

30 Church Road (B5248)
☎ (01772) 433531
11.45–11.30; 12–10.30 Sun
**Burtonwood Bitter, Forshaw's, Top Hat, Buccaneer; guest beer** ℍ
Ancient inn with a bowling green, near the even more ancient parish church and open-air market. Lunches Mon–Fri. ⊛ ◁ ♣ P

## George IV

63 Towngate ☎ (01772) 422165
11.45–11; 12–10.30 Sun
**Boddingtons Bitter; Greenalls Bitter; guest beers** ℍ
Attractive pub near the proposed new shopping centre. Meals till 5 Sun.
◁ ⊟ ♣ P

# Little Eccleston

## Cartford Hotel

Cartford Lane (by toll bridge, ½ mile off A586)
☎ (01995) 670166
12–3, 7 (6.30 summer)–11; 12–4, 6–10.30 Sun
**Boddingtons Bitter; guest beers** ℍ
Delightfully situated CAMRA award-winning, free house by the River Wyre. An extensive bar menu offers children's meals. Six changing guest beers. Hart Brewery is at the rear and at least two Hart beers are always available.
ﬦ ⊛ ⇔ ◁ & ♣ ⌂ P

# Longridge

## Alston Arms

Inglewhite Road
☎ (01772) 783331
11.30–11; 12–10.30 Sun
**Matthew Brown Mild, Bitter; Theakston Best Bitter; guest beer** ℍ
Scenically situated pub on the way to Beacon Fell. The garden has a play area, animals and a double-decker bus. Popular with families, diners and drinkers.
ﬦ Q ⛵ ⊛ ◁ ▶ Å ♣ P

## Forrest Arms

2 Derby Road (near town centre)
12–2 (not Wed), 7–11 (may extend in summer); 12–11 Fri & Sat; 12–10.30 Sun
**Boddingtons Bitter; guest beers** ℍ
Splendid, refurbished, three-roomed, drinkers' pub fielding

sports teams. Two guest beers – one often unusual and/or cheap. ❀ ◗ ◁ ♣

## Towneley Arms

41 Berry Lane
☎ (01772) 782219
11–11; 12–10.30 Sun
**Tetley Mild, Bitter** Ⓗ
Town-centre, multi-roomed pub next to the long-closed station. A pub for the mature drinker. ♨ Q ⊞ ▲ ♣ P

## Lytham

### Hole in One

Forest Drive (off B5261)
☎ (01253) 730598
11–3, 6–11; 11–11 Fri & Sat; 12–10.30 Sun
**Thwaites Bitter** Ⓗ
Busy, friendly, modern local by Fairhaven golf course. Full of golfing memorabilia, it features a large games room, plus good, home-made food (extensive menu). Wheelchair WC.
Q ❀ ◗ ⊞ & ♣ P

### Taps

12 Henry Street (off Lytham Sq) ☎ (01253) 736226
11–11; 12–10.30 Sun
**Boddingtons Bitter; Whitbread Abroad Cooper; guest beers** Ⓗ
Busy, friendly, basic ale house serving a wide choice of changing guest beers. Wheelchair WC. Difficult parking.
♨ Q ❀ ◗ & ⇌ ♣ ⏏

## Mawdesley

### Black Bull

Hall Lane (off B5246) OS499151
☎ (01704) 822202
12–11; 12–10.30 Sun
**Greenalls Mild, Bitter, Original; Tetley Bitter; guest beers** Ⓗ
Welcoming, 700-year-old country pub with an excellent food menu.
♨ Q ☎ ❀ ◗ ▶ & ♣ P ⅄

## Morecambe

### New Inn

2 Poulton Square
☎ (01524) 831120
11–11; 12–10.30 Sun
**Boddingtons Bitter; John Smith's Bitter** Ⓗ
Down-to-earth pub in the centre of the old village of Poulton-le-Sands. Two small bars and a games room.
❀ ⊞ ♣ P

### Smugglers' Den

56 Poulton Road
☎ (01524) 421684
11–3, 7–11; 11–11 Fri & Sat (& Tue–Thu in summer); 12–10.30 Sun

**Boddingtons Bitter; Jennings Bitter; Tetley Bitter; guest beer** Ⓗ
The smugglers have long since gone, but the stained-glass and nautical knick-knacks remind customers of this low-beamed, stone-floored pub's past. Busy in summer (when food is available).
♨ ❀ ◗ ⊞ ♣ P

## Nelson

### Shooters Arms

Southfield Lane, Southfield (leave Nelson centre via Barkerhouse Rd)
☎ (01282) 614153
12–3.30 (not Wed), 6.30–11; 12–11 Fri & Sat; 12–10.30 Sun
**Thwaites Bitter, seasonal beers** Ⓗ
Country pub on the outskirts of town, offering superb views of Pendle Hill. Popular with locals. ♨ ❀ P

## Ormskirk

### Hayfield

22 County Road (A59)
☎ (01695) 571157
12–3, 5–11; 12–11 Fri & Sat; 12–10.30 Sun
**Courage Directors; John Smith's Bitter; Webster's Yorkshire Bitter; guest beers** Ⓗ
Once a derelict restaurant, now a popular free house, comfortably furnished. Good wheelchair access. Up to ten guest beers. CAMRA Lancs *Pub of the Year* 1995. Worth the short walk from the centre.
❀ ◗ ▶ & ⇌ P ⏢

### Yewtree

Grimshaw Lane
☎ (01695) 573381
12–3, 5–11.30; 12–3, 7–10.30 Sun
**Cains Mild, Bitter; guest beers** Ⓗ
Modern, spacious pub in a residential area: a well-patronised public bar and a pleasantly furnished snug. Good value food (not served Sun). Worth the walk from the centre.
Q ❀ ◗ ▶ ♣ P

## Oswaldtwistle

### Stop & Rest

Fielding Lane
☎ (01254) 231951
12–3, 7–11; 11–11 Sat; 12–3, 7–10.30 Sun
**Boddingtons Bitter; Whitbread Trophy; guest beer** Ⓗ
Two-roomed, six-pump local with a spacious lounge. Charity events; occasional beer festivals.
◗ ♣ P

## Overton

### Ship ☆

9 Main Street ☎ (01524) 858231
11.30–4, 7–11; 11–11 Sat; 12–4, 7–10.30 Sun
**Thwaites Best Mild, Bitter, Craftsman** (summer), **seasonal beers** Ⓗ
Unspoilt, multi-roomed, Victorian pub displaying cases of stuffed animals and birds' eggs. Craft shop upstairs; bowling green.
♨ Q ❀ ◗ ▶ ▲ ♣ P

## Padiham

### Hare & Hounds

58 West Street
☎ (01282) 774749
11–11; 12–10.30 Sun
**Tetley Bitter** Ⓗ
Originally a brewhouse for the Huntroyd estate, circa 17th-century, extended in the 1950s and little changed since. Set in the Padiham conservation area.
♨ Q ☎ ❀ ⋈ ◗ & ♣ P

## Penwortham

### St Teresa's Social Centre

Queensway (off A59)
☎ (01772) 743523
7–11; 1–5, 7–11 Sat; 1–4, 7–10.30 Sun
**Burtonwood Mild, Bitter, Forshaw's; Ind Coope Burton Ale; Tetley Mild, Bitter; guest beers** Ⓗ
Thriving, Catholic club in a residential area: a large function room, a games room and a lounge, each with its own bar; a total of 18 handpumps. Annual beer festival. Entry restrictions: CAMRA members anytime, non-members 50p six times a year. Family room lunchtime.
♿ ⊞ ♣ ⏏ P

## Pleasington

### Railway Hotel

Pleasington Lane
☎ (01254) 201520
12–3, 6.30–11; 12–11 Sat; 12–10.30 Sun
**Boddingtons Bitter; Wilson's Mild, Bitter; guest beer** Ⓗ
Old farmhouse converted to a pub about 1850; a cosy, intimate local, with a bowling green. Eve meals 7–9, Tue–Sat.
♨ Q ☎ ❀ ◗ ▶ ⇌ ♣ P

## Poulton-le-Fylde

### Thatched House

Ball Street
11–11; 12–10.30 Sun
**Boddingtons Bitter; Wells Bombardier; guest beer** Ⓗ
Recently altered, very popular pub in the centre of town, part of St Chad's Norman

159

churchyard. No music; no
games. Difficult parking.
🏚 Q & ⇌

# Preston

## Ashton Institute
10–12 Wellington Road (off
Blackpool Rd, A5085)
☎ (01772) 726582
7 (4 Fri, 1 Sat)–11; 12–10.30 Sun
**Boddingtons Bitter; Chester's
Mild; Whitbread Trophy;
guest beers** ℍ
Enterprising, good value social
club, the oldest club in Preston
(founded in 1944 in its original
premises, two terraced houses
knocked into one). Show this
guide or CAMRA card to be
signed in. 🍴 ♣

## Blackamoor
92 Lancaster Road
☎ (01772) 251590
10.30–5, 7–11; 12–3 Sun, closed Sun
eve
**John Smith's Bitter;
Moorhouse's Premier; Yates
Bitter; guest beer**
(occasional) ℍ
Lively, town-centre free house
facing the outdoor market and
serving some of the cheapest
beer in town (but the range
may change). ♣

## Fox & Grapes
15 Fox Street (off Fishergate)
☎ (01772) 252448
10.30–11; 12–10.30 Sun
**Theakston Best Bitter, XB,
Old Peculier; Wells
Bombardier; Younger IPA,
No. 3** ℍ
Popular, town-centre pub; one
room, decorated in traditional
ale house style. Two guest
beers. No food Sun.
◖ ⇌

## Hogshead
99 Fylde Road (A583)
☎ (01772) 252870
11–11; 12–10.30 Sun
**Boddingtons Bitter;
Whitbread Abroad Cooper** ℍ**;
guest beers** ℍ**/** ℊ
Former doctor's house and
surgery restored as an open-
plan cask ale house. Brisk
lunch trade (food is served all
day until 7); very busy
weekend eves. Up to 12 guest
beers, but prices are high.
Q ❀ ◖ ▶ & ✄

## Mitre Tavern
90–91 Moor Lane (A6 jct)
☎ (01772) 251918
12–3, 5.30–11; 12–11 Sat; 12–10.30 Sun
**Vaux Samson; Ward's Thorne
BB; guest beers** ℍ
Friendly pub, not far from the
town centre and the university
halls of residence: a
comfortable lounge and a
well-used vault (pool). Good
value lunches. ◖ 🍴 ♣ P

## Moorbrook
370 North Road (A6 jct)
☎ (01772) 201127
4 (12 Sat)–11; 12–3, 7–10.30 Sun
**Thwaites Best Mild, Bitter,
seasonal beers** ℍ
Small, welcoming local with
two small rooms off the main
bar area. Summer barbecues.
Q ❀ ♣

## New Britannia
6 Heatley Street (off Friargate)
☎ (01772) 253424
11–3 (4 Sat), 6–11; 7–10.30 Sun, closed
Sun lunch
**Castle Eden Ale; Flowers
Original; Marston's Pedigree;
Whitbread Trophy; guest
beers** ℍ
Small, cosy, single bar in a
terraced town-centre pub, close
to the university. Splendid
Britannia windows. Weekday
lunches. ❀ ◖ & ⇌ ♣ ↻

## Old Black Bull
35 Friargate (Ringway jct)
☎ (01772) 254402
10.30–11; 12–10.30 Sun
**Boddingtons Bitter; guest
beers** ℍ
Tudor-fronted pub, extended
into the shop next door, and
now having a snug, a games
area and a main lounge. It
sports an alehouse theme, with
barrels racked behind the bar.
The tiny vault has been
retained. Three changing guest
beers. Weekday lunches.
❀ ◖ ▤ ♣ ↻

## Olde Blue Bell
114 Church Street (off A6)
☎ (01772) 251280
11–3.30 (4 Sat), 6 (7 Sat)–11; 12–10.30
Sun
**Samuel Smith OBB** ℍ
The oldest pub in Preston, like
a country cottage, with two
small rooms off a main bar
area. Good for conversation,
but it can be packed Fri and Sat
nights. Good value food; the
cheapest beer in town.
🏚 ❀ ◖ ♣

## Olde Dog & Partridge
44 Friargate ☎ (01772) 252217
11–3, 6–11; 12–3, 7–10.30 Sun
**Draught Bass; Highgate Dark;
Worthington Bitter; guest
beers** ℍ
Popular pub, which recently
re-acquired the 'Olde'. Good
value meals make it popular
with all, but it mainly attracts
bikers and students eves. Basic
decor; good rock jukebox. No
food Sun. ❀ ◖ ⇌ ♣

## Plungington Tavern
85 Plungington Road (off
A5085)
12 (11 Sat)–11; 12–3, 7–10.30 Sun
**Bass Toby Cask; Hancock's
HB; Highgate Dark; Stones
Bitter; Webster's Green
Label** ℍ

Well-maintained drinkers' pub
which is steadily building up a
reputation for its ales. The fine,
red-brick exterior hides a plain
but comfortable interior.
🍴 ♣

## Real Ale Shop
47 Lovat Road (off A6)
☎ (01772) 201591
11–2, 5–10; 12–2, 6–10 Sun
**Beer range varies** ℍ**/** ℊ
Superb off-licence offering an
extensive range of bottled
beers (foreign and bottle-
conditioned): a 1995 local
CAMRA award-winner. Up to
four beers on draught.
↻

## Sumners
Watling Street Road, Fulwood
(B6242) ☎ (01772) 705626
11.30–11; 12–10.30 Sun
**Boddingtons Mild, Bitter;
guest beers** ℍ
Large, busy, modern pub
handy for the football ground:
a large, wood-panelled lounge
with a no-smoking dining area
and spacious games room.
Meals served all day until 7.
Whitbread-supplied guest
beer. ❀ ◖ ▶ 🍴 ♣ P

## Wall Street
1 Fishergate ☎ (01772) 823323
11–11; 7–10.30 Sun, closed Sun lunch
**Greenalls Bitter, Original** ℍ
Huge, town-centre bar,
extremely popular, especially
at weekends when queues
often form for eve admission.
The main feature is a huge
revolving video screen.
Upstairs dining (10–5). Smart
dress essential. Converted in
1993 from a bank. ◖ ▶ & ⇌

# Rishton

## Rishton Arms
Station Road ☎ (01254) 886396
7 (11 Sat)–11; 12–10.30 Sun
**Thwaites Best Mild, Bitter,
Craftsman** ℍ
Pleasant, two-roomed pub next
to the station. Grandfather
clock in the lounge.
⇌ ♣ P

# Salterforth

## Anchor Inn
Salterforth Lane
☎ (01282) 813186
12–11; 12–10.30 Sun
**Bass Mild, Draught Bass;
Theakston Best Bitter;
Worthington Bitter; guest beer**
(summer) ℍ
Grade II listed building, dating
from 1655. The history can be
found on a plaque inside.
Stalactites can be seen in the
cellar. A popular stop for
boaters on the Leeds–Liverpool
Canal.
🏚 Q ⛺ ❀ ◖ ▶ & ▲ ♣ P

## Scarisbrick

### Heatons Bridge Inn

2 Heatons Bridge Road (B5242, by Leeds–Liverpool Canal)
☎ (01704) 840549
11–11; 12–10.30 Sun
**Tetley Mild; Walker Best Bitter; guest beers** H
Popular, welcoming canalside inn, extended at the rear without loss of character. The small rooms off the small bar area are ideal for conversations. Excellent value food (all day Sun). Children welcome in the dining area.
🏰 Q 🏶 ◑ ▶ ♣ P ⅟

## Thornton Cleveleys

### Tavern at the Mill

Marsh Mill Village, Fleetwood Road ☎ (01253) 862586
11–11; 12–10.30 Sun
**Boddingtons Bitter; Flowers IPA, Original; Higsons Bitter; Morland Old Speckled Hen; Whitbread Trophy** H
Friendly, Brewers' Fayre pub in a shopping village next to Marsh Windmill. Food served all day; children's certificate and play area. Busy weekend lunchtimes. 🏶 ◑ ▶ ♿ P

## Tockholes

### Royal Arms

Tockholes Road
☎ (01254) 705373
12–3, 7–11; 12–11 Fri, Sat & summer; 12–10.30 Sun
**Thwaites Best Mild, Bitter, Craftsman, seasonal beers** H
Very cosy, attractive moorland pub with a fire in each of its four rooms. Handy for walks. Recommended food.
🏰 Q 🏰 🏶 ◑ ▶ ♣ P ⅟

## Tontine

### Delph Tavern

☎ (01695) 622239
11.30–11; 12–10.30 Sun
**Boddingtons Bitter; Flowers IPA; Moorhouse's Premier; guest beers** H
Popular, open-plan pub appealing to all ages. Eve meals finish at 8.30.
◑ ▶ ♿ ♣ P

## Up Holland

### White Lion

10 Church Street
☎ (01695) 622727
12–3, 7–11; 12–3, 7–10.30 Sun
**Tetley Bitter; guest beers** H
Genuine local with a comfortable, L-shaped lounge; reputedly haunted. No food Sat. 🏰 🏶 ◑ P

## Waddington

### Buck Inn (Lower)

Church Road ☎ (01200) 28705
11–3, 6–11; 11–11 Thu–Sat; 12–3, 7–10.30 Sun
**Ruddles County; Taylor Best Bitter, Landlord; Younger No. 3** H
Friendly coaching house dating from 1760, serving excellent, home-cooked food.
🏰 Q 🏰 🏶 🏰 ◑ ▶ ♿ ♠ ♣ P

## Walmer Bridge

### Longton Arms

2 Liverpool Old Road (off Longton bypass, A59)
☎ (01772) 612335
2 (12 Sat)–11; 12–4, 7–10.30 Sun
**Greenalls Mild, Bitter** H
Cosy, welcoming, terraced village pub, a haven in an area of poor choice: a tiny public bar and a cosy lounge.
🏰 Q 🏰 🏶 🏶 ♣

## Walton-le-Dale

### Yew Tree

100 Victoria Road (A6/A675 jct) ☎ (01772) 555103
11.30–3, 6–11; 12–10.30 Sun
**Boddingtons Bitter; Taylor Landlord; guest beers** H
Large pub with an emphasis on food and a following for its three guest beers.
🏶 ◑ ▶ ♿ ♣ P

## Wennington

### Bridge

Low Tatham
☎ (0152 42) 21326
12–2, 6.30–11; 12–11 Sat; 12–10.30 Sun
**Mitchell's Original** H
Small, out-of-the-way, two-room pub, where it is hard not to be part of the conversation. Lunches Thu–Mon.
🏰 🏶 🏰 ◑ ♠ 🏰 ♣ P

## Westhead

### Prince Albert

109 Wigan Road
☎ (01695) 573656
12–3 (5 Sat), 5 (7 Sat)–11; 12–3, 7–10.30 Sun
**Beer range varies** H
Comfortable, friendly village pub, enjoying good local support. Up to two changing guest beers; excellent value lunches. A Tetley *Golden Huntsman* award-winner.
🏰 Q 🏶 🏰 ◑ ♠ ♣ P

## Whalley

### Swan

62 King Street
☎ (01254) 822195
11–11; 12–10.30 Sun
**Boddingtons Bitter; Moorhouse's Premier; Taylor Landlord; Thwaites Bitter; guest beers** H
Excellent pub in the centre of an historic village, catering for all. Good value meals. The house beer is brewed by Commercial.
🏰 ◑ ▶ ♿ ♣ ⇌ P

## Wharles

### Eagle & Child

Church Road (2 miles off B5269, near radar station)
OS448356 ☎ (01772) 690312
12–3 (not winter Mon–Fri), 7–11; 12–3, 7–10.30 Sun
**Boddingtons Bitter; guest beers** H
Pleasant, country free house with a thatched roof, beamed ceilings and antique furnishings (including grandfather clocks). House beer from Commercial.
🏰 Q ♿ ♠ P

## Wheelton

### Red Lion

196 Blackburn Road (off A674)
☎ (01254) 830378
12–11; 12–10.30 Sun
**Boddingtons Bitter; Theakston Best Bitter; guest beers** H
Popular, village-centre pub with a split-level interior, a comfortable bar and a games room. A short walk from the Leeds–Liverpool Canal at Johnsons Hillock. Eve meals Fri and Sat (until 8).
🏰 🏶 ◑ ♣ P

## Whitestake

### Farmer's Arms

Wham Lane (½ mile W of A582) ☎ (01772) 613210
11–11; 12–10.30 Sun
**Boddingtons Bitter; Castle Eden Ale; Marston's Pedigree; guest beers** H
Large, roadside Brewers' Fayre. The real ale bar offers five guests. Live music Thu. Occasional cider.
🏰 🏰 🏶 ◑ ▶ ♿ ♣ P ⅟

## Whittle-le-Woods

### Royal Oak

216 Chorley Old Road
☎ (01257) 276485
2.30–11; 12–10.30 Sun
**Matthew Brown Mild, Bitter; Theakston Black Bull; Young's Special; guest beer** H
Welcoming, small, one-bar, terraced village pub, a meeting place for mature motorcycle enthusiasts. Note the Nuttalls cut-glass windows. Monthly guest beer. 🏰 Q 🏶 ♣

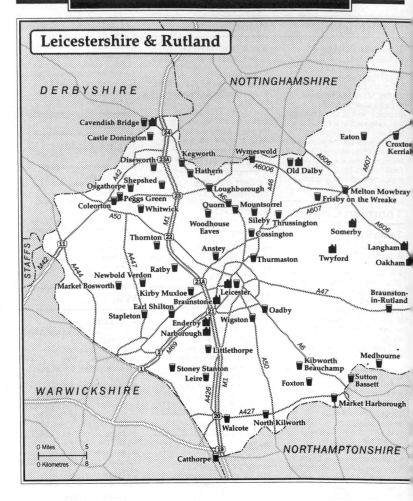

## Leicestershire & Rutland

DERBYSHIRE
NOTTINGHAMSHIRE
STAFFS
WARWICKSHIRE
NORTHAMPTONSHIRE

Cavendish Bridge
Castle Donington
Eaton
Croxton Kerrial
Kegworth
Wymeswold
Diseworth
Hathern
Old Dalby
Shepshed
Osgathorpe
Loughborough
Melton Mowbray
Peggs Green
Frisby on the Wreake
Coleorton
Quorn
Mountsorrel
Whitwick
Sileby
Thrussington
Somerby
Woodhouse Eaves
Cossington
Langham
Thornton
Anstey
Thurmaston
Twyford
Oakham
Newbold Verdon
Ratby
Market Bosworth
Kirby Muxloe
Leicester
Braunston-in-Rutland
Earl Shilton
Braunstone
Stapleton
Oadby
Enderby
Wigston
Narborough
Littlethorpe
Medbourne
Kibworth Beauchamp
Stoney Stanton
Sutton Bassett
Leire
Foxton
Market Harborough
Walcote
North Kilworth
Catthorpe

0 Miles 5
0 Kilometres 8

## Anstey

### Old Hare & Hounds
34 Bradgate Road (opp. church)
☎ (0116) 236 2496
11–3.30, 6.30–11; 11–11 Fri & Sat;
12–3, 7–10.30 Sun
**Marston's Bitter, Pedigree, HBC** Ⓗ
Split-level pub with three rooms and one central bar; a popular local with a warm atmosphere.
Q ❀ ♣ P

## Barrowden

### Exeter Arms
Main Street
☎ (01572) 747247
12–3, 6–11; 12–3, 7–10.30 Sun
**Marston's Bitter, Pedigree; guest beers** Ⓗ
Stone pub on the village green, opposite a duck pond. Local

CAMRA *Pub of the Year* 1995. Home-cooked menu (no food Sun eve or Mon). Cider in summer.
🏚 ❀ ◑ ▶ ♿ ♣ ⇔ P ⌿

## Braunston-in-Rutland

### Old Plough Inn
High Street
☎ (01572) 722714
11–3, 6–11; 12–3, 6–10.30 Sun
**Grainstore Cooking; Oakham JHB; Ruddles Best Bitter, County; guest beers** Ⓗ
Nicely decorated country pub with a cosy lounge. The conservatory restaurant has a false ceiling made from parasols. The first pub to have beer from all three Rutland breweries together.
🏚 ❀ ◑ ▶ ▲ ♣ P

## Castle Donington

### Nag's Head Inn
Hilltop
☎ (01332) 850652
11–2.30, 5.30–11; 12–3, 7–10.30 Sun
**Marston's Bitter, Pedigree** Ⓗ
Comfortable pub on the hilltop side of the village. Whilst food is important, the bar still maintains a good atmosphere. The dining rooms are no-smoking (closed Sun eve).
🏚 Q ❀ P

## Catthorpe

### Cherry Tree
Main Street (½ mile from M1/M6/A14)
☎ (01788) 860430
12–3 (4 Sat; not Mon or Tue), 7–11;
12–4, 7–10.30 Sun
**Ansells Bitter; Draught Bass; Hook Norton Best Bitter; guest beers** Ⓗ

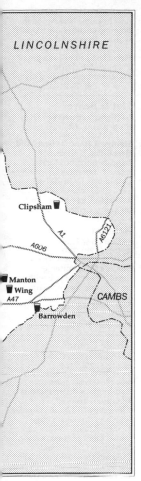

LINCOLNSHIRE

Clipsham

Manton
Wing
A47
CAMBS

Barrowden

popular with locals. The most southerly pub in Leicestershire.
Q ֎ ◖ ♣ P

## Cavendish Bridge

### Old Crown
400 yds from A6 turning near Trent Bridge ☎ (01332) 792392
11–3, 5–11; 12–4, 7–10.30 Sun
**Draught Bass; Marston's Pedigree; guest beers** Ⓗ
Riverside village pub decorated with breweriana, old advertisements and water jugs. Good range of beers. Popular for food. ֎ ◖ P

## Clipsham

### Olive Branch
Main Street ☎ (01780) 410355
12–2.30 (3 Sat; not Mon), 7–11; 12–3, 7–10.30 Sun
**Draught Bass; M&B Brew XI; guest beers** Ⓗ
Refurbished village pub, retaining its old charm.

Usually two guest beers; occasional live music; good food. Only two miles from the A1. ⚐ Q ֎ ◖ ◗ ⅋ P

## Coleorton

### George
Loughborough Road (A512)
☎ (01530) 834639
11.30–2.30, 6–11; 12–2.30, 7–10.30 Sun
**Draught Bass; guest beer** Ⓗ
Smartly furnished pub on the outskirts of a village with early coalmining history. The Nine Mile Mining Heritage Trail runs through the pub car park making it a good place to break a weekend stroll. A large garden at the rear caters for children.
⚐ ֎ ◖ ◗ ⅋ ⅋ ♣ P

## Cossington

### Royal Oak
105 Main Street
☎ (01509) 813937
12–2.30 (3 Sat), 6–11; 12–3, 7–10.30 Sun
**Everards Beacon, Tiger, Old Original; guest beer** Ⓗ
Small village local recently refurbished after serious fire damage: a wood-panelled, single L-shaped bar with plain wooden tables. Very popular with diners. Two guest beers from Everards Old English Ale Club. ֎ ◖ ◗ ♣ P

## Croxton Kerrial

### Peacock Inn
1 School Lane (A607)
☎ (01476) 870324
11.30–2.30 (3 Sat), 6.30–11; 12–3, 7–10.30 Sun
**Boddingtons Bitter; Flowers Original; Greene King Abbot; Marston's Pedigree; Morland Old Speckled Hen; guest beers** Ⓗ
Warm, comfortable village pub dating back over 300 years. Excellent range of beers, plus cider in summer. Good, home-cooked food. Children's certificate.
⚐ Q ⅋ ֎ ◖ ◗ ⅋ ♣ ◠ P ⅋

## Diseworth

### Plough
Hall Gate ☎ (01332) 810333
11–2.30 (3 Sat), 4.45 (6 Sat)–11; 12–3, 7–10.30 Sun
**Draught Bass; Hancock's HB; Highgate Dark; Marston's Pedigree; guest beer** Ⓗ
Popular village pub with a large garden and car park. Welcoming and cosy, it is popular with personnel from the nearby airport. No food Sat eve or Sun. ⚐ ֎ ◖ ◗ ♣ P

## Earl Shilton

### Red Lion Inn
168 High Street
☎ (01455) 840829
11–2.30, 5.30–11; 12–3, 7–10.30 Sun
**Draught Bass; M&B Mild** Ⓗ
Basic beer drinkers' pub with three rooms and one central bar. No food at all.
֎ ♣ P

## Eaton

### Castle Inn
33 Vicarage Lane
☎ (01476) 870949
12–3, 7–11; 12–3, 7–10.30 Sun
**Mansfield Riding Mild, Bitter, Old Baily; guest beers** Ⓗ
Friendly village free house in beautiful countryside near Belvoir Castle, extended to include a skittle alley and a pool room. Facilities for campers and caravanners at the rear.
⅋ ֎ ⅋ ◖ ◗ ⅋ ▲ ♣ P ⅋

Try also: **Red Lion**, Stathern (Free)

## Foxton

### Black Horse
94 Main Street ☎ (01858) 545250
11–3, 6–11; 12–4, 7–10.30 Sun
**Marston's Bitter, Pedigree, HBC** Ⓗ
Large village pub, close to the Grand Union Canal and Foxton locks: two rooms plus a conservatory dining area (no-smoking). Live jazz Wed eve.
⚐ ֎ ◖ ◗ ⅋ ▲ ♣ P

---

### 🍺 INDEPENDENT BREWERIES

| | |
|---|---|
| **Belvoir:** Old Dalby | **Oakham:** Oakham |
| **Everards:** Narborough | **Original:** Braunstone |
| **Featherstone:** Enderby | **Parish:** Somerby |
| **Fulbeck:** Twyford | **Ruddles:** Langham |
| **Grainstore:** Oakham | **Shardlow:** Cavendish Bridge |
| **Hoskins:** Leicester | |
| **Hoskins & Oldfield:** Leicester | |

## Frisby on the Wreake

### Bell Inn

2 Main Street
☎ (01664) 434237
12–2.30, 6–11; 12–2.30, 7–10.30 Sun
**Draught Bass; Bateman Mild, XB, XXXB; Marston's Pedigree; Tetley Bitter; guest beer** H
Large, friendly, village local dating from 1759, popular with diners; once tied to Allied, but now free. 🏚 Q ☎ ❀ ◖ ▮ P

## Hathern

### Three Crowns

Wide Lane ☎ (01509) 842233
12–2.30, 5.30–11; 12–11 Sat; 12–3, 7–10.30 Sun
**Draught Bass; Highgate Dark; M&B Mild; Worthington Bitter; guest beer** H
Lively village local with three drinking areas serving different clientele. Home to the village sports teams. Skittle alley to the rear.
🏚 Q ❀ ⚑ ♣ P ▯

Try also: **Dew Drop**, Loughborough Rd (Hardys & Hansons)

## Kegworth

### Cap & Stocking

20 Borough Street (one-way street between Nottingham Rd and Derby Rd)
☎ (01509) 674814
11.30–3, 6–11; 12–3, 7–10.30 Sun
(varies in summer)
**Draught Bass** G; **Hancock's HB; M&B Mild; guest beers** H
Popular but cosy, village local where Bass is served from the jug. Occasional food theme nights. Petanque in the garden. Good, chip-free meals till 8.45.
🏚 Q ❀ ◖ ▮ ♣

### Red Lion

High Street ☎ (01509) 672466
11–3, 5–11; 11–11 Fri & Sat; 12–10.30 Sun
**Draught Bass; Bateman XB; M&B Mild; Marston's Pedigree; Theakston Best Bitter; guest beers** H
Popular, friendly, old-fashioned local, renowned for its reasonable prices. Substantial fare – strictly no chips (eve meals 6–8). Camping by arrangement.
🏚 Q ☎ ❀ ◖ ▮ ▲ ♣ ⌂ P

## Kibworth Beauchamp

### Coach & Horses

2 Leicester Road (A6)
☎ (0116) 279 2247
11.30–2.30, 5–11; 11–11 Sat; 12–3, 7–10.30 Sun

---

**Ansells Mild, Bitter; Draught Bass; Tetley Bitter** H
Warm, cosy, old coaching inn on the main A6, featuring coin-filled beams and horse brasses. Popular with locals and passing custom. Traditional, home-cooked food. 🏚 ◖ ▮ ♣ P

## Kirby Muxloe

### Royal Oak

35 Main Street
☎ (0116) 239 3166
11–2.30, 6.30–11; 12–2.30, 7–10.30 Sun
**Adnams Bitter; Everards Mild, Beacon, Tiger, Old Original; guest beer** H
A modern exterior conceals a comfortable, traditionally-styled lounge bar with a restaurant, popular with both business folk and locals. The guest beer is supplied by the Everards Old English Ale Club.
❀ ◖ ▮ P

## Leicester

### Black Boy

35 Albion Street
☎ (0116) 254 0422
11–11; 12–10.30 Sun
**Draught Bass; Highgate Dark; Worthington Bitter** H
City-centre local with the feel of a country pub: a basic bar and a comfortable, L-shaped lounge with wood panelling and a decorative ceiling. Family room open eves by arrangement. Q ❀ ◖ ⇌ ♣

### Black Horse

1 Foxon Street, Braunstone Gate ☎ (0116) 254 0030
12–2.30 (3 Thu–Sat), 5.30–11; 12–3, 7–10.30 Sun
**Everards Beacon, Tiger; guest beers** H
120-year-old beer drinkers' pub close to the city centre and popular with students. Two rooms untouched by refurbishment, with one central bar. Guest beers come from the Everards Old English Ale Club – always two available. ❀

### Clarendon

7–9 West Avenue, Clarendon Park (near A6)
☎ (0116) 270 7530
12 (11.30 Sat)–11; 12–10.30 Sun
**Draught Bass; M&B Mild; guest beers** H
Friendly, two-roomed, corner pub in a terraced residential area. Popular with students eves. Q ❀ ▮ ♣ ✦

### Fuzzock & Firkin

203 Welford Road (A50)
☎ (0116) 270 8141
12–11; 12–10.30 Sun
**Firkin Fuzzock, Ass, Dogbolter; guest beers** H

---

The Stork's Head until 1993, now featuring basic wooden flooring and furniture. Popular with students and the young eves, but for all in the day. The Firkin beers come from the Phantom & Firkin in Loughborough. Meals daily 12–6. ❀ ◖ ♣ ⌂ P

### Hat & Beaver

60 Highcross Street (off High St) ☎ (0116) 262 2157
11–3, 6–11; 12–3, 7–10.30 Sun
**Hardys & Hansons Best Mild, Best Bitter** E, **Classic** H
Basic, two-roomed local with a relaxed atmosphere, formerly a Bass house. TV in the bar. Well-filled cobs usually available. Close to the Shires Shopping Centre. ❀ ⚑ ♣

### Salmon

19 Butt Close Lane
☎ (0116) 253 2301
11–11; 12–3 Sun, closed Sun eve
**Banks's Mild, Bitter** E
Small, city-centre pub with a modern interior – one large U-shaped room; close to St Margarets bus station and the Shires Shopping Centre. No food Sun. ❀ ◖ ▯

### Three Cranes

82 Humberstone Gate
☎ (0116) 251 7164
11–11; 12–10.30 Sun (doors closed football match afternoons)
**Boddingtons Bitter; Flowers IPA; guest beers** H
City-centre free house, popular with beer drinkers: a large U-shaped lounge with a very varied range of guest beers – Hoskins & Oldfield and Oakham are usually on. Called the Boulevard in the 1980s, but the cast picture of three cranes survived on the outer wall. Food always available.
❀ ⇌ ◖ ♣ ⌂

### Tudor

100 Tudor Road
☎ (0116) 262 0087
11–2.30 (3 Sat), 6–11; 12–3, 7–10.30 Sun
**Everards Beacon, Tiger** H
Street-corner pub in a Victorian residential area. It still has two rooms and one central bar. There is evidence on the outside wall of the old decorative entrance, no longer used. ❀ ♣

### Victoria Jubilee

112 Leire Street (off Melton Rd, A46) ☎ (0116) 266 3599
11–2.30 (3.30 Sat), 6–11; 12–4, 7–10.30 Sun
**Marston's Bitter, Pedigree** H
Friendly, two-roomed local on a terraced street corner; the Full Moon until Queen Victoria celebrated her jubilee in 1887.
❀ ♣

## Wilkie's Continental Bar

29 Market Street
☎ (0116) 255 6877
11–11; closed Sun
**Adnams Bitter, Extra; Boddingtons Bitter; Marston's Pedigree; Shepherd Neame Spitfire; guest beers** Ⓗ
Well-established continental bar in the city centre stocking six ales, three German beers, cider and guest Belgian beers on draught, plus over 100 bottled beers. Spanish and German food at reasonable prices. Friendly atmosphere.
⊛ ◖ ≈ ○

## Wyvern Ale House

157 Granby Street
☎ (0116) 247 1978
11.30–11; 12–3, 7–11 Sat; 12–3, 7–10.30 Sun
**Mansfield Riding Bitter, Bitter, Old Baily; guest beers** Ⓗ
City-centre ale house, popular with students and the young. It was recently refurbished to make it more spacious, but retaining some original features. Previously called Kings – Wyvern comes from the Midland Railway coat of arms (station close by). Always three guest beers. No children.
⊛ ◖ ≈ P

## Leire

### Queens Arms

Main Street
☎ (01455) 209227
12–3, 5.30–11; 12–3, 7–10.30 Sun
**Marston's Bitter, Pedigree, HBC** Ⓗ
Warm, traditional, rural village pub: one open bar and a lounge with a beamed ceiling, popular with regulars and passing custom. Barbecues in summer.
♨ Q ➶ ⊛ ◖ ▶ ὁ ♣ P

## Littlethorpe

### Plough

7 Station Road (200 yds from Narborough station)
☎ (0116) 286 2383
11–2.30 (3 Sat), 6–11; 12–3, 7–10.30 Sun
**Everards Beacon, Tiger, Old Original; guest beers** Ⓗ
Friendly, thatched village local featuring a cosy, unspoilt bar and a lounge with a separate dining area. The guest beer is supplied by the Everards Old English Ale Club. Long alley skittles available by arrangement. Wheelchair access is from the car park.
Q ⊛ ◖ ▶ ὁ ≈ (Narborough) ♣ P

## Loughborough

### Paget Arms

41 Oxford Street (between A6 and A512)
☎ (01509) 239712
11–3, 5–11; 11–10.30 Sun
**Everards Tiger, Old Original; guest beer** Ⓗ
Busy, very traditional, backstreet pub, especially popular with students: three rooms of very different character, but always a warm welcome. ⊛ ◖ ὁ ♣

### Priory

Nanpantan Road, Nanpantan
☎ (01509) 216333
11–2.30 (3 Sat), 5.30 (6 Fri & Sat)–11; 12–3, 7–10.30 Sun
**Home Mild, Bitter; Marston's Pedigree; Theakston XB** Ⓗ
Imposing pub in Nanpantan, on the forest side of town. The pub is comfortable, with the choice of lounge or snug-style bars. The function room often hosts jazz. Eve meals until 8.30.
➶ ⊛ ◖ ▶ ♣ P

### Royal Oak

70 Leicester Road (A6)
☎ (01509) 263860
11–3, 7–11; 11–11 Thu–Sat; 12–4, 7–10.30 Sun
**Burtonwood Bitter, Forshaw's, Buccaneer** *or* **seasonal beers** Ⓗ
Genuine locals' boozer on the main road, welcoming and friendly, with a basic bar and a comfortable lounge.
⊛ ◖ ♣ P

### Swan in the Rushes

21 The Rushes (A6)
☎ (01509) 217014
11–2.30, 5–11; 11–11 Thu–Sat; 12–3.30, 7–10.30 Sun
**Archers Golden; Bateman XB; Marston's Pedigree; Tetley Bitter; guest beers** Ⓗ
Popular and roomy free house and restaurant. An interesting range of draught beers is supplemented by a wide selection of foreign bottled beers and draught ciders (occasionally including a perry). Live music and speciality food nights. Good B&B.
♨ Q ◖ ◖ ▶ ⊞ ὁ ♣ ○ P

### Tap & Mallet

36 Nottingham Road
☎ (01509) 210028
11.30–2.30, 5–11; 11.30–11 Sat; 12–10.30 Sun
**Courage Best Bitter, Directors; Marston's Pedigree; guest beers** Ⓗ
Popular free house between the town centre and the station. Interesting guest beers (at least three), many from micro-breweries which are discounted to CAMRA members. Large patio and garden with a children's play area.
♨ ⊛ ≈ ♣ ○

**Try also: Gate**, Meadow Lane (Banks's); **Lonsdale**, Burder St (Bass); **Old Packe Horse**, Woodgate (Hardys & Hansons); **Tap & Spile**, Woodgate (Free)

## Manton

### Horse & Jockey

2 St Mary's Road
☎ (01572) 737335
11–2.30, 7–11; 12–3, 7–10.30 Sun (extends in summer)
**Mansfield Riding Bitter, Old Baily** Ⓗ
A rarity near Rutland Water – an unspoilt 250-year-old village local. Cycle repair outfits on sale. Camping by arrangement. Good food.
♨ ⊛ ⇌ ◖ ▶ ♨ ▲ ♣

## Market Bosworth

### Red Lion

1 Park Street
☎ (01455) 291713
11–2.30, 7–11; 11–11 Sat; 12–3, 7–10.30 Sun
**Banks's Mild, Bitter; Camerons Bitter; Marston's Pedigree; Theakston XB, Old Peculier** Ⓗ
Village pub, popular with locals and tourists from the nearby Bosworth railway and battlesite and Ashby Canal: a large, split-level, L-shaped pub.
♨ ⊛ ⇌ ◖ ▲ ♣ P ⊞

## Market Harborough

### Red Cow

58–59 High Street (old A6)
☎ (01858) 463637
11–3 (4 Sat), 6 (7 Sat)–11; 12–3, 7–10.30 Sun
**Marston's Bitter, Pedigree, HBC** Ⓗ
Unspoilt, town-centre pub: a single small bar with no frills or music, but with games and conversation. Q ♣

## Medbourne

### Nevil Arms

12 Waterfall Way
☎ (01858) 565288
12–2.30, 6–11; 12–3, 7–10.30 Sun
**Adnams Bitter; Ruddles Best Bitter, County; guest beers** Ⓗ
Built in 1876 as a coaching inn on the village green. Next to an attractive stream, it is a popular weekend venue for families (the ducks are friendly). Unusual pub games by prior arrangement for parties. Two varying guest beers.
♨ ➶ ⊛ ⇌ ◖ ▶ ▲ ♣ P

## Melton Mowbray

### Crown

10 Burton Street
☎ (01664) 64682
11–4, 7–11; 11–11 Fri & Sat; 12–10.30 Sun

**Everards Beacon, Tiger, Old Original; guest beer** Ⓗ
Welcoming, town-centre pub with a comfortable lounge and a friendly bar.
🏚 🍺 🌳 ◑ 🍴 ⇌ ♣

## Mountsorrel

### Waterside Inn

Sileby Road ☎ (0116) 230 2758
11–2.30, 6–11; 12–3, 7 (6 summer)–10.30 Sun

**Everards Beacon, Tiger, Old Original; guest beer** Ⓗ
Pub in a lovely situation by the canal, with large windows six feet from the lockgates. The site has housed a pub for 200 years; the old stables have long been made into a sitting area. Very popular in summer. Easy access for wheelchairs. Good bar menu. 🌳 ◑ ▶ ♿ ♣ P

## Newbold Verdon

### Jubilee Inn

80 Main Street
☎ (01455) 822698
11–3 (not Tue or Wed), 6 (5.30 Fri)–11; 12–2.30, 7–10.30 Sun

**Marston's Bitter, Pedigree** Ⓗ
Friendly, two-roomed village local; cosy and unspoilt.
🏚 🌳 ♣ P

## North Kilworth

### White Lion

Lutterworth Road
☎ (01858) 880260
12–2.30, 5.30–11; 12–11 Sat; 12–10.30 Sun

**Marston's Bitter, Pedigree, HBC** Ⓗ
Former coaching inn on the main road, close to the Grand Union Canal (Bridge 45). The large single bar has a number of distinct areas, including a tile-floored games area with darts and table skittles. No food Mon eve. 🏚 🌳 ◑ ▶ ♣ P

## Oadby

### Cow & Plough

Stoughton Farm Park, Gartree Road (follow Farmworld signs off A6) ☎ (0116) 272 0852
5–9; 5–9 Sun

**Bateman Mild; Fuller's London Pride; Hoskins & Oldfield HOB Bitter; Parish Farm Gold; Steamin' Billy Bitter; guest beers** Ⓗ
E Midlands CAMRA *Pub of the Year* 1995. Part of a leisure park during the day, its atmospheric vaults are adorned with breweriana. Guest beers are from small breweries. The house beers come from Steamin' Billy.
Q 🌳 🌳 🍺 ◑ 🍴 P ♿

## Oakham

### White Lion Hotel

30 Melton Road (A606, near level crossing)
☎ (01572) 724844
11.30–3, 6–11; 12–3, 7–10.30 Sun

**Draught Bass; Highgate Dark; Worthington Bitter; guest beers** Ⓗ
Split-level pub in a Grade II listed building. Note the collection of ties. Good food.
🏚 ⇌ ◑ ▶ ♿ ♣ P

**Try also:** Wheatsheaf, Northgate (Everards)

## Old Dalby

### Crown

Debdale Hill
☎ (01664) 823134
12–3, 6–11; 12–3, 7–10.30 Sun

**Hardys & Hansons Bitter; Marston's Pedigree; guest beers** Ⓖ
Cosy 17th-century pub with one bar where beers are served from the wood. Excellent food. Small intimate rooms, all with log fires in winter; large, attractive garden.
🏚 Q 🌳 🌳 ◑ ▶ P ♿

## Osgathorpe

### Royal Oak Inn

20 Main Street
☎ (01530) 222443
7–11; 12–3, 7–10.30 Sun

**M&B Mild; Marston's Pedigree** Ⓗ
Friendly local in a picturesque, rural valley. Note: closed lunchtime Mon–Sat.
🏚 Q 🌳 🌳 ⇌ ♿ ♠ ♣ P

## Peggs Green

### New Inn

Zion Hill (B587)
☎ (01530) 222293
11.30–2.30, 7–11; 12–3, 7–10.30 Sun

**Draught Bass; M&B Mild; Marston's Pedigree** Ⓗ
Excellent country pub with a multitude of cosy corners. The large garden is ideal for families. Monthly Irish folk club. 🏚 🌳 🌳 ♣ P

## Quorn

### Apple Tree

2 Stoop Lane ☎ (01509) 412296
12–3 (3.30 Sat), 7–11; 12–3, 7–10.30 Sun

**Draught Bass; M&B Mild** Ⓗ
Traditional local with two rooms, both small and with their own separate entrances. It can be very busy.
🏚 🌳 ⊞ ♣ P

### Blacksmith's Arms

29 Meeting Street
☎ (01509) 412751
12–2 (11–2.30 Sat), 5.30–11; 12–3, 7–10.30 Sun

**Marston's Bitter, Pedigree** Ⓗ
Old beamed pub in a picturesque village, now bypassed: a tiny lounge and a comfortable bar. The famous Great Central Railway passes through Quorn – the pub is within a mile of the station.
🏚 Q 🌳 ⊞ ♣ P

## Ratby

### Plough Inn

6 Burroughs Road
☎ (0116) 239 2103
11–3, 6–11; 12–3, 7–10.30 Sun

**Bateman Mild; Marston's Bitter, Pedigree, HBC** Ⓗ
Large, refurbished regulars' pub, also popular with diners.
🏚 🌳 🌳 ◑ ♣ P

## Shepshed

### Black Swan

21 Loughborough Road
☎ (01509) 502659
12–2.30, 7–11; 12–3, 7–10.30 Sun

**Draught Bass; M&B Mild; Tetley Bitter; Worthington Bitter; guest beer** Ⓗ
Smart, large, multi-roomed pub satisfying both beer drinkers and 'foodies'. Children welcome in the restaurant (no eve food Sun or Mon unless booked).
🌳 ◑ ▶ P

### Bull & Bush

61 Sullington Road
☎ (01509) 506783
12–3, 5.30–11; 12–4, 7–10.30 Sun

**Banks's Mild; Marston's Bitter, Pedigree** Ⓗ
Friendly local: a traditional and largely unspoilt, single-room pub with a particularly fine, carved wood servery. A true community pub. 🌳 ♣ P

## Sileby

### White Swan

Swan Street
☎ (01509) 814832
11–3, 7–11; 12–3, 7–10.30 Sun

**Ansells Bitter; Marston's Pedigree; Ruddles Best Bitter; guest beers** Ⓗ
Grand pub with high ceilings, tucked away in the village. Many games are played, including long alley skittles. A popular monthly antique valuation night includes food (phone to book). Excellent meals: à la carte restaurant and bar food (no meals Sun eve).
Q 🌳 ◑ ▶ ♿ ⇌ ♣ P

## Stapleton

### Nag's Head
15 Main Street (A447, 2½ miles
E of Hinckley)
☎ (01455) 845056
11–2.30 (11.30–3 Sat), 5.30–11; 12–3,
7–10.30 (12–10.30 summer) Sun
**Marston's Bitter, Pedigree** Ⓗ
Typical country pub, popular
with both regulars and passing
trade. Recently extended to
cater for increased demand for
meals. ✿ ◖ ▶ P

## Stoney Stanton

### Francis Arms
Huncote Road
☎ (01455) 272034
12–2.30, 5.30–11; 11–11 Sat; 12–3,
7–10.30 Sun
**Bateman Mild; Marston's
Bitter, Pedigree** Ⓗ
Basic village pub dominated by
beer drinkers: two rooms with
one central bar. A collection of
old rifles adorns the ceiling.
🚶 ⊞ ♣ P

## Sutton Bassett

### Queen's Head
Main Street (B664)
☎ (01858) 463530
11.45–3, 6.30–11; 12–3, 7–10.30 Sun
**Adnams Bitter; Ruddles Best
Bitter, County; guest beers** Ⓗ
Unspoilt, rural village pub
which offers a minimum of five
guest beers (at least seven in
summer): two adjoining rooms
with a restaurant (good food).
Beer festivals. 🚶 ✿ ◖ ▶ P

## Thornton

### Bricklayers Arms
Main Street
☎ (01530) 230808
12–3, 7 (6 summer)–11; 12–3, 7–10.30
Sun
**Everards Mild, Beacon, Tiger,
Daredevil; guest beer** Ⓗ
Old, traditional village local,
part of which dates from the
16th century, with a basic,
quarry tiled bar area and a
cosy, comfortable lounge. It
overlooks Thornton trout
fisheries and is totally unspoilt.
Guest beers come from the
Everards Old English Ale Club.
🚶 Q ☎ ◖ ▶ ♣ P

## Thrussington

### Blue Lion
5 Rearsby Road
☎ (01664) 424266
12–2 (3 Sat), 6–11; 12–3, 7–10.30 Sun
**Marston's Bitter, Pedigree,
HBC or guest mild** Ⓗ
Welcoming, large village pub
whose landlord has historic
links with the previous
owners, Sileby Brewery.
Bizarre collection of teapots.
✿ ◖ ▶ ⊞ ☼ ▲ ♣ P

## Thurmaston

### Unicorn & Star
796 Melton Road
☎ (0116) 269 2849
11–3, 6–11; 12–3, 7–10.30 Sun
**Greenalls Shipstone's Mild,
Shipstone's Bitter** Ⓗ
Pub with a basic beer drinkers'
bar with no frills, and a
comfortable, cosy lounge;
known to locals as the 'Top
House'. ✿ ♣ P

## Walcote

### Black Horse
Main Street
☎ (01455) 552684
12–2 (not Mon or Tue), 6.30–11;
12–2.30, 7–10.30 Sun
**Hook Norton Old Hooky;
Hoskins & Oldfield HOB
Bitter; Taylor Landlord; guest
beers** Ⓗ
Single-bar free house, near M1
jct 20 and well worth the
detour for excellent, home-
cooked Thai food, independent
breweries' guest beers, plus
occasional cider.
🚶 Q ◖ ▶ ☼ P

## Whitwick

### Three Horseshoes
11 Leicester Road
☎ (01530) 837311
11–3, 6.30–11; 12–2, 7–10.30 Sun
**Draught Bass; M&B Mild** Ⓗ
Traditional, two-roomed pub
with a welcoming public bar.
🚶 ✿ ⊞ ☼ ♣ P

## Wigston

### Meadowbank
Kelmarsh Avenue (300 yds
from A50) ☎ (0116) 281 1926
12 (11.30 Sat)–2.30, 6–11; 12–3,
7–10.30 Sun
**Banks's Mild, Bitter** Ⓔ**;
Marston's Pedigree** Ⓗ
Modern estate pub with a basic
bar and a comfortable lounge.
✿ ◖ ⊞ ♣ P ⊟

## Wing

### Cuckoo
Top Street
☎ (01572) 737340
11.30–3 (not Tue), 6.30–11; 12–3,
7–10.30 Sun
**Marston's Pedigree; guest
beers** Ⓗ
White-washed, unspoilt
village local which stages a
beer festival and steam
rally in summer. Varied,
reasonably-priced menu
specialising in curries.
🚶 ✿ ◖ ▶ ▲ ♣ P

## Woodhouse Eaves

### Wheatsheaf
Brand Hill (½ mile from
village)
☎ (01509) 890320
12 2.30, 7 (6.30 Fri & Sat)–11; 12–3,
7–10.30 Sun
**Draught Bass; Boddingtons
Bitter; Marston's Pedigree;
Ruddles County; Taylor
Landlord; guest beers** Ⓗ
Comfortable country pub, near
the Great Central steam
railway, offering a very relaxed
atmosphere and a good range
of guest beers. Gale's country
fruit wines are also available.
No children. No food Sun eve.
🚶 Q ✿ ◖ ▶ P

## Wymeswold

### Hammer & Pincers
5 East Road
☎ (01509) 880735
12–2.30 (3 Sat), 6–11; 12–3, 7–10.30
Sun
**Draught Bass; Marston's
Pedigree; Ruddles County;
Tetley Bitter; Theakston XB;
guest beers** Ⓗ
Welcoming pub; a popular
eating place where local Stilton
is used in dishes. A listed water
pump is a feature of the back
room and the highly polished
handpumps originate from St
Pancras station. Well
patronised by locals.
✿ ◖ ▶ ☼ ♣ P ⊬

---

# UPDATES

Updates to pubs and breweries featured in the *Good Beer Guide* are
published monthly in the CAMRA members' newspaper,
*What's Brewing*. For details of how to join and receive copies, see the
back of this book.

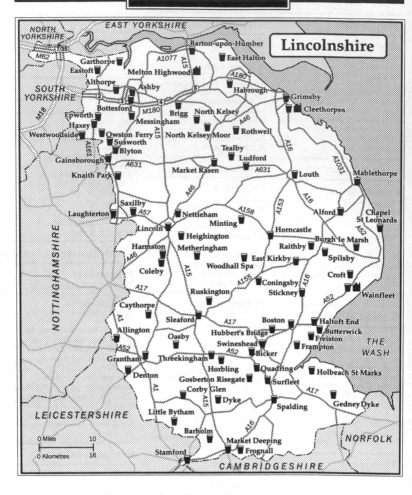

Lincolnshire

## Alford

### Half Moon

West Street ☎ (01507) 463477
10–11 (1am Fri & Sat); 12–10.30 Sun
**Draught Bass; Vaux Samson;
Worthington Bitter; guest
beers** H
Welcoming, ever-expanding,
pub with a lively atmosphere,
in a craft-oriented market town
which is an ideal base for
exploring the Wolds and
Tennyson country. Popular
restaurant and a large garden.
🛏 🕮 ◑ ▶ 🍴 ♣ P

## Allington

### Welby Arms

The Green ☎ (01400) 281361
12–2.30 (3 Sat), 5.30 (6.30 Sat)–11;
12–4, 7–10.30 Sun
**Draught Bass; John Smith's
Bitter; Taylor Landlord; guest
beers** H

Perfect village pub; a regular
*Guide* entry, serving over 60
guest beers per year.
Traditional pub atmosphere in
the bar area; the no-smoking
dining area features good
home cooking (no meals Sun
eve). Well worth seeking out.
🛏 Q 🕮 ◑ ▶ & P

## Althorpe

### Dolphin

27 Trunk Road
☎ (01724) 784510
12–3, 5–11; 12–11 Fri & Sat; 12–4,
7–10.30 (12–10.30 summer) Sun
**Vaux Samson, Waggle Dance;
Ward's Thorne BB** H
Roadside pub with an
emphasis on, and an excellent
reputation for, food. The first
pub in the area to be in
CAMRA's *Good Pub Food*
guide. No meals Mon eve.
Well-equipped family room.
🛏 🕮 ◑ ▶ 🛏 ⇌ ♣ P 🍴

## Ashby

### Malt Shovel

219 Ashby High Street
☎ (01724) 843318
11–11; 12–10.30 Sun
**Barnsley Bitter; Boddingtons
Bitter; John Smith's Bitter;
Theakston Old Peculier; guest
beer** H
Converted snooker hall,
located in a busy shopping
area, featuring country-style
decor with oak beams and
floral furnishings. Good value
meals (two for the price of one

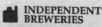

**INDEPENDENT
BREWERIES**

**Bateman:** Wainfleet

**Highwood:**
Melton Highwood

**Willy's:** Cleethorpes

deals). Guest beers come from independent brewers. Licensed snooker facilities have been retained next door.
🔥 ◐ ◑

### Queen Bess
Derwent Road
☎ (01724) 840827
11.30–3.30 (4 Sat), 6–11; 12–3, 7–10.30 Sun
**Samuel Smith OBB** Ⓗ
Established estate pub with a strong local following: a public bar and a recently refurbished lounge with a real fire.
🔥 ❀ ⊞ ♣ P

## Barholm

### Five Horseshoes
Horseshoe Lane
☎ (01778) 560238
5–11; 12–3, 5–11 Sat; 12–10.30 Sun
**Adnams Bitter; Theakston XB; guest beers** Ⓗ
Estate-owned 18th-century stone pub, sympathetically restored and always serving two guest beers. Winter and summer beer festivals.
🔥 Q ⛟ ❀ ▲ P

## Barton-upon-Humber

### Volunteer Arms
13 Whitecross Street
☎ (01652) 632309
11–3 (5 Sat), 6.45–11; 12–5, 7–10.30 Sun
**Burtonwood Mild, Bitter, Top Hat, seasonal beers** Ⓗ
Friendly, refurbished, two-roomed pub with a comfortable lounge and pool in the bar. ❀ ⊞ ♿ ▲

## Bicker

### Red Lion
Donington Road
☎ (01775) 821950
11–3, 6–11; 11–11 Sat; 12–10.30 Sun
**Draught Bass; Bateman XB** Ⓗ
17th-century, friendly, village pub recently renovated. Quality home-cooked food.
Q ◐ ◑ ♿ P

## Blyton

### Black Horse Inn
93 High Street (A159)
☎ (01427) 628277
11.45–3.30, 7 (5 Fri)–11; 12–4, 7–10.30 Sun
**Beer range varies** Ⓗ
Small, cosy village local on the main Scunthorpe–Gainsborough road. Two distinct drinking areas are served by a single bar; real fires in both. Separate dining room; small garden to the rear. Two guest beers are generally available. 🔥 ❀ ◐ ◑ ♣ P

## Boston

### Ball House
Wainfleet Road (A52, 1 mile N of town) ☎ (01205) 364478
11–3, 6.30–11; 12–3, 7–10.30 Sun
**Draught Bass; Bateman Mild, XB** Ⓗ
Recently extended, mock-Tudor pub with a large roaring fire in winter. The home-cooked food is popular (booking advised weekend eves). Its unusual name is derived from its site – a former cannon-ball store.
🔥 ❀ ◐ ◑ ♿ ♣ P

### Eagle
144 West Street
☎ (01205) 361116
11–2.30, 6 (5 Thu & Fri)–11; 11–11 Sat; 12–3, 7–10.30 Sun
**Adnams Broadside; Marston's Pedigree; Taylor Landlord; guest beers** Ⓗ
Traditional town pub always with six real ales, including ever-changing guest beers, one always low priced. The good-sized function room is home to a folk club (alternate Mon) and other clubs. Biddenden cider.
❀ ⊞ ⇌ ♣ ⌓

### Golden Lion
46 High Street
☎ (01205) 352745
12–3, 7–11; 11–11 Sat; 12–3, 7–10.30 Sun
**Hardys & Hansons Best Mild, Best Bitter, Classic** Ⓗ
Cosy, friendly pub within easy walking distance of the town centre, overlooking the River Witham. Pictures of boats once using the local port adorn the walls.
❀ ⇌ ♣

### Olde Magnet Tavern
South Square
☎ (01205) 369186
11–4, 5.30–11; 11–11 Fri & Sat; 12–4, 7–10.30 Sun
**Bass Mild, Draught Bass; Bateman XB; Theakston Old Peculier; Stones Bitter; Worthington Bitter** Ⓗ
Friendly riverside pub set amongst warehouses that have been converted to an arts centre and for residential use; opposite the historic Guildhall Museum.
❀ 🛏 ◐ ◑ ⊞ ⇌

### Ropers Arms
33 Horncastle Road
☎ (01205 355741
11–11; 12–10.30 Sun
**Bateman Mild, XB** Ⓗ
Corner local which has been refurbished in a traditional style. It can be lively, particularly Sun afternoons.
❀ 🛏 ⇌ ♣

**Try also: Ship Tavern,** Custom House Lane (Bateman)

## Bottesford

### Black Beauty
Keddington Road
☎ (01724) 867628
11–11; 12–10.30 Sun
**Mansfield Riding Mild, Riding Bitter, Bitter, Old Baily** Ⓗ
Estate pub, popular with regulars and families. It comprises a public bar, a large lounge bar with wide-screen Sky TV and live music Sat, plus a family room with a children's play area and access to the outside playground.
⛟ ❀ ⊞ ♣ P

**Try also: Beckwood,** Bottesford Lane (Whitbread)

## Brigg

### Brocklesby Ox Inn
Bridge Street (A15/A18)
☎ (01652) 650292
12–3, 6 (5 Thu–Sat)–11; 12–3, 7–10.30 Sun
**Burtonwood Bitter, seasonal beers** Ⓗ
Attractive, two-roomed, 18th-century inn: a well-appointed lounge with olde-worlde charm and a public bar. The family dining area offers good value meals and children's portions. Sing-along Wed and Sat eves.
❀ ◐ ◑ ⊞ ♣ P

**Try also: Black Bull,** Wrawby St (Old Mill)

## Burgh le Marsh

### Olde Burgh Inn
High Street
☎ (01754) 810204
11.30–2.30, 7–11; 12–2.30, 7–10.30 Sun
**Bateman XB; Courage Directors; Theakston Old Peculier; guest beers** Ⓗ
This Grade II-listed building, which houses an authentic beam dated 1699, first became a pub shortly after the Battle of Waterloo. Today it is a very busy establishment which serves fine food. Games room.
Q ❀ ◐ ◑ ♿ ▲ ♣ P ⌷

### Red Lion
Storeys Lane
☎ (01754) 810582
11–11; 12–4, 7–10.30 Sun
**Bateman XB; Vaux Samson** Ⓗ
Welcoming, traditional country pub; the only no-food pub in this large village. Fine collection of brassware and stuffed fauna. The pool/games room and sports area at the rear are popular.
🔥 Q ♿ ▲ ♣ P

# Butterwick

## Five Bells

1 Church Road
☎ (01205) 760282
12–4, 7–11; 12–11 Fri & Sat; 12–4,
7–10.30 Sun
**Bateman Mild, XB** Ⓗ
Family-run pub which always
affords a warm welcome.
Known as 'Horry's Folly', it
was built as a station hotel,
complete with platform
buildings, in anticipation of the
railway which eventually
followed a different route.
Restaurant open eves (booking
advised). 🏨 ֎ ◖❱ ♣ P

# Caythorpe

## Red Lion Inn

62 High Street
☎ (01400) 272632
11–3, 6–11; 11–11 Sat; 12–10.30 Sun
**Draught Bass; Boddingtons
Bitter; Higsons Bitter** Ⓗ**; guest
beers** Ⓗ/Ⓖ
Friendly village pub with an
ever-changing range of beers
and at least one ale served by
gravity. Renowned for its 'beer
and curry' festivals; extensive
menu of home-cooked meals.
Varied cider in summer.
🏨 Q ☏ ֎ ◖❱ ⊞ & Ａ ♣ ⟲ P

# Chapel St Leonards

## Ship

109 Sea Road ☎ (01754) 872640
11–3.30, 7–11; 12–3, 7–10.30 Sun
**Bateman Mild, XB, Valiant,
Salem Porter, XXXB, seasonal
beers** Ⓗ
Recently refurbished,
welcoming, busy local, away
from the hustle and bustle of
the resort. The cosy bar/lounge
features two real fires and the
full range of beers from the
local brewery. 🏨 ֎ Ａ ♣ P

# Cleethorpes

## Kings Royal

20 Kingsway ☎ (01472) 691012
11–11; 12–10.30 Sun
**Theakston XB; Younger
Scotch, No. 3** Ⓗ
Seafront pub with a Victorian-
style theatre bar and another
room used mainly at weekends
and for private functions.
Children welcome until 8.
☏ ֎ 🏘 ◖❱

## Nottingham House

7 Seaview Street (just off
seafront) ☎ (01472) 694386
12 (11 Sat)–11; 12–3, 7–10.30 Sun
**Tetley Mild, Bitter** Ⓗ
Town drinking pub with a
superb facade. Unusually for
the area, it has three rooms,
including a snug. Free bread

and dripping Sun lunch.
Highly recommended.
Q & ≋ ♣

## No.2 Refreshment Room

Station Approach
☎ (01472) 697951
11–11; 12–10.30 Sun
**Mansfield Riding Mild;
Ruddles Best Bitter; John
Smith's Magnet; guest beer** Ⓗ
Basic one-roomer; a proper
drinkers' pub known to locals
as 'Under the Clock'.
≋ ♣

## Willy's Pub & Brewery

17 High Cliff Road
☎ (01472) 602145
11–11; 12–10.30 Sun
**Bateman XB; Willy's Original;
guest beers** Ⓗ
An ever-changing range of
beers makes this seafront bar a
drinker's haven. The brewery
can be viewed from the bar.
Annual beer festival Nov.
Wide range of good value
meals. ◖ ≋

# Coleby

## Tempest Arms

Hill Rise ☎ (01522) 810287
11.30–2.30, 6.30–11; 12–3, 7–10.30 Sun
**Bateman XB; Courage
Directors; Marston's Pedigree;
Ruddles Best Bitter, County;
guest beer** Ⓗ
Welcoming village local on the
Lincoln Edge, with fine views
over the Vale of Trent towards
Newark. Also on the Viking
Way long distance footpath, it
is the centre of village life,
hosting fundraising events and
occasional live music. Guest
beers tend to coincide with
events. ֎ ◖❱ & ♣ P

# Coningsby

## Leagate Inn

Leagate Road
☎ (01526) 342370
11.30–3, 7 (6 winter Sat)–11; 12–3,
7–10.30 (12–10.30 summer) Sun
**Bateman XB; Boddingtons
Bitter; Marston's Pedigree;
Taylor Landlord; guest beer** Ⓗ
Built in 1542, this largely
unchanged pub, with a priest
hole and antique furniture,
offers a superb atmosphere
and excellent food (in the bar
and restaurant). The garden is
popular with children and the
16th-century yew tree stands
close to the site of the old
gibbet. 🏨 ֎ ◖❱ & P

# Corby Glen

## Woodhouse Inn

2 Bourne Road
☎ (01476) 550316
12–3, 5.30–11; 12–4, 7–10.30 Sun

**Oakham JHB, Old Tosspot;
Ruddles County; Theakston
Best Bitter, XB, Old Peculier** Ⓗ
Popular village inn with an
excellent range of beers. The
restaurant serves good, home-
cooked meals.
🏨 Q ☏ ֎ 🏘 ◖❱ & P

# Croft

## Old Chequers Inn

Lymn BankOS503611
☎ (01754) 880320
11–3, 7–11; 12–3, 7–10.30 Sun
**Bateman Mild, XB** Ⓗ
Small, rural watering hole
reputed to be the oldest pub in
Lincolnshire; well off the
beaten track. Enjoy the roaring
open fire in the snug bar,
which is adorned with old
agricultural implements.
Excellent food (booking
advised for the restaurant).
🏨 Q ֎ ◖❱ ♣ P

# Denton

## Welby Arms

Church Street
☎ (01476) 870304
12–2.30 (3 Fri & Sat), 7–11; 12–3,
7–10.30 Sun
**Mansfield Riding Mild,
Riding Bitter, Bitter, Old
Baily** Ⓗ
Attractive, stone-built village
inn with coal fires in both bars.
No meals Sun eve.
🏨 Q ֎ ◖❱ & ♣ P

# Dyke

## Wishing Well Inn

Main Street
☎ (01778) 422970
11–3, 6–11; 12–3, 7–10.30 Sun
**Greene King Abbot; Tetley
Bitter; guest beers** Ⓗ
Originally a row of three
shops, including a baker's
(note the oven in the lounge
wall). The village takes its
name from the nearby Roman
car-dyke.
🏨 ☏ 🏘 ◖❱ ⊞ ♣ P

# East Halton

## Black Bull

Townside (main street)
☎ (01469) 540207
11–3.30, 5–11 (11–11 summer); 12–3,
7–10.30 Sun
**Bateman Mild; Marston's
Bitter, Pedigree, HBC** Ⓗ
Pub with a good-sized,
traditional bar, complemented
by a plush lounge, which has
been well extended to provide
a dining area. The food is
deservedly popular (no meals
Sun eve). Regular live music.
Children welcome in the
restaurant and garden play
area.
🏨 Q ֎ ◖❱ ⊞ ♣ P

## East Kirkby

### Red Lion

Main Road ☎ (01790) 763406
11–3, 7–11; 12–3, 7–10.30 Sun
**Bateman XB; John Smith's Bitter; guest beers** Ⓗ
An extensive breweriana collection adorns every available space within and without this popular rural pub which maintains links with aircrews once stationed at the nearby wartime airfield (now an air museum).
🏨 🛏 🕸 ◑ ▶ ᕫ ▲ ♣ P

## Eastoft

### River Don Tavern

Sampson Street (A161)
☎ (01724) 798225
12–2.30, 7–11; 12–3, 7–10.30 Sun
**John Smith's Bitter** Ⓗ
250-year-old village pub offering excellent food (not served Tue eve) and a warm welcome. Comprehensive vegetarian menu. Large games room.
🏨 Q 🛏 🕸 ◑ ▶ ♣ P

## Epworth

### Red Lion Hotel

2 Market Place
☎ (01427) 872208
11–11; 12–10.30 Sun
**Ind Coope Burton Ale; John Smith's Bitter; Tetley Bitter; guest beer** Ⓗ
Large, lively hotel in the village centre, particularly popular with diners and younger drinkers. Extensive menu (sizzling steaks a speciality); separate restaurant.
🏨 Q 🕸 🛏 ◑ ▶ ᕫ P

## Frampton

### Moores Arms

Church End ☎ (01205) 722408
10–11; 12–10.30 Sun
**Draught Bass; Bateman XB; guest beers** Ⓗ
Popular village local with a deserved reputation for meals; a supper licence allows drinking until midnight.
🕸 ◑ ▶

## Freiston

### King's Head

Church Road
☎ (01205) 760368
11–2.30, 7–11; 11–11 Sat; 12–3, 7–10.30 Sun
**Draught Bass; Bateman Mild, XB; guest beers** Ⓗ
15th-century, traditional village pub. The Lancaster Restaurant (open Tue–Sat eves) serves quality home-cooked food and hosts frequent theme

nights. Popular at lunchtimes and weekends.
🏨 Q 🕸 ◑ ▶ ♣ P

## Frognall

### Goat

155 Spalding Road
☎ (01778) 347629
11–2.30 (3 Sat), 6–11; 12–3, 7–10.30 (12–10.30 summer) Sun
**Adnams Bitter; Draught Bass; guest beers** Ⓗ/Ⓖ
Pub with an excellent food menu. The family room is ideal for meetings on quiet nights. Since the guest beer policy started, 566 different ales from 181 breweries have been featured.
🏨 Q 🛏 🕸 ◑ ▶ ▲ P

## Gainsborough

### Eight Jolly Brewers

Ship Court, Silver Street
☎ (01427) 677128
11–3, 7–11; 11–11 Sat; 12–4, 7–10.30 Sun
**Barnsley Bitter; Bateman XB; Old Mill Bitter; guest beer** Ⓗ
Award-winning, real ale haven, specialising in the products of small and micro-breweries. CAMRA East Midlands *Pub of the Year* 1996. Lunchtime snacks.
Q 🍴 🗗

## Garthorpe

### Bay Horse

Shore Road
☎ (01724) 798306
12–3, 7.30–11; 12–11 Sat; 12–3, 7–10.30 Sun
**Mansfield Riding Bitter, Old Baily** Ⓗ
Comfortable, traditional pub with a small entrance bar, a public bar, a games room and a large lounge. Frequent live entertainment. Close to Blacktoft Sands RSPB Reserve. Lunches Wed–Sat, eve meals Wed–Sun.
🏨 ◑ ▶ 🍴 ♣ P

## Gedney Dyke

### Chequers

Main Street
☎ (01406) 362666
12–2.30, 7–11; 12–2.30, 7–10.30 Sun
**Adnams Bitter; Draught Bass; Elgood's GSB; Greene King Abbot; Morland Old Speckled Hen** Ⓗ
Comfortable country pub and restaurant with an accent on food, confirmed by its entry in CAMRA's *Good Pub Food* guide. Situated in a quiet village, the pub dates back to 1795 and is understandably popular. Worth seeking out.
🏨 🕸 ◑ ▶ ᕫ P

## Gosberton Risegate

### Duke of York

106 Risegate Road (B1397, 1½ miles from Gosberton)
☎ (01775) 840193
12–11; 12–3, 7–10.30 Sun (flexible for diners)
**Draught Bass; Bateman XB; John Smith's Bitter; guest beers** Ⓗ
Village local transformed by its present landlord: a rambling pub, resulting from combining several buildings, including a former petrol station. Good food (no-smoking dining room) and bar snacks. Pool room. Occasional cider.
🏨 🕸 ◑ ▶ ▲ ♣ 🕰 P

## Grantham

### Beehive

10–11 Castlegate
☎ (01476) 67794
11.30–3 (5 Sat), 7–11; 11.30–11 Thu & Fri; 7–10.30 Sun, closed Sun lunch
**Beer range varies** Ⓗ
Renowned as the pub with a living sign; popular with young people and hiker friendly. The beers are from Bateman, plus two guests.
🕸 ◑ 🐝 🗗

### Blue Bull

64 Westgate
☎ (01476) 70929
11–3 (4 Sat), 7–11; 12–3, 7–10.30 Sun
**Bateman XB; Fuller's London Pride; guest beers** Ⓗ
Welcoming 1850s pub with a restaurant. Joint local CAMRA *Pub of the Year* 1996. Wide range of guest beers; good, home-cooked food (not served Wed or Sun eves). Occasional cider. Q ◑ ▶ 🐝 ♣ 🕰 P

### Blue Pig

9 Vine Street
☎ (01476) 63704
11–11; 12–10.30 Sun
**Draught Bass; Boddingtons Bitter; Castle Eden Ale; Flowers Original; Wadworth 6X; guest beer** Ⓗ
One of only three remaining Tudor buildings in the town, a pub with a friendly atmosphere and excellent, good value, lunchtime food.
🏨 ◑ 🍴 🕰

### Chequers

25 Market Place
☎ (01476) 76083
5–11; 12–3, 5–11 Thu; 11–11 Fri & Sat; 12–10.30 Sun
**Beer range varies** Ⓗ
Lively, thriving, free house, with an art gallery, popular with a wide range of people. Joint local CAMRA *Pub of the Year* 1996. Seven handpumps; over 400 beers sold in 1995.
◑

## Shirleycroft Hotel

Harrowby Road (off A52,
Boston road) ☎ (01476) 63260
11–11; 12–10.30 Sun
**Draught Bass; Bateman XB;
guest beer** H
Victorian-style hotel set in its
own grounds: one large
drinking area, with seating in
various nooks and crannies.
Weekly guest beer.
❀ 🛏 ≉ P

## Grimsby

### Royal Oak

Victoria Street
☎ (01472) 354562
11–11; 11–5, 7–11 Sat; 12–3, 7–10.30
Sun
**Bass Mild, Draught Bass;
Stones Bitter; Worthington
Bitter** H
Drinkers' pub close to the town
centre and the National Fishing
Heritage Centre. Folk Club
alternate Fri.
Q 🍴 ≉ (Town) ♣

### Rutland Arms

Rutland Street (off Cleethorpe
Rd) ☎ (01472) 241345
11–11; 12–4, 7–10.30 Sun
**Old Mill Mild, Bitter, Old
Curiosity** H
Former workingman's club,
cleverly converted into a one-
room pub with a games area at
one end. It caters for locals and
shoppers.
& ≉ (New Clee) ♣

### Swigs

21 Osborne Street
☎ (01472) 354773
11–11; 7–10.30 Sun, closed Sun lunch
**Bateman XB; Willy's Original;
guest beers** H
Cosmopolitan, narrow, town-
centre pub, a free house within
a couple of mins' walk from
the station. Popular with office
workers and shoppers at
lunchtimes; quiet during the
afternoon and early eve;
noisier later. The second outlet
for Willy's Brewery. No food
Sun. ◖ ≉ (Town)

### Tap & Spile

Garth Lane ☎ (01472) 357493
11.30–4, 7–11; 11.30–11 Fri & Sat;
12–3, 7–10.30 Sun
**Beer range varies** H
Large, one-roomed, open-plan,
former flour mill retaining old
stone, brick and woodwork;
well-kept, particularly eves,
with a good atmosphere.
CAMRA local *Pub of the Year*
1995. Up to nine ales; the cider
varies.
❀ ◖ & ≉ (Town) ♣ ➘

### Tivoli Tavern

Old Market Place
☎ (01472) 342231
11–11; 12–10.30 Sun
**Bass Mild, Draught Bass;
guest beers** (occasional) H

Comfortable, town-centre pub,
a haven from the hurly-burly
of the shopping centre.
≉ (Town)

## Habrough

### Station Hotel

1 Station Road
☎ (01469) 572896
11–11; 12–3, 7–10.30 Sun
**Courage Directors; Marston's
Pedigree; Morland Old
Speckled Hen; Ruddles
County; John Smith's Bitter;
guest beer** (occasional) H
One-roomed pub, divided into
areas, giving the impression of
three rooms. It was originally
based in the shop next door.
🍴 Q ❀ 🛏 ◖ ▶ & ♠ ≉ ♣ P

## Haltoft End

### Castle

Wainfleet Road (A52, 2 miles
NE of Boston)
☎ (01205) 760393
11–11; 12–10.30 Sun
**Bateman Mild, XB** H
Friendly roadside local which
can be very busy summer
weekends. A keen darts and
domino pub with matches
most eves. Food available all
day until 8.15. Excellent
adventure playground for
children. 🍴 ❀ 🛏 ◖ ▶ ♣ P

## Harmston

### Thorold Arms

High Street ☎ (01522) 720358
11–3, 7–11; 12–3, 7–10.30 Sun
**Draught Bass; Worthington
Bitter; guest beer** H
Centuries-old, two-bar pub at
the centre of a Lincoln Edge
village. Reputedly haunted, it
is a friendly, cosy pub.
Breakfast available Mon–Sat
from 7.30.
🍴 ❀ ◖ ▶ 🍴 ♣ P ♨

## Haxey

### Loco

31–33 Church Street
☎ (01427) 752879
6.30–11; 12–10.30 Sun
**Courage Directors; John
Smith's Bitter** H
Pub converted from the village
Co-op and fish and chip shop;
a must for railway enthusiasts,
packed with railwayana.
🍴 Q 🛏 ◖ ▶ 🍴 ♣ P

## Heighington

### Butcher & Beast

High Street ☎ (01522) 790386
11–3 (4 Fri, 5 Sat), 7–11; 12–5, 7–10.30
Sun
**Draught Bass; Bateman Mild,
XB, XXXB; guest beer** H
Popular local in a pleasant
village on the edge of Lincoln.

Award-winning floral displays
outside; large range of
ornaments inside. Guest beers,
provided by Bateman, are sold
at reasonable prices. No food
Sun or Mon.
🍴 🛏 ❀ ◖ ▶ & ♠ P ⚉ ♨

## Holbeach St Marks

### New Inn

Main Road ☎ (01406) 701231
12–2.30, 7–11 (midnight Sat); 12–4.30,
7–10.30 Sun
**Bateman Mild; Boddingtons
Bitter; Tetley Bitter; guest
beers** H
Popular village local with a
cosy atmosphere. A lively
music venue, it also hosts
regular art exhibitions. Close to
the Wash Marshlands and
nature reserves. A 'get-you-
home service' is provided.
🍴 Q ❀ 🛏 ◖ ▶ ♠ ♣ P ♨

## Horbling

### Plough Inn

4 Spring Lane
☎ (01529) 240263
12–3, 7–11; 12–3, 7–10.30 Sun
**Greene King IPA; guest
beers** H
Late 17th-century building,
owned by the parish council.
Fred, the resident ghost,
wanders the premises after
time searching for a late drink.
Speciality eves in the
restaurant monthly.
🍴 🛏 ◖ ▶ & ♣ P

## Horncastle

### Fighting Cocks

West Street ☎ (01507) 527307
11–4, 7–11; 12–3, 7–10.30 Sun
**Draught Bass; Bateman XB;
Courage Directors; Fuller's
London Pride; Marston's
Pedigree; John Smith's
Bitter** H
Modernised 200-year-old pub
with a bright, cheerful and
bustling atmosphere; reputed
to be haunted by a cat and a
cavalier. Separate restaurant
(closed Sun and Wed eves in
winter). 🍴 ❀ 🛏 ◖ ▶ ♣ P

### Red Lion

Bullring ☎ (01507) 523338
11–3, 7–11; 12–3, 7–10.30 Sun
**Courage Directors; John
Smith's Bitter** H
Pleasant, friendly pub, a
meeting place for clubs. It
supports a flourishing theatre
in the converted stables.
🍴 Q 🛏 🛏 ◖ & ♣ P

## Hubbert's Bridge

### Wheatsheaf

Station Road ☎ (01205) 290347
11–2.30, 5–11; 11–11 Mon & Sat; 12–3,
7–10.30 Sun

**Vaux Samson, Double Maxim; Ward's Thorne BB** Ⓗ
Welcoming, family-run, bankside pub, ideal for fishing and near good golfing facilities. Excellent food in both the bar and restaurant; specials and imaginative vegetarian dishes available.
🏠 ⊛ 🛏 ◖◗ ▲ ≈ ♣ P

## Knaith Park

### Stag's Head

Willingham Road (B1241)
☎ (01427) 612917
11–3, 7–11; 12–3, 7.30–10.30 Sun
**Castle Eden Ale; Marston's Pedigree; Tetley Bitter; Ward's Best Bitter** Ⓗ
Cosy village local, extensively renovated a few years ago.
Q ⊛ ◖◗ P 🗓

## Laughterton

### Friendship

Main Road ☎ (01427) 718681
11–3, 5.30–11; 11–11 Sat; 12–3, 6–10.30 Sun
**Draught Bass; Bateman Valiant; Ward's Best Bitter; guest beer** Ⓗ
Cosy village local with a busy food trade. Frequent live music; own art gallery.
⊛ ◖◗ ♣ P

## Lincoln

### Dog & Bone

10 John Street
☎ (01522) 522403
12–3, 7 (5 Fri)–11; 11–11 Sat; 12–10.30 Sun
**Draught Bass; Bateman XB, Valiant, XXXB, Salem Porter; guest beer** Ⓗ
Friendly, one-roomer, formerly known as the Gay Dog. Popular with students, it stages occasional fun nights during term-time and boasts an array of antiques and old relics with a touch of humour. Big screen TV for major sporting events. Lunches Tue–Fri.
🏠 ⊛ 🛏 & ≈ ♣ P

### Golden Eagle

21 High Street
☎ (01522) 521058
11–3, 5–11; 11–11 Fri & Sat; 12–10.30 Sun
**Bateman XB; Everards Beacon; Fuller's London Pride; guest beer** Ⓗ
Friendly, two-bar pub, near the football ground: a lively bar with a quieter lounge. Regularly changing guest beers and ciders. ⊛ 🍺 ♣ ○ P

### Jolly Brewer

26 Broadgate ☎ (01522) 528583
11–11; 12–10.30 Sun
**Draught Bass; Everards Tiger; Theakston XB; Younger Scotch, No. 3; guest beer** Ⓗ

Very popular, city-centre pub, attracting a wide range of customers. Formerly the Unity, it has been a *Guide* entry since 1983. No food Sun.
🏠 ⊛ ◖ ≈ ♣ ○ P

### Lincolnshire Poacher

84 Bunkers Hill
☎ (01522) 511788
11–11; 12–10.30 Sun
**Mansfield Riding Mild, Riding Bitter, Bitter, Old Baily** Ⓗ
Very comfortable pub and restaurant converted from an empty listed building: two eating areas, one no-smoking, plus a separate bar area. Excellent indoor and outdoor play areas. Children's certificate. 🛏 ⊛ ◖◗ & P

### Peacock Inn

23 Wragby Road
☎ (01522) 524703
11–11; 12–10.30 Sun (may vary winter)
**Hardys & Hansons Best Mild, Best Bitter, Classic, seasonal beers** Ⓗ
Popular local on the edge of the tourist area. Eve meals Fri–Sun in summer. 🏠 ⊛ ◖◗ ♣ P

### Portland Arms

50 Portland Street
☎ (01522) 513912
11–11; 12–10.30 Sun
**Draught Bass; Bateman XXXB; Courage Directors; John Smith's Bitter; Wilson's Mild; guest beer** Ⓗ
Simple, friendly, town pub with no ties. Guest beers from near and far are served in a newly extended, lively tap room and a cosy, quiet best room. A traditional gem. The cider varies.
Q 🍺 ≈ ♣ ○ P

### Queen in the West

12–14 Moor Street
☎ (01522) 526169
11.30–3, 5.30–11; 11.30–11 Fri & Sat; 12–4, 7–10.30 Sun
**Bateman XB; Courage Directors; John Smith's Bitter; Morland Old Speckled Hen; Ruddles Best Bitter; Taylor Landlord** Ⓗ
Friendly sidestreet pub, popular with factory and office workers at lunchtime, and locals eves. Fine collection of miniature bottles. ◖ 🍺 ♣

### Sippers

26 Melville Street
☎ (01522) 527612
11–2.30, 5 (4 Fri, 7 Sat)–11; 7–10.30 Sun, closed Sun lunch
**Courage Directors; Marston's Pedigree; Morland Old Speckled Hen; John Smith's Bitter; Wilson's Mild; guest beer** Ⓗ
Handy pub for both rail and bus stations; popular at lunchtimes with workers from nearby factories and offices,

quieter eves. Usually two guest beers from small and independent brewers are sold. The excellent food is not available Sat eve or Sun.
◖ ≈ ♣

### Strugglers

83 Westgate
☎ (01522) 524702
11–3, 5.30–11; 11–11 Fri & Sat; 12–3, 7–10.30 Sun
**Bass Mild, Draught Bass** Ⓗ
Compact, 19th-century beerhouse with an almost unaltered lounge. Thriving pub sports scene. Q ⊛ 🍺 ♣

### Victoria

6 Union Road
☎ (01522) 536048
11–11; 12–10.30 Sun
**Bateman XB; Everards Old Original; Taylor Landlord; guest beer** Ⓗ
Flagship pub of the Small Beer Company, serving up to seven guests, including a mild. Brewery feature nights are held on a regular basis; occasional live music. Good food in good portions.
Q ⊛ 🍺 ♣ ○

## Little Bytham

### Willoughby Arms

Station Road (B1176, opp. old station)
☎ (01780) 410276
6 (12 Sat)–11; 12–3, 7–10.30 Sun
**Ruddles County; guest beers** Ⓗ
Very cosy, welcoming, old-style village pub serving two guest ales at all times. Great views over the rolling countryside from the back room bar. Food available every eve, plus weekend lunch, in the restaurant.
🏠 Q ⊛ ◖◗ & ♣ P

## Louth

### Lincolnshire Poacher

211 Eastgate
☎ (01507) 603657
11–3, 5–11; 11–11 Sat; 12–3, 7–10.30 Sun
**Hardys & Hansons Best Mild, Best Bitter, Classic** Ⓗ
Georgian building, a residential house till 1955. The single long bar offers darts, pool and push-ha'penny. Family-run B&B; a restaurant serves home-made fare.
⊛ 🛏 ◖◗ & ♣ P

### Malt Shovel

21 Northgate (next to Leo's supermarket)
☎ (01507) 608904
11–5 (3 Tue & Thu; not Mon), 7–11; 12–3, 7–10.30 Sun
**Bass Mild, Draught Bass; Boddingtons Bitter; guest beers** Ⓗ

Edwardian building, now a
single bar with a lounge and a
games area, refurbished in
1995. Occasional live
entertainment. ♨ ♣

## Masons Arms

Cornmarket
☎ (01507) 609525
11–11; 12–3, 7–10.30 Sun
**Draught Bass; Bateman Mild,
XB, Salem Porter, XXXB;
Marston's Pedigree; guest
beer** H
Friendly, family-run,
18th-century posting inn,
restored sympathetically.
Charming accommodation;
home-made fare (listed in
CAMRA's *Good Pub Food*
guide). Q ⌂ ♨ ◑ ♦ ♣

## Newmarket

Newmarket Road
☎ (01507) 605146
7–11; 12–3, 7–10.30 Sun
**Black Sheep Best Bitter;
Castle Eden Ale; Flowers IPA;
guest beer** H
Pleasantly decorated, two-
roomed pub in a rural town.
Friendly atmosphere; popular
with all ages. Eve meals Wed–
Sat. Limited parking.
Q ♨ ◑ ♦ P

## Wheatsheaf

62 Westgate
☎ (01507) 603159
11–3, 5–11; 11–11 Sat; 12–4, 7–10.30
Sun
**Draught Bass; Bentley's
Yorkshire Bitter; Boddingtons
Bitter; Flowers Original; guest
beers** H
Attractive, traditional old inn,
dated 1612, in a Georgian
terrace, in a prestigious
position in the town: three bars
all with real fires. Weekday
lunches. The house beer, Tipsy
Toad, is not brewed here.
Children welcome until 9.
♨ Q ⌂ ♨ ◑ ♦ P

## Woodman Inn

134 Eastgate
☎ (01507) 602100
11–3 (4 Wed & Fri), 7–11; 11–11 Sat;
12–3, 7–10.30 Sun
**John Smith's Bitter; guest
beers** H
Popular, town-centre pub
serving a constantly changing
selection of guest beers. Good
value food; children's portions
available. ♨ ◑ ♦ ♣ P

## Ludford

### White Hart

Magna Mile
☎ (01507) 313489
12–3 (not winter Mon–Fri), 7–11; 12–3,
7–10.30 Sun
**John Smith's Bitter, Magnet;
guest beer** H
Two-roomed pub on the main
road. Handy for walkers on the
Viking Way. ♨ ♨ ♨ ◑ ♦ P

# Mablethorpe

## Montalt Arms

George Street (off High St)
☎ (01507) 472794
11.30–3, 7–11; 12–3, 7–10.30 Sun
**Draught Bass; Bateman XB;
Stones Bitter; guest beer**
(occasional) H
Real ale oasis in a town awash
with keg beer. Named in
honour of a 13th-century
knight, Robert de Montalt, it
has a pleasant lounge bar with
an adjoining restaurant (no
food Mon). Always a warm
welcome. Limited parking.
♨ ♨ ◑ P

# Market Deeping

## Bull

19 Market Place
☎ (01778) 343320
11–3, 5–11; 11–11 Fri & Sat; 12–10.30
Sun
**Adnams Bitter; Everards
Tiger, Old Original; guest
beer** H
Old coaching house in the
village centre: a traditional,
friendly bar and a comfortable,
busy lounge. Book eve meals.
⌂ ♨ ◑ ♦ ♣

## Vine

19 Church Street
☎ (01778) 342387
11–2, 5.30–11; 12–3, 7–10.30 Sun
**Wells Eagle, Bombardier,
Fargo; guest beers** H
Former 1870s prep school, now
a friendly local with a large,
busy bar and a smaller, quieter
lounge. ♨ Q ♨ ♦ ♣ P

# Market Rasen

## Chase

1 King Street ☎ (01673) 842308
11–3, 7–11; 12–3, 7–10.30 Sun
**Boddingtons Bitter; Marston's
Bitter; Morland Old Speckled
Hen; Ruddles Best Bitter; John
Smith's Bitter** H
Centrally situated, opposite the
Market Square, this well-
appointed town pub is
renowned for its food.
◑ ♦ ♨ P

# Messingham

## Horn Inn

High Street ☎ (01724) 762426
11–11; 12–10.30 Sun
**John Smith's Bitter, Magnet;
guest beer** H
Popular village local on the
main road. Open-plan in
layout, it has separate drinking
areas, original oak beams and
dark wood fittings. Small
garden. Live music midweek.
A regular outlet for Highwood
Brewery's beers.
♨ ♨ ◑ ♣ P

# Metheringham

## White Hart

High Street ☎ (01526) 320496
11–4.30, 7–11; 11–11 Thu–Sat;
12–10.30 Sun
**Mansfield Riding Mild,
Riding Bitter, Bitter, Old
Baily, seasonal beers** H
Friendly, one-roomed, village
local with a warm welcome
from the licensees. Quizzes
and karaoke on occasions.
♨ ◑ ♦ ♣ ☗

# Minting

## Sebastapol Inn

Church Lane (2 miles off A158)
☎ (01507) 578688
11–3, 6.30–11; 11–11 Fri & Sat;
12–10.30 Sun
**Draught Bass; Bateman Mild,
XB; guest beer** H
Popular, 16th-century, village
local offering good food in
comfortable surroundings.
♨ ♨ ◑ ♦ ♨ ♦ ♣ P ♨ ☗

# Nettleham

## White Hart

14 High Street
☎ (01522) 751976
11.30–3.30, 7–11; 12–3.30, 7–10.30 Sun
**Draught Bass; Bateman XB,
XXXB; Marston's Pedigree;
guest beer** H
Very busy, friendly, village
pub serving excellent cuisine
(particularly in the eve). Tue
night is games night. Very
friendly and hospitable host.
♨ Q ⌂ ♨ ◑ ♦ ♨ ♦ P

# North Kelsey

## Royal Oak

High Street ☎ (01652) 678544
12–2 (may extend; 12–4 Sat), 7–11;
12–4, 7–10.30 Sun
**Draught Bass; Vaux Samson;
Ward's Best Bitter; guest beer**
(occasional) H
Fine old village pub with a
friendly atmosphere. The
lounge bar has an open fire at
one end and a wood-burning
stove at the other; there is also
a games room and a snug.
Popular for meals (not served
Mon). ♨ ◑ ♦ ♣ P

# North Kelsey Moor

## Queen's Head

Station Road (near disused
N Kelsey station)
☎ (01652) 678055
7–11; 12–2, 7–11 Fri; 12–4, 7–11 Sat;
12–3, 7–10.30 Sun
**Theakston Best Bitter; guest
beer** H
Friendly, three-room free
house, a little out of the way,
but well worth finding. The
genial landlord is enthusiastic
about his guest beers. Eve

meals Tue–Sat (booking advised). Tue is gourmet sausage night (free).
🚶 Q ◁ 🛏 🐕 ♿ ♣ P

## Oasby

### Houblon Arms
Village Street
☎ (01529) 455215
12–2.30, 6.30 (6 Fri & Sat)–11; 12–3, 7–10.30 Sun
**Draught Bass; Bateman XB; guest beers** Ⓗ
Charming old village inn with low, beamed ceilings and open fires. Popular with locals and diners. 🚶 ❀ 🛏 ◁ ▷ ♣ P

## Owston Ferry

### Crooked Billet
Silver Street ☎ (01427) 728264
11.30–3 (not Mon, except bank hols), 6 (7 Mon & Sat)–11; 12–3, 7–10.30 Sun
**Ward's Thorne BB; guest beer** Ⓗ
Friendly local beside the River Trent with its own amateur boxing club. Weekend sing-alongs. Excellent food; eve meals Tue–Fri (till 8).
🚶 Q ↻ ❀ ◁ ▷ ♣ P ⏷

## Quadring

### White Hart
Town Drove (50 yds W of A152) ☎ (01775) 821135
12–3 (not Mon), 7–11; 12–3, 7–10.30 Sun
**Bateman XB; Boddingtons Bitter** Ⓗ
Lively, popular village pub with a warm welcome. Darts and pool played. Wheelchair access is from the car park at the rear. 🚶 ❀ ♿ ♣ P

## Raithby

### Red Lion
Main Street ☎ (01790) 753727
11–3 (not Mon–Fri, except bank hols), 7–11; 12–3, 7–10.30 Sun
**Home Bitter; Tetley Bitter; guest beers** Ⓗ
Inviting and friendly pub in an attractive Wolds village with an excellent food reputation and comfortable accommodation. An adjoining barn has been rebuilt and converted to a small, full mash brewery, expected to brew exclusively for the pub.
🚶 Q ❀ 🛏 ◁ ▷ ♣ P

## Rothwell

### Nickerson Arms
Hill Rise ☎ (01472) 371300
12–2, 7–11 (closed Mon eve); 12–3, 7–10.30 Sun (may vary in summer)
**Bateman XB; guest beers** Ⓗ
Deservedly popular pub in a pretty Wolds village. A wide range of draught and bottled

foreign beers complements the excellent food menu.
🚶 Q ↻ ❀ ◁ ▷ ♣ P ⏣

## Ruskington

### Black Bull
10 Rectory Road
☎ (01526) 832270
11.30–2.30 (3 Fri, 3.30 Sat), 6.30–11; 12–3, 7–10.30 Sun
**Draught Bass; Bateman XB; guest beers** Ⓗ
Friendly, comfortable, village local which hosts a lively quiz Wed eve. Sun lunches are very popular; these and eve meals must be booked.
❀ 🛏 ◁ ▷ 🐕 ♿ ⇌ ♣ ⏷

## Saxilby

### Ship Inn
21 Bridge Street
☎ (01522) 702259
11.30–2.30 (3 Fri & Sat), 7 (5.30 summer)–11; 12–3, 7–10.30 Sun
**John Smith's Bitter** Ⓗ
Plain village pub, popular with sports enthusiasts and boaters on England's oldest canal (across the road). Home-cooked food at reasonable prices; try 'Pat's home-made pie'. Book eve meals and to camp in the garden.
❀ ◁ ▷ 🐕 ♿ ▲ ⇌ ♣ P

## Sleaford

### Carre Arms
Mareham Lane
☎ (01529) 303156
11–3, 5.30–11; 12–3, 7–10.30 Sun
**Draught Bass; M&B Brew XI** Ⓗ
Large, comfortable, hotel that can get busy. A brasserie off the lounge area is open weekday lunch and Sun eve.
❀ 🛏 ◁ ▷ 🐕 ⇌ ♣ P

### Rose & Crown
2 Watergate ☎ (01529) 303350
11–2.30, 7–11; 12–10.30 Sun
**Mansfield Riding Bitter, Bitter, Old Baily** Ⓗ
Welcoming, busy, town pub with a good-sized games area on a lower level from the bar. No food weekends.
❀ ▷ ⇌ ⌂ P

## Spalding

### Lincoln Arms
4 Bridge Street
☎ (01775) 722691
11–3 (4 Sat), 6.30 (7 winter)–11; 12–3, 7–10.30 Sun
**Mansfield Riding Mild, Riding Bitter, Bitter, Old Baily, seasonal beers** Ⓗ
18th-century riverside pub, popular with the locals; cosy and unpretentious with a friendly welcome. The meeting place of Spalding Pigeon Club.
❀ 🛏 ⇌ ♣

### Ship Albion
37 Albion Street (next to Castle Sports Complex)
☎ (01775) 769644
11.30–11; 12–10.30 Sun
**Bateman XB; Boddingtons Bitter; Marston's Pedigree; guest beers** Ⓗ
Comfortable, two-bar pub with a quiet front bar and a sometimes lively rear bar, used by all ages. Home of Spalding Folk Club. 🚶 ❀ 🛏 ◁ ▷ ♣ P

## Spilsby

### Nelson Butt
10 Market Street
☎ (01790) 752258
10.30–3, 7–11; 12–3, 7–10.30 Sun
**Draught Bass; Bateman XB** Ⓗ
Basic, friendly, no-frills pub in an interesting market town.
Q ❀ 🐕 ♣ P

## Stamford

### Daniel Lambert
20 St Leonard's Street (2 mins' walk from centre)
☎ (01780) 55991
11.30–3, 6–11, 11–11 Fri, 12–3, 7–10.30 Sun
**Adnams Bitter; Courage Directors; John Smith's Bitter; Taylor Landlord; guest beer** Ⓗ
Named after one of Britain's heaviest men: a one-room pub with a restaurant downstairs. Prints of Stamford adorn the walls; a huge open fire has a picture of Daniel Lambert above. A friendly local.
🚶 Q ◁ ▷ ⇌

### Dolphin
12 East Street (near police station) ☎ (01780) 55494
11–3, 5.30–11; 12–3, 7–10.30 Sun
**Badger Dorset Best, Tanglefoot; Wells Eagle, Bombardier, Fargo; guest beer** Ⓗ
300-year-old pub with four small rooms and a restaurant. Reasonably-priced food and beer. Annual beer festival. Wheelchair WC. Car park opposite.
🚶 ❀ 🛏 ◁ ▷ 🐕 ⇌ ♣ ⏣

### St Peter's Inn
11 St Peter's Street (5 mins' walk from centre)
☎ (01780) 63298
12–2.30, 5.30–11; 12–11 Fri & Sat; 12–4, 7–10.30 Sun
**Marston's Bitter, Pedigree; guest beer** Ⓗ/Ⓖ
Over 200-year-old, stone-built pub with a restaurant at the rear and a Cloister Bar downstairs (gravity dispense). A friendly local with an extensive menu, including a wide range of vegetarian and vegan meals. Limited parking.
🚶 Q ❀ ◁ ▷ 🐕 ⇌ ♣ P

## Stickney

### Plough & Dove
Main Road ☎ (01205) 480965
11.30–3.30, 6.30–11; 12–3.30, 7–10.30
Sun
Bateman XB; Webster's
Yorkshire Bitter; Wilson's
Mild; guest beer
(occasional) Ⓗ
Lively village pub, reputedly
frequented by Arthur Lucan
(Old Mother Riley) during his
travels. Occasional
entertainment and theme
nights.
ⓂⓀ◖◗♿Å♠P▯

## Surfleet

### Mermaid
2 Gosberton Road
☎ (01775) 680275
11.30–3, 6.30–11; 12–3, 7–10.30 Sun
Adnams Broadside;
Federation Buchanan's Best
Bitter; John Smith's Bitter;
guest beers Ⓗ
Former brewery by the River
Glen with a warm and friendly
atmosphere. Very popular for
meals. The large garden is
perfect for children.
ⓂQⓀ⌂◖◗P

## Susworth

### Jenny Wren
Main Street (3 miles off A159 at
Scotter, by River Trent)
☎ (01724) 784000
12–2.30 (3.30 Sat), 6.30 (7 Sat)–11;
12–3.30, 7–10.30 (12–5.30, 6.30–10.30
summer) Sun
John Smith's Bitter; Webster's
Yorkshire Bitter; guest beer Ⓗ
Large village inn dating back
to the 18th century. It features
attractive rural decor with bare
brickwork, wooden beams and
many nooks and crannies for
drinking and eating. Excellent
food in the bar and upstairs
restaurant.
ⓂⓀ◖◗▣♿♠P✁

## Swineshead

### Wheatsheaf Hotel
Market Place ☎ (01205) 820349
12–2.30, 6–11; 12–11 Sat; 12–3, 7–10.30
Sun
Draught Bass; Bateman XB;
Tetley Bitter; guest beers Ⓗ
Traditional village pub with a
good selection of bar and
restaurant meals (no bar food
Mon); children's meals
available. Traditional jazz
nights (second and fourth Thu
of the month).
ⓂⓀ⌂◖◗♠P

## Tealby

### Olde Barn Inn
Cow Lane ☎ (01673) 838304
12–3 (not Mon), 7–11; 12–3, 7–10.30
Sun
Bateman XB; Everards Beacon,
Tiger, Old Original; guest
beer Ⓗ
Situated in a picturesque
village, this country pub
features a 16th-century barn as
a restaurant. Families
welcome. ⓂⓀ◖◗P

## Threekingham

### Three Kings
Salters Way ☎ (01529) 240249
11–4, 7–11; 12–3, 7–10.30 Sun
Draught Bass; M&B Brew XI;
guest beers Ⓗ
This pub and its village take
their names from three Danish
chieftains who were killed in
the 9th-century Battle of Stow
Green nearby. Good food.
☿Ⓚ◖◗♿Å♠P

## Wainfleet

### Jolly Sailor Inn
19 St John Street
☎ (01754) 880275
11–2, 4.30–11; 11–11 Fri & Sat; 12–3,
7–10.30 Sun (may extend in summer)
Draught Bass; Bateman Mild,
XB Ⓗ

Welcoming local with a large
bottle collection and sporting
photographs. Note the
interestingly-shaped table
made from ship's timber.
Lunches served in summer.
Ⓜ◖♿Å⇌♣♠

### Royal Oak
73 High Street
☎ (01754) 880328
11–3 (later in summer), 7–11; 12–3,
7–10.30 summer
Bateman Mild, XB Ⓗ
Cheerful pub; apparently the
building once belonged to
Bethlehem Hospital for the
Insane. The detailed model of
*HMS Vanguard* on display took
two years to build.
ⓂⓀ⌂◖◗Å⇌♠P

## Westwoodside

### Park Drain
400 yds off B1396 OS726988
☎ (01427) 752255
11–11; 12–3, 7–10.30 (extends
summer) Sun
Mansfield Riding Mild,
seasonal beers; John Smith's
Bitter Ⓗ
Unusual, remote, Victorian
pub built to serve the mining
community of a pit that was
never sunk: a comfortable
lounge and an excellent
restaurant (which is closed
Mon lunch).
Ⓜ◖◗♿Å♠P

## Woodhall Spa

### Mall
Station Road ☎ (01526) 352342
11–11; 12–10.30 Sun
Bateman XB; Courage
Directors; John Smith's
Bitter Ⓗ
Thriving village local in the
heart of a genuine spa village: a
large mock-Tudor building
with a traditional village bar
and a recently extended, cosy
lounge/restaurant.
Ⓚ◖◗▣♠P✁

---

# STOUTS AND PORTERS

The revival in cask-conditioned stouts and porters in recent years
has been long overdue. These wonderful beer styles, strong in
roast grain flavours, date back to Victorian London but had been
forced out of the market by cleverly advertised Irish keg stouts. Then
along came the micro-brewers. Never afraid to experiment, the likes
of Linfit, Malton and Nethergate produced English Guineas Stout,
Pickwick's Porter and Old Growler. The regionals followed suit:
Bateman's Salem Porter, amongst others, won awards. Now the
wheel has turned full circle with the arrival of Harwood's Porter –
named after the father of stout and porter, Ralph Harwood, and
brewed by none other than Guinness! It has been extremely well
received and looks likely to become a permanent fixture.

# THE BEER LOVER'S BOOKSHELF

To complement the *Good Beer Guide*, CAMRA produces a whole series of other beer- and pub-related titles. These range from guides to pub food and accommodation, to Continental beer guides and home brewing manuals. Highlights of our collection are displayed below. Copies are available from all good bookshops, or direct (and post-free) from CAMRA, 230 Hatfield Road, St Albans, Hertfordshire AL1 4LW. Discounts are available for CAMRA members. Credit card orders can be taken on (01727) 867201.

### The Good Beer Guide to Belgium and Holland £9.99
The Low Countries have long been celebrated for their weird and wonderful variety of beers. Tim Webb reveals all you need to know about Lambics, Guezes, Krieks and Trappist Ales, plus the best places in which to enjoy them. (2nd edition)

### The Good Beer Guide to Prague and the Czech Republic £7.99
The Czechs drink more beer than any other nation. Graham Lees explains why – and where – in this essential guide to the land of real Pilsner. (1st edition)

### The Good Beer Guide to Munich and Bavaria £8.99
The best bars and all you need to know about beer in the world's foremost brewing region, compiled by Graham Lees. (1st edition)

### Good Pub Food £9.99
The CAMRA guide to original and exciting, genuine pub catering, researched and presented by Susan Nowak. The best food pubs in the country. (4th edition)

### Room at the Inn £8.99
The CAMRA guide to pub accommodation – the passport to a comfortable bed, a decent breakfast and a well-kept pint of beer, compiled by Jill Adam. (1st edition)

### The CAMRA Guide to Real Cider £7.99
The cider bandwagon is rolling and demand is rising for quality, traditional ciders (without the processed fizz and burp of the major commercial brands). Ted Bruning has compiled this definitive guide to a fine British drink. (1st edition)

### The CAMRA Guide to Home Brewing £6.99
Tips for beginners and for the more experienced in CAMRA's guide to the basics of brewing-it-yourself, from the knowledgeable Graham Wheeler. (Revised 1st edition)

### Brew Your Own Real Ale at Home £6.99
Graham Wheeler and Roger Protz have combined to reveal how many famous commercial brews can now be emulated at home. Recipes for all kinds of beers. (1st edition)

### Brew Classic European Beers at Home £8.99
Your chance to brew Continental favourites like wheat beers, Pilsners and even Belgian Guezes, guided by authors Graham Wheeler and Roger Protz. (1st edition)

### Known Treasures and Hidden Gems £7.99
CAMRA's new, slimline, pocket-sized guide to over 400 London pubs, compiled by award-winning pub writer Peter Haydon. (1st edition)

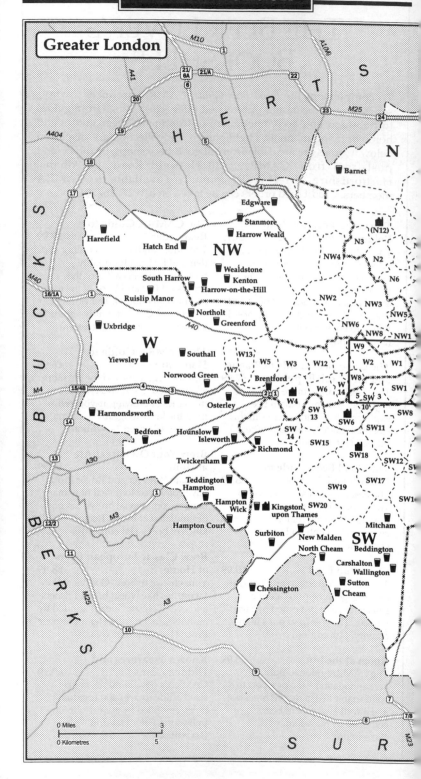

Greater London

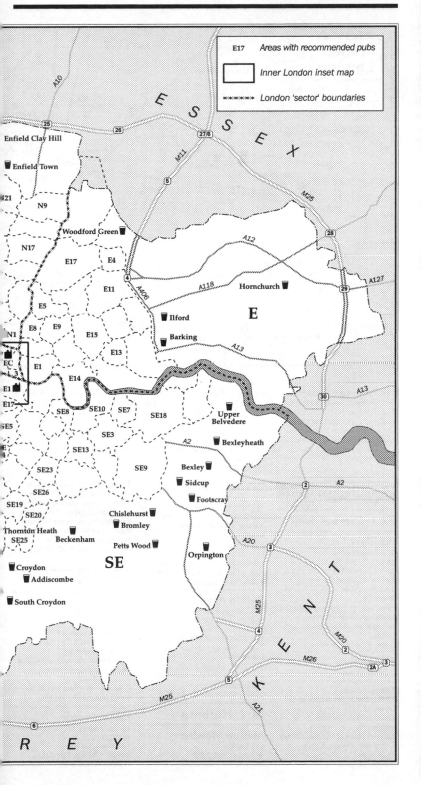

E17    *Areas with recommended pubs*

*Inner London inset map*

*London 'sector' boundaries*

ESSEX

E

SE

KENT

SURREY

Enfield Clay Hill
Enfield Town
N21
N9
N17
Woodford Green
E17
E4
E11
E5
E8
E9
E15
N1
EC
E1
E17
E1
E14
SE8
SE10
SE7
SE18
SE5
SE3
SE13
SE23
SE9
SE26
SE19
SE20
Thornton Heath
SE25
Beckenham
Croydon
Addiscombe
South Croydon

Hornchurch
Ilford
Barking
Upper Belvedere
Bexleyheath
Bexley
Sidcup
Footscray
Chislehurst
Bromley
Petts Wood
Orpington

A10
A11
A12
A118
A406
A13
A127
A2
A20
M25
M26
M20
A21

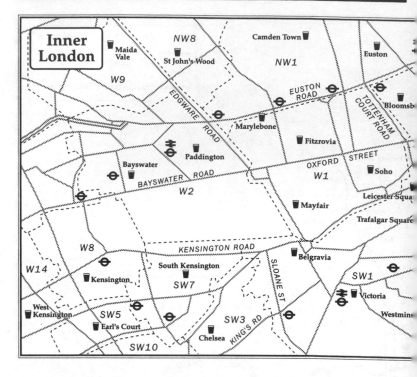

NB: Pubs within Greater London are divided into seven geographical sectors: Central, East, North, North-West, South-East, South-West and West, reflecting London postal boundaries (see Greater London map on previous pages). Look under Central London for postal districts EC1 to EC4, and WC1 and WC2. For each of the surrounding sectors, postal districts are listed in numerical order (E1, E4, etc.), followed in alphabetical order by the outlying areas which do not have London postal numbers (Barking, Hornchurch, etc.). The Inner London map, above, shows the area roughly covered by the Circle Line and outlines regions of London (Bloomsbury, Holborn, etc.) which have featured pubs. Some regions straddle more than one postal district.

## Central London

## EC1: Clerkenwell

### Artillery Arms
102 Bunhill Row
☎ (0171) 253 4683
11–11; 12–10.30 Sun
**Fuller's Chiswick,
London Pride, ESB, seasonal
beers** Ⓗ
Small city pub opposite Bunhill
burial grounds, drawing a
mixture of office workers and
locals.
Ⓓ ≣ (Old St) ⊖ ♣

### O'Hanlon's
8 Tysoe Street
11–11; 12–10.30 Sun
**Draught Bass;
O'Hanlon's Dry Stout; guest
beers** Ⓗ
Small Irish brew pub on the
edge of the city, with a
conservatory at the rear. Other
O'Hanlon's beers may be
available.
Ⓓ ▶ ⊖ (Angel)

### Sekforde Arms
34 Sekforde Street
☎ (0171) 253 3231
11–11; 12–3 Sun, closed Sun eve
**Young's Bitter, Special,
seasonal beers** Ⓗ
Small, popular, pub frequented
by London branches of
northern football supporters'
clubs. Pavement tables. Q ✤ Ⓓ
▶ ≣ (Farringdon) ⊖ ♣

### Sutton Arms
15 Great Sutton Street
☎ (0171) 253 3251
11–11 (4 Sat); closed Sun
**Boddingtons Bitter; Everards
Tiger; Flowers Original; guest
beers** Ⓗ
Popular, sidestreet pub which
can be loud Fri eve. The beer
range may vary.
Ⓓ ≣ (Barbican) ⊖ ♣

## EC1: Holborn

### Melton Mowbray
18 Holborn
☎ (0171) 405 7077
11–11 (10 Fri); closed Sat & Sun

**Fuller's Chiswick, London
Pride, ESB, seasonal beers** Ⓗ
Tasteful shop conversion with
a split-level ground floor bar. A
downstairs room is used for
meals lunchtime and private
functions eve. Q Ⓓ ▶ &
≣ (Farringdon) ⊖ (Chancery
Lane)

## EC3: City

### Elephant
119 Fenchurch Street
☎ (0171) 623 8970
11–10.30; closed Sat & Sun
**Young's Bitter, Special,
seasonal beers** Ⓗ
Basic bar at street level, with a
smarter bar downstairs.
Pavement seating.
Q ✤ Ⓓ ▶ ≣ (Fenchurch St)
⊖ (Aldgate) ♣

### Lamb Tavern
10–12 Leadenhall Market
☎ (0171) 626 2454
11–9; closed Sat & Sun
**Young's Bitter, Special,
Winter Warmer** Ⓗ

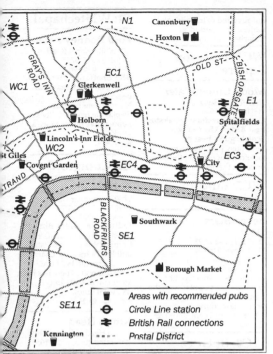

| | |
|---|---|
| | Areas with recommended pubs |
| | Circle Line station |
| | British Rail connections |
| | Postal District |

Single-bar, friendly pub, popular with locals and ITN workers. Very popular restaurant upstairs. Q ❀ ◖ ▮ ⇌ (King's Cross) ⊖ (Russell Sq)

### King's Arms
11A Northington Street
☎ (0171) 405 9107
11–11; closed Sat & Sun
**Adnams Bitter; Draught Bass; Fuller's London Pride; Greene King IPA** Ⓗ
Single-bar, corner house in a quiet street within London's legal community, relaxing and welcoming with a notable Thai restaurant upstairs. The Charles Dickens Museum is nearby. Q ◖ ▮ ⊖ (Chancery Lane) ⌿

### Lamb
94 Lamb's Conduit Street
☎ (0171) 405 0713
11–11; 12–4, 7–10.30 Sun
**Young's Bitter, Special, seasonal beers** Ⓗ
Well-preserved, popular pub which retains its original etched glass snob screens and resplendent interior, with pictures and memorabilia of the music hall. Comfortable, no-smoking snug.
Q ❀ ◖ ⊖ (Russell Sq) ✦ ⌿

## WC1: Holborn

### Cittie of Yorke ☆
22 High Holborn
☎ (0171) 242 7670
11.30–11; closed Sun
**Samuel Smith OBB** Ⓗ
Distinctive Gothic building on the site of a 15th-century inn and coffee house. The baronial hall at the rear boasts huge vats, screened compartments and an unusual triangular stove. There are also a comfortable panelled front bar and a cellar bar. ㎰ Q ❀ ◖ ▮ ⇌ (Farringdon) ⊖ (Chancery Lane)

### Three Cups
21–22 Sandland Street
☎ (0171) 831 4302
11–11; closed Sat & Sun
**Young's Bitter, Special, Ram Rod, Winter Warmer** Ⓗ

Large, three-bar pub in a Victorian covered market. The street-level bar is for standing only; a bar with seating is upstairs (no-smoking area). Often packed lunchtime and early eve. Pavement drinking. Q ❀ ◖ ⇌ (Liverpool St) ⌿

### Swan
Ship Tavern Passage, 77–80 Gracechurch Street
☎ (0171) 283 7712
11–10.30 (may close earlier); closed Sat & Sun
**Fuller's Chiswick, London Pride, ESB, seasonal beers** Ⓗ
Pub with a small bar downstairs and the main bar above. Q ◖ ⇌ (Fenchurch St) ⊖ (Bank/Monument)

## EC4: City

### Banker
Cousin Lane
☎ (0171) 283 5206
11–9; closed Sat & Sun
**Fuller's Chiswick, London Pride, ESB, seasonal beers** Ⓗ
Lofty, split-level pub in an arch under Cannon St station, overlooking the Thames, with a riverside patio. Eve meals to order.
❀ ◖ & ⇌ (Cannon St) ⊖

### Old Bank of England
194 Fleet Street
☎ (0171) 430 2255
11–11; closed Sat & Sun

**Fuller's Chiswick, London Pride, ESB, seasonal beers; guest beers** Ⓗ
Pub with an impressive classical interior (this was the law courts branch of the Bank of England), featuring murals of 17th-century London. A gallery provides extra space. One of Fuller's 'Ale & Pie' managed houses.
Q ◖ ⇌ (City Thameslink/ Blackfriars) ⊖ (Temple)

## WC1: Bloomsbury

### Calthorpe Arms
252 Gray's Inn Road
☎ (0171) 278 4732
11–11; 11–3, 5.30–11 Mon–Wed; 12–10.30 Sun
**Young's Bitter, Special, Winter Warmer, seasonal beers** Ⓗ

One-bar pub, popular with office workers. Eve meals to order.
Q ᴥ ❀ ◖ ⊖ ♣

## WC2: Covent Garden

### Hogshead

21 Drury Lane
☎ (0171) 240 2489
11–11; 12–10.30 Sun
**Beer range varies** Ⓗ/Ⓖ
Small, friendly pub opposite the New London Theatre. Lunches Mon–Fri. ◖ ⊖

### Hogshead in Covent Garden

23 Wellington Street
☎ (0171) 836 6930
11–11; 12–10.30 Sun
**Beer range varies** Ⓗ
Corner pub near the Lyceum Theatre (which is being rebuilt), featuring a bank of 11 handpulls.
◖ ⇌ (Charing Cross) ⊖ ◔

### Lamb & Flag ☆

33 Rose Street
☎ (0171) 497 9504
11–11 (10.45 Fri & Sat); 12–10.30 Sun
**Courage Best Bitter, Directors; John Smith's Bitter; Wadworth 6X** Ⓗ
Reputedly the oldest pub in Covent Garden, dating from the early 18th century; formerly known as the 'Bucket of Blood'. The poet Dryden was mugged in the alleyway at the side. ⊖ (Leicester Sq)

### Marquess of Anglesey

39 Bow Street
☎ (0171) 240 3216
11–11; 12–10.30 Sun
**Young's Bitter, Special, Winter Warmer, seasonal beers** Ⓗ
Busy corner pub, handy for all Covent Garden's attractions. Another bar and a restaurant are on the first floor.
◖ ▮ ⇌ (Charing Cross) ⊖

### Marquis of Granby

51 Chandos Place
11–11; 12–10.30 Sun
**Adnams Bitter; Ind Coope Burton Ale; Tetley Bitter** Ⓗ
Small, wedge-shaped, corner pub, popular with office workers and tourists. The house beer is brewed by Carlsberg-Tetley and sold at a promotional price.
Q ᴥ ◖ ▮ ⇌ (Charing Cross) ⊖ ♣

### Prince of Wales

150–151 Drury Lane
☎ (0171) 836 5183
11–11; 12–10.30 Sun
**Courage Directors; Theakston Best Bitter, XB, Old Peculier; guest beers** Ⓗ

Spacious, corner pub which has reverted to its original name after a period as 'Charlie's'. Pricey. ◖ ▮ ⊖

## WC2: Leicester Square

### Moon Under Water

28 Leicester Square
11–11; 12–10.30 Sun
**Courage Directors; Theakston Best Bitter, XB; Younger Scotch; guest beer** Ⓗ
Very busy pub thanks to its location, but offering the best prices in the area. ◖ ▮ ⊖

## WC2: Lincoln's Inn Fields

### Seven Stars

53 Carey Street
☎ (0171) 242 8521
11–11; closed Sat & Sun
**Courage Best Bitter, Directors** Ⓗ
Built in 1602; an unspoilt, two-bar pub, popular with the legal profession from the nearby law courts.
◖ ▮ ⇌ (City Thameslink) ⊖ (Temple)

## WC2: St Giles

### Angel

61 St Giles High Street
☎ (0171) 240 2816
11–11; closed Sun
**Courage Best Bitter, Directors; Theakston Best Bitter; Wadworth 6X** Ⓗ
'Local' in the shadow of Centre Point; reputedly haunted.
Q ❀ ◖ ▮ ⊖ (Tottenham Ct Rd) ♣

## East London

## E1: Spitalfields

### Alma

41 Spelman Street
☎ (0171) 247 5604
11–11; 12–3, 7–10.30 Sun
**Fuller's London Pride; Young's Bitter; guest beers** Ⓗ
Small, old pub that was once a brewery, now with a large, new room at the rear in what was previously a courtyard.
◖ ⊖ (Aldgate E) ♣

### Pride of Spitalfields

3 Heneage Street
☎ (0171) 247 8933
11–11; 12–10.30 Sun
**Fuller's London Pride, ESB; guest beers** Ⓗ
Small, backstreet pub, very handy for Brick Lane market and curry houses. Many old photos of the East End feature.
ᴘᴀ ❀ ◖ ⇌ (Liverpool St) ⊖ (Aldgate E)

## E1: Whitechapel

### Lord Rodney's Head

285 Whitechapel Road
☎ (0171) 247 9795
11–11; 12–10.30 Sun
**B&T Shefford Bitter, SOD, SOS, Black Bat, seasonal beers** Ⓗ
Narrow, one-bar pub displaying over 130 clocks. Popular live music twice a week.
❀ ⊖ ♣ ◔

## E4: Chingford

### Bull & Crown

The Green (near station)
☎ (0181) 529 5773
11–11; 12–10.30 Sun
**Ridleys IPA; Tetley Bitter; guest beer** (occasional) Ⓗ
Comfortable pub in a listed building, a friendly, charming local. Jazz club Wed eve. Over-25s only. There has been an inn on this site since medieval times.
ᴘᴀ ◖ ⇌ ⊖ P

### King's Head

King's Head Hill (by police station) ☎ (0181) 521 1655
12 (11 Sat)–11; 12–10.30 Sun
**Hardy Royal Oak; Tetley Bitter; Young's Special; guest beers** Ⓗ
Comfortable pub with a good atmosphere and beer selection. Well worth a visit.
Q ❀ ◖ ⊖ ♣ P

## E5: Clapton

### Anchor & Hope

15 High Hill Ferry
☎ (0181) 806 1730
11–3, 5.30 (6 Sat)–11; 12–3, 7–10.30 Sun (may vary)
**Fuller's London Pride, ESB** Ⓗ
Small, one-bar, riverside pub which can get crowded in winter. Same licensee for over 20 years.
❀ ⊖ ♣

### Prince of Wales

146 Lea Bridge Road
☎ (0181) 533 3463
11–11; 12–10.30 Sun
**Young's Bitter, Special, Winter Warmer, seasonal beers** Ⓗ
Large, two-bar, riverside pub with a collection of prints of former Princes of Wales.
Q ❀ ◖ ⊟ ⇌ ♣ P

## E8: Hackney

### Lady Diana

95 Forest Road
☎ (0171) 254 3439
11.30–11; 11.30–3.30, 7–11 Sat; 12–3, 7–10.30 Sun

**Fuller's Chiswick, London Pride; Greene King Abbot; Marston's Pedigree** H
Small, sidestreet pub, famous for its pizzas. Paved outside drinking area. ❀ ◖ ▶ ♣

## E9: Hackney

### Falcon & Firkin
360 Victoria Park Road
☎ (0181) 985 0693
12–11; 12–10.30 Sun
**Firkin Falcon, Hackney, Dogbolter, Golden Glory** H
Brew pub which features monthly brew specials, next to Victoria Park. A very popular, friendly pub. Live music weekend eves. Good facilities for families.
🕭 ❀ ◖ ▶ ♿ ♣ ♱ P ⚲

## E11: Leytonstone

### Bell
468 High Road
☎ (0181) 539 3704
11–11; 11–3, 7.30–10.30 Sun
**Draught Bass; Worthington Bitter** H
Comfortable, traditional Charrington's house, squeezed between the fire station and the police station. Three bars.
❀ ◖ ▶ 🍺 ➡ (High Rd) ♣

### Birkbeck Tavern
45 Langthorne Road
☎ (0181) 539 2584
11–11; 12–10.30 Sun
**Draught Bass; Courage Best Bitter; John Smith's Bitter; Tetley Bitter; guest beers** H
Popular, backstreet pub, with a lively public bar and a quieter lounge, serving the most varied beer range for miles.
❀ 🍺 ➡ (Leyton) ♣

## E11: Wanstead

### George
High Street
11–11; 12–10.30 Sun
**Courage Directors; Greene King Abbot; Theakston Best Bitter, XB; Younger Scotch; guest beers** H
Large, two-bar corner pub displaying photos and pictures of Wanstead and famous Georges. Q ◖ ▶ ♿ ➡ ⚲

## E13: Plaistow

### The Village
140 Balham Street
☎ (0181) 472 2024
12–2.30 (3 Sat), 5.30 (7 Sat)–11; 12–3, 7–10.30 Sun
**Beer range varies** H
Small, two-bar pub which, during 1995, served over 200 different ales; up to five available at any time. Book for meals (lunch Thu–Sun; eves daily). ❀ ◖ ▶ 🍺 ♣ ♣

## E14: Isle of Dogs

### Cat & Canary
Fisherman's Walk, Canary Wharf ☎ (0171) 512 9187
11–11; closed Sat & Sun
**Fuller's Chiswick, London Pride, ESB, seasonal beers; guest beer** H
Waterside pub at the foot of an office block. ◖ ▶ ♿
➡ (Canary Wharf DLR) ♣

## E14: Stepney

### Queen's Head
8 Flamborough Street
11–2.30, 5.30 (7.30 Sat)–11; 12–3, 7–10.30 Sun
**Young's Bitter, Special, Winter Warmer** H
Friendly, backstreet local, unspoilt by 'progress'. Note the London 'Fives' dartboard in the back bar. ◖ 🍺 ➡ (Limehouse) ➡ (DLR) ♣

## E15: Stratford

### Goldengrove
146–148 The Grove
☎ (0181) 519 0750
11–11; 12–10.30 Sun
**Courage Directors; Theakston Best Bitter, XB, Old Peculier; Younger Scotch; guest beers** H
Large, one-bar pub whose walls are covered with prints and photos of former industries and of the nearby Theatre Royal. Regular beer festivals and promotions.
Q ❀ ◖ ▶ ♿ ➡ ➡ ⚲

## E17: Walthamstow

### Coppermill
205 Coppermill Lane
☎ (0181) 520 3709
11–11; 12–10.30 Sun
**Fuller's London Pride, ESB; Greene King IPA; Tetley Bitter; guest beers** H
Friendly, down-to-earth, backstreet local near the market.
Q ❀ ➡ (St James's St) ♣

## Barking

### Britannia
1 Church Road (near A123)
☎ (0181) 594 1305
11–3, 5–11; 11–11 Sat; 12–3, 7–10.30 Sun
**Young's Bitter, Special, Winter Warmer, seasonal beers** H
Three-bar pub: a roomy, comfortable lounge with a connecting private bar and a more basic public bar; Young's most easterly tied pub (north of the Thames). Note the caryatids on the exterior. Local

CAMRA *Pub of the Year* 1996. No food Sat/Sun.
❀ ◖ ➡ ➡ ⚲ P

## Hornchurch

### Pit Bar (Queen's Theatre)
Billet Lane (near A124)
☎ (01708) 456118
12–3, 6–11; 12–3, 7–10.30 Sun (closed Sun eve if no performance)
**Greene King IPA, Rayments Special, Abbot, seasonal beers** H; **guest beers** G
Modern theatre bar open to the public. Jazz Sun lunch, when beer prices are increased by 20p from their usual low level. Details of guest beers are shown on a small handwritten notice behind the bar. Eve meals finish at 7.
Q 🕭 ◖ ➡ (Emerson Pk) ➡ (Hornchurch)

## Ilford

### Prince of Wales
63 Green Lane (A1083)
☎ (0181) 478 1326
11–3, 5.15–11; 11–11 Fri & Sat; 12–3, 7–10.30 Sun
**Ind Coope Burton Ale; Tetley Bitter** H
Lively, atmospheric pub half a mile from Ilford centre. Three distinct drinking areas include a public bar and a small garden. The house beer comes from Carlsberg-Tetley. Meals Mon–Fri.
❀ 🍺 ♣ P

### Rose & Crown
16 Ilford Hill
☎ (0181) 478 7104
11–11; 12–10.30 Sun
**Adnams Bitter; Alloa Arrol's 80/-; Hardy Country; Ind Coope Burton Ale; Young's Winter Warmer; guest beers** H
Still the best beer choice in Ilford, despite increasing competition, in a large, one-bar pub with friendly staff. Some swan necks, but a sparkler is only used on Tetley, if available.
◖ ▶ ➡ ♱

Try also: **Bell**, 308 Ley St (Scottish Courage)

## Woodford Green

### Cricketers
299–301 High Road (A11)
☎ (0181) 504 2734
11–3, 5.30–11; 11–11 Sat; 12–10.30 Sun
**McMullen AK, Country, Gladstone, seasonal beers; guest beer** H
Pleasant, two-bar pub with extensive wood panelling in the comfortable saloon and more basic public. No food Sun.
Q ❀ ◖ 🍺 ♣ P

### Traveller's Friend

496–498 High Road
☎ (0181) 504 2435
11–11; 12–3.30, 7–10.30 Sun
**Courage Best Bitter, Directors; Ridleys IPA, Rumpus; guest beers** Ⓗ
Superb, small, friendly, wood-panelled pub with snob screens which has never sold keg bitter. Usually two guest beers. Q ⚘ ◑ ⇔

## North London

## N1: Canonbury

### Earl of Radnor

106 Mildmay Grove
☎ (0171) 241 0318
11–11; 12–10.30 Sun
**Fuller's London Pride, ESB, seasonal beers** Ⓗ
Cosy locals' bar with wrought iron fittings and Art Deco glass. ⚘ ◑ ▶ ⇌ (Dalston Kingsland) ♣

### Marquess Tavern

32 Canonbury Street
☎ (0171) 354 2975
11–11; 12–10.30 Sun
**Young's Bitter, Special, Ram Rod** Ⓗ**, Winter Warmer** Ⓖ/Ⓗ
Magnificent 19th-century local serving home-cooked food.
🏚 Q ⚘ ◑ ▶ ⇌ (Essex Rd) ⊖ (Highbury & Islington) ♣

## N1: Hoxton

### Rosemary Branch

2 Shepperton Road
☎ (0171) 704 2730
12–3, 5.30 (5 Fri)–11; 12–11 Sat; 12.30–10.30 Sun
**Boddingtons Bitter; Brakspear Bitter; Fuller's London Pride; Marston's Pedigree; Morland Old Speckled Hen; Taylor Landlord** Ⓗ
Large, refurbished canalside pub. Memorabilia displays its former canal connections. Live music at weekends; fringe theatre. Weekend supper licence until midnight.
🏚 ⚘ ◑ ▶ ⇌ (Essex Rd) ♣

### Wenlock Arms

26 Wenlock Road
☎ (0171) 608 3406
11–11; 12–10.30 Sun
**Nethergate IPA; Tetley Bitter; guest beers** Ⓗ
Extra handpumps have been installed to cope with demand for the ever-changing ales in this thriving free house, adjacent to the site of the former Wenlock Brewery and close to the Regent's Canal.
🏚 ⇌ (Old St) ⊖ ♣ ⇔ ⛫

## N1: Islington

### Compton Arms

4 Compton Avenue
☎ (0171) 359 6883
12–11; 12–10.30 Sun
**Greene King IPA, Rayments Special, Abbot** Ⓗ
Small, friendly local in cottage style; a country pub in central London. It can get very busy at weekends. Meals served 12–9. Q ⚘ ◑ ▶ ⇌ (Highbury & Islington) ⊖

### Crown

116 Cloudesley Road
☎ (0171) 837 7107
11–11; 12–10.30 Sun
**Fuller's Chiswick, London Pride, ESB** Ⓗ
Weave your way through an intricate pattern of squares and streets to find the Crown's distinctive and ornate interior. Wooden panels and etched glass divide the open-plan pub into distinct areas. 🏚 Q ☞ ⚘ ◑ ▶ ⊞ ⊖ (Angel) ♣

## N2: East Finchley

### Welch's Ale House

130 High Road
☎ (0181) 444 7444
11–11; 12–10.30 Sun
**Adnams Broadside; Fuller's London Pride; Greene King Abbot; Wadworth 6X; guest beers** Ⓗ
Long-standing shop conversion offering four or five guest beers plus a selection of country wines. ⊖ ♣

## N3: Finchley Central

### Catcher in the Rye

317 Regent's Park Road
☎ (0181) 343 4369
11–11; 12–10.30 Sun
**Draught Bass; Theakston XB; guest beer** Ⓗ
Tasteful shop conversion with exposed brickwork and wood panelling much in evidence. One large bar serves three split-level areas. The house bitter, Catcher, is Hancock's HB. Occasional beer festivals. No food Sun eve. ◑ ▶ ⊖ ♣

## N6: Highgate

### Flask ☆

77 Highgate West Hill
☎ (0181) 340 7260
11–11; 12–10.30 Sun
**Marston's Pedigree; Young's Bitter, Special, Winter Warmer** Ⓗ
Splendid building dating back to 1663, retaining many original features. Over the centuries many notables, such as Dick Turpin and Karl Marx, have passed through. No food Sun eve.
🏚 ⚘ ◑ ▶ ⊖ ♣

## N8: Hornsey

### Tollgate

26–30 Turnpike Lane
☎ (0181) 889 9085
11–11; 12–10.30 Sun
**Greene King Abbot; Theakston Best Bitter, XB; Younger Scotch; Wadworth 6X; guest beers** Ⓗ
One of Wetherspoon's first superpubs, with all the now familiar facilities and decor. It can get very crowded. Q ⚘ ◑ ▶ ⊖ (Turnpike Lane) ⇔ ⛌

## N9: Lower Edmonton

### Beehive

24 Little Bury Street
☎ (0181) 360 4358
11–11; 12–10.30 Sun
**Adnams Bitter; Ind Coope Burton Ale; Tetley Bitter; Young's Bitter; guest beer** Ⓗ
Large, comfortable, friendly local where the TV and piped music are not too intrusive. Small, enclosed garden. No food Sun eve. ⚘ ◑ ▶ ♣ P

### Lamb

52–54 Church Street
☎ (0181) 887 0128
11–11; 12–10.30 Sun
**Courage Directors; Marston's Pedigree; Theakston Best Bitter, XB; guest beers** Ⓗ
Familiar Wetherspoon conversion of restaurant premises, with wood-panelling much in evidence. The pub is named after the 19th-century poet Charles Lamb who lived locally. Two guest beers. Wheelchair WC. Q ⚘ ◑ ▶ ♿ ⇌ (Edmonton Green) ⇔ ⛌

### William IV

102 Hertford Road
☎ (0181) 807 2605
11–11; 12–10.30 Sun
**Adnams Bitter; Ind Coope Burton Ale; Tetley Bitter; Young's Bitter** Ⓗ
One island bar serves two distinct drinking areas in this Edwardian street-corner local. Fine tiled exterior with attractive etched glass and ironwork. Big Steak menu. ⚘ ◑ ♿ ⇌ (Edmonton Green) ♣

## N17: Tottenham

### Elbow Room

503–505 High Road
☎ (0181) 801 8769
11–11; 12–10.30 Sun
**Courage Directors; Marston's Pedigree; Theakston Best**

**Bitter; Younger Scotch; guest beers** Ⓗ
Smaller, split-level Wetherspoon shop conversion beneath the station, with a tiny, non-segregated, no-smoking area.
◖ ▶ ⇌ (Bruce Grove) ✄

## N21: Winchmore Hill

### Dog & Duck
74 Hoppers Road
☎ (0181) 886 1987
12–11; 12–4, 7–10.30 Sun
**Boddingtons Bitter; Flowers Original; Fuller's London Pride; Wethered Bitter; Whitbread seasonal beers** Ⓗ
Tucked-away local with a loyal clientele; local CAMRA *Pub of the Year*. The beer range may vary.
🏨 ☸ ⇌ (Palmers Green) ♣

### Orange Tree
18 Highfield Road
☎ (0181) 360 4853
11–11; 12–10.30 Sun
**Adnams Bitter; Greene King IPA** Ⓗ
Friendly, down-to-earth local, tucked away off Green Lanes. TV for sport. Under-21s may not be admitted. Eve meals finish at 7. ☸ ◖ ▶ ⇌ ♣ P

### Salisbury Arms
Hoppers Road/The Green
☎ (0181) 886 1945
11–11; 12–10.30 Sun
**Draught Bass; Fuller's London Pride; guest beer** Ⓗ
Large pub by the green. The popular, good value, restaurant offers an extensive menu. Occasional beer festivals. ☸ ◖ ▶ ⇌ P

## N22: Wood Green

### Starting Gate
Station Road
☎ (0181) 889 9789
12–11; 12–10.30 Sun
**Adnams Bitter; Hardy Dorchester; Ind Coope Burton Ale; Tetley Bitter; Young's Bitter; guest beers** Ⓗ
Named after the former Alexandra Palace racecourse, this pub has 1930s-style wood decor, alcoves with panoramic paintings and impressive etched glass windows and interior panels. It attracts a mainly local crowd, is often busy and may be very smoky. No food Sun.
☸ ◖ ⇌ (Alexandra Palace) ⊖

## Barnet

### King William IV
18 Hadley Highstone, Hadley
☎ (0181) 449 6728
11–3, 5.30–11; 12–4, 7–10.30 Sun

**Adnams Bitter; Benskins BB; Hook Norton Best Bitter; Ind Coope Burton Ale** Ⓗ
Unspoilt, 17th-century pub with three distinct drinking areas free of fruit machines and piped music. Extensive lunchtime menu (not served Sun). The house beer is brewed by Ushers. Q ☸ ◖

### Olde Mitre
58 High Street
☎ (0181) 449 6582
11.30–11; 12–3, 7–11 Sat; 12–3, 7–10.30 Sun
**Friary Meux BB; Ind Coope Burton Ale; Tetley Bitter; guest beers** Ⓗ
Traditional coaching inn, now an ale house which can get very crowded. Pleasant ambience – in contrast to some neighbouring pubs. It may close Sat afternoon if Barnet FC are at home. No food Sun.
Q ◖ ⊖ (High Barnet) ♣ P

### White Lion
50 St Albans Road
☎ (0181) 449 4560
11–2.30 (3 Sat), 5 (6 Sat)–11; 12–3, 7–10.30 Sun
**Ansells Bitter; Greene King IPA; Abbot; Tetley Bitter; Wadworth 6X; guest beers** Ⓗ
Comfortable, rejuvenated free house on the edge of town. Many awards decorate the walls. The house beer, Healy's Sanctuary, is ABC Best Bitter. The beer range may vary.
☸ ◖ ♣ P

## Enfield Clay Hill

### Fallow Buck
☎ (0181) 363 9467
12–2.30 (3 Thu–Sat), 6 (5.30 Fri)–11; 12–3, 7–10.30 Sun
**Ind Coope Burton Ale; Marston's Pedigree; Tetley Bitter; Young's Bitter; guest beer** Ⓗ
Located in rural Enfield, this pub partly dates from the 16th century. The largest bar contains several distinct drinking areas. Children welcome in the restaurant area. Note the hitching rail for horses in the car park. Live jazz Thu.
☸ ◖ ▶ ⊟ P

## Enfield Town

### Stag
Little Park Gardens
☎ (0181) 363 1836
11–3, 5.30–11; 12–4, 7–10.30 Sun
**Draught Bass; Fuller's London Pride; Greene King IPA; Tetley Bitter** Ⓗ
Well-refurbished, town-centre pub, overlooking the bus terminus. TV for major sports events. No food Sun eve.
☸ ◖ ▶ ♿ ⇌ (Enfield Chase) ♣

## NW1: Camden Town

### Spread Eagle
141 Albert Street (Parkway jct)
☎ (0171) 267 1410
11–11; 12–10.30 Sun
**Young's Bitter, Special, Ram Rod, Winter Warmer** Ⓗ
Friendly pub, now knocked through into one bar but still separated into different areas. Built in 1858, it was expanded into adjoining buildings in the 1930s and 1963.
☸ ◖ ▶ ⇌ (Camden Rd) ⊖

## NW1: Euston

### Head of Steam
Euston Station Colonnade,
1 Eversholt Street
☎ (0171) 388 2221
11–11; 12–3, 6–10.30 Sun
**B&T Shefford Mild; Draught Bass; Banks's Mild, Hop Back Summer Lightning; Shepherd Neame Master Brew Bitter; guest beers** Ⓗ
Railway-themed pub offering a good range of ales, including guests from micros. Some beers are expensive.
◖ ⇌ ⊖ ⇌

## NW1: Marylebone

### Perseverance
11 Shroton Street
☎ (0171) 723 7469
11–3, 4.30–11; 12–3.30, 7–10.30 Sun
**Draught Bass; Fuller's London Pride; guest beer** Ⓗ
Former 19th-century coaching inn, with a horseshoe bar and a friendly atmosphere. The guest beer is sometimes a mild. Food available at all times.
☸ ◖ ▶ ⇌ ⊖

## NW2: Cricklewood

### Beaten Docket
50–56 Cricklewood Broadway
☎ (0181) 450 2972
11–11; 12–10.30 Sun
**Courage Directors; Greene King Abbot; Theakston XB; Younger Scotch; guest beer** Ⓗ
Large Wetherspoons pub in an area not known for good beer. It draws a mixed clientele and can get very busy at weekends.
◖ ▶ ♿ ⇌ ✄

## NW3: Hampstead

### Duke of Hamilton
23–25 New End
☎ (0171) 794 0258
11–11; 12–10.30 Sun

**Fuller's London Pride, ESB; guest beers** H
Friendly, comfortable local, hidden away in a sidestreet.
❀ ⊖ ♣

## Flask

14 Flask Walk
☎ (0171) 435 4580
11–11; 12–10.30 Sun
**Young's Bitter, Special, Ram Rod, Winter Warmer** H
Famous watering hole in a picturesque location, attracting a good mix of customers. Keen rugby following – it can get crowded on match days.
🚌 Q ⅏ ❀ ◑ ▶ ⊖ ♣

## Holly Bush ☆

22 Holly Mount
☎ (0171) 435 2892
11–3, 5.30–11; 12–4, 6–11 Sat; 12–3, 7–10.30 Sun
**Benskins BB; Ind Coope Burton Ale; Tetley Bitter; guest beer** H
Pleasant, secluded local, first established as a pub in 1896 (the back bar was a stable). The interior retains its gas lights and Benskins memorabilia. No food Mon.
🚌 Q ◑ ⊖ ♣

## NW4: Hendon

### Chequers

20 Church End
☎ (0181) 203 5658
11.30–11; 12–10.30 Sun
**Courage Best Bitter, Directors; Theakston Best Bitter** H
An island bar serves two distinct drinking areas in this popular local near Church Farm House Museum. No food Sun.
❀ ◑ ▶ ♣ P

## NW5: Kentish Town

### Pineapple

51 Leverton Street
☎ (0171) 209 4961
12 (11 Sat)–11; 12–10.30 Sun
**Boddingtons Bitter; Greene King IPA; Marston's Pedigree** H
Cosy, Victorian, backstreet pub. Local artists' paintings are for sale. Banjo players Mon eve. ≢ ⊖ ♣

## NW6: Kilburn

### Queen's Arms

1 Kilburn High Road
☎ (0171) 624 5735
11–11; 12–10.30 Sun
**Young's Bitter, Special, Ram Rod, Winter Warmer** H
This pub's three separate lounge bars were linked during a recent refurbishment, creating a pleasant atmosphere. Many old

photographs are on display. A real gem in a real ale wilderness. Food served 12–9 (2.30 Sun).
🚌 Q ❀ ◑ ▶ ⅏ & ≢ (High Rd) ⊖ (Park) ♣

## NW8: St John's Wood

### Clifton

96 Clifton Hill
☎ (0171) 624 5233
11–11; 12–10.30 Sun
**Adnams Bitter; Ind Coope Burton Ale; Marston's Pedigree, Tetley Bitter** H
Victorian villa, split into different areas, featuring many original fittings and framed prints, plus an unusual Temperance Society mirror. Expensive, even for this area. No food Sun eve.
❀ ◑ ▶ ≢ (Kilburn High Rd) ⊖ (Kilburn Pk) ♣

## Edgware

### Change of Hart

21 High Street
☎ (0181) 952 0039
11–11; 12–10.30 Sun
**Adnams Bitter; Marston's Pedigree; Tetley Bitter; guest beers** H
Formerly the White Hart, this pub has three distinct areas served by an island bar. Very busy lunchtimes with local employees and residents. Garden adjacent to the Dean's Brook. Eve meals until 7.
Q ❀ ◑ ▶ & ⊖ ♣ P

## Harefield

### Plough

Hill End Road
☎ (01895) 822129
11–3, 5.30–11; 12–3, 7–10.30 Sun
**Adnams Bitter; Brakspear Bitter; Fuller's London Pride; Rebellion IPA, Smuggler; Ruddles Best Bitter; Taylor Landlord; guest beers** H
Excellent, single-bar free house near the famous Harefield Hospital. Busier in summer, when it is popular with walkers. Good food (not served Sun).
❀ ◑ P

### White Horse

Church Hill
☎ (01895) 822144
11–3, 6–11; 12–4, 7–10.30 Sun
**Greenalls Bitter, Shipstone's Bitter, Original; guest beers** H
Excellent, lively, traditional local on the south side of the village: a Grade II listed, 17th-century building. An exciting menu includes children's choices.
🚌 ❀ ◑ ▶ ⅏ ♣ ⌂ P ⅍

## Harrow-on-the-Hill

### Castle

30 West Street
☎ (0181) 422 3155
11–11; 12–10.30 Sun
**Fuller's London Pride, ESB** H
Relaxing, homely pub, one of the few left with a real 'woody' public bar, which has a separate games/darts room at the rear. Q ❀ ◑ ⅏ ♣

## Harrow Weald

### Seven Balls

749 Kenton Lane
☎ (0181) 954 0261
11–11; 12–4, 7–10.30 Sun
**Benskins BB; Tetley Bitter; guest beer** H
A good mix of locals and passing trade frequents this welcoming old pub. The guest beer is usually from the Tapster's Choice range. Occasional beer festivals.
❀ ◑ ▶ ⅏ ♣ P ⅍

## Hatch End

### Moon & Sixpence

250 Uxbridge Road
☎ (0181) 420 1074
11–11; 12–10.30 Sun
**Courage Directors; Theakston Best Bitter, XB; Younger Scotch; guest beers** H
Popular, often crowded, pub that attracts a good mix. A welcome change in an area dominated by Allied-Domecq pubs. Pleasant garden. Up to two guest beers; occasional beer festivals.
Q ❀ ◑ ▶ ≢ ⌂ ⅍

## Kenton

### New Moon

25–26 Kenton Park Parade, Kenton Road
☎ (0181) 909 1103
11–11; 12–10.30 Sun
**Courage Directors; Theakston Best Bitter, XB; Younger Scotch; guest beers** H
L-shaped pub, converted from two shops and well-appreciated by its regulars, in a very under-pubbed part of London. Q ◑ ▶ ≢ ⊖ ⅍

## Stanmore

### Malthouse

7 Stanmore Hill
☎ (0181) 420 7265
11–11; 12–10.30 Sun
**Beer range varies** H
Community pub, a boon to the real ale scene in an area dominated by big brewers' pubs. Over 350 ales were served in its first year, mostly from independents. Always

something happening.
Occasional cider in summer.
❀ ◁ ⊖ ♣

# Wealdstone

## Royal Oak

60 Peel Road
☎ (0181) 427 3122
12–11; 12–10.30 Sun
**Adnams Bitter; Ind Coope
Burton Ale; Tetley Bitter;
guest beers** Ⓗ
Imposing 1930s pub in a
backstreet off the busy high
street. The large lounge retains
separate drinking areas,
including a pleasant
conservatory. Small car park.
❀ ◁ ⬗ ⇌ (Harrow &
Wealdstone) ⊖ ♣ P

## Sarsen Stone

32 High Street
☎ (0181) 863 8533
11–11; 12–10.30 Sun
**Courage Directors; Theakston
Best Bitter, XB; Younger
Scotch; guest beers** Ⓗ
One of Wetherspoon's smaller
establishments, frequented by
local workers lunchtimes and
lively regulars other times.
Occasional beer festivals.
Q ◁ ▶ ⇌ (Harrow &
Wealdstone) ⊖

# South-East London

# SE1: Lambeth

## Windmill

44 Lambeth High Street
11–11; closed Sat & Sun
**Courage Best Bitter, Directors;
Wadworth 6X** Ⓗ
Very friendly, newly decorated
pub, but retaining the original
Courage style. Upstairs dining
area. ◁ ▶ ⇌ (Vauxhall)
⊖ (Lambeth N)

# SE1: Southwark

## Founders Arms

52 Hopton Street
☎ (0171) 928 1899
11–11; 12–10.30 Sun
**Young's Bitter, Special,
seasonal beers** Ⓗ
Modern pub on the south
bank of the Thames, with
excellent views of St Paul's
and the City. Popular with
tourists, and, unusually for
the area, open (with food
available) all weekend
(no meals Sun eve).
Q ❀ ◁ ▶ ⇌ (Blackfriars) ⊖

## George Inn ☆

77 Borough High Street
☎ (0171) 407 2056
11–11; 12–10.30 Sun
**Bishops Cathedral;
Boddingtons Bitter; Brakspear**

Bitter; Castle Eden Ale;
Flowers Original; guest
beer Ⓗ
Large, galleried, coaching inn,
built in 1677. Owned by the
National Trust and often
busy with tourists and
commuters. The old
bedrooms now serve as a
restaurant (booking
advisable). Monthly beer
festivals. ♨ ❀ ◁ ▶
⇌ (London Bridge) ⊖ ♣

## Ship

68 Borough Road
☎ (0171) 403 7059
11–11; 12–3, 8–10.30 Sun
**Fuller's Chiswick, London
Pride, ESB, seasonal beers** Ⓗ
Long, narrow pub where the
back of the bar is decorated
with model ships. No food Sun
eve. ❀ ◁ ▶
⇌ (London Bridge) ⊖
(Borough)

## Trinity Arms

29 Swan Street
☎ (0171) 207 5662
11–11; 12–10.30 Sun
**Beer range varies** Ⓗ
Friendly, two-bar pub, serving
some beers from micros. Jazz
Thu; piano Wed.
❀ ⊖ (Borough) ↻

## Wheatsheaf

6 Stoney Street
☎ (0171) 407 1514
11–11; 12–3, 7–10.30 Sun
**Courage Best Bitter; guest
beers** Ⓗ
Early Victorian pub
overlooking Borough Market.
Prints of old Southwark adorn
the walls of the lounge. A mild
is always available. Lunches
Mon–Fri.
◁ ⇌ (London Bridge) ⊖ ↻

# SE3: Blackheath

## Bitter Experience

129 Lee Road
11 (10 Sat)–9.30 (10 Fri & Sat)
**Beer range varies** Ⓖ
Outstanding off-licence
offering a wide range of ales
and foreign and British bottled
beers. Friendly staff.
⇌ (Lee) ↻

# SE5: Camberwell

## Fox on the Hill

149 Denmark Hill
☎ (0171) 738 4756
11–11; 12–10.30 Sun
**Courage Directors; Theakston
Best Bitter, XB; Younger
Scotch; guest beers** Ⓗ
Large Wetherspoons
roadhouse at the top of
Denmark Hill, offering the
usual standard of service and
range of beers. Q ❀ ◁ ▶ ♿
⇌ (Denmark Hill) ↻ P ✗

# SE7: Charlton

## Bugle Horn

6 The Village
☎ (0181) 856 9656
11–11; 12–4, 7–10.30 Sun
**Draught Bass; Hancock's HB;
Worthington Bitter** Ⓗ
Comfortable, busy pub with a
restaurant (children welcome).
The bar is decorated with
unusual rural items.
◁ ▶ ⇌ P

# SE8: Deptford

## Crystal Palace Tavern

105 Tanners Hill
3–midnight (2am Fri); 12–2am Sat;
1–10.30 Sun
**Beer range varies** Ⓗ
Live music pub offering an
excellent beer range with up to
nine ales, including rare beers
from micros, seasonal ales and
ales brewed for the pub. Sun
lunch served 2–7. Occasional
cider. ❀ ⇌ ↻ ⛁

## Dog & Bell

116 Prince Street
☎ (0181) 692 5664
11–11; 12–5, 7–10.30 Sun
**Fuller's London Pride, ESB;
guest beers** Ⓗ
Despite its unprepossessing,
backstreet location, this former
CAMRA SE London *Pub of the
Year* is worth seeking out.
Excellent choice of ales and
malt whiskies. An old fireplace
has recently been restored. No
food Sun eve. ♨ ◁ ▶ ⛁

## Old Manor House

58 Bush Road
☎ (0171) 394 1796
11–11; 12–10.30 Sun
**Young's Bitter, Special; guest
beers** Ⓗ
Pleasant local near Surrey
Quays Shopping Centre. Two
guest beers.
⊖ (Surrey Quays) ♣

# SE9: Eltham

## Banker's Draft

80 Eltham High Street
☎ (0181) 294 2578
11–11; 12–10.30 Sun
**Courage Directors; Theakston
Best Bitter, XB; Younger
Scotch; guest beer** Ⓗ
Typical, friendly
Wetherspoons pub, but
smaller! Decor commemorates
celebrities born locally.
Q ◁ ▶ ♿ ⇌ ♣ ↻

## Old Post Office

4 Passey Place (off High St)
☎ (0181) 850 2942
11–11; 12–10.30 Sun
**Beer range varies** Ⓗ
Friendly, spacious pub with
old post office memorabilia –
note the old motorbike near the

bar. Seaside postcard-style cartoons show the way to the toilets. The house bitter (George's) is Hancock's HB. Freshly prepared food.
◁ ▶ & ⇌ ⊭

## SE10: Greenwich

### Ashburnham Arms

25 Ashburnham Grove
☎ (0181) 692 2007
12–3, 6–11; 12–3, 7–10.30 Sun
**Shepherd Neame Master Brew Bitter, Best Bitter, Spitfire, Bishops Finger** *or* **Porter** Ⓗ
Former London CAMRA *Pub of the Year*, serving excellent food, including vegetarian (no meals Mon/Tue eves). Extended at the back but retaining its character.
❀ ◁ ▶ ♣

## SE11: Kennington

### Greyhound

336 Kennington Park Road
☎ (0171) 735 2590
11–11; 12–10.30 Sun
**Courage Best Bitter, Directors; Wadworth 6X** Ⓗ
Long, narrow pub close to the Oval cricket ground. It can get crowded eves. Good lunches Mon–Sat. ◁ ⊖ (Oval)

### Mansion House

46 Kennington Park Road
☎ (0171) 735 2291
11–11; 12–10.30 Sun
**Flowers Original; Greene King Abbot; Marston's Pedigree; Morland Old Speckled Hen** Ⓗ
Spacious pub not far from Elephant and Castle. Good value lunches (Mon–Fri). Pavement drinking area.
❀ ◁ ⊖ ♣

## SE13: Lewisham

### Hogshead

354 Lewisham High Street
☎ (0181) 690 2054
11–11; 12–10.30 Sun
**Boddingtons Bitter; Flowers Original; Whitbread Fuggles IPA** Ⓗ**; guest beers** Ⓖ
Friendly pub in the typical Hogshead style. Gale's fruit wines available. No food Sun.
❀ ◁ ⇌ (Ladywell) ↻

## SE17: Walworth

### Beehive

60–62 Carter Street
☎ (0171) 703 4992
11–11; 12–10.30 Sun
**Courage Best Bitter, Directors; Fuller's London Pride; Wadworth 6X** Ⓗ
Well-hidden pub in a beer desert. Wide range of food available until 10pm, plus a

good choice of whiskies and wines. ❀ ◁ ▶ ♣

## SE18: Shooters Hill

### Bull

151 Shooters Hill
☎ (0181) 856 0691
11–3, 5.30–11; 12–3, 7–10.30 Sun
**Courage Best Bitter, Directors** Ⓗ
Near the top of Shooters Hill, this is one of the few unspoilt Courage pubs in an area dominated by pubs acquired by the company from the former Beasley Brewery. No food weekends. Q ❀ ◁ ⊈

## SE18: Woolwich

### Prince Albert (Rose's)

49 Hare Street
☎ (0181) 854 1538
11–11; 12–3 Sun, closed Sun eve
**Beer range varies** Ⓗ
Pub situated in the middle of Woolwich, serving an excellent range of ales (three from a changing list of up to 14).
◁ ▶ ⇌ (Arsenal/Dockyard) ♣

## SE19: Crystal Palace

### Railway Bell

14 Cawpore Street
11–11; 12–3, 7–10.30 Sun
**Young's Bitter, Special, Winter Warmer** Ⓗ
Cosy pub, decorated with railway memorabilia. No food Sun.
Q ❀ ◁ ⇌ (Gipsy Hill) ♣

## SE20: Penge

### Moon & Stars

164–166 High Street
☎ (0181) 776 5680
11–11; 12–10.30 Sun
**Courage Directors; Hop Back Summer Lightning; Theakston Best Bitter; Younger Scotch; guest beers** Ⓗ
Typical, large, Wetherspoons pub, on the site of a former cinema. At least three guest beers. Q ❀ ◁ ▶ & ⇌ (Kent House/Penge E) ↻ P ⊭

## SE23: Forest Hill

### Bird in Hand

35 Dartmouth Road
☎ (0181) 699 7417
11–11; 12–10.30 Sun
**Courage Directors; Hop Back Summer Lightning; Theakston Best Bitter, XB; Younger Scotch; guest beers** Ⓗ
Victorian pub with a local following, especially amongst pensioners at lunchtime. A smaller Wetherspoons house offering the usual standards.
Q ❀ ◁ ▶ ⇌ ↻ P ⊭

## SE24: Herne Hill

### Lord Stanley

31 Hinton Road
☎ (0171) 738 4280
12–11; 12–3, 7.30–10.30 Sun
**Fuller's London Pride; Ruddles Best Bitter; guest beers** Ⓗ
Friendly free house in a real ale desert. Decor includes car number plates from nearly every American state. Good value meals at all times; summer barbecues in the enlarged garden. Q ❀ ◁ ▶ ⇌ (Loughborough Jct)

## SE25: South Norwood

### Alliance

91 High Street (A213)
☎ (0181) 653 3604
11–11; 12–10.30 Sun
**Courage Best Bitter, Directors; Young's Special; guest beer** Ⓗ
Corner pub, with an unspoilt exterior, near the station and shops: one L-shaped bar. One guest beer from a small independent brewery; Imperial Russian stout stocked. Good food lunchtimes (not served Sun). ◁ ⇌ (Norwood Jct) ♣

### Clifton Arms

21 Clifton Road
☎ (0181) 771 2443
11–11; 12–10.30 Sun
**Fuller's London Pride; Ind Coope Burton Ale; Tetley Bitter; guest beers** Ⓗ
Friendly, one-bar, backstreet local near Selhurst Park (it can be busy before some football matches and closed afterwards). Two guest beers, generally from regional brewers. No food Sat or Sun.
❀ ◁ ⇌ (Selhurst) ♣

### Portmanor

1 Portland Road (A215)
☎ (0181) 655 1308
11–11; 12–10.30 Sun
**Fuller's London Pride; Greene King Abbot; Young's Special; guest beers** Ⓗ
Lively, comfortable, one-bar pub with an extra serving area on the balcony in summer. Popular with all ages, it can be rather crowded eves. Always six beers at competitive prices, with guests generally from small breweries. No food Sun.
❀ ◁ ⇌ (Norwood Jct)

## SE26: Upper Sydenham

### Dulwich Wood House

39 Sydenham Hill
☎ (0181) 693 5666
11–11; 12–10.30 Sun

Young's Bitter, Special,
seasonal beers Ⓗ
Large, country-style pub with
an extensive garden, including
a petanque piste. Local
CAMRA *Pub of the Year*
1995/96. Barbecues daily in
summer. 🏠 ❀ Ⓓ ♠
≉ (Sydenham Hill) ♣ P

## Addiscombe

### Builder's Arms
65 Leslie Park Road (between
Cherry Orchard Rd – A222 –
and Lower Addiscombe Rd)
☎ (0181) 654 1803
12–3, 5 (6.30 Sat)–11; 12–11 Fri; 12–
10.30 Sun
Fuller's Chiswick, London
Pride, ESB, seasonal beers Ⓗ
Popular, backstreet pub with a
country pub atmosphere in its
two cosy bars. Good food
Mon–Sat. The excellent garden
is popular with families.
Q ❀ Ⓓ ♪ ≉ (Addiscombe/E
Croydon) ♣

### Claret Free House
5A Bingham Corner, Lower
Addiscombe Road (A222)
☎ (0181) 656 7452
11.30–11; 12–10.30 Sun
Hardy Royal Oak; Palmers
IPA; Shepherd Neame
Spitfire; guest beers Ⓗ
Cosy bar in a shopping parade
which attracts ale lovers from a
wide area (two regularly
changing guest beers from all
over the country). Lunches
Mon–Fri. Ⓓ ≉

## Beckenham

### Jolly Woodman
9 Chancery Lane
☎ (0181) 650 3664
11–11; 12–10.30 Sun
Draught Bass; Fuller's London
Pride; M&B Brew XI; guest
beer Ⓗ
Friendly country pub
transported to the London
suburbs, hosting numerous
sports clubs, including a
motorcycling club. No food
Sun. Q ❀ Ⓓ ♪ (Jct) ♣

## Bexley

### Black Horse
63 Albert Road
☎ (01322) 523371
11–3, 5–11; 11–11 Fri; 12–3, 7–10.30
Sun
Courage Best Bitter; Younger
Scotch; guest beers Ⓗ
Fine example of a cosy,
backstreet pub. Winner of
various *'Bexley in Bloom'*
awards. ❀ Ⓓ ≉ ♣

### Cork & Cask
3 Bourne Parade
☎ (01322) 528884
11–2, 4–10; 10–10 Sat; 12–3, 7–10 Sun
Beer range varies Ⓗ

Off-licence with usually five
ales available, plus at least one
cider and an excellent range of
English and foreign bottled
beers. Containers available.
♿ ≉ ♻

## Bexleyheath

### Robin Hood & Little John
78 Lion Road
☎ (0181) 303 1128
11–11; 12–10.30 Sun
Courage Best Bitter, Directors;
Ruddles County; John Smith's
Bitter; Wadworth 6X; guest
beer Ⓗ
Popular, two-bar backstreet
local in a Grade II listed
building. Home-made meals
and snacks lunchtimes (not
served Sun). The tables are
made from Singer sewing
machines. Over-21s only.
♻ ❀ Ⓓ ♬ ♣

### Royal Oak (Polly Clean Stairs)
Mount Road
☎ (0181) 303 4454
11–3, 6–11; 12–3, 7–10.30 Sun
Courage Best Bitter; Ruddles
County; Wadworth 6X; guest
beers Ⓗ
The former Upton village store,
now a village-style local in a
residential area: a gem. Cold
food only served lunchtimes
(not Sun). Q ❀ ♣ P

## Bromley

### Bitter End
139 Masons Hill
☎ (0181) 466 6083
12–3 (not Mon), 5–10 (9 Mon); 11–10
Sat; 12–2, 7–9 Sun
Beer range varies Ⓖ
Outstanding off-licence
situated in a beer desert,
offering a wide range of
imported and British bottled
beers. ≉ (South) ♻

## Chislehurst

### Bull's Head
Royal Parade
☎ (0181) 467 1727
11–11; 12–10.30 Sun
Young's Bitter, Special,
seasonal beers Ⓗ
Large, ivy-clad wayside house,
popular with all. The ballroom
is often booked for wedding
receptions. The family room
closes at 8.
🏠 ♻ ❀ 🏠 Ⓓ ♪ ≉ P

## Croydon

### Cricketers Arms
23 Southbridge Place (under
Old Town flyover)
☎ (0181) 688 1403
11–11; 12–4, 7–11 Sat; 12–3, 7–10.30
Sun

Fuller's London Pride;
Harveys BB; Worthington
Bitter; guest beers Ⓗ
Quiet, one-bar, backstreet pub
offering a country pub
atmosphere in four separate
bar areas, all very traditional in
character. Regular events and
quiz nights.
Q Ⓓ ♪ ♣

### Dog & Bull ☆
24–25 Surrey Street (off the
High Street) ☎ (0181) 688 3664
11–11; 12–4, 8–10.30 Sun
Young's Bitter, Special,
Winter Warmer Ⓗ
Lively market pub, a Grade II
listed building with an
excellent garden, popular in
summer. Greater London
CAMRA *Pub of the Year* 1994,
visited by Prince Charles in
1995 (pictures in the bar). Food
Mon–Fri.
Q ❀ Ⓓ ≉ (East/West) ♣

### Porter & Sorter
Station Road (between post
office and East Croydon
station) ☎ (0181) 688 4296
11–11; 11–3, 7–11 Sat; 12–4 Sun,
closed Sun eve
Courage Best Bitter, Directors;
Ruddles Best Bitter, County;
Young's Bitter; guest beer Ⓗ
A rare building of character in
an area of modern office
blocks, its comfortable interior
decorated with railway
memorabilia. Popular with
local office workers and
commuters. Guests are from
the larger independents. Meals
Mon–Fri.
❀ Ⓓ ≉ (East) P

### Princess Royal
22 Longley Road (off Summer
Rd, Broad Green)
☎ (0181) 684 4056
11–3, 5.30 (7.30 Sat)–11; 11–11 Fri;
12–3, 8–10.30 Sun
Greene King XX Mild, IPA,
Rayments Special, Abbot,
seasonal beers Ⓗ
Small, cosy pub with a friendly
welcome: a real local with a log
fire, known locally as the 'Glue
Pot' (see reverse of the pub
sign). No food Sun.
🏠 ❀ Ⓓ ♣

### Royal Standard
1 Sheldon Street (off the High
St) ☎ (0181) 688 9749
11–3, 5–11; 11–11 Fri & Sat; 12–3,
7–10.30 Sun
Fuller's Chiswick, London
Pride, ESB, seasonal beers Ⓗ
Friendly, traditional and
popular backstreet local;
extended and completely
refurbished without loss of
character. It still has fine etched
glass windows and a small
serving hatch into the new,
rear bar. The garden is across
the road. No food Sun.
Q ❀ Ⓓ ≉ (East) ♣

## Footscray

### Seven Stars
High Street
☎ (0181) 300 2057
11–11; 12–3, 7–10.30 Sun
**Bass Toby Cask, Draught
Bass; Greene King IPA** Ⓗ
16th-century pub, retaining
many original features. Live
music Fri eve. ❀ ◖

## Orpington

### Cricketers
93 Chislehurst Road
☎ (01689) 812648
11–11; 12–10.30 Sun
**Courage Best Bitter; guest
beers** Ⓗ
Cosy, backstreet pub on
Broomhill Common, with three
handpumps. Guest beers
change regularly. No food Sun.
Small car park.
☎ ❀ ◖ P

## Petts Wood

### Sovereign of the Seas
109–111 Queensway
☎ (01689) 891606
11–11; 12–10.30 Sun
**Courage Directors; Theakston
Best Bitter, XB; Younger
Scotch; guest beers** Ⓗ
Large, one-bar pub which
emerged from a shop
conversion two years ago; in a
beer desert. Local photos adorn
the walls. Quiet during the
day, it can be overpowering
weekend eves, but is still worth
visiting.
Q ◖ ▶ ᵫ ⇌ ◔ ⊁

## Sidcup

### Alma
Alma Road
11–2.30, 5.30 (7 Sat)–11; 12–3, 7–10.30
Sun
**Courage Best Bitter; Young's
Bitter, Special** Ⓗ
Deservedly popular, backstreet
local retaining some of its
Victorian-style interior.
Q ◖ ⇌

## South Croydon

### Stag & Hounds
26 Selsdon Road (B275, 200 yds
from A235 jct)
☎ (0181) 688 1908
11–11; 12–10.30 Sun
**Fuller's London Pride;
Harveys BB; guest beer** Ⓗ
Attractive, one-bar, street-
corner pub in typical brewer's
Tudor style, decorated with
prints, old photos and a brick-
built bar. Very popular,
especially at weekends with
the football/rugby fraternity,
but not rowdy. No food Sun.
❀ ◖ ⇌ ♣ P

## Thornton Heath

### Railway Telegraph
19 Brigstock Road (B266)
☎ (0181) 684 5809
11–11; 12–4, 7–10.30 Sun
**Young's Bitter, Special,
Winter Warmer** Ⓗ
Attractive, street-corner pub
near the station, with two
comfortable bars, both with
real fires. Dartboard and
cheaper prices in the public
bar. No food Sun.
ᵫ ❀ ◖ ⇌ ♣

## Upper Belvedere

### Royal Standard
39 Nuxley Road
☎ (01322) 432774
11–11; 12–10.30 Sun
**Adnams Bitter; Draught Bass;
Caledonian Deuchars IPA;
Fuller's London Pride** Ⓗ;
**Highgate Old** Ⓖ; **guest
beers** Ⓗ
Centrally-located pub offering
regularly changing guest beers.
Two beer festivals a year – one
specialising in Scottish beers.
☎ ❀ ◖ ᵫ P

### Victoria
Victoria Street
☎ (01322) 433773
11–11; 12–10.30 Sun
**Courage Best Bitter;
Hancock's HB; Shepherd
Neame Master Brew Bitter,
Spitfire** Ⓗ
Back after a few years' absence,
now a single-bar free house
under a new landlord.
❀ ◖ ▶ ♣

---

### South-West London

## SW1: Belgravia

### Fox & Hounds
29 Passmore Street
11–3, 5.30–11; 12–3, 7–10.30 Sun
**Adnams Bitter; Draught Bass;
Greene King IPA; Harveys
BB** Ⓗ
Tiny, unchanging local with
the last known beer and wine
only licence in London.
◖ ⊖ (Sloane Sq)

### Nag's Head ☆
53 Kinnerton Street
☎ (0171) 235 1135
11–11; 12–10.30 Sun
**Adnams Bitter; Benskins BB;
Tetley Bitter** Ⓗ
Small, cosy, multi-level pub,
sometimes called the 'Upstairs
Downstairs'. Totally unspoilt,
it has two ancient lever-type
fruit machines for which old
pennies can be had at the bar.
◖ ▶ ⊖ (Hyde Pk Crnr)

### Star Tavern
6 Belgrave Mews West
☎ (0171) 234 2806
11.30–3, 5 (6.30 Sat)–11; 11.30–11 Fri;
12–3, 7–10.30 Sun
**Fuller's Chiswick, London
Pride, ESB, seasonal beers** Ⓗ
Unchanging, unspoilt, mews
pub. Meals Mon–Fri.
ᴁ ◖ ▶ ⊖ (Hyde Pk Crnr)

### Turk's Head
10 Motcomb Street
☎ (0171) 235 7850
11–11; 12–3, 7–10.30 Sun
**Draught Bass; Wadworth 6X;
guest beer** Ⓗ
Gas-lit, corner pub with a
raised area at the rear.
◖ ⊖ (Hyde Pk Crnr)

## SW1: Trafalgar Square

### Lord Moon of the Mall
16–18 Whitehall
☎ (0171) 839 7701
11–11; 12–10.30 Sun
**Courage Directors; Theakston
Best Bitter, XB; Younger
Scotch; guest beers** Ⓗ
Large Wetherspoons pub in
former bank premises, with a
magnificent vaulted ceiling;
next door to the Whitehall
Theatre. Wheelchair WC. Q ◖ ▶
ᵫ ⇌ (Charing Cross) ⊖

## SW1: Victoria

### Wetherspoons
Victoria Island, Victoria Station
☎ (0171) 931 0445
11–11; 12–10.30 Sun
**Courage Directors; Theakston
Best Bitter, XB; Younger
Scotch; guest beers** Ⓗ
Relief for the thirsty traveller;
the destinations and
departures indicator is visible
from the bar. It may close Sat
3–7 when local football
matches are on.
◖ ▶ ⇌ ⊖

## SW1: Westminster

### Buckingham Arms
62 Petty France
☎ (0171) 222 3386
11–11; 11–3, 5.30–11; 12–3, 7–10.30
Sun
**Young's Bitter, Special, Ram
Rod, Winter Warmer** Ⓗ
Popular pub near the Passport
Office with a corridor drinking
area behind the bar. Food
served until 9.30.
◖ ▶ ⊖ (St James's Pk)

### Royal Oak
2 Regency Street
☎ (0171) 834 7046
11–11; 12–10.30 Sun
**Young's Bitter, Special,
Winter Warmer** Ⓗ
Quiet corner local.
Q ⊖ (St James's Pk)

## SW2: Streatham

### Crown & Sceptre

2 Streatham Hill
☎ (0181) 671 0843
11–11; 12–10.30 Sun
**Courage Directors; Greene King Abbot; Theakston Best Bitter, XB; Younger Scotch; guest beers** Ⓗ
Early Wetherspoons conversion which has continued to thrive. Standing on a major crossroads, it attracts a varied clientele who appreciate the guest beers. Q ❀ ◖ ▶ ⌂ P ⌇

## SW3: Chelsea

### Blenheim

27 Cale Street
☎ (0171) 349 0056
11–11; 12–10.30 Sun
**Badger Dorset Best, Tanglefoot; Wadworth 6X** Ⓗ
Spacious, former Charrington pub, now owned by Badger. No food Sun. Q ◖ ♣

### Builders

13 Britten Street
☎ (0171) 352 6660
11–11; 12–10.30 Sun
**Boddingtons Bitter; Brakspear Bitter; Marston's Pedigree; guest beer** Ⓗ
Two-bar, backstreet pub, once the tap of Matthews & Canning's Anchor Brewery (closed 1907), the gate of which still survives. The public bar has an interesting frieze depicting the area. ◖ ⌸

### Coopers Arms

87 Flood Street
11–11; 12–10.30 Sun
**Young's Bitter, Special, Ram Rod** Ⓗ
Busy, café bar-style pub with an extensive food menu. The bar is dominated by a large bull's head. Q ◖

### Crown

153 Dovehouse Street
☎ (0171) 352 9505
11–11; 12–10.30 Sun
**Beer range varies** Ⓗ
Small, busy, friendly local with a constantly varying range of beers. It runs regular fundraising events for local hospitals – quiz nights, draws, etc.
◖ ⊖ (S Kensington) ⊟

### Surprise

6 Christchurch Terrace
☎ (0171) 352 4699
11–11; 12–3, 7–10.30 Sun
**Draught Bass; Hancock's HB; Taylor Landlord** Ⓗ
Popular local with an interesting frieze around the top of the bar. Meals Mon–Fri.
◖

## SW5: Earl's Court

### Blackbird

209 Earl's Court Road
☎ (0171) 835 1855
11–11; 12–10.30 Sun
**Fuller's Chiswick, London Pride, ESB, seasonal beers** Ⓗ
Fuller's 'Ale & Pie' house – a former bank opposite Earl's Court station. Smart dress required. ◖ ▶ ⊖

## SW6: Fulham

### White Horse

1 Parsons Green
☎ (0171) 730 2115
11–11; 12–10.30 Sun
**Draught Bass; Harveys BB; Highgate Dark; guest beers** Ⓗ
Large, popular, upmarket pub with a front terrace (covered in winter) for outside drinking. Many beer festivals; large range of foreign beers, often sold with indigenous methods of dispense. Very good, varied food. ﹍ ❀ ◖
⊖ (Parsons Green) ♣

## SW7: South Kensington

### Anglesea Arms

15 Selwood Terrace
11–11; 11–4, 7–11 Sat; 12–4, 7–10.30 Sun
**Adnams Bitter; Brakspear Special; Boddingtons Bitter; Marston's Pedigree; guest beer** Ⓗ
Renowned free house, often extremely busy. Charles Dickens and DH Lawrence lived nearby. ▶ ⌸

## SW8: South Lambeth

### Royal Albert

43 St Stephen's Terrace (off Albert Sq, off South Lambeth Rd)
☎ (0171) 735 3789
11–11; 12–10.30 Sun
**Boddingtons Bitter; Flowers Original; Wadworth 6X; Whitbread Fuggles IPA, seasonal beers** Ⓗ
Friendly, traditional ale house that hosts regular beer festivals and charity events. Pool room upstairs. The garden is popular all year. Eve meals 5–7.
﹍ ❀ ◖ ▶ ⊖ (Stockwell) ♣

### Surprise

16 Southville
☎ (0171) 622 4623
11–11; 12–10.30 Sun
**Young's Bitter, Special, Winter Warmer, seasonal beers** Ⓗ
Homely, friendly local by Larkhall Park. A big fundraiser

for charities. Eve meals finish at 7.30.
﹍ Q ❀ ◖ ▶ ⊖ (Stockwell) P

## SW8: Stockwell

### Priory Arms

83 Landsdowne Way
☎ (0181) 622 1884
11–11; 12–3, 7–10.30 Sun
**Harveys BB; Young's Bitter, Special; guest beers** Ⓗ
Friendly, backstreet, genuine free house offering three changing guest beers daily; 1000 beers to date. CAMRA SW London *Pub of the Year* 1992 and 1994. Perry in summer.
❀ ◖ ⊖ ♣ ⌂ ⊟

## SW10: West Brompton

### Fox & Pheasant

1 Billing Road
☎ (0171) 352 2943
12–3, 5.30–11; 12–3, 6–10.30 Sun
**Greene King IPA, Abbot, seasonal beers** Ⓗ
Small, two-bar local, just off Fulham Rd near Chelsea FC. Billing Rd is private, so parking is very difficult. Busy on match days. No food Sun eve. Q ❀ ◖ ♣

## SW11: Battersea

### Duke of Cambridge

228 Battersea Bridge Road
☎ (0171) 223 5662
11–11; 12–10.30 Sun
**Young's Bitter, Special, Winter Warmer, seasonal beers** Ⓗ
Refurbished Victorian local near Battersea Park with a keen racing following. Meals can be requested at any time.
❀ ◖ ▶ ⌸ ♣

### Eagle Ale House

104 Chatham Road
☎ (0171) 228 2328
11–11; 12–10.30 Sun
**Boddingtons Bitter; Flowers Original; Marston's Pedigree** Ⓗ**; Wadworth 6X** Ⓖ**; Whitbread Pompey Royal** Ⓗ
Friendly, backstreet pub, frequented by market traders and locals. Large screen TV for sporting events. No food Sun. ❀ ◖ ♣

## SW11: Clapham

### Beehive

197 St John's Hill
☎ (0171) 207 1273
11–11; 12–3, 6–10.30 Sun
**Fuller's Chiswick, London Pride, ESB, seasonal beers** Ⓗ
Small, friendly, one-bar pub used by locals and visitors. Note the ironwork above the bar. Two TVs. The only Fuller's

tied house in the area. No
meals Sun eve.
❀ ◑ ▶ ⇌ (Jct)

## Mistress P's

North Street, Clapham Old
Town ☎ (0171) 622 5347
11–11; 12–10.30 Sun
**Boddingtons Bitter; Flowers
Original; Fuller's London
Pride** H
Small, cosy pub, off the main
road, with a real fire in the bar.
A friendly clientele makes it a
pleasure to visit. Home-cooked
food. ⚏ ◑ ▶ ⊖ (Common) ♣

# SW12: Balham

## Nightingale

97 Nightingale Lane
☎ (0181) 673 1637
11–3, 5.30–11; 11–11 Wed–Sat; 12–
10.30 Sun
**Young's Bitter, Special,
Winter Warmer** H
Comfortable, but at times
crowded, Victorian pub in a
residential area. The pub has
changed with the area.
Convivial clientele; extensive
menu (not served Sun eve).
Q ⬥ ❀ ◑ ▶ ♣ ✂

# SW13: Barnes

## Coach & Horses

27 Barnes High Street
☎ (0181) 876 2695
11–11; 12–10.30 Sun
**Young's Bitter, Special,
Winter Warmer** H
Small, popular, one-bar pub
near the Thames. Lovely log
fire; garden with a children's
play area. No food Sun.
⚏ Q ⬥ ❀ ◑ ⇌ (Barnes
Bridge)

## Red Lion

2 Castelnau ☎ (0181) 748 2984
11–11; 12–10.30 Sun
**Fuller's Chiswick, London
Pride, ESB, seasonal beers** H
Large, refurbished pub with a
strong emphasis on food,
particularly in the back bar.
Part of Fuller's 'Ale & Pie
House' chain.
⚏ ❀ ◑ ▶ ⇌ ♣ P

# SW14: Mortlake

## Hare & Hounds

216 Upper Richmond Road,
East Sheen ☎ (0181) 876 4304
11–11; 12–10.30 Sun
**Young's Bitter, Special,
Winter Warmer** H
Comfortable, roomy pub: the
oak-panelled lounge has a
pleasant atmosphere, part of
the bar is set aside for snooker,
and a large, walled garden
provides a children's play area
and hosts barbecues. Wide
choice of good value food. Live
music Sun eve (when no food
is served). ⚏ Q ❀ ◑ ▶ ⇌ ♣

# SW15: Putney

## Green Man

Wildcroft Road, Putney Heath
☎ (0181) 788 8096
11–11; 12–10.30 Sun
**Young's Bitter, Special,
seasonal beers** H
Fine, old, two-bar ale house on
the edge of Putney Heath. The
large outdoor drinking area
has playground facilities –
popular in summer. Try the
fiendishly difficult Ring the
Bull game in the public bar.
Eve meals in summer.
Q ❀ ◑ ▶ ⇌ ♣

## Spotted Horse

122 Putney High Street
☎ (0181) 788 0246
11–11; 12–4, 7–10.30 Sun
**Young's Bitter, Special, Ram
Road, seasonal beers** H
Large high street pub,
attracting a good mix of
customers; recently
refurbished to appeal more to a
younger crowd, but not spoilt.
No-smoking area lunchtime.
⚏ ◑ ▶ ⚅ ⇌ ⊖ ✂

# SW16: Streatham

## Pied Bull

498 Streatham High Road
☎ (0181) 764 4003
11–11; 12–10.30 Sun
**Young's Bitter, Special, Ram
Road, Winter Warmer** H
Large, friendly pub opposite
the common: four separate
drinking areas and a large back
room with notable pot plants.
Live music is a regular feature.
Handy for the supermarket;
very popular in summer. Eve
meals Tue–Sat. ⚏ Q ❀ ◑ ▶ ⊖
⇌ (Streatham/Streatham
Common) P

# SW17: Tooting

## Castle

38 Tooting High Street
☎ (0181) 672 7018
11–11; 12–10.30 Sun
**Young's Bitter, Special, Ram
Road, Winter Warmer** H
Large, welcoming pub near the
tube and handy for the shops.
Darts area at the rear; cricket
club in summer. ⚏ ❀ ◑ ▶ ⚅
⇌ ⊖ (Bdwy) ♣ P

## Prince of Wales

646 Garratt Lane
11–11; 12–4, 7–10.30 Sun
**Young's Bitter, Special,
Winter Warmer, seasonal
beers** H
Two-bar corner house, well
renovated and comfortable.
The public bar has lower
prices. Large games room
(many games) at the rear; the

family room is open until 9.
Generous bar food lunchtime.
Q ⬥ ◑ ▶ P

# SW18: Earlsfield

## Country House

2 Groton Road (near station)
☎ (0181) 874 2715
12–11; 12–10.30 Sun
**Courage Best Bitter, Directors;
Morland Old Speckled Hen;
John Smith's Bitter** H
Welcoming, two-bar pub in a
residential area, off the main
road. Good basic pub food.
Darts, crib and dominoes
played. Q ◑ ⇌ ♣

# SW18: Wandsworth

## Old Sergeant

104 Garrett Lane
☎ (0181) 874 4099
11–11; 11–3, 5–11 Tue & Wed; 12–10
Sun
**Young's Bitter, Special, Ram
Rod, Winter Warmer** H
Two-bar, roadside pub,
friendly and welcoming.
Copper ornaments adorn the
lounge. Handy for the shops.
Weekday lunches. ❀ ◑ ♣ P

## Queen Adelaide

35 Putney Bridge Road
☎ (0181) 874 1695
11–11; 12–10.30 Sun
**Young's Bitter, Special, Ram
Rod, Winter Warmer, seasonal
beers** H
Comfortable pub with a
relaxed atmosphere, five mins'
walk from Wandsworth town
centre. Large-screen TV in the
bar. Summer barbecues in the
garden. Wheelchair access is
via the garage. ⚏ ❀ ◑ ♣

# SW19: Merton

## Prince of Wales

98 Morden Road
☎ (0181) 542 0573
11–3, 5–11; 11–11 Fri & Sat; 12–10.30
Sun
**Young's Bitter, Special, Ram
Rod, Winter Warmer** H
Welcoming, two-bar pub with
an unspoilt, mid-Victorian
frontage. The spacious saloon
features prints of Princes of
Wales through the ages with
some ruthless captions. Darts
in the public bar. Family room
open in summer. No food Sun.
⚏ Q ⬥ ❀ ◑ ⚅ ⇌ (Morden
Rd) ⊖ (S Wimbledon) ♣ P

## Princess Royal

25 Abbey Road
☎ (0181) 542 3273
11–3, 5.30–11; 11–11 Fri (if busy) & Sat;
12–3.30, 7–10.30 Sun
**Courage Best Bitter, Directors;
Fuller's London Pride;
Morland Old Speckled Hen** H
Charming, 200-year-old corner
pub with comfortable public

and saloon bars. Abundant decorations include mugs hanging from ceilings. Excellent service. Q ✿ ◑ ⊕ ⊖ (S Wimbledon) ♣

## SW19: South Wimbledon

### Sultan

78 Norman Road
☎ (0181) 542 4532
12–11; 12–4, 7–10.30 Sun
**Hop Back Mild or Special or Thunderstorm, GFB, Entire Stout, Summer Lightning** Ⓗ
Well-proportioned pub with a lounge and a saloon, rebuilt in the late 1950s and reopened in 1994 as the third Hop Back tied house. Four- and 18-pint take-aways; excellent value. Local CAMRA *Pub of the Year* 1995.
Q ✿ ⅄ ♣

## SW19: Wimbledon

### Hand & Racket

25–27 Wimbledon Hill Road
☎ (0181) 947 9391
11–11; 12–10.30 Sun
**Boddingtons Bitter; Flowers IPA, Original; Fuller's London Pride; Marston's Pedigree; Whitbread Fuggles IPA** Ⓗ; **guest beers** Ⓖ
Whitbread Hogshead Ale House near the station; wood panels and bare brick walls feature. Up to four guest beers and a selection of Belgian beers are served but swan neck/sparklers are used. Convenient for the shops. Pictures on the walls carry a tennis theme.
◑ ▶ ⅄ ⇌ ⊖ ⌁

### Wibbas Down Inn

6–12 Gladstone Road (off Wimbledon Broadway)
☎ (0181) 540 6788
11–11; 12–10.30 Sun
**Courage Directors; Marston's Pedigree; Theakston Best Bitter; Younger Scotch; guest beers** Ⓗ
Huge, new, two-bar pub which nevertheless manages to provide distinct welcoming areas in typical Wetherspoon style, with notes on local history, books and varied seating. Handy for the theatre. Guest beers vary between the bars and are constantly changing.
Q ◑ ▶ ⅄ ⇌ ⊖ ⌂ ⌁

## SW19: Wimbledon Common

### Hand in Hand

7 Crooked Billet
☎ (0181) 946 5720
11–11; 12–10.30 Sun
**Young's Bitter, Special, seasonal beers** Ⓗ
Early 19th-century bakehouse

on the site of a house owned by Watney's grandfather; a family-owned beer house for 100 years before Young's bought it in 1974. It has since been renovated and enlarged internally, but retains warmth and intimacy. ♨ Q ✿ ◑ ♣

## SW20: Raynes Park

### Cavern

100 Coombe Lane
☎ (0181) 944 8211
11–11; 12–10.30 Sun
**Boddingtons Bitter; Fuller's London Pride; Marston's Pedigree; Young's Bitter** Ⓗ
Creatively designed, split-level, single bar opened in 1990, featuring rock 'n' roll memorabilia, a good jukebox, an original red phone box and an illuminated Budweiser guitar. Busy and lively; great atmosphere. Jugs available.
✿ ◑ ⇌

## Beddington

### Plough

The Broadway, Croydon Road (A232/B272 jct)
☎ (0181) 647 1122
11–3, 5.30–11; 11–11 Fri & Sat; 12–10.30 Sun
**Young's Bitter, Special, Ram Rod, Winter Warmer** Ⓗ
Imposing, Tudor-style pub with covered balconies and a single bar, opened in 1897 to replace an 18th-century building. The original coach house still stands in the old stable yard, now used for outside drinking. Good lunches Mon–Fri. ♨ ✿ ◑ ⅄ ⇌ (Waddon) ♣ P

## Carshalton

### Racehorse

17 West Street (B278, off A232)
☎ (0181) 647 6818
11–11; 12–3, 7–10.30 Sun
**Courage Best Bitter, Directors; King & Barnes Sussex; guest beers** Ⓗ
Smart, two-bar pub with a formal eating area in the lounge; excellent menu and good bar meals (no food Sun eve). Guest beers from independent breweries.
Q ✿ ◑ ▶ ⅄ ⇌ ♣ P

### Railway Tavern

47 North Street (B277, off A232)
☎ (0181) 669 6818
12–3, 5–11; 12–11 Sat; 12–3, 7–10.30 Sun
**Fuller's London Pride, ESB, seasonal beers** Ⓗ
Small, street-corner local decorated with mirrors and railwayana. Popular, especially with its many teams, from marbles to morris dancing.
⇌ ♣

### Windsor Castle

378 Carshalton Road (A232)
☎ (0181) 669 1191
11–11; 12–10.30 Sun
**Draught Bass; Fuller's London Pride; Hancock's HB; Worthington Bitter; guest beers** Ⓗ
Large, one-bar pub at the main crossroads. Good range of guest beers from micro- and family breweries. Good food in the restaurant or bar (not served Sun eve). A separate cottage-style meeting room has its own bar. Popular with all ages. ✿ ◑ ▶ ⇌ P

## Cheam

### Railway

32 Station Way (off A217/A213) ☎ (0181) 642 7416
11–11; 12–10.30 Sun
**Courage Best Bitter, Directors; Theakston Best Bitter or XB; guest beer** (occasional) Ⓗ
Detached, 19th-century pub. A real local with an emphasis on beer and conversation; no music. No food Sun lunch.
Q ◑ ▶ ⇌

## Chessington

### North Star

271 Hook Road, Hook
☎ (0181) 391 5248
12 (11 Sat)–11; 12–3.30, 7–10.30 Sun
**Draught Bass; Hancock's HB; Highgate Dark; guest beer** (occasional) Ⓗ
Popular and lively 150-year-old pub, close to the Ace of Spades roundabout: a rare mild outlet for the area. The menu offers a choice for vegetarians and children (no eve food Tue or Sun). Bar billiards table. The garden has children's play facilities.
Q ⅏ ✿ ◑ ▶ ♣ P

## Kingston upon Thames

### Bricklayers Arms

53 Hawks Road (off A2043)
☎ (0181) 546 0393
12–11; 12–7 Sun (maybe later in summer)
**Morland Original, Old Masters, Old Speckled Hen, seasonal beers** Ⓗ
Marvellous pub – traditional and homely, with an accent on food; deservedly popular with diners. The interesting menu changes several times a year. No food Sun eve. Q ✿ ◑ ▶ ♣

### Cocoanut

16 Mill Street
☎ (0181) 546 3978
11–3, 5.30–11; 11–11 Sat; 12–3, 7–10.30 Sun
**Fuller's London Pride, ESB** Ⓗ

Large, horseshoe-shaped bar with a pool table in the 'public' side; quieter in the 'saloon' side. The pub dog is a legend in these parts (try leaving before closing time). No food Sun.
🝲 ❀ ◖

### Park Tavern
19 New Road
10.30–11; 12–3, 7–10.30 Sun
**Boddingtons Bitter; Brakspear Special; Young's Bitter, Special; guest beer** Ⓗ
Comfortable, friendly, sidestreet local near Richmond Park gate. Parking is difficult. Annual pig roast (Nov).
⌂ ❀

### Ram
34 High Street
☎ (0181) 546 4518
11–11; 12–10.30 Sun
**Courage Best Bitter, Directors; Theakston Best Bitter, XB, Old Peculier; guest beers** Ⓗ
Refurbished T&J Bernard outlet, much improved and crowded eves with a mainly young clientele. The outdoor drinking area (children welcome) backs onto the Thames. Food always available. ❀ ◖◗ ⌓

### Two Brewers
19 Wood Street (A308)
☎ (0181) 549 3712
11–11; 12–3, 7–10.30 Sun
**Beer range varies** Ⓗ
Genuine free house on Kingston's inner ring road, next to the shopping centre; its reasonably-priced lunches are popular with shoppers. Occasional mini-beer festivals. Local CAMRA *Pub of the Year* 1995. ◖ ≠ ♣

## Mitcham

### Queen's Head
70 The Cricket Green
☎ (0181) 648 3382
11–11; 12–3, 7–10.30 Sun
**Greene King IPA, Abbot** Ⓗ
Welcoming community pub with a growing real ale trade, right opposite Mitcham Cricket Club, which is said to have the oldest cricket green in the country. Bar snacks always available. Q ≠ ♣ P

**Try also: Windmill,** Commonside North (Carlsberg-Tetley)

## New Malden

### Woodies
Thetford Road
☎ (0181) 949 5824
11–11; 12–10.30 Sun
**Boddingtons Bitter; Flowers Original; Fuller's London Pride; Young's Bitter, Special; guest beer** Ⓗ
Ex-cricket pavilion, decorated with a staggering montage of sports, theatrical and film memorabilia. It can get crowded eves. Families welcome if eating. The guest beer changes monthly.
⌂ Q ❀ ◖ ♣ P

## North Cheam

### Wetherspoons
552–556 London Road (A24)
☎ (0181) 644 1808
11–11; 12–10.30 Sun
**Courage Directors; Theakston Best Bitter, XB; Younger Scotch; guest beers** Ⓗ
Wetherspoon conversion of a former Sainsbury's cold store. A statue of Henry VIII, whose hunting lodge was nearby at Nonsuch Park, stands inside the entrance. Pictures on the walls commemorate local history. Guest ales from micro-breweries.
Q ◖◗ ♿ ⚟

## Richmond

### Coach & Horses
8 Kew Green
☎ (0181) 940 1208
11–11; 12–10.30 Sun
**Young's Bitter, Special, Ram Rod, seasonal beers** Ⓗ
Large, traditional, edge-of-town coaching inn with many preserved features from the 19th century. Popular with both families (particularly for Sun lunch) and visitors to Kew. Occasional summer jazz sessions in the large garden. Generous food portions; no meals Sun eve.
⌂ Q ❀ 🛏 ◖◗ ≠ (Kew Bridge) ⊖ (Kew Gardens) P

### Orange Tree
45 Kew Road
☎ (0181) 940 0944
11–11; 12–10.30 Sun
**Young's Bitter, Special, Ram Rod, Winter Warmer** Ⓗ
Fine, popular pub in a large Victorian building, with a fringe theatre upstairs and a restaurant downstairs. A good variety of excellent bar food is served from a counter in the lounge; no food Sun eve.
⌂ Q ❀ ◖◗ ≠ ⊖

### Triple Crown
15 Kew Foot Road
☎ (0181) 940 3805
11–11; 12–10.30 Sun
**Beer range varies** Ⓗ
Small, popular pub, close to London Scottish Rugby Club, serving a changing range of beers and a large selection of whiskies. Local CAMRA *Pub of the Year* 1994 and '95.
❀ ◖ ≠ ⊖

### Waterman's Arms
12 Water Lane
☎ (0181) 940 2893
11–3, 5.30–11; 11–11 Sat; 12–4, 7–10.30 (12–10.30 summer) Sun
**Young's Bitter, Special, Winter Warmer** Ⓗ
Small, Victorian pub in a cobbled stone lane leading to the river, with an attractive bar in its cosy, two-room layout. Simple, home-made meals (soups, casseroles and a wide range of cheeses). Try the games – Horsey-Horsey and Shut-the-Box.
⌂ Q 🝲 ❀ ◖◗ ♣

### White Cross Hotel
Water Lane ☎ (0181) 940 6844
11–11; 12–10.30 Sun
**Young's Bitter, Special, Ram Rod, Winter Warmer** Ⓗ
Extremely popular, Thames-side pub in a splendid, picturesque setting, offering excellent bar food and service. The riverside terrace bar is open in summer. Local CAMRA *Pub of the Year* 1992.
⌂ Q ❀ ◖◗

## Surbiton

### Black Lion
58 Brighton Road
☎ (0181) 399 1666
11–3, 5–11; 11–11 Sat; 12–10.30 Sun
**Young's Bitter, Special, Ram Rod, Winter Warmer** Ⓗ
Friendly, traditional Young's pub where you can usually get a seat and can converse with no problem. One bar, with a separate room which used to be the public bar; smart, comfortable and quite ornate.
❀ ◖◗ ≠

### Denby Dale
84 Victoria Road
☎ (0181) 390 2778
11–11; 12–10.30 Sun
**Fuller's Chiswick, London Pride, ESB, seasonal beers** Ⓗ
Former bank premises, next to the station. Impressive internal decor includes wood panelling, snob screens and stained-glass. Pies and other home-made food are a speciality, but it retains a good pub atmosphere. ◖◗ ♿ ≠ ♣

### Waggon & Horses
1 Surbiton Hill Road
11–2.30 (3 Fri), 5–11; 11–11 Sat; 12–4, 7–10.30 Sun
**Young's Bitter, Special, Winter Warmer, seasonal beers** Ⓗ
Pub run by the same tenant since 1967 and retaining many separate rooms. It can get busy, especially at weekends, and now offers a good lunchtime menu (not served Sat). Local CAMRA *Pub of the Year* 1993 and '96. Tiny car park.
Q 🝲 ❀ ◖ 🗗 ♣ P

## Sutton

### Moon on the Hill
5–9 Hill Road
☎ (0181) 643 1202
11–11; 12–10.30 Sun
**Courage Directors; Theakston Best Bitter, XB; Younger Scotch; guest beer** H
Large Wetherspoons conversion of a former department store in the town square. A double staircase leads to a no-smoking area and a terrace garden at the rear. Regular price promotions and beer festivals. Guest ales from micro-breweries.
Q ❀ ⬤ 🕭 ⬤ ≉ ○ ✇

### New Town
7 Lind Road (off A232)
☎ (0181) 642 0567
11–3, 5–11; 11–11 Sat; 12–3, 7–10.30 Sun
**Young's Bitter, Special, Winter Warmer** H
Popular, friendly, street-corner pub in the New Town area: a carpeted public bar, with an adjoining games room, and a contrasting, three-level saloon. No food Sun eve.
Q ❀ ⬤ ◗ ⬤ ⬤ ♣

### Windsor Castle
13 Greyhound Road (off A232)
☎ (0181) 643 2574
11–3, 5–11; 11–11 Sat; 12–3, 7–10.30 Sun
**Fuller's Chiswick, London Pride, ESB, seasonal beers** H
Popular local known as the 'Little' Windsor to distinguish it from the one in Carshalton. The smart single bar is one of the smallest in the area. Eve meals until 8.30, Mon–Fri.
❀ ⬤ ◗ ≉

## Wallington

### Duke's Head
6 Manor Road, The Green (off A232) ☎ (0181) 647 1595
11–11; 12–10.30 Sun
**Young's Bitter, Special, Winter Warmer** H
Traditional, historic, two-bar pub, a Grade II listed building. The main bar is decorated with tankards and brass. Very popular with locals who spill onto the green in summer. Note the sign for the livery stables in the back yard. No lunches Sun.
Q ❀ ⬤ ◗ ⬤ ≉ ♣ P

### West London

## W1: Fitzrovia

### Bricklayers Arms
31 Gresse Street
☎ (0171) 636 5593
11–11; 7–10.30 Sun, closed Sun lunch

**Samuel Smith OBB** H
Small pub on two floors. Food is served in the upper bar.
◗ ◗ ⬤ (Tottenham Ct Rd)

### Duke of York
47 Rathbone Street
11–11 (5 Sat); closed Sun
**Greene King IPA, Rayments Special, Abbot, seasonal beers** H
Friendly local at the end of a pedestrian street. ◗ ⬤ ♣

### Jack Horner
236 Tottenham Court Road
☎ (0171) 656 2868
11–11; closed Sun
**Fuller's Chiswick, London Pride, ESB, seasonal beers** H
Fuller's 'Ale & Pie House' in former bank premises, handy for Oxford St shops and London University. It can get extremely crowded.
◗ ◗ 🕭 ⬤ (Tottenham Ct Rd)

### Rising Sun
46 Tottenham Court Road
☎ (0171) 636 6530
11–11; 12–10.30 Sun
**Courage Best Bitter, Directors; Taylor Landlord; Theakston Best Bitter, XB, Old Peculier; guest beers** H
Long, busy, corner pub which for a while was called Presleys but has, thankfully, reverted to its original name.
◗ ▶ ⬤ (Goodge St)

## W1: Marylebone

### Beehive
7 Homer Street
11–3, 5.30–11; 11–11 Fri; 12–3, 7–10.30 Sun
**Boddingtons Bitter; Fuller's London Pride; Marston's Pedigree** H
Tiny, welcoming, backstreet pub, very much a local.
◗ ≉ ⬤

### Golden Eagle
59 Marylebone Lane
11–11; 11–3, 7–11 Sat; 12–3, 7–10.30 Sun
**Draught Bass; Brakspear Bitter; Fuller's London Pride** H
Tiny, popular, corner local featuring a piano player at weekends. ◗ ⬤ (Baker St) ♣

### Harcourt Arms
32 Harcourt Street
☎ (0171) 723 6634
11–11; 12–10.30 Sun
**Adnams Bitter; Marston's Pedigree; Tetley Bitter; guest beers** H
Pleasant pub with a horseshoe bar and Tapster's Choice guest beers. ❀ ◗ ≉ ⬤

### Turners Arms
26 Crawford Street
11–11; 12–10.30 Sun
**Shepherd Neame Master Brew Bitter, Spitfire** H

Small pub, recently given a much needed refurbishment.
◗ ≉ ⬤

### Wargrave Arms
42 Brendon Street
☎ (0171) 723 0559
11–11; 11–3, 7–11 Sat; 12–3, 7–10.30 Sun
**Young's Bitter, Special, Ram Rod, Winter Warmer** H
Long, narrow, corner local, handy for Edgware Road shops. ◗

### Westmorland Arms
34 George Street
☎ (0171) 935 4753
11 (12 Sat)–11; 12–3 Sun, closed Sun eve
**Bateman XB; Boddingtons Bitter; Jennings Bitter; Marston's Pedigree; guest beers** H
Pub built in 1795 as a wine vault. Downstairs Dungeons and Dragons is played Mon–Tue eves; the split-level main bar has an original mahogany and glass back fitting which is listed. Q ◗ ⬤ (Baker St)

### Worcester Arms
39 George Street
11–11; 12–10.30 Sun
**Beer range varies** H
Popular corner local with an impressive Courage Alton mirror. ◗ ≉ ⬤

## W1: Mayfair

### Guinea
30 Bruton Place
☎ (0171) 409 1728
11 (6.30 Sat)–11; closed Sun
**Young's Bitter, Special, seasonal beers** H
Small, intimate, mews pub with an exclusive restaurant at the rear. ◗ ▶

## W1: Soho

### Ain't Nothin' But
20 Kingly Street
☎ (0171) 287 0514
5.30–1am (3am Fri & Sat); closed Sun
**Adnams Bitter; guest beers** H
Small blues bar staging live music six days a week. It attracts a wide range of customers and creates an atmosphere all of its own. Two ever-changing guest beers from independent breweries. Admission charge after 10 Fri; beer is more expensive after 11.
▶ ⬤ (Oxford Circus)

### Burlington Bertie
39 Shaftesbury Avenue
☎ (0171) 437 0847
12–1am; 12–10.30 Sun
**Badger Tanglefoot; Draught Bass; Brakspear Bitter; guest beers** H
Modern pub in an old shop premises in Theatreland, featuring a large ground-floor

195

bar, plus a balcony bar. Wine bar downstairs. House beer.
◑ ◗ ⊖ (Piccadilly Circus)

## W2: Bayswater

### Prince Edward
73 Princes Square
☎ (0171) 722 2221
11–11; 12–10.30 Sun
**Boddingtons Bitter; Flowers Original; Fuller's London Pride; Marston's Pedigree; guest beer** [H]
Busy, comfortable, corner local near Queensway. Extensive food menu. Wine bar downstairs. ◑ ◗ ⊖

## W2: Paddington

### Archery Tavern
4 Bathurst Street
☎ (0171) 402 4916
11–11; 12–10.30 Sun
**Badger Dorset Best, Tanglefoot; Gribble Black Adder II; Wadworth 6X; Wells Eagle** [H]
Very popular pub next to a working stables; named after an archery ground which once stood nearby.
◑ ◗ ⇌ ⊖

### Victoria
10A Strathearn Place
☎ (0171) 724 1191
11–11; 12–3, 7–10.30 Sun
**Fuller's Chiswick, London Pride, ESB, seasonal beers** [H]
Corner pub, recently refurbished but retaining much original woodwork and magnificently etched mirrors. Queen Victoria is alleged to have rested here on the way to opening Paddington Station. Piano bar upstairs. No food Sun.
Q ◑ ⇌ ⊖

## W3: Acton

### Duke of York
86 Steyne Road
☎ (0181) 992 0463
11–11; 12–10.30 Sun
**Courage Best Bitter; Morland Old Speckled Hen; Wadworth 6X; Webster's Yorkshire Bitter; Young's Special** [H]
Friendly pub, tucked away off the busy high street. ♘ ❀ ◑ ◗ ⇌ (Central) ⊖ (Town) ♣

### King's Head
214 High Street
☎ (0181) 992 0282
11–11; 12–10.30 Sun
**Fuller's Chiswick, London Pride, ESB** [H]
Busy, cosmopolitan pub; imposing from the front but the interior is very comfortable.
❀ ◑ ◗ ⇌ (Central) ⊖ (Town)

## W4: Chiswick

### Bell & Crown
13–17 Strand on the Green
☎ (0181) 994 4164
11–11; 12–10.30 Sun
**Fuller's Chiswick, London Pride, ESB** [H]
Pleasant, riverside pub with a conservatory. Drinkers tend to overflow on to the towpath at times. ❀ ◑ ◗ ♿

### Duke of York
Devonshire Road (just N of Hogarth Roundabout)
☎ (0181) 994 2118
11–3, 5–11; 11–11 Fri & Sat; 12–10.30 Sun
**Fuller's Chiswick, London Pride, ESB** [H]
Backstreet local with a strong TV following. When ordering Chiswick ask for the real one as the pub has keg as well. ⊞

### George & Devonshire
8 Burlington Lane
☎ (0181) 994 1859
11–11; 12–10.30 Sun
**Fuller's Chiswick, London Pride, ESB, seasonal beers** [H]
Two-bar pub, next to Hogarth Roundabout. The function room doubles as a family room. Limited parking. Good value meals. ♨ ♘ ❀ ◑ ◗ ⊞ ⇌ ⊖ (Turnham Green) ♣ P

### George IV
185 Chiswick High Road
☎ (0181) 994 4624
11.30–11; 12–10.30 Sun
**Fuller's Chiswick, London Pride, ESB, seasonal beers** [H]
Recently converted into a Fuller's 'Ale & Pie House', this pub now sports a large ground-floor bar and a first-floor seating area at the rear, with a projection TV for occasional use. The patio has been enlarged and improved.
♨ Q ❀ ◑ ◗ ♿ ⊖ (Turnham Green)

### JJ Moon's
80–82 Chiswick High Road
☎ (0181) 742 7263
11–11; 12–10.30 Sun
**Courage Directors; Morland Old Speckled Hen; Theakston Best Bitter, XB; guest beers** [H]
Modern pub with an old pub atmosphere. The guest beers change every three months. Regular beer festivals, plus allegedly the cheapest beer locally. Food served all day until 10. Q ❀ ◑ ◗ ♿ ⊖ (Turnham Green) ⊘

## W5: Ealing

### Duffy's
124 Pitshanger Lane
☎ (0181) 998 6810
11–11; 12–10.30 Sun
**Draught Bass; Brakspear Bitter; Fuller's London Pride; Young's Special; guest beers** [H]
This former dairy has been expanded since last year's *Guide*, and has more drinking and eating space. Very much a community pub, with a lively ambience. House bitter available. No food Sun eve.
Q ❀ ◑ ◗ ♣

### Fox & Goose
Hanger Lane
☎ (0181) 997 2441
11–11; 12–10.30 Sun
**Fuller's Chiswick, London Pride, ESB, seasonal beers; guest beers** [H]
Pub where a tiny public bar, a large, comfortable saloon and a very pleasant garden at the rear combine to offer a welcome refuge from the nearby infamous Hanger Lane gyratory system.
❀ ◑ ⊞ ⊖ ♣ ▯

### Red Lion
13 St Mary's Road
☎ (0181) 567 2541
11–11; 12–10.30 Sun
**Fuller's Chiswick, London Pride, ESB, seasonal beers** [H]
Small and friendly gem of a pub opposite the Ealing film studio, from which it takes its alternative name, 'Stage Six', and the many photographs which line the walls. Absolutely no electronic intrusions. Excellent, award-winning garden. Q ❀ ◑ ⇌ (Bdwy) ⊖ (South)

### TJ Duffy
282 Northfields Avenue
☎ (0181) 932 1711
11–11; 12–10.30 Sun
**Adnams Bitter; Draught Bass; Fuller's London Pride** [H]
Ex-wine bar, totally refurbished, with a warm, convivial atmosphere. Sun lunch 12–4; no food Sun eve.
◑ ◗ ⊖ (Northfield)

### Wheatsheaf
41 Haven Lane
☎ (0181) 997 5240
11–11; 12–10.30 Sun
**Fuller's Chiswick, London Pride, ESB, seasonal beers** [H]
Pub refurbished in 1993 (including the addition of a small public bar and the extension of the saloon bar), with much wood and exposed brickwork. Live music Sun eve; regular quizzes. Good value food (no meals Sun eve). ♨ ❀ ◑ ◗ ⊞ ⇌ (Bdwy) ⊖ ♣

**Try also: Rose & Crown,** St Mary's Rd (Fuller's)

## W6: Hammersmith

### Andover Arms
57 Aldensley Road
☎ (0181) 741 9794
11–11; 12–3, 7–10.30 Sun
**Fuller's Chiswick, London Pride, ESB, seasonal beers** Ⓗ
Small, well-hidden local, very pleasantly furnished. Weekday lunches; Thai food eves (except Sun). Ⓓ ▶ ❺ (Ravenscourt Pk)

### Dove                          ☆
19 Upper Mall
☎ (0181) 748 5405
11–11; 12–10.30 Sun
**Fuller's London Pride, ESB, seasonal beers** Ⓗ
Famous riverside pub dating from the 17th century. It is claimed that Charles II and Nell Gwynne drank here. The public bar has been listed in the *Guinness Book of Records* as the smallest in London.
Q ❀ Ⓓ ▶ ❺ (Ravenscourt Pk)

### Salutation
154 King Street
☎ (0181) 748 3668
11–11; 12–3, 7–10 (12–10.30 summer) Sun
**Fuller's Chiswick, London Pride, ESB, seasonal beers** Ⓗ
Former coaching house with an imposing tiled frontage.
❀ Ⓓ ❺ (Ravenscourt Pk)

## W7: Hanwell

### Fox
Green Lane ☎ (0181) 567 3912
11–11; 12–10.30 Sun
**Courage Best Bitter, Directors; Marston's Pedigree** Ⓗ
Welcoming pub at the confluence of the River Brent and the Grand Union, midway along the 12 locks between the Thames and the London summit level of the canal. Last orders for massive Sun roasts taken at 3.30. No straight glasses used; pricey beer.
Q ❀ Ⓓ ♣

## W8: Kensington

### Britannia
1 Allen Street
☎ (0171) 937 1864
11–11; 12–10.30 Sun
**Young's Bitter, Special, Winter Warmer** Ⓗ
Two-bar pub off Kensington High St, with a large conservatory at the rear. Note the Toby jug, teapot and plate collections and the wood-panelled bars. The conservatory is a no-smoking area at lunchtime. No food Sun eve. Q Ⓓ ▶ ❺ (High St) ⌇

### Churchill Arms
119 Kensington Church Street
☎ (0171) 727 4242
11–11; 12–10.30 Sun
**Fuller's Chiswick, London Pride, ESB, seasonal beers** Ⓗ
Extremely busy pub with a large collection of Churchillian memorabilia as well as butterflies and photos of US presidents. It specialises in Thai food eves; take-aways available. 🍴 Q Ⓓ ▶
❺ (Notting Hill Gate)

## W9: Maida Vale

### Truscott Arms
55 Shirland Road
☎ (0171) 286 0310
11–11; 12–10.30 Sun
**Adnams Broadside; Boddingtons Bitter; Brakspear Bitter; Greene King Abbot; guest beers** Ⓗ
Large, comfortable pub with an impressive bank of handpulls. Live music at weekends.
❀ Ⓓ ❺ (Warwick Ave)

### Warrington Hotel        ☆
93 Warrington Crescent
☎ (0171) 286 2929
11–11; 12–10.30 Sun
**Brakspear Special; Fuller's London Pride, ESB; Marston's Pedigree; Young's Special; guest beers** (occasional) Ⓗ
Large 'gin palace'-type pub featuring woodwork, tiles, stained-glass and a semi-circular, marble-topped bar. Thai restaurant upstairs (eves).
Q Ⓓ ❺ (Warwick Ave)

### Warwick Castle
6 Warwick Place
☎ (0171) 286 6868
11–11; 12–10.30 Sun
**Draught Bass; Fuller's London Pride; Morland Old Speckled Hen; Worthington Bitter** Ⓗ
Canalside pub boasting an impressive coloured print of Paddington Station. 🍴 Q Ⓓ ❺ (Warwick Ave)

## W12: Shepherd's Bush

### Crown & Sceptre
57 Melina Road
☎ (0181) 743 6414
11–11; 12–4.30, 7–10.30 Sun
**Fuller's London Pride, ESB** Ⓗ
Backstreet, two-bar pub: an oasis in a beer desert, displaying much QPR memorabilia. ❀ Ⓓ

### Moon on the Green
172–174 Uxbridge Road
☎ (0181) 749 5709
11–11; 12–10.30 Sun
**Courage Directors; Greene King IPA; Theakston Best Bitter, XB; Younger Scotch; guest beers** Ⓗ
Two-bar pub in ex-shop premises, overlooking the green. Glass-fronted, it has wood panelling throughout, particularly in the basement bar. Q Ⓓ ❺ ⌇

## W13: West Ealing

### Drayton Court Hotel
2 The Avenue
☎ (0181) 997 1019
11–11; 12–10.30 Sun
**Fuller's Chiswick, London Pride, ESB, seasonal beers** Ⓗ
A massive refurbishment in 1995 realised the full potential of this classic late Victorian edifice (known locally as 'Dracula's Castle'). Live theatre Sun–Thu in the basement function room. Food always available, except 3–7 winter Sun.
⛱ ❀ Ⓓ ▶ ⊟ ⇌ ♣

### Kent
2 Scotch Common
☎ (0181) 997 5911
11–11; 12–10.30 Sun
**Fuller's London Pride, ESB, seasonal beers; guest beers** Ⓗ
Large pub, literally on the edge of London, with an extensive garden backing on to the Brent Valley Park. As well as the split-level lounge, there is a public bar and a children's room (once the off-licence). The garden has its own kids' 'tuck shop'. No food Sun eve. Wheelchair WC. Q ⛱ ❀ Ⓓ ⊟ ⇌ (Castlebar Halt) ♣ P

## W14: West Kensington

### Britannia Tap
150 Warwick Road
☎ (0171) 602 1649
11–11; 12–4, 8–10.30 Sun
**Young's Bitter, Special** Ⓗ
Small, narrow, comfortable local, refurbished in 1994; now part-wood-panelled with a new real fire. The many prints all carry a beer/brewery theme. Weekday lunches.
🍴 Q ❀ Ⓓ ⇌ (Olympia) ❺ (Earl's Ct) ♣

### Seven Stars
253 North End Road
☎ (0171) 385 3571
11–11; 12–10.30 Sun
**Fuller's London Pride, ESB, seasonal beers** (occasional) Ⓗ
Main road, 1930s, Art Deco, two-bar pub which draws a predominantly local trade with its community atmosphere (Sun eve sing-alongs).
❀ Ⓓ ▶ ⊟ ⇌ (Olympia) ❺ (W Brompton)

### Warwick Arms
160 Warwick Road
☎ (0171) 603 3560
11–11; 12–10.30 Sun
**Fuller's Chiswick, London Pride, ESB, seasonal beers** Ⓗ

Traditional local, built in 1828 for the now defunct canal basin. Note the attractive Wedgwood handpumps. Handy for Earl's Court and Olympia halls. No food Sun eve. ⚶ Q ✿ ◑ ≋ (Olympia) ⊖ (Earl's Ct) ♣

## Bedfont

### Beehive

333 Staines Road
☎ (0181) 890 8086
11–11; 12–2, 7–10.30 Sun
**Fuller's London Pride, ESB** Ⓗ
Excellent pub with a friendly atmosphere, an attractive lounge and a well-kept garden. Good value meals from a Thai and traditional menu (not served Sat lunch or Sun); barbecues in summer.
✿ ◑ ▶ P

## Brentford

### Beehive

227 High Street
☎ (0181) 560 2421
11–11; 12–10.30 Sun
**Fuller's Chiswick, London Pride, ESB** Ⓗ
Large, prominent and popular pub at the centre of Brentford. Sun lunches are recommended. Bar skittles played.
⚶ ✿ ◑ ▶ ≋ ♣

### Brewery Tap

47 Catherine Wheel Road
☎ (0181) 560 5200
11–11; 12–10.30 Sun
**Fuller's London Pride, ESB, seasonal beers** Ⓗ
Small, friendly local with music most eves (jazz Tue and Thu), near the Grand Union Canal. TV football on match days. Excellent Sun lunches.
◑ ♣

### Magpie & Crown

128 High Street
☎ (0181) 560 5658
11–11; 12–10.30 Sun
**Beer range varies** Ⓗ
1920s brewers' Tudor pub, offering interesting beers plus cider and perry. Lunches weekdays; snacks generally available at other times.
✿ ◑ ≋ ♣ ○

## Cranford

### Queen's Head

123 High Street
☎ (0181) 897 0722
11–11; 12–10.30 Sun
**Fuller's Chiswick, London Pride, ESB, seasonal beers** Ⓗ
Large, Tudor-style pub in the aerodrome conservation area; close to Heathrow, but not spoilt by its proximity.
⚶ Q ☙ ✿ ◑ ♣ P

## Greenford

### Black Horse

425 Oldfield Lane
☎ (0181) 578 1384
11–11; 12–4, 7–10.30 (12–10.30 summer) Sun
**Fuller's Chiswick, London Pride, ESB** Ⓗ
Busy, friendly, canalside pub, in the middle of an industrial area, popular with anglers, walkers and the boating fraternity alike. The large garden has a children's play area. ✿ ◑ ⌸ ≋ ⊖ ♣ P

## Hampton

### White Hart

70 High Street
☎ (0181) 979 5352
11–3, 5.30–11; 11–11 Fri & Sat; 12–10.30 Sun
**Boddingtons Bitter; Flowers Original; Greene King Abbot; guest beers**
Genuinely free house with a log fire and no music. Its history goes back at least to 1730, though it was rebuilt in 1898. Once owned by the actor David Garrick, it was known as the Six Bells until 1780. Dickens mentioned it in *Oliver Twist*.
⚶ Q ✿ ◑

## Hampton Court

### King's Arms

Lion Gate, Hampton Court Road ☎ (0181) 977 1729
11–11; 12–10.30 Sun
**Badger Dorset Best, Tanglefoot** Ⓗ
Fine, imposing, historic pub backing on to the palace grounds. ✿ ◑ ▶ ⌸

## Hampton Wick

### White Hart

1 High Street
☎ (0181) 977 1786
11–3, 5–11; 11–11 Fri & Sat; 12–10.30 Sun
**Fuller's Chiswick, London Pride, ESB** Ⓗ
Large, mock-Tudor pub: a spacious oak-panelled lounge with a real fire.
⚶ ✿ ◑ ▶ ≋ ♣

## Harmondsworth

### Crown

High Street ☎ (0181) 759 1007
11–11; 12–10.30 Sun
**Courage Best Bitter, Directors; King & Barnes Sussex; Marston's Pedigree; Young's Special** Ⓗ
Despite its proximity to Heathrow Airport, this is still a true village local; convivial, characterful and occasionally lively. Local newspapers and enamel signs feature. Coaches welcome. ⚶ Q ✿ ◑ ▶ ♣ ○

## Hounslow

### Cross Lances

236 Hanworth Road (A314)
☎ (0181) 570 4714
11–11; 12–10.30 Sun
**Fuller's London Pride, ESB** Ⓗ
Early Victorian, traditional tiled local, with a popular public bar. The saloon has a large, welcoming fire. Wholesome meals are served at all hours on request (booking advised for Sun lunch).
⚶ Q ✿ ◑ ⌸ ≋ ♣ P

### Jolly Farmer

177 Lampton Road (100 yds S of A4) ☎ (0181) 570 1276
11–11; 12–3, 7–10.30 Sun
**Courage Best Bitter, Directors; Marston's Pedigree** Ⓗ
Popular, cosy local serving excellent weekday lunches.
✿ ◑ ⌸ ⊖ (Central) ♣ P

## Isleworth

### Castle

18 Upper Square, Old Isleworth ☎ (0181) 560 3615
11–11; 12–10.30 Sun
**Young's Bitter, Special, Ram Rod, seasonal beers** Ⓗ
Prominent pub, a long-standing *Guide* entry, housing a large, comfortable bar, plus a games room. Families are welcome in the conservatory. The building is pre-1930 and replaced an old inn that once served nearby Isleworth Docks on the Thames.
⚶ Q ☙ ✿ ◑ ⌸ ♣ P

## Northolt

### Plough

Mandeville Road
☎ (0181) 845 1750
11–11; 12–10.30 Sun
**Fuller's London Pride, ESB** Ⓗ
Surprisingly quiet pub for its location; if you could ignore the traffic you would think you were in a small village pub.
✿ ◑ ⌸ ⊖ ♣ P

## Norwood Green

### Plough

Tentelow Lane (off main green)
☎ (0181) 574 1945
11–11; 12–10.30 Sun
**Fuller's Chiswick, London Pride, ESB** Ⓗ
Very pleasant pub where one substantial bar houses various discrete areas. A number of fires, unfortunately no longer real, complete the atmosphere within this 17th-century building. No food Sun; eve meals end at 8. Q ✿ ◑ ▶ ♣ P

## Osterley

### Hare & Hounds

Wyke Green, Windmill Lane
☎ (0181) 560 5438
11–11; 12–10.30 Sun
**Fuller's London Pride, ESB, seasonal beers** Ⓗ
Rural pub near the SE entrance to Osterley Park, set back from one of the few remaining old Middlesex lanes, albeit heavily trafficked nowadays. Ideal for family outings with its large garden and children's playground. Beware the keg Chiswick Bitter. Food always available. ❀ ◖ ◗ ♣ P

## Ruislip Manor

### JJ Moon's

12 Victoria Road
☎ (01895) 622373
11–11; 12–10.30 Sun
**Courage Directors; Greene King Abbot; Theakston Best Bitter, XB; Younger Scotch; guest beer** Ⓗ
Traditional-style, mock Victorian ale house, converted from an old Woolworth's store. Very popular with all ages.
Q ◖ ◗ ♿ ⊖ ⚟

## Southall

### Hambrough Tavern

The Broadway, Uxbridge Road (by Grand Union Canal at Hayes Bridge)
☎ (0181) 813 9522
11–11; 12–10.30 Sun
**Beer range varies** Ⓗ
Although the current building is just 15 years old, a pub has stood on this site for 200 years. Four constantly changing independents' ales in the saloon. ❀ ◖ ⊞ ♿ ♣ P

### Three Tuns

45 The Green (100 yds S of station)
11–11; 12–8.30 Sun
**Adnams Bitter; Samuel Smith OBB; guest beers** Ⓗ
Former Mann's keg-only house, one of a diminishing band of outlets serving OBB as nature intended in London. A somewhat run-down exterior belies a salubrious saloon area, complete with a real fire; a doorway leads to the old public bar. ⌂ ❀ ⇌ ♣ P

**Try also: Beaconsfield Arms,** West End Rd (Free)

## Teddington

### Hogarth

58 Broad Street
☎ (0181) 977 3846
11–11; 12–10.30 Sun
**Fuller's Chiswick, London Pride, ESB, seasonal beers** Ⓗ
Popular pub, right in the town centre. Recent structural alterations have made it much roomier. Open at 9.30 for breakfast; no food Sun eve.
Q ❀ ◖ ◗ ⚟

### Queen Dowager

49 North Lane
☎ (0181) 943 3474
11–11; 12–4, 7–10.30 Sun
**Young's Bitter, Special, Winter Warmer** Ⓗ
Friendly, comfortable pub, just off the main street with a first-class garden. Named after Queen Adelaide, widow of William IV. Local CAMRA *Pub of the Year* 1993. No food Sun.
Q ❀ ◖ ⊞ ⇌ ♣

## Twickenham

### Eel Pie

9–11 Church Street
☎ (0181) 891 1717
11–11; 12–10.30 Sun
**Badger Tanglefoot; Gribble Black Adder II; Smiles Best Bitter; Wadworth 6X** Ⓗ
Highly recommended modern pub in an old shopping area, yards from the river and town centre. Deservedly high reputation for its selection of weekday lunches. Roomy and comfortable, it is popular with all ages. Q ◖ ⇌ ♣ ⌓

### Pope's Grotto

Cross Deep ☎ (0181) 892 3050
11–3, 5.30–11; 11–11 Sat; 12–10.30 Sun
**Young's Bitter, Special, Ram Rod, Winter Warmer** Ⓗ
Large, modern, three-bar pub overlooking pretty riverside public gardens. It enjoys a good reputation for catering (dining area in the lounge). Completely rebuilt following wartime bomb damage.
⌂ Q ❀ ◖ ⊞ ⇌ (Strawberry Hill) ♣ P

### Prince Albert

30 Hampton Road
☎ (0181) 894 3963
11–11; 12–3, 7–10.30 Sun
**Fuller's Chiswick, London Pride, ESB** Ⓗ
Small, Victorian pub with a friendly atmosphere. No food Sun eve. ❀ ◖ ◗ ⚟

### Prince Blucher

124 The Green
☎ (0181) 894 1824
11–11; 12–10.30 Sun
**Fuller's Chiswick, London Pride, ESB, seasonal beers** Ⓗ
Large, comfortable, one-bar pub which, although modernised, still reveals great character. ❀ ◖

## Uxbridge

### Crown

Colham Green Road
☎ (01895) 442303
11–11; 12–4.30, 7–10.30 Sun
**Fuller's Chiswick, London Pride, ESB** Ⓗ
Comfortable local with a lively public bar; handy for Hillingdon Hospital visitors. Well-laid-out patio garden.
⛀ ❀ ◖ ⊞ ♣ P

### Load of Hay

33 Villier Street
☎ (01895) 234676
11–3, 5.30 (7 Sat)–11; 12–3, 7–10.30 Sun
**Beer range varies** Ⓗ
Town pub with a real country feel. The main bar was formerly a stabling area; the superb smaller bar is opened occasionally and is available for functions. Local CAMRA *Pub of the Year* 1995.
❀ ◖ ◗ P ⚟


## KNOWN TREASURES AND HIDDEN GEMS

Over 400 great London pubs are featured in CAMRA's new, slimline, pocket-sized guidebook, *Known Treasures and Hidden Gems*. Compiled by award-winning pub writer Peter Haydon, in association with the London branches of CAMRA, it highlights all the famous London pubs but also reveals a host of classic hostelries which are off the tourist's beaten track. Priced at only £7.99, it is an essential travelling companion when in the Capital. See page 542 for details of how to order your copy.

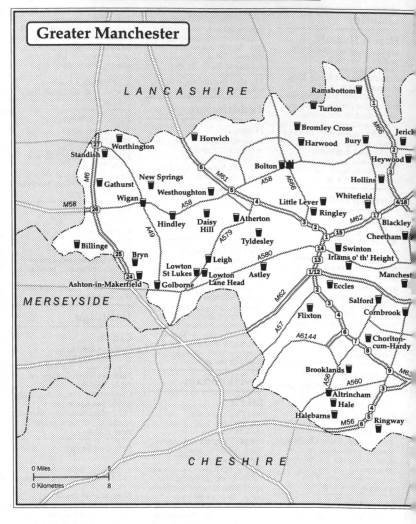

**Greater Manchester**

## Altrincham

### Hogshead Ale House
Old Market Place
☎ (0161) 927 7062
11–11; 12–10.30 Sun
**Boddingtons Bitter; Marston's
Pedigree; Wadworth 6X;
Whitbread Abroad Cooper,
Fuggles IPA; guest
beers** Ⓗ/Ⓖ
Once known as the Unicorn
and owned by Altrincham
brewers Richardson & Goodall
(taken over by Chester's in
1890), this pub now holds
regular beer festivals. All types
of live music are performed
Sun. Food served 12–7 (good
value steaks). Bulmers Old
Hazy cider is stocked.
🛏 🏵 ◑ ▶ ⇌ ⊖ ♠ ☺ ⚄

### Malt Shovels
68 Stamford Street
☎ (0161) 928 2053
11.30–11; 12–4.30, 7–10.30 Sun
**Samuel Smith OBB** Ⓗ
Friendly, town-centre pub
serving good value lunches.
Live trad jazz Wed and Fri,
modern jazz Thu and Sat.
Pool room upstairs. No
food Sun.
🏵 ◑ ⇌ ⊖ ♠

### Orange Tree
Old Market Place
☎ (0161) 928 2600
12–11; 12–10.30 Sun
**Courage Directors;
Marston's Pedigree; Morland
Old Speckled Hen;
Wilson's Bitter; guest
beer** Ⓗ
Once the smallest pub in

Altrincham: legend has it that a
man sold his wife for 1/6d in
1823 in the pub. Note the old
photos of Altrincham and
neighbouring pubs long since
gone. Upstairs room/bar
available for hire.
🛏 🏵 ◑ ▶ ⇌ ⊖ ♠ ⚄

### Tatton Arms
3–5 Tipping Street (next to
Sainsbury)
☎ (0161) 941 2502
11–11; 12–10.30 Sun
**Boddingtons Bitter** Ⓗ
Thriving, two-roomed,
football-oriented local
where pictures reflect the
long-serving landlord's
nautical background and
the two Manchester football
clubs. No food Sun.
🛏 🏵 ◑ 🍴 ⇌ ⊖ ♠ P

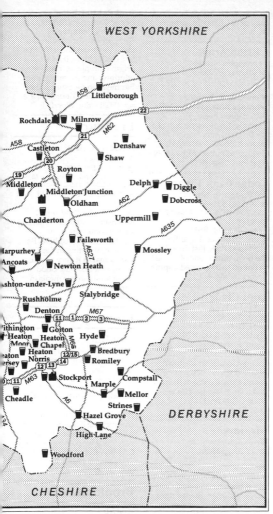

**Robinson's Hatters Mild, Best Bitter** Ⓗ
Stone, terraced local with small tap (Sky TV) and pool rooms, a lounge and a cosy bar. Next to open walking country.
Q ⊛ ◑ 🍽 ♣ P

## Oddfellows
King's Road, Hurst
☎ (0161) 330 6356
12–11; 12–10.30 Sun
**Robinson's Hatters Mild, Best Bitter** Ⓗ
Popular, multi-roomed local taking full advantage of the new Sun hours. Many original features – not least the splendid bar – alongside more modern comforts. Cosy and welcoming. ⊛ ♣ ✴

## Station
2 Warrington Street
☎ (0161) 330 6776
11.30–11; 12–3, 7–11 Sat; 12–3, 7–10.30 Sun
**Boddingtons Bitter; Chester's Mild; Marston's Pedigree; guest beers** Ⓗ
Now boasting seven guest handpumps, the Station continues to set the pace for free houses in the area. It hosts regular beer festivals where unusual brews feature and places an emphasis on smaller regional breweries. Occasional cider in summer. ⊛ ◑ ⇌ ○

## Witchwood
152 Old Street
☎ (0161) 344 0321
12–11 (midnight Venue Bar); 12–4 (3 Venue Bar), 7–10.30 Sun
**Courage Directors; Marston's Pedigree; John Smith's Bitter; Theakston Best Bitter, XB; guest beers** Ⓗ
Lively pub staging good live music. Three guest beers add interest to the regular brews.
◑ ⇌

## Astley

### Cart & Horses
221 Manchester Road
☎ (01942) 870751
12–11; 12–10.30 Sun
**Holt Mild, Bitter** Ⓗ
Impressive roadside local: a large, comfortable lounge, a

## Ancoats

### Mitchell Arms
215 Every Street (A662)
☎ (0161) 273 3097
12–11; 12–10.30 Sun
**Banks's Mild, Bitter** Ⓔ
Lively two-roomer, still under threat from a road scheme. A pub for the community, run with a refreshing, no-nonsense approach. 🍽 ♣ 🛏

## Ashton in Makerfield

### Commercial
21 Heath Road
☎ (01942) 726955
12–3, 7–11; 12–11 Fri & Sat; 12–10.30 Sun
**Burtonwood Bitter, Top Hat, seasonal beers; guest beers** Ⓗ
Backstreet local, now open-plan, well worth seeking out. ♿

## Ashton-under-Lyne

### Dog & Pheasant
528 Oldham Road
☎ (0161) 330 4894
12–5, 7.30–11; 12–3, 7.30–10.30 Sun
**Banks's Mild; Marston's Bitter, Pedigree, HBC** Ⓗ
Popular, friendly, lively local close to Daisy Nook Country Park. Good value food lunchtime; quizzes Tue and Thu eves. 🍴 ⊛ ◑ ♣ P

### Junction Inn
Mossley Road (A670, near Ashton golf course)
☎ (0161) 343 1611
12–3, 5.30–11; 12–11 Fri & Sat; 12–4, 7–10.30 Sun

## 🍺 INDEPENDENT BREWERIES

**Bank Top:** Bolton

**Cobden's:** Stockport

**Holt:** Cheetham

**Hydes' Anvil:** Manchester

**Lees:** Middleton Junction

**McGuinness:** Rochdale

**Phoenix:** Heywood

**Robinson's:** Stockport

no-smoking room and a sporting tap room.
⊛ ◖ ⊟ P ⊁

## Atherton

### Atherton Arms
6 Tyldesley Road
☎ (01942) 882885
11.30–11; 12–10.30 Sun
**Holt Mild, Bitter** H
Immense public house: a large, well-appointed, L-shaped lounge with a long central bar which also serves a tap room which has pool and snooker tables. Plenty of room in the wide corridor. ⊟ ⅋ ♣ P

### Pendle Witch
2–4 Warburton Place
☎ (01942) 884537
12–11; 12–10.30 Sun
**Moorhouse's Black Cat Mild, Premier, Pendle Witches Brew, seasonal beers; guest beer** H
One-roomed, popular local off the main road; Moorhouse's only pub in the area. A lounge contains a pool table and a jukebox. ⊛ ♣

## Billinge

### Hare & Hounds
142 Upholland Road
12–11; 12–10.30 Sun
**Moorhouse's Premier; Tetley Dark Mild; Walker Mild, Bitter; guest beer** H
Popular, large redbrick pub with two rooms. The lounge is free from distractions.
Q ⊟ ♣ P

## Blackley

### Pleasant Inn
370 Chapel Lane (off A6104, foot of Crab Lane)
☎ (0161) 740 3391
1 (12 Sat)–11; 12–10.30 Sun
**Robinson's Hatters Mild, Best Bitter** H
Small, three-roomed community pub in an ancient urban village. The lively vault, golf society room and lounge attract a loyal local clientele in this fairly remote location. Children welcome until 8.
⅋ ⊛ ⊟ ♣

## Bolton

### Bob's Smithy Inn
1448 Chorley Old Road (B6226)
☎ (01204) 842622
12–3.30 (4 Sat), 4.30 (7 Sat)–11; 12–3, 7–10.30 Sun
**Boddingtons Bitter; Taylor Best Bitter; Walker Mild, Bitter; guest beers** H
Popular pub on the fringes of the moors, with panoramic views of Bolton; named after the local blacksmith who used

to frequent it. Meals Tue–Fri. It may open all day in summer.
🏭 ⊛ ◖ P

### Clifton Arms
94 Newport Street
☎ (01204) 392738
11–11; 11–3, 6–11 Sat; 12–2, 7–10.30 Sun
**Moorhouse's Premier; Jennings Bitter; Walker Mild, Bitter; guest beers** H
Friendly, town-centre pub near the bus/rail interchange. Folk music Mon eve; quiz Wed. Regular mini-beer festivals. No food Sun. ◖ ≋ ♣

### Lodge Bank Tavern
260 Bridgeman Street
☎ (01204) 531946
12–5, 7.30–11; 11–11 Fri & Sat; 12–10.30 Sun
**Lees GB Mild, Bitter** H
Comfortable local near Bobby-Heywood Park, just outside the town centre; one of the last in Bolton to be granted a spirits licence. ⊛ ≋ ♣ P

### Lord Clyde
107 Folds Road
☎ (01204) 521705
12–11; 12–4, 7–10.30 Sun
**Hydes' Anvil Dark Mild, Light, Bitter, seasonal beers** G
Friendly, traditional, multi-roomed local near the town centre: a small L-shaped tap room, a small room at the rear, and a large lounge. Home-cooked lunches Fri.
Q ⊛ ⊟ ♣ P ⊟

### Maxims
26–28 Bradshawgate
☎ (01204) 523486
11.30–4, 7.30–11; 7–10.30 Sun, closed Sun lunch
**Vaux Samson, Waggle Dance; guest beer** H
Large Victorian, town-centre pub, very busy at weekends. Minimal dress restrictions (no workclothes, etc.). Food is served on two floors Mon–Sat. Lively, nightly entertainment.
◖ ⅋ ≋ ○

### Sweet Green Tavern
127 Crook Street (opp. bus/rail interchange) ☎ (01204) 392258
11.30–3 (3.30 Sat), 6.30–11; 11.30–11 Thu & Fri; 12–3, 7–10.30 Sun
**Walker Mild, Bitter; guest beers** H
Multi-roomed, deceptively large pub serving two changing guest beers. Bolton CAMRA *Pub of the Year* 1992 and '95. Home fans only on Bolton Wanderers home match days. No food Sun.
🏭 Q ⊛ ◖ ≋ ♣ P

### Watermillock
Crompton Way (A58, ring road) ☎ (01204) 591798
11–3, 5–11; 12–10.30 Sun

**Banks's Mild, Bitter, seasonal beers; Camerons Strongarm; Marston's Pedigree** H
Sympathetic conversion of a large Victorian house. Built in a late Gothic style, it retains original fireplaces, mullioned windows and plaster ceilings. Bar meals in the Squires Bar; restaurant next door. ⊛ ◖ ⅋
≋ (Hall i' the' Wood) P ⊟

## Bredbury

### Arden Arms
Ashton Road
☎ (0161) 430 2589
11.30–11 (11.30–3, 5–11 winter Mon & Tue); 12–3.30, 6–11 Sat; 12–10.30 Sun
**Robinson's Hatters Mild, Best Bitter** E
One of the few traditional Robinson's pubs left, retaining small rooms with a comfortable atmosphere. Its semi-rural setting in the Tame Valley makes it very popular summer weekends. Good value food (no eve meals in winter.)
Q ⊛ ◖ ▶ ♣ P

## Bromley Cross

### Flag Inn
50 Hardmans Lane (B6472, off A666; follow signs for Last Drop village)
☎ (01204) 302236
11–11; 12–3, 7–10.30 Sun
**Boddingtons Bitter; guest beers** H
Whitbread ale house with an enterprising licensee, serving a wide range of beers. It can be very busy weekend eves. Local CAMRA *Pub of the Year* 1994. The cellar is visible from the pub. 🏭 ♣ ○

## Brooklands

### Brook
Brooklands Station Approach, Brooklands Road
☎ (0161) 973 3773
12–11; 12–10.30 Sun
**Lees Bitter** H
Converted station master's house retaining a railway theme. The bistro upstairs is open Thu–Sun eves. Happy hour 5–7 weekdays.
⊛ ◖ ▶ ⅋ ≋ ⊖ ♣ P

**Try also: Legh Arms**, Sale Moor (Holt)

## Bryn

### Bath Springs
455 Wigan Road
☎ (01942) 202716
11–11; 12–10.30 Sun
**Boddingtons Bitter; Ind Coope Burton Ale; Tetley Dark Mild; Walker Mild, Best Bitter; guest beers** H

Formidable redbrick building, named after Bath Springs Brewery of Ormskirk. Excellent value, home-cooked lunches Mon–Fri. Smart function room upstairs.
◖ ⊞ ≈ ♣

## Bury

### Blue Bell

840 Manchester Road (A56, near Blackford Bridge)
☎ (0161) 766 2496
12–11; 12–10.30 Sun
**Holt Mild, Bitter** Ⓗ
Large, three-roomed pub with a traditional vault and a friendly host; popular with mature Manchester Utd supporters. The large, comfortable lounge is well patronised by friendly locals.
Q ✿ ♣ P

### Bridge Inn

731 Manchester Road (A56, at Blackford Bridge)
☎ (0161) 796 8122
12–3, 5–11; 12–11 Sat; 12–3, 7–10.30 Sun
**Courage Directors; Marston's Pedigree; John Smith's Bitter; guest beers** Ⓗ
Detached, traditional pub with traditional values. A beamed lounge with lots of brass and bric-a-brac provides a relaxing atmosphere. Extensive lunchtime menu; curries a speciality. No food Sun.
🚪 ✿ ◖ ♣ P

### Dusty Miller

87 Crostons Road (B6213/B6214 jct)
☎ (0161) 764 1124
12–11; 12–4, 7–11 Sat; 12–10.30 Sun
**Moorhouse's Black Cat Mild, Premier, Pendle Witches Brew; guest beers** Ⓗ
One of only a handful of Moorhouse's tied houses, this two-roomed pub has a central bar and an enclosed courtyard. No food Wed. Note the stone fingerpost outside. Worth the short walk from the town centre.
✿ ◖ ♣

### Old Blue Bell

2 Bell Lane (B6221/B6222 jct)
☎ (0161) 761 3674
11–11; 12–10.30 Sun
**Hold Mild, Bitter** Ⓗ
Grandly-fronted, large, multi-roomed, drinking man's pub. The traditional vault is very popular for cards and dominoes. The large lounge hosts live music Thu and Sat afternoons; disco Sun. A room with no bar can be used by families until 6.
🛏 ♿ ♣

*Try also: Two Tubs, The Wylde (Thwaites)*

## Castleton

### Blue Pits Inn

842 Manchester Road (A664)
☎ (01706) 32151
12–4 (5 Fri & Sat), 7.30–11; 12–4, 7.30–10.30 Sun
**Lees GB Mild, Bitter** Ⓗ
Welcoming, friendly local in a former railway building, reputedly once used as a mortuary. Three distinct drinking areas and a large upstairs function room now provide a much more cheerful note. ≈ P

*Try also: Midland Beer Co., Manchester Rd (Free)*

## Chadderton

### Horton Arms

Streetbridge (B6195, almost under A627M)
☎ (0161) 624 7793
11.30–11; 12–10.30 Sun
**Lees GB Mild, Bitter, Moonraker** Ⓗ
Popular, comfortable pub which has a rural feel, despite its easy access to Oldham and Rochdale. Neatly laid out in distinct drinking areas, it has one quiet room. Lunches weekdays. ✿ ◖ P

*Try also: Hunt Lane Tavern, Middleton Rd (Lees)*

## Cheadle

### Old Star Inn

13 High Street
☎ (0161) 428 5423
11.30 (11 Sat)–11; 12–10.30 Sun
**Hydes' Anvil Mild, Bitter, seasonal beers** Ⓔ
High Street local in a well-pubbed urban village. Dominoes in the vault; quiet muzak in the lounge. Lunchtime meals Mon–Sat. Good range of whiskies. Prices are generally lower than managed Hydes' houses.
◖ ⊞ ♣ 🍴

### Queens Arms

177 Stockport Road
☎ (0161) 428 3081
11 (4 Mon)–11; 12–10.30 Sun
**Robinson's Hatters Mild, Old Stockport, Best Bitter** Ⓗ
Traditional, multi-roomed community local, popular with families, especially in summer when the large garden with its safe play area is well used. Weekday lunches in summer.
🚪 🛏 ✿ ◖ ♣ P ⌿

## Cheetham

### Queen's Arms

4–6 Honey Street (off A665, near A6010 jct)
☎ (0161) 834 4239

12–11; 12–10.30 Sun
**Federation Buchanan's Mild, Best Bitter, Special; Hughes Ruby Mild; Taylor Best Bitter** *or* **Ram Tam, Landlord; guest beers** Ⓗ
Pub displaying an original Empress Brewery tiled facade, recently doubled in size by sideways expansion. Noted for food, including ethnic dishes, it has a children's certificate (play area in the garden, with views of the Irk Valley and the city centre). Ever-changing range of guest beers. 🚪 ✿ ◖ ▶
≈ (Victoria) ⊖ ♣ ⌂

## Chorlton-cum-Hardy

### Beech Inn

72 Beech Road
☎ (0161) 881 1180
11–11; 12–4, 7–10.30 (12–10.30 summer) Sun
**Bentley's Yorkshire Bitter; Chester's Best Bitter; Flowers Original; Morland Old Speckled Hen; Taylor Best Bitter, Landlord; guest beers** Ⓗ
Thriving, three-room pub, just off the village green. No food, no music, no gimmicks; popular with all ages.
Q ✿ ⊞ ♣

## Compstall

### Andrew Arms

George Street
☎ (0161) 427 2281
11–11; 12–10.30 Sun
**Robinson's Hatters Mild, Best Bitter** Ⓗ
A constant entry in the *Guide* since 1975: a pub which pleases all who visit. Open fire in the comfortable lounge; vault for darts and card lovers. Good lunches. Close to the Etherow Park Nature Reserve.
🚪 Q ✿ ◖ ♣ P

## Cornbrook

### Hope Inn

297 Chester Road
☎ (0161) 848 0038
11–4, 7–11; 12–3, 7–10.30 Sun
**Hydes' Anvil Light, Bitter** Ⓔ
Basic, two-roomed, street-corner local in an area which once boasted a multitude of pubs and breweries. A lone handpump stands on the bar for use in power cuts.
♣

## Daisy Hill

### Rose Hill Tavern

321 Leigh Road, Westhoughton (B5235) ☎ (01942) 815529
12–11; 12–10.30 Sun
**Holt Mild, Bitter** Ⓗ

Large, busy, ex-Tetley pub, nicely refurbished.
◁ ▲ ♣ P

## Delph

### Royal Oak (Th' Heights)
Broad Lane, Heights (1 mile above Denshaw Rd) OS982090
☎ (01457) 874460
7–11; 12–3, 7–10.30 Sun
**Coach House Gunpowder Mild; Commercial Alesman; guest beers** Ⓗ
Isolated, 250-year-old stone pub on an historic pack horse route overlooking the Tame Valley: a cosy bar and three rooms. Good, home-cooked food Fri–Sun (home-bred beef is on the menu).
🏚 Q ❀ ◑ & P

## Denshaw

### Black Horse Inn
2–4 The Culvert, Oldham Road (A672) ☎ (01457) 874375
12–3, 6–11; 12–10.30 Sun
**Banks's Mild, Bitter** Ⓗ
Attractive, 17th-century stone pub in a row of terraced cottages: a cosy L-shaped bar area and two rooms, one available for functions. Wide range of meals lunchtime and early eve. ❀ ◑ P

Try also: **Junction**, Rochdale Rd (Lees)

## Denton

### Chapel House
145 Stockport Road
☎ (0161) 336 3058
11–11; 12–10.30 Sun
**Holt Mild, Bitter** Ⓗ
Imposing addition to the Holt tied estate: a comfortable lounge and a traditional vault.
❀ ⏣ ♣ P

### Jolly Hatters
67 Stockport Road
☎ (0161) 336 3682
11–11; 12–10.30 Sun
**Hydes' Anvil Light, Bitter** Ⓔ
No-nonsense local, often busy, with a strong accent on games.
❀ ◑ ♣ P

## Diggle

### Diggle Hotel
Station Houses (½ mile off A670) ☎ (01457) 872741
12–3, 5–11; 12–11 Sat; 12–3, 5–10.30 Sun
**Boddingtons Bitter; Flowers Original; OB Mild, Bitter; Taylor Golden Best, Landlord** Ⓗ
18th-century, stone pub in a pleasant hamlet: a bar area and two rooms, busy and popular, especially in summer. The

## Dobcross

### Navigation
Wool Road (A670)
☎ (01457) 872418
11.30–3, 5 (6 Sat)–11; 12–4, 7–10.30 Sun
**Banks's Hanson's Mild, Bitter; Marston's Pedigree; guest beer** (occasional) Ⓗ
Next to the Huddersfield Narrow Canal: a stone pub built in 1806 to slake the thirst of navvies cutting the Standedge tunnel under the Pennines. The open-plan lounge is a shrine to brass band music. Eve meals finish early (no eve meals Sun).
❀ ◑ & ♣ P ⏛

### Swan Inn
The Square ☎ (01457) 873451
12–3, 7–11; 12–3, 7–10.30 Sun
**Marston's Pedigree; Moorhouse's Pendle Witches Brew; Theakston Mild, Bitter, XB; guest beers** Ⓗ
Stone-built, village local dating from 1765; a renovated bar area with a flagged floor, plus three distinct drinking areas. Excellent food at reasonable prices lunchtime and early eve (not Sun eve).
🏚 Q ❀ ◑ ♣ ✂

## Eccles

### Grapes Hotel ☆
439 Liverpool Road, Peel Green (A57, near M63 jct 2)
☎ (0161) 789 6971
11–11; 12–10.30 Sun
**Holt Mild, Bitter** Ⓗ
Magnificent, listed Edwardian gem featuring rich mahogany, etched-glass and green tiling. Four rooms include a billiard room, now with pool tables. The upstairs function room hosts angling clubs. A garden is planned. ⏣ ♣ P

### Lamb Hotel ☆
33 Regent Street (A57, opp. bus station) ☎ (0161) 789 3882
11.30–11; 12–10.30 Sun
**Hold Mild, Bitter** Ⓗ
Listed, Edwardian pub in the same style as the Grapes (above). Much mahogany and etched-glass are in evidence with Art Nouveau tiling lining the walls and staircase. As well as a billiards room (still with full-size table), there are three other rooms and a standing area around the bar. Very busy at times. ◑ ⏣ ≩ P

### Queen's Arms
Green Lane, Patricroft (B5231, next to station, up long slope)
☎ (0161) 789 2019

12–3, 6 (5 Fri)–11; 12–11 Sat; 12–4, 7–10.30 Sun
**Boddingtons Mild, Bitter; guest beer** (occasional) Ⓗ
Britain's first railway pub on the oldest passenger line, named after Queen Victoria's journey along the route. Listed by CAMRA activists a few years ago, this four-room classic was facing internal changes as we went to press. Fine view of the track and trains.
👶 ❀ ⏣ ≩ (Patricroft) ♣ P

## Failsworth

### Millgate
Ashton Road West (off A62)
☎ (0161) 688 4910
11.30–11; 12–10.30 Sun
**Boddingtons Bitter; Holt Mild, Bitter; guest beers** Ⓗ
Very popular, large, low-level pub, a completely revamped former British Legion club. Extensive restaurant menu (meals all day Sun). Ideal for families – the garden has adventure play equipment.
👶 ❀ ◑ ⏣ & P

Try also: **Woodhouse Gardens**, Woodhouses (Lees)

## Flixton

### Church Inn
34 Church Road (B5213)
☎ (0161) 748 2158
11–3.30, 5.30–11; 11–11 Fri & Sat; 12–10.30 Sun
**Greenalls Mild, Bitter, Original; guest beer** Ⓗ
Former schoolhouse and court-room, licensed for 120 years and now comfortably furnished with various seating areas. Well-behaved children welcome till 7.30pm.
❀ ◑ ≩ ♣ P

## Gathurst

### Gathurst Station Inn
Station Approach
☎ (01257) 251410
12–3, 5.30–11; 12–11 Sat & summer; 12–10.30 Sun
**Flowers IPA; Moorhouse's Pendle Witches Brew; Tetley Bitter; guest beers** Ⓗ
Recently refurbished, converted railway station (on the Wigan to Southport line) which serves up to seven ales and traditional pub food. No meals Mon; eve meals end at 8 (7 Sat/Sun).
❀ ◑ ⏏ & ▲ ≩ ♣ P

## Golborne

### Railway
131 High Street
☎ (01942) 728202
12–11; 12–10.30 Sun

accent is on home-cooked food (served all day Sat).
❀ 🛏 ◑ ⏏ & P

Theakston Mild, Best Bitter; guest beers Ⓗ
Pub where a central bar serves both the tap room and a smart, comfortable, friendly lounge. Occasional live music; ever-changing range of guest beers. The pub has its own beer club and stages occasional beer festivals. ❀ ⇔ ⚑ ♣ P

## Gorton

### Coach & Horses
227 Belle Vue Street (A57)
5.30 (12 Sat)–11; 12–10.30 Sun
Robinson's Hatters Mild, Best Bitter Ⓗ
Everything that a community local should be, this warm-hearted two-roomer boasts many original features including a fine tiled bar. Loyal local custom is augmented by trade from the multi-screen cinema over the road.
⚑ ≩ (Belle Vue) ♣ P

### Travellers Call
521 Hyde Road (A57/A6010 jct) ☎ (0161) 223 1722
11–11; 12–10.30 Sun
Hydes' Anvil Mild, Bitter, seasonal beers Ⓔ
This basic, no-frills boozer, whose demolition for road widening has been frequently threatened, but always postponed, offers a reminder of Manchester's drinking past in a robust but friendly atmosphere. ⚑ ♣

### Vale Cottage
Croft Bank (footpath off Hyde Rd, A57, at Lord Nelson)
☎ (0161) 223 2477
11.45–3, 5.30–11; 12–4, 7–10.30 Sun
Taylor Landlord; Theakston Best Bitter; Webster's Yorkshire Bitter; Wilson's Bitter Ⓗ
Country pub in the town, overlooking Gore Brook and offering a relaxed, comfortable ambience for social drinking. Food, while popular and excellent, does not take over. HQ for Gorton Morrismen's Rushcart ceremony, which tours the district every Sept. Eve meals end at 8.30. No food Sun eve or Sat. ❀ ◖ ▷ P

### Waggon & Horses
736 Hyde Road (A57)
☎ (0161) 231 6262
11–11; 12–10.30 Sun
Holt Mild, Bitter Ⓗ
Comfortably furnished, main road drinkers' pub consisting of a single drinking area, well divided into a large lounge with a recent extension, a lively vault, and an area for pool and darts (with a Manchester 'log-end' board). Keen prices.
⚑ ≩ (Ryder Brow) ♣ P

## Hale

### Railway
128–130 Ashley Road
☎ (0161) 941 5327
11–11; 12–10.30 Sun
Robinson's Hatters Mild, Old Stockport, Hartleys XB, Best Bitter Ⓗ, Old Tom Ⓖ
Reputedly haunted, unspoilt, 1930s, multi-roomed local retaining much wood panelling. Families welcome until 8.30. No food Sun.
Q ☎ ❀ ◖ ⚑ ≩ ⊖ (Altrincham) ♣

## Halebarns

### Bull's Head
Wicker Lane (off A538, at Cenotaph) ☎ (0161) 980 3050
11.30–11; 12–10.30 Sun
Robinson's Hatters Mild, Hartleys XB, Best Bitter, Frederics Ⓗ
Pub refurbished in 1993 in a variety of styles, but retaining separate drinking areas. The garden has a play area and a bowling green. Children's certificate. Meals end at 7.30 Sun. ⇔ ◖ ▷ ♿ ♣ P ✗

### Unicorn Hotel
329 Hale Road (A538, 1 mile from M56 jct 6)
☎ (0161) 980 4347
11.30–3.30, 5.30–11; 12–3, 7–10.30 Sun
Hydes' Anvil Mild, Bitter Ⓔ, seasonal beers Ⓗ
Smart, comfortable roadside pub with a dining area where children are welcome. No meals Sun eve.
Q ⇔ ◖ ▷ ⚑ ♿ ♣ P

## Harpurhey

### Junction
Hendham Vale (A6010)
☎ (0161) 203 4723
11.30–11; 12.30–10.30 Sun
Boddingtons Bitter; Holt Bitter; Lees Bitter Ⓗ
Serious drinkers' pub with an unusual curved frontage, a very deep, two-level cellar and a traditional vault. Irish music on the jukebox. ♫ Q ⇔ ⚑ ⊖ (Woodlands Rd) ♣

## Harwood

### House Without a Name
75–77 Lea Gate
☎ (01204) 300063
12–11; 12–10.30 Sun
Boddingtons Bitter; Holt Bitter Ⓗ
Small pub in a row of stone cottages dating from 1832, with separate lounge and public bars. Originally an unlicensed brew pub, it was given its unusual name by an impatient magistrate. ❀ ⚑ ♣

## Hazel Grove

### Three Tunnes
194 London Road (A6)
11.30–11; 12–3, 7–10.30 Sun
Robinson's Hatters Mild, Best Bitter Ⓗ
Fine, village-centre local with a good choice of rooms, in an area dominated by Robinson's; the best bet for both a pub and beer. The car park is off a sidestreet at the rear. No food Sun. Q ◖ ⚑ ≩ P

## Heaton Chapel

### Hind's Head
Manchester Road
☎ (0161) 431 9301
11–11; 12–10.30 Sun
Castle Eden Ale; Higsons Bitter; Marston's Pedigree; guest beers Ⓗ
Attractive, welcoming, newly built pub in cottage style on the site of a former night club. It is larger than it looks, with a smart, well-divided lounge and a conservatory restaurant. No jukebox. Children welcome if eating. No food Sun eve. Large garden. ❀ ◖ ▷ ♿ P

## Heaton Mersey

### Crown
6 Vale Close, Didsbury Road (A5145) ☎ (0161) 442 4531
11–11; 12–10.30 Sun
Robinson's Hatters Mild, Best Bitter Ⓗ
Traditional pub which claims to be the oldest in Stockport; not too large, but very busy, with two bars. Award-winning food (eve meals Mon–Fri).
❀ ◖ ▷ P

## Heaton Moor

### Crown Hotel
98 Heaton Moor Road (B5169)
11–11; 12–10.30 Sun
Boddingtons Mild, Bitter, guest beer Ⓗ
Fine, multi-roomed local in a busy suburban shopping area; a favourite with a range of customers. A thriving vault supports dart teams. Ask for the mild – there's no pumpclip. ♫ Q ❀ ⚑ ≩ (Heaton Chapel) ♣

## Heaton Norris

### Moss Rose
63 Didsbury Road (A5145)
☎ (0161) 442 9510
11.30–3.30 (4 Sat), 5.30 (7 Sat)–11; 11.30–11 Mon & Fri; 12–10.30 Sun
Hydes' Anvil Light, Bitter Ⓔ, seasonal beers Ⓗ

An unpromising, early 1970s exterior conceals a comfortable, welcoming local with a traditional feel. Good contrast between the lounge and the vault. No food Sun or Tue.
Ⓓ ⊞ ♣ P ⊟

## Nursery ☆

Green Lane (off A6)
☎ (0161) 432 2044
11.30–3, 5.30–11; 11.30–11 Sat & bank hols; 12–10.30 Sun
**Hydes' Anvil Mild, Bitter** Ⓔ, **seasonal beers** Ⓗ
Comfortable, unspoilt 1930s pub, with its own bowling green, in a conservation area in a pleasant suburb. A good choice of rooms includes a fine, wood-panelled lounge. Excellent food (set lunches only Sun). Children welcome if dining. Q ⊛ Ⓓ ⊞ ♣ P ⊟

## Heywood

### Engineers Arms

11–13 Aspinall Street (off A58)
☎ (01706) 368365
11–3, 7–11; 11–11 Fri & Sat; 12–4, 7–10.30 Sun
**Samuel Smith OBB** Ⓗ
Corner pub, just out of town, that has an interesting tiled interior, having survived a careful renovation. ♣ P

### Wishing Well

89 York Street (A58)
☎ (01706) 620926
12–11; 12–10.30 Sun
**Jennings Bitter; Moorhouse's Premier, Pendle Witches Brew; Taylor Landlord; guest beers** Ⓗ
Atmospheric free house offering a splendid array of independent brewers' beers. The house beers include Wigwam (Phoenix) and Millers Brook (Moorhouse's). ⋓ Ⓓ ♣

**Try also: Oddfellows Arms,** Peel Lane (Lees)

## High Lane

### Royal Oak

Buxton Road ☎ (01663) 762380
11–11 (closes weekday afternoon in winter); 12–10.30 Sun
**Burtonwood Bitter, Buccaneer** Ⓗ
A recently recrafted bar has added to the appeal of this roadside pub where the landlord puts much effort into attracting custom. Rather unusual, mock hunting-lodge feel.
Q ⊛ Ⓓ ▶ ⇌ (Middlewood) P

## Hindley

### Cumberland

39 Chapel Green Road
☎ (01942) 225117
12–4.45, 7–11; 12–3, 7–10.30 Sun
**Tetley Dark Mild, Bitter** Ⓗ

End of terrace local that oozes tradition and atmosphere. One of the last of a dying breed.
🏭 ⊞ ⇌ ♣

### Minstrel

174 Wigan Road
11–11; 12–10.30 Sun
**Stones Bitter; guest beers** Ⓗ
Small but lively local which offers six ales, usually including a mild. Food available all day. Children welcome.
⊛ Ⓓ ♣

## Hollins

### Hollins Bush Inn

257 Hollins Lane (off A56 at Blackford Bridge)
☎ (0161) 766 5692
12–3, 6–11; 12–11 Fri & Sat; 12–10.30 Sun
**Lees GB Mild, Bitter** Ⓔ
Traditional, friendly, three-roomed pub, very popular with locals. Thought to be about 200 years old, it was recently commended by Lees for having the *Best Kept Cellar*. Typical bar food served (except Sun lunch and Tue eve).
Q ⊛ Ⓓ ▶ ♣ P

## Horwich

### Old Original Bay Horse

206 Lee Lane (B6226)
☎ (01204) 696231
11–11; 12–10.30 Sun
**Boddingtons Bitter; Chester's Mild; Flowers Original; Lees Bitter; guest beer** Ⓗ
Small pub in the town centre, very busy at weekends. Small, cosy vault.
Q ⊛ ⊞ ♣ P

**Try also: Gallaghers,** Little Scotland, Blackrod (Free)

## Hyde

### Godley Hall Inn

Godley Hall (200 yds along Station Rd)
☎ (0161) 368 4415
11–3.30, 7–11; 12–3, 7–10.30 Sun
**Vaux Mild, Bitter, Samson** Ⓗ
Small, historic pub, formerly a manorial hall and licensed since the early 19th century. Somewhat off the beaten track and apparently in the middle of a meat packing factory! The low ceilinged rooms add to the cosy feel.
Q ⊛ Ⓓ ⇌ (Godley) ♣ P

### White Lion

7 Market Place
☎ (0161) 368 2948
11.30–3, 7.30–11; 11–11 Sat; 12–3, 7–10.30 Sun
**Robinson's Hatters Mild, Best Bitter** Ⓔ, **Old Tom** Ⓗ

Popular, town-centre pub prominently located next to the market, which supplies much daytime custom: a comfortable lounge, plus a tap room sporting an impressively long bar. A rare all year outlet for Old Tom.
Ⓓ ⊞ ⇌ (Central/Newton) ♣

## Irlams o'th' Height

### Red Lion

279 Bolton Road
☎ (0161) 736 9680
11–11; 12–10.30 Sun
**Holt Mild, Bitter** Ⓔ
Pre-war pub catering for the older drinker with a lounge and a public bar. One of three Joseph Holt pubs in the village.
Q ⊞ ♣ P

## Jericho

### Famous Gamecock Inn

455 Rochdale Old Road (B6222, opp. Fairfield Hospital)
☎ (0161) 761 4784
12–4, 6–11; 12–11 Fri & Sat; 12–10.30 Sun
**Banks's Mild; Marston's Bitter, Pedigree; Thwaites Bitter; guest beer** Ⓗ
Originally a beer house and once a blacksmith's, this pub, built in 1824, retains three rooms. Good range of bar meals. Quiz night Tue.
⋓ ⊛ Ⓓ ♣ P

## Leigh

### Musketeer

15 Lord Street
☎ (01942) 701143
11–11; 12–7, 10.30 Sun
**Boddingtons Mild, Bitter; guest beer** Ⓗ
Two-roomed, town-centre local. The lounge is divided into three areas; the main area in front of the bar houses a large collection of Lancashire colliery plates. The sporting tap room displays local RLFC photographs. Ⓓ ♣

### Victoria

68–70 Kirkhall Lane
☎ (01942) 606114
7.30–11; 2–5, 7.30–11 Fri; 12–11 Sat; 12–10.30 Sun
**Tetley Mild, Bitter; guest beers** (occasional) Ⓗ
Welcoming, edge-of-town, multi-roomed local, handy for Leigh RLFC. ⊛ ♣

## Littleborough

### Red Lion Hotel

6 Halifax Road (A58/B6225 jct)
☎ (01706) 378195
3 (12 Fri & Sat)–11; 12–10.30 Sun
**Webster's Yorkshire Bitter; Wilson's Mild, Bitter; guest beers** Ⓗ

Parts of this traditional, multi-roomed pub date back to the 16th century. At some time in its history it was a boat repair yard and re-opened as a pub in the 1800s. Two scrumpies. Red Lion house beer is brewed by Phoenix. ♨ Q ☸ ♠ ▲ ⌂ P

## Little Lever

### Horseshoe Inn
71 Lever Street
☎ (01204) 572081
12–4, 7–11; 11–11 Sat; 12–4, 7–10.30 Sun
**Hydes' Anvil Mild, Bitter, seasonal beers** Ⓗ
Busy, two-roomed pub with a lounge, a vault and many sports teams. Q ⊟ ♣ ⊟

## Lowton Lane Head

### Red Lion
324 Newton Road
☎ (01942) 671429
12–3.30, 5.30–11; 12–11 Sat; 12–10.30 Sun
**Greenalls Mild, Bitter, Davenports Bitter, Original; Tetley Bitter; guest beers** Ⓗ
Popular with drinkers and diners alike, this pub attracts all ages to its comfortable lounges, pool room, bowling green and garden (next to the landlord's war games centre). Meals all day Sun until 9.30.
☸ ⊯ ◑ ▶ ⊟ ♣ P

## Lowton St Lukes

### Hare & Hounds
1 Golborne Road
☎ (01942) 728387
12–11; 12–10.30 Sun
**Tetley Mild, Bitter; guest beers** Ⓗ
Large, open-plan pub catering for all, with a large children's playground. Occasional barbecues and beer festivals. Up to four guest beers.
☸ ◑ ▶ ♣ P

## Manchester City Centre

### Beer House
6 Angel Street (off A664, near A665 jct) ☎ (0161) 839 7019
11.30–11; 12.30–10.30 Sun
**Burtonwood Bitter; Moorhouse's Pendle Witches Brew; Theakston Best Bitter, XB; guest beers** Ⓗ
Basic, extremely popular free house where a large blackboard shows the ever-changing beer and cider range. Beer festivals and cider festivals are held regularly, often in the upstairs function room. Watch out for food promotions. Eve meals Thu–Fri, finishing at 7.30.
☸ ◑ ▶ ⇌ (Victoria) ⊖ ⌂

### Castle
66 Oldham Street (400 yds from Piccadilly Gdns, near A62/A665 jct)
☎ (0161) 236 2945
11.30–11; 12–4, 7.30–10.30 Sun
**Robinson's Hatters Mild, Old Stockport, Best Bitter, Frederics, Old Tom** Ⓗ
Robinson's only city-centre pub. A tiled facade and a mosaic floor lead into a comfortable front bar, with a cosy snug behind and a large pool room. Children's room lunchtimes. Q ☎ ⊟ ⇌ (Victoria/Piccadilly) ⊖ (High St/Piccadilly Gdns) ♣

### Circus Tavern ☆
86 Portland Street
☎ (0161) 236 5818
12–11; 12–3, 7–10.30 Sun (may vary)
**Tetley Bitter** Ⓗ
This tiny two-roomer has often been compared to a Dublin bar, but in truth it is one of a kind. The Quadrant bar has room only for two handpumps – no keg is sold. The two small rooms and corridor hold no more than 40 drinkers, so the pub can close its doors when full. Impromptu music at times.
♨ Q ⇌ (Piccadilly) ⊖ (Piccadilly Gdns)

### City Arms
48 Kennedy Street
11.30–11; 11.30–3, 7–11 Sat; closed Sun
**Tetley Bitter; guest beers** Ⓗ
Very popular, two-roomed pub, much frequented by the city-centre business community. Good value food. A listed building with a noteworthy frontage.
◑ ☒ ⇌ (Oxford Rd) ⊖ (St Peter's Sq)

### Crown & Cushion
192 Corporation Street (200 yds N of Victoria station)
☎ (0161) 839 1844
11–11; 12–10.30 Sun
**Hold Mild, Bitter** Ⓗ
Comfortable, open-plan pub, just beyond the bustle of the city centre and close to Holt's Brewery. ⇌ (Victoria) ⊖ ♣

### Crown Inn
321 Deansgate
☎ (0161) 834 1930
12–11; 12–10.30 Sun
**Vaux Mild, Samson; guest beer** Ⓗ
Former Wilson's pub in the Castlefield area. Its one bar manages to capture the feel of a vault in one part and a comfortable lounge in the other. Games include table football. Good value food (weekday lunches) and accommodation. ⊯ ◑ ⇌ (Deansgate) ⊖ (G Mex) ♣

### Hare & Hounds
46 Shudehill (near Arndale bus station) ☎ (0161) 832 4737
11–11; 12–10.30 Sun
**Tetley Dark Mild, Bitter; guest beer** Ⓗ
Popular, city-centre pub with the atmosphere of a local, featuring extensive tiling and leaded glass in its front bar, lobby and snug back room. Home-made food (eve meals on request).
♨ Q ◑ ⊟ ⇌ (Victoria) ⊖ (High St/Market St) ♣

### Jolly Angler
47 Ducie Street (near A665/Gt Ancoats St jct)
☎ (0161) 236 5307
12–4, 5.30–11; 12–11 Fri & Sat; 12–4, 7–10.30 Sun
**Hydes' Anvil Light, Bitter, seasonal beers** Ⓗ
Authentic backstreet boozer which has stood the test of time. It is difficult to put your finger on what makes this such an inviting local. An Irish pub without the clichés!
♨ ⇌ (Piccadilly) ⊖

### Old Monkey
90–92 Portland Street
11.30–11; 12–10.30 Sun
**Holt Mild, Bitter** Ⓗ
Opened in 1993, this brewery flagship has a ground floor saloon bar and an upstairs lounge. High quality materials are used throughout, with local memorabilia as decor. Low prices and high standards make it (sometimes very) busy. Weekday lunches.
Q ◑ ⊟ ⇌ ⊖

### Peveril of the Peak ☆
127 Great Bridgewater Street
☎ (0161) 236 6364
12–3 (not Sat), 5.30 (7 Sat)–11; 7–10.30 Sun, closed Sun lunch
**Webster's Yorkshire Bitter; Wilson's Bitter; Ruddles Best Bitter; guest beer** Ⓗ
Named after a famous 19th-century stagecoach: a classic multi-roomed, triangular-shaped pub, with a glazed tile exterior and wood and stained-glass panels inside. Popular with students and home to Manchester's longest serving landlady (25 years). Open Sat lunch when Man. Utd are at home.
♨ ☸ ◑ ⊟ ⇌ (Oxford Rd) ⊖ (St Peter's Sq) ♣

### Smithfield Hotel
37 Swan Street (A665)
☎ (0161) 839 4424
12–11; 7–10.30 Sun, closed Sun lunch
**Freetraders Twelve Bore; Fuller's London Pride; Highgate Dark; guest beers** Ⓗ
Former Smithfield Market pub, now one long, narrow room with a bar halfway along and a dining area at the back. See the

old 'magic lantern' on top of
the piano. Eve meals 5.30–7.30.
Three ciders. 🍴 ◖ ▮ ⇌
(Victoria) ⊖ (High St) ○

## White House

122 Great Ancoats Street
☎ (0161) 228 3231
12–4, 8–11; 12–11 Fri & Sat; 12–3,
8–10.30 Sun
**Holt Bitter; Thwaites Bitter;
guest beers** Ⓗ
Welcoming corner local,
fronted by a curved lounge,
decorated with sherry casks
and photos of long dead film
stars. Popular vault to the rear.
❀ ◖ 🍴 ⇌ (Piccadilly) ⊖ ♣

## White Lion

43 Liverpool Road, Castlefield
☎ (0161) 832 7373
11.30–11; 12–10.30 Sun
**Boddingtons Bitter;
Taylor Landlord;
guest beers** Ⓗ
Pub at the heart of the
Castlefield area, close to the
canal basin and museums. The
old city photographs are
worthy of study. The good
value food is all made and
cooked on the premises (no eve
meals Fri; meals till 6 Sun).
❀ ◖ ▮ ⅊ ⇌ (Deansgate)
⊖ (G Mex)

**Try also: Unicorn**, Church St
(Bass); **Vine**, Kennedy St
(Scottish Courage)

## Marple

### Pineapple

Market Street
☎ (0161) 427 3935
11–11; 12–10.30 Sun
**Robinson's Hatters Mild,
Hartleys XB, Best Bitter,
Frederics** Ⓗ
Enterprising, comfortable and
welcoming redbrick pub in the
centre of Marple, built to last in
1892. Inventive, good value
food includes Tapas. Well-used
by locals of all ages.
🍴 Q 🍴 ◖ ▮ ♣ P ✕

**Try also: Travellers Call**, Lane
Ends, Glossop Rd (Robinson's)

## Mellor

### Oddfellows Arms

73 Moor End Road
☎ (0161) 449 7826
12–3, 5.30–11; 12–3, 7–10.30 Sun
**Banks's Mild; Marston's
Bitter, Pedigree;
guest beer** Ⓗ
Elegant, stone, three-storey
building sympathetically
altered internally, in a picture-
postcard setting, in a dip on the
Marple Bridge to New Mills
road. Enterprising cuisine;
excellent choice of beer.
🍴 Q ❀ ◖ ▮ P ✕

## Middleton

### Crown Inn

52 Rochdale Road (A664)
☎ (0161) 654 9174
11.30–11; 12–10.30 Sun
**Lees GB Mild, Bitter** Ⓗ
End of terrace pub with a small
snug and a much larger
lounge, hung with horse
brasses. Almost always busy.
♣ P

### Lancashire Fold

77 Kirkway, Alkrington (½ mile
off A664) ☎ (0161) 643 4198
11.30–11; 12–10.30 Sun
**Lees GB Mild, Bitter,
Moonraker** Ⓗ
Exceptionally busy, popular
estate-style pub with a large
lounge and a lively public bar.
It was recently renovated to
high standards but the prices
remain extremely reasonable.
♋ ❀ ◖ ▮ ⅊ ♣ P

### Tandle Hill Tavern

Thornham Lane, Slattocks
(unmetalled road, 1 mile off
A671 / A664) OS898091
☎ (01706) 345297
7 (4 summer)–11; 12–11 Sat; 12–10.30
Sun
**Lees GB Mild, Bitter,
Moonraker** (winter) Ⓗ
Welcoming, two-roomed pub
at the heart of a small farming
community, near Tandle Hill
Country Park. Soup and
sandwich Sun lunches.
Children welcome until early
eve. 🍴 ♋ ❀ ♣

**Try also: Oddfellows Arms**,
Oldham Rd (Scottish Courage)

## Milnrow

### Waggon Inn

Butterworth Hall (off B6225)
☎ (01706) 48313
11–11; 12–10.30 Sun
**Burtonwood Mild, Bitter** Ⓗ
Purpose-built public house
from 1732: a friendly and
popular pub which retains a
multi-room layout. Table
football played. ❀ ⇌ ♣ P

## Mossley

### Tollemache Arms

415 Manchester Road
☎ (01457) 832354
11–3, 5–11; 11–11 Fri & Sat; 12–3,
7–10.30 Sun
**Robinson's Hatters Mild, Best
Bitter** Ⓗ
Popular, cosy, sociable, stone-
built local next to the
Huddersfield Narrow Canal,
which is overlooked by the
small garden. Compact oak-
panelled rooms and a polished
bar feature. In the same family
since 1959. 🍴 Q ❀ ♣ P

## New Springs

### Colliers Arms

192 Wigan Road
☎ (01942) 831171
12.30–5.30 (not Thu), 7.30–11; 12–5,
7–10.30 Sun
**Burtonwood Mild, Bitter** Ⓗ
18th-century pub by the
Leeds–Liverpool Canal.
♋ ♣ P

## Newton Heath

### Railway Hotel

82 Dean Lane (off A62, Oldham
Rd, opp. station)
☎ (0161) 681 8199
11.30–11; 12–10.30 Sun
**Holt Mild, Bitter** Ⓔ
Friendly, recently refurbished
local with a large main bar and
a popular vault. Victorian
tiling and stained-glass
windows feature.
⅊ ⇌ (Dean Lane)

### Robin Hood

237 Droylsden Road (500 yds
from Oldham Rd)
☎ (0161) 681 5167
12–4.30, 7–11; 12–11 Sat; 12–10.30 Sun
**Bateman Mild; Marston's
Bitter** Ⓗ
Well-maintained two-roomed
local with a comfortable lounge
and an extensive, well-
furnished vault. Its traditional
atmosphere attracts a cross-
section of customers.
❀ ⅊ ♣ P

## Oldham

### Beer Emporium

92–94 Union Street (near
central library)
☎ (0161) 628 7887
12–11; 12–4, 7.30–11 Sat; 12–3,
7.30–10.30 Sun
**Marston's Bitter, Pedigree;
Newcastle Exhibition;
Theakston Best Bitter, Old
Peculier; guest beer** Ⓗ
Popular, town-centre free
house with six regular beers,
plus guests usually including a
mild. Free jukebox; live music
at least once a week. Table
football and pool played.
⇌ (Mumps)

### Dog & Partridge

376 Roundthorn Road (off
B6194)
☎ (0161) 624 3335
7–11; 11.30–3, 7–11 Sat; 11–11 Fri;
12–5, 7–10.30 Sun
**Lees GB Mild, Bitter** Ⓗ
Popular, comfortably
furnished, detached pub in a
semi-rural setting, with low,
beamed ceilings. Busy Sun
lunch with local football teams.
♋ ❀ ♣ P

### Hark to Topper

5 Bow Street
☎ (0161) 624 7950

11.30–3, 7–11; 12–3, 7–10.30 Sun
**Samuel Smith OBB** H
Detached town-centre pub (a former Rochdale & Manor house, known as the Manor Inn), with an impressive brick exterior dating from 1835. Just off the high street, its pleasant, open-plan, interior has a central bar and etched-glass windows. ♨ ◖ ⇌ (Mumps)

Try also: **Gardeners Arms**, Mill Bottom (Robinson's); **Hogshead**, Union St (Whitbread)

## Ramsbottom

### Royal Oak
39 Bridge Street
☎ (01706) 822786
12–11; 12–4, 7–10.30 Sun
**Thwaites Best Mild, Bitter, Craftsman** H
Friendly, three-roomed village-centre pub in a conservation area, popular with visitors to the nearby East Lancs Railway, a preserved line which runs steam locos at weekends and bank hols. Bar meals Wed–Sun lunchtimes.
⛟ ◖ ⇌ (E Lancs) ♣

Try also: **Old Dun Horse**, Bolton St (Thwaites)

## Ringley

### Lord Nelson
Kearsley Hall Road, Stoneclough (off A667)
☎ (01204) 579456
12–3 (4 Sat), 7–11; 12–3, 7–10.30 Sun (may open all day in summer)
**Thwaites Best Mild, Bitter** H
Traditional village local in a scenic riverside setting. Railway buffs should check out the 'railwayana' in the appropriately titled Railway Room.
♨ Q ❀ ⇌ (Kearsley) ♣ P

## Rochdale

### Albert
62 Spotland Road (A608)
☎ (01706) 45666
11–11; 12–10.30 Sun
**Burtonwood Mild, Bitter** H
Corner local with an open-plan bar and a separate vault that can get boisterous. Free 'oldies' jukebox. ♨ ♣

### Albion
600 Whitworth Road (A671, 2 miles from centre)
☎ (01706) 48540
12–3, 4.30–11; 11–11 Thu–Sat; 12–10.30 Sun
**Adnams Bitter; Bateman Mild; Lees Bitter; Marston's Bitter, Pedigree; Taylor Landlord** H
Traditional, three-roomed local given a new lease of life by an enthusiastic landlord. Excellent

range of wines. Food is very well presented and includes oxtail, steaks and sometimes ostrich. Lunches served Thu and Fri. ♨ ⛟ ◖ ▶

### Cask & Feather
1 Oldham Road
☎ (01706) 711476
11–11; 12–10.30 Sun
**McGuinness Feather Plucker Mild, Best Bitter, Junction Bitter, Tommy Todd Porter, seasonal beers** H
Distinctive stone-fronted pub on the main road near the town centre; a comfortable and well-appointed pub, home of Thomas McGuinness Brewery.
◖ ⇌

### Eagle
59 Oldham Road (A671/Wood St jct)
☎ (01706) 45453
12–3 (4 Sat), 5 (7 Sat)–11; 12–11 Fri; 12–10.30 Sun
**Samuel Smith OBB** H
Popular, stone-built pub, on the outskirts of the town centre, retaining many interesting period features and artefacts. ⇌ ♣

### Healey Hotel
172 Shawclough Road, Healey (B6377) ☎ (01706) 45453
12–3, 5–11; 12–3, 5–10.30 Sun
**Robinson's Best Bitter** H
Out-of-town, terraced hostelry with several drinking areas. It is subtly decorated and friendly, and retains much of its original splendid tiled interior. Boules played.
Q ❀ ◖ ▶

### Merry Monk
234 College Road (near A6060/B6222 jct)
☎ (01706) 46919
12–11; 12–3, 7–10.30 Sun
**Marston's Bitter, Pedigree; guest beers** H
Friendly, unpretentious free house selling up to four guest beers. Unusual Ring the Bull game. Free jukebox. ♣ P

### Success to the Plough
179 Bolton Road, Marland (A58) ☎ (01706) 33270
12–11; 12–10.30 Sun
**Lees GB Mild, Bitter** H
Imposing, detached redbrick pub displaying its name in glazed tiles on a gable wall. The extensive interior is divided into separate areas. Home of the John Willie Lees Crown Green Bowling Classic. No food Sat or Sun.
❀ ◖ ♨ ♣ P

Try also: **Flying Horse**, Town Hall Sq (Free)

## Romiley

### Duke of York
Stockport Road
☎ (0161) 430 2806

11.30–11; 12–10.30 Sun
**Courage Directors; Ruddles County; John Smith's Bitter; Webster's Green Label; guest beer** H
Long, low pub of harmonious proportions, just as pleasing inside with its beamed lounge and vault. Close to the Peak Forest Canal. Good, home-cooked food.
❀ ◖ ▶ ♨ ♣ ⇌ ♣ P

Try also: **Spread Eagle**, Hatherlow (Whitbread)

## Royton

### Marston Tavern
83 Rochdale Road
☎ (0161) 628 0569
12–3, 7–11; 12–3, 7–10.30 Sun
**Bateman Mild; Marston's Bitter, Pedigree; guest beers** H
Detached, town-centre pub with two distinct drinking areas. A former Rothwell house called the Radcliffe Arms, it was acquired by Marston's in 1961, who renamed it after refurbishment in 1976. Good, friendly atmosphere. No food Sat or Sun. ◖ ♣

### Puckersley Inn
22 Narrowgate Brow (off A671 via Dogford Rd)
☎ (0161) 624 4973
5 (4.30 Fri, 12 Sat)–11; 12–3, 7.30–10.30 Sun
**Lees GB Mild, Bitter** H
Popular, detached, stone-fronted pub on the edge of town, with panoramic views of Royton and Oldham. Well-furnished lounge; more basic, yet lively, vault. Q ♨ ♣ P

Try also: **Dog & Partridge**, Middleton Rd (Lees)

## Rusholme

### Albert
5 Walmer Street (off B5177 at Shere Khan)
☎ (0161) 224 2287
11–11; 12–3, 7–10.30 Sun
**Hydes' Anvil Bitter** E
Forget fake Irish theme pubs – this is the real thing. Irish writers and classic Guinness posters feature in this lively two-roomer (pool and cards to the fore in the back room), where the Republic's football team is fanatically supported. Sun eves see traditional music sessions. ♨ ♣ ☷

## Salford

### Crescent
20 Crescent (A6, near University)
☎ (0161) 736 5600
12 (7.30 Sat)–11; 1–4, 7.30–10.30 Sun
**Beer range varies** H

Cosy, multi-roomed pub with a splendid cat population. A noteworthy painting of Salford Old Tech hangs on the wall above the fireplace. The house beers, Crescent and Son of Crescent, are brewed by Scottish Courage and Titanic respectively. Eve meals finish at 8. No food weekends. ⚏ ❀ ◗
◗ ⊞ ≢ (Crescent) ♣ ↻ P

## Dock & Pulpit

1 Encombe Place (off Chapel St, A6)
☎ (0161) 834 0121
11–3 (not Sat), 5 (7.30 Sat)–11; 12–3, 7.30–10.30 Sun
**Beer range varies** Ⓗ
Small, friendly, gas-lit, one-room free house with an old-fashioned cast iron fireplace. It can be difficult to find, but is well worth the effort. The name derives from the nearby former law courts and the church. House beer available.
⚏ Q ◗ ≢ (Central) ♣ ↻

## Eagle Inn

19 Collier Street (near A6041/A6042 jct)
☎ (0161) 832 7530
11–11; 12–10.30 Sun
**Holt Mild, Bitter** Ⓗ
Archetypal, small, unspoilt backstreet local in an area of old terraced housing and modern car showrooms, dissected by a new dual carriageway.
Q ⊞ ≢ (Victoria) ⊖ ♣

## Egerton Arms

Gore Street (A6 jct, by station)
☎ (0161) 834 3182
11–11; 12–5 Sun
**Boddingtons Bitter; Holt Mild, Bitter; Lees Bitter; Marston's Bitter, Pedigree** Ⓗ
Exuberant and flamboyant, with chandeliers and Art Nouveau lamps, but most of all a cracking pub with class. Probably the cheapest pint in Salford.
❀ ⊭ ◗ ⊞ ≢ (Central) ♣

## King's Arms

11 Bloom Street (off A6, opp. A34 jct)
☎ (0161) 839 4388
11–11; 12.30–10.30 Sun
**OB Bitter; Taylor Landlord; Theakston Best Bitter; guest beers** Ⓗ
Popular and friendly pub offering ten or more ales and many foreign bottled beers. The bar serves a large main room; a small counter serves a snug across the corridor with its popular pinball machine. Live music at times.
◗ ≢ (Central) ♣ ↻

## Union Tavern

105 Liverpool Street
☎ (0161) 736 2885

11–11; 12–10.30 Sun
**Holt Mild, Bitter** Ⓗ
Gem of a Holt's outlet in an area surrounded by industrial property. Friendly bar staff; popular darts teams (ten).
Q ⊞ ♿ ≢ (Crescent) ♣ P

## Welcome

Robert Hall Street, Ordsall (off A5066)
☎ (0161) 872 6040
12–4, 7–11; 12–3, 7.30–10.30 Sun
**Lees GB Mild, Bitter** Ⓔ
A valued rarity – Lees beers are uncommon in Salford, and good pubs are almost extinct in Ordsall. This 1970s (ex-Wilson's) building, with a lounge, games room and function room, is a true community local. The handpumps work electric pumps. Q ⊞ ♣ P

## Shaw

## Black Horse

203A Rochdale Road (B6194)
☎ (01706) 847173
2 (12 Sat)–11; 12–10.30 Sun
**Lees GB Mild, Bitter** Ⓗ
Friendly, stone built pub, ten mins' walk from Shaw station. A cosy, comfortable lounge area and a vault.
⊞ ♣ P

**Try also: Blue Bell**, Market St (Robinson's)

## Stalybridge

## Q

3 Market Street
☎ (0161) 303 9157
5–11; 12–3, 7–11 Sat; 12–3, 7.30–10.30 Sun
**Marston's Bitter; guest beers** Ⓗ
Cosy pub with a continental feel, incorporating an upstairs cocktail bar and a conservatory. Much needed space is soon to be provided by extension into the shop next door. The name, recognised as the shortest in the UK, originally belonged to a long-gone pub nearby.
Q ≢ P

## Rose & Crown

7 Market Street
☎ (0161) 303 7098
11–11; 12–10.30 Sun
**Vaux Mild, Bitter, Samson; guest beers** Ⓗ
Excellent urban local with a staunch local following. The pokey back room has been opened up into the main room. A games room is also available.
≢ P

## White House

1 Water Street
☎ (0161) 303 2288
11–11; 12–3, 7–10.30 Sun

**Marston's Bitter, Pedigree; guest beers** Ⓗ
Enterprising free house with a well deserved reputation. Three rooms and a popular bar area are well used by locals and clubs. Extensive range of whiskies and foreign bottled beers. Q ◗ ≢ P

## Standish

## Dog & Partridge

33 School Lane
☎ (01257) 401218
1–11; 12–10.30 Sun
**Boddingtons Bitter; Tetley Dark Mild, Mild, Bitter** Ⓗ
Modern, male-dominated, open-plan pub featuring sport on TV. Limited parking.
❀ ♣ P

## Stockport

## Arden Arms ☆

23 Millgate (behind Asda)
☎ (0161) 480 2185
12–11; 12.30–3, 7–10.30 Sun
**Robinson's Hatters Mild, Best Bitter, Old Tom** Ⓗ
Classic, multi-roomed pub on the edge of town. Find the snug, accessed through the bar area. Music Wed eve. A listed gem, not to be missed.
Q ❀ ⊭ ◗ ♣ P

## Armoury

Greek Street, Shaw Heath (off A6) ☎ (0161) 480 5055
11.30–11; 11.30–4, 8–11 Sat; 12–3, 7–10.30 Sun
**Robinson's Hatters Mild, Best Bitter** Ⓔ
Don't be put off by the plain exterior: inside is a warm and welcoming local with fine, unspoilt 1920s decor. The bright lounge and superb vault form the core of the pub but there is also a lobby and a back room. Handy for Edgeley Park.
Q ⊞ ≢ ♣

## Blossoms

2 Buxton Road, Heavily (A5102/A6 jct)
12–11; 12–10.30 Sun
**Robinson's Hatters Mild, Best Bitter, Frederics, Old Tom** Ⓗ
Classic, multi-roomed local with a friendly welcome. Three rooms and a lobby lead to a central bar. A rare outlet for Frederics and Old Tom.
Q ◗ ♿ ♣ P

## Crown

154 Heaton Lane (150 yds W of A6, beneath viaduct)
☎ (0161) 429 8646
12–11; 12–10.30 Sun
**Boddingtons Bitter; Lees Bitter; guest beers** Ⓗ
Attractive, multi-roomed ale house usually stocking nine beers and a guest cider. Occasional beer festivals.
❀ ◗ ≢ ↻ ✦

### Florist
100 Shaw Heath
☎ (0161) 480 2734
11–11; 12–3, 7–10.30 Sun
**Robinson's Hatters Mild, Best Bitter** Ⓗ
Although somewhat altered, this is still a classic multi-roomer, now thriving under new licensees. The garden is a sun trap in summer. Despite its size, the pub can be difficult to spot – look for the name high on the side wall. No meals Sat eve or Sun. Q ⊛ ◖ ▶ ⇌ ♣

### Greyhound
27 Bowden Street, Edgeley
☎ (0161) 480 5699
12 (11.30 Fri & Sat)–11; 12–10.30 Sun
**Boddingtons Mild, Bitter; guest beers** Ⓗ
An estate-pub exterior conceals a warm, friendly local, improved by refurbishment in 1995. An increasingly rare outlet for real Boddingtons Mild. Up to three guest beers are usually available. It may open earlier when County play at home. ⊛ ⊞ ⇌ ♣ P

### Olde Woolpack
70 Brinksway
☎ (0161) 429 8821
11.30–3, 5.30 (6.30 Sat)–11; 11.30–11 Fri; 12–10.30 Sun
**Marston's Pedigree; Tetley Bitter; Theakston Best Bitter; Thwaites Best Mild; guest beers** Ⓗ
Cosy, semi-open-plan local with three rooms and a lobby, offering one, ever-changing guest beer. Overshadowed by a giant blue pyramid, it is easily accessed from the motorway. Opening hours and the availability of food may change as offices and other developments are erected nearby. ◖ ♣ P

## Strines

### Sportsman's Arms
105 Strines Road (1 mile from Marple on New Mills road)
☎ (0161) 427 2888
11.30–3, 5.30–11; 12–3, 7–10.30 Sun
**Bateman Mild; Mitchell's Original; guest beers** Ⓗ
Welcoming country pub with two rooms (a vault and a lounge/dining room), plus impressive views over to Mellor. At least two guest beers, always changing.
Q ⊛ ◖ ▶ ⊞ & ⇌ P

**Try also: Romper**, Ridge End (Free)

## Swinton

### Buckley Arms
135–137 Partington Lane
☎ (0161) 794 2657
12–3.30, 5.30–11; 12–11 Fri & Sat; 12–4, 7–10.30 Sun

**Tetley Mild, Bitter** Ⓗ
Deservedly popular, thriving community local with two rooms. The landlord holds Tetley *Master of Cellarcraft* awards for 1993 and '95. Meals weekdays. ⊛ ◖ ⊞ ⇌ ♣ P

### Cricketers' Arms
227 Manchester Road (A6, near A572 jct) ☎ (0161) 281 5382
11.30–11; 11.30–4, 7–11 Sat; 12–10.30 Sun
**Holt Mild, Bitter** Ⓗ
Thriving, two-room local, recently smartened up and ever popular, especially with older customers. ⊞

### White Swan
186 Worsley Road
☎ (0161) 794 1504
12–11; 12–10.30 Sun
**Holt Mild, Bitter** Ⓗ
Large, smart, four-room, late 1920s pub. The vault has its own entrance, the main room is wood-panelled, while the side room retains a vestige of a dividing wall. The former pool room at the rear has been converted to a sumptuous function/family room.
Q ⌂ ⊛ ◖ ⊞ ♣ P

## Turton

### Bull's Head
857 Bradshaw Road
☎ (01204) 852411
12–3 (4 Sat), 6.30–11 (12–11 summer); 12–4, 7–10.30 (12–10.30 summer) Sun
**Ruddles Best Bitter; John Smith's Bitter; guest beer** Ⓗ
Stone pub, rebuilt in 1891, situated on the Lancs boundary, on the original Watling Street (Roman road). Reputedly haunted. Excellent views across the moors. Regular piano nights. Busy summer food trade (ring to check summer hours).
⌂ Q ⊛ ◖ ▲ ♣ P

## Tyldesley

### Half Moon
115–117 Elliot Street
☎ (01942) 873206
11–4 (4.30 Sat), 7–11; 12–3, 7–10.30 Sun
**Holt Mild, Bitter; guest beers** Ⓗ
Popular pub with all ages, especially at weekends: a low-beamed lounge and a pool room. ⊛ ♣

### Mort Arms
235 Elliot Street
☎ (01942) 883481
12–11; 12–10.30 Sun
**Holt Mild, Bitter** Ⓗ
Town local popular with all ages: a comfortable, panelled lounge, where the bowed bar is complete with etched-glass screens, and a bright, lively tap room. ⊞ P

## Uppermill

### Cross Keys
Off Running Hill Gate (off A670, up Church Rd)
☎ (01457) 874626
11–11; 12–10.30 Sun
**Lees GB Mild, Bitter, Moonraker** Ⓗ
Attractive, 18th-century, stone building overlooking Saddleworth Church. The public bar has a stone-flagged floor and a Yorkshire range. The hub of many activities, including mountain rescue and clay pigeon shooting. Folk night Wed.
⇌ Q ⊛ ◖ ▶ ⊞ & ▲ ♣ P

**Try also: Waggon Inn**, High St (Robinson's)

## Westhoughton

### Cross Guns
25–27 Bolton Road (½ mile off A6) ☎ (01942) 811124
11.30–4 (4 Fri & Sat), 7–11; 12–3, 7–10.30 Sun
**Tetley Mild; Walker Bitter** Ⓗ
Large, open-plan pub, recently extended to incorporate a pool table. Warm welcome.
⇌ Q ⊛ ♣

## Whitefield

### New Grove Inn
183 Bury New Road (A56)
☎ (0161) 766 2190
12–11; 12–4, 7–11 Sat; 12–10.30 Sun
**Holt Mild, Bitter** Ⓗ
Recently modernised, spacious, friendly two-roomer. The interior belies its 1920s brick exterior. Strong sporting and social support ensures that both bars are well frequented. Impressive local prints in the bar. ⊖ ♣

**Try also: Beehive**, Bury New Rd (Whitbread)

## Wigan

### Beer Engine
69 Poolstock Lane
☎ (01942) 321820
11–11; 12–10.30 Sun
**Courage Directors; Marston's Pedigree; John Smith's Bitter; guest beers** Ⓗ
Pub with a comfortable lounge and a large concert room which stages an annual beer, pie and music festival. Excellent bowling green. Meals served 11–7 Fri–Sun. ⊛ ◖ ▶ ⇌ (Wallgate/NW) ♣ P

### Bird i'the' Hand (Th' En 'Ole)
102 Gidlow Lane
☎ (01942) 241004
12–11; 12–10.30 Sun
**Tetley Mild, Bitter; Theakston**

**Best Bitter; guest beers** H
Tiny, comfortable local with impressive mosaicwork above the door. ✿ ◖ ▶ ⚥ ♣ P

### Bold Hotel

161 Poolstock Lane, Worsley Mesnes ☎ (01942) 241095
12–4.30, 7–11; 12–3, 7–10.30 Sun
**Burtonwood Mild, Bitter** H
Unchanged local on the edge of town. The tap room is full of Rugby League memorabilia.
Q ◖ ♣

### Gems

15 Upper Dicconson Street
☎ (01942) 826588
11–11; 12–10.30 Sun
**Boddingtons Bitter; Holt Bitter; Tetley Mild, Bitter; Walker Best Bitter** H
Busy, modern, one-roomer, popular with office workers lunchtime and crowded at weekends. The TV is constantly tuned to sport.
✿ ◖

### Old Pear Tree

44 Frog Lane ☎ (01942) 243677
11.30–11; 11.30–4, 7–11 Sat; 12–10.30 Sun
**Burtonwood Mild, Bitter, Top Hat** H
Excellent, town-centre pub near the bus station with a relaxing lounge and a lively vault (the haunt of darts and dominoes devotees). Good value food until 7.30; no eve meals Fri–Sun. 🛏 ✿ ◖ ▶ ⚥ ዾ ≠ (Wallgate/NW)

### Orwell

Wallgate ☎ (01942) 323034
11–11 (10.30–5 winter); 12–3, 7–10.30 Sun
**Greenalls Original; Walker Best Bitter; guest beers** H

Large, open-plan pub at the heart of the Wigan Pier complex. Food available all afternoon in summer (busy with tourists); eves are quieter. Large function rooms. Children welcome.
◖ ዾ ≠ (Wallgate/NW)

### Swan & Railway

80 Wallgate ☎ (01942) 495032
11–11; 12–4, 7–10.30 Sun
**Banks's Mild, Bitter, seasonal beers; Marston's Pedigree** H
Pub recently Grade II listed, and converted to Banks's beers (unusual for the area). It boasts a large collection of clocks and railway memorabilia. Not to be missed. Weekday lunches are excellent value.
🛏 ◖ ≠ (Wallgate/NW)

### Tudor House

New Market Street (by bus station) ☎ (01942) 700296
11–11; 12–10.30 Sun
**Draught Bass; Highgate Dark; guest beers** H
Earthy, town-centre boozer, popular with a younger crowd. Rapidly changing range of beers; Biddenden cider. Good value food. 🛏 ✿ ◖ ▶ ≠ (Wallgate/NW) ዾ

## Withington

### Red Lion

532 Wilmslow Road (B5093, 200 yds from Christie Hospital) ☎ (0161) 434 2441
11–11; 12–10.30 Sun
**Banks's Mild, seasonal beers; Marston's Bitter, Pedigree** H
Popular pub on a busy main road, famous for its garden and bowling green. Extended at the rear, its front lounges and bar exude character. Wide range of

food lunchtime and Mon–Thu eves. Children welcome in the conservatory until 8.
⚥ ✿ ◖ ▶ ⚥ ♣ ዾ P

## Woodford

### Davenport Arms (Thief's Neck)

550 Chester Road (A5102)
☎ (0161) 439 2435
11–3.30, 5.15–11; 11–11 Sat; 12–3, 7–10.30 Sun
**Robinson's Hatters Mild, Best Bitter** H, **Old Tom** E, **seasonal beers** H
Superb, unspoilt farmhouse pub on the edge of suburbia. The multi-roomed layout includes a no-smoking snug where children are admitted lunchtime. Large attractive garden at the rear. Local CAMRA *Pub of the Year* 1995.
🛏 Q ⚥ ✿ ◖ ♣ P ⚥

## Worthington

### Crown Hotel

Platt Lane OS576114
☎ (01257) 421354
12–11; 12–10.30 Sun
**Boddingtons Bitter; Tetley Bitter; Walker Mild, Best Bitter; guest beers** H
Quiet, rural pub featuring an attractive mahogany-panelled bar area. Renowned for its extensive menu (restaurant open Tue–Sat eves, and 12–8.30 Sun). 🛏 Q ◖ ▶ P

---

For further information about the beers listed in the above entries, check the breweries section at the back of this book.

---

# LINING UP A PINT

Take a good look at the front cover of this book, and, in particular, at the glass of beer it features. The glass may seem to be short-measured but, on close inspection, it can be seen that it is, in fact, an oversized glass, with the pint measured not at the brim but at a special line on the side. CAMRA has introduced such lined glasses into all its beer festivals as a means of ensuring that drinkers get a pint when they pay for a pint. Many publicans have also adopted lined glasses, particularly for the service of beers which are designed to be drunk with a thick, creamy head (predominantly northern beers served through a swan neck and sparkler). Sadly, too many landlords have seized their chance to short-measure customers by serving excessively frothy beer in standard pint pots. The oversized, lined glass is your best guarantee of getting a full pint, so we are happy to recognise *Good Beer Guide* pubs which use these glasses for some or all of their beers, by awarding the lined glass symbol at the end of their entries.

# Merseyside

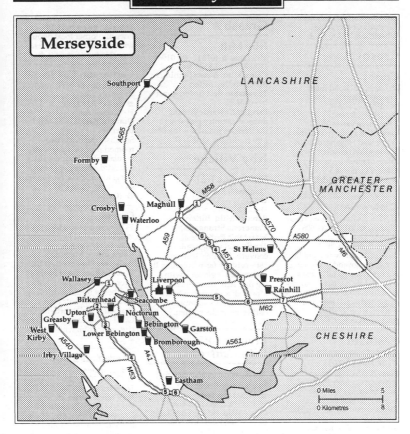

Merseyside

---

## Bebington

### Cleveland
31 Bebington Road, New Ferry
☎ (0151) 645 2847
11.30–11; 12–3, 7–10.30 Sun
**Thwaites Best Mild, Bitter,
seasonal beers** H
Ever-popular, open-plan local
in a pedestrianised area.
≹ ♣ P

## Birkenhead

### Commodore
25 Broad Street
☎ (0151) 647 6558
11–11; 12–10.30 Sun
**Cains Bitter; Marston's
Pedigree; Phoenix Wobbly
Bob; Theakston Best Bitter,
XB; guest beers** H
Backstreet bikers' pub with a
licensee whose views do not
always accord with those of
CAMRA. Live bands Sat eve.
Three regularly changed
guest beers.
⛺ ✿ ◖ ≹ (Central) ⊖
(Hamilton Sq) ♣

### Crown Ale House
128 Conway Street (by Europa
Centre)
☎ (0151) 647 9108
11.30–11; 12–3, 7–10.30 Sun
**Cains Bitter; Jennings Mild,
Sneck Lifter; guest beers** H
Multi-roomed, town-centre ale
house offering up to five guest
beers from independent
breweries. Excellent value
lunches – all one price. Handy
for the market and the shops.
Children welcome when
parents are eating at
lunchtimes (no food Sun).
◖ ⊞ ≹ (Central) ⊖
(Hamilton Sq) ♣ ◔

### Crown & Cushion
60 Market Street
☎ (0151) 647 8870
11–11; 12–10.30 Sun
**Highgate Dark; guest
beers** H
Recently refurbished, two-
roomed, backstreet pub, once
the haunt of market traders.
Warm, friendly atmosphere.
Regular live music. Three
guest beers.
◖ ▶ ≹ (Hamilton Sq) ⊖ ♣ ⏚

### Old Colonial
167 Bridge Street
☎ (0151) 666 1258
11–11; 12–10.30 Sun
**Cains Mild, Bitter, FA; guest
beers** H
Cains's second pub,
undergoing a sympathetic
refurbishment. The beer range
will stay the same. Q ◖ ⅋ ≹
(Hamilton Sq) ♣ P ⅄

## Bromborough

### Archers
149 Mark Rake
☎ (0151) 334 3406
11–11; 12–10.30 Sun
**Cains Bitter; Jennings Bitter;
Tetley Bitter; guest beer** H
Large, two-roomed pub
attracting all ages. Live music
Thu–Sun. The guest beer is

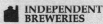

**INDEPENDENT
BREWERIES**

**Cains:** Liverpool

**Liverpool:** Liverpool

**Passageway:** Liverpool

213

from the Carlsberg-Tetley
Tapster's Choice range.
Wheelchair WC. Q ⚓ ♿

## Crosby

### Crosby

75 Liverpool Road (near
Crosby Village)
☎ (0151) 924 2574
11–11; 12–10.30 Sun
**Beer range varies** H/G
Large, busy pub, part of the
Whitbread Hogshead chain.
The landlord ensures a wide
range of guest beers at all
times. Eve meals 5–7.
❀ ◖ ➤ ♿ ⇌ (Blundellsands/
Crosby)

### Crow's Nest

63 Victoria Road (near Crosby
Village) ☎ (0151) 931 5081
11.30–11; 12–10.30 Sun
**Cains Bitter, FA** H
Busy little pub with a public
bar, a lounge and a tiny snug.
An exterior sign advertises
what it does *not* have – no food,
no music, no pool, no machines
– just traditional beer and
conversation. Q ⚓ ⇌
(Blundellsands/Crosby)

## Eastham

### Pier Bar (Tap)

Ferry Road (follow signs for
Eastham Country Park, off
A41) ☎ (0151) 327 6089
11.30–11; 12–10.30 Sun
**Burtonwood Bitter, Top Hat;
guest beer** H
Smallish, traditional pub
overlooking the Mersey
Estuary, at the entrance to
Wirral Country Park. Coaches
are welcome. ❀ P

## Formby

### Freshfield Hotel

1 Massams Lane, Freshfield (N
of centre, ½ mile from B5424)
☎ (01704) 874871
11.30–11; 12–10.30 Sun
**Boddingtons Mild, Bitter;
Castle Eden Ale; Flowers IPA;
Whitbread Trophy** H**; guest
beers** H/G
Popular, suburban pub,
converted to a Hogshead
Alehouse, with a large bar
serving up to 12 ales on
handpump and two on gravity.
❀ ◖ ⇌ (Freshfield) P

## Garston

### Dealers Arms

79–81 St Mary's Road
☎ (0151) 427 5877
11.30–11; 12–10.30 Sun
**Cains Mild, Bitter** H
Medium-sized pub, on the
main shopping street, with a
small, cosy room at the rear.
Cable TV. ⚓ ⇌ ♣

## Greasby

### Irby Mill

Mill Lane ☎ (0151) 604 0194
11.30–3, 5–11; 11.30–11 Sat
**Cains Mild, Bitter; Jennings
Bitter; Tetley Bitter;
Theakston Best Bitter; guest
beers** H
Excellent, award-winning,
unspoilt country pub where
the licensee maintains the best
pub traditions. Q ❀ ◖ P

## Irby Village

### Shippons Inn

Thingwall Road
☎ (0151) 648 0449
11–11; 12–10.30 Sun
**Banks's Mild, Bitter;
Camerons Strongarm;
Marston's Pedigree** H
Traditional village pub
converted in 1994 from an
18th-century farm building. It
features an inglenook with a
log fire. Attractions include
Mon folk music and a lively
Wed quiz, plus summer
barbecues in the garden.
🛏 ❀ ◖ ➤ P

## Liverpool:
### *City Centre*

### Anderson's Piano Bar

26 Exchange Street East
☎ (0151) 236 0649
11–8 (11 Fri); closed Sat & Sun
**Cains Mild, Bitter; Theakston
Best Bitter; guest beer** H
Surprising bar hidden in a
business area; the city's only
piano bar. A good range of
lunches includes Chinese
dishes. German Weissbiers are
a speciality. Friendly service.
◖ ✆ (Moorfields)

### Blackburne

24 Catharine Street
☎ (0151) 708 0252
11–11; 12–10.30 Sun
**Cains Mild, Bitter** H
Medium-sized pub, handy for
the Anglican Cathedral and the
city centre. It attracts mainly
locals, with some students and
musicians from the Liverpool
Philharmonic.

### Bonapartes

21A Clarence Street
☎ (0151) 709 0737
12–12.30am; 7–12.30am Sat; 7–10.30
Sun, closed Sun lunch
**Vaux Samson, Waggle Dance;
Ward's Best Bitter** H
Bare boards, candlelight, music
and a late licence create an
atmosphere that's especially
popular with students.
◖

### Cambridge

Mulberry Street (near
university)11.30–11; 12–10.30 Sun

**Burtonwood Bitter, Forshaw's,
Top Hat; guest beer** H
Friendly corner local popular
with students; busy in term
time. No food Sat. ❀ ◖ ♣

### Carnarvon Castle

Tarleton Street (off Church St
shopping area)
☎ (0151) 709 3153
11–11; closed Sun
**Draught Bass; Cains Mild,
Bitter** H
Smallish and busy, two-
roomed pub, popular with
regulars and shoppers alike.
Splendid display of Dinky/
Corgi toy models. No food Sat.
🛏 Q ◖ ⇌ (Lime St)
✆ (Central)

### Cracke

13 Rice Street (off Hope St)
☎ (0151) 709 4171
11.30–11; 12–10.30 Sun
**Cains Mild; Marston's
Pedigree; Phoenix Best Bitter,
Wobbly Bob; guest beers** H
Ever-popular old pub with a
number of unusual drinking
areas, each with its own
character. Well worth finding.
Good value lunches. The only
city-centre pub with a garden.
❀ ◖ ♣

### Everyman Bistro

9 Hope Street
☎ (0151) 708 9545
12–midnight; closed Sun
**Beer range varies** H
Bar and bistro beneath the
Everyman Theatre (plus a bar
in the foyer where Cains FA is
served). Usually four guest
beers sold. Very busy after
11pm, it is popular with diners
and theatregoers and has an
entry in CAMRA's *Good Pub
Food* guide for its extensive,
unusual dishes. The theatre
was 'saved' by the bar.
Q ◖ ➤ ⌂

### Excelsior

121 Dale Street
11.30–11; closed Sat & Sun
**Cains Mild, Bitter; guest
beers** H
Ale house concept pub which
offers up to six unusual guest
beers: a comfortable pub with a
central bar that is popular at
lunchtimes with business folk
and in the eve with drinkers.
◖ ⇌ ✆ ♣

### Flying Picket

24 Hardman Street
☎ (0151) 709 3995
12–11; closed Sun
**Coach House Coachman's,
Gunpowder Mild; Jennings
Bitter** H
Recently refurbished bar in the
Unemployed Resource Centre,
but open to all. It employs a
keen anti-sexist and anti-racist
policy. Function rooms hold

many art and music events.
Wheelchair WC. ❀ ◖ ❧ P

## Globe

17 Cases Street (opp. Central
Station) ☎ (0151) 709 5060
11–11; 12–10.30 Sun
**Cains Mild, Bitter** Ⓗ
Authentic, welcoming, lively,
city-centre local with a snug at
the rear.
≢ (Lime St) ⊖ (Central)

## Peter Kavanagh's

2–6 Egerton Street (off
Catharine St)
☎ (0151) 709 3443
11–11; 12–10.30 Sun
**Cains Bitter; Courage
Directors; Ind Coope Burton
Ale** Ⓗ
Quaint, Victorian pub, full of
bric-a-brac, on the edge of the
city centre, drawing a wide-
ranging clientele. A good
starting-off point for a city
crawl to the station.
Q ◖ ⊬

## Poste House

23 Cumberland Street (off
Victoria St) ☎ (0151) 236 4130
11–11; 12–10.30 Sun
**Cains Mild, Bitter; guest
beer** Ⓗ
Popular, traditional pub with a
business trade for its good
value weekday meals, plus a
good local trade. One of the
area's oldest pubs, it is the
home of Scouse (the meal that
is); free lunchtime buffet
weekends. ◖ ≢ (Lime St) ⊖
(Moorfields)

## Railway

18 Tithebarn Street
☎ (0151) 236 7210
11.30–11; 12–3, 7.30–10.30 Sun
**Cains Mild, Bitter** Ⓗ
Pub close to the remains of the
Exchange Station, popular
with white-collar workers for
lunchtime food and visited by
locals in the eve. Breakfast
served from 9.30. No food Sun.
◖ ⊖ (Moorfields) ♣

## Roscoe Head

Roscoe Street (opp. bombed
out church) ☎ (0151) 709 4490
11.30 (12 Sat)–11; 12–10.30 Sun
**Ind Coope Burton Ale;
Jennings Bitter** Ⓗ
A bar, a snug, a back lounge
and a side lounge off a small
main bar make up this gem. No
music or electronic invaders
spoil the friendly atmosphere.
An ever-present entry in the
*Guide*, fully deserving of its
many awards. No food
weekends. Q ◖ ≢ (Lime
Street) ⊖ (Central)

## Ship & Mitre

133 Dale Street (near
Birkenhead Tunnel entrance)
☎ (0151) 236 0859
11.30–11; closed Sun

**Cains Mild; guest beers** Ⓗ
The city's foremost real ale
pub: up to eight unusual guest
beers served in a friendly
atmosphere at a fair price and
with full measure. Local
CAMRA *Pub of the Year*. Very
good value lunches (no food
Sat). Two guest ciders.
◖ ≢ (Lime St) ⊖
(Moorfields) ⌂ ⛉

## Swan

86 Wood Street (behind Bold
St) ☎ (0151) 709 5281
11.30–11; 12–10.30 Sun
**Cains Mild, Bitter; Marston's
Pedigree; Phoenix Wobbly
Bob; guest beers** Ⓗ
Basic, backstreet, free house
with up to two guest beers and
the best rock jukebox in town.
Good value, home-cooked
lunches. No food Sat; Sun
breakfasts served. There's also
an upstairs bar.
◖ ⊖ (Central) ♣ ⌂

## United Powers

66–68 Tithebarn Street
☎ (0151) 236 5205
11–11; closed Sun
**Beer range varies** Ⓗ
Friendly pub on the edge of the
business quarter. Up to four
guest beers; good value
lunches (not served Sat). Live
jazz Wed eve. Note the
impressive old station clock.
◖ ⊖ (Moorfields)

## Wetherspoons

Unit 1, Charlotte Row
☎ (0151) 709 4802
11–11; 12–10.30 Sun
**Banks's Mild; Cains Bitter;
Courage Directors; Theakston
Best Bitter; Younger Scotch;
guest beer** Ⓗ
Large, modern pub with good
service and always one beer on
special offer. Occasional beer
festivals. Popular all day. Food
served 11–10 (12–9.30 Sun).
Wheelchair WC.
Q ◖ ▶ ❧ ≢ (Lime St) ⊖ ⌂ ⊬

## White Star (Quinn's)

2–4 Rainford Gardens
☎ (0151) 236 4572
11–11; 12–3, 7–10.30 Sun
**Draught Bass; Cains Bitter;
guest beers** Ⓗ
Near the site of the Cavern, of
Beatles fame, this pub caters
for shoppers, business people
and regulars. Bass maintains
the pub sympathetically and
supplies the guest beers.
Occasional beer festivals.
≢ (Lime St) ⊖ (Moorfields)

## Liverpool: *East*

## Albany

40–42 Albany Road
☎ (0151) 228 8597
11–11; 12–10.30 Sun
**Cains Mild, Bitter** Ⓗ

Lively, friendly local in a
backstreet terrace. No food at
weekends. ◖ ♣

## Childway Fiveways

Fiveways, Queens Drive
☎ (0151) 722 3314
11–11; 12–10.30 Sun
**Cains Mild, Bitter** Ⓗ
Large, suburban landmark on a
major road junction.
Extensively altered in recent
years, it has retained separate
drinking areas. Eve meals until
7 (6 Sun). ◖ ▶ P

## Clubmoor

119 Townsend Lane, Anfield
☎ (0151) 263 4220
12 (11.30 Sat)–11; 12–10.30 Sun
**Cains Mild, Bitter** Ⓗ
Handsome, detached pub on a
main road with a large lounge,
and a public bar with darts and
Sky TV. Not far from Everton
and Liverpool FC grounds.
Quiz night Wed. ❀ ⊕ ♣

## Edinburgh

4 Sandown Lane
☎ (0151) 733 7830
12–11; 12–10.30 Sun
**Cains Bitter** Ⓗ
Tiny local, hidden away from
the busy Wavertree High
Street: a small lounge and an
even smaller bar, but a big
welcome. ⊕

## Kensington

189 Kensington
☎ (0151) 263 6807
12–11; 12–10.30 Sun
**Cains Mild, Bitter** Ⓗ
Classic, street-corner local; a
popular pub, often with table
service in the lounge.
⊕ ♣

## Lord Nelson

146 East Prescot Road
☎ (0151) 220 1894
11.30–11; 12–10.30 Sun
**Cains Bitter** Ⓗ
Friendly local on a main road,
with a small bar and a back
lounge. Formerly Joseph Jones
Knotty Ash Brewery tap.
♣ P

## Rocket

2 Bowring Park Road (A57, end
of M62) ☎ (0151) 228 5080
11.30–11; 12–10.30 Sun
**Cains Bitter; guest beers** Ⓗ
Relatively modern pub, named
after a famous loco which is
depicted in relief on the side.
No food Sat.
Q ❀ ◖ ≢ (Broad Green) P

## Wheatsheaf

186 East Prescot Road (A57)
☎ (0151) 228 5080
11.30–11; 12–10.30 Sun
**Cains Bitter; guest beer** Ⓗ
Popular, traditional pub
offering waitress service in the
two lounges, plus a busy bar.
Q ⊕ P

## Liverpool: *South*

### Brewery Tap

35 Stanhope Street (by Cains Brewery) ☎ (0151) 709 2129
11–11; 12–10.30 Sun
**Cains Mild, Bitter, FA; guest beers** Ⓗ
Deservedly popular; Cains's first tied house and winner of CAMRA's *Best Refurbishment* award 1994. See the interesting local breweriana. Many music, quiz and charity events. Three guest beers and Cains special brews. The base for Cains brewery visits. Q ❀ ◖ P

### Royal George

99 Park Road, Toxteth
☎ (0151) 708 9277
11–11; 12–10.30 Sun
**Beer varies** Ⓗ
Popular, friendly pub known locally as 'Blacks', selling a house beer brewed by Ind Coope at Burton, plus one changing guest beer, very reasonably priced. Happy hours Mon–Thu, 5–8. Live music Fri–Sun eve. Cable TV. Note: in an area not for the unwary. ⊕ ♣

## Lower Bebington

### Rose & Crown

Village Road
☎ (0151) 643 1312
11–3, 5–11; 11–11 Fri & Sat; 12–10.30 Sun
**Thwaites Best Mild, Bitter, seasonal beers** Ⓗ
Bustling, friendly, multi-roomed local, popular with office workers and shoppers at lunchtime and with local residents at night.
Q ◖ ⊕ ♣ P

## Maghull

### Red House

31 Foxhouse Lane
☎ (0151) 526 1376
11–11; 12–10.30 Sun
**Beer range varies** Ⓗ
Friendly, suburban local: an oasis for pub-lovers in Maghull and not dominated by 'yoof' culture. Guest beers from Carlsberg-Tetley's Tapster's Choice range are served. No food Sun. ❀ ◖ ⊕ ⇌ ♣ P

## Noctorum

### Wirral Hundred

45 Noctorum Way
11–11; 12–10.30 Sun
**Draught Bass; Boddingtons Bitter; Cains Mild, Bitter** Ⓗ
Large, one-roomed, modern estate pub with a friendly licensee. Live entertainment and a good atmosphere.
❀ ◖ ♿ ⇌ (Upton)

## Prescot

### Clockface

54 Derby Street
☎ (0151) 430 0701
11–11; 12–3, 7–10.30 Sun
**Thwaites Bitter, Craftsman** Ⓗ
Attractive, old sandstone mansion, converted to a pub in the 1980s. An oasis of pleasant relaxation. Q ❀ ◖ P

### Hare & Hounds

10 Warrington Road
11–11; 12–10.30 Sun
**Cains Mild, Bitter; guest beer** Ⓗ
Small, ex-Joseph Jones house which used to be two-roomed, but is now L-shaped. It retains a good atmosphere. Also known as Tommy Hall's and the Weighing Machine. ⇌

## Rainhill

### Commercial

Station Road
☎ (0151) 426 6446
12–11; 12–10.30 Sun
**Cains Bitter; guest beer** Ⓗ
Old Joseph Jones (of Knotty Ash) pub with windows to match, now back to its busy best thanks to an enthusiastic licensee. ❀ ⊕ ⇌ ♣ P

## St Helens

### Phoenix Inn

Canal Street ☎ (01744) 21953
11–11; 12–10.30 Sun
**Taylor Landlord; guest beers** Ⓗ
Pub with a busy, lively bar with a rugby league theme. Live bands in the 'best side' at weekends. ⊕ ♣ ☖

### Turk's Head

Cooper Street
☎ (01744) 26949
11–11; 12–3, 7–10.30 Sun
**Cains Mild, Bitter, FA; Holt Bitter** Ⓗ
Unusual, half-timbered pub set in the backstreets. It hosts many clubs and is at the heart of the community. It even owns its own racehorse (Crabbie's Pride). Book Sun lunch. ♨ ❀ ◖ ♣

## Seacombe

### Prince Alfred

3 Church Road
☎ (0151) 638 1674
11–11; 12–10.30 Sun
**Boddingtons Mild, Bitter; Cains Bitter; guest beers** Ⓗ
*The* pub to visit for the area's best choice of beers. Small, comfortable and friendly, it stands just up the road from the Seacombe ferry terminal. Good value guest ales.
❀ ♿ ♣ ☖

## Southport

### Barons Bar

Scarisbrick Hotel, Lord Street
☎ (01704) 543000
11–11; 12–10.30 Sun
**Boddingtons Bitter; Morland Old Speckled Hen; Shepherd Neame Bishops Finger; Tetley Bitter; guest beers** Ⓗ
Baronial, traditional lounge bar within a hotel complex; a drinking bar, comfortably furnished, with a cosmopolitan clientele. Busy at weekends. Annual beer festival in May. The house beer, Flag & Turret, is brewed by Little Avenham. Food in the adjacent bars.
🛏 ◖ ⇌

### Berkeley Hotel

19 Queens Road (right out of station, 400 yds)
☎ (01704) 530163
12–11; 12–10.30 Sun
**Holt Bitter; Marston's Bitter; Moorhouse's Black Cat Mild, Pendle Witches Brew; guest beers** Ⓗ
Small hotel near the town centre. Ten beers are stocked, including five guests. The house beer, Berkeley Bitter, is brewed by Moorhouse's. Fun quizzes Thu. Good food (sandwiches only Mon lunch).
Q ❀ 🛏 ◖ ▶ P

### Cheshire Lines Inn

81 King Street (700 yds from station) ☎ (01704) 532178
11–11; 12–3, 4–7, 10.30 (12–10.30 summer) Sun
**Tetley Bitter; Walker Mild, Bitter; guest beer** Ⓗ
Attractive, friendly, mid-terrace pub, very close to the town centre. ♨ ❀ ♿ ⇌

### Lakeside Inn

Marine Lake, Promenade (200 yds N of pier entrance)
☎ (01704) 530173
11–11; 12–10.30 Sun
**Fuller's London Pride; Marston's Pedigree** Ⓗ
Tiny, lakeside, one-room bar, adjacent to the Floral Hall and tourism offices, and close to the pier and old Promenade Hospital. Listed in the *Guinness Book of Records* as Britain's smallest pub. Theatre entertainers are often customers. Q ❀

### Up Steps

20 Upper Aughton Road, Birkdale ☎ (01704) 569245
11.30–11; 12–10.30 Sun
**Matthew Brown Bitter; Theakston Mild, Bitter, Black Bull, XB; guest beers** Ⓗ
Friendly, Birkdale local; home to darts, dominoes and quiz teams. A warm welcome is always guaranteed in this

traditional, old-fashioned pub.

❀ ⏚ ⇌ (Birkdale) ♣ P

## Zetland

53 Zetland Street
☎ (01704) 544541
11.30–11; 12–10.30 Sun
**Burtonwood Mild, Bitter, Forshaw's, Top Hat** *or* **Buccaneer** Ⓗ

Large, Victorian pub with its own bowling green (which can be hired). It retains separate rooms; the family room is open until 8.30pm. No food Mon.

❧ ❀ ⏚ ⏚ P

## Upton

### Eagle & Crown

149 Ford Road
☎ (0151) 677 5045
11–11; 12–10.30 Sun
**Thwaites Bitter, seasonal beers** Ⓗ

Popular, community pub near the village crossroads. Two function rooms. ♣ P

## Wallasey

### Cheshire Cheese

2 Wallasey Village
☎ (0151) 638 3152
12–11; 12–10.30 Sun
**Cains Mild, Bitter; Theakston Best Bitter** Ⓗ

Wallasey's oldest licensed premises, rebuilt in 1884. Beer has been sold on this site for more than 500 years. A lounge, a snug and a bar are served by a central bar. Popular with all ages, it is a rare Wirral Cains Mild outlet.

❀ ⏚ ⏚ ⇌ ♣

### Farmers Arms

225 Wallasey Village
☎ (0151) 638 2110
11.30–11; 12–10.30 Sun
**Cains Bitter; Tetley Bitter; Theakston Best Bitter; guest beer** Ⓗ

Deservedly popular pub, a previous local CAMRA *Pub of the Year*: a front bar, a side snug and a back lounge. The guest pump is in the bar. No jukebox. No food weekends.

⏚ ⏚ ☙ ⇌ (Grove Rd)

### Primrose Hotel

1 Withens Lane (off Manor Rd)
☎ (0151) 637 1340
12–11; 12–10.30 Sun
**Cains Bitter; Theakston Best Bitter; guest beers** Ⓗ

Unmistakeable, half-timbered pub with wood-panelled walls,
an ornate ceiling and a mixed clientele.

❀ ♣ P

## Waterloo

### Volunteer Canteen

45 East Street (near marina)
☎ (0151) 928 6594
11–11; 12–10.30 Sun
**Cains Bitter; Theakston Best Bitter** Ⓗ

No distractions spoil the buzz of conversation in this small, comfortable, two-bar pub. Friendly welcome; table service. Absorbing local photos. Regular summer barbecues. Q ⇌ ♣

## West Kirby

### Hilbre Court

Banks Road
☎ (0151) 625 7811
11–11; 12–10.30 Sun
**Tetley Dark Mild, Bitter; guest beers** Ⓗ

Popular, friendly pub with a restaurant. The lounge bar is open-plan but with defined drinking areas. Try the excellent lunches. Close to the promenade and Wirral Way.

❀ ⏚ ▸ ⇌ ♣ P

---

# LONG DISTANCE WALKER

Less than six years after a famous Merseyside brewing name was usurped and cheapened, local drinkers have again suffered a blow to their brewing heritage. In 1991, Whitbread closed Higsons brewery, transferring production of the two ales to Sheffield (they have since moved again, to Castle Eden). Now Carlsberg-Tetley has axed the Tetley Walker brewery in Warrington, home of Peter Walker beers.

Peter Walker was a revolutionary brewer. As well as establishing the Warrington brewery in 1852, he invented the famous Burton Union method of fermentation which is still employed by Marston's of Burton upon Trent. Pubs bearing his name are a familiar sight in Liverpool and its environs, and they serve four Peter Walker beers – Mild, Bitter, Best Bitter and Winter Warmer. These will now be produced many miles away, somewhere else in Carlsberg-Tetley's brewing empire but, inevitably, will not taste the same.

This transfer of beers is a familiar trick of the big brewers. When drinkers decide the beers do not taste as good as before and switch to other products, the brewers claim lack of demand and discontinue them, replacing them with hugely profitable, nationally advertised brands.

The future of Peter Walker beers is, therefore, uncertain. They will survive in the short term but how long will it be before the name of Peter Walker is simply allowed to fade away?

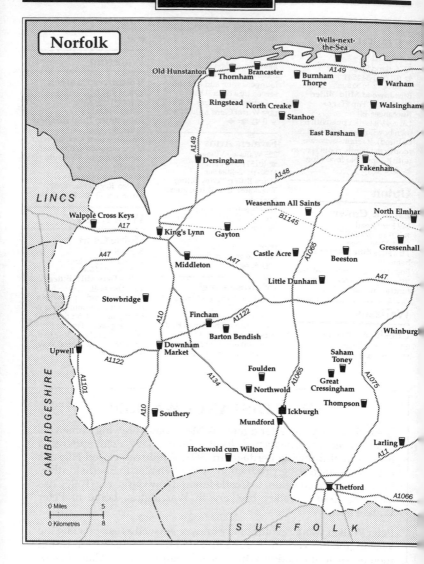

## Attleborough

### Griffin Hotel
Church Street
☎ (01953) 452149
10.30–3, 5.30–11; 12–3, 7–10.30 Sun
**Draught Bass; Greene King Abbot; Wethered Bitter; Wolf Bitter; guest beers** H
Welcoming, old coaching inn retaining much charm with oak beams. Strong guest beers from all over the country; wide-ranging menu.
🏚 Q 🛏 ◑ 🕭 💺 🛱 ➤ ♣ P

## Aylsham

### Feathers
54 Cawston Road (B1145, 300 yds from fire station)
☎ (01263) 732314
11–3, 7–11; hours vary Sat & Sun
**Adnams Bitter; Boddingtons Bitter; Wells Eagle; guest beers** H
Good local and family pub. Quiz night Tue; good selection of pub games available. Don't miss it.
🏚 ❀ ♿ ♣ P

## Banningham

### Crown Inn
Church Road ☎ (01263) 733534
12–2.30, 7–11 (11.30–3, 6.45–11 summer); 12–3, 7–10.30 Sun
**Boddingtons Bitter; Flowers IPA; Greene King Abbot; Tetley Bitter** H
Comfortable village pub. The bar is divided into several sections and the restaurant area has a wheelchair ramp. Good food. Children welcome.
🏚 Q ❀ ♿ ◑ 💺 ♣

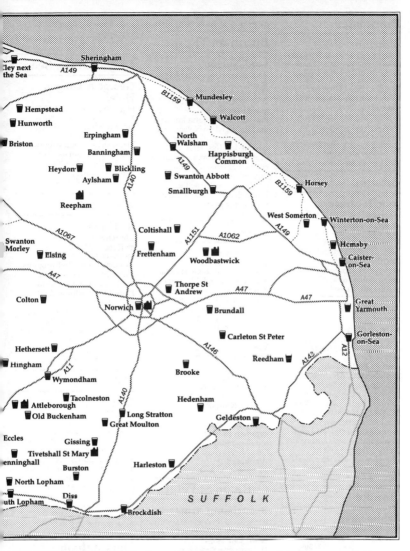

## Barton Bendish

### Spread Eagle
☎ (01366) 347295
12–3 (not Mon), 7–11; 12–3, 7–10.30
Sun
**Boddingtons Bitter; Flowers
IPA, Original** Ⓗ
Quiet village inn with a
children's play area set in
lovely gardens: a lounge and a
games bar, plus a dining room.
🏚 Q ⛄ ⚘ ◑ ◗ ⬥ ♠ P ⤢ ⛉

## Beeston

### Ploughshare
The Street ☎ (01328) 701485
12–2.30, 6–11; 12–11 Sat; 12–3, 7–10.30
Sun

**Greene King IPA, Rayments
Special, Abbot; guest beer** Ⓗ
A pub has occupied this site
since circa 1420; this friendly
local was built in the 17th
century, but has been extended
and modernised. Cider in
summer. 🏚 ⛄ ⚘ ◑ ◗ ♣ P

## Blickling

### Buckinghamshire Arms
☎ (01263) 732133
12–3, 6–11; 12–3, 7–10.30 Sun
**Adnams Bitter, Broadside;
Reepham Granary** Ⓗ
Pub next to Blickling Hall, with
its lovely walking and cycling
routes: a delightful snug and a
separate bar with a real fire.

Local brews are a special
feature, and the food is
recommended. A good place to
stay. 🏚 Q ⚘ 🛏 ◑ ◗ P

## Brancaster

### Ship Inn
Coast Road ☎ (01485) 210333
12–3, 7–11 (11.30–3.30, 6–11 summer);
12–3, 7–10.30 (12–3.30, 6–10.30
summer) Sun
**Boddingtons Bitter; Ind
Coope Burton Ale; guest
beer** Ⓗ
Welcoming, traditional inn
with a wood-panelled bar.
Local seafood dishes are a
speciality. Large garden with a
children's play area.
🏚 Q ♿ ⊛ 🛏 ◖▶ ₺ P ⌦

## Briston

### John H Stracey
Norwich Road (B1354)
☎ (01263) 860891
11–3, 6.30–11; 12–3, 7–10.30 Sun
**Beer range varies** Ⓗ
Built in 1565, a former coaching
inn, this friendly roadside pub
serves excellent food in the
comfortable bar and
restaurant. 🏚 ⊛ 🛏 ◖▶ P

## Brockdish

### Greyhound
The Street ☎ (01379) 668775
7–11; 12–2, 7–11 Fri & Sat; 12–2,
7–10.30 Sun
**Buffy's Polly's Folly, Mild,
Polly's Extra, Ale, Strong Ale;
Woodforde's Wherry** Ⓖ
17th-century village pub on the
Suffolk border near the River
Waveney. No machines, pool
nor loud music; award-
winning food. Second-hand
books and records are on sale.
Buffy's ales are sold as
'Greyhound' ales. Eve meals
end at 8.45.
🏚 Q ⊛ ◖▶ ♣ P ⌦ ⊟

## Brooke

### White Lion
The Street ☎ (01508) 550443
12–2.30 (3 Sat), 5.30–11 (12–11
summer Sat); 12–4, 7–10.30 Sun
**Adnams Bitter, Extra,
Broadside; Boddingtons
Bitter; guest beers** Ⓗ
Attractive village-centre pub
just off the main road, facing
the mere. No food Mon.
🏚 ⊛ ◖▶ ₺ ♣ P

## Brundall

### Yare
Station Road
☎ (01603) 713786
10.30–2.30, 5.30–11; 10.30–11 Sat &
summer; 12–10.30 Sun
**John Smith's Bitter;
Woodforde's Wherry; guest
beers** Ⓗ
Large Georgian building
overlooking boatyards with an
unusual wattle ceiling, an
inglenook and a display of

nautical memorabilia.
🏚 ♿ ⊛ ◖▶ ⇌ ♣ P

## Burnham Thorpe

### Lord Nelson
Walsingham Road (off A149)
☎ (01328) 738241
11–3, 6–11; 12–3, 7–10.30 Sun
**Greene King IPA, Abbot;
guest beer** Ⓖ
Pub built in 1650 and known as
the Plough when Nelson held a
party here in 1793 (it was
renamed in 1807 after his
death). Four drinking areas but
still no bar (friendly table
service), a stone-flagged floor
and high wooden settles.
Wheelchair WC. Note: mild is
kept under gas in winter.
🏚 Q ⊛ ◖▶ ₺ ♣ P

## Burston

### Crown Inn
☎ (01379) 741257
11.30–3, 5.30–11; 12–3, 6–10.30 Sun
**Adnams Bitter, Old; Greene
King Abbot; guest beers** Ⓖ
Typical, two-bar village pub
serving local beers, plus some
from further afield.
🏚 ⊛ ◖▶ ♣ P

## Caister-on-Sea

### Ship
2 Victoria Street
☎ (01493) 728008
10.30–11; 12–3, 7–10.30 Sun
**Greene King IPA; guest
beers** Ⓗ
Pretty, backstreet pub, busy in
summer. Its single bar is nicely
sectioned into different areas.
Guest beers come from
Whitbread.
🏚 ♿ ⊛ ◖▶ ₺ ♣ P

## Carleton St Peter

### Beauchamp Arms
Ferry Road (between Claxton
and Langley) OS350043
☎ (01508) 480247
11–3 (not winter Wed–Fri), 6 (7
winter)–11 (closed winter Mon & Tue);
11–11 (11.30–4, 7–11 winter) Sat;
12–10.30 (12–4, 7–10.30 winter) Sun
**Adnams Bitter; Draught Bass;
Woodforde's Wherry** Ⓗ
Large, multi-roomed free
house in a remote location on
the south bank of the River
Yare (moorings for boats).
Good, home-cooked food.
🏚 Q ♿ ⊛ ◖▶ ₺ ♣ P

## Castle Acre

### Ostrich
Stocks Green (follow priory
signs from B1065)
☎ (01760) 755398
12–3, 7–11; 12–10.30 Sun
**Greene King XX Mild, IPA,
Abbot** Ⓗ
Coaching inn in a village with

a ruined castle and a priory to
visit. Prize-winning
sandwiches.
🏚 Q ⊛ ◖▶ ♣ P

## Cley next the Sea

### George & Dragon Hotel
High Street ☎ (01263) 740652
11–3, 6–11; 12–2.30, 7–10.30 Sun
**Greene King IPA, Abbot,
seasonal beers** Ⓗ
Birdwatcher's pub with two
bars, plus a room for diners
and families. Good food.
Unusual games.
🏚 ♿ ⊛ 🛏 ◖▶ ₺ ♣ P

## Coltishall

### Red Lion
Church Street
☎ (01603) 737402
11–3, 5–11; 12–3, 7–10.30 Sun
**Adnams Bitter; Boddingtons
Bitter; Flowers Original;
Fuller's Chiswick; Greene
King Abbot; Morland Old
Speckled Hen** Ⓗ
Pub with bars on two levels, a
restaurant area and a large
outdoor play area for children.
House brew from
Woodforde's.
⊛ ◖▶ ₺ ♣ ⌂ P

## Colton

### Ugly Bug Inn
High House Farm Lane
☎ (01603) 880794
12–3, 5.30–11; 12–3, 7–10.30 Sun
**Adnams Bitter; Morland Old
Speckled Hen; guest beers** Ⓗ
Single-bar pub converted from
an old barn, featuring a brick
and wood interior, a dining
area and a children's area.
Large gardens with a pond.
The house beer comes from
Iceni. Wheelchair WC.
♿ ⊛ 🛏 ◖▶ ₺ P ⌦

## Dersingham

### Feathers
Manor Road ☎ (01485) 540207
11–2.30, 5.30–11; 12–10.30 Sun
**Adnams Bitter; Draught Bass;
guest beer** Ⓗ
Pub close to Sandringham
House; a quiet, wood-panelled
bar contrasts with the Stable
Bar which has games and loud
music. Fine food in the
restaurant. Large garden with
summer barbecues.
🏚 ⊛ 🛏 ◖▶ P

## Diss

### Cock Inn
63 Lower Denmark Street
11.30–3, 5 (6.30 Sat)–11; 11.30–11 Fri;
12–3, 7–10.30 Sun

Adnams Bitter; Greene King
Abbot; Woodforde's Nelson's
Revenge; guest beers ℍ
Pleasant, welcoming, two-bar
pub.
🏚 ❀ ⇔ ◑ ♣ P

## Downham Market

### Cock Tavern

Lynn Road ☎ (01366) 384175
11–3, 7–11 (11–11 summer Sat);
12–2.30, 7–10.30 Sun
Ansells Mild; Benskins BB;
guest beers ℍ
Cosy, friendly local with a
good range of home-cooked
food, and interesting beers.
Pleasant garden to the rear.
Cider in summer.
🏚 Q ❀ ◑ ▶ ♣ ⇪ P

### Crown Hotel

Bridge Street ☎ (01366) 382322
11–11; 12–3, 7–10.30 Sun
Bateman XB; Courage
Directors; Theakston Best
Bitter; guest beers ℍ
300-year-old coaching inn with
a wood-panelled bar
displaying local memorabilia.
🏚 Q ❀ ⇔ ◑ ▶ P

## East Barsham

### White Horse Inn

Fakenham Road
☎ (01328) 820645
11–3, 7 (6 summer)–11; 12–3, 7–10.30
Sun
Boddingtons Bitter; Greene
King Abbot; Theakston Best
Bitter; Woodforde's Wherry;
guest beers ℍ
Old, beamed building, set in an
unspoilt village and lovely
countryside, next to a quaint
old manor house. The bar has a
large inglenook; two restaurant
areas.
🏚 Q ❀ ⇔ ◑ ▶ ▲ ♣ P

## Eccles

### Old Railway Tavern
(Eccles Tap)

Station Road
12–2.30, 5.30–11; 12–3, 7–10.30 Sun
(may extend)
Adnams Bitter 🄶; Greene
King IPA; guest beers ℍ
Traditional welcoming local in
a peaceful village. 🏚 Q ❀ ❀
(Eccles Rd, limited service) ♣
P ⇪

## Elsing

### Mermaid Inn

Church Street
☎ (01382) 637640
12–3, 7–11; 12–3, 7–10.30 Sun
Adnams Bitter, Broadside;
Woodforde's Wherry; guest
beer ℍ
Old village pub with a single
bar and a restaurant.
🏚 ❀ ◑ ▶ P ⇪

## Erpingham

### Spread Eagle

Eagle Lane ☎ (01263) 761591
11–3, 6.30–11; 12–3, 6.30–10.30 Sun
Woodforde's Wherry, Gt
Eastern, Norfolk Nog,
Headcracker ℍ
Very friendly local: a long bar
with a games room at one end
and a dining room leading on
to the garden at the other.
Good food. The house beers
come from Woodforde's.
🏚 ⛵ ❀ ◑ ▶ ⅄ ♣ P

## Fakenham

### Bull

Bridge Street ☎ (01328) 862560
11–3, 7–11 (11–11 Thu–Sat in
summer); 12–3, 7–10.30 Sun
Marston's Pedigree; John
Smith's Bitter; Webster's
Yorkshire Bitter; Woodforde's
Wherry ℍ
Comfortable, two-bar, market
town pub with a no-smoking
area lunchtime. Tiny car park.
❀ ◑ ♣ P ⅄

### Star

Oak Street ☎ (01328) 862895
11–2.30, 7–11; 12–3, 7–10.30 Sun
Tolly Cobbold Original; guest
beer ℍ
With parts dating back to the
15th century, this listed
building also boasts a natural
cellar. The open-plan drinking
area is sympathetically divided
(pool table in a separate room).
Q ❀ ▲ P

## Fincham

### Swan

High Street ☎ (01366) 347765
11.30–3, 6.30–11; 12–3, 7–10.30 Sun
Greene King IPA; guest
beers ℍ
You won't be short of things to
look at in this roadside pub
where good value food
includes enormous specials.
⇔ ◑ ▶ ⅃ ♣ P ⅄

## Foulden

### White Hart Inn

White Hart Street
☎ (01366) 328638
11–3, 6–11; 12–3, 7–10.30 Sun
Greene King XX Mild, IPA,
Abbot, seasonal beers;
Marston's Pedigree; guest
beer ℍ
17th-century, characterful pub
with flagstone floors and oak
beams. Good quality food.
🏚 Q ⛵ ❀ ◑ ▶ ♣ P

## Frettenham

### Rose & Crown

Buxton Road ☎ (01603) 898341
7–11; 12–2.30, 7–11 Sat & summer;
12–3, 7–10.30 Sun

Flowers IPA; Ind Coope
Burton Ale; Tetley Bitter;
Tolly Cobbold Mild; guest
beer ℍ
Friendly, sporting local with a
large, wood-panelled interior
and brick fireplaces.
🏚 ❀ ♣ P ⅄

## Gayton

### Crown

Lynn Road ☎ (01553) 636252
11–3, 6.30–11; 12–2, 7–10.30 Sun
Greene King XX Mild, IPA,
Rayments Special, Abbot ℍ
Real village local which,
despite having all the tourist
facilities, such as a restaurant
and a children's room, has a
strong local following.
🏚 Q ⛵ ❀ ◑ ▶ ♣ P

## Geldeston

### Wherry

The Street ☎ (01508) 518371
11–3, 7 (6 summer)–11; 12–3, 7–10.30
Sun
Adnams Bitter, Old,
Broadside ℍ
Friendly pub which retains the
charm of a small village inn,
with its original old bar. An
extension provides plenty of
drinking room and a
restaurant.
🏚 Q ⛵ ❀ ◑ ▶ ▲ ♣ P

## Gissing

### Crown Inn

Lower Street ☎ (01379) 677718
11–3, 6.30–11; 12–3, 7–10.30 Sun
Adnams Bitter, Old; Greene
King Abbot; guest beers ℍ
Village pub with a half-
timbered interior. Restaurant
at the rear.
❀ ◑ ▶ ♣ P

## Gorleston-on-Sea

### Dock Tavern

Dock Tavern Lane
☎ (01493) 442255
11–11; 12–10.30 Sun
Adnams Broadside; Draught
Bass; Greene King IPA,
Abbot; guest beers ℍ
Attractive, comfortable open-
plan, one-room local featuring
china jugs, brass and seafaring
objects. ❀ ♣

## Great Cressingham

### Windmill Inn

Water End (off A1065)
☎ (01760) 756232
11.30–3, 6–11; 12–3, 6.30–10.30 Sun
Adnams Bitter, Broadside;
Draught Bass; Samuel Smith
OBB; guest beers ℍ
Pub with a room for every day
of the week, with character and
charm. A good place to drink

and eat – it can get very busy eves. 🏠 🍽 ⚘ ◁ ▶ & ⚓ ♣ P

## Great Moulton

### Fox & Hounds
Frith Way ☎ (01379) 677506
11–2.30, 7–11; 12–2.30, 7–10.30 Sun
**Adnams Bitter; Boddingtons Bitter; Greene King Abbot; guest beer** Ⓗ
Small village pub with a large garden and a pond. The cosy interior boasts beams from the 15th century. No food Mon. Cider in summer.
🏠 Q ⚘ 🛏 ◁ ▶ ▲ ♣ ⬥ P

## Great Yarmouth

### Mariners Tavern
69 Howard Street South (between market place and South Quay) ☎ (01493) 332299
11–3, 8–11; closed Mon–Wed eves and Sun
**Woodforde's Mardler's Mild, Wherry, Norfolk Nog; guest beers** Ⓗ
First-class, friendly free house, staging regular beer festivals: a true real ale pub (no keg), Norfolk Nog recently replacing draught Guinness. 🏠 Q ⚘ ◁ ▶
▲ ⇌ (Vauxhall) ♣ P

### Red Herring
24–25 Havelock Road (behind seafront, off St Peters Rd) ☎ (01493) 853384
11–3, 6–11; 12–3, 7–10.30 Sun
**Adnams Bitter; Woodforde's Mardler's Mild; guest beers** Ⓗ
Photographs of bygone fishing days adorn the walls of this hard to find, single-bar, corner local. Four guest ales are from independent brewers. Two beer festivals a year.
Q 🍽 ⚘ ◁ ▶ ♣ ⬥

## Gressenhall

### Swan
The Green ☎ (01623) 860341
12–2.30 (not Mon), 7–11; 12–10.30 Sun
**Greene King Abbot; Tetley Bitter, Imperial; guest beer** Ⓗ
Comfortable, single-bar local near the Rural Life Museum. Pool and darts in one area; screened-off dining area. Eve meals Thu–Sun.
🏠 Q ⚘ ◁ ▶ ▲ ♣ P

## Happisburgh Common

### Victoria
Lower Street ☎ (01692) 650228
11–3, 6–11 (11–11 summer); 12–3, 7–10.30 (12–10.30 summer) Sun
**Courage Directors; John Smith's Bitter; Woodforde's Wherry; guest beer** Ⓗ
Extended rural pub, well positioned for Broadland and

the coast with facilities for caravans. 🏠 Q ⚘ ◁ ▶ ▲ P ⊟

## Harleston

### Cherry Tree
London Road
☎ (01379) 852345
11–2.30 (3 Sat), 6–11; 12–4.30, 7–10.30 Sun
**Adnams Bitter, Broadside, seasonal beers** Ⓗ
Popular Adnams local with a comfortable atmosphere in an historic, beamed, traditional interior: two bars and a dining area. Extensively renovated in 1995. Eve meals Thu–Sat.
🏠 Q ⚘ ◁ ▶ & ♣ P

## Hedenham

### Mermaid
Norwich Road
☎ (01508) 482480
11–3, 6 (7 Sat)–11; 12–3, 7–10.30 Sun
**Adnams Bitter; Draught Bass; Greene King IPA** Ⓗ
Comfortable, refurbished country pub, which has retained much of its original character. 🏠 ⚘ ◁ ▶ ▲ ♣ P

## Hempstead

### Hare & Hounds
Baconsthorpe Road
☎ (01263) 713285
11–3, 5.30–11; 12–3, 7–10.30 Sun
**Adnams Bitter; Greene King Abbot; Woodforde's Wherry** Ⓗ
Long bar in a genuine, old beamed pub with a wood burner in the inglenook.
🏠 ⚘ ◁ ▶ ♣ P ⌫

## Hemsby

### Kings Head
North Road ☎ (01493) 730568
11–11; 12–10.30 Sun
**Greene King IPA; John Smith's Bitter; Woodforde's Gt Eastern** Ⓗ
Pleasant, one-bar pub with a no-smoking dining area.
🏠 🍽 ⚘ ◁ ▶ & ▲ P ⊟

## Hethersett

### Kings Head
36 Old Norwich Road (off B1172) ☎ (01603) 810206
11–2.30, 5.30 (5 Fri, 6 Sat)–11; 12–3, 7–10.30 Sun
**Courage Directors; Marston's Pedigree; Morland Old Speckled Hen; John Smith's Bitter; Wadworth 6X; Woodforde's Wherry** Ⓗ
17th-century ale house: a small, cosy, traditional snug bar, and a carpeted, beamed lounge with a log fire. Home-cooked food (not served Sun or Mon eves). The large, well-kept

garden has a play area.
🏠 Q 🍽 ⚘ ◁ ▶ 🛏 & ♣ P

## Heydon

### Earle Arms
The Street ☎ (01263) 587376
11 (12 winter)–3, 6 (7 winter)–11; 12–2.30, 7–10.30 Sun
**Morland Old Speckled Hen, Woodforde's Wherry, Gt Eastern** Ⓗ
Pub with two bars, each distinctly different in character; also two additional rooms, one light, one dark. Heydon is often used for filming period drama. Eve meals Tue–Sat.
🏠 🍽 ⚘ ◁ ▶ & P

## Hingham

### White Hart Hotel
Market Place ☎ (01953) 850214
11–3, 6.30–11; 12–3, 7–10.30 Sun
**Adnams Bitter; Morland Old Speckled Hen; Webster's Yorkshire Bitter** Ⓗ
An imposing hotel frontage hides a plush locals' bar, plus a no-smoking dining area, at the centre of Abraham Lincoln's ancestral village.
🏠 Q 🍽 🛏 ◁ ▶ P

## Hockwold cum Wilton

### New Inn
Station Road ☎ (01842) 828668
11–3, 6–11; 11–11 Sat & bank hols; 12–10.30 Sun
**Flowers IPA; Greene King Abbot; guest beers** Ⓗ
Welcoming, 16th-century, thatched village local, active for local charities. The large garden is ideal for children. Food includes home-cooked specials (no-smoking dining room). 🏠 Q ⚘ 🛏 ◁ ▶ ♣ P

## Horsey

### Nelson Head
The Street ☎ (01493) 393378
11–2.30 (3 Sat), 6 (7 winter)–11; 12–3, 7–10.30 Sun
**Woodforde's Wherry, Nelson's Revenge** (summer) Ⓗ
Friendly, one-bar country pub with nautical artefacts, handy for the marshes and Horsey Mill, and within walking distance of the Broads and the beach. Austrian food is a speciality.
🏠 Q 🍽 ⚘ ◁ ▶ ▲ ♣ P

## Hunworth

### Hunny Bell
The Green ☎ (01263) 712300
11–3, 5.30–11; 12–3, 7–10.30 Sun
**Adnams Bitter; Greene King Abbot; Woodforde's Wherry** Ⓗ
Pub with a comfortable,

L-shaped bar with a log fire, plus a dining room.
🏛 ⛲ ❀ ◐ ▶ ♣ P

## Kenninghall

### White Horse Inn
Market Place ☎ (01953) 887379
11–3, 6–11 (11–11 if busy); 12–3, 7–10.30 (12–10.30 if busy) Sun
**Adnams Bitter** Ⓖ**; Greene King IPA** Ⓗ
16th-century coaching inn with a beamed interior. A popular village local serving an extensive range of food.
⛲ ❀ ◐ ▶ ♣ P

## King's Lynn

### Duke's Head
(Lynn Bar)
Tuesday Market Place
☎ (01553) 774996
11–2.30, 6–11; 12–3, 6–10.30 Sun
**Adnams Bitter; Draught Bass; Woodforde's Gt Eastern; guest beer** Ⓗ
An oasis of calm: a small, comfortable, quiet, wood-panelled bar. Q ⛲ ◐ ▶ P

### London Porterhouse
78 London Road
☎ (01553) 766842
12–0, 0–11, 12–11 Sat, 12–10.30 Sun
**Greene King IPA, Abbot** Ⓖ
Tiny, lively pub, close to the town's historic South Gates, with casks racked behind the bar. Q ❀ ◐ ♣

### Seven Sisters
3 Extons Road
☎ (01553) 766707
12–3, 7–11; 12–3, 7–10.30 Sun
**Iceni Celtic Queen, Gold; John Smith's Bitter; guest beer** Ⓗ
Locals' pub, close to the Walks football ground. Small, no-smoking restaurant (no food Wed); live music Fri. Interesting guest beers.
❀ ◐ ♣

### White Horse
9 Wootton Road, Gaywood
☎ (01553) 763258
11–3, 5.30–11; 11–11 Fri & Sat; 12–3, 7–10.30 Sun
**Greene King IPA; John Smith's Bitter; Morland Old Speckled Hen; guest beers** Ⓗ
No food, no frills – this is a drinkers' pub, out of town, close to the Gaywood Clock. The heart of the community.
P ☗

## Larling

### Angel
On A11 ☎ (01953) 717963
11–3, 5–11; 11–11 Fri & Sat; 12–10.30 Sun
**Adnams Bitter; Tetley Bitter; guest beers** Ⓗ

Farming and football-friendly: a two-bar free house with an ever-increasing guest ale turnover and a great mix of locals and travellers.
🏛 Q ❀ 🛏 ◐ ▶ 🍴 🏕 ☗ P

## Little Dunham

### Black Swan
The Street ☎ (01760) 722200
12–2, 7–11; 12–3, 7–10.30 Sun
**Beer range varies** Ⓗ
Pub built in 1735 and once owned by Nelson: a large, single bar divided into several areas. Horse brasses and saddlery adorn the walls. No lunches Tue.
🏛 Q ❀ ◐ ♣ P

## Long Stratton

### Queen's Head
The Street ☎ (01508) 530164
11–2.30, 6.30–11; 11–11 Sat; 12–3, 7.30–10.30 Sun
**Adnams Bitter, Broadside; guest beer** Ⓗ
Large, single-bar pub with drinking areas on different levels. A collection of plates adorns one area that can be isolated from the main bar for functions. Q ❀ ◐ ▶ ♣ P

## Middleton

### Gate Inn
Fair Green ☎ (01553) 840518
12–3, 7–11; 12–3, 7–10.30 Sun
**Boddingtons Bitter; Flowers IPA; guest beer** Ⓗ
Turn north off the A47, just out of King's Lynn, to find this small village local which serves excellent food and features award-winning floral displays.
🏛 Q ❀ ◐ ♣ P

## Mundesley

### Royal Hotel
Paston Road ☎ (01263) 720416
11–3, 6–11; 12–3, 7–10.30 Sun
**Adnams Bitter; Greene King IPA, Abbot; guest beer** Ⓗ
Hotel whose Nelson Bar has comfortable, olde-worlde charm with an inglenook, leather chairs, and Lord Nelson memorabilia.
🏛 ⛲ ❀ 🛏 ◐ ▶ P

## Mundford

### Crown Hotel
Crown Street ☎ (01842) 878233
11–11; 12–3, 7–10.30 Sun
**Marston's Pedigree; Samuel Smith OBB; Woodforde's Wherry; guest beers** Ⓗ
Attractive, two-bar 17th-century village inn, popular for food. Limited parking.
🏛 Q ❀ 🛏 ◐ ▶ ♣ P

## North Creake

### Jolly Farmers
Burnham Road
☎ (01328) 738185
11–3, 6–11; 12–3, 7–10.30 Sun
**Greene King Abbot; Tetley Bitter, Imperial** Ⓗ
Comfortable, two-bar local in the centre of a pretty, unspoilt village, within easy reach of the north Norfolk coast. Good food. 🏛 Q ❀ ◐ ▶ 🅰 ♣ P

## North Elmham

### Railway Hotel
Station Road ☎ (01362) 668300
11–2.30, 7–11; 12–2.30, 7–10.30 Sun
**Ansells Bitter; Flowers IPA; Tetley Imperial; guest beer** Ⓗ
Single-bar, drinkers' pub, close to the old railway, now run by Mid-Norfolk Railway Trust. The bar retains a pre-1930s feel. The large garden has camping space. 🏛 ❀ ◐ ▶ ♿ 🅰 P

## North Lopham

### Kings Head
The Street ☎ (01379) 687320
12–4, 7–11; 12–4, 7–10.30 Sun
**Flowers IPA; Friary Meux BB; guest beers** Ⓗ
Magnificent, thatched, 15th-century pub with an oak-beamed interior and inglenooks in both bars. A dining area adjoins the main bar; pool table in the second bar. Families welcome. Good meals.
🏛 ❀ ◐ ▶ ♿ 🅰 ♣ P ☗

## North Walsham

### Orchard Gardens
Mundesley Road
☎ (01692) 405152
11.30–11; 12–10.30 Sun
**Beer range varies** Ⓗ
Two-bar pub with a games room. Five handpumps; large garden. ❀ 🚆 ♣ P

## Northwold

### Crown Inn
High Street ☎ (01366) 727317
12–3, 6–11; 11–11 Sat; 12–3, 7–10.30 Sun
**Greene King IPA, Abbot; guest beers** Ⓗ
Well-restored example of a 'chalk lump' inn. Iceni beer is usually available. Good food in generous portions.
🏛 Q ❀ ◐ ▶ ♣ P ☗

## Norwich

### Alexandra Tavern
16 Stafford Street (between Earlham Rd and Dereham Rd)
☎ (01603) 627772
10.30–11; 12–10.30 Sun

Chalk Hill Tap Bitter;
Courage Best Bitter; Marston's
Pedigree; Morland Old
Speckled Hen Ⓗ
Unspoilt Victorian, two-bar
pub with bare boards and a
pool table in the public bar.
Highly recommended.
🚲 ❀ ♿ ♣ ⏁

## Billy Bluelight

27 Hall Road
☎ (01603) 623768
12–2.30, 5.30–11; 12–11 Fri & Sat;
12–4, 7–10.30 Sun
Woodforde's Mardler's Mild,
Wherry, Emerald Ale Ⓗ, Gt
Eastern, Nelson's Revenge,
Norfolk Nog Ⓖ; guest beers Ⓗ
Popular pub, the only
Woodforde's house in
Norwich. Beers include a
Woodforde's house ale.
🚲 Q ❀ ♿ ⏁

## Coach & Horses

82 Thorpe Road (200 yds from
station) ☎ (01603) 620704
11–11; 12–10.30 Sun
Chalk Hill Tap Bitter, CHB,
Porter, Dreadnought, Old
Tackle; guest beers Ⓗ
Busy pub, home of the Chalk
Hill Brewery. Regular live
music (Sat eve/Sun lunch). No
hot food Sat and Sun eves.
Guest beers usually include a
mild. 🚲 ❀ ◖ ▶ ⇌ ⏁ P

## Eaton Cottage

75 Mount Pleasant
☎ (01603) 453048
11–11; 12–10.30 Sun
Adnams Bitter; Marston's
Pedigree; John Smith's Bitter;
guest beers Ⓗ
Attractive, suburban local: two
rooms with comfortable
furnishings. Off-licence sales
from the snug. Centenary
(house ale) is brewed by
Scott's. ♿ ♣

## Fat Cat

49 West End Street (off
Dereham Rd, 1 mile from city)
☎ (01603) 624364
12 (11 Sat)–11; 12–10.30 Sun
Adnams Bitter; Fuller's
London Pride; Greene King
Abbot; Kelham Island Pale
Rider; Woodforde's Nelson's
Revenge; guest beers Ⓗ/Ⓖ
Highly regarded, backstreet
pub, offering a wide selection
of fine beers – many on gravity.
Live folk music Thu.
🚲 Q ❀ ♣ ⏁

## Horse & Dray

137 Ber Street
☎ (01603) 624741
11–11; 12–3, 7–10.30 Sun
Adnams Mild, Bitter, Old,
Extra, Broadside; guest
beers Ⓗ
Friendly local, close to the
central shopping area; popular
at lunchtime. 🚲 ❀ ◖ ♿ ♣

## Mustard Pot

101 Thorpe Road
☎ (01603) 432393
12–3, 5.30–11; 12–11 Fri & Sat; 12–3,
7–10.30 Sun
Adnams Bitter, Old;
Marston's Pedigree; guest
beers Ⓗ
Comfortable pub with an
emphasis on beer and wine.
High-backed settles split a
large room into drinking areas.
Within walking distance of the
football ground, it can be busy
on match days. No food Sun.
❀ ◖ P

## Plasterers Arms

43 Cowgate (off Magdalen St)
11–11; 12–2.30, 7–10.30 Sun
Adnams Mild, Bitter, Extra;
Ind Coope Burton Ale; Tetley
Bitter; guest beers Ⓗ
Corner pub, with a traditional
feel, decorated with old curios
and theatre posters. Good
value lunches Mon–Sat. Q ◖

## Ribs of Beef

24 Wensum Street
☎ (01603) 619517
10.30–11; 12–10.30 Sun
Adnams Bitter; Boddingtons
Mild, Bitter; Fuller's London
Pride; Hop Back Summer
Lightning; Reepham Rapier;
Woodforde's Wherry; guest
beers Ⓗ
Busy riverside pub popular
with students and young
people eves. The downstairs
room overlooks the river. Food
served all afternoon Sat/Sun.
◖

## Rosary Tavern

95 Rosary Road (300 yds from
yacht and railway stations)
☎ (01603) 666287
11.30–11; 12–5, 7–10.30 Sun
Adnams Bitter; B&T Shefford
Bitter Ⓗ; guest beers Ⓖ/Ⓗ
Friendly, cosy, local offering a
good range of beers, whiskies
and games.
⚡ ◖ ▶ ⇌ (Thorpe) ♣ P

## St Andrew's Tavern

4 St Andrew's Street (opp.
Duke St car park)
☎ (01603) 614858
11–11; 12–10.30 Sun
Adnams Bitter, Broadside,
seasonal beers; guest beers Ⓗ
Very popular, breweriana-
adorned, city-centre pub with a
cellar bar (no-smoking) open at
busy times and weekends.
Secure cycle parking. Eve
meals Sat. ❀ ◖ ♿ ⏁ ⊬ ⏁

## Tap & Spile

73 Oak Street (just inside Inner
Link Road) ☎ (01603) 620630
12–3.30, 5.30–11; 11–11 Fri & Sat;
12–3, 7–10.30 Sun
Beer range varies Ⓗ
Formerly the White Lion; a pub
has stood on this site since

1514. The three bars house
skittles and bar billiards and
host live music Sat/Sun eves.
🚲 ☏ ◖ ▶ ♣ ⏁

## Trafford Arms

61 Grove Road
☎ (01603) 628466
11–11; 12–10.30 Sun
Boddingtons Bitter; Tetley
Bitter; Woodforde's Mardler's
Mild; guest beers Ⓗ
Large, popular, one-bar city
pub offering an ever-changing
range of guest ales and varied
live music. St Valentine's Day
beer festival. Limited parking.
❀ ◖ ▶ ♿ ♣ ⏁ P

## Vine Tavern

7 Dove Street (off market place)
☎ (01603) 629258
10.30–11; 12–10.30 Sun
Adnams Mild (summer),
Bitter, Old, Extra, Broadside;
guest beer Ⓗ
Norwich's smallest pub; with a
pavement drinking area and
classical music, it has a
continental feel. The single
compact bar is popular with
shoppers and locals.
❀ ⇌ (Thorpe) ♣ ⏁

## Wig & Pen

6 St Martin at Palace Plain
☎ (01603) 625891
11–11; 12–10.30 Sun
Samuel Smith OBB;
Woodforde's Wherry;
Worthington Bitter; guest
beer Ⓗ
Pub opposite the north gate of
the cathedral, deriving its
name from the nearby law
courts: a comfortable mix of
stone floors and carpets, wood
and brickwork, settles and
window seats. Eve meals end
early. 🚲 ❀ ◖ ▶ ⇌ (Thorpe)

## Windmill

Knox Road
☎ (01603) 434531
11.30–2.30 (3.30 Sat), 6 (6.30
winter)–11; 12–10.30 Sun
Greene King XX Mild, IPA,
Abbot; seasonal beers Ⓗ
Pub displaying a definite
contrast between its quiet
lounge and larger, refurbished,
brightly-lit bar. New garden
and play area. Regular live
music. ❀ ◖ ♣

## Old Buckenham

## Ox & Plough

The Green
☎ (01953) 860004
12–2 (3 summer), 6.30–11; 12–11 Sat;
12–3, 7–10.30 Sun
Adnams Bitter; guest beers Ⓗ
Large, single-bar pub with a
pool table at one end,
overlooking the green in the
village centre.
🚲 ❀ ◖ ▶ ♿ ♣ P

## Old Hunstanton

### Ancient Mariner

Golf Course Road
☎ (01485) 534411
11–3, 6–11; 11–11 Sat & summer; 12–4,
7–10.30 (may vary summer) Sun
**Adnams Bitter, Broadside;
Draught Bass; guest beer** H
Adjoining the Le Strange Arms
Hotel, this free house features
bare boards and nautical decor.
There are no-smoking family
rooms and a pleasant patio
garden.
🏰 ⛺ 🌳 🛏 ◁ ▶ ⅋ ♣ P ✗

## Reedham

### Railway Tavern

17 The Havaker (opp. station)
☎ (01493) 700340
12–3, 6.30–11; 11–11 Fri & Sat; 12–
10.30 Sun
**Adnams Extra; Woodforde's
Gt Eastern; guest beers** H
Welcoming pub offering
interesting guest ales, beer
festivals and very good food.
🏰 ⛺ 🛏 ◁ ▶ 🖢 Å ⇌ ♣ P

## Ringstead

### Gin Trap

☎ (01485) 525264
11–3, 7–11; 12–4, 7–10.30 Sun
**Adnams Bitter; Draught Bass;
Greene King Abbot;
Woodforde's Norfolk Nog** H
Comfortable and welcoming
village pub with a split-level
bar, a small restaurant
(excellent food) and a large
garden. Fearsome display of
animal traps. The house beer is
from Woodforde's.
🏰 ⛺ ◁ ▶ P

## Saham Toney

### Bell

Bell Lane ☎ (01953) 884934
12–3, 6–11; 12–3, 7–10.30 Sun
**Adnams Bitter; guest beers** H
Traditional, 18th-century
village pub of 'clay lump'
construction (visible in the
restaurant).
🏰 Q ⛺ ◁ ▶ ♣ P

## Sheringham

### Lobster

High Street ☎ (01263) 822716
11–3, 5.30–11; 11–11 Fri & Sat;
12–4, 7–10.30 Sun
**Adnams Bitter; Marston's
Pedigree; John Smith's
Bitter** H
Traditional, two-bar pub with
a no-smoking family/garden
room; popular with locals and
holidaymakers. Pool table and
darts in the public bar; nautical
atmosphere in the lounge. Eve
meals Fri and Sat.
🏰 Q ⛺ ⛺ ◁ ▶ 🍴 ⇌ ♣ P ✗

## Smallburgh

### Crown

North Walsham Road (A149)
☎ (01692) 536314
12–3 (4 Sat), 5.30 (7 Sat)–11; 12–3,
7–10.30 Sun (closed Sun eve in winter)
**Boddingtons Bitter; Flowers
IPA; Greene King Abbot;
Tetley Bitter; guest beers** H
Comfortable, two-bar village
pub and restaurant, in a
thatched and beamed, 15th-
century building. The games
room opens on to a lovely
garden. 🏰 Q ⛺ 🛏 ◁ ▶ Å ♣ P

## Southery

### Jolly Farmers

60 Feltwell Road
☎ (01366) 377327
11–2.30, 6–11; 12–4, 7–10.30 Sun
**Adnams Bitter; Greene King
IPA, Abbot** H
Friendly, excellent value pub
in all respects. No-smoking
dining area; imaginative menu.
Q ⛺ ◁ ▶ 🖢 ♣ P

## South Lopham

### White Horse

The Street ☎ (01379) 687252
11–3 (4 Sat), 6–11; 12–4, 7–10.30 Sun
**Adnams Bitter; Greene King
IPA, Abbot** H
Pleasant, 18th-century village
pub with oak beams. Good
food.
🏰 Q ⛺ ◁ ▶ 🖢 ♣ P ✗

## Stanhoe

### Crown Inn

Burnham Market Road (B1155)
☎ (01485) 518330
11–3, 6–11; 12–3, 7–10.30 Sun
**Elgood's Cambridge Bitter** H,
**GSB** G
Cosy, friendly village local.
Excellent, home-cooked food
(not served Sun eve). Small
caravan park for CC members.
🏰 Q ⛺ ◁ ▶ Å ♣ P

## Stowbridge

### Heron

Station Road ☎ (01366) 384147
11–3, 7–11; 12–3, 7–10.30 Sun
**Adnams Bitter; Draught Bass;
Greene King IPA, Abbot;
guest beers** H
Pub situated between the Great
Ouse and the relief channel,
with a games room and a
comfortable main bar adorned
with curios and an impressive
row of seven handpumps.
🏰 Q ⛺ ⛺ 🛏 ◁ ▶ Å ♣ P

## Swanton Abbott

### Jolly Farmers

Aylsham Road
☎ (01692) 538542

11–11; 12–10.30 Sun
**Greene King IPA, Abbot;
guest beers** H
Sociable local with a games
room and a parrot. Friendly
bar; good food (but not all-
pervading). Book Sun lunch.
⛺ ◁ ▶ ♣ P

## Swanton Morley

### Darby's

Elsing Road ☎ (01362) 637647
11–2.30, 6–11; 11–11 Sat; 12–3, 7–10.30
Sun
**Adnams Bitter, Broadside;
Badger Tanglefoot;
Woodforde's Mardler's Mild,
Wherry; guest beers** H
Single-bar pub, converted from
two cottages, retaining original
character through beams and
brickwork, an original range
and a fireplace. Separate
restaurant; children's room
with games. Wheelchair access
is via the back door.
🏰 Q ⛺ 🛏 ◁ ▶ 🖢 Å P

## Tacolneston

### Pelican

136 Norwich Road (B1113)
☎ (01508) 489521
11–3, 5.30–11; 11–11 Sat; 12–10.30 Sun
**Flowers IPA, Original, guest
beers** H
Subtly-lit pub with a single,
timbered bar, a large open fire,
a conservatory where children
are welcome and a very large
garden/play area with a
menagerie. No-smoking dining
area. No lunches Tue.
🏰 ⛺ ◁ ▶ 🖢 ♣ P

## Thetford

### Albion

93–95 Castle Street (opp. Castle
Hill ancient monument)
☎ (01842) 752796
11–2.30 (3 Fri), 6 (5 Fri)–11; 12–2.30,
7–10.30 Sun
**Greene King seasonal beers** H
Small, traditional local, set
amongst flint-faced cottages in
the older part of town. Good
value ales, but note the IPA
and Abbot are kept using a
cask breather. Q ⛺ ♣ P

### Anchor Hotel

Bridge Street (near bus station)
☎ (01842) 763925
11–3, 6–11; 12–3, 7–10.30 Sun
**Theakston Best Bitter;
Younger IPA; guest beers** H
Popular beer and food haven
with intimate, low-ceilinged
drinking areas on various
levels. Q ⛺ 🛏 ◁ ▶ 🖢 P

## Thompson

### Chequers Inn

Griston Road OS923969
☎ (01953) 483360

11–3, 6–11; 12–3, 7–10.30 Sun
**Adnams Bitter; Draught Bass;
Fuller's London Pride; Tetley
Bitter; guest beers** H
16th-century thatched inn, off
the beaten track but worth
finding. Good value food.
🏚 Q 🌲 ❀ ◑ ▲ ♣ P

## Thornham

### Lifeboat

Ship Lane (off A149)
☎ (01485) 512236
11–11; 12–10.30 Sun
**Adnams Bitter; Greene King
IPA, Abbot; Woodforde's
Wherry** H; **guest beers** G/H
Classic, 16th-century inn
beside the salt marshes, with
views of the harbour. Play
'Penny in the Hole' by the light
of oil lamps in the Smugglers'
Bar. 🏚 Q ❀ � ◑ ♣ 👄 P

## Thorpe St Andrew

### Gordon

88 Gordon Avenue
☎ (01603) 434658
11–3, 7–11; 12–3, 7–10.30 Sun
**Tetley Bitter; guest beers** H
Large, suburban, family pub,
popular with locals; a mock
Tudor building, dating from
1934. ❀ ♣ P

## Upwell

### Five Bells

New Road ☎ (01945) 772222
11–3, 5–11 (11–11 summer); 12–3,
7–10.30 Sun
**Draught Bass; Courage Best
Bitter; John Smith's Bitter** H
Spacious, friendly, family inn
with a bar counter made from
redundant pew ends from the
church next door. Plush dining
room. An Iceni beer is also
sold. 🏚 Q 🌲 ❀ � ◑ ◑ 🛆 ♣ P

## Walcott

### Lighthouse Inn

Coast Road (B1159)
☎ (01692) 650371
11–3, 6–11; 11–11 Sat; 12–10.30 Sun
**Adnams Bitter; Tetley Bitter;
guest beers** H
Friendly pub, popular with
visitors and locals. Good value
food. 🏚 🌲 ❀ ◑ ▲ ♣ P

## Walpole Cross Keys

### Woolpack Inn

Sutton Road ☎ (01553) 828327
12–3, 7–11; 12–3.30, 7–10.30 Sun
**Adnams Bitter, Broadside;
guest beer** H
Attractive, 16th-century inn on
the old A17, catering for all in
two bars, a games room and a
restaurant. Live music Sun eve.
🏚 Q 🌲 ❀ ◑ ◑ P

## Walsingham

### Bull Inn

Common Place, Shirehall Plain
☎ (01328) 820333
11–3, 6–11 (11–11 summer Sat); 12–3,
7–10.30 Sun
**Boddingtons Bitter; Flowers
IPA, Original; Ind Coope
Burton Ale; guest beers** H
15th-century inn, with one wall
originally part of a priory. The
lounge contains beams charred
during a fire caused by
pilgrims who accused the
landlord of overcharging! Eve
meals in summer.
🏚 Q ❀ � ◑ ◑ ♣ P

## Warham

### Three Horseshoes ☆

The Street ☎ (01328) 710547
11–2.30, 6–11; 11–11 Sat; 12–3, 7–10.30
Sun
**Greene King IPA, Abbot;
Woodforde's Wherry** G
Pub with a timeless interior
featuring scrubbed wood
tables, a grandfather clock and
local memorabilia. Busy in
summer. Excellent food.
🏚 🌲 ❀ � ◑ ◑ P

## Weasenham All Saints

### Ostrich Inn

On A1065 ☎ (01328) 838221
11–3, 7–11; 12–3, 7–10.30 Sun
**Adnams Bitter; guest beer**
(occasional) H
Welcoming, totally unspoilt
pub which sells fruit and veg.
🏚 Q ❀ ▲ ♣ P

## Wells-next-the-Sea

### Crown Hotel

The Buttlands
☎ (01328) 710209
11–2.30, 6–11; 12–2.30, 7–10.30 Sun
**Adnams Bitter; Draught Bass;
Marston's Pedigree** H
Comfortable hotel bar and
large restaurant with an
imposing Georgian facade.
Children are catered for in a
south-facing sun lounge.
🏚 🌲 ❀ � ◑ ◑ P

### Edinburgh Hotel

Station Road ☎ (01328) 710120
11–3, 6.30–11; 12–3, 6.30–10.30 Sun
**Draught Bass; Hancock's HB;
guest beers** H
Pub whose long bar is broken
into areas. A large brick
chimney divides off a lounge,
which leads to a courtyard
with small caged animals
(popular with families).
Lunches in summer; eve meals
restricted in winter to
weekends.
🏚 ❀ � ◑ ◑ 🛆 ▲ 🍺

## West Somerton

### Lion

Martham Road (B1159/B1152)
☎ (01493) 393289
11–4 (3 winter), 6–11; 12–4 (3 winter),
7–10.30 Sun
**Draught Bass; Greene King
IPA, Abbot, seasonal beers;
Mauldons Black Adder;
Worthington Bitter; guest
beers** H
Comfortable, two-bar, village
pub, which re-opened 20 years
ago after being de-licensed for
several years. Excellent range
of beers. Q 🌲 ◑ ◑ ♣ P

## Whinburgh

### Mustard Pot

Dereham Road (B1135)
☎ (01362) 692179
11–3, 6.30–11; 12–3, 7–10.30 Sun
**Woodforde's Wherry; guest
beer** H
Friendly village local, formerly
a row of houses. Accomm-
odation is available next to the
pub. Additional guest beer in
summer. 🏚 Q ❀ ◑ ◑ 🛆 ♣ P

## Winterton-on-Sea

### Fisherman's Return

The Lane (off B1159)
☎ (01493) 393305
11–2.30 (3 Sat), 6 (7 winter)–11 (11–11
summer Sat); 12–3, 7–10.30 Sun
**Adnams Bitter** G; **Draught
Bass; Boddingtons Mild;
Courage Directors; John
Smith's Bitter; Whitbread
Fuggles IPA; guest beers** H
Popular, two-bar local handy
for the beach. Family room and
cider in summer.
🏚 Q 🌲 ❀ � ◑ ◑ 🍺 ♣ 👄 P

## Woodbastwick

### Fur & Feather Inn

Slad Lane ☎ (01603) 720003
12–3, 6–11; 12–3, 7–10.30 Sun
**Woodforde's Mardler's Mild,
Broadsman, Wherry, Gt
Eastern, Nelson's Revenge,
Norfolk Nog, Baldric,
Headcracker** G
Woodforde's tap – a purpose-
built pub. Families welcome in
the no-smoking area. Good
food (restaurant); large garden.
❀ ◑ ◑ 🛆 👄 P 🍴

## Wymondham

### Feathers Inn

Town Green ☎ (01953) 605675
11–2.30, 7 (6 Fri)–11; 12–2.30, 7–10.30
Sun
**Adnams Bitter; Greene King
Abbot; Marston's Pedigree;
guest beers** H
Popular local; a large single-
room bar. House beer from
Sam Smith. Q ❀ ◑ ◑ ♣ P

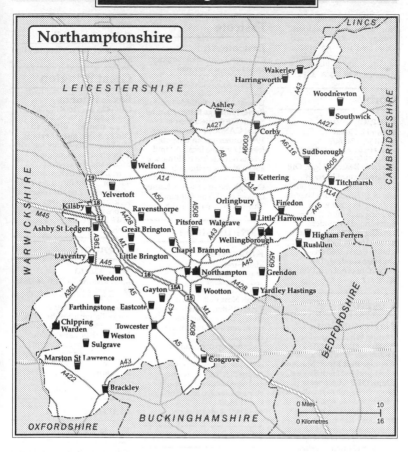

## Northamptonshire

*(Map showing locations including:)*

LINCS

LEICESTERSHIRE

Wakerley
Harringworth
Woodnewton
Ashley
Southwick
Corby
Sudborough
CAMBRIDGESHIRE
Welford
Kettering
Titchmarsh
Yelvertoft
Kilsby
Ravensthorpe
Orlingbury
Finedon
Ashby St Ledgers
Pitsford
Walgrave
Little Harrowden
Great Brington
Wellingborough
Higham Ferrers
WARWICKSHIRE
Chapel Brampton
Rushden
Daventry
Little Brington
Weedon
Northampton
Grendon
Gayton
Wootton
Yardley Hastings
Farthingstone
Eastcote
Chipping Warden
Towcester
Weston
Sulgrave
BEDFORDSHIRE
Marston St Lawrence
Cosgrove
Brackley
BUCKINGHAMSHIRE
OXFORDSHIRE

0 Miles 10
0 Kilometres 16

---

## Ashby St Ledgers

### Old Coach House Inn
Main Street (off A361)
☎ (01788) 890349
12–2.30, 6–11; 12–11 Sat; 12–4, 7–10.30
Sun (may extend in summer)
**Boddingtons Bitter; Everards
Old Original; Flowers IPA;
guest beers** H
Popular pub all year round,
with wood panelling and open
fires for a warm winter
welcome and a large garden
for summer barbecues. Beer
festivals in March and Oct. St
Ledger Special is brewed for
the pub.
🏤 ❀ ⇔ ◑ ▶ ⊟ ♿ ➪ P ⊟

## Ashley

### George
21 Main Street (off B664)
☎ (01858) 565881
12–2.30 (3 Sat; not Thu), 6–11; 12–3,
7–10.30 Sun
**Mansfield Riding Bitter,
Bitter, Old Baily** H
Friendly village pub: a superb

tiled bar with wooden settles, a
comfortable lounge and a
skittles room with a small
serving hatch to the main bar.
Well worth a detour. No food
Tue.
🏤 ❀ ◑ ▶ ♣

## Brackley

### Greyhound Inn
101 High Street
☎ (01280) 703331
12–2.30, 7–11; 12–3, 7–10.30 Sun
**Banks's Bitter; guest beers** H
Pub with an L-shaped bar, plus
a snug room, games room and a
restaurant where Mexican
dishes are a speciality. Four
guest ales and 40 malt
whiskies. 🏤 ◑ ▶ ♣

### Red Lion
11 Market Place
☎ (01280) 702228
11–11; 12–10.30 Sun
**Wells Eagle, Bombardier,
Fargo** H
16th-century, stone-built pub,
recently refurbished. The
public bar has a pool table.

Regular music events in the
barn bar in the garden.
🏤 ❀ ⇔ ◑ ▶ ♣

**Try also: Great Western Arms,
Aynho (Hook Norton)**

## Chapel Brampton

### Brampton Halt
Pitsford Road (between A508
and A50) ☎ (01604) 842676
11–3, 5–11; 12–3, 7–10.30 Sun
**Adnams Bitter, Old; Everards
Tiger, Old Original; guest
beers** H
Excellent pub conversion from
a former station master's

| 📇 INDEPENDENT BREWERIES | |
|---|---|
| **Cannon:** Wellingborough | |
| **Frog Island:** Northampton | |
| **Hop House:** Northampton | |
| **Leyland:** Wellingborough | |
| **Merivales:** Chipping Warden | |

house, adjacent to the Northampton and Lamport Preservation Railway. Good value food always available. Extensive lawn and gardens; popular with families in summer. Q ❀ ◖▮ ◒ Ⅰ ♿ ▲ P

## Corby

### Knights Lodge
Tower Hill Road
☎ (01536) 742602
12–3 (4 Fri & Sat), 6 (6.30 Sat)–11;
12–3, 7–10.30 Sun
**Everards Beacon, Tiger, Old Original; guest beers** H
Early 17th-century pub on the site of a 12th-century knights' lodgings in what was a clearing in the forest. Now surrounded by modern housing, it is an oasis in an ex-steel town. Eight ghosts; graffiti dated 1860 on a staircase window. The restaurant is not open Sun eve.
🏚 ❀ ◖▮ P

## Cosgrove

### Navigation Inn
Thrupp Wharf (signed on A508) ☎ (01908) 543156
11–3.30, 6–11; 12–3, 7–10.30 Sun
**Courage Best Bitter; Morland Old Speckled Hen; Samuel Smith OBB; guest beers** H
Stone-built pub set in attractive countryside alongside the Grand Union Canal. A spacious balcony offers views of boats and summer sunsets. The restaurant boasts two pianos and offers excellent food. 🏚 ❀ ◖▮ ▲ P

## Daventry

### Coach & Horses
Warwick Street
☎ (01327) 76692
11–2.30, 5 (4.30 Fri)–11; 12–3, 7–11 Sat;
12–3, 7–10.30 Sun
**Ind Coope Burton Ale; Marston's Pedigree; Tetley Bitter; guest beers** H
Open fires, boarded floors and stone walls give a warm feel to this town-centre pub. The stables across the coaching yard host a jazz night alternate Thu. Changing guest beers. No food Sun. 🏚 Q ❀ ◖ ♣

### Dun Cow
Brook Street ☎ (01327) 71545
10.30–3, 5 (7 Sat)–11; 10.30–11 Fri;
12–3, 7–10.30 Sun
**Greenalls Davenports Bitter, Original** H
Early 17th-century coaching inn with an unspoilt snug bar. The landlord is only the third this century. Monthly folk music. No food Sun.
🏚 Q ❀ ◖ P

## Eastcote

### Eastcote Arms
6 Gayton Road (take Banbury Lane turn for Duncote)
☎ (01327) 830731
12–2.30 (not Mon), 6–11; 12–3, 7–10.30 Sun
**Draught Bass, Fuller's London Pride; Jennings Bitter; Samuel Smith OBB; guest beer** H
Local CAMRA *Pub of the Year* 1995 runner-up: an unspoilt friendly village local. A family area is outside but children are also welcome in the pub. A small no-smoking dining room through the snug serves home-cooked food (Tue–Sat lunch, Thu–Sat eve). 🏚 Q ❀ ◖▮ P

## Farthingstone

### Kings Arms
Main Street
☎ (01327) 361604
12–2.30 (not Mon), 6.30–11; 12–3, 7–10.30 Sun
**Hook Norton Best Bitter; Tetley Bitter; guest beers** H
Outstanding village pub, listed for its architectural interest; an unusual combination of ages and styles, partly built with stone from the church opposite. Cosy and low-beamed, it has an inglenook and a collection of jugs and china plates. No food Sun eve or Mon.
🏚 Q ❀ ◖▮ ♣ P

## Finedon

### Bell
Bell Hill ☎ (01933) 680332
11.30–2.30, 5.30 (6 Sat)–11; 12–3, 7–10.30 Sun
**Boddingtons Bitter; Ruddles Best Bitter, County; Vaux Samson; Ward's Best Bitter; guest beers** H
Reputed to be the county's oldest pub, AD1043. A real gem: a large ironstone building with a Gothic Revival period archway entrance. The large bar has an inglenook and a wood burner. The rear bar is packed with memorabilia. It also has a restaurant (no eve meals Sun or Mon). Good atmosphere. 🏚 ❀ ◖▮ ♣ P

## Gayton

### Eykyn Arms
20 High Street (A43 Blisworth road) ☎ (01604) 858361
12–2 (not Mon), 7 (earlier summer)–11;
12–3, 7–10.30 Sun
**Theakston XB; Wells Eagle, Fargo; guest beers** H
Good, basic, popular local with a bar and a lounge. The front bar bears a nautical/aviation

theme. Floral patio. Dogs welcome.
🏚 ☂ ❀ ◖ ▲ ♣ P ▯

**Try also: Queen Victoria**, High St (Free)

## Great Brington

### Fox & Hounds
Off A428 ☎ (01604) 770651
12–2.30, 5.30–11; 12–10.30 Sun
**Theakston Best Bitter, XB, Old Peculier; guest beers** H
350-year-old coaching inn with flagstoned floors, original beams and some wood panelling. The olde-worlde interior is split into three areas of character. Log fires create a welcoming atmosphere. The games room affords a view of casks in the cellar; six guest beers. 🏚 ❀ ◖▮ ♣ P

## Grendon

### Half Moon
Main Road ☎ (01933) 663263
12–3 (4 Sat), 6 (6.30 Sat)–11; 12–3, 7–10.30 Sun
**Badger Tanglefoot; Wells Eagle, Fargo; guest beers** H
17th-century, country inn. The large bar has a low ceiling, original beams and lots of gleaming brass and copper. Totally pink decor in the gents' loo; Laura Ashley has found her way into the ladies'.
🏚 Q ☂ ❀ ◖▮ ◒ ♣ P

## Harringworth

### White Swan
Seaton Road ☎ (01572) 747543
11.30–2.30, 6.30–11; 12–3, 7–10.30 Sun
**Greene King IPA, Abbot; Marston's Pedigree** H
16th-century coaching inn of local limestone with a collweston roof: a bar area, a games and drinking area and a restaurant. The stairs up to the accommodation have a trip step – an early form of burglar alarm. Close to the famous railway viaduct over the River Welland. Q ❀ 🛏 ◖▮ ♣ P

## Higham Ferrers

### Green Dragon Hotel
4 College Street (A6)
☎ (01933) 312088
11.30–11; 12–10.30 Sun
**Badger Tanglefoot; Banks's Bitter; Federation Buchanan's Special; Shepherd Neame Spitfire; Tetley Bitter; guest beers** H
Stone-built, 17th-century, Grade II listed pub on a conservation high street. Thirteen beers are available, including a mild and a stout or porter. Beer festivals held in May and Aug. Two acres of garden include a children's

adventure playground and a boules pitch. Cider in summer.
⊛ ⇔ ◑ ▮ ⊟ ♣ ◌

## Kettering

### Piper

Windmill Avenue (off A6)
☎ (01536) 513870
11–3 (4 Sat), 5 (6 Sat)–11; 12–10.30 Sun
**Ansells Mild; Tetley Bitter; Theakston Best Bitter, XB, Old Peculier** ⊞
Much-improved 1950s pub, near Wicksteed Park: a pleasantly furnished lounge and a games room with pool. A rare outlet for mild. Food served at all times.
⊛ ◑ ▮ ⊟ ♣ P

### Talbot Inn

Meadow Road
☎ (01536) 514565
11–11; 12–10.30 Sun
**Marston's Bitter, Pedigree** ⊞
Close to the town centre, this friendly establishment has two comfortable lounges, a public bar and a conservatory. Limited accommodation available. ⇔ ◑ ▮

## Kilsby

### George Hotel

11 Watling Street
☎ (01788) 822229
11.30–3, 6–11; 12–3, 7–10.30 Sun
**Draught Bass; M&B Brew XI** ⊞
Pleasant old village hotel on the old A5. The wood-panelled lounge is quiet and relaxing; the rather basic bar is quite a contrast. Good value, home-cooked bar meals plus a restaurant.
Q ⊛ ⇔ ◑ ▮ ⊟ ♣ P

## Little Brington

### Saracen's Head

High Street ☎ (01604) 770640
11–3, 5.30–11; 11–11 Sat; 12–3, 7–10.30 Sun
**Flowers Original; Frog Island Best Bitter; Fuller's London Pride; Morland Old Speckled Hen; Wadworth 6X; guest beers** ⊞
300-year-old village pub with a cosy log fire; refurbished both to enhance its character and to further accommodate diners. Special rates for pensioners' meals Wed lunch. Games eves held. ⚄ ⊛ ◑ ▮ ♣ P

## Little Harrowden

### Lamb

Orlingbury Road
☎ (01604) 673300
11–2.30, 7 (6 Fri)–11; 12–3, 7–10.30 Sun
**Adnams Broadside; Badger Tanglefoot; Morland Old Speckled Hen; Wells Eagle, Bombardier** ⊞

Well-run, village local with a good reputation for its food. The beamed lounge has an adjoining eating area. The games room features table skittles. Note the framed print of the history of the English monarchy.
⚄ Q ⊛ ◑ ▮ ⊟ ♣ P

## Marston St Lawrence

### Marston Inn

1½ miles off B4525
☎ (01295) 711906
12–3 (not Mon), 7 (6 Sat)–11; 12–3, 7–10.30 Sun
**Hook Norton Best Bitter, seasonal beers; guest beers** ⊞
Welcoming village local which offers excellent, home-cooked food in the restaurant or bar. Aunt Sally is played in the back garden. Unusually for the area, real cider is stocked. Camping, with caravans allowed, behind the pub. No food Sun eve or Mon. ⚄ ⊛ ◑ ▮ ▲ ♣ ◌ P

## Northampton

### Bold Dragoon

48 High Street, Weston Favell
☎ (01604) 401221
11–3, 5.30–11; 11–11 Sat; 12–3, 7–10.30 Sun
**Banks's Bitter; Boddingtons Bitter; Flowers IPA; Wadworth 6X; guest beers** ⊞
Well-patronised pub with two to three constantly changing guest beers drawing people in. Comfortable lounge with a central fireplace; busy games room with a loud jukebox and occasionally louder rugby players. ⊛ ⊟ ♣ P

### Crown & Cushion

276 Wellingborough Road
☎ (01604) 33937
11–11; 12–10.30 Sun
**Banks's Bitter; Ruddles Best Bitter; John Smith's Bitter** ⊞
Large, popular pub, one of several on the always busy Wellingborough Road. It attracts all ages; drinkers on one side, games-players on the other, served from a central bar. Safe, secure garden.
⊛ ♣ 🍺

### Duke of Edinburgh

3–5 Adelaide Street (off Barrack Road) ☎ (01604) 37903
11–3, 5–11; 11–11 Sat; 12–3, 7–10.30 Sun
**Wells Eagle, Bombardier; guest beers** ⊞
Recently refurbished Charles Wells backstreet local: a large L-shaped bar with a central serving area. Northants skittles team. Impromptu piano players are welcome, as are any musicians. Live music Sat

eve; quiz Tue; 50s/60s discos Fri. ⊛ ♣

### Fish Inn

11 Fish Street
☎ (01604) 234040
11–11; 7–10.30 Sun, closed Sun lunch
**Courage Directors; Morland Old Speckled Hen; Theakston Best Bitter, XB; Younger No. 3; guest beers** ⊞
Traditional pub with a friendly atmosphere in a town-centre location. Wide range of sandwiches and main meals (lunchtime); T&J Bernard's famous pies available until 10. Regular beer festivals.
⇔ ◑ ◌

### Old Black Lion

Marefair/Black Lion Hill (2 mins from station, turn left)
☎ (01604) 39472
11–11; 12–3, 7–10 Sun
**Courage Directors; Marston's Pedigree; Webster's Yorkshire Bitter; guest beers** ⊞
Basic, two-roomed lounge/bar, stone built in the 12th century. It features a pool table, skittles and darts, plus a 50s/60s music night. Guest beers include the Tapster's Choice range and the local Frog Island beers. Ask for oversized glasses.
⊛ ⊟ ⮞ P 🍺

### Queen Adelaide

50 Manor Road, Kingsthorpe
☎ (01604) 714524
11–2.30 (3 Sat), 5.30–11; 12–3, 7–10.30 Sun
**Banks's Bitter; Wadworth 6X; Webster's Yorkshire Bitter** ⊞
Well-patronised, unspoilt pub in the middle of old Kingsthorpe village. A listed building, it dates back to 1640. The original ceiling and panelling can be seen in the atmospheric bar. The adjoining games area houses table skittles.
Q ⊛ ◑ ▮ ⊟ ♣ P

### Racehorse

15 Abington Square
☎ (01604) 31997
11–11; 12–10.30 Sun
**Adnams Bitter; Everards Tiger; Morland Old Speckled Hen; guest beers** ⊞
Popular, town-centre pub with a good range of beers in its wood-panelled bar and split-level drinking area. Live bands Sun and Tue. Vegetarian menu. Friendly, well informed staff. ⊛ ◑

### Victoria Inn

2 Poole Street, Military Road
☎ (01604) 33660
12–3, 5.30–11; 11–11 Fri & Sat; 12–10.30 Sun
**Flowers IPA; Fuller's London Pride; guest beers** ⊞
This good old, backstreet corner local has had a chequered history, but is now a

thriving real ale house. Four ever-changing guest beers, plus a house beer around £1 a pint. Popular with students, it is frequented by football teams at the weekend. ❧ ♣

## Wig & Pen

19 St Giles Street (near Town Hall) ☎ (01604) 22178
11–2.30, 5 (7 Sat)–11; closed Sun
**Courage Directors; Everards Tiger; Marston's Pedigree; Morland Old Speckled Hen** Ⓗ
Pub which has risen from the decay of the Black Lion and features a drastically altered interior, reclaimed beams and old pine doors. A popular lunchtime venue, it can get a bit crowded Fri and Sat eves. Large verdant patio. ❀ ◖

# Orlingbury

## Queen's Arms

11 Isham Road
☎ (01933) 678258
11–2.30, 5.30–11; 12–3, 7–10.30 Sun
**Fuller's London Pride; Hook Norton Best Bitter; Morland Old Speckled Hen; guest beers** Ⓗ
Recently refurbished (in green) village pub; Northants CAMRA *Pub of the Year* 1994. Up to ten real ales on at one time (over 400 different brews to date). No food at weekends. ▲ Q ❀ ◖ P

# Pitsford

## Griffin

High Street
☎ (01604) 880346
11–2.30, 5.30–11; 12–11 Sat (if busy); 12–3, 7–10.30 Sun
**Theakston Best Bitter, Old Peculier; guest beer** Ⓗ
Listed, stone-built village local, well supported by various sporting groups. Ideal after a walk around the reservoir.
Q ❀ ◖ ♣ P

# Ravensthorpe

## Chequers

Church Lane (off A428)
☎ (01604) 770379
11–3, 6–11; 11–11 Sat; 12–3, 7–10.30 Sun
**Fuller's London Pride; Jennings Bitter; Samuel Smith OBB; Thwaites Bitter; guest beers** Ⓗ
One of the county's few free houses, set in rolling countryside and well worth finding. A beamed, single, L-shaped bar is adorned with bric-a-brac, creating a warm atmosphere. Excellent value food and beer. Family room across the courtyard.
Q ⛲ ❀ ◖ ♣ P

# Rushden

## Rushden Historical Transport Society

Station Approach (A6, N end of town, on one-way system)
☎ (01933) 318988
7.30–11; 12–2.30, 7.30–10.30 Sun
**Fuller's London Pride; guest beers** Ⓗ
Midland railway station saved by locals after a 1962 branch closure. The private gas-lit bar and adjoining museum are packed with transport memorabilia. The bar sometimes extends into the no-smoking carriage at the platform edge. Usually four guest beers. ▲ Q ❀ P ✗ ⊟

# Southwick

## Shuckburgh Arms

Main Street ☎ (01832) 274007
12–2 (3 Sat; not Mon), 6–11; 12–3, 7–10.30 Sun
**Fuller's London Pride; guest beer** Ⓗ
Cosy village local, dating from the 16th century: a through-bar with games and eating areas at one end and a large fireplace at the other. Situated by the cricket pitch and opposite Southwick Hall, it is popular with all sections of the community. Weekly guest beer. ▲ Q ⛲ ❀ ◖ ◗ ♣ P

# Sudborough

## Vane Arms

Main Street ☎ (01832) 733223
11.30–3 (not Mon), 5.30 (6 Sat)–11; 12–3, 7–10.30 Sun
**Beer range varies** Ⓗ
1996 Northamptonshire CAMRA *Pub of the Year*: an outstanding free house of great character in a thatched village. It stocks over ten real ales plus country wines and draught Kriek and Frambozen. Good B&B (special weekend rates). Mexican food a speciality (no meals Sun or Mon eves). ▲ Q ❀ ⛺ ◖ ◗ ❧ ♣ ⌂ P

# Sulgrave

## Star

Manor Road (off B4525, follow Sulgrave Manor signs)
☎ (01295) 760389
11–2.30, 6–11; 12–3, 7–10.30 Sun
**Hook Norton Mild, Best Bitter, Old Hooky, Twelve Days; guest beers** Ⓗ
Popular village local with good tourist trade from nearby Sulgrave Manor (the ancestral home of George Washington). The single bar has a large fireplace with a resident customer – George the skeleton. ▲ Q ❀ ⛺ ◖ ◗ P

# Titchmarsh

## Dog & Partridge

6 High Street ☎ (01832) 732546
12–2.30, 6–11; 12–3, 7–10.30 Sun
**Adnams Bitter, Broadside; Wells Eagle; Bombardier** Ⓗ
Welcoming, 18th-century village local where one large bar incorporates quiet and games areas. Popular with all ages; ramblers and hikers most welcome. A rural gem.
▲ Q ❀ ◖ ♣ P

# Towcester

## Plough

Market Square, Watling Street (A5) ☎ (01327) 350738
11–11; 12–3, 7–10.30 Sun
**Adnams Broadside; Wells Eagle; guest beer** Ⓗ
Pub facing a small market square; the small front bar leads to a larger seating area at the rear. Take-away food available. ▲ ◖ ◗ P

# Wakerley

## Exeter Arms

Main Street ☎ (01572) 747817
12–3, 6–11; 12–3, 7–10.30 Sun
**Adnams Broadside; Bateman XB; Marston's Pedigree** Ⓗ
17th-century, stone pub: a comfortable lounge with a woodburning stove. Wheelchair access at the side door. ▲ ❀ ⛺ ◖ ◗ ❧ ♣ P

# Walgrave

## Royal Oak

Zion Hill ☎ (01604) 781248
11–2.30, 6–11; 12–4, 6.30–10.30 Sun
**Boddingtons Bitter; Webster's Yorkshire Bitter; guest beers** Ⓗ
Exceptionally well-run pub in the centre of the village. Very popular for food – an interesting menu is augmented with daily blackboard specials. Cosy, three-section front bar; the rear games room doubles as a well-appointed restaurant at weekends. Four guest beers. Q ❀ ◖ ◗ ❧ ♣ P ✗

# Weedon

## Globe Hotel

High Street (A5/A45 jct)
☎ (01327) 340336
11–11; 12–3, 7–10.30 Sun
**Marston's Bitter, Pedigree; Webster's Yorkshire Bitter; guest beers** Ⓗ
Very professional countryside inn, maintaining a pub feel in the bar which also serves home-cooked fare. High quality food also features in the restaurant. Ideal for a weekend

break (excellent B&B), or a
drink whilst passing through.
🏨 Q 🍴 ◑ ◐ & P

**Try also: Wheatsheaf**, High St
(Banks's)

## Welford

### Shoulder of Mutton

12 High Street (A50)
☎ (01858) 575375
12–2.30, 7–11; 12–3, 7–10.30 Sun
**Draught Bass; Worthington
Bitter** Ⓗ
Welcoming, friendly,
17th-century village local with
a single bar divided by arches.
The games room is also the
family room. The large garden
has swings and a slide. Good
value food in the bar and
restaurant (no meals Thu).
Q 🌸 ⊛ ◑ ◐ & 🅰 ♣ P

## Wellingborough

### Cannon

Cannon Street
☎ (01933) 279629
11–11; 12–4, 7–10.30 Sun
**Cannon Light Brigade, Florrie
Night-in-Ale, Pride, Fodder;
Wells Eagle; guest beers** Ⓗ
Brew pub on the edge of the
town centre: a friendly local in
two halves – games on one
side, seats by the fire on the
other. Up to nine ales. Admire
the enormous bottled beer
collection. 🏨 ⊛ ♣ P

### Vivian Arms

153 Knox Road (side street,
between station and town
centre) ☎ (01933) 223660
11–2.30 (3 Sat), 6 (7 Sat)–11; 12–3,
7–10.30 Sun
**Badger Tanglefoot; Wells
Eagle; guest beers** Ⓗ

Rare, unspoilt, traditional,
street-corner local: a friendly
bar, a cosy lounge and a large
games room. Some way from
the town centre but worth
finding. 🏨 Q ⊛ 🍴 ⇌ ♣ P

## Weston

### Crown

2 Helmdon Road
☎ (01295) 760310
12–2.30 (3 Sat), 6–11; 12–3, 7–10.30
Sun
**ABC Best Bitter; Friary Meux
BB; guest beers** Ⓗ
Attractive, beamed pub, in part
dating back to 1593, with a
cosy log fire in the lounge area,
a children's area and a function
room. Three guest beers.
🏨 Q ⊛ 🍴 ◑ ◐ ♣ P

## Woodnewton

### White Swan

Main Street (4 miles N of
Oundle, between A43 and
A605) ☎ (01780) 470381
12–3, 6.30–11; 12–3.30, 7–10.30 Sun
**Badger Tanglefoot; Fuller's
London Pride; Oakham JHB;
Shepherd Neame Spitfire;
guest beers** Ⓗ
Popular, 200-year-old village
free house, comprising a single
bar and a restaurant with an
extensive menu (no food Sun
eve). Always a warm welcome.
Boules played. ⊛ ◑ ◐ & ♣ P

## Wootton

### Wootton
Workingmen's Club

23 High Street
☎ (01604) 761863
12–2 (2.30 Fri & Sat), 7–11; 12–2.30,
7–10.30 Sun

**Draught Bass; Wells Eagle;
guest beers** Ⓗ
East Midlands CAMRA *Club of
the Year* 1993: a superb club,
recently refurbished to include
a games room. The function
room offers live entertainment
at weekends, while the lounge
provides a pub atmosphere.
CIU entry restrictions apply.
Excellent range of real ales.
♣ P

## Yardley Hastings

### Red Lion

89 High Street (off Bedford Rd)
☎ (01604) 696210
11–2.30 (3 Sat), 6–11; 12–3, 7–10.30
Sun
**Adnams Broadside; Wells
Eagle** Ⓗ
Cosy, village pub featuring
loads of gleaming brass and
copperware in its wood-
beamed lounge. The bar has
darts and Northamptonshire
skittles. Excellent lunches
(not served Sun).
Q ⊛ ◑ ⊟ & ♣ P

## Yelvertoft

### Knightley Arms

49 High Street (off A428)
☎ (01788) 822401
11.30–2.30 (not winter Mon), 7 (5
Fri)–11; 11–11 Sat; 12–4.30, 7–10.30
Sun
**Draught Bass; Marston's
Pedigree; Theakston XB; guest
beer** Ⓗ
Village local with a tiled floor.
The public bar offers
Northants skittles; the
lounge is wood-panelled and
displays a plate collection and
local canal maps.
🏨 Q ⊛ ◑ ◐ ⊟ ♣ P

---

## ROOM AT THE INN

Whilst the *Good Beer Guide* provides, by way of the bed symbol,
an indication of the accommodation available at a pub, the
*Guide* often does not have the space to comment on the quality of the
bed and board on offer. That's why CAMRA has produced a sister
publication which details the best pubs in which to stay in the UK.

*Room at the Inn* has been compiled by *Good Beer Guide* deputy editor
Jill Adam, in conjunction with CAMRA members across the country.
The book features well over 300 pubs where the practice of offering
generous hospitality to travellers has not been forgotten. Designed to
appeal to both the holidaymaker and the travelling businessperson,
it's a passport to a comfortable bed, a decent breakfast and, of course,
a well-kept pint of beer. Copies are available at £8.99 from all good
bookshops or direct (post-free) from CAMRA, 230 Hatfield Road,
St Albans, Hertfordshire AL1 4LW.

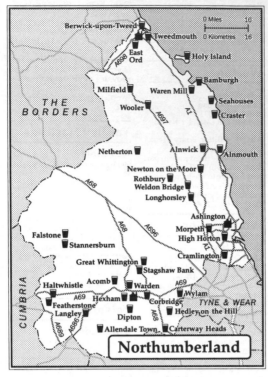

**Northumberland**

---

dirty bottles which are believed to be cursed.

## Bamburgh

### Victoria Hotel
Front Street ☎ (01668) 214431
11–11; 12–10.30 Sun
**Boddingtons Bitter; Border Rampart; Butterknowle Conciliation; guest beers** H
Imposing, historic hotel with a comfortable bar near magnificent Bamburgh Castle. Excellent food and accommodation.

## Berwick-upon-Tweed

### Auld Brewers Arms
119 Marygate
☎ (01289) 302641
11–11; 12–10.30 Sun
**Border Noggins Nog, Rampart** H
An unusual concave window dominates the exterior of this fine, pleasant Scottish-style pub. ◑ ♧

### Barrels
59 Bridge Street
☎ (01289) 308013
11–3, 6–11; 7–10.30 Sun, closed Sun lunch
**Boddingtons Bitter; Border Noggins Nog; Flowers IPA; guest beers** H
Interesting ground-floor pub with a changing guest beer from local independent breweries. Bar billiards and excellent chalk drawings of local scenes help create a pleasant atmosphere.
◑ ▶ ♧

### Free Trade ☆
Castlegate ☎ (01289) 306498
11–2, 8–11 (may vary); 7–10.30 Sun, closed Sun lunch
**Vaux Lorimer's Best Scotch** H
Historic, friendly, unspoilt pub near the station, serving arguably the best Lorimer's Scotch in a county with a taste for Scotch. Irregular opening hours, but well worth a visit.
Q ⊕ ≢

## Carterway Heads

### Manor House Inn
On A68, 6 miles S of Corbridge.
☎ (01207) 255268
12–3, 6–11; 12–3, 7–10.30 Sun

| INDEPENDENT BREWERIES |
|---|
| **Border:** Tweedmouth |
| **Hexhamshire:** Hexham |
| **Northumberland:** Ashington |

---

## Acomb

### Miners Arms
Main Street
☎ (01434) 663909
5 (11 Sat & Summer)–11; 12–10.30 Sun
**Big Lamp Bitter; Federation Buchanan's Best Bitter; guest beers** H
A house beer, Miner's Lamp, brewed by Big Lamp, alternates with the bitter in this 18th-century stone-built, traditional village pub. One guest beer in winter, increasing to three in summer.
 Q ◑ ▲

## Allendale Town

### King's Head Hotel
Market Place
☎ (01434) 863681
11–11; 12–10.30 Sun
**Jennings Cumberland Ale; Theakston Best Bitter; guest beers** H
Comfortable, busy, hotel bar in a market town high in the Pennines, offering good food. An ideal base for exploring the wonderful countryside.
 Q ⊨ ◑ ▶ ▲ ♧

**Try also: Golden Lion**, Market Place (Federation); **Hotspur**, Main Rd (Free)

## Alnmouth

### Schooner Hotel
Northumberland Street
11–11; 12–10.30 Sun
**Belhaven 80/-; guest beers** H
Welcoming pub in a busy village, popular with locals and tourists. A good base from which to explore the coastline.
◑ P

## Alnwick

### John Bull
Howick Street
☎ (01665) 602055
11–3, 7–11; 12–2, 7–10.30 Sun
**Tetley Bitter; guest beers** H
Basic, 1820s pub in the middle of a terrace of houses. At one time it had its own maltings and brewery. Probably the finest selection of whiskies in town – over 60. Lunchtime sandwiches. Q ♧

### Old Cross
Narrowgate ☎ (01665) 602735
11–11; 12–3, 7–10.30 Sun
**Theakston Best Bitter; guest beers** H
Welcoming, listed building, over 200 years old and known locally as the 'Dirty Bottles', referring to sealed windows of

Butterknowle Bitter; guest
beers ⊞
Northumberland CAMRA *Pub
of the Year* and tourist board
winner; a welcoming country
inn. Usually a guest stout or
porter is available, plus guest
ciders. Splendid views over the
Derwent Valley. Good food.
🏠 Q ✿ 🛏 🕻 ▶ ⌂ P ⚥

## Corbridge

### Dyvels Hotel

Station Road ☎ (01434) 633566
7–11; 7–10.30 Sun (may vary in
summer)
**Black Sheep Best Bitter;
Draught Bass; guest beers** ⊞
A warm welcome from
landlord and locals alike
makes this pub worth seeking
out. An ideal base for
exploring Hadrian's Wall
country.
🏠 Q ✿ 🛏 ▶ ⇌ ✦ P

## Cramlington

### Plough

Middle Farm Buildings
☎ (01670) 737633
11–3, 6–11; 11–11 Fri & Sat; 12–3,
7–10.30 Sun
**Theakston Best Bitter, XB;
guest beers** ⊞
Architecturally interesting
pub, a sympathetic conversion
of farm buildings. Catering for
a cross-section of visitors, it
offers several drinking areas
and a wide selection of guest
beers served from a central bar.
✿ 🕻 🍺 ⇌ ✦ P

## Craster

### Jolly Fisherman

Haven Hill ☎ (01665) 576461
11–3, 6–11; 11–11 Sat & summer; 12–3,
7–10.30 Sun
**Vaux Lorimer's Best Scotch;
Ward's Thorne BB** ⊞
Welcoming, busy pub in a tiny
coastal village. Excellent
seafood (try the crab
sandwiches) and marvellous
sea views.
🏠 ⛵ ✿ 🕻 🍴 ✦ P

## Dipton

### Dipton Mill Inn

Dipton Mill Road (off B6306, 2
miles S of Hexham)
☎ (01434) 606577
12–2.30, 6–11; 12–3, 7–10.30 Sun
**Hexhamshire Shire Bitter,
Devil's Water, Whapweasel;
guest beers** ⊞
An excellent advertisement for
Hexhamshire Brewery: cosy
and welcoming with coal fires
throughout (although the
family room is basic). Set in
beautiful countryside, the
garden has its own burn.
Noted for home-cooked food.
🏠 Q ⛵ ✿ 🕻 ▶ 🍴 ✦ P 🍺

## East Ord

### Salmon

☎ (01289) 305227
11–3, 7–11; 12–3, 7–10.30 Sun (may
vary)
**Vaux Lorimer's Best Scotch,
Samson, Waggle Dance** ⊞
Friendly village local outside
Berwick, a short walk from the
remains of hill forts along the
Tweed. A two-roomed oasis in
the Tweedside desert. Q 🕻

## Falstone

### Blackcock

☎ (01434) 240200
11–3, 6–11; 11–11 Fri & Sat; 12–3,
7–10.30 Sun
**Boddingtons Bitter;
Federation Buchanan's Best
Bitter; guest beers** ⊞
Cosy and friendly, historic pub
near Kielder Water, popular
with water-sports enthusiasts.
Very good food. 🏠 Q ⛵ 🛏 🕻
▶ 🍴 🍴 ✦ ⌂ P 🍺

## Featherstone

### Wallace Arms

Rowfoot ☎ (01434) 321872
12–2.30 (not Mon or Tue), 4–11; 11–11
Fri & Sat; 12–3, 7–10.30 Sun (hours
extended in summer)
**Hexhamshire Shire Bitter,
Whapweasel; guest beers** ⊞
Friendly hostelry in beautiful
countryside, near Featherstone
Castle. Enjoyable music nights.
Meals are not always available
early on weekdays.
🏠 Q ✿ 🕻 ▶ 🍴 ✦ P

## Great Whittington

### Queen's Head Inn

☎ (01434) 672267
12–2, 6–11; 12–3, 7–10.30 Sun
**Boddingtons Bitter;
Hambleton Bitter; guest
beers** ⊞
Pub dating back to the 15th-
century, set in lovely
countryside close to Hadrian's
Wall. Queen's Head Bitter is
brewed by Hadrian. Good
quality food.
🏠 Q 🕻 ▶ P

## Haltwhistle

### Black Bull

Market Place ☎ (01434) 320463
12–11 (closed Mon lunch in winter);
12–3, 7–10.30 Sun
**Jennings Bitter, Cumberland
Ale; guest beers** ⊞
Very cosy, unspoilt, stone pub
with low ceilings, beams and a
tiny snug. Changing guest
beers. 🏠 Q 🕻 ⇌ ✦

### Grey Bull

Wapping ☎ (01434) 321991
11–11; 12–3, 7–10.30 Sun

Stones Bitter; Webster's
Yorkshire Bitter; guest
beers ⊞
Busy town pub, popular with
locals, who make visitors more
than welcome. The front bar is
always busy; the panelled back
bar is quieter. Ever-changing
guest beers. Quoits played. 🏠
Q ⛵ ✿ 🛏 🕻 ▶ 🍺 🍴 ⇌ ✦ P

## Hedley on the Hill

### Feathers Inn

☎ (01661) 843607
6–11; 12–3, 6–11 Sat; 12–3, 7–10.30
Sun
**Boddingtons Bitter; guest
beers** ⊞
Friendly hilltop pub with an
excellent atmosphere and
changing guest beers. Lunch
and eve meals Sat. 🏠 Q P

## Hexham

### Tap & Spile

Battle Hill ☎ (01434) 602039
11–11; 12–10.30 Sun
**Tap & Spile Premium; guest
beers** ⊞
Busy, two-roomed, market
town pub with a changing
range of ales from far and
wide. Q 🕻 ⇌

## High Horton

### Three Horse Shoes

Hathery Lane
☎ (01670) 822410
11–11; 12–10.30 Sun
**Ind Coope Burton Ale; Taylor
Landlord; Tetley Bitter; guest
beers** ⊞
Large, friendly, 18th-century
coaching inn, serving a wide
variety of guest ales and
whiskies. Children welcome in
the conservatory.
✿ 🕻 ▶ P

## Holy Island

### Ship

Marygate (across causeway –
check tide table)
☎ (01289) 389311
11–11; 12–10.30 Sun (may vary in
winter)
**Beer range varies** ⊞
400-year-old pub with stone
walls, wood panelling and low
beams. Old photographs and
fishing memorabilia add
interest. No real ale in winter.
Eve meals in summer.
🏠 Q 🕻 ▶

## Langley

### Carts Bog Inn

On A686 ☎ (01434) 684338
12–3, 7–11; 12–3, 7–10.30 Sun (extends
in summer)
**Marston's Pedigree;
Theakston Best Bitter; guest
beers** ⊞

Unspoilt, family-run country pub built in 1730 on a site where brewing commenced in 1521. An extended menu offers Japanese, Chinese, Indian and Thai meals, freshly made. Music and beer festivals held. 🏠 Q 🍴 ❀ ◖ ▌ ♣ P

## Longhorsley

### Linden Pub

Linden Hall Hotel (on A697)
☎ (01670) 516611
11–3, 6–11; 12–3, 7–10.30 Sun
**Boddingtons Bitter; Federation Buchanan's Best Bitter; Jennings Cumberland Ale; Marston's Pedigree** ⊞
Secluded country pub converted from an old granary in the grounds of Linden Hall Hotel. Excellent range of beer and good food. Giant chess in the courtyard. Summer barbecues. 🍴 ❀ ◖ ▌ ♣ P

## Milfield

### Red Lion

Main Road (A697)
☎ (01688) 216224
11–11; 12–10.30 Sun
**Draught Bass; Stones Bitter; guest beers** ⊞
Friendly village pub close to the Scottish border, ideal when exploring the Cheviots. Changing range of guest beers. 🏠 Q 🚗 ◖ ▌ P

## Morpeth

### Joiners Arms

6 Wansbeck Street
☎ (01670) 513540
11–11; 12–10.30 Sun
**Draught Bass; Tetley Bitter; Theakston XB; guest beers** ⊞
Friendly, two-roomed pub in a thriving market town, within walking distance of the river. Fine range of ever-changing guest beers. Q 🚲 ♣

### Tap & Spile

23 Manchester Street
☎ (01670) 513540
12–2.30, 4–11; 11–11 Fri & Sat; 12–10.30 Sun
**Beer range varies** ⊞
Comfortable, friendly, award-winning pub with an excellent range of up to eight real ales. Traditional pipe and fiddle music Sun lunch. Q ◖ ♣ ⌂

## Netherton

### Star Inn ☆

On B634 ☎ (01669) 630238
12–1.30, 7–11; 12–1.30, 7–10.30 Sun
(may vary in winter)
**Castle Eden Ale** ⌷
Marvellously unspoilt, rural pub where the beer is served direct from the cellar. Popular with walkers. 🏠 Q ❀ P

## Newton on the Moor

### Cook & Barker Arms

½ mile off A1 ☎ (01665) 575234
11–3, 6–11; 12–3, 7–10.30 Sun
**Castle Eden Ale; Theakston Best Bitter; guest beers** ⊞
Large, multi-roomed pub and restaurant with a welcoming atmosphere. Good food. 🏠 Q ❀ 🚗 ◖ ▌ P ✂

## Rothbury

### Turks Head

High Street ☎ (01669) 20434
11–11; 12–10.30 Sun
**Ward's Best Bitter** ⊞
Basic, multi-roomed locals' pub. 🏠 ◖ ▌ ⊟

## Seahouses

### Olde Ship Hotel

Main Street ☎ (01665) 720200
11–3, 6–11; 12–3, 7–10.30 Sun
**McEwan 80/-; Marston's Pedigree; Morland Old Speckled Hen; guest beers** (summer) ⊞
Warm, cosy, treasure house of nautical and antique memorabilia, close to the harbour; popular with visitors and locals. Meals in the bar and dining room. Small family room. 🏠 Q 🍴 ◖ ▲ P

## Stagshaw Bank

### Fox & Hounds Inn

On A68 ☎ (01434) 633024
11–11; 12–10.30 Sun
**McEwan 80/-; Theakston Best Bitter; guest beers** ⊞
Welcoming old stone building near Hadrian's Wall. The large conservatory serves as a restaurant.
🏠 ❀ 🚗 ◖ ▌ ♣ P

## Stannersburn

### Pheasant Inn

On minor road near Falstone, 1 mile from Kielder Water
☎ (01434) 240382
11–3, 6–11; 12–3, 7–10.30 Sun
**Ind Coope Burton Ale; Tetley Bitter; guest beers** ⊞
Over 400-year-old building, originally a farm, hence the old farm implements featured in the bar. Note the pictures of the valley and the antique brass and copperware.
🏠 Q ❀ 🚗 ◖ ▌ ▲ P ✂

## Tweedmouth

### Angel

Brewery Bank
☎ (01289) 306273
11–3, 7–11; 12–3, 7–10.30 Sun

**Border Noggins Nog; Shepherd Neame Bishops Finger; guest beers** ⊞
The nearest pub to Border Brewery – the brewery sign hangs outside – but this is a free house with a wide and regularly changing portfolio of beers. A pool table dominates one room, but the bar is light and comfortable. 🏠 ❀

## Warden

### Boatside

☎ (01434) 602233
12–3, 5.30–11; 12–3, 7–10.30 Sun
**Theakston Best Bitter; guest beers** ⊞
Small, busy country pub with a warm welcome. 🏠 Q ◖ ▌ P

## Waren Mill

### Burnside

☎ (01668) 214544
12–3 (not winter Mon–Fri), 6 (7.30 winter, 7 winter Sat)–11; 12–3, 7–10.30 Sun
**Border Special; Theakston Best Bitter; guest beers** (summer) ⊞
Modern, open-plan pub with a thriving summer trade from an adjacent campsite.
◖ ▌ ▲ P

## Weldon Bridge

### Anglers Arms

☎ (01665) 570271
11–3, 6–11; 12–3, 7–10.30 Sun
**Theakston Best Bitter; guest beers** ⊞
1760s coaching inn beside picturesque Weldon Bridge. Fishing is available on the inn's private stretch of the River Coquet. Good food.
🏠 Q ❀ 🚗 ◖ ▌ P

## Wooler

### Red Lion

High Street ☎ (01668) 281629
11–11; 12–10.30 Sun
**Vaux Lorimer's Best Scotch, Waggle Dance** ⊞
Small, unpretentious but friendly pub in a thriving market town. 🏠 ◖

## Wylam

### Boathouse

Station Road ☎ (01661) 853431
6–11; 12–3, 6–11 Fri; 12–11 Sat; 12–3, 7–10.30 Sun
**Butterknowle Conciliation Ale; Marston's Pedigree; Mordue Five Bridge; Morland Old Speckled Hen; Taylor Landlord; Theakston Best Bitter; guest beers** ⊞
Standing next to Wylam station, on the banks of the River Tyne, this pub offers a choice of eight cask ales.
🏠 Q ▌ ⊟ 🚲 ⌂ P

# Nottinghamshire

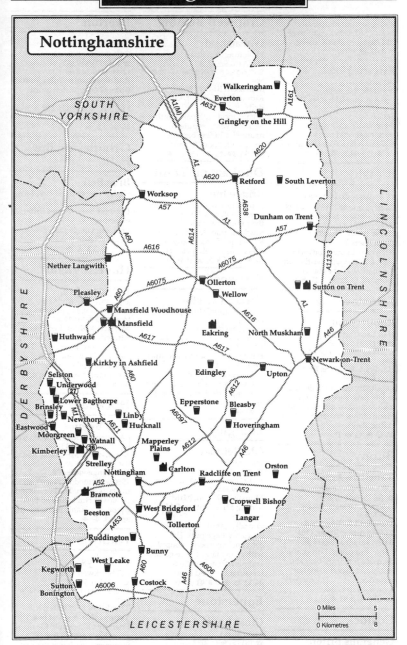

## Nottinghamshire

SOUTH YORKSHIRE

Walkeringham
Everton
Gringley on the Hill
Retford
South Leverton
Worksop
Dunham on Trent
Nether Langwith
Ollerton
Wellow
Sutton on Trent
Pleasley
Mansfield Woodhouse
Mansfield
Eakring
North Muskham
Huthwaite
Kirkby in Ashfield
Edingley
Newark-on-Trent
Selston
Underwood
Upton
Brinsley
Lower Bagthorpe
Epperstone
Bleasby
Newthorpe
Linby
Hoveringham
Eastwood
Hucknall
Moorgreen
Watnall
Mapperley Plains
Kimberley
Strelley
Carlton
Orston
Nottingham
Radcliffe on Trent
Bramcote
Cropwell Bishop
Beeston
West Bridgford
Langar
Tollerton
Ruddington
Bunny
West Leake
Kegworth
Sutton Bonington
Costock

LEICESTERSHIRE

DERBYSHIRE

LINCOLNSHIRE

| 0 Miles | 5 |
| 0 Kilometres | 8 |

---

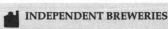 **INDEPENDENT BREWERIES**

**Bramcote:** Bramcote

**Hardys & Hansons:** Kimberley

**Mallard:** Carlton

**Mansfield:** Mansfield

**Maypole:** Eakring

**Springhead:** Sutton on Trent

## Beeston

### Commercial Inn
19 Wollaton Road
☎ (0115) 925 4480
11–3, 5.30–11; 11–11 Fri & Sat; 12–10.30 Sun
**Hardys & Hansons Best Mild, Best Bitter** E, **Classic,**

235

**seasonal beers** H
Well-established, friendly
local. The bar has pictures of
Old Beeston. Skittle alley.
✿ ⍟ ⬦ ♣ P ☐

### Victoria Hotel
Dovecote Lane
☎ (0115) 925 4049
11–3, 5 (6 Sat)–11; 11–11 Fri; 12–4.30,
7–10.30 Sun
**Beer range varies** H
Busy Victorian architectural
gem, an ale and fine food
haven. Over 100 malt whiskies.
🏨 ✿ ⍟ ▶ ⬦ ᗒ ➡ ♣ ⌂ P

## Bleasby

### Waggon & Horses
Gypsy Lane ☎ (01636) 830283
12–2.30 (not Mon or Tue), 6.30–11;
12–3, 7–10.30 Sun
**Home Bitter; Theakston XB;
guest beers** H
200-year-old pub, converted
from a farmhouse, nestling in
the shadow of the church. Pool
room. 🏨 Q ᗒ ✿ ⍟ ♣ P

## Brinsley

### Robin Hood
Hall Lane (off A608)
☎ (01773) 713604
12–2 (3 summer), 7–11; 12–3, 7–10.30
Sun
**Hardys & Hansons Best Mild,
Best Bitter** H
Reputedly haunted village pub
in DH Lawrence country,
maintaining traditional values.
Piano nights; singers Sat. Two
skittle alleys.
🏨 Q ✿ ⬦ ♣ P

## Bunny

### Rancliffe Arms
139 Loughborough Road
☎ (0115) 984 4727
11.30–2.30, 6 (7 Mon)–11; 12–3,
7–10.30 Sun
**Mansfield Riding Mild,
Riding Bitter, Bitter, Old
Baily, seasonal beers** H
Large, imposing, 17th-century
roadside inn: three bars and a
restaurant. Good food (not
served Sun eve). The car park
is on a sharp bend.
🏨 Q ✿ ⍟ ▶ ⬦ ♣ P

## Costock

### Generous Briton
14 Main Street
11.30–2.30, 6.30–11; 12–2.30, 7–10.30
Sun
**Mansfield Riding Bitter,
Bitter, Old Baily, seasonal
beers** H
Fine example of an unspoilt,
two-roomed village inn where
games and conversation
dominate the bar. Famous
flowered courtyard in summer.
🏨 Q ⍟ ⬦ ♣ P

## Cropwell Bishop

### Wheatsheaf
11 Nottingham Road
☎ (0115) 989 2247
12–3, 6–11; 11–11 Fri & Sat; 12–10.30
Sun
**Mansfield Riding Mild,
Riding Bitter, Bitter, Old
Baily** H
Village local with parts dating
back 500 years; reputedly
haunted. Chinese banquets in
an upstairs room for parties
(book). 🏨 ᗒ ✿ ⍟ ⬦ ♣ P

## Dunham on Trent

### Bridge Inn
Main Street ☎ (01777) 778385
11–3, 7–10.30; 12–3, 7–10.30 Sun
**Beer range varies** H
Roadside pub close to Dunham
toll bridge. Three changing
beers (one keenly-priced).
🏨 ✿ ⍟ ▶ ⬦ Å P ✄ ☐

## Eastwood

### Greasley Castle
1 Castle Street, Hilltop (off
B6010)
☎ (01773) 761080
10.30–3 (5 Fri and Sat), 6–11; 12–4,
7–10.30 Sun
**Hardys & Hansons Best Mild,
Best Bitter** E
Friendly corner pub, on a
one-way terraced street, with a
Victorian exterior. Live local
artistes Fri and Sun.
✿ ⍟ ♣

## Edingley

### Old Reindeer
Main Street
☎ (01623) 882253
12–2.30 (not Mon), 6–11; 12–11 Sat;
12–4, 7–10.30 Sun
**Mansfield Riding Mild,
Riding Bitter, Bitter, Old
Baily** H
Friendly, family-run, 18th-
century village pub. The
convivial tap room is popular
with rugby fans. Large garden
and play area. Excellent
restaurant (closed Mon).
🏨 Q ᗒ ✿ ⍟ ▶ ⍟ Å ♣ P ☐

## Epperstone

### Cross Keys
Main Street
☎ (0115) 966 3033
11.45–2.30 (not Mon), 6–11; 12–3,
7–10.30 Sun
**Hardys & Hansons Best Mild,
Best Bitter** E, **Classic,
seasonal beers** H
Classic country village inn: the
three rooms include a simply
furnished bar and a
comfortable lounge. High
quality food (eve meals Thu–
Sat, 6.30–8.30).
🏨 Q ᗒ ✿ ⍟ ▶ ⍟ ♣ P

## Everton

### Sun Inn
Gainsborough Road
☎ (01777) 817260
12–11; 12–10.30 Sun
**Ruddles County; John Smith's
Bitter; Tetley Bitter; guest
beer** H
Multi-roomed pub with a good
choice of food.
🏨 ✿ ⍟ ▶ ⬦ ✄ ☐

## Gringley on the
Hill

### Blue Bell
High Street ☎ (01777) 817406
6 (12 Sat)–11; 12–10.30 Sun
**Draught Bass; Stones Bitter;
guest beer** H
Relaxing village pub. Eve
meals Wed–Sat.
🏨 Q ✿ ⍟ Å ♣

## Hoveringham

### Reindeer Inn
Main Street ☎ (0115) 966 3629
12–3 (not Mon), 5–10 (5.30–11 Sat &
Mon); 12–3, 7–10.30 Sun
**Marston's Bitter, Pedigree** H
Attractive country pub with a
view of the cricket pitch. The
bar is for drinkers in the eve,
with meals taken in the
restaurant. No food Sun or
Mon eves. 🏨 ✿ ⍟ ▶ ♣ P

## Hucknall

### Lord Byron
6A Annesley Road (off Market
Sq) ☎ (0115) 963 0193
7–11; 12–3, 7–11 Sat; 12–4.30, 7–10.30
Sun
**Beer range varies** H
1960s-oriented local with an
upstairs disco. The bar has old
photos of Hucknall and Lord
Byron. Pool table in a separate
area. ✿ ⍟ ♣

## Huthwaite

### Godfreys
222 Blackwell Road
☎ (01623) 550087
11–3, 5–11; 11–11 Sat; 12–4, 7–10.30
Sun
**Theakston Best Bitter, XB;
Younger No. 3; guest beers** H
Friendly village pub: the main
room has a central bar.
Summerhouse bar at the back.
Live music Fri eve. Eve meals
Wed–Sat. 🏨 Q ✿ ▶ ⬦ P

## Kegworth

### Station Hotel
Station Road (towards Sutton
Bonington)
☎ (01509) 672252
11.30–2.30, 6–11; 11.30–11 Sat; 12–3,
7–10.30 Sun

Draught Bass; M&B Mild; guest beers Ⓗ
Built in 1847 as an hotel for the now-closed station: three characterful rooms with an upstairs restaurant, serving excellent, home-cooked food. Large garden with fine views. ⚫ Q ⚫ ⛵ ◗ ● P

## Kimberley

### Nelson & Railway
Station Road
☎ (0115) 938 2177
11–3, 5–11; 11–11 Thu–Sat; 12–10.30 Sun
Hardys & Hansons Best Mild Ⓔ, Best Bitter Ⓗ/Ⓔ, Classic, seasonal beers Ⓗ
Excellent village local with a fine, wood-panelled bar plus a restored, beamed lounge and dining area, noted for good value food. Sun eve meals end at 6. ⚫ ⛵ ◗ ● ⊞ ● P

## Kirkby in Ashfield

### Countryman
Park Road (B6018, S of town)
☎ (01623) 752314
12–3 (4 Fri & Sat), 7–11; 12–3, 7–10.30 Sun
Theakston Best Bitter, XB; guest beers Ⓗ
18th-century inn with beamed alcoves. Its bar was decorated by a wandering sculptor in the late 1970s. Children welcome. ⚫ ◗ ● ● P

## Langar

### Unicorn's Head
Main Street
11–2.30, 6–11; 12–2.30, 7–10.30 Sun
Home Mild, Bitter; guest beers Ⓗ
Comfortable, beamed village pub in the Belvoir Valley with an emphasis on sporting activities. ⚫ ⚫ ● P

## Linby

### Horse & Groom
Main Street ☎ (0115) 963 2219
11.30–3.30, 6–11 (may be 11–11 summer Sat); 12–3, 7–10.30 Sun
Home Mild, Bitter; Theakston XB, Old Peculier (summer) Ⓗ
Popular, four-roomed village pub and restaurant. The bar boasts an inglenook. Eve meals in summer. ⚫ Q ⛵ ⚫ ◗ ● ⊞ A ● P

## Lower Bagthorpe

### Dixie's Arms
School Road (off B600 at Underwood) ☎ (01773) 810505
12.30–3.30 (4 Fri; 12–4 Sat), 7–11; 12–4, 7–10.30 Sun
Home Mild, Bitter; guest beer Ⓗ
Old country pub with a tap room, a lounge and a snug.

Guest beers change twice-weekly.
⚫ ⛵ ⚫ ⊞ A ● P

## Mansfield

### Bleak House Club
117 Sutton Road (near A38/ Skegby Lane jct)
☎ (01623) 659850
12–4 (not Tue–Thu), 7–11; 12–3, 7–10.30 Sun
Draught Bass; Mansfield Bitter; guest beers Ⓗ
Established in 1926 as a men-only emporium, now much more accommodating: a homely lounge and a games room with a TV.
⚫ ⚫ ● ⊟

### Boothy's Club
2 Westhill Drive (ring road)
☎ (01623) 23729
11–11; 12–3, 7–10.30 Sun
Adnams Bitter; Mansfield Riding Bitter, Bitter, seasonal beers; Wells Bombardier Ⓗ
Large, private club with a lounge and a concert room (Sat/Sun cabaret; Thu is country and western eve). Mansfield supplies the house mild. Wheelchair WC.
⚫ ◗ ● ≠ ● P

### Ling Forest
Eakring Road ☎ (01623) 23202
11.30 (11 Sat)–11; 12–3, 7–10.30 Sun
Mansfield Riding Mild, Riding Bitter, Bitter, seasonal beers Ⓗ
Friendly, two-roomed pub: a jukebox-free lounge and a busy tap room with modern facilities. Q ⊞ ● P ⊟

### Plough
180 Nottingham Road (A60, 1 mile from centre)
☎ (01623) 23031
11–11; 12–10.30 Sun
Boddingtons Bitter; Flowers IPA, Original; Whitbread Fuggles IPA, seasonal beers; guest beers Ⓗ
Refurbished, large, friendly one-roomed pub with good food and eight beers. Live music weekly.
⚫ ◗ ● ≠ P

## Mansfield Woodhouse

### Greyhound Inn
High Street ☎ (01623) 643005
12–5, 7–11; 12–3, 7–10.30 Sun
Home Mild, Bitter; Mansfield Riding Bitter; Theakston Best Bitter, XB, Old Peculier; guest beers Ⓗ
Village local, popular with all ages: a lounge bar and a tap room. ⚫ ⊞ ≠ ● P

### Star Inn
Warsop Road ☎ (01623) 24145
12–3, 6–11; 12–10.30 Sun

Vaux Waggle Dance; Ward's Thorne BB, Best Bitter; guest beer Ⓗ
Old, low-beamed, three-roomed pub. Excellent play facilities for children (who are welcome inside for meals). Good food (not served Sat/Sun eves). ⚫ ◗ ● ⊞ ⚫ ≠ P

## Mapperley Plains

### Traveller's Rest
Plains Road ☎ (0115) 926 4412
11–11; 12–10.30 Sun
Home Bitter; Theakston Mild, Best Bitter, XB; guest beers Ⓗ
Comfortable roadhouse affording good views. Excellent home-cooking includes children's specials. No food Sun or Mon eves.
⚫ ⛵ ⚫ ◗ ● ● P

## Moorgreen

### Horse & Groom
On B600 ☎ (01773) 713417
11–2.30, 5–11; 11–11 Sat & summer; 12–10.30 Sun
Hardys & Hansons Best Mild, Best Bitter, Classic, seasonal beers Ⓗ
17th-century pub, originally a farmhouse on the Greasley Castle estate; now one large room with an upstairs restaurant. Well-equipped garden.
⚫ ⚫ ◗ ● ● P

## Nether Langwith

### Jug & Glass
Queens Walk
☎ (01623) 742283
11.30–4, 7–11; 12–3, 7–10.30 Sun
Hardys & Hansons Best Bitter, Classic Ⓔ
Unpretentious, stone pub, dating from the 15th century, beside the village stream – popular for outdoor drinking. No eve meals Wed or Sun.
⚫ ⛵ ⚫ ⛵ ◗ ● ⊞ ⚫ ● P

## Newark-on-Trent

### Mailcoach
13 London Road
☎ (01636) 605164
11–2.30 (3 Wed & Fri), 5.30–11; 11–4, 7–11 Sat; 12–3, 7–10.30 Sun
Benskins BB; Ind Coope Burton Ale; Marston's Pedigree; Tetley Bitter; guest beers Ⓗ
Large, busy, one-roomer, offering good home-cooking (not served Sun). Blues at weekends. Cider in summer.
⚫ ⚫ ⛵ ≠ (Castle) ● ○ P

### Newcastle Arms
34 George Street (150 yds from Northgate station)
12–2.30 (3 Fri & Sat), 7–11; 12–3, 7–10.30 Sun

# NOTTINGHAMSHIRE

Home Mild, Bitter; Mansfield
Riding Bitter; Theakston XB;
Wells Bombardier; guest
beer H
Traditional Victorian local with
a basic public bar and a
comfortable lounge. A short
walk from the town centre.
Q ❀ ⊟ ⇌ (Northgate) ♣ ⊟

## Old King's Arms

19 Kirkgate ☎ (01636) 703416
11–3, 5 (5.30 Sat)–11; 11–11 Fri; 12–3,
7–10.30 Sun
Bateman Mild; Fuller's
London Pride; Marston's
Bitter, Pedigree; Morland Old
Speckled Hen; guest beers H
In the shadow of the church,
this recently refurbished pub
has lost all of its previous
character, it remains busy.
⊲ ⇌ (Castle/Northgate) ♣

## Old Malt Shovel

25 Northgate ☎ (01636) 702036
11.30–3, 7 (5 Fri)–11; 12–3, 7–10.30 Sun
Taylor Landlord; Ward's Best
Bitter; guest beers H
Friendly pub serving four
guest beers. Traditional Sun
lunches. Mexican and
Portuguese food a speciality
(no food Mon/Tue eves).
🏨 ☎ ❀ ⊲ ▶ ⊟ ⇌ (Castle/
Northgate) ♣ ✂

## Wheatsheaf

Slaughterhouse Lane (opp.
Morrison's supermarket)
11–3, 7–11; 11–11 Fri & Sat; 12–10.30
Sun
Mansfield Riding Mild,
Riding Bitter, Bitter, Old
Baily, seasonal beers H
Bustling, often loud, one-
roomed bar, just off the town
centre. Frequented mainly by
younger people, its darts teams
hold two world records.
❀ ⇌ (Castle/Northgate) ♣

# Newthorpe

## Ram Inn

Beauvale Road (B6010)
☎ (01773) 713312
11–4, 5.30–11; 11–11 Sat; 12–3.45,
7–10.30 (12–10.30 summer) Sun
Hardys & Hansons Best Mild,
Best Bitter E, Classic,
seasonal beers H
Community local, popular for
darts and quizzes. Good food.
🏨 Q ❀ ⊲ ▶ ⊟ ♣ P

# North Muskham

## Crown Inn

Main Street ☎ (01636) 640316
12–3 (4 Sat; not Mon or Tue), 7–11;
12–3, 7–10.30 Sun
Mansfield Riding Bitter,
Bitter, Old Baily or seasonal
beers H
Small, cosy, village local with
lots of pub teams. Award-
winning garden. No food Sun.
❀ ⊲ ♿ ⚓ ♣ P

# Nottingham

## Bell Inn

18 Angel Row, Old Market
Square
☎ (0115) 947 5241
10.30–11; 10–2.30, 5.30–11 Sat; 12–3,
7–10.30 Sun
Draught Bass; Black Sheep
Special; Boddingtons Bitter;
Jennings Mild, Cocker Hoop;
Marston's Pedigree; guest
beers H
Popular, timber-framed, 15th-
century inn, with original
beams in the entrance; owned
by the Jackson family since
1898. Jazz Sun lunch and Sun-
Tue eves. Guest beers are in the
back room. Q ❀ ⊲ ⌂

## Canal Tavern

2 Canal Street
☎ (0115) 941 2281
11.30–11; 12–3, 7–10.30 Sun
Mansfield Riding Mild,
Riding Bitter, Bitter, Old
Baily, seasonal beers; guest
beers H
Small, single-bar ale house, just
south of the centre, renovated
with an original tiled wall as a
feature. Q ⊲ ⇌ ♣ ⌂

## Coopers Arms

3 Porchester Road,
Thorneywood (just off Carlton
Rd)
☎ (0115) 950 2433
11–3 (4.30 Sat), 6 (5.30 Fri, 7 Sat)–11;
12–3, 7–10.30 Sun
Home Mild, Bitter E
Large, Victorian local featuring
a comfortable lounge, a bar, a
darts room and a tiny family
room, plus a covered skittle
alley outside.
♿ ⊟ ♣ P ⊟

## Golden Fleece

105 Mansfield Road (500 yds N
of Victoria Centre)
☎ (0115) 947 2843
11–11; 12–10.30 Sun
Draught Bass; Greenalls Mild,
Shipstone's Mild, Shipstone's
Bitter, Original; Tetley
Bitter H
Refurbished corner pub; one
room with nooks and crannies.
Live music Sun–Tue eves.
Deep sandstone cellars;
unusual roof garden. Book eve
meals. ❀ ⊲ ▶ ♣

## Hole in the Wall

63 North Sherwood Street
☎ (0115) 947 3162
11–11; 12–3, 7–10.30 Sun
Mansfield Riding Bitter,
Bitter, Old Baily, seasonal
beers; guest beers H
Well-refurbished pub, popular
with students: one room with a
long bar. Originally the pub
was extremely small – literally,
just a hole in the wall! Eve
meals till 7; no food Sun eve.
Wheelchair WC. ❀ ⊲ ▶ ♿

## Langtry's

4 South Sherwood Street (opp.
Royal Concert Hall)
☎ (0115) 947 2124
10.30–11; 12–10.30 Sun
Boddingtons Bitter; Castle
Eden Ale; Chester's Mild;
Flowers IPA; Marston's
Pedigree; Whitbread
Trophy H; guest beers H/G
One-roomed, street-corner
Hogshead pub serving guest
ales from micros and a good
selection of cheap food till 5pm
(3 Sun). Typical Hogshead
floorboards and bare brick
decor. Ten beers. ⊲ ▶ ⌂

## Limelight Bar

Wellington Circus
(Nottingham Playhouse
Complex) ☎ (0115) 941 8467
11–11; 12–10.30 Sun
Adnams Bitter; Boddingtons
Bitter; Courage Directors;
Marston's Pedigree;
Theakston XB; guest beers H
Pub with a traditional interior
in a 1960s building: a welcome
retreat from the nearby city
centre. Q ❀ ⊲ ⌂ ✂

## Lincolnshire Poacher

161–163 Mansfield Road (600
yds N of Victoria Centre)
☎ (0115) 941 1584
11–3, 5.30–11; 11–11 Sat; 12–10.30 Sun
Bateman Mild, XB, Valiant,
XXXB, Victory; Marston's
Pedigree; guest beer H
The city's leading ale house.
Brewery nights first Tue of the
month; always at least ten
beers on, plus over 80
whiskies. Two rooms, and a
no-smoking dining area (no
food Sun eve). Q ❀ ⊲ ▶ ⌂

## Lion

44 Mosley Street, New Basford
(behind old Shipstone's site)
☎ (0115) 970 3506
10.30–11; 12–10.30 Sun
Draught Bass; Highgate Dark;
Mallard Bitter; Stones Bitter;
guest beer H
Popular, corner local. The deep
sandstone cellar can be seen
from the bar in this one-
roomed, bare brick and board
pub. Music Fri/Sat eves; jazz
Sun eve. Eve meals end at 8.30.
🏨 ⊲ ▶ ♿ ⌂ P

## Lord Nelson

Thurgaton Street, Sneinton
☎ (0115) 911 0069
11–3 (3.30 Sat), 5.30–11; 12–4, 7–10.30
Sun
Hardys & Hansons Best Mild,
Best Bitter, Classic, seasonal
beers H
Two farm cottages, converted
into a village pub about 200
years ago, now enveloped by
the city. Four separate rooms in
a Grade II listed building.
Pleasant garden. No food Sat.
No-smoking area lunchtime.
🏨 ❀ ⊲ ▶ ♣ ✂

## Magpies

Meadow Lane
☎ (0115) 986 3851
11–2.30, 5–11; 11–11 Fri; 12–2.30, 7–10.30 Sun
**Home Mild, Bitter** Ⓔ; **Marston's Pedigree; Theakston XB** Ⓗ
On the city's eastern edge, this pub is handy for both football and cricket grounds. The drinkers' bar has pool and Sky TV; L-shaped lounge. Eve meals till 8.30; no food Sat eve or Sun. ❀ ◑ ♣ P

## March Hare

248 Carlton Road, Sneinton
☎ (0115) 950 4328
11.30–2.30, 6–11; 12–2.30, 7–10.30 Sun
**Courage Directors; John Smith's Bitter** Ⓗ
Typical 1950s-style pub, run since opening by the same landlord: a comfortable front lounge, with pool in the bar. Remarkable value lunches Mon–Sat. ❀ ◑ ♣ P

## Navigation Inn

6 Wilford Street
☎ (0115) 941 7139
11.30–2.30, 5–11; 11.30–11 Sat; 12–3, 7–10.30 Sun
**Banks's Mild, Bitter, seasonal beers; Camerons Strongarm; Marston's Pedigree; guest beers** Ⓗ
Pub next to the locks. Plenty of canal memorabilia in one split-level bar. House beer sold.
❀ ◑ ≠ ♣ ◠ ☗

## Portland Arms

24 Portland Road (off A610, at Canning Circus)
☎ (0115) 978 2429
11.30–3, 7–11; 12–3, 7–10.30 Sun
**Hardys & Hansons Best Mild, Best Bitter** Ⓗ
Friendly Victorian local, open-plan, but retaining a traditional feel. Good snacks. ❀ ♣

## Red Lion

21 Alfreton Road (A610)
☎ (0115) 952 0309
11–11; 12–10.30 Sun
**Boddingtons Bitter; Marston's Pedigree; Morland Old Speckled Hen; Taylor Landlord; Wadworth 6X; guest beers** Ⓗ
Enterprising pub, just north of the centre: one open-plan room with well-defined areas. Open 11 Sun for brunch. Eve meals Tue only. ❀ ◑ ♣

## Trip to Jerusalem ☆

1 Brewhouse Yard, Castle Road
☎ (0115) 947 3171
11–11; 12–10.30 Sun
**Hardys & Hansons Best Mild, Best Bitter, Classic, seasonal beers; Marston's Pedigree** Ⓗ
One of England's oldest inns, dating back to 1189; the back rooms are cut out of the cliff

below Nottingham Castle. Flagged floor; blackened beams. ♨ Q ❀ ◑ ≠ ♣

## White Lion

43 Carlton Road (A612)
☎ (0115) 911 0115
11–3, 5.30–11; 12–3, 7–10.30 Sun
**Banks's Mild, Bitter; Camerons Strongarm** Ⓗ
Friendly local with two rooms in 1930s style. Q ❀ ◑ ⊞ ♣

## Ollerton

### Snooty Fox

Main Street, Old Ollerton
☎ (01623) 823073
12–3.30 (4 Sat), 6–11; 12–4, 7–10.30 Sun
**Barnsley Bitter; Theakston Best Bitter, XB; guest beers** Ⓗ
Pub in modernised old buildings with several small rooms. ❀ ◑ ◗ P

## Orston

### Durham Ox

Church Street
☎ (01949) 850059
12 (11 Sat)–3, 6–11; 12–3, 7–10.30 Sun
**Home Bitter; Marston's Pedigree; Theakston Mild, Best Bitter; Young's Special; guest beer** Ⓗ
Pleasant, split-room, country pub with large garden and pavement café-type areas. Filled rolls. Table and long alley skittles. Q ⛫ ❀ ♣ P ⚲

## Pleasley

### Olde Plough

Chesterfield Road North
☎ (01623) 810386
11–3, 5.30–11; 11–11 Sat; 12–3, 7–10.30 Sun
**Marston's Bitter, Pedigree, Owd Rodger, HBC** Ⓗ
Old stone pub, tastefully renovated, with beams and posts in one large, open-plan room with alcoves. No food Sun eve. Q ❀ ◑ ◗ P ⚲

## Radcliffe on Trent

### Royal Oak

Main Road ☎ (0115) 933 3798
11–11; 12–3, 7–10.30 Sun
**Boddingtons Bitter; Castle Eden Ale; Fuller's London Pride; Morland Old Speckled Hen; Taylor Landlord; guest beers** Ⓗ
Convivial village local with a cosy lounge and a boisterous bar. Nine ales, but they can be pricey. ♨ ◑ ⊞ ≠ ♣ P

## Retford

### Clinton Arms

Albert Road ☎ (01777) 702703

11–11; 12–10.30 Sun
**Courage Directors; Morland Old Speckled Hen; John Smith's Bitter; Webster's Green Label; guest beers** Ⓗ
Refurbished pub, especially busy at weekends. Large screen satellite TV. Live rock and blues Thu. The lounge is quieter. Cider in summer.
⛫ ❀ ◑ ◗ ≠ ◠ P ☗

## Market Hotel

West Carr Road
☎ (01777) 703278
11–3, 5.30–11; 11–11 Sat; 12–10.30 Sun
**Adnams Broadside; Draught Bass; Fuller's London Pride; Marston's Pedigree; Taylor Landlord; Theakston XB; guest beers** Ⓗ
On the site of the old cattle market, a warm, homely pub serving bar and restaurant meals. Bands in the function room. Guest beers come from Springhead Brewery.
❀ ◑ ◗ & ≠ P ☗

## Turk's Head

Grove Street
☎ (01777) 702742
11–3.30, 7–11; 12–3.30, 7–10.30 Sun
**Vaux Samson; Ward's Best Bitter** Ⓗ
Traditional, oak-panelled pub with a warm atmosphere. Pool, darts and Ring the Bull played.
♨ ❀ ⇥ ◑ & ♣ P ☗

## Ruddington

### Three Crowns

23 Easthorpe Street
☎ (0115) 921 3226
11.45–4, 6–11; 12–4, 7–10.30 Sun
**Boddingtons Bitter; Mansfield Riding Bitter, Bitter, Old Baily; Tetley Bitter** Ⓗ
Known as the 'Top House', this quiet, village local is handy for the Great Central Railway Walk. Lunchtime snacks. Q ❀

## Selston

### Horse & Jockey

Church Lane ☎ (01773) 863022
11–11; 12–10.30 Sun
**Draught Bass; Bateman XB; Hook Norton Old Hooky, Morrells Graduate; Shepherd Neame Spitfire; guest beers** Ⓖ
Small, popular village pub, dating from 1664: three rooms with low, beamed ceilings. Folk/unplugged music Wed eve. Wheelchair WC.
⛫ ❀ ◑ ◗ & ♣ P ☗

## South Leverton

### Plough Inn

Town Street ☎ (01427) 880323
2 (12 Sat)–11; 12–4, 7–10.30 Sun
**Adnams Bitter; Ansells Bitter** Ⓗ

True little gem – one of the smallest pubs in Notts, which also doubles as a post office (hence the opening hours). No frills: old wooden trestle tables and benches. ♨ Q ❀ ♣ P ⊟

## Strelley

### Broad Oak Inn
Main Street ☎ (0115) 929 3340
11–11; 12–10.30 Sun
**Hardys & Hansons Best Mild, Best Bitter, Classic, seasonal beers** Ⓗ
Pleasant, 17th-century, listed building in a rural setting: one drinking and two dining areas (one for non-smokers). Special offer meals 3–6, Mon–Sat.
Q ❀ ◑ ▶ & P ⌦

## Sutton Bonington

### Anchor Inn
Bollards Lane
☎ (01509) 673648
7 (11 Sat)–11; 12–3.30, 7–10.30
Sun
**Marston's Pedigree, HBC** Ⓗ
Friendly, cosy, reputedly haunted local with one bar serving a split-level, single room. Beware of Banks's Mild, kept under gas.
♨ Q ❀ & ♣ P ⊟

## Sutton on Trent

### Lord Nelson
Main Street
12–2.30 (not Mon), 6.30–11; 12–3,
7–10.30 Sun
**Springhead Bitter; Theakston Best Bitter; guest beers** Ⓗ
Old village pub, popular with farmers, fishermen and locals: two bars, one a restaurant (eves).
❀ ◑ ▶ ⌑ & P ⊟

## Tollerton

### Air Hostess
Stanstead Avenue
☎ (0115) 937 2485
11.30–2.30 (3 Sat), 5.30 (6.30 Sat)–11;
12–2.30, 7–10.30 Sun
**Home Mild, Bitter; Marston's Pedigree; Theakston XB; guest beers** Ⓗ
Modern estate pub serving beers at sensible prices in a lounge and a bar. Children's swings. ♣ P

## Underwood

### Red Lion
Church Lane, Bagthorpe (off B600) ☎ (01773) 810482
12–3, 6–11; 12–11 Sat; 12–3.30, 6–10.30
Sun
**Boddingtons Bitter; Flowers Original; Marston's Pedigree; guest beer** Ⓗ

300-year-old beamed, friendly village pub with an eating area where children are welcome. Large garden and children's play area; barbecues in summer. Independent guest beers. ❀ ◑ ▶ P

## Upton

### Cross Keys
Main Street ☎ (01636) 813269
11.30–2.30, 5.30 (6 Sat)–11; 12–2.30,
7–10.30 Sun (may open all day Sat/
Sun in summer)
**Bateman XXXB; Boddingtons Bitter; Marston's Pedigree; Springhead Bitter; guest beer** Ⓗ
Attractive, 17th-century pub with a split-level single bar. Excellent food in the bar and restaurant (open Fri–Sun). Live folk music Sun eve.
♨ Q ❀ ◑ ▶ ♣ P

## Walkeringham

### Three Horseshoes
High Street ☎ (01427) 890959
11.30–3, 7–11; 12–4, 7–10.30 Sun
**Draught Bass; Boddingtons Bitter; Stones Bitter; guest beer** Ⓗ
Friendly village pub with a lounge and a restaurant serving an excellent choice of food and beers (no food Mon). Marvellous summer flowers.
Q ❀ ◑ ▶ & ▲ ♣ P ⊟

## Watnall

### Queen's Head
Main Road ☎ (0115) 938 3148
11–2.30 (3 Sat), 5.30–11; 12–3, 7–10.30
Sun
**Home Mild, Bitter; Theakston XB, Old Peculier; guest beer** Ⓗ
17th-century village inn, carefully renovated: a wood-panelled bar with a very small, intimate snug. Splendid back lawn. Eve meals Mon–Fri till 8.
♨ Q ❀ ◑ ▶ ♣ P

### Royal Oak
Main Road ☎ (0115) 938 3110
11–3.30, 5.30–11 (11–11 summer);
12–4, 7–10.30 Sun
**Hardys & Hansons Best Mild, Best Bitter** Ⓗ/Ⓔ**, Classic, seasonal beers** Ⓗ
Friendly, comfortable village local with an upstairs lounge. Happy hour 5.30–8 Mon–Fri. No lunches Sun.
Q ⌑ ❀ ◑ ⌑ ♣ P

## Wellow

### Old Red Lion
Eakring Road (off A616)
☎ (01623) 861000
11.30–3.30, 5.30–11 (11.30–11 summer
Sat); 12–4, 7–10.30 (12–10.30 summer)
Sun
**Ruddles Best Bitter, County; guest beers** Ⓗ

Pub with cosy, small rooms, popular with diners. The house beer comes from Maypole Brewery.
Q ❀ ◑ ▶ P ⌦

## West Bridgford

### Real Ale Shop
116 Melton Road
☎ (0115) 981 6181
6–11; 7–10.30 Sun; closed Mon
**Oakham JHB; guest beers** Ⓖ
Off-licence stocking three changing guest beers, often from local micros. Containers available; parties catered for (casks can be delivered). Fine selection of bottled beers/ ciders. & ⌂ P

## West Leake

### Star Inn (Pit House)
Melton Lane (Sutton Bonington road)
☎ (01509) 852233
11–3, 6–11; 12–3, 7–10.30 Sun
**Draught Bass; Theakston XB; guest beer** Ⓗ
Former coaching inn with low beams and a flag-tiled bar, plus a recently opened additional lounge and a fine, half-panelled lounge. Large garden and patio. ♨ Q ❀ ◑ ▶ ⌑ P

## Worksop

### Greendale Oak
Norfolk Street (near market place) ☎ (01909) 489680
12–4.30, 7–11; 11–11 Fri & Sat; 12–3,
7–10.30 Sun
**Stones Bitter; Tetley Bitter** Ⓗ
Small, cosy, gas-lit, mid-terrace pub, built in 1790. Keen darts and dominoes teams. Good food. Q ❀ ◑ ▲ ♣ P ⊟

### Old Norfolk Arms
Norfolk Street (off market place) ☎ (01909) 475280
11–11; 12–10.30 Sun
**Boddingtons Bitter; Marston's Bitter, Pedigree; Stones Bitter; guest beers** Ⓗ
Tom Cobleigh house: a renovated, cosy, classic Edwardian interior in which to enjoy bargain meals and a good selection of guest beers. Car park opposite.
Q ❀ ◑ ▶ & ▲ ♣

### Top House
Park Street ☎ (01909) 478125
11.30–3.30, 5.30–11; 12–10.30 Sun
**Adnams Bitter, Broadside; Mansfield Riding Bitter, Bitter, seasonal beers; Wells Bombardier** Ⓗ
Small, cosy pub boasting four separate rooms, with low ceilings, and a conservatory.
Q ⌑ ❀ ◑ ▶ & ▲ P

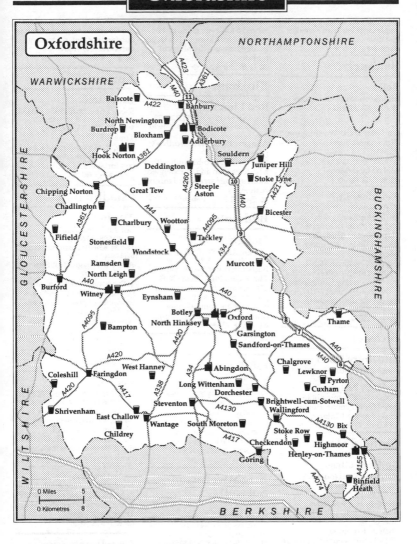

## Oxfordshire

NORTHAMPTONSHIRE

WARWICKSHIRE

Balscote
Banbury
North Newington
Burdrop
Bodicote
Bloxham
Adderbury
Hook Norton
Souldern
Deddington
Juniper Hill
Stoke Lyne
Chipping Norton
Great Tew
Steeple Aston
Chadlington
Bicester
Charlbury
Wootton
Fifield
Stonesfield
Tackley
Woodstock
Ramsden
Murcott
North Leigh
Burford
Witney
Eynsham
Botley
Oxford
Thame
Bampton
North Hinksey
Garsington
Sandford-on-Thames
West Hanney
Chalgrove
Coleshill
Faringdon
Abingdon
Lewknor
Pyrton
Long Wittenham
Cuxham
Dorchester
Shrivenham
Steventon
Brightwell-cum-Sotwell
East Challow
Wantage
South Moreton
Wallingford
Childrey
Bix
Stoke Row
Checkendon
Highmoor
Goring
Henley-on-Thames
Binfield Heath

GLOUCESTERSHIRE

BUCKINGHAMSHIRE

WILTSHIRE

BERKSHIRE

0 Miles 5
0 Kilometres 8

---

## Adderbury

### White Hart
Tanners Lane, West
Adderbury (off Horn Hill Rd)
☎ (01295) 810406
11–2.30, 5–11; 12–3, 7–10.30 Sun
**Boddingtons Bitter; guest
beers** Ⓗ
Idyllic, unassuming, 17th-
century back of village local,
small, quiet and friendly.
🏚 Q ❀ 🛏 ◁ ▷ ♣ P

## Balscote

### Butcher's Arms
Shutford Road (off A422)
☎ (01295) 730750
12–3, 6–11; 12–3, 7–10.30 Sun
**Hook Norton Best Bitter** Ⓗ

Classic one-roomed village
pub popular with hikers and
locals. Conversation rules!
🏚 Q ❀ ♣ P

## Bampton

### Morris Clown
17 High Street
☎ (01993) 850217
12–3, 6–11; 12–3, 7–10.30 Sun
**Courage Best Bitter;
Wadworth 6X; guest beer** Ⓗ
Cosy, 800-year-old pub, its
name relating to the village
history of morris dancing.
Opening hours are drinker-
flexible.
🏚 ❀ 🛏 ◁ ▷ ⊡ ♣ P

### Romany
Bridge Street ☎ (01993) 850237
11–11; 12–4, 7–10.30 Sun

**Archers Village; Hook Norton
Best Bitter; Morland Original;
guest beers** Ⓗ
Very attractive village free
house with a deserved
reputation for good food and

---

| 🏠 INDEPENDENT BREWERIES | |
|---|---|
| **Brakspear:** | Henley-on-Thames |
| **Hook Norton:** | Hook Norton |
| **Morland:** Abingdon | |
| **Morrells:** Oxford | |
| **Plough Inn:** Bodicote | |
| **Wychwood:** Witney | |

241

ale at very reasonable prices: a single large bar with a smaller restaurant area to the side.
🏚 ❀ 🍴 ◑ 🄳 ♿ ♣ ✦

## Banbury

### Bell
Middleton Road, Grimsbury
☎ (01295) 253169
11–3, 7–11; 11–11 Sat; 12–3, 7–10.30 Sun
**Highgate Dark; Worthington Bitter; guest beers** 🄷
Pleasant and friendly, two-roomed pub. Good home-cooked food (Mon–Fri).
🏚 ❀ ◑ 🄳 ⇌ ✦ P

### Reindeer Inn
47 Parsons Street
☎ (01295) 264031
11–2.30, 5 (7 Sat)–11; closed Sun
**Hook Norton Mild, Best Bitter, Old Hooky; guest beers** 🄷
Superbly restored, 15th-century, town-centre coaching inn with a relaxed atmosphere (tidy dress; no under-21s). See the outstanding Jacobean, panelled back room.
🏚 ❀ ◑ ⇌ ✦ P

## Bicester

### Littlebury Hotel
Kings End ☎ (01869) 252595
11–3, 5–11; 12–3, 7–10.30 Sun
**Marston's Pedigree** 🄷
Pleasant, welcoming hotel noted for functions. Home-cooked meals. Children welcome. Q ❀ 🛏 ◑ 🄳 ♿ P

## Binfield Heath

### Bottle & Glass
Harpsden Road (off A4155, ½ mile NE of centre)
☎ (01491) 575755
11–4, 6–11; 12–4, 7–10.30 Sun
**Brakspear Bitter** 🄷, **Old** 🄷/🄶, **Special** 🄷
Thatched, beamed, 17th-century, country pub with a flagstoned floor in its larger bar. Excellent home-cooked food, including vegetarian options (no meals Sun eve). Large garden. Gas-assisted pumps (no gas in contact with the beer), activated by handpumps, may be used.
Q ❀ ◑ 🄳 ✦ P

## Bix

### Fox at Bix
Oxford Road (A4130)
☎ (01491) 574134
11–3, 7–11; 12–3, 7–10.30 Sun
**Brakspear Bitter, Old** *or* **Special** 🄷
Large, solidly built, creeper-covered roadside pub, with 53 doors. The two wood panelled bars each have a log fire. Friendly and famous dog!

Good, home-cooked food (not served Mon eve); game dishes a speciality in season. The large garden boasts a hitching rail for horses.
🏚 Q ❀ ◑ 🄳 🄴 🄰 ✦ P

## Bloxham

### Red Lion Inn
High Street ☎ (01295) 720352
11.30–2.30 (3 Sat), 7–11; 12–3, 7–10.30 Sun
**Adnams Bitter; Wadworth 6X; guest beers** 🄷
Welcoming, two-bar pub with a large garden and an extended lounge-diner area. Good mix of customers.
🏚 Q ❀ ◑ 🄴 🄰 ✦ P

## Bodicote

### Plough
9 High Street ☎ (01295) 262327
11–3, 5.45–11; 12–3, 7–10.30 Sun
**Bodicote Bitter, No. 9, Porter, Three Goslings, Triple X** 🄷
14th-century, two-room brew pub. Home-cooked food is served in the lounge-diner (meals cooked to order Sun).
🏚 ❀ ◑ 🄳 🄴 ✦

## Botley

### Fair Rosamund
Chestnut Road
☎ (01865) 243376
12–2.30, 7–11; 12–3, 7–10.30 Sun
**Marston's Bitter** 🄷
Friendly, 1950s estate pub, pleasantly refurbished: a large, L-shaped bar and a very comfortable lounge. Very competitive beer prices.
❀ 🄴 ✦ P

## Brightwell-cum-Sotwell

### Red Lion
The Street (off A4130)
☎ (01491) 837373
11–2.30, 6–11; 12–3, 7–10.30 Sun
**Beer range varies** 🄷
Two-bar, 15th-century, thatched pub with an inglenook in the lounge: a popular village local. No meals Sun. At least six ales available, most from local micro-breweries. The house beer is from Hampshire Brewery. Gas-assisted handpumps used (no gas touches the beer).
🏚 Q ❀ ◑ 🄳 🄴 ✦ P

## Burdrop

### Bishop Blaize
Between Sibford Gower and Sibford Ferris
☎ (01295) 780323
12–2.30 (not Mon), 6–11 (12–3, 6–11 Bank Hol Mon); 12–3, 7–10.30 Sun
**Hook Norton Best Bitter; Theakston XB; guest beers** 🄷

Friendly, 17th-century village inn where the large garden has outstanding views. Quizzes, darts and crib enjoyed.
🏚 ❀ ◑ 🄳 ✦ P

## Burford

### Lamb Inn
Sheep Street ☎ (01993) 823155
11–2.30, 6–11; 12–2.30, 7–10.30 Sun
**Wadworth IPA, 6X, Old Timer** 🄷
Cosy, flagstone-floored locals' bar in a very smart hotel: comfortable and homely – a gem. 🏚 Q 🛏 ◑ 🄳 🄴

## Chadlington

### Tite Inn
Mill End (near A361)
☎ (01608) 676475
12–2.30, 6.30–11; closed Mon, except bank hols
**Archers Village, Best Bitter; guest beers** 🄷
16th-century free house and restaurant with no jukebox, machines or pool. The lovely garden has country views. No-smoking garden/family room in summer.
🏚 Q 🛏 ❀ ◑ 🄳 ♿ 👜 P ⌖

## Chalgrove

### Red Lion
High Street ☎ (01865) 890625
11.30–3, 6–11; 12–3, 7–10.30 Sun
**Brakspear Bitter; Fuller's London Pride; guest beers** 🄷
Popular, 350-year-old, attractive village pub, Grade II listed. Several drinking areas; families welcome. A wide range of good-value, home-cooked food includes vegetarian (no eve meals Sun or Mon). Separate no-smoking dining room. Wheelchair WC. Three guest beers.
🏚 ❀ ◑ 🄳 ♿ ✦ P

## Charlbury

### Rose & Crown
Market Street
☎ (01608) 810103
12–3, 5.30–11; 11–11 Fri & Sat; 12–3, 7–10.30 Sun
**Archers Best Bitter** 🄷; **guest beers** 🄷/🄶
Popular, one-room, town-centre pub with a patio-courtyard. Excellent rotation of guest beers. Regular live music. 🏚 ❀ ⇌ ✦

## Checkendon

### Black Horse ☆
Burncote Lane (off A4074 towards Stoke Row; left up narrow lane) OS667841
☎ (01491) 680418
12–2.30, 7–11; 12–3, 7–10.30 Sun

Brakspear Bitter; Old Luxters Barn Ale; Rebellion IPA; West Berkshire Good Old Boy G
Pub in the same family for over 90 years, with thankfully no major changes in that time; hidden away in the woods next to a farm. Tasty filled rolls. Real fires, real outside gents', real countryside, really difficult to find, but worth the effort. A classic!
♨ Q ⛬ 🍴 ✿ ♿ ♣ P

## Childrey

### Hatchet

High Street ☎ (01235) 751213
11.30–2.30, 7–11; 12–3, 7–10.30 Sun
Brains Dark; Flowers Original; Morland Original; guest beers H
Family-run, friendly village local with an impressive range of beers.
✿ ◑ ▶ ♿ ♣ P

Try also: Star, Sparsholt (Free)

## Chipping Norton

### Chequers

Goddards Lane (off main street) ☎ (01608) 644717
11–2.30, 5.30 (6 Sat)–11; 12–3, 7–10.30 Sun
Fuller's Chiswick, London Pride, ESB H, seasonal beers H/ G
Friendly, traditional pub next to the theatre: Fuller's Town Pub of the Year.
♨ Q ✿ ◑ ▶ ♣

## Coleshill

### Radnor Arms

32 Coleshill (B4019)
☎ (01793) 762366
11–3, 7 (6 summer)–11; 12–3, 7–10.30 Sun
Flowers Original; guest beers G
Old rural Cotswold building with split bars and a friendly atmosphere. Good food.
♨ ⛬ ◑ ▶ ♣ P

## Cuxham

### Half Moon

On B480 ☎ (01491) 614110
12–2.30, 6–11; 12–3, 7–10.30 Sun
Brakspear Bitter, Old (winter), Special H
16th-century, thatched, village inn with a big garden. The 1993 renovation retained many original features – beams, open fireplace and a tiled floor. Extensive menu of home-cooked food (not served Sun eve in winter). Children welcome in the dining room lunchtime and early eve. Gas-assisted handpumps (no gas touches the beer).
♨ Q ✿ ◑ ▶ ♿ ✿ ♣ P

## Deddington

### Crown & Tuns

New Street (main road)
☎ (01869) 337371
11–11; 12–10.30 Sun
Hook Norton Mild, Best Bitter, Old Hooky H
16th-century inn, tastefully re-designed: in every issue of the Guide.
♨ Q ◑ ◐ ♣

## Dorchester

### Chequers

20 Bridge End (off High St; from S turn sharp left after bridge) ☎ (01865) 340015
12–2 (3 Sat & summer; not Mon), 7–11; 12–3, 7–10.30 Sun
Courage Best Bitter; Wadworth IPA; guest beer G
Genuine, 17th-century local in an attractive village which has an historic abbey. Lots of games, including Aunt Sally on summer Fri. Handy for walkers and the Rivers Thames and Thame.
♨ Q ⛬ ✿ 🍴 ♣ P ✗

## East Challow

### Coach & Horses

Main Street (A417)
☎ (01235) 762251
12–2.30, 6–11; 12–3, 7–10.30 Sun
Fuller's London Pride; Morland Original; Theakston XB; guest beer H
Friendly, comfortable, one-bar pub with a split-level back room/restaurant. Small car park. ♨ ✿ ◑ ▶ P

## Eynsham

### Queen's Head

Queen Street
☎ (01865) 881229
12–2.30, 6–11; 12–2.30, 7–10.30 Sun
Morland Original; guest beers H
Very convivial, 18th-century, two-bar village local. Railway memorabilia abounds. Ask which guest beers are available.
♨ ✿ 🍴 ◑ ◐

## Faringdon

### Folly

54 London Street
☎ (01367) 240620
10.30–2.30, 5.30–11; 12–3, 7–10.30 Sun
Morrells Varsity H
Friendly little pub at the top of the town, with a small public bar and lounge and a larger, recently opened and tastefully decorated lounge which was originally part of the pub's private accommodation.
♨ Q ✿ ◐ ♣

## Fifield

### Merrymouth Inn

Stow Road (A424)
☎ (01993) 831652.
11–2.30, 6–11; 12–3, 7–10.30 Sun
Banks's Bitter; Donnington BB, SBA; guest beers (occasional) H
13th-century inn with a beamed bar and a stone floor; mentioned in the Domesday Book. Home cooking.
♨ Q ⛬ ✿ 🍴 ◑ ▶ ♿ ✿ ♣ P ⛾

## Garsington

### Three Horseshoes

The Green ☎ (01865) 361395
11–11; 12–10.30 Sun
Draught Bass; Morrells Bitter, Varsity, Graduate H
Popular village pub, with a large garden and children's area. Good food is served in the bars and a no-smoking conservatory restaurant.
♨ Q ✿ ◑ ◐ ♿ ✿ ♣ P

## Goring

### Catherine Wheel

Station Road (off B4009, High St) ☎ (01491) 872379
11–2.00 (3 Sat), 6–11; 12–3, 7–10.30 Sun
Brakspear Mild, Bitter, Old, Special, OBJ H
The oldest pub in a lovely riverside village, near the Ridgeway footpath. Extended into the old village forge, it serves good value, freshly prepared food (daily specials); no meals Sun eve. Children are welcome in the restaurant area.
♨ Q ✿ ◑ ▶ ➤ ♣

### John Barleycorn

Manor Road (off B4009, High St, ¼ mile from the Thames)
☎ (01491) 872509
10–2.30, 6–11; 12–3, 7–10.30 Sun
Brakspear Bitter, Special H
16th century, low-beamed inn with a cosy lounge. Extensive good-value menu (daily specials). Children allowed in the lounge/restaurant.
Q ✿ 🍴 ◑ ▶ ➤ ♣

## Great Tew

### Falkland Arms

Off B4022 ☎ (01608) 683653
11.30–2.30 (not Mon except bank hols), 6–11; 12–2, 7–10.30 Sun
Badger Tanglefoot; Donnington BB; Hook Norton Best Bitter; Wadworth 6X H; guest beers G/ H
Classic, thatched, 16th-century inn in a preserved village, featuring oak panels, oil lamps, settles and flagstoned floors. Malt whiskies and fruit wines stocked. No food Sun. A gem!
♨ Q ✿ 🍴 ◑ ♣ ⟳

## Henley-on-Thames

### Bird in Hand
61 Greys Road (off A4155; near Greys Rd car park)
☎ (01491) 575775
11.30–3, 5–11; 11.30–11 (may be 11.30–3, 5–11 winter) Sat; 12–10.30 Sun
**Adnams Broadside; Fuller's London Pride; guest beers** H
Comfortable, welcoming, one-bar, town local: the only real ale free house in Henley. Safe garden for children. No meals Sun. Two guest beers.
Q ❀ ◑ ▲ ⇌ (summer only Sun) ♣

## Highmoor

### Dog & Duck
On B481, S of Nettlebed
☎ (01491) 641261
11.30–2.30, 6–11; 12–3, 7–10.30 Sun
**Brakspear Mild, Bitter, Special** H
Cosy, three-roomed, roadside pub in Chiltern woodland and near a pond. The large, enclosed garden hosts occasional barbecues summer weekends. Restaurant quality, home-made food (including vegetarian); reasonable prices and generous portions. No meals Mon.
⛫ Q ❀ ◑ ◗ ⊞ ♣ P

## Hook Norton

### Pear Tree Inn
Scotland End (W of village)
☎ (01608) 737482
12–2.30 (3 Sat), 6–11 (12–11 summer); 12–3, 7–10.30 (12–10.30 summer) Sun
**Hook Norton Mild, Best, Bitter, Old Hooky, seasonal beers** H
Charming, 18th-century, one-room, brick-faced pub featuring log fires and beams. The large gardens have a children's area and animals. Award-winning, healthy food. No eve meals Tue or Sun. Children's certificate.
⛫ Q ❀ ⛟ ◑ ◗ ▲ ♣ P

## Juniper Hill

### Fox
Off A43 ☎ (01869) 810616
12–2 (3 Sat), 7–11; 12–3, 7–10.30 Sun
**Hook Norton Best Bitter** H**, Old Hooky, seasonal beers** G
Friendly and attractive, two-bar, 18th-century rural inn at the centre of a hamlet; described as the 'Wagon and Horses' in the book *Lark Rise to Candleford*. ⛫ Q ❀ ♣ P

## Lewknor

### Olde Leathern Bottel
1 High Street (off B4009, near M40 jct 6) ☎ (01844) 351482
11–2.30, 6–11; 12–3, 7–10.30 Sun
**Brakspear Bitter, Old, Special** H
Comfortable, inviting, family-run village pub with a large, well-kept garden, large inglenook and low beams. The food is good quality, home-made and reasonably priced (vegetarian options).
⛫ ⛄ ❀ ◑ ◗ ⊞ ♿ ♣ P

## Long Wittenham

### Machine Man Inn
Fieldside (1 mile off A415 at Clifton Hampden, follow signs) ☎ (01865) 407835
11–3, 6–11; 12–4, 6–10.30 Sun
**Adnams Bitter; Cotleigh Barn Owl Bitter; Hardy Country, Royal Oak; guest beers** H
Basic, friendly village local serving good value, home-made food (including vegetarian); book Sun eve. ETB-approved accommodation. Three changing guest beers. The nearest pub to the annual World Pooh Sticks Championships (Jan). Families welcome. ⛫ ❀ ⛟ ◑ ◗ ♿ ♣ P

## Murcott

### Nut Tree Inn
Main Street ☎ (01865) 331253
11–3.30, 6.30–11; 12–3, 7–10.30 Sun
**Beer range varies** H/G
Very attractive, welcoming village pub offering five or six ever-changing, well chosen ales and a superb menu. Although food plays an important role, the drinker is not overlooked.
⛫ Q ❀ ◑ ◗ ♣ P

## North Hinksey

### Fishes Inn
Signed from A34
☎ (01865) 249796
11–3, 6–11 (11–11 summer Sat); 12–3, 7–10.30 (12–10.30 summer) Sun
**Morrells Bitter, Mild, Varsity, Graduate, College; guest beer** H
Recently refurbished village inn with a large, quiet, open-plan bar and a conservatory overlooking a two-acre garden with safe children's play area. Try the wholesome food.
⛫ Q ❀ ◑ ◗ ♿ ♣ P

## North Leigh

### Woodman Inn
New Yatt Road (off A4095)
☎ (01993) 881790
12–2.30 (4 Sat), 6–11; 12–10.30 Sun
**Hook Norton Best Bitter; Wadworth 6X; guest beers** H
Small, friendly village pub, recently refurbished, serving freshly cooked food (no eve meals Mon). The large terrace and garden host beer festivals Easter and Aug Bank Hol.
⛫ ❀ ⛟ ◑ ◗ ♿ ♣ P

## North Newington

### Roebuck Inn
Banbury Road (take B4035 from Banbury Cross; 1st right)
☎ (01295) 730444
12–3 (not Mon), 7–11; 12–3, 7–10.30 Sun
**Morland Original, Old Speckled Hen; guest beers** H
Welcoming, 17th-century inn with an emphasis on freshly prepared food. Relaxed bistro atmosphere (no food Sun eve). Well-behaved children welcome. ⛫ ❀ ◑ ◗ ♿ P

## Oxford

### Angel & Greyhound
30 St Clement's Street, St Clement's (A420)
☎ (01865) 242660
11–11; 12–10.30 Sun
**Young's Bitter, Special, Ram Rod, Winter Warmer** H
Light, airy, relaxed and friendly pub with a public car park behind. Small outside seating areas at the front and rear. ⛫ Q ❀ ◑ ◗ ♣

### Black Boy
91 Old High Street, Headington (off A420)
☎ (01865) 63234
11–3, 6–11; 11–11 Sat; 12–3, 7–10.30 Sun
**Morrells Bitter, Mild, Varsity, Graduate, College** H
Popular, 1930s-style pub with a through bar and a quiet saloon. Award-winning garden. No meals Sun. Q ❀ ◑ ◗ ⊞ ♣ P

### Bookbinder's Arms
17 Victor Street, Jericho
☎ (01865) 53549
11–3, 6–11; 11–11 Thu–Sat; 12–10.30 Sun
**Morrells Bitter, Mild** H
Very popular and friendly, corner local: a no-frills pub with two drinking areas.
◑ ♣

### Butcher's Arms
5 Wilberforce Street, Headington (off New High St)
☎ (01865) 61252
11.30–2.30, 5.30 (4.30 Fri)–11; 12–3, 7–10.30 Sun
**Fuller's Chiswick, London Pride, ESB, seasonal beers** H
Lively, welcoming, backstreet local with a single bar and a mixed clientele. Quiz Sun. Worth finding. ⛫ ❀ ◑ ♿ ♣

### Fir Tree Tavern
163 Iffley Road (A4158)
☎ (01865) 247373
12–3, 5.30–11; 12–11 Sat; 12–10.30 Sun
**Morrells Bitter, Mild, Varsity, Graduate, College; guest beer** H
Small, split-level, Victorian

pub, recently sympathetically refurbished. Popular folk session Tue eve; live music also Sun, Wed and Sat eves. Food all day weekends; freshly-made pizzas a speciality. Cider and perry in summer.
❀ ◑ ▶ ♣ ◠

### Folly Bridge Inn
38 Abingdon Road, Grandpont
☎ (01865) 790106
11–11; 12–3, 7–10.30 Sun
**Badger Tanglefoot; Wadworth IPA, 6X, Farmers Glory, Old Timer; guest beers** Ⓗ
Large, open-plan, single-bar pub tastefully refurbished; a short walk south from the city centre and the Thames. Regular mini-beer festivals; function room with a skittle-alley. ❀ ◑ ▶ ♣ P

### Half Moon
17–18 St Clement's Street, St Clement's (A420)
☎ (01865) 247808
11–11; 12–3, 7–10.30 Sun
**Greene King IPA, Abbot, seasonal beers** Ⓗ
Small, recently refurbished, cosy, single-bar pub, popular with the Irish community. Snacks available. ♣

### King's Arms
40 Holywell Street
☎ (01865) 242369
10.30–11; 12–10.30 Sun
**Morland Original; Wadworth 6X; Younger No. 3; Young's Bitter, Special, Ram Rod, seasonal beers** Ⓗ
Large, bustling city-centre institution: a large main bar with separate rooms at the front and rear; six different areas in all. The atmospheric Don's Bar at the rear is worth seeking out. No music – just the hum of conversation. Open 10.30 Sun for snacks.
♨ Q ▭ ❀ ◑ ♣ ✄

### Marsh Harrier
40 Marsh Road, Cowley (off B480)
☎ (01865) 775937
12–2.30, 6–11; 12–11 Fri & Sat; 12–10.30 Sun
**Fuller's London Pride, ESB, seasonal beers** Ⓗ
Small, friendly, two-bar pub with an attractive, cosy lounge. Recently refurbished, it caters for all the local community and is an oasis in a part of the city not renowned for good beer.
♨ ❀ ◑ ▶ ⊟ ♣

### Prince of Wales
73 Church Way, Iffley
☎ (01865) 778543
11–2.30, 6–11; 12–3, 7–10.30 Sun
**Badger Dorset Best, Tanglefoot; Wadworth IPA, 6X, Farmers Glory; guest beers** Ⓗ
Friendly, attractively furnished

pub in a pleasant riverside village, a short walk from Iffley Lock. Popular for its wide range of ales and good, home-made food. Mini-beer festival last weekend of each month.
❀ ◑ ♣ P

### Rose & Crown
North Parade Avenue (off A4165)
☎ (01865) 510551
10.30–3, 5 (6 Sat)–11; 12–3, 7–10.30 Sun
**ABC Best Bitter; Ind Coope Burton Ale; guest beers** Ⓗ
Popular, unspoilt pub, purpose-built in the 1870s, with an unusual corridor drinking area and small bars front and rear. The large covered courtyard is heated. The swear box is treated very seriously!
Q ❀ ◑ ♣

### Somerset
241 Marston Road, New Marston
☎ (01865) 243687
11–3, 5.30–11; 11–11 Fri & Sat; 12–3, 7–10.30 Sun
**Banks's Bitter; Camerons Strongarm** Ⓗ
Two-bar, 1930s pub with a small, cosy lounge and a large, enclosed garden. Access to University Parks and pleasant walks to the city centre from Ferry Road. No meals Mon.
Q ❀ ◑ ⊟ ♣ P 🕭

## Pyrton

### Plough
Knightsbridge Lane (off B4009, N of Watlington)
☎ (01491) 612003
11.30–2.30, 6 (7 Tue)–11; closed Mon eve; 12–3, 7–10.30 Sun
**Adnams Bitter; Brakspear Bitter; guest beer** Ⓗ
Attractive, 17th-century, thatched pub in a quiet country village, popular for its extensive menu of home-made food, served in the bar and separate restaurant. Families welcome in the restaurant lunchtime. The beer range may vary. ♨ ❀ ◑ ▶ ♠ P

## Ramsden

### Royal Oak
High Street (off B4022)
☎ (01993) 868213
11.30–2.30, 6.30–11; 12–3, 7–10.30 Sun
**Archers Golden; Hook Norton Best Bitter, Old Hooky; guest beers** Ⓗ
17th-century former coaching inn with a courtyard. The restaurant serves high quality local produce. Long serving staff help create an efficient, friendly atmosphere.
♨ Q ❀ 🛏 ◑ ▶ ⚄ P

## Sandford-on-Thames

### Fox
25 Henley Road
☎ (01865) 777803
12–2.30, 7–11; 12–2.30, 7–10.30 Sun
**Morrells Bitter; guest beer** Ⓗ
In the same family for 77 years and 19 years in the *Guide*: a basic, but friendly, local serving the cheapest Morrells beer in the area.
♨ Q ❀ ⊟ ♣ P

## Shrivenham

### Prince of Wales
High Street
☎ (01793) 782268
11–2.30, 6–11; 12–3, 7–10.30 Sun
**Badger Tanglefoot; Wadworth IPA, 6X; guest beer** Ⓗ
17th-century, stone coaching inn with a comfortable, beamed interior. No-smoking dining area.
♨ Q ❀ ◑ ▶ ♣ P

## Souldern

### Fox
Fox Lane (off B4100)
☎ (01869) 345281
11–3, 5 (6 Sat)–11; 12–4, 7–10.30 Sun
**Draught Bass; Fuller's London Pride; Hook Norton Old Hooky; Worthington Bitter; guest beers** Ⓗ
Friendly, Cotswold stone pub in the village centre, noted for its food, served in the bar and restaurant (not Sun eve).
♨ Q ❀ 🛏 ◑ ♣ P

## South Moreton

### Crown
High Street (off A4130 and A417) ☎ (01235) 812262
11–3, 5.30–11; 12–3, 7–10.30 Sun
**Adnams Bitter; Badger Tanglefoot; Wadworth IPA Ⓗ, 6X Ⓖ; guest beer Ⓖ/Ⓗ**
Enthusiastically-run village local, deservedly popular for meals, including vegetarian. Water coolers are used on the casks behind the bar.
♨ ▭ ❀ ◑ ▶ ♣ P

## Steeple Aston

### Red Lion
South Street (600 yds off A4260) ☎ (01869) 340225
11–2.30, 6–11; 12–2.30, 7–10.30 Sun
**Badger Tanglefoot; Hook Norton Best Bitter; Wadworth 6X** Ⓗ
Friendly adult retreat with a floral summer terrace and a library. Bar lunches served, except Sun; the dining room serves eve meals (Tue–Sat).
♨ Q ❀ ◑ P

## Steventon

### Cherry Tree
High Street
☎ (01235) 831222
11.30–2.30, 6–11; 12–3, 7–10.30 Sun
**Wadworth IPA, 6X, Farmers Glory, Old Timer; guest beer** Ⓗ
Comfortable roadside pub with a good choice of food; very popular lunchtime and early eve (plenty of space).
🏃 🍴 ☀ ◖ ▸ ♣ P ⊁

## Stoke Lyne

### Peyton Arms ☆
Off B4100
☎ (01869) 345285
11.30–3 (not Mon), 6–11; 11–11 Sat; 12–2.30, 7–10.30 Sun
**Hook Norton Mild, Best Bitter, Old Hooky; guest beers** Ⓖ
Small, basic, two-bar village pub, unchanged by time: a real rural gem. Aunt Sally played. Cold snacks lunchtime.
🏃 Q ☀ ♣ P

## Stoke Row

### Cherry Tree
Off B481 at Highmoor
☎ (01491) 680430
11–3, 6–11; 12–3, 7–10.30 Sun
**Brakspear Mild, Bitter, Special** Ⓖ
Low-beamed, attractive village local close to the famous Maharajah's Well. Families are welcome in the lounge and the games room; the garden has swings and a slide. Snacks available (rolls only Mon).
🏃 Q 🍴 ☀ ⊟ ♣ P

## Stonesfield

### Black Head
Church Street
☎ (01993) 891616
10.30–2.30, 5.30–11; 12–3, 7–10.30 Sun
**Courage Best Bitter; guest beers** Ⓗ
Basic local with an hospitable atmosphere. Two guest beers.
🏃 ☀ ⊟ ♣ P

## Tackley

### Gardiners Arms
95 Medcroft Road (main street)
☎ (01869) 331266
11–3, 6.30–11; 12–4, 6.30–10.30 (12–10.30 summer) Sun
**Morrells Bitter, Varsity, Graduate; guest beers** Ⓗ
Popular and comfortable, 17th-century Cotswold stone pub with two bars and a skittle alley. Barbecue summer Sun.
🏃 ☀ ◖ ▸ ⊟ ≑ ♣ P

## Thame

### Six Bells
44 Lower High Street
☎ (01844) 212088
11.15–3, 6–11; 12–3, 7–10.30 Sun
**Fuller's Chiswick, London Pride, ESB, seasonal beers** Ⓗ
Comfortable, old two-bar pub with some original 16th-century ship's timbers. The lounge bar ceiling has straps to assist perpendicular drinkers. The food is recommended (not served Sun eve).
Q 🍴 ☀ ◖ ♣ P

### Swan Hotel
9 Upper High Street
☎ (01844) 261211
11–11; 12–10.30 Sun
**Brakspear Bitter; Hook Norton Best Bitter; guest beers** Ⓗ
Popular 15th-century coaching inn overlooking the market place, with many unusual fittings (spot the boar's head). Excellent restaurant and bar meals include vegetarian and children's options.
🏃 Q 🍴 ◖ ▸ ⊛

## Wallingford

### King's Head
2 St Martin's Street (A329, near A4130 jct)
☎ (01491) 838309
11–11; 12–10.30 Sun
**Brakspear Bitter** Ⓗ
Lively town-centre local. Families welcome until 4pm.
⊛ ♣ P

## Wantage

### Royal Oak
Newbury Street
☎ (01235) 763129
6–11; 12–2.30, 6–11 Fri; 12–2.30, 7–11 Sat; 12–3, 7–10.30 Sun
**Draught Bass; Wadworth 6X; guest beers** Ⓖ/Ⓗ
Boisterous pub with two large bars and a landlord who loves beer (wide variety of guests, which change frequently). Whiskies for the connoisseur.
🍴 ◖ ⊟ ♣

## West Hanney

### Lamb Inn
School Road (off A338)
☎ (01235) 868917
11.30–3, 6–11; 12–3, 7–10.30 Sun
**Draught Bass; Flowers Original; Morland Original; Shepherd Neame Spitfire; guest beers** Ⓗ
Very friendly free house serving good food. Beer festival Aug Bank Hol.
Q 🏃 🍴 ◖ ▸ ⊛ ⚲ ♣ ⟳ P

## Witney

### Carpenter's Arms
132 Newland
☎ (01993) 702206
10.30–2.30, 6–11; 12–2.30, 7–10.30 Sun
**Morrells Bitter, Varsity** Ⓗ
Very comfortable, one-bar (with small games room) pub, popular with all ages. Ideal for a quiet drink. ☀ ◖ ▸ P

### Three Horseshoes
29 Corn Street
☎ (01993) 703086
11–2.30, 6.30–11; 11–11 Sat; 12–2.30, 7–10.30 Sun
**Morland Original; Wells Bombardier; guest beer** (occasional) Ⓗ
16th-century inn with a stone floor, exposed beams, antique furniture (including a grandfather clock) and oriental rugs. 🏃 Q 🏃 ☀ ◖ ▸

## Woodstock

### Black Prince
2 Manor Road (A44)
☎ (01993) 811530
12–2.30, 6.30–11; 12–2.30, 6.30–10.30 Sun
**Archers Village; Theakston XB, Old Peculier; guest beer** Ⓗ
Superb, 16th-century ex-coaching inn on the bank of the River Glyme. A beautiful suit of armour stands in the bar. Recently threatened by developers, but it looks safe now. Mexican food a speciality.
🏃 ☀ ◖ ▸ P

### Queen's Own
59 Oxford Street
☎ (01993) 813582
11–3, 6–11; 11–11 Sat; 11–3, 6–10.30 Sun
**Boddingtons Mild; Hampshire Lionheart; Hook Norton Best Bitter, Old Hooky; guest beers** Ⓗ
Very pleasant, stone free house, narrow at the front but opening into quite a spacious bar. A very rare local outlet for Hampshire Brewery. ◖

## Wootton

### Killingworth Castle Inn
Glympton Road (B4027)
☎ (01993) 811401
12–2.30 (not Tue), 7–11; 12–3, 7–10.30 Sun
**Morland Original; guest beers** Ⓗ
Warm, friendly, 17th-century, Cotswold stone coaching inn popular with locals and tourists, near the Oxfordshire Way and Blenheim Palace. Excellent, freshly-cooked, varied English meals. No food Tue. 🏃 Q ☀ ⚲ ◖ ▸ P ⊁

# Shropshire

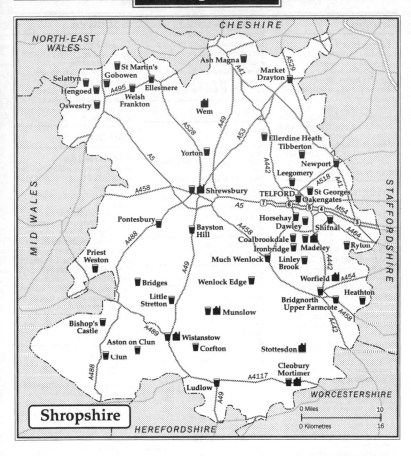

## Shropshire

---

## Ash Magna

### White Lion
Off A525 bypass
☎ (01948) 663153
12–2 (3 Sat; not Mon), 6–11; 12–3,
7–10.30 Sun
**Draught Bass; Highgate
Saddlers; Worthington
Bitter** Ⓔ**; guest beers** Ⓗ/Ⓔ
Two-bar pub where the lounge
has a collection of hickory-
handled golf clubs. Along with
bar billiards and skittles, there
is also a bowling green.
♨ Q ❀ ◑ ▶ ♣ 🖵

## Aston on Clun

### Kangaroo
☎ (01588) 660263
12–3, 7–11; hours vary weekends and
summer
**Draught Bass; Highgate Dark;
Worthington Bitter; guest
beers** (summer) Ⓗ
Pub whose landlord's time in
Australia is reflected in
mementoes: a large bar and a
no-smoking lounge. Spacious

garden. The village tradition of
tree dressing survives.
♨ ◑ ▶ ♠ ♣ ✄

## Bayston Hill

### Compasses
29 Hereford Road (A49)
☎ (01743) 872921
5 (12 Fri & Sat)–11; 12–10.30 Sun
**Draught Bass; Highgate Dark;
M&B Brew XI; Stones Bitter;
guest beer** Ⓗ
Pub with a snug and an
extended bar, boasting a huge
collection of carved elephants
and other mementoes. The rear
overlooks the old village
common. ❀ ⊞ ♿ ♣ P ✄

## Bishop's Castle

### Castle Hotel
Market Square
☎ (01588) 638403
12–2.30, 5.30–11; 12–3, 7–10.30 Sun
**Draught Bass; Worthington
Bitter; guest beers** Ⓗ
Fine country town hotel. The
front entrance leads to a snug

bar with much original
woodwork in evidence. There
is a larger room off and a
public bar at the rear. Good
selection of games; popular
with locals. Large garden. Up
to two guest beers.
♨ Q ❀ 🛏 ◑ ▶ ♣ P

---

 **INDEPENDENT
BREWERIES**

**All Nations:** Madeley

**Crown Inn:**
Munslow

**Davenports Arms:**
Worfield

**Fox & Hounds:** Stottesdon

**Hanby:** Wem

**Hobsons:**
Cleobury Mortimer

**Salopian:** Shrewsbury

**Wood:** Wistanstow

---

## Bridges

### Horseshoe Inn

OS394964 ☎ (01588) 650260
12–3 (not Mon, or winter Tue–Thu),
6–11; 12–3, 7–10.30 Sun
**Adnams Bitter, Extra;
Shepherd Neame Spitfire;
guest beer** H
Excellent local, attractively
situated in a quiet valley by the
River Onny, much appreciated
by walkers from the Long
Mynd and Stiperstones hills.
Local CAMRA *Pub of the Year*
1995. Two guest beers.
🏚 Q ♣ ❀ ◖ ⬥ ▲ ♣ ⬠ P ⚤

## Bridgnorth

### Bear Inn

Northgate ☎ (01746) 763250
11–2.30 (10.30–3 Fri & Sat), 5.15 (6
Sat)–11; 12–2.30, 7.30–10.30 Sun
**Batham Mild, Best Bitter;
Boddingtons Bitter; Ruddles
Best Bitter; guest beer** H
Comfortable and friendly,
two-roomed former brew pub
off the high street of this
historic market town; a locals'
pub with a daily-changing
guest beer and good quality
food (gourmet eve Thu – book;
no food Sun). Above average
accommodation.
Q ❀ ◖ ⬠ ▲ ♣ P

### Railwayman's Arms

SVR station, Hollybush Road
(off B4364) ☎ (01746) 764361
11–4 (12–2 winter), 7–11; 11–11 Sat;
12–3, 7–10.30 Sun
**Batham Best Bitter; Highgate
Dark; Hobsons Best Bitter;
guest beers** H
Favourite watering hole of
steam railway enthusiasts,
located directly on the
platform of SVR's famous
preserved line. Very good
selection of guest beers,
usually from independent
breweries; autumn beerex. Hot
snacks served.
🏚 ❀ ⬥ ▲ ⬱ (SVR) ♣ ⬠ P

## Cleobury Mortimer

### Bell Inn

Lower Street ☎ (01299) 270305
11–3, 7 (6 Fri & Sat)–11; 12–3, 7–10.30
Sun
**Banks's Mild, Bitter** E
Pub with a smart, split-level
lounge and a good, old-
fashioned bar, plus a private
snooker club room at the rear
(day membership available)
and a pool room. 🏚 Q ⬠ ♣ P

### King's Arms Hotel

High Street (opp. church)
☎ (01299) 270252
11.30–11; 12–10.30 Sun
**Hobsons Best Bitter; Hook
Norton Best Bitter; Wye
Valley HPA; Taylor Landlord;
guest beers** H

16th-century coaching inn with
a central fireplace and a
separate eating area. At
lunchtimes classical music is
played; during the eve the
sounds are a little faster.
Helpful bar staff. Toasted
sandwiches all day. Occasional
cider. 🏚 ❀ ⬙ ◖ ▶ ⬥ ⬠

## Clun

### White Horse

The Square
☎ (01588) 640305
11.30–3, 6.30–11; 12–3, 7–10.30 (may
vary) Sun
**Draught Bass; Worthington
Bitter; guest beer** H
Set in the centre of this timeless
village, a pub with one
L-shaped bar which provides
spaces for customers of all
ages. The guest beer is usually
from Wye Valley.
🏚 ❀ ◖ ▲ ♣

## Corfton

### Sun Inn

On B4368 ☎ (01584) 861239
11–2.30, 6–11; 12–3, 7 (6
summer)–10.30 Sun
**Boddingtons Mild; Flowers
IPA; Wye Valley HPA; guest
beers** H
Family-run, 17th-century inn
serving good food. Award-
winning facilities for guests
with disabilities. Good views
of Clee Hill from the garden.
Cider in summer.
🏚 Q ❀ ◖ ⬥ ▲ ♣ ⬠ P ⚤ ⬙

## Ellerdine Heath

### Royal Oak

1 mile off A53 OS603226
☎ (01939) 250300
11–3, 5–11; 11–11 Sat; 12–3, 7–10.30
Sun
**Brains Dark, SA; Hanby
Drawwell; Hobsons Best
Bitter; Wood Parish; guest
beers** H
Splendid rural local nicknamed
the 'Tiddly', with a small,
simple bar joined by a games
room; large outside drinking
area. Regular special events;
children's certificate; good
food (no meals Tue).
🏚 ⬝ ❀ ◖ ▶ ▲ ♣ ⬠ P

## Ellesmere

### White Hart Inn

Birch Road
☎ (01691) 622333
7–11; 11.30–5, 7–11 Sat; 12–3, 7–10.30
Sun
**Bateman Mild; Marston's
Bitter, Pedigree** H
Delightful, two-roomed, early
17th-century, listed, cosy local
near the Llangollen Canal in
Shropshire's Lake District.
Q ⬝ ❀ ⬠ ⬥ ♣ P

## Gobowen

### Cross Foxes

By station ☎ (01691) 670827
11–11; 10.30 Sun
**Banks's Mild; Marston's
Pedigree, HBC** H
Welcoming, sympathetically
refurbished village local. Sun
lunches served.
❀ ⬥ ▲ ⬱ ♣ P ⬙

## Heathton

### Old Gate Inn

From Claverley village follow
signs to Bobbington OS813924
☎ (01746) 710431
12–2.30, 6.30–11; 12–3 (not winter),
7–10.30 Sun
**Enville Ale; HP&D Entire;
Tetley Bitter; guest beer** H
Bustling, traditional country
pub off the beaten track: two
rooms with exposed beams
and log fires. First licensed in
1784, this is the only HP&D
pub in Shropshire. Families
welcome (play equipment and
barbecue in the rear garden).
Quality, home-cooked food.
🏚 ❀ ◖ ▶ ▲ P

## Hengoed

### Last Inn

On B4579 ☎ (01691) 659747
7–11; 12–3, 7–10.30 Sun
**Draught Bass; Boddingtons
Bitter; guest beers** H
Welcoming rural pub on the
Welsh border, offering a varied
selection of guest beers.
Families are well catered for.
Note the beer tray collection.
Good food (lunches Sun; no
eve meals Tue).
🏚 Q ⬝ ▶ ⬥ ♣ ⬠ P

## Linley Brook

### Pheasant Inn

Britons Lane (off B4373)
☎ (01746) 762260
12–2.30, 6.30–11; 12–2.30, 7–10.30 Sun
**Beer range varies** H
Out of the way, two-room pub
in a picturesque valley; 12
consecutive years in the *Guide*.
Two coal fires warm the
inviting lounge. Three
handpulls dispense ever-
changing guest beers. Good
food. 🏚 Q ❀ ◖ ▶ ♣ P

## Little Stretton

### Ragleth

Ludlow Road
☎ (01694) 722711
12–2.30, 6–11 (12–10.30 bank hols;
extends in summer); 12–11 Sat;
12–10.30 Sun
**Banks's Mild; Marston's
Pedigree; guest beer** H
Comfortable, 17th-century pub
of character, set in the South
Shropshire hills. Brick and tiled

floor together with woodwork and an inglenook in the bar; larger lounge. Children's certificate.
🏚 ✿ 🛏 ◖ ▶ 🍺 ♿ Å ♣ P

## Ludlow

### Church Inn

Buttercross ☎ (01584) 872174
11–11; 12–10.30 (12–3, 7–10.30 Dec–Feb) Sun
**Courage Directors; Ruddles County; Webster's Yorkshire Bitter; guest beers** (summer) Ⓗ
Tucked away in Ludlow's pedestrian area, on one of the town's most ancient sites, this upmarket inn stands near the church of St Lawrence, the largest and most majestic in Shropshire. Q 🛏 ◖ ▶ ≠

### Old Bull Ring Tavern

44 Bull Ring ☎ (01584) 872311
11–11; 12–3, 7–10.30 Sun
**Ansells Mild, Bitter; Tetley Bitter; guest beer** Ⓗ
Cosy, two-roomed pub going back 650 years; very popular with all ages. No eve meals Sun. 🏚 ◖ ▶ 🍺 ≠ ♣

## Market Drayton

### Star

Stafford Street
☎ (01630) 652530
12–3, 7–11; 11–11 Wed, Fri & Sat; 12–3, 7–10.30 Sun
**Hanby Drawwell; guest beers** Ⓗ
Hanby's own tavern is a 17th-century coaching inn, now a friendly, one-bar town pub. Snacks and bar meals are planned. At least two other Hanby beers are sold.
✿ ♣ P

## Much Wenlock

### George & Dragon ☆

2 High Street ☎ (01952) 727312
11–2.30 (3 Sat), 6–11; 12–2.30, 7–10.30 Sun
**Hook Norton Best Bitter; guest beers** Ⓗ
Friendly, popular and untouched by refurbishment, this delightful, traditional pub is packed with character. Breweriana adorns the walls; a large collection of jugs hangs from the beams. A keen crosswording clientele enjoys three guest beers. No meals Sun eve. ◖ ▶ ♣

## Munslow

### Crown Inn

☎ (01584) 841205
12–2.30, 7–11; 12–3, 7–10.30 Sun
**Banks's Mild; Marston's Pedigree; Crown Munslow Boy's Pale Ale, Munslow Ale; guest beers** (occasional) Ⓗ

Interesting roadside inn brewing its own beers and serving meals prepared by an award-winning chef (specialities include Thai and French dishes). The brew house is visible from the bar.
🏚 Q ✿ ◖ ▶ 🍺 ♣ ⌂ P

## Newport

### New Inn

Stafford Road
☎ (01952) 814729
11.30–3.30, 7–11; 12–4, 7–10.30 Sun
**Banks's Hanson's Mild, Mild, Bitter; Draught Bass** Ⓗ
Three-room local with a friendly atmosphere in its average-sized, basic bar, cosy and warm snug, and good-sized family room. The servery is a tiny bar between the snug and the main bar.
🏚 Q 🛏 ✿ 🍺 ♣

### Shakespeare

Upper Bar (main street)
☎ (01952) 811924
11–11; 12–10.30 Sun
**Banks's Mild; Draught Bass; Theakston Best Bitter; guest beers** Ⓗ
Clean and friendly town pub frequented by all ages and very busy Fri and Sat nights.
✿ Å ♣ P ⌷

## Oswestry

### Bell

Church Street
☎ (01691) 657068
11–11; 12–10.30 Sun
**Draught Bass; Highgate Dark; M&B Brew XI; guest beer** Ⓗ
Busy town local opposite the parish church; reputedly the oldest pub in town.
✿ ♣ P

### Oak Inn

47 Church Street
☎ (01691) 652304
11–3, 6–11; 12–3, 7–10.30 Sun
**Draught Bass** Ⓗ**; M&B Brew XI** Ⓗ**/**Ⓔ**; guest beers** Ⓗ
Old pub opposite the church, with a small front bar and a rear lounge. It has had only three licensees in 74 years (25 years for the present licensee).
Q ✿ 🍺 ♿ ♣

## Pontesbury

### Horseshoes Inn

Minsterley Road (A488)
☎ (01743) 790278
12–3, 6–11; 12–4, 7–10.30 Sun
**Boddingtons Bitter; Castle Eden Ale; Flowers IPA; guest beer** Ⓗ
Busy local in a large village, conveniently placed for walking in the South Shropshire hills. The service is friendly. Teams from the pub participate in several local

games leagues. Up to two guest beers. ◖ ▶ 🍺 ♣ P

## Priest Weston

### Miners Arms

OS293973 ☎ (01938) 561352
11–4, 7–11; 12–3, 7–10.30 Sun
**Draught Bass; Worthington Bitter** Ⓗ
Remote, classic country pub, still largely unspoilt, drawing walkers visiting a nearby stone circle. The well can be viewed en route to the toilet. Folk singing first Wed of the month; folk festival Easter.
🏚 ✿ ◖ ▶ Å ♣ ⌂ P

## Ryton

### Fox

E of A49 at Dorrington
☎ (01743) 718499
12–3, 7–11; 12–3, 7–10.30 Sun
**Draught Bass; guest beers** Ⓗ
Its elevated position gives this pub's L-shaped bar and restaurant expansive views towards the South Shropshire hills. Along with one guest beer in winter, and two in summer, locals and visitors sample an imaginative range of home-prepared food. Boules played. ✿ ◖ ▶ P

## St Martin's

### Greyhound Inn

Overton Road (B5069, 1 mile from village) ☎ (01691) 774307
12–11; 12–10.30 Sun
**Banks's Mild; Marston's Pedigree** or **guest beer; Webster's Yorkshire Bitter** Ⓗ
Comfortable, refurbished rural pub with an extensive outdoor area, including children's play facilities. The bar has a collection of rare artefacts from the nearby (closed) Ifton Colliery. 🏚 🍺 ✿ ◖ ▶ ♿ P

## Selattyn

### Cross Keys ☆

On B4579 ☎ (01691) 650247
6–11; 6–10.30 Sun (phone for lunchtime hours)
**Banks's Mild, Bitter** Ⓗ
Unspoilt, 17th-century village local with various rooms, including a skittle area; popular with Offa's Dyke walkers. Holiday flat to let.
🏚 Q 🍺 ✿ 🛏 ♿ ♣ P

## Shifnal

### Wheatsheaf Taphouse

61 Broadway ☎ (01952) 460938
11–11; 12–10.30 Sun
**Banks's Mild, Bitter, seasonal beers; Camerons Strongarm; guest beer** Ⓗ
Friendly Banks's ale house pub with coal fires in two rooms. Hanson's Mild and Camerons

Bitter are sold as house beers. Food available all day.

🏠 Q ⊛ ◖ ▮ ⧓ ▵ ⇌ ♣ P ⊓

## White Hart

4 High Street ☎ (01952) 461161
12–3, 6–11; 12–11 Fri & Sat; 12–4, 7–10.30 Sun

**Ansells Bitter; Enville Simpkiss Bitter, Ale; Ind Coope Burton Ale; guest beers** Ⓗ

Welcoming, two-bar, 16th-century coaching house which is timber framed and features ships' oak beams. A free house, it has served 400 guest beers in two years. The landlord is a Burton Ale *Master Cellarman* and a keen angler. Local CAMRA *Pub of the Year* 1996. Reputedly haunted.

Q ⊛ ◖ ⧓ ⇌ ♣ P

# Shrewsbury

## Boat House

New Street, Port Hill (A488)
☎ (01743) 362965
11–11; 12–10.30 Sun

**Boddingtons Bitter; Flowers IPA; Fuller's London Pride; Whitbread Abroad Cooper, Fuggles IPA; guest beers** Ⓗ

Hogshead ale house reached by footbridge from Quarry Park. Tables in the terraced garden overlook the river (bouncy castle in summer). Guest beers from Shropshire breweries. Eve meals end at 8.

🏠 Q ⊛ ◖ ▮ ⧓ ⇌ ♣ ⊂ P

## Castle Vaults

16 Castle Gates
☎ (01743) 358807
11.30–3, 6–11; 7–10.30 Sun, closed Sun lunch

**Hobsons Best Bitter; Marston's Pedigree; guest beers** Ⓗ

Free house with a roof garden, in the shadow of the castle, specialising in home-cooked Mexican food served in an open bar area. The house beer is brewed by Plassey Brewery. Three guest beers include one from Wood.

🏠 Q ⊛ ◖ ◪ ◖ ▮ ⇌ ⊂ ⅍ ⊓

## Coach & Horses

Swan Hill ☎ (01743) 365661
11–11; 12–10.30 Sun

**Draught Bass; guest beers** Ⓗ

Unspoilt Victorian pub in a quiet part of town, attracting a mixed clientele. The bar is wood panelled, with a partitioned area at the side. The house beer is brewed by Salopian Brewery. A separate restaurant is planned.

Q ◖ ▮ ⇌

## Dolphin

48 St Michaels Street
☎ (01743) 350419
5 (3 Fri & Sat)–11; 12–3, 7–10.30 Sun

**Beer range varies** Ⓗ

Early Victorian, gas-lit drinking house with a porticoed entrance. Up to six hand-pulled beers; no lager, not even in bottles.

Q ⇌ ♣

## Nag's Head

22 Wyle Cop
☎ (01743) 362455
11–11; 12–10.30 Sun

**Beer range varies** Ⓗ

Often lively, reputedly haunted, historic house of considerable architectural interest. Work is in hand to preserve and enhance its features. Three or four Carlsberg-Tetley beers are on sale. ⊛ ⇌ ♣

## Peacock

42 Wenlock Road (A458, 300 yds from Shire Hall)
☎ (01743) 355215
11–3, 6–11; 12–3, 7–10.30 Sun

**Bateman Mild; Marston's Bitter, Pedigree, Owd Rodger, HBC** Ⓗ

Spacious, open-plan pub near Lord Hill's Column (the tallest Doric column in Britain). Food includes vegetarian meals. Note the ornate peacock on the wall by the lounge entrance. ⊛ ◖ ▮ ♣ P

## Proud Salopian

Smithfield Road
☎ (01743) 236887
11–11; 7–10.30, closed Sun lunch

**Draught Bass; Boddingtons Bitter; Castle Eden Ale; Whitbread Fuggles IPA; guest beers** Ⓗ

Busy pub just off the town centre, occasionally threatened by the nearby River Severn. Three guest beers. Thomas Southam, the Shrewsbury brewer, was the Proud Salopian.

◖ ▮ ◪ ⇌ ♣

## Three Fishes

4 Fish Street
☎ (01743) 344793
11.30–11; 11–11 Sat; closed Sun

**Boddingtons Bitter; Flowers Original; Fuller's London Pride; Morland Old Speckled Hen; Taylor Landlord; guest beers** Ⓗ

Single-roomed, timber-framed pub, one of the few nationally where smoking is not allowed anywhere. It stands amongst other buildings of the same era in a narrow sidestreet. Good food. Q ◖ ▮ ⇌ ⅍

# Telford: *Coalbrookdale*

## Coalbrookdale Inn

12 Wellington Road (opp. Museum of Iron)
☎ (01952) 433953

12–3, 6–11; 12–3, 7–10.30 Sun

**Courage Directors; Enville Bitter, Mild; HP&D Entire; guest beers** Ⓗ

CAMRA national *Pub of the Year* 1995: a popular, one-bar pub with an enthusiastic landlord. The beer range is always varied. Eve meals end at 8; no food Sun.

🏠 Q ⅍ ⊛ ◖ ⌣

# Dawley

## Three Crowns

Hinksay Road (off B4373 at Finger Road garage)
☎ (01952) 590868
11–3 (4 Sat), 6.30–11; 12–4, 7–10.30 Sun

**Marston's Bitter, Pedigree, HBC** Ⓗ

Small, friendly, well-decorated open-plan local. Rolls and sandwiches served eves.

⊛ ◖ ♣ P

# Horsehay

## Traveller's Joy

Woodhouse Lane
☎ (01952) 501802
12–3, 6 (6.30 Sat)–11; 12–3, 7–10.30 Sun

**Banks's Mild; Draught Bass; Hook Norton Old Hooky; guest beers** Ⓗ

Comfortable, open-plan, U-shaped pub serving good value food at all sessions, except Sun eve. Live music Fri and Sat eves. The garden has swings and a slide. Two guest beers are available.

⊛ ◖ ▮ ♣ P

# Ironbridge

## Golden Ball

1 Newbridge Road (off A4169, Madeley Hill, at Jockey Bank)
☎ (01952) 432179
12–3, 6–11 (12–11 summer Sat); 12–3, 7–10.30 Sun

**Courage Best Bitter, Directors; Marston's Pedigree; Ruddles Best Bitter, County; guest beer** Ⓗ

Multi-roomed pub still retaining a sense of its 18th-century roots, only ten mins' walk from the famous iron bridge. Good food from a wide-ranging menu.

🏠 ⊛ ◪ ◖ ▮ ♣ P

## Horse & Jockey

15 Jockey Bank (set back from A4169, Madeley Hill)
☎ (01952) 433798
12–3, 6.30–11; 12–3, 7–10.30 Sun

**Flowers IPA; guest beer** Ⓗ

Food-oriented, two-roomed pub pleasantly refurbished and comprised of a small bar and a larger lounge catering mainly for diners. The varied menu includes prize-winning steak

and kidney pies.
✿ ◖ ▶ ⊞ ♣ P

## Old Vaults Wine Bar
29 High Street
☎ (01952) 432716
11–3 (not Mon), 6.30–11; 12.30–10.30 Sun
**Beer range varies** ⊞
Friendly, cosy wine bar with a street-level eating area and a bar downstairs for food and drink. Shropshire's micros feature strongly among the three handpulled beers. A varied menu includes Sun roasts and Spanish Tapas; monthly theme nights.
🏚 ✿ ◖ ▶

## *Leegomery*

### Malt Shovel Inn
Hadley Park Road (off A442, at Leegomery roundabout)
☎ (01952) 242963
12–2.30 (3 Sat), 5–11; 12–3, 7–10.30 Sun
**Banks's Mild; Marston's Bitter, Pedigree, Owd Rodger** (winter), **HBC** ⊞
Welcoming, two-roomed pub with open fires and horse brasses. Weekday lunches.
🏚 ✿ ◖ ▶ ⊞ ♣ P

## *Madeley*

### All Nations
20 Coalport Road (opp. Blist Hill Museum)
☎ (01952) 585747
12–3 (4 Sat), 7–11; 12–3, 7–10.30 Sun
**All Nations Pale Ale** ⊞
Famed, family-owned, one-bar pub which has been brewing for over 200 years. Strong local following. In every edition of the *Guide*.
✿ ▲ ♣ P

### Royal Oak
High Street
☎ (01952) 585598
12–3, 7–11; 12–3, 7–10.30 Sun
**Burtonwood Bitter; Chester's Mild; guest beers** ⊞
Basic and friendly, drinkers' pub with a bar, cosy lounge and separate pool playing area. All ten handpulls are utilised occasionally. Live music at weekends.
🏚 Q ✿ ⊞ ▲ ♣ ⇔ P

## *Oakengates*

### Crown Inn
Market Street
☎ (01952) 610888

11.30–2.30 (3 Fri & Sat), 7 (5 Thu & Fri)–11; 12–3, 7–10.30 Sun
**Hobsons Best Bitter; Hook Norton Old Hooky; Mansfield Riding Mild; guest beers** ⊞
Friendly, town-centre pub with three distinct drinking areas, specialising in ales from independent breweries (over 130 in seven months; up to nine at a time). Level entrance at the rear from the bus station.
🏚 ◖ ⇌ ♣ P

## *St Georges*

### Albion Inn
Station Hill
☎ (01952) 614193
12–2.30 (4 Sat), 5 (7 Sat)–11; 12–3, 7–10.30 Sun
**Banks's Mild; Marston's Bitter, Pedigree** ⊞
Smart, one-bar pub between St Georges and Oakengates, popular with locals. Home-cooked food. Panoramic views towards North Shropshire from the bar. ✿ 🛏 ◖ ▶
⇌ (Oakengates) ♣ P

## Tibberton

### Sutherland Arms
☎ (01952) 550533
12–2.30, 6–11; 12–11 Sat; 12–10.30 Sun
**Banks's Mild; Marston's Bitter, Pedigree, Owd Rodger** (winter) ⊞
Village community pub with several open, but distinctive, drinking areas, real fires and a selection of 40 single malt whiskies. Games include bar skittles, Pot the Pudding and Broke 'Id 'Ole. Eve meals Tue–Sat, till 8.30
🏚 Q ✿ ◖ ▶ ⊞ ♣ P

## Upper Farmcote

### Lion O'Morfe
Off Bridgnorth–Stourbridge road, follow Claverley sign
☎ (01746) 710678
11.30–3 (5 Sat), 7–11; 12–4, 7–10.30 Sun
**Banks's Mild, Bitter** Ⓔ; **Draught Bass; guest beer** ⊞
Georgian farmhouse with a modern feel; a quiet pub which welcomes families and functions. Live jazz, folk or comedy second Thu of the month. Games room; floodlit boules piste. Locals meet in the bar. The good selection of food is not available Fri–Sun eves.
🏚 Q ✿ ◖ ▶ ⊞ ♣ ⊁ Ⓓ

## Welsh Frankton

### Narrow Boat
Ellesmere Road
☎ (01691) 661051
11–3, 7–11; 12–3, 7–10.30 Sun
**Tetley Bitter; guest beers** ⊞
Well-appointed pub alongside a busy section of the Shropshire Union (Llangollen) Canal. Two guest beers, plus Tapster's Choice, available. Sun lunches a speciality.
🏚 Q ✿ ◖ ▶ ⑂ ▲ P ⊁

## Wenlock Edge

### Wenlock Edge Inn
Hilltop (B4371, 4½ miles from Much Wenlock)
☎ (01746) 785678
11.30–2.30 (not Mon), 6.30–11; 12–3, 7–10.30 Sun
**Beer range varies** ⊞
Family-run pub on top of Wenlock Edge, attracting a mostly mature clientele. Small, but inspired, menu of home-made dishes (no food Mon). Storytelling nights second Mon of the month. Good walking nearby.
🏚 Q ✿ 🛏 ◖ ▶ P

## Wistanstow

### Plough
400 yds off A49 / A489
☎ (01588) 673251
12–3, 7–11; 12–3, 7–10.30 Sun
**Wood Parish, Special, Shropshire Lad, Wonderful; guest beers** ⊞
Wood's brewery tap serving a wide choice of excellent food. Two bars: the public is split into snug and games areas. Families welcome in the bottom bar. Large car park.
🏚 ✿ ◖ ▶ ⊞ ♣ P

## Yorton

### Railway
By station
☎ (01939) 28240
11.30–3, 6–11; 12–3.30, 7–10.30 Sun
**Wadworth 6X; Wood Parish, Special, Shropshire Lad** ⊞; **guest beers** ⊞/Ⓖ
This pub's unchanging atmosphere reflects the 60 years' occupation by the same family: a friendly, simple bar with a large lounge. Shropshire CAMRA *Pub of the Year* 1996.
🏚 Q ✿ ⇌ (request stop) ♣ P

---

# SYMBOLISM

A full explanation of the symbols used in the *Good Beer Guide* can be found on the inside front cover.

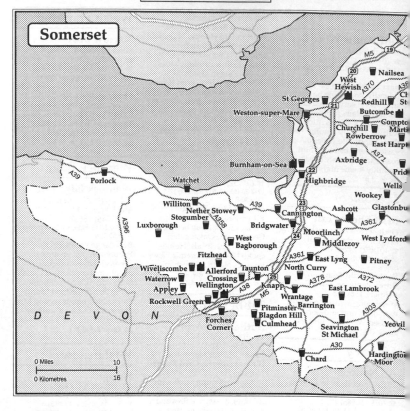

Somerset

## Allerford Crossing

### Victory

½ mile S of B3227 OS182249
☎ (01823) 461282
11–3, 6–11; 12–4, 6–10.30 Sun
**Badger Tanglefoot; Cotleigh Tawny; guest beers** Ⓗ
Large, multi-roomed pub which caters for all, especially families. Up to 11 real ales; good value food in the bar and restaurant. Two gardens – the family one features a full-sized train and a bouncy castle in summer. Cider in summer (Lanes). Somerset CAMRA *Pub of the Year* 1996.
🏚 🐂 🏵 ◑ ▮ 🍴 🅖 🔥 🗢 P 🚲

## Appley

### Globe Inn ☆

2½ miles N of A38 at White Ball Hill OS071215
☎ (01823) 672327
11–3 (not Mon), 6.30–11; 12–3, 7–10.30 Sun
**Cotleigh Tawny; guest beer** Ⓗ
Lovely old village inn, deep in the country. The bar is a simple hatchway in a flagstoned corridor, with several cosy rooms leading off. Attractive garden with children's play equipment. Good quality, good value food always available. Well worth the journey down winding lanes.
🏚 Q 🐂 🏵 ◑ ▮ 🅐 🔥 🗢 P

## Axbridge

### Lamb Inn

The Square
☎ (01934) 732253
12–2.30 (3 Sat), 6.30–11; 12–3, 7–10.30 Sun
**Draught Bass; Butcombe Bitter; Wadworth 6X; guest beers** Ⓗ
Rambling old pub, now owned by Butcombe, opposite King John's Hunting Lodge. Large terraced garden. The unusual bar is made of bottles.
Q 🏵 🚪 ◑ ▮ 🅖 🔥

## Barrington

### Royal Oak

☎ (01460) 53455
12–3, 6.30 (6 Fri)–11; 12–11 Sat; 12–4, 7–10.30 Sun
**Theakston Best Bitter; guest beers** Ⓗ
Popular village pub where families are made welcome: a quiet lounge, a busy public bar and a large upstairs function room with games. At least six guest ales from all over the country feature on an ever-changing list. Taunton Traditional cider, plus Burrowhill in summer.
🏚 Q 🐂 🏵 ◑ ▮ 🅖 🔥 🗢 P 🍺

## Bath

### Bell Inn

103 Walcot Street
☎ (01225) 460426
11.30–11; 12–3, 7–10.30 Sun
**Bath Barnstormer; Courage Best Bitter, Directors; Fuller's London Pride; Smiles Best Bitter; John Smith's Bitter** Ⓗ
Pub with an open-plan bar, renowned for its music. It now boasts an Internet café for computer buffs at the rear of the premises. Bar billiards.
🏵 🔥

### Belvedere

25 Belvedere, Lansdown Road
☎ (01225) 330264
12–2.45, 5.30–11; 12–3, 7–10.30 Sun
**Draught Bass; Hancock's HB** Ⓗ
Welcoming, unpretentious local with a quiet lounge bar.
Q 🅖 🔥

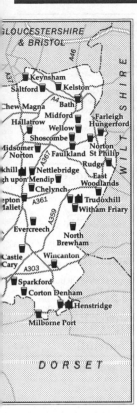

**Bladud Arms**

Gloucester Road, Lower
Swainswick (A46)
☎ (01225) 420152
11–3, 5.30–11; 12–3, 7–10.30 Sun
**Draught Bass; Butcombe
Bitter; Wickwar Brand Oak;
guest beer** Ⓗ
Long, lounge-bar local with a
public bar section. Skittle alley
and a garden patio area below
the main road. Eve meals finish
at 8. ☀ ⓓ ▶ ♣ P

**Cross Keys Inn**

Midford Road, Combe Down
(B3110) ☎ (01225) 832002
11–2.30 (3 Sat), 6–11; 12–3, 7–10.30
Sun
**Courage Best Bitter; Ushers
Best Bitter, Founders, seasonal
beers** Ⓗ
Attractive Bath stone
'roadhouse'-type pub on the
southern edge of the city: two
traditional bars, one with an
annexe for private parties and
meetings. An aviary is a
feature of the large, walled
garden. Good value food.
🚶 ☀ ⓓ ▶ ⓔ ☘ 日

**Fairfield Arms**

1 Fairfield Park Road, Fairfield
☎ (01225) 310594
11–2.30, 6–11; 11–11 Sat; 12–10.30 Sun

**Courage Best Bitter; Ushers
Best Bitter, seasonal beers** Ⓗ
Welcoming local, with an
award-winning garden, on the
north-eastern outskirts of the
city. ☀ ⓔ ♣

**Foresters Arms**

Bradford Road, Combe Down
☎ (01225) 837671
11.30–3.30, 5–11; 11.30–11 Sat;
12–3.30, 7.30–10.30 Sun
**Draught Bass; Courage Best
Bitter; Otter Bitter, Head;
guest beer** Ⓗ
Pub with a comfortable,
friendly main bar and an
adjacent skittle alley. One wall
of the public bar is dominated
by a vast, mirror-like mural of
itself which depicts many of
the regulars grouped around
the pool table. No food Sat.
ⓓ ⓔ ♣ P

**Golden Fleece**

1–3 Avon Buildings, Lower
Bristol Road ☎ (01225) 429572
11–2.30 (3 Sat), 5.30 (4.30 Fri, 6
Sat)–11; 12–3, 7–10.30 Sun
**Courage Georges BA, Best
Bitter; guest beer** Ⓗ
Popular, street-corner local,
convenient for Twerton Park
football ground. The two guest
beers change daily. Weekday
lunches. ⓓ ⓔ ♣ P

**Hatchetts**

6–7 Queen Street (off Queen
Sq) ☎ (01225) 425045
11–11; 12–3, 7–10.30 Sun
**Beer range varies** Ⓗ
Popular, sidestreet free house
with a selection of five, usually
higher gravity, beers which
change on a day-to-day basis.
Beer prices are well below
average for the area. No food
Sun. ⓓ ⇌ (Spa)

**King's Arms**

1 Monmouth Place
☎ (01225) 425418
11–11; 12–10.30 Sun
**Courage Best Bitter; Ruddles
County; Smiles Best Bitter;
Wadworth 6X; guest beer** Ⓗ
Former coaching inn on the last
leg of the London–Bristol
mailcoach run. A popular
weekend music venue for its
mainly local clientele. Good
value food. ☀ 🚶 ⓓ ⓔ ♣

**Larkhall Inn**

St Saviours Road, Larkhall (400
yds off A4/A46 jct)
☎ (01225) 425710
11–2 (2.30 Sat), 6–10.30 (11 Fri & Sat);
12–2, 7–10.30 Sun
**Courage Best Bitter,
Directors** Ⓗ
Distinctive local on the
outskirts of the city. Note the
early closing hours.
🚶 Q ☀ ⓔ ♣

**Old Crown**

1 Crown Hill, Weston
☎ (01225) 423371

11–2.30, 5–11; 11–11 Fri & Sat; 12–3,
7–10.30 Sun
**Draught Bass; Boddingtons
Bitter; Courage Best Bitter;
Smiles Best Bitter; guest
beer** Ⓗ
Originally a staging post
during the Civil War, this
pleasant village local has a
single, spacious bar and a
walled garden which is very
popular with families in
summer. No meals Sun eve.
☀ ⓓ ▶ ♣ ⅍

**Old Farmhouse**

1 Lansdown Road
☎ (01225) 316162
12–11; 7–10.30 Sun
**Badger Tanglefoot; Draught
Bass; Butcombe Bitter;
Wadworth IPA, 6X, Old
Timer** Ⓗ
Lively local of great character.
The unusual pub sign is a
caricature of its landlord. Live
music four nights a week. No
food Sun. Tiny car park.
🚶 ☀ ⓓ ▶ ⓔ ♣ P

**Pig & Fiddle**

2 Saracen Street
☎ (01225) 460868
11.30–3, 5–11; 11.30–11 Fri & Sat;
12–3, 7–10.30 Sun
**Ash Vine Bitter, Challenger,
Black Bess Porter, Hop &
Glory; guest beer** Ⓗ
Former fish restaurant, now an
extremely popular city-centre
pub: Ash Vine's only pub in
the Bath area, apart from the
White Hart at Trudoxhill.
Thatcher's cider. ☀ ⓓ ♣ ⌣

**Porter Butt**

York Place, London Road
☎ (01225) 425084
12–3, 5.30–11; 12–11 Sat; 12–5, 7–10.30
Sun
**Courage Georges BA, Best
Bitter; Fuller's London Pride;
guest beer** Ⓗ
Two-bar local with an upstairs
meeting room and regular live
music in the 'Walcot Palais'

---

🍺 **INDEPENDENT
BREWERIES**

**Ash Vine:** Trudoxhill

**Bath:** Henstridge

**Berrow:** Burnham-on-Sea

**Butcombe:** Butcombe

**Cotleigh:** Wiveliscombe

**Cottage:** West Lydford

**Exmoor:** Wiveliscombe

**Henstridge:** Henstridge

**Juwards:** Wellington

**Moor:** Ashcott

**Oakhill:** Oakhill

**RCH:** West Hewish

downstairs. Next to the local bus depot. No food Sun.
💺 🌀 🍺 ♣ P

### Star Inn ☆
23 The Vineyards (on Paragon, ½ mile NE of centre)
☎ (01225) 425072
12 (11 Sat)–2.30, 5.30–11; 12–3, 7–10.30 Sun
**Draught Bass** Ⓖ**; Exmoor Ale; Wadworth 6X; guest beer** Ⓗ
Enjoy the atmosphere of this classic town pub. The Bass is served from the jug.
Q 🌀 ♣

## Blagdon Hill

### Lamb & Flag
On unclassified road 3 miles S of Taunton ☎ (01823) 421736
12 (11.30 summer)–2.30, 6.30–11; 12–2.30, 7–10.30 Sun
**Boddingtons Bitter; Flowers Original; Greenalls Royal Wessex Bitter; Otter Bitter** Ⓗ
17th-century country pub with exposed beams, bar food, a restaurant and a large open fire. Friendly atmosphere. Skittle alley; large garden. Children welcome.
🏨 Q 🌙 🍺 ♣ P

Try also: **White Lion** (Free)

## Bridgwater

### Commercial Inn
Redgate Street (off A372)
☎ (01278) 426989
11–2.30, 7–11; 12–2.30, 7–10.30 Sun
**Butcombe Bitter; Castle Eden Ale; guest beer** Ⓗ
Popular local next to the station: a bar with a pool table, plus a lounge area, skittle alley and a garden. No food Sun. 💺 ⅄ & ⯊ ♣ P

### Fountain Inn
1 West Quay ☎ (01278) 424115
11.30 (11 Fri & Sat)–3, 6.30–11; 12–3, 7–10.30 Sun
**Badger Tanglefoot; Butcombe Bitter; Wadworth IPA, 6X, Old Timer; guest beer** Ⓗ
Single-roomed pub on the river, providing a friendly local feel in the town centre. Guest beers come from Wadworth's list. Good value bar snacks (not served Sun). Q & ⯊ ♣

Try also: **Cross Rifles**, Bath Rd (Free)

## Burnham-on-Sea

### Royal Clarence Hotel
31 The Esplanade
☎ (01278) 783138
11–11; 12–10.30 Sun
**RCH PG Steam, Pitchfork, East St Cream, Old Slug Porter; guest beers** Ⓗ
The RCH Brewery tap: a large seafront hotel catering for a wide range of customers. It

hosts two major beer festivals each year (Feb and Oct) and stocks the full range of RCH beers, plus a good selection of bottled beers. The Addlestones cider is under gas; try the Crossmans or Wilkins Traditional.
Q 🍃 🛏 🌙 & 🅰 ⟳ ⅄

## Cannington

### Malt Shovel Inn
Blackmoor Lane (off A39)
☎ (01278) 653432
11.30–3, 6.30 (7 winter)–11; 12–3, 7–10.30 Sun
**Butcombe Bitter; Morland Old Speckled Hen; John Smith's Bitter; guest beer** Ⓗ
Family-run free house overlooking the Quantocks. Rich's and Larie's cider available. No meals Sun eve. Short mat bowls played.
🏨 Q 🍃 🛏 🌙 & ⟳ P

## Castle Cary

### George Hotel
Market Place ☎ (01963) 350761
10.30–3, 6–11; 12–2.30, 7–10.30 Sun
**Draught Bass; Butcombe Bitter** Ⓗ
Thatched, Grade II coaching inn (1470), on the Leyland trail; walkers welcome. This privately-owned hotel enjoys a good reputation for food.
🏨 Q 🛏 🌙 & P

Try also: **Horse Pond**, The Triangle (Free)

## Chard

### Bell & Crown
Combe Street, Crimchard
☎ (01460) 62470
11–3 (not Mon), 7–11; 12–3, 7–10.30 Sun
**Shepherd Neame Best Bitter; guest beers** Ⓗ
Ten minutes' walk from the town centre, this popular local still has gas lighting. Good value food (not served Sun/ Mon eves). Occasional beer festivals. Q 🌙 🌙 ♣ P

## Chelynch

### Poachers Pocket
½ mile N of A361 at Doulting OS648438 ☎ (01749) 880220
11.30 (12 Mon)–2.30, 6–11; 12–3, 7–10.30 Sun
**Butcombe Bitter; Cottage Southern Bitter or Oakhill Best Bitter; Wadworth 6X** Ⓗ
Part-14th-century pub in a small village some way from the A361. Though mostly given over to food, it remains popular as a locals' drinking pub. The large garden is well patronised summer weekends. Wilkins cider.
🏨 Q 🌙 🌙 ♣ ⟳ P

## Chew Magna

### Bear & Swan
South Parade
☎ (01275) 332577
12–3, 6–11; 12–11 Sat; 12–3, 7–10.30 Sun
**Courage Georges BA, Best Bitter; Mole's Tap; John Smith's Bitter** Ⓗ
Friendly, two-bar country local. Old maps decorate the walls in the lounge. Generous portions of food.
🏨 Q 🌙 & P

## Chew Stoke

### Stoke Inn
Old Bristol Road
☎ (01275) 332120
11.30–2.30, 6–11; 11–11 Sat; 12–5, 7–10.30 Sun
**Draught Bass; Butcombe Bitter; Courage Best Bitter; Smiles Best Bitter; guest beer** Ⓗ
Large, stone-built pub near Chew Valley lake. Traditional public bar; the lounge bar is popular with diners. Skittles and table skittles played.
🏨 Q 🌙 🌀 & ⯊ ⟳ P

## Churchill

### Crown Inn
The Batch, Skinners Lane (off A38 S of A368 jct)
☎ (01934) 852995
11.30–3.30, 5–11; 12–4, 7–10.30 Sun
**Draught Bass; Cotleigh Tawny; RCH PG Steam; guest beers** Ⓖ
Characterful and unspoilt pub down a small lane, with three indoor, and two outdoor, drinking areas. The two bars have real fires and can get busy at times. Always a good range of beers, including local independents. The house beer, 'Batch Bitter' is Cotleigh Harrier. Good food; eve meals must be booked.
🏨 Q 🌙 🅰 ♣ P

## Compton Martin

### Ring O' Bells
Bath Road ☎ (01761) 221284
11.30–2.30, 6.30–11; 12–3, 7–10.30 Sun
**Draught Bass** Ⓖ**; Butcombe Bitter; Wadworth 6X; guest beer** Ⓗ
Pleasant, 200-year-old, two-bar pub with wonderful food, an excellent family room and a large, safe garden.
🏨 Q 🍃 🌙 🌙 ♣ P ⅄

## Corton Denham

### Queens Arms Inn
3 miles S of A303
☎ (01963) 220317
12–2.30, 7–11; 11.30–2.30, 6–11 Fri, Sat & summer; 12–3, 7–10.30 Sun

Cotleigh Tawny; RCH PG
Steam; guest beer Ⓗ
Comfortable, rural pub in
superb walking country. Guest
ales of the month are featured
on a chalkboard. Good choice
of specials on the food menu.
Taunton and Inch's cider. Well
worth a visit. ⚲ Q ✿ 🛏 ◑ ▶
🍴 ♿ ♣ ◔ P

## Culmhead

### Holman Clavel
On B3170 OS222162
☎ (01823) 421432
11–3 (not Tue), 6–11; 12–3, 7–10.30
Sun
Butcombe Bitter; Cotleigh
Tawny; guest beers Ⓗ
Reputedly 14th-century inn on
the Blackdowns, which is
haunted by a ghost named
Charlie (a defrocked monk).
Beamed ceilings and log fires
feature; families are welcome.
Good food (not served Sun
eve). Live music Fri/Sat eves;
jazz Sun lunch. Camping and
caravan site close by.
⚲ ✿ ◑ ▶ ♣ ♠ P

## East Harptree

### Castle of Comfort
On B3143, ½ mile N of B3135
☎ (01761) 221321
12–2.30, 7–11; 12–2.30, 7–10.30 Sun
Draught Bass; Butcombe
Bitter; guest beers Ⓗ
Stone-built coaching inn on the
old Roman road. Two bars
serve up to four real ales, with
regularly changing guest beers,
and good food. The huge
garden has children's playthings. ⚲ ✿ ◑ ▶ ♣ P

## East Lambrook

### Rose & Crown
Off A303 ☎ (01460) 240433
11.30–2.30 (3 Sat), 7–11; 12–3, 7–10.30
Sun
Otter Ale; Worthington Bitter;
guest beers Ⓗ
Traditional, oak-beamed,
two-bar village pub, one of the
few in Somerset to stock a
guest dark mild. Good value
food (not served Sun eve in
winter). Burrowhill cider.
Children's certificate.
⚲ Q ✿ ◑ ▶ ♠ ♣ ◔ P ⚥ 🍴

## East Lyng

### Rose & Crown
☎ (01823) 698235
11–2.30, 6.30–11; 12–3, 7–10.30 Sun
Butcombe Bitter; Hardy
Country; Royal Oak Ⓗ
Comfortable, civilised village
pub, popular with locals and
visitors alike. It features a large
stone fireplace, beams and
antique furniture. A small
restaurant area leads off the

main bar. The food is good and
the garden pleasant.
⚲ Q ✿ 🛏 ◑ ▶ ♠ ♣ P

## East Woodlands

### Horse & Groom
1 Mile SE of A361/B3092 jct
OS792445 ☎ (01373) 462802
11.30 (12 Mon)–2.30, 6.30–11; 12–3,
7–10.30 Sun
Bateman XB; Butcombe Bitter;
Wadworth 6X; guest beer Ⓖ
17th-century inn on the
western edge of Longleat
estate: a cosy bar with an open
fireplace and a flagstone floor,
plus a small dining room. A
new extension incorporates a
family room. No food Sun eve
or Mon. ⚲ Q ✿ ✿ ◑ ▶ ♣ P

## Evercreech

### Bell Inn
Bruton Road (B3081)
☎ (01749) 830287
11.30–3, 6.30–11; 11.30–11 Sat; 12–3,
7–10.30 Sun
Butcombe Bitter; Cottage Our
Ken; guest beer Ⓗ
17th-century inn with roaring
fires: one bar with a restaurant
area, plus a games room.
⚲ Q ◑ ▶ 🛏 ♣ P

## Farleigh Hungerford

### Hungerford Arms
On A366 ☎ (01225) 752411
11–3, 6–11; 12–3, 7–10.30 Sun
Draught Bass; Ushers Best
Bitter; Wadworth 6X; guest
beer Ⓗ
Pub with a long lounge bar and
a separate garden lobby,
overlooking Farleigh Castle.
Bar billiards table.
⚲ Q ✿ ✿ ◑ ▶ ♣ P

## Faulkland

### Tuckers Grave Inn ☆
On A366, 1 mile E of village.
☎ (01373) 834230
12–3, 6–11; 12–3, 7–10.30 Sun
Draught Bass; Butcombe
Bitter Ⓖ
The burial site of a suicide in
1747; a former cottage that has
doubled as an inn for over 200
years. Three old-fashioned
rooms without a bar counter;
the stillage is set in a small bay
window. The story of the
unfortunate Edward Tucker
can be found above the parlour
fireplace.
⚲ Q ✿ 🛏 ♠ ♣ ◔ P

## Fitzhead

### Fitzhead Inn
Off B3187 at Milverton
OS285124 ☎ (01823) 400667
12–3, 7–11; 12–3, 7–10.30 Sun
Cotleigh Tawny; guest
beers Ⓗ

Cosy village pub used by
regulars as well as those
attracted by excellent food
(booking recommended).
Three guest beers always
available; Bolhayes cider.
⚲ Q ✿ ✿ ◑ ▶ ♠ ♣ ◔

## Forches Corner

### Merry Harriers
OS184171
☎ (01823) 421270
11–2.30 (not Mon), 6.30–11; 12–3,
7–10.30 Sun
Badger Tanglefoot; Exmoor
Gold; Fuller's London Pride;
Otter Bitter; guest beer Ⓗ
Isolated, but friendly, old inn
on the Devon border, high on
the Blackdown Hills. The large
garden has a children's play
area. Live music Thu and Sat.
Lunchtime snacks.
⚲ ✿ ♠ ♣ P

## Glastonbury

### Who'd a Thought It
17 Northload Street
☎ (01458) 834460
11–2.30, 6–11; 12–2.30, 7–10.30 Sun
Draught Bass; Hardy Country;
Palmers IPA; guest beer Ⓗ
Attractive town pub featuring
numerous collections and
war-time posters. It has its own
phonebox inside, along with a
well. The accommodation is
recommended. Regional *Loo of
the Year* winner for the second
time (wheelchair WC).
⚲ Q ✿ 🛏 ◑ ▶ ♠ ♣ P ⚥

Try also: Beckets, High St
(Wadworth)

## Hallatrow

### Old Station Inn
Wells Road (A39, 400 yds from
A37 jct)
☎ (01761) 452228
11–3, 5 (6 Sat)–11; 12–3, 7–10.30 Sun
Draught Bass; Mole's Best
Bitter; Oakhill Best Bitter;
Otter Ale; Wadworth 6X; guest
beer Ⓗ
Friendly village free house,
where bric-a-brac covers every
wall and ceiling.
⚲ Q ✿ 🛏 ◑ ▶ ♣ P

## Hardington Moor

### Royal Oak
Moor Lane (off A30)
☎ (01935) 862354
12–3 (not Mon), 7–11; 12–3, 7–10.30
Sun
Butcombe Bitter; Hook
Norton Old Hooky; guest
beers Ⓗ
Former farmhouse offering a
warm and friendly atmosphere
and a good choice of snacks
and meals (not served Mon).
Three ciders are usually
available. Skittle alley for

functions. Camping by arrangement.
🏕 Q ❀ ◖ ▲ ♣ ⌂ P

# Henstridge

## Bird in Hand

Ash Walk (off A30)
☎ (01963) 362255
11–2.30, 5.30–11; 11–11 Sat; 12–3, 7–10.30 Sun
**Draught Bass; Smiles Brewery Bitter; guest beer** Ⓗ
Classic village pub where wooden beams, a low roof and suitable lighting create a pleasant atmosphere. Taunton Traditional cider. No food Sun.
❀ ◖ 🍴 ♿ ▲ ♣ ⌂ P

# Highbridge

## Coopers Arms

Market Street
☎ (01278) 783562
11–3.30, 5.15–11; 12–3, 7.30–10.30 Sun
**Berrow Topsy Turvy; Fuller's London Pride; Ringwood Fortyniner; guest beers** Ⓗ
Large, long-roomed pub with two lounges and a bar skittle alley. A large blackboard displays the ever-changing guest beers (at least four plus two house beers, usually from big brewers). The station is on the doorstep. No food.
❀ 🍴 ♿ ▲ ⇌ ♣ P

# Kelston

## Old Crown Inn

Bath Road ☎ (01225) 423032
11.30–2.30 (3 Sat), 5–11; 12–3, 7–10.30 Sun
**Draught Bass; Butcombe Bitter; Smiles Best Bitter; Wadworth 6X** Ⓗ
Attractively restored, stone-built, 18th-century inn with a flagstone floor and cosy drinking areas. Note the original bank of unusual beer engines. Large garden at the rear. Children under 14 are not allowed in the bar or restaurant. No food Sun.
🏕 Q ❀ ◖ ▲ ♣ P

# Keynsham

## Ship Inn

Temple Street
☎ (0117) 986 9841
12–3 (5 Sat), 7–11; 12–4, 7–10.30 Sun
**Draught Bass; Courage Georges BA, Best Bitter; guest beers** Ⓗ
Friendly, popular, two-bar community pub near the high street. Barbecues in summer. Good value food. Shove ha'penny played. Normally at least two or three guest beers available.
❀ ◖ ⇌ ♣ P

# Knapp

## Rising Sun

Off A361, then follow signs OS301254
☎ (01823) 490436
11–2.30, 6.30–11; 12–3, 7–10.30 Sun
**Draught Bass; Boddingtons Bitter; Exmoor Ale** Ⓗ
15th-century inn: a fine example of a Somerset longhouse with many original features, including two inglenooks. Winner of many national awards for its extensive fish menu, it has a busy weekend food trade (eve meals also in the restaurant). Local farm cider in summer.
🐕 ▶ ⌂

# Leigh upon Mendip

## Bell

High Street
☎ (01373) 812316
12–3, 7–11; 12–3, 7–10.30 Sun
**Draught Bass; Butcombe Bitter; Wadworth IPA, 6X** Ⓗ
Much altered and extended village inn, now comfortably furnished, with an emphasis on the food trade (separate restaurant, but food is served throughout the pub). Friendly locals' atmosphere at the bar.
🏕 ❀ ◖ ▶ ♣ P

# Luxborough

## Royal Oak

☎ (01984) 640319
11–2.30, 6–11; 12–3, 7–10.30 Sun
**Cotleigh Tawny** Ⓖ**; Exmoor Gold; Flowers IPA** Ⓗ**; guest beers** Ⓗ/Ⓖ
Unspoilt, rural village pub at the heart of the Brendon Hills (superb walks). Flagstone floors, open log fires, beamed ceilings and noted, home-cooked food are features. Folk club Fri. Dogs welcome. Rich's and Cheddar Valley cider. Good B&B.
🏕 Q ❀ 🛏 ◖ ▶ ♣ ⌂ P

# Middlezoy

## George Inn

42 Main Road
☎ (01823) 698215
12–3 (not Mon or Tue), 7–11; 12–3, 7–10.30 Sun
**Butcombe Bitter; Courage Best Bitter; guest beers** Ⓗ
Thriving village pub, now owned by a local couple. Old beams and a flagged floor enhance the main bar; there is also a dining room and a large skittle alley with a bar. Good value food (not served Sun eve). Lanes cider in summer.
🏕 🐕 ❀ 🛏 ◖ ▶ ♿ ▲ ♣ ⌂ P 🚲

# Midford

## Hope & Anchor

On B3110 ☎ (01225) 832296
12–2.30, 6.30–11; 12–3, 7–10.30 Sun
**Draught Bass; Butcombe Bitter; Mole's Best Bitter** Ⓗ
Large pub, split into eating and drinking areas, with a patio at the rear. Next to the car park are the remains of Midford railway station on the old Somerset and Dorset line.
🏕 Q ❀ ◖ ▶ P

# Midsomer Norton

## White Hart ☆

The Island ☎ (01761) 418270
11–3, 5.30–11; 12–3, 7–10.30 Sun
**Draught Bass** Ⓖ
Large, rambling building with several rooms, retaining many of its original Victorian features. No food Sun. Skittles played. 🏕 🐕 ◖ ♿ ♣ ⌂

# Milborne Port

## Queen's Head

High Street (A30)
☎ (01963) 250314
11–11; 12–10.30 Sun
**Butcombe Bitter; Flowers Original** or **Ringwood Fortyniner; guest beers** Ⓗ
Busy, multi-room village pub with a restaurant and a skittle alley/function room, plus a pleasant outdoor courtyard drinking area and a garden. Good food (especially the curries). A mystery beer is featured each week.
🏕 Q 🐕 ❀ 🛏 ◖ ▶ ♿ ♣ ⌂ P

# Moorlinch

## Ring o' Bells

Pit Hill Lane ☎ (01458) 210358
12–2.30 (3 Sat; not Mon; not Tue–Thu in winter), 7–11; 12–3, 7–10.30 Sun
**Draught Bass; guest beers** Ⓗ
Traditional village local with a welcoming atmosphere, near Moorlinch Vineyard: a friendly lounge and a lively bar with games. Superb range of home-cooked, farmhouse-style food. Six beers, mostly from micros, plus Wilkins cider.
🏕 Q ❀ ◖ ▶ ♣ ⌂ P

# Nailsea

## Blue Flame

West End OS449690
☎ (01275) 856910
12–3 (4.30 Sat), 6–11; 12–4.30, 7–10.30 Sun
**Draught Bass** Ⓗ**; Bath Gem** Ⓖ**; Oakhill Best Bitter** Ⓗ**; Smiles Best Bitter, Exhibition** Ⓖ
Wonderful, small, cottage-style pub popular with a mixed clientele.
🏕 Q 🐕 ❀ ♿ ♿ ▲ ♣ ⌂ P

## Nether Stowey

### Rose & Crown

St Mary Street
☎ (01278) 732265
12–3, 6–11; 12–3, 7–10.30 Sun
**Cotleigh Barn Owl; Oakhill Yeoman** H
16th-century coaching inn at the village centre; a popular multi-roomed pub with a public bar and a strong local following. Large function room upstairs. Good food. Lanes cider.
⚫ ❀ 🛏 ◑ ▶ ⊟ ♣ ↻

## Nettlebridge

### Nettlebridge Inn

On A367, 1 mile N of Oakhill
☎ (01749) 841360
11.30–2.30, 5–11; 12–11 Sat; 12–10.30 Sun
**Oakhill Mendip Gold, Best Bitter, Black Magic Stout, Yeoman; guest beer** H
Big roadside pub in a pretty valley on the edge of the Mendips. Priority is given to food in the large main bar; bar snacks only in the smaller 'Bridges Bar', which has been given a sophisticated city pub decor. ❀ 🛏 ◑ ▶ ⊟ P

## North Brewham

### Old Red Lion

On Maiden Bradley–Bruton road OS722368
☎ (01749) 850287
11–3, 6–11; 12–3, 7–10.30 Sun
**Butcombe Bitter; guest beer** H
Stone-built, former farmhouse in an isolated rural setting. The bar is in the old dairy, with flagged floors. Two regular guest beers, one is usually a mild during summer.
⚫ Q ❀ ◑ ▶ ♣ ↻ P

## North Curry

### Bird in Hand

Queen Square
☎ (01823) 490248
12–3, 7–11; 12–3, 7–10.30 Sun
**Badger Tanglefoot; Butcombe Bitter; Otter Ale; Teignworthy Reel Ale; guest beers** H
Superbly renovated village local with low beams and ever-changing guest ales. The pub runs many special eves and produces a *What's On* news-sheet for the village. Rich's farmhouse cider.
⚫ Q ❀ ◑ ▶ & ▲ ♣ ↻ P

## Norton St Philip

### Fleur de Lys

High Street (B3110)
☎ (01373) 834333

11–3, 5–11; 11–11 Sat; 12–3, 7–10.30 Sun
**Draught Bass; Oakhill Best Bitter; Wadworth 6X; Worthington Bitter** H
Ancient stone building, part of which dates from the 13th century. A recent extensive, but mainly sympathetic refurbishment has unfortunately left the resited bar blocking the old passageway through which the pub ghost was said to pass on his way to the gallows.
⚫ Q ⚫ ❀ ◑ ▶ ♣ P

## Pitminster

### Queen's Arms

Off B3170 at Corfe
☎ (01823) 421529
11–3, 5–11; 11–11 Sat; 12–3, 7–10.30 Sun
**Cotleigh Tawny; guest beers** H
Cosy, popular village pub. The main bar is divided by a black iron, wood-burning stove. Usually six guest beers, mainly from small brewers. Interesting bar meals plus an excellent restaurant. Large function room. Cider in summer. Camping by arrangement.
⚫ Q ❀ 🛏 ◑ ▶ & ▲ ↻ P

## Pitney

### Halfway House

☎ (01458) 252513
11.30–2.30, 5.30–11; 12–3, 7–10.30 Sun
**Berrow Topsy Turvy; Butcombe Bitter; Cotleigh Tawny; Oakhill Best Bitter; Teignworthy Reel Ale; guest beers** G
Old village pub featuring real fires, flagstone floors and rudimentary wooden furniture. It always has six–nine beers available, mostly from South-West micros. Try the home-cooked curries (no food Sun). A real gem; CAMRA *National Pub of the Year 1996*.
⚫ Q ⚫ ❀ ◑ ▶ ▲ ♣ P

## Porlock

### Ship Inn

High Street
☎ (01643) 862507
10.30–3, 5.30–11; 12–3, 7–10.30 Sun
**Draught Bass; Cotleigh Barn Owl (summer); Old Buzzard (winter); Courage Best Bitter; guest beer** H
Old pub mentioned in *Lorna Doone*. A traditional bar area attracts the locals; the restaurant specialises in local food cooked on an Aga. Perry's cider. Good for families.
⚫ ⚫ ❀ 🛏 ◑ ▶ & ▲ ♣ ↻ P

## Priddy

### New Inn

☎ (01749) 676465
11.30 (12 Mon)–2.30, 7–11; 12–2.30, 7–10.30 Sun
**Draught Bass; Hardy Country; Wadworth 6X** H
15th-century farmhouse on the village green, with flagstoned bars. Warm and friendly, it enjoys a reputation for good food, including a choice of vegetarian meals. Popular at weekends. Wilkins cider.
⚫ Q ⚫ ❀ 🛏 ◑ ▶ & ▲ ♣ ↻ P

## Redhill

### Bungalow Inn

Winford Lane (½ mile off A38, 1 mile S of Bristol Airport)
OS513640 ☎ (01275) 472386
12–3, 5.30–11; 12–11 Fri, Sat & summer; 12–10.30 Sun
**Draught Bass** E; **Wadworth IPA, 6X; guest beer** H
Pub with two cosy bars and a separate function room. Handy for Bristol Airport.
⚫ ❀ ◑ ▲ ♣ P

## Rockwell Green

### Weavers Arms

102 Rockwell Green
☎ (01823) 662466
11–2.30, 6–11; 11–11 Fri & Sat; 12–2.30, 7–10.30 Sun
**Boddingtons Bitter; Castle Eden Ale; Flowers IPA, Original; Whitbread Fuggles IPA; guest beer** H
Comfortable village pub with several drinking areas enjoying a busy local trade. Check the new family room is ready before taking children. Whitbread cask collection guest beers.
⚫ ⚫ ❀ ▲ ♣ ↻ P

## Rowberrow

### Swan Inn

☎ (01934) 852371
12–3, 6–11; 12–2.30, 7–10.30 Sun
**Draught Bass; Butcombe Bitter; Wadworth 6X; guest beers** H
Former cider house converted from three stone cottages, now housing two bars and a large open fireplace. No food Sun eve. ⚫ Q ❀ ◑ ▶ P

## Rudge

### Full Moon

1 mile N of A36 bypass at Standerwick OS829518
☎ (01373) 830936
12–3, 6–11; 12–3, 7–10.30 Sun
**Draught Bass; Butcombe Bitter; Wadworth 6X** H
Splendid, 300-year-old building, greatly extended in 1991 but retaining most of its

original features, including stone floors. The emphasis is on food trade, the skittle alley, families and accommodation. Country and western music Sun eve (when no food is served).
♨ Q ❀ 🚐 ◖❿ 🍴 ♣ ⏚ P

## St Georges

### Woolpack Inn
Shepherds Way (off M5 jct 21; take 1st left off Weston Rd) ☎ (01934) 521670
12–2.30 (3 Sat), 6–11; 12–3, 7–10.30 Sun
**Courage Best Bitter; guest beers** H
Warm, friendly, former 17th-century coaching house and woolpacking station, well-patronised by locals. Two bars and a restaurant serve good value, high quality food. Three changing guest beers; up to five in summer. ♨ Q ❀ ◖❿ 🍴 ≈ (Worle) ♣ P

## Saltford

### Bird in Hand
High Street ☎ (01225) 873335
11–3, 6.30 (6 Fri & Sat)–11; 12–4, 7–10.30 Sun
**Draught Bass; Courage Best Bitter; Wadworth 6X; guest beers** H
Food-oriented pub with access from the Bristol–Bath Cycle Track. The no-smoking conservatory for diners offers a good view over the Avon Valley and an excellent value, varied menu. Petanque played.
Q ❀ ❀ ◖❿ ♣ ⏚ P

## Seavington St Michael

### Volunteer
On old A303 ☎ (01460) 240126
12–2.30 (not Mon), 5.30–11; 12–11 Sat; 12–3, 7–10.30 Sun
**Cottage S&D; guest beers** H
Friendly, family-run, roadside pub with two bars; the lounge has low beams and a central fireplace. Good food, including Sun lunches and Fri eve curries (no food Mon). ♨ Q ◖❿ ♣ P

## Shepton Mallet

### Kings Arms
Leg Square ☎ (01749) 343781
11–11; 12–10.30 Sun
**Ansells Bitter; Hardy Country; Ind Coope Burton Ale** H
Originally 17th-century, but much altered, this is a pub of some character. Boasting a large games room with a skittle alley it also has a cosy snug and a large main bar where food dominates. A

conservatory looks out onto a paved, sheltered courtyard.
❀ 🚐 ◖❿ ⏚ ♣ P

## Shoscombe

### Apple Tree
1 mile S of A367 bypass at Peasedown OS712565 ☎ (01761) 432263
7–11; 12–3, 7–11 Sat; 12–3, 7–10.30 Sun
**Draught Bass; Oakhill Best Bitter; guest beer** G
Friendly village local, nestling in a hidden valley; well worth seeking out for the warm welcome. Note: closed weekday lunch; meals available Sat lunch. Thatcher's cider.
♨ ❀ ♣ ⏚ P

## Sparkford

### Sparkford Inn
Off A303 ☎ (01963) 440218
11–2.30, 6.30–11; 12–3, 7–10.30 Sun
**Draught Bass; Worthington Bitter; guest beers** H
15th-century coaching inn, retaining many of its original features, including several rooms and corridors. Catering for all the family, it has indoor and outdoor children's play areas. Inch's cider in summer. Regular music eves.
♨ Q ≈ ❀ 🚐 ◖❿ 🍴 ♣ ⏚ P

## Stogumber

### White Horse Inn
The Square ☎ (01984) 656277
11–2.30, 6–11; 12–2.30, 7–10.30 Sun
**Cotleigh Tawny; Exmoor Ale** H
Traditional pub in an historic village. Accommodation and a restaurant are housed in the adjoining market house. Look out for memorabilia of the long-defunct Stogumber Brewery. Sheppy's cider in summer. Limited parking. The family room is not always open – check. (WSR) ♣ ⏚ P

## Taunton

### Hankridge Arms
Hankridge Way, Riverside (off M5 jct 25) ☎ (01823) 444405
11–11; 12–10.30 Sun
**Badger Dorset Best, Tanglefoot** H
Superbly converted, listed farmhouse on the new trading area just off the motorway. Many original features have been retained. Good food; large function room. The house beer, Hankridge Ale, is brewed by Badger.
♨ Q ❀ ◖❿ ⏚ P

### Masons Arms
Magdalene Street ☎ (01823) 288916
10–3, 5 (6 Sat)–11; 12–3, 7–10.30 Sun
**Draught Bass; Exe Valley Dob's Best Bitter; guest beers** H
Comfortable, one-bar pub with a relaxing atmosphere, away from the main streets. Fresh food is always available, including grillstone steaks. Self-catering flat to let.
Q 🚐 ◖❿ ≈ ♣

### Minstrels
Castle Hotel, Castle Green (entrance in Castle Bow, just off town centre) ☎ (01823) 337780
11–3, 7–11; 11–11 Thu–Sat; 7–10.30 Sun, closed Sun lunch
**Draught Bass; Hardy Dorchester; guest beers** H
Town-centre bar, part of the Castle Hotel but run separately. It features wooden beams and high ceilings. Live music two eves a week. Popular for lunch, served Mon–Sat. ♨ 🚐 ◖ ≈

### Wood Street Inn
Wood Street ☎ (01823) 333011
11–3 (4 Sat), 6–11; 12–2.30, 7–10.30 Sun
**Beer range varies** H
Basic, backstreet local, 14 years in the *Guide* and popular with all ages. The three changing beers tend to be from local independent breweries; Lanes cider in summer. Large public car park opposite. Very reasonable accommodation.
❀ 🚐 ♿ ≈ ♣ ⏚ 🛏

## Trudoxhill

### White Hart
½ mile S of A361 at Nunney Catch OS749438 ☎ (01373) 836324
12–3, 7 (6.30 Fri & Sat)–11; 12–3, 7–10.30 Sun
**Ash Vine Bitter, Challenger, Hop & Glory; Wadworth 6X; guest beers** H
Comfortable, food-oriented, open-plan village pub with exposed beams and a large fireplace. Ash Vine Brewery is behind the pub. The beer range includes Ash Vine's monthly special brews. Thatcher's cider.
♨ ❀ ◖❿ ⏚ P

## Watchet

### West Somerset Hotel
Swain Street ☎ (01984) 634434
11–11; 12–10.30 Sun
**Courage Directors; John Smith's Bitter; guest beer** H
Lively local; a former coaching inn at an historic port. Accommodation and matches are arranged for touring cricket teams. Good value food.
≈ ❀ 🚐 ◖❿ 🍴 ♿ ♣

## Waterrow

### Rock Inn
On B3227 ☎ (01984) 623293
11–2.30, 6–11; 12–3, 7–10.30 Sun
**Cotleigh Tawny; Exmoor Gold; John Smith's Bitter** H
Interesting old inn, set against a rockface, which forms the rear wall of part of the bar area (public style at one end with a lounge and restaurant at the other). Sheppy's cider in summer.
🏨 Q 🛏 ◐ ▮ ♿ ▲ ♣ ○ P

## Wellington

### Cottage Inn
Champford Lane (200 yds from Mantle St) ☎ (01823) 664650
11–3, 6–11; 12–3, 7–10.30 Sun
**Draught Bass; Cotleigh Tawny; Fuller's London Pride; John Smith's Bitter; guest beers** H
Popular, friendly pub close to the town centre and cinema. Usually at least three guest beers served, plus good value, basic bar lunches.
❀ ◐ ▮ ♣ P

## Wellow

### Fox & Badger
Railway Lane (2 miles W of B3110 at Hinton Charterhouse) OS741583 ☎ (01225) 832293
11–3, 6–11; 11–11 Fri & Sat; 12–10.30 Sun
**Boddingtons Bitter; Butcombe Bitter; Exmoor Ale; Wadworth 6X; guest beer** H
Pretty Wellow's only pub: a two-bar local where, unusually, the public bar is carpeted and the lounge bar is flagstoned. It can be difficult to park. 🏨 Q ❀ ◐ ▮ ▱ ♣ ○

## Wells

### Britannia Inn
Bath Road (B3139)
☎ (01749) 672033
11–3, 5–11; 11–11 Sat; 12–3, 7–10.30 Sun
**Butcombe Bitter; Ushers Best Bitter; guest beer** H
'Top of the town' local serving housing estates to the north end of the city. Eve meals Fri–Sun. Wilkins cider.
Q ◐ ▮ ♿ ○ P

## West Bagborough

### Rising Sun
☎ (01823) 432575
12–3, 7–11 (closed winter Mon); 12–3, 7–10.30 Sun
**Cotleigh Tawny, Old Buzzard, Exmoor XV; Oakhill Bitter; guest beer** H
16th-century, country pub with oak beams and a log fire. Set in the Quantock Hills – ideal for walkers and cyclists. Families welcome. Good food. Overnight accommodation includes one room for guests with disabilities. Lanes cider.
🏨 ❀ 🛏 ◐ ▮ ♿ ▲ ♣ ○

## Weston-super-Mare

### Major from Glengarry
10–14 Upper Church Road (off the seafront) ☎ (01934) 629260
11–3, 6–11 (11–11 summer); 12–3, 7–10.30 Sun
**Butcombe Bitter** H**; Wadworth IPA, 6X, Old Timer** G**; guest beers** H
Friendly, open-plan pub, popular with locals and enjoying a busy summer trade.
Q ❀ ◐ ▮ ♣ P

## Williton

### Foresters Arms
55 Long Street
☎ (01984) 632508
11–11; 12–3, 7–10.30 Sun
**Cotleigh Tawny; Flowers Original; John Smith's Bitter; guest beers** H
17th-century inn close to the West Somerset Railway station; an ideal base for walking the Quantock Hills. Reputed to be haunted by the ghost of a 14-year-old girl from the neighbouring old workhouse.
🏨 🛏 ❀ 🛏 ◐ ▮ ▲ 🚄 (WSR) ♣ ○ P

## Wincanton

### Bear Inn
12 Market Place
☎ (01963) 32581
11–2.30, 5.30–11; 12–3, 7–10.30 Sun
**Draught Bass; Worthington Bitter; guest beer** H
Large, former coaching inn, with several drinking areas, plus a substantial games and function room. Weekly archery in the skittle alley. Guest beers include a session, as well as a stronger, beer.
🏨 Q 🛏 ◐ ▮ ♣ P

### Red Lion Inn
Market Place ☎ (01963) 33095
11–11; 12–3, 7–10.30 Sun
**Draught Bass; Oakhill Best Bitter; Worthington Bitter; Young's Special** H
Welcoming, one-bar, town-centre pub with a congenial atmosphere; popular with locals and visitors alike.
◐ ♣ ○

## Witham Friary

### Seymour Arms ☆
On minor road, off B3092, by old station ☎ (01749) 850742
11–3, 6–11; 12–3, 7–10.30 Sun
**Ushers Best Bitter** H
Old village local, unspoilt by progress, with a central serving hatch and a fine garden. Rich's cider on gravity.
🏨 Q ❀ ▱ ▲ ♣ ○

## Wiveliscombe

### Bear Inn
10 North Street
☎ (01984) 623537
11–3, 6–11; 11–11 Sat & summer; 12–10.30 Sun
**Cotleigh Barn Owl; Exmoor Gold; guest beers** H
Former 17th-century coaching inn, near the town centre: a friendly bar and a dining room serving good, home-cooked food. It organises beer lovers' weekends in conjunction with local breweries. Local farm cider in summer. Skittles played.
🏨 🛏 ❀ 🛏 ◐ ▮ ♣ ○ P

## Wookey

### Burcott Inn
☎ (01749) 673874
11–2.30 (3 Sat), 6–11; 12–2.30, 7–10.30 Sun
**Cotleigh Tawny; RCH PG Steam; guest beers** H
Popular roadside pub with a friendly atmosphere. The L-shaped bar has a copper serving top. There is also a small games room and a good-sized garden featuring an old cider press. Good food (no meals Sun eve).
🏨 Q 🛏 ❀ ◐ ▮ ♿ ♣ P

## Wrantage

### Canal Inn
On A378, 1½ miles from A358 jct
☎ (01823) 480210
12–2.30, 7–11; 12–3, 7–10.30 Sun
**Exmoor Ale; Flowers Original; guest beer** H
16th-century country pub with a friendly atmosphere; families welcome. Bar food available seven days a week. Coach parties by arrangement. Children's outdoor play area. Skittle alley; darts played.
🏨 ❀ ◐ ▮ ♣ ○

## Yeovil

### Armoury
1 The Park
☎ (01935) 71047
12–2.30, 6 (6.30 Mon & Tue)–11; 11–11 Fri & Sat; 12–3, 7–10.30 Sun
**Adnams Broadside; Butcombe Bitter; Wadworth 6X; guest beer** H
Lively, simply furnished town pub, formerly an armoury. Snacks and salads available lunchtimes (not Sun). Live bands play alternate Sat eves. Taunton cider.
Q ❀ ♿ ♣ ○ P

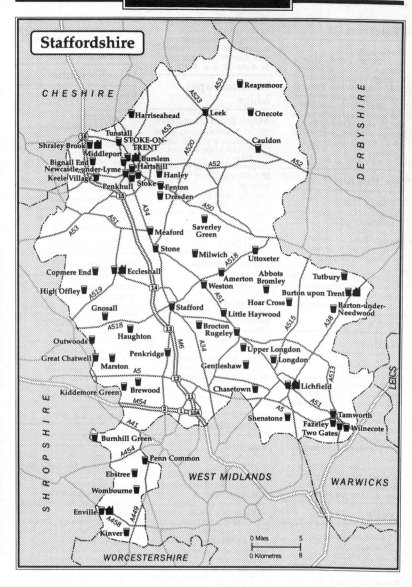

## Staffordshire

*CHESHIRE*

Reapsmoor

Harriseahead

Leek

Onecote

Tunstall

STOKE-ON-TRENT

Cauldon

Shraley Brook

Middleport

Bignall End

Burslem

Newcastle-under-Lyme

Hartshill

Keele Village

Hanley

Penkhull

Stoke

Fenton

Dresden

*DERBYSHIRE*

Meaford

Saverley Green

Stone

Milwich

Uttoxeter

Copmere End

Eccleshall

Abbots Bromley

Tutbury

High Offley

Amerton

Weston

Burton upon Trent

Gnosall

Hoar Cross

Barton-under-Needwood

Stafford

Little Haywood

Outwoods

Haughton

Brocton

Rugeley

Great Chatwell

Penkridge

Upper Longdon

Marston

Gentleshaw

Longdon

Kiddemore Green

Brewood

Chasetown

Lichfield

Burnhill Green

Shenstone

Tamworth

Penn Common

Fazeley

Two Gates

Wilnecote

Ebstree

Wombourne

*WEST MIDLANDS*

*WARWICKS*

Enville

*LEICS*

Kinver

*SHROPSHIRE*

*WORCESTERSHIRE*

0 Miles 5

0 Kilometres 8

---

## Abbots Bromley

### Bagot Arms
Bagot Street ☎ (01283) 840371
11–2.30, 5.30–11; 12–3, 7–10.30 Sun
**Marston's Pedigree, HBC** Ⓗ
18th-century coaching inn
specialising in good food, close
to Blithfield Reservoir.
Q ❀ ◖ ▶ ♣ P

## Amerton

### Plough
On A518 ☎ (01889) 270308
11–3, 6.30–11 (11–11 summer); 12–3,
7–10.30 Sun

**Marston's Bitter, Pedigree;
Morland Old Speckled Hen;
guest beer** Ⓗ
Traditional country inn
opposite Amerton Working
Farm Craft and Garden Centre.

The restaurant boasts an
extensive high class menu. The
large garden has a children's
play area.
🎣 ☞ ❀ ◖ ▶ ⊟ ♿ ▲ ♣ P

 **INDEPENDENT BREWERIES**

**Burton Bridge:**
Burton upon Trent

**Eccleshall:** Eccleshall

**Enville:** Enville

**Lichfield:** Lichfield

**Marston's:**
Burton upon Trent

**Rising Sun:** Shraley Brook

**Titanic:** Burslem

## Barton-under-Needwood

### Top Bell

52 Barton Gate (B5016)
☎ (01283) 712510
12–3.30, 6–11; 12–3.30, 7–10.30 Sun
**Burtonwood Bitter, Forshaw's, Tom Thumper, Top Hat, Buccaneer** H
Typical, beamed country pub. Live music Wed, Fri, Sat and Sun nights. Meals available other eves.
🎠 🛏 ✿ 💷 ◑ 🅓 & P

## Bignall End

### Plough

Ravens Lane (B5500, ½ mile E of Audley) ☎ (01782) 720469
12–3, 7–11; 12–11 Fri & Sat; 12–10.30 Sun
**Banks's Bitter; Marston's Pedigree; guest beers** H
Popular roadside hostelry, with a beer enthusiast landlord, catering for local and passing trade in a traditional bar and a split-level lounge. Constantly changing guest beers; good range of meals. 1995 local CAMRA *Pub of the Year.* ✿ ◑ 🅓 ♣ P

## Brewood

### Swan

15 Market Square
☎ (01902) 850330
12–2.30 (3 Sat), 7–11; 12–3, 7–10.30 Sun
**Draught Bass; Mansfield Riding Bitter; Theakston XB, guest beer** H
Comfortable village pub with low-beamed ceilings and two cosy snugs, plus a skittle alley at the back. 🎠 ◑ ♣ P

## Brocton

### Chetwynd Arms

Cannock Road (A34)
☎ (01785) 661089
11.30–3, 5.45–11; 11–11 Sat; 12–10.30 Sun
**Banks's Mild, Bitter** E**; Marston's Pedigree; guest beers** H
Bustling main road pub at the north-western boundary of Cannock Chase with a genuine, unspoilt bar. No meals Sat eve, or Sun.
✿ ◑ 🅓 🍴 & ♣ P

## Burnhill Green

### Dartmouth Arms

Snowdon Road
☎ (01746) 783268
11–3, 7–11; 12–3, 7–10.30 Sun (extends in summer)
**Ansells Bitter; Ind Coope Burton Ale; guest beers** H

Popular village pub, renowned for home-made bar meals served in a small restaurant area (book at busy times). No meals Mon, Tue lunch or Sun eve. 🎠 Q ✿ ◑ 🅓 P

## Burton upon Trent

### Blackpool Inn

237 Blackpool Street (Leicester St jct, off Branston Rd)
☎ (01283) 517826
11–11; 12–3, 7–10.30 Sun
**Marston's Pedigree; Morland Old Speckled Hen; Taylor Landlord; guest beers** H
Friendly, backstreet free house: a long, single room with a split-level lounge area with wood panelled walls and matching decor. ✿ ♣

### Boat House

The Dingle, Stapenhill (off Ferry St) ☎ (01283) 538831
12–3, 7–11; 12–3, 7.30–10.30 Sun
**Draught Bass; Greene King Abbot; Marston's Pedigree; Morland Old Speckled Hen; Ruddles County; Taylor Landlord** H
Pub on a bank of the Trent beside the ferry bridge, with a garden play area for children and an upstairs restaurant. Jazz Thu eve. Q ✿ ◑ 🅓 & P

### Burton Bridge Inn

24 Bridge Street (A50, by Trent Bridge) ☎ (01283) 536596
11.30–2.15, 5.30–11; 12–2, 7–10.30 Sun
**Burton Bridge Summer Ale, XL, Bridge Bitter, Porter, Top Dog Stout, Festival Ale, seasonal beers; guest beer** (Sun) H
Snug, two-roomed brewery tap with wooden pews and award-covered walls. Good range of whiskies and country wines. Easter beer festival. No food Sun. Q ◑ ♣

### Cooper's Tavern

Cross Street (off Station St)
☎ (01283) 532551
12–2.30, 5 (7 Sat)–11; 12–3, 7–10.30 Sun (may extend)
**Draught Bass; Hardys & Hansons Best Mild** G**, Best Bitter** H**, Classic** G**; Marston's Pedigree** H
Truly traditional ale house with a renowned tap room: note the stillaged casks, barrel tables and 'top bench' seat. Simple, good value food (not served Sun). Coaches welcome. Staffordshire CAMRA *Pub of the Year 1994.* Q ◑ 🍴 ♣

### Derby Inn

17 Derby Road
☎ (01283) 564460
11 (10.30 Sat)–3, 5.30 (4 Sat)–11; 12–3, 7–10.30 Sun
**Marston's Pedigree** H
Small, down to earth local on a busy road: a bustling bar and a

cosy lounge serving arguably the best Pedigree in Marston's home town. 🔔 ♣ P

### New Inn

273 Horninglow Road North (A50) ☎ (01283) 540812
11.30–3, 6–11; 11–11 Sat; 12–3, 7–10.30 Sun
**Marston's Bitter, Pedigree** H
Originally a coaching inn, now with a public bar and a comfortable, two-level lounge with a homely atmosphere. It reputedly has three ghosts. Large function room.
🎠 Q ✿ ◑ 🅓 🔔 ♣ P

### Roebuck

Station Street ☎ (01283) 568660
11–11; 11–3, 6–11 Sat; 12–3, 7–10.30 Sun
**Ansells Bitter; HP&D Entire; Ind Coope Burton Ale; Marston's Pedigree; Tetley Bitter; guest beers** H
Pub known locally as the 'Ale House', offering a good selection of Carlsberg-Tetley ales as well as the Tapster's Choice and a guest ale. Nearly 500 guest beers have been served – the pump clips can be seen over the bar.
🔔 ◑ 🚋 ♣

### Thomas Sykes

Heritage Brewery, Anglesey Road (off Moor St, B5017)
☎ (01283) 510246
11.30–3, 5 (7 Sat)–11; 12–3, 7–10.30 Sun
**Draught Bass; Marston's Pedigree, Owd Rodger; guest beers** H
Classic ale house in the former stables and wagon sheds of the old Thomas Sykes Brewery. Stone cobbled floors, high ceilings and breweriana create a traditional, friendly atmosphere. Burton Bridge beers are also on sale.
Q 🛏 ✿ ♣ P

## Cauldon

### Yew Tree

Off A52 / A523
☎ (01538) 308348
11–3, 6–11; 12–3, 7–10.30 Sun
**Draught Bass; Burton Bridge Bridge Bitter; M&B Mild** H
One of the finest pubs in the country, dating back to the 17th century, housing a fine collection of working antiques, including polyphonia, pianolas (both manual and electric) and grandfather clocks. Look for the 'Acme dog carrier'.
Q ✿ ▲ ♣ P

## Chasetown

### Uxbridge Arms

2 Church Street
☎ (01543) 674853
12–3, 6–11; 12–11 Sat; 12–10.30 Sun

**Draught Bass; Highgate Dark; Worthington Bitter; guest beers** Ⓗ
Popular local with a games room and two changing guest beers.
✧ ◖▶ ⬜ ♣ P

## Copmere End

### Star
12–3, 6–11; 12–11 Fri & Sat; 12–3, 7–10.30 Sun
**Draught Bass; guest beer** Ⓗ
Cosy country pub: a meeting place for a cycling club, popular with walkers. Sun lunchtime auctions in summer for seasonal produce.
♨ Q ☜ ✧ ◖▶ ⬜ ▲ ♣ P

## Ebstree

### Hollybush Inn
Ebstree Road, Trysull
OS854959 ☎ (01902) 895587
11.30–3, 6–11; 12–3, 7–10.30 Sun
**Ansells Bitter; Ind Coope Burton Ale; Tetley Bitter; guest beers** Ⓗ
Pleasant country inn half a mile west of the Staffs and Worcs Canal: a large lounge area (children welcome) and a more traditional public bar with games and a piano. No meals Sun. ♨ ✧ ◖▶ ⬜ ♣ P

## Eccleshall

### George Hotel
Castle Street ☎ (01785) 850300
11–11; 12–10.30 Sun
**Eccleshall Slaters Bitter, Original, Premium, seasonal beers; guest beers** Ⓗ
Originally a coaching inn, this town-centre hotel now has ten excellent bedrooms and a separate bistro (supper licence). Eccleshall's first brewery for over a century opened behind the hotel in 1995. ♨ ☜ ✧ ⊨ ◖▶ ▲ P

## Enville

### Cat
Bridgnorth Road (A458)
☎ (01384) 872209
12–3, 7–11; closed Sun
**Enville Ale, Gothic; Theakston XB; guest beers** Ⓗ
Part-16th-century inn with a defunct brewery at the rear and four different, oak-beamed rooms with real fires. Not far from Enville Brewery.
♨ Q ✧ ◖▶ ♣ P

## Fazeley

### Three Horseshoes
New Street ☎ (01827) 289754
12–3, 7–11; 12–3, 7–10.30 Sun
**Draught Bass; Marston's Pedigree** Ⓗ

Small, cosy, traditional pub with a strong local following, an old coaching inn near the junction of the Birmingham and Fazeley and Coventry canals and Drayton Manor Park.
☜ ✧ ◖ ⇌ (Wilnecote) ♣

## Gentleshaw

### Olde Windmill
Windmill Lane (on common)
☎ (01543) 682468
12–11; 12–10.30 Sun
**Draught Bass; Highgate Dark; Worthington Bitter** Ⓗ
Pleasant common-side pub next to an old windmill on the edge of picturesque Cannock Chase forest, complete with its own crown bowling green.
♨ ☜ ✧ ◖▶ ⬜ ♣ P

## Gnosall

### Boat
Wharf Road ☎ (01785) 822208
12 (11 summer)–11; 12–10.30 Sun
**Marston's Bitter, Pedigree, HBC** Ⓗ
Popular pub next to Bridge 34 on the Shropshire Union Canal.
♨ ☜ ✧ ◖▶ ♣ ○ P

## Great Chatwell

### Red Lion
2 miles E of A41 OS792143
☎ (01952) 691366
12–3 (not Mon, or winter Tue/Wed), 6 (7 winter)–11 (12–11 summer Sat); 12–3, 7–10.30 Sun
**Draught Bass; Theakston Best Bitter; Worthington Bitter; guest beers** Ⓗ
Friendly, family-run country pub with a range of guest beers. Excellent children's play area in the garden. Good value food in the bar and restaurant.
♨ ☜ ✧ ◖▶ ⬜ ▲ ♣ P ⊟

## Harriseahead

### Royal Oak
42 High Street
☎ (01782) 513362
7–11; 12–3, 7–11 Sat; 12–3, 7–10.30 Sun
**Courage Directors; John Smith's Bitter; guest beers** Ⓗ
Genuine free house in a semi-rural location on the Kidsgrove side of Mow Cop Folly (NT): a smallish bar and a larger lounge. Constantly changing guest beers (the best choice in the area); occasional mini-beer festivals. Popular with old and young alike. ✧ ⬜ ♣ P ⊟

## Haughton

### Bell
Newport Road (A518)
☎ (01785) 780301
11.30–3, 6–11; 12–3.30, 7–10.30 Sun

**Boddingtons Bitter; Mansfield Riding Mild; Marston's Pedigree; guest beer** Ⓗ
One-roomed village free house with a large collection of book matches. ♨ ✧ ◖▶ ♣ P

## High Offley

### Anchor ☆
Old Lea (by Bridge 42 of the Shropshire Union Canal)
OS775256 ☎ (01785) 284569
11–3, 6–11; 12–3, 6–10.30 Sun (winter hours: 7–11 Fri; 12–3, 7–11 Sat; 12–3 Sun; closed Sun eve–Fri lunch)
**Marston's Pedigree** (summer), **Owd Rodger** (summer); **Wadworth 6X** Ⓖ/Ⓗ
Once called the Sebastopol Inn, this classic, two-bar, canalside pub is not easily found by road. Behind the pub is a canalware gift shop.
♨ Q ✧ ⬜ ▲ ○ P

## Hoar Cross

### Meynell Ingram Arms
1 mile W of A515 at Newchurch OS133234
☎ (01283) 575202
12–3, 6–11; 12–11 Sat; 12–5, 7–10.30 Sun
**Marston's Pedigree; guest beer** Ⓗ
Extended former estate pub with hunting memorabilia, in a rural setting. No food Sun eve.
♨ Q ✧ ◖▶ ♣ P

## Keele Village

### Sneyd Arms
1 The Village (off A525)
☎ (01782) 614533
12–3 (4 Sat), 7–11; 12–4, 7–10.30 Sun
**HP&D Entire; Ind Coope Burton Ale; Tetley Bitter; guest beers** Ⓗ
Solid stone village local built in 1846 and used by locals and students (close to the university). ✧ ◖▶ ⬜ & ♣ P

## Kiddemore Green

### New Inns
Between Brewood and Bishop's Wood OS858089
☎ (01902) 850614
12–3 (not winter Mon–Wed), 6–11; 12–3, 7–10.30 Sun
**Burtonwood Mild, Bitter, Forshaw's, Buccaneer** Ⓗ
Small, cosy country inn with a comfortable, L-shaped lounge with two fires. ♨ ✧ ◖ P

## Kinver

### Crown & Anchor
115A Enville Road
☎ (01384) 872567
12–3, 7–11 Sat; 12–10.30 Sun
**Banks's Mild, Bitter** Ⓔ, **seasonal beers; Marston's Pedigree** Ⓗ

Dating from 1853, a lively pub with an island front bar and a rear pool room. ⚿ ♣ P

## Plough & Harrow

High Street ☎ (01384) 872659
7–11; 12–3.30, 7–11 Fri; 12–4.30, 7–11 Sat; 12–4.30, 7–10.30 Sun
**Batham Mild, Best Bitter** Ⓗ
Popular pub known locally as 'the Steps' – its three rooms are on different levels. Film star pictures decorate the lounge. Cider in summer.
🏚 Q ⛵ ◖ Ⅱ ♣ ⌂ P

## Whittington Inn

On A449 S of A458 jct
☎ (01384) 872110
11–2.30 (3 Sat), 5.30–11 (11–11 summer); 12–3, 7–10.30 (12–10.30 summer) Sun
**Banks's Mild, Bitter** Ⓔ, **seasonal beers; Marston's Pedigree** Ⓗ
Converted 14th-century manor house visited by Charles II after the Battle of Worcester. It boasts panelled walls, ornate moulded ceilings, with low beams, and a walled Tudor garden. 🏚 Q ⚿ ◖ Ⅱ ⚰ P Ⓤ

## Leek

### Abbey Inn

Abbey Green Road (1 mile from Leek, off A523)
☎ (01538) 382865
12–3, 7–11; 12–3, 7–10.30 Sun
**Draught Bass; guest beers** Ⓗ
Large, impressive, stone establishment with two rooms served from a central bar; close to the former site of the Cistercian Abbey of Dieulacres. Good value food. Children's certificate. Q ⚿ 🚃 ◖ Ⅱ P

### Blue Mugge

17 Osborne Street (300 yds from centre, off Buxton Rd)
☎ (01538) 384450
11–2.30, 6–11; 11–11 Sat; 12–10.30 Sun
**Draught Bass; Worthington Bitter; guest beer** Ⓗ
Street corner local free of brewery tie. The Tardis-like interior has several rooms and areas radiating off a central island bar. Ever changing beer at a most reasonable price. Good value lunches. Sidestreet parking close by. ⚿ ◖ Ⅱ ♣

### Swan

2 St Edward Street
☎ (01538) 382081
11–3, 7–11; 12–3, 7–10.30 Sun
**Draught Bass; Highgate Dark; Worthington Bitter; guest beer** Ⓗ
Three-roomed former coaching inn opposite St Edward's church. The lounge is mainly given over to non-smoking diners at lunchtime (eve meals Oct–March). Ever-changing guest beers; range of malt whiskies. Function room for mini-beer festivals. Car park opposite. ⚿ ◖ Ⅱ Ⅱ ♣

## Wilke's Head

16 St Edward's Street (by church) ☎ (01538) 383616
11 (10 Wed)–11; 12–3, 7–10.30 Sun
**Coach House seasonal beers; Whim Magic Mushroom Mild, Hartington Bitter, Old Izaak, Black Christmas; guest beer** (occasional) Ⓗ
Whim Brewery tied outlet serving a fine selection of beers and malt whiskies to lively, discerning drinkers in basic, two-roomed premises. ⚿ ♣

## Lichfield

### Earl of Lichfield Arms

10 Conduit Street (opp. market square) ☎ (01543) 251020
11–11; 11–4, 7–11 Sat; 12–3, 7–10.30 Sun
**Banks's Mild; Marston's Bitter, Pedigree, HBC** Ⓗ
Traditional, city-centre bar on three levels, frequented by all ages. Lunches Mon–Sat.
⚿ ◖ 🚃 (City)

### Greyhound

Upper St John Street
☎ (01543) 262303
12–3, 5.30–11; 11–11 Fri & Sat; 12–3, 7–10.30 Sun
**Ansells Bitter; Draught Bass; guest beers** Ⓗ
Popular local with an extended lounge. The guests are premium bitters.
⛵ ◖ Ⅱ 🚃 (City) ♣ P

### Queen's Head

14 Queen Street
☎ (01543) 410932
11–11; 12–10.30 Sun
**Adnams Bitter; Marston's Pedigree; Taylor Landlord; guest beers** Ⓗ
Marston's first ale house: a two-room local converted into a busy, one-roomed pub with changing guest beers. It attracts all ages. Excellent cheese board.
Q ◖ 🚃 (City) ♣ ⌂

### Scales

24 Market Street
☎ (01543) 410653
11–11; 12–10.30 Sun
**Draught Bass; Highgate Dark; Lichfield Steeplejack; Worthington Bitter; guest beers** Ⓗ
Completely renovated city-centre pub: a very busy example of the Bass 'real ale shrine' concept.
⚿ ◖ ⚷ 🚃 (City) ♣

## Little Haywood

### Red Lion

Main Road
☎ (01889) 881314

11–11; 12–3.30, 7–10.30 (12–10.30 summer) Sun
**Bateman Mild; Marston's Bitter, Pedigree, HBC** Ⓗ
Lively village pub, very much a community-based local. The landlady plays the organ in the lounge. Award-winning garden.
🏚 ⚿ Ⅱ Å ♣ P

## Longdon

### Swan With Two Necks

40 Brook End (100 yds off A51)
☎ (01543) 490251
12–3, 7–11; 12–3, 7–10.30 Sun
**Ansells Bitter; HP&D Entire; Ind Coope Burton Ale; guest beers** Ⓗ
400-year-old, beamed village pub with a stone-flagged bar, a comfortable lounge and a restaurant. Two guest beers. Home-cooked food (good choice).
🏚 Q ⚿ ◖ P

## Marston

### Fox

1 mile NW of Wheaton Aston
OS935140 ☎ (01785) 840729
11–11; 12–10.30 Sun
**Draught Bass; Joule Old Priory; Lloyds Country Bitter; Mansfield Riding Mild; Wells Eagle; guest beers** Ⓗ
Isolated country free house with an adjoining restaurant. The garden has a children's play area.
🏚 Q ⚿ ◖ Å ♣ ⌂ P

## Meaford

### George & Dragon

The Highway (100 yds S of A34 Darlaston roundabout)
☎ (01785) 818497
11–11; 12–10.30 Sun
**Burtonwood Bitter, Forshaw's Top Hat, Buccaneer** Ⓗ
Large, main road pub with a spacious, wood-panelled lounge, plus a large restaurant on the first floor. Lunches served downstairs Mon–Sat.
⚿ ◖ Ⅱ ⚷ ♣ P

## Milwich

### Green Man

Sandon Lane (B5027)
☎ (01889) 505310
12–2 (not Mon or Tue), 5–11; 12–11 Sat; 12–4, 7–10.30 Sun
**Draught Bass; Worthington Bitter; guest beers** Ⓗ
Welcoming village pub, well-situated for hikers. A list of landlords since 1792 is displayed in the bar. Large selection of whiskies. Happy hour 5–6 weekdays.
🏚 ⚿ ◖ Å ♣ P

## Newcastle-under-Lyme

### Bull's Vaults

Hassell Street (near bus station) ☎ (01782) 616555
11–11; 12–2.30, 7–10.30 Sun
**Banks's Mild, Bitter** E, **seasonal beers; Camerons Strongarm; Marston's Pedigree** H
One-roomed, town-centre pub with bar, lounge and games areas. It caters for shoppers and a wide range of drinkers in the daytime, and a mainly younger element eves.
◑ ♣ ⬛

### Castle Mona

4 Victoria Street (off A34)
☎ (01782) 612849
12–4 (not Mon–Thu), 7–11; 12–4, 7–10.30 Sun
**Greenalls Mild, Davenports Bitter, Original** H
Very busy, street-corner local just outside the town centre; built in 1876. Music in the bar most times (jukebox); pleasant lounge and separate pool room. ❀ ⬛ ♣

### Crossways

Nelson Place (A52/A527 jct)
☎ (01782) 616953
11–11; 11–4, 7–11 Sat; 12–3, 7–10.30 Sun
**Vaux Samson, Waggle Dance; Ward's Best Bitter; guest beers** H
Large, town-centre pub with a bar and a smaller games area off. Popular with a wide range of drinkers. The house beer, Bearcross, is brewed by Coach House. Occasional other beers from Vaux. ⬛ ◑ ♣

### Dunkirk Tavern

Dunkirk (just off A34)
☎ (01782) 618735
12–3.30, 7–11; 12–3, 7–10.30 Sun
**Burtonwood Bitter, Top Hat, Buccaneer, seasonal beers** H
Cosy community local just out of the town centre; always a friendly welcome. Book eve meals. ◑ ▶ ♣

**Try also: Albert**, Liverpool Rd (Burtonwood)

## Onecote

### Jervis Arms

On B5053 ☎ (01538) 304206
12–3, 7–11; 12–3, 7–10.30 Sun
**Draught Bass; Marston's Pedigree; Ruddles County; Theakston Mild, Best Bitter; Old Peculier** H
Free house in a superb country setting, beside the River Hamps, with an emphasis on good quality food. Family-oriented (good play area), it takes its name from a former

aide to Lord Nelson, Admiral Jervis. Q ⬛ ❀ ◑ ▶ ▲ P

## Outwoods

### Village Tavern

Signed from A518
☎ (01952) 691216
12–3 (not winter Mon–Fri), 6 (7.30 winter)–11; 12–3, 7–10.30 Sun
**Boddingtons Bitter; Hobsons Best Bitter; guest beers** H
Friendly country inn in a small village, frequented by walkers and cyclists. Good value food; families are made welcome. Wildman's, the house beer, is brewed by Enville.
🐾 Q ❀ ◑ ▶ ▲ P

## Penkridge

### Boat

Cannock Road (by Bridge 86 of Staffs and Worcs Canal)
☎ (01785) 714178
12–3, 6.30–11; 12–3, 7–10.30 Sun
**Ansells Bitter; Ind Coope Burton Ale; Marston's Pedigree; Tetley Bitter** H
Comfortable, homely canalside pub with plenty of brass. Bar skittles in the corridor. Sun eve meals are only served in summer. ❀ ◑ ▶ ♣ P

## Penn Common

### Barley Mow

Pennwood Lane (off Wakeley Hill) OS949902
☎ (01902) 333510
12–3, 6.30–11; 11.30–11 Sat; 12–10.30 Sun
**Ansells Mild; Ind Coope Burton Ale; guest beer** H
Hidden gem, circa 1630, with a warm welcome and a popular children's playground. Food is served in the small bar. Guest bitter from Ind Coope, plus one Holden's brew.
🐾 Q ❀ ◑ ▶ ⬒ P ⬛

## Reapsmoor

### Butcher's Arms

Off B5053 ☎ (01298) 84477
12–3, 7–11; 12–3, 7–10.30 Sun
**Marston's Pedigree; guest beers** H
Gem of a pub in the heart of the Staffordshire moorlands, popular with the local farming community and sometimes isolated during severe winter conditions. Superb value meals.
🐾 Q ◑ ▶ ▲ P

## Rugeley

### Red Lion

Market Street
☎ (01889) 570328
11–11; 12–10.30 Sun
**Banks's Mild, Bitter** E

Small, three-roomed pub with bags of atmosphere. Pool and darts room and a cosy bar.
❀ ♣ P

## Saverley Green

### Hunter

Sandon Road OS970385
☎ (01782) 392067
12–3, 7–11; 12–3, 7–10.30 Sun (may vary)
**Burtonwood Bitter, Forshaw's Top Hat** H
Cosy country pub offering great hospitality. Antique items in every nook and cranny. Snacks only eves.
🐾 ❀ ◑ ▲ ♣ P

## Shenstone

### Bull's Head

Birmingham Road (A5127)
☎ (01543) 480214
11.30–11; 12–10.30 Sun
**Draught Bass; Highgate Dark; M&B Brew XI** H; **guest beer** G
18th-century, semi-rural inn with log fires and beams. Traditional British food all day. Changing guest ale.
🐾 Q ⬛ ❀ ◑ ▶ ら ⇌ P ⅄

### Railway

Main Street ☎ (01543) 480503
12–11; 12–10.30 Sun
**Marston's Bitter, Pedigree, Owd Rodger, HBC** H
Popular village pub for locals and rail travellers; formerly a butcher's shop and a chapel. Winner of a *Best Garden* competition and runner-up for local CAMRA *Pub of the Year* 1996. Good food.
Q ❀ ◑ ▶ ⬛ ら ⇌ ♣ P

## Shraley Brook

### Rising Sun Inn

Knowle Bank Road (B52)
☎ (01782) 720600
12–3, 6.30–11; 12–11 Fri & Sat; 12–10.30 Sun
**Rising Sun Rising, Setting, Porter, Sunstroke, Total Eclipse, Solar Flare** H
Brew pub with a large selection of whiskies and foreign beers. Vegetarian meals a speciality.
🐾 ⬛ ❀ ◑ ▶ ら ▲ ♣ ⬒ P

## Stafford

### Bird in Hand

Mill Street (between town centre and station)
☎ (01785) 252198
11–11; 12–3, 7–10.30 Sun
**Courage Best Bitter, Directors; John Smith's Bitter; Worthington Bitter; guest beer** H
Popular and enterprising pub with a bar, snug, games room and lounge. No meals Sun.
🐾 ⬛ ❀ ◑ ▶ ⇌ ♣

### Forester & Firkin
3 Eastgate Street
☎ (01785) 223742
11–11; 12–3, 7–10.30 Sun
**Firkin Forester, Pecker, Dogbolter** Ⓗ
Pub furbished in a similar style to other Firkin pubs, with basic decor, live music some sessions and many student customers. No food Sun. Stafford's first brewery since 1952.
❀ ◖ ♣ P

### Stafford Arms
Railway Street (opp. station)
☎ (01785) 253313
12–11; 12–3, 7–10.30 Sun
**Titanic Best Bitter, Lifeboat, Premium, Stout, White Star, Captain Smith's, Wreckage; guest beers** Ⓗ
Local CAMRA *Pub of the Year* 1994 and 1996, Titanic's second pub selling four guests from independents. Games include bar billiards and corridor skittles. No meals Sun, or Sat eve (other eves till 8). Cider in summer.
❀ ◖ ▶ ⇌ ♣ ⌂ P

### Sun
7 Lichfield Road
☎ (01785) 242208
11.30–3 (5 Sat), 7–11; 12–10.30 Sun
**Draught Bass; Worthington Bitter; guest beer** Ⓗ
Pleasant, multi-roomed, town-centre pub with an olde-worlde restaurant.
❀ ⇌ ◖ ▶ ⊞ ⇌ ♣ P

### Tap & Spile
59 Peel Terrace (just off B5066, 1 mile from centre)
☎ (01785) 223563
12–2, 6.30–11; 12–11 Thu–Sat; 12–3, 7–10.30 Sun
**Beer range varies** Ⓗ
Sympathetic Tap & Spile conversion which has greatly increased choice in northern Stafford. Seven changing guest beers (200 a year). Free bar billiards. Staffordshire CAMRA *Pub of the Year* 1995.
❀ ◖ ▶ ⊞ ♣ ⌂ ✄

### Telegraph
Wolverhampton Road
☎ (01785) 258858
11–11; 12–10.30 Sun
**Draught Bass; Highgate Dark; Worthington Bitter; guest beers** Ⓗ
Good, honest local, with a lounge and a bar, not far from the centre. Good value meals. Function room.
◖ ▶ ⊞ ♣ P

## Stoke on Trent: *Burslem*

### Bull's Head
14 St John's Square (near Woolworth's)
☎ (01782) 834153

12–2.30 (3 Sat), 5 (6.30 Sat)–11; 12–11 Fri; 12–3, 7–10.30 Sun
**Titanic Best Bitter, Lifeboat, Premium, Stout, White Star, Captain Smith's; guest beers** Ⓗ
Titanic-owned, town-centre pub with a bar and a lounge. Beer festivals June and Sept. Articles on the walls refer to Captain Smith of the *Titanic*, a Potteries man. Cider in summer. ⚏ Q ❀ ⊞ ♣ ⌂

### George Hotel
Swan Square
☎ (01782) 577544
11.30–2, 7–11; 12–2, 7–10.30 Sun
**Marston's Bitter, Pedigree; Morland Old Speckled Hen** Ⓗ
Fine pseudo-Georgian building on the site of Arnold Bennett's 'Dragon'. The bar is ideal for a quiet drink, but smart casual dress is required. Special accommodation rates for CAMRA members. Highly recommended restaurant.
Q ⇌ ◖ ▶

### New Inn
Market Place ☎ (01782) 838654
11–4, 7–11; 12–4, 7–10.30 Sun
**Burtonwood Bitter, Top Hat, Buccaneer** Ⓗ
Popular, town-centre pub: a traditional bar, a comfortable lounge and an open corridor/lounge; once the only Joule's house in Burslem. Good value food always available.
◖ ▶ ⊞

## *Dresden*

### Sir Robert Peel
58 Peel Street (just off A5035)
☎ (01782) 313821
7–11; 12–3, 7–11 Sat; 12–3, 7–10.30 Sun
**Draught Bass; Tetley Bitter; Worthington Bitter; guest beer** Ⓗ
Community local with a Victorian bridlepath at the side. ❀ ⊞ ♣

## *Fenton*

### Malt 'n' Hops
295 King Street (A50)
☎ (01782) 313406
12–3, 7–11; 12–3.30, 7–10.30 Sun
**Beer range varies** Ⓗ
Welcoming, well-run house where at least 15 ever-changing guest beers are sold each week. Bursley Bitter (Burtonwood), Turners Tipple and Fenton Special (Hardington) are house beers. ⇌ (Longton) ⊟

## *Hanley*

### Coachmaker's
65 Lichfield Street (next to bus station) ☎ (01782) 262158
11.30–11; 12–4, 7–10.30 Sun

**Draught Bass; Worthington Bitter** Ⓗ
Fine example of a Potteries town pub; mid-terraced, with three small rooms and a corridor. An unpretentious drinkers' pub.
⚏ Q ⊞ ♣

### Golden Cup
65 Old Town Road
☎ (01782) 212405
11.30–11; 12–3, 7.30–10.30 Sun
**Draught Bass; Ruddles County** Ⓗ
Friendly locals' beer house – the last in Hanley to obtain a liquor licence – boasting splendid bar fittings. The ornate Edwardian exterior proudly proclaims 'Bass only'. Famous for its 'big breakfast'.
❀ ◖ ♿ ♣

## *Hartshill*

### Jolly Potters
296 Hartshill Road
☎ (01782) 845254
11–3 (4 Sat), 6 (7 Sat)–11; 11–11 Fri; 12–4, 7–10.30 Sun
**Draught Bass; M&B Mild; guest beer** (occasional) Ⓗ
Rare example of a typical Potteries town pub, first licensed as a beer house in 1834, on the edge of the 40-acre Hartshill Farm. Situated in a conservation area, it has four small rooms and a central corridor. Q ❀ ⊞ ♿ ♣

## *Middleport*

### White Swan
107 Newport Lane (off Newcastle St)
☎ (01782) 813639
11–11; 11–4, 7–11 Sat; 11–3, 7–10.30 Sun
**Vaux Mild, Bitter, Samson, Double Maxim; Ward's Thorne BB; guest beers** Ⓗ
Popular, friendly free house.
⚏ ⇌ (Longport) ♣

## *Penkhull*

### Marquis of Granby
51 St Thomas's Place
☎ (01782) 847025
11–3 (4 Thu–Sat), 6–11; 12–3, 7–10.30 Sun
**Banks's Mild; Marston's Bitter, Pedigree, HBC** Ⓗ
Red-brick corner pub opposite the church. The public bar, full of locals, is popular for games; the large, comfortable lounge holds quiz nights. Wheelchairs can use the Penkhull New Rd entrance. ❀ ◖ ⊞ ♿ ♣ P

## *Stoke*

### Glebe
35 Glebe Street
11–11; 12–10.30 Sun

**Banks's Mild, Bitter;
Camerons Strongarm;
Marston's Pedigree** H
Large, refurbished pub
between the town hall and
civic offices, popular with
students. ◑ ♿ ♣ ♠

## Tunstall

### Globe
53 High Street
☎ (01782) 835817
11–11; 12–2.30, 7–10.30 Sun
**Bass Toby Cask, Draught
Bass** H
Old-fashioned, town-centre
pub with a separate bar and
lounge. No swan neck on the
Bass. Q ♨ ♣ ☖

## Stone

### Pheasant
Old Road ☎ (01785) 814603
11.30–4, 6–11; 11.30–11 Fri & Sat;
12–3, 7–10.30 Sun
**Banks's Mild; Bateman Mild;
Marston's Bitter, Pedigree;
guest beers** H
Busy, friendly local where
darts, dominoes, crib and
football are well supported.
Major selection of home-
cooked meals at sensible
prices. Eve meals Fri and Sat;
no lunches Sun. ֎ ◑ ▸ ⇌ ♣

### Star
21 Stafford Street (by Bridge 93
of Trent and Mersey Canal)
☎ (01785) 813096
11–11; 12–10.30 Sun
**Banks's Mild, Bitter;
Camerons Strongarm;
Marston's Pedigree** H
Dating from 1568, this
canalside pub is located on 13
different floor levels. Very
busy in summer.
♨ Q ☙ ֎ ◑ ▸ ♨ ♣ P ☖

## Tamworth

### Albert
Albert Road ☎ (01827) 64694
11.30–3, 6–11; 12–3, 7–10.30 Sun
**Banks's Mild, Bitter, seasonal
beers; Marston's Pedigree** H
Pleasant local close to the town
centre: a previous local
CAMRA *Pub of the Year*. Good
value bar meals; separate
restaurant. No eve meals Sun.
֎ ﬚ ◑ ▸ ♨ ⇌ ♣ P

### Boot Inn
Lichfield Street
☎ (01827) 68024
11–11; 12–10.30 Sun
**Marston's Pedigree, HBC** H
Busy, town-centre pub
attracting a varied clientele.
֎ ◑ ⇌

### White Lion
Aldergate (next to council
offices) ☎ (01827) 64630

12–3, 6–11; 11–11 Fri & Sat; 12–3,
7–10.30 Sun
**Banks's Mild, Bitter, seasonal
beers; Marston's Pedigree** H
Basic, three-roomed corner pub
with a restaurant area. Busy at
weekends.
♨ ◑ ⇌ P

## Tutbury

### Cross Keys
Burton Street (A50)
☎ (01283) 813677
10.30–3, 5.30–11; 12–3, 7–10.30 Sun
**Ind Coope Burton Ale; Tetley
Bitter; guest beer** H
Village local with a friendly
atmosphere. Separate
restaurant (home-cooking a
speciality). Wheelchair WC.
Q ֎ ◑ ▸ ♨ ♿ ⇌ ♣ P

## Two Gates

### Bull's Head
Watling Street
☎ (01827) 287820
12–2.30 (3 Sat), 6.30–11; 12–2.30,
7–10.30 Sun
**Banks's Mild; Marston's
Pedigree** H
Comfortable, two-roomed
local, tastefully modernised.
Darts and dominoes teams.
Q ֎ ◑ ♨ ⇌ (Wilnecote) P

## Upper Longdon

### Chetwynd Arms
57 Upper Way (¾ mile off A51)
☎ (01543) 490266
12–3 (not Mon), 5.30–11; 12–11 Sat;
12–10.30 Sun
**Lichfield Steeplejack;
Marston's Pedigree; Tetley
Bitter; guest beer** H
Popular local on the edge of
Cannock Chase, catering for
most tastes (families welcome).
Tapster's Choice guest beer.
♨ ֎ ◑ ▸ ▲ ♣ P

## Uttoxeter

### Black Swan
Market Street
☎ (01889) 564657
11 (10.30 Sat)–11; 12–3.30, 7–10.30
Sun (may vary)
**Draught Bass; Worthington
Bitter** H
17th-century listed building of
great character. Visitors are
made welcome.
♨ ⇌ ♣ P

### Vaults
Market Place
☎ (01889) 562997
11–3, 5.30 (7 Fri & Sat)–11; 12–3.30,
7–10.30 Sun
**Draught Bass; Worthington
Bitter** H
Friendly, unspoilt, three-
roomed pub with a large bottle
collection.
♨ ⇌ ♣

## Weston

### Saracen's Head
Stafford Road (A518)
☎ (01889) 270286
11.30–11; 12–3, 7–10.30 Sun
**Draught Bass; Worthington
Bitter** E; **guest beer** H
Situated below Weston Bank,
this country pub has a new
conservatory for meals.
Courtesy bus for regulars and
parties of at least six diners.
♨ ֎ ◑ ▸ ♨ ♣ P ☖

### Woolpack
The Green ☎ (01889) 270238
11.30–3, 5.30–11; 11.30–11 Fri & Sat;
12–3, 7–10.30 Sun
**Marston's Bitter, Pedigree;
guest beer** H
This 17th-century 'Inn on the
Green' has been carefully
extended, retaining separate
drinking and dining areas.
Good selection of quality,
home-cooked food at sensible
prices (no food Sun eve).
♨ ֎ ◑ ▸ ♨ ♣ P

## Wilnecote

### Globe
91 Watling Street
☎ (01827) 280885
1–3.30, 7–11; 12–3, 7–10.30 Sun
**Banks's Mild; Marston's
Pedigree, HBC** H
Basic, one-room local with
darts and dominoes. ֎ ♣ ⇌

## Wombourne

### New Inn
Station Road ☎ (01902) 892037
11–3, 5.30–11; 11–11 Fri & Sat; 12–4,
7–10.30 Sun
**Banks's Mild, Bitter** E,
**seasonal beers** H
Friendly village-centre local: a
plain bar and a large,
refurbished lounge. No meals
Sun. ֎ ◑ ♨ ♣ P ☖

### Red Lion
Old Stourbridge Road (off
A449) ☎ (01902) 892270
12–11; 12–3, 7–10.30 Sun
**Banks's Mild** E; **Draught
Bass; guest beers** H
Two-roomed, 17th-century
coaching inn on the old main
road. Split-level bar; the lounge
is geared towards food service.
♨ ֎ ◑ ▸ ♿ P

### Round Oak
Ounsdale Road (next to Staffs
and Worcs Canal)
☎ (01902) 892083
12–3, 5.30–11; 11–11 Sat; 12–3, 7–10.30
(12–10.30 summer) Sun
**Banks's Mild, Bitter, seasonal
beers** H
Multi-level, canalside, family-
oriented pub. Wheelchair
access to both floors (but toilets
on ground floor only). No eve
meals Sun. ☙ ֎ ◑ ▸ ♿ P ⌦ ☖

*Burton's newest micro-brewery? Actually, it's the 'guest beer'
production plant at Carlsberg-Tetley's main Ind Coope brewery.
The short-run brewery was established in 1994, reviving a classic
Staffordshire brewing name.*

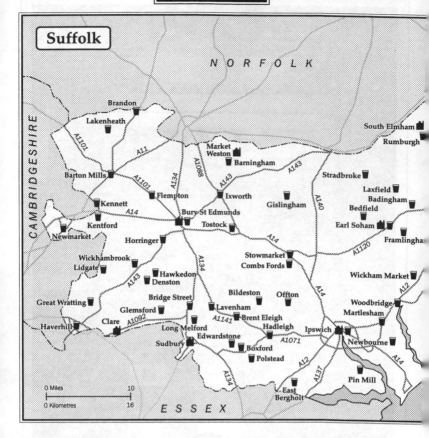

## Aldeburgh

### Cross Keys

Crabbe Street
☎ (01728) 452637
11–11; 12–10.30 Sun
**Adnams Mild** (summer), **Old, Extra, Broadside** H
16th-century smugglers' haunt and fishermen's pub now comfortably refurbished. The menu features good local seafood. ♨ Q ◑ ▷ ▲ ♣

### Mill

Market Cross Place (opp. Moot Hall) ☎ (01728) 452563
11–3, 6–11; 11–11 Fri & Sat; 12–3, 7–10.30 Sun
**Adnams Mild** (summer), **Bitter, Old, Broadside** H
Early 19th-century, friendly pub, popular with fishermen and lifeboatmen. Seafront location. Q ⇔ ◑ ▷ ▲ ♣

## Badingham

### White Horse

By A1120. ☎ (01728) 638280
11–3, 6–11 (11–11 summer Sat); 12–3, 6–10.30 (12–10.30 summer) Sun
**Adnams Mild** (summer), **Bitter, Old, Broadside** (summer) H
Attractive pub serving good food. An excellent children's play area in the garden overlooks a bowling green. Outside gents'.
♨ ❀ ◑ ▷ ⊕ P

## Barningham

### Royal George

Church Road
☎ (01359) 221246
11–3, 6–11; 11–11 Fri & Sat; 12–10.30 Sun
**Greene King XX Mild, IPA, Abbot, seasonal beers** H
Beautifully situated thatched pub in the village centre, quite spacious inside with many old beams and a huge inglenook. A nice outside drinking area has shady trees. Extensive menu, mainly home-made.
⚲ ❀ ◑ ▷ ⊕ P ⊟

## Barton Mills

### Bull Inn

The Street ☎ (01638) 713230
11–11; 12–3, 5–10.30 Sun
**Draught Bass; Greene King IPA** G; **guest beers** H/G
Large, old coaching inn, now bypassed by the A11. Family-run, with full hotel facilities, it has a new bar which is very beer-oriented and totally separate from the restaurant.
♨ ❀ ⇔ ◑ ▷ P

## Bedfield

### Crown

Church Lane (leave A1120 at Earl Soham) ☎ (01728) 628431
11.30–3, 6–11; 11–11 Sat; 12–3, 7–10.30 Sun
**Greene King IPA; guest beer** H
Village local with a friendly welcome. Good selection of pub games. ♨ ❀ ◑ ▷ ♣ P

## Bildeston

### King's Head

132 High Street
☎ (01449) 741434
12–3, 5–11; 11–11 Sat; 12–10.30 Sun
**Greene King IPA; Tolly Cobbold Mild; guest beer** H
Large, lively pub retaining

many original features. Live music weekends; beer festival Whitsun bank hol. Bildeston Bitter is brewed by Mauldons. Cider in summer.
🍺 ❀ 🍴 🍷 🍽 ♣ 🚬 P

## Blaxhall

### Ship
The Street ☎ (01728) 688316
11–3 (not Mon), 7–11; 12–3, 7–10.30 Sun
**Adnams Mild, Bitter, Broadside** Ⓗ
Traditional pub whose basic bar features a high-back settle and games. The dining area offers good value meals. The pub has a strong folk singing tradition. Chalet accommodation. ❀ 🍴 🍷 🍽 ♣ 🚬 P

## Boxford

### White Hart
Broad Street ☎ (01787) 211071
12–3, 6 (6.30 Mon–Fri in winter)–11; 12–3, 7–10.30 Sun
**Adnams Extra *or* Broadside; Greene King IPA; guest beers** Ⓗ
Timber-framed pub with a stream nearby. Boxford

---

Brewery operated on this site during the 19th century. Good seafood menu; interesting guest beers. 🍺 ❀ 🍷 🍽 ♣ 🚬 P 🍽

## Brandon

### Five Bells
Market Hill ☎ (01842) 813472
11–2.30, 5–11; 11–11 Fri & Sat; 12–3, 7–10.30 Sun
**Greene King IPA** Ⓗ
200-year-old, flint-faced building, typical of the town and simply run by a fastidious landlord and staff. The lively locals provide various games teams. Limited food (no lunch Sun). Q ❀ 🍷 🍽 🚆 P

## Brent Eleigh

### Cock ☆
Lavenham Road
☎ (01787) 247371
12–3, 6–11; 12–3, 7–10.30 Sun
**Adnams Mild** Ⓗ, **Bitter** Ⓖ; **Greene King IPA** Ⓗ, **Abbot** Ⓖ
An absolute gem – thatched, unspoilt and at peace with the world. Note the pitch-penny settle in the bar.
🍺 Q ❀ 🍽 ♣ 👝 P

## Bridge Street

### Rose & Crown
Bridge Street (A134)
☎ (01787) 247022
12–3, 6 (6.30 Sat)–11; 12–3, 7–10.30 Sun
**Greene King IPA, Abbot, seasonal beers** Ⓖ
Homely village pub with an abundance of exposed beams and a friendly atmosphere. The ales are drawn straight from the cask; excellent home-made food. Near Long Melford and Kentwell Halls.
Q ❀ 🍷 🍽 ♣ P

## Bungay

### Chequers
23 Bridge Street
☎ (01986) 893579
12–3, 5–11; 11–11 Fri & Sat; 12–4, 7–10.30 Sun
**Adnams Bitter; Draught Bass; Worthington Bitter; guest beers** Ⓗ

---

Popular, 17th-century pub downhill from the market place. Four changing guest beers come from all over the country. Covered patio area behind the pub. Extremely good value, comprehensive menu, including doorstep sandwiches. No food Sat/Sun.
❀ 🍷 🅰 ♣ P 🍽

### Green Dragon
29 Broad Street
☎ (01986) 892681
11–3, 5–11; 11–11 Fri & Sat; 12–4, 7–10.30 Sun
**Adnams Bitter; Green Dragon Chaucer, Bridge Street, Dragon, seasonal beers** Ⓗ
Formerly the Horse & Groom, purchased from Brent Walker in 1991. Its friendly atmosphere caters for all tastes. The award-winning beers are brewed behind the pub. Good value food. The restaurant doubles as a family room.
🍺 🐕 ❀ 🍷 🍴 🅰 ♣ P 🍽

## Bury St Edmunds

### Black Boy
69 Guildhall Street
☎ (01284) 752723
11–3, 6–11; 12–3, 7–10.30 Sun
**Greene King IPA, Abbot, seasonal beers** Ⓗ
Characterful, timbered, 15th-century pub, near the town centre, decorated extensively with cartoons painted onto the walls by Terry Willers of the *Daily Express*. Good value lunches. Clubs meet in the upstairs function room. The car park is reached via St Andrews St South. Q 🍷 🚆 ♣ P

### Flying Fortress
Mount Road, Great Barton (Thurston road)
☎ (01284) 787665
12–3, 5–11; 12–3, 6–10.30 Sun
**Adnams Bitter; Draught Bass; Flowers IPA; Worthington Bitter; guest beers** Ⓔ
Friendly free house displaying WWII artefacts from the airfield nearby (the original farmhouse stood at the end of the main runway!). The large garden includes an old fire engine for children. Full menu and carvery. Q ❀ 🍷 P

---

## 🏠 INDEPENDENT BREWERIES

| | |
|---|---|
| **Adnams:** Southwold | **Mauldons:** Sudbury |
| **Blue Boar:** Oulton | **Nethergate:** Clare |
| **Earl Soham:** Earl Soham | **Old Chimneys:** Market Weston |
| **Green Dragon:** Bungay | |
| **Greene King:** Bury St Edmunds | **St Peter's:** South Elmham |
| | **Scott's:** Lowestoft |
| **Green Jack:** Oulton Broad | **Tolly Cobbold:** Ipswich |

## Ipswich Arms

1 Tayfen Road (200 yds from station) ☎ (01284) 703623
11–2 (2.30 Fri), 6.30–11; 11–11 Sat; 12–10.30 Sun
**Greene King XX Mild, IPA, Abbot, seasonal beers** Ⓗ
Interesting, semi-circular, 19th-century, light brick pub on a busy corner. Good value food. Ⓓ ≠ P

## Queen's Head

39 Churchgate Street
☎ (01284) 761554
11–11; 12–10.30 Sun
**Adnams Broadside; Boddingtons Bitter; Courage Best Bitter; Webster's Green Label; guest beers** Ⓗ
White-brick, 18th-century coaching inn with plenty of history, beneath a Victorian-style refurbishment. Young trade at weekends. ❀ Ⓓ Ⓓ ≠

## Rose & Crown

48 Whiting Street
☎ (01284) 755934
11–11; 11–3, 7–11 Sat; 12–2.30, 7–10.30 Sun
**Greene King XX Mild, IPA, Abbot, seasonal beers** Ⓗ
Characterful, unspoilt, family-run town local in sight of the brewery and frequented by its staff. Mild outsells the bitter. The pub fronts on to Westgate St. No food Sun. Q Ⓓ Ⓓ ♣

# Butley

## Oyster

The Street ☎ (01394) 450790
11–3, 5–11; 11–11 Sat; 12–10.30 Sun
**Adnams Mild, Bitter, Old, Broadside** Ⓗ
15th-century building, much altered in recent years. Vintage motor cycle meetings are held here. Local folk groups Sun.
🚶 ❀ Ⓓ ♿ ▲ ♣ P

# Combs Fords

## Gladstone Arms

2 Combs Fords (1 mile from Stowmarket on Needham road) ☎ (01449) 612339
11–2.30, 5 (6 Sat)–11; 12–3, 7–10.30 Sun
**Adnams Bitter, Old, Extra (summer), Broadside** Ⓗ
Adnams tied house with areas to suit all tastes; a good games venue. Cross the stream to the beer garden. 🚶 ❀ ♣ P

# Denston

## Plumbers Arms

Wickham Street
☎ (01440) 820350
11–2.30, 5–11; 12–3, 7–10.30 Sun
**Greene King IPA, Rayments Special, Abbot, seasonal beers** Ⓗ
Large country pub on the main road from Bury to Haverhill.

---

Note: mild is kept under a cask breather. 🚶 Q ❀ Ⓓ Ⓓ ♣ P

# Earl Soham

## Victoria

By A1120 ☎ (01728) 685758
11.30–3.30, 5.30–11; 12–3, 7–10.30 Sun
**Earl Soham Gannet Mild, Victoria, Albert, Jolabrugg; guest beers** Ⓗ
Simple country pub with its own brewery. 🚶 Q ❀ Ⓓ Ⓓ ♣ P

# East Bergholt

## Hare & Hounds

Heath Road ☎ (01206) 298438
11–2.30, 5–11; 11–11 Sat; 12–3, 7–10.30 Sun
**Adnams Mild, Bitter, Broadside; Draught Bass; guest beers** Ⓗ
Grade II listed building dating from the 16th century, boasting a fine pargetted ceiling with heavy relief in the main bar. Well situated for Constable Country. Eve meals Sat/Sun.
Q 🐄 ❀ 🏠 Ⓓ Ⓓ ♿ ▲ P

# Edwardstone

## White Horse

Mill Green OS951429
☎ (01787) 211211
11–2.30, 7 (6.30 summer)–11; 12–3, 7–10.30 Sun
**Greene King XX Mild, IPA, seasonal beers** Ⓗ
Homely, two-bar pub, tucked away down lanes which can make it difficult to find. It attracts various local vehicle rallies in summer. Snacks available all week; meals served Thu–Sun.
🚶 Q ❀ Ⓓ Ⓓ 🍴 ▲ ♣ 🍽 P

# Flempton

## Greyhound

The Green ☎ (01284) 728400
11–2.30, 5–11; 11–11 Sat; 12–3, 7–10.30 Sun
**Greene King IPA, Abbot, seasonal beers** Ⓗ
Easy to miss village pub, tucked away behind the church, overlooking the village green and attractive thatched cottages. A good pub for tourists visiting the nearby country park with its replica Saxon village. Good food. Note: mild is kept under a cask breather.
🚶 Q ❀ Ⓓ Ⓓ 🍴 ♣ P

# Framlingham

## Railway Inn

Station Road ☎ (01728) 723693
12–3, 5.30–11; 12–3, 7–10.30 Sun
**Adnams Mild or Extra or Old, Bitter, Broadside** Ⓗ
Fine small town pub of quality and real atmosphere where the

---

plush lounge bar boasts a Victorian fireplace. The public bar has basic tables, settles and a barrel seat. New games room.
🚶 Q ❀ 🍴 ▲ ♣ P

# Friston

## Old Chequers

Aldeburgh Road
☎ (01728) 688270
11–3, 6–11; 12–3, 7–10.30 Sun
**Adnams Bitter; John Smith's Bitter; Woodforde's Wherry; guest beers** Ⓗ
Well-modernised village pub, specialising in good food.
🚶 Q ❀ 🏠 Ⓓ Ⓓ ♿ P

# Gislingham

## Six Bells

High Street ☎ (01379) 783349
12–3, 7 (5.30 Fri)–11; 12–3, 7–10.30 Sun
**Greene King IPA; Shepherd Neame Master Brew Bitter; guest beers** Ⓗ
Village-centre pub, occupying a spacious brick building. The landlord is keen to support local micro-breweries. Excellent food from an interesting menu (no meals Mon). Children's certificate. Annual Dwile Flonk for charity. Guest beers include a mild. 🐄 ❀ Ⓓ Ⓓ 🍴 ♣ P

# Glemsford

## Angel Inn

Egremont Street
☎ (01787) 281671
12–2.30, 5–11; 12–3, 7–10.30 Sun
**Greene King IPA, Abbot** Ⓖ
Quiet, traditional pub, the oldest house in the village and once the home of Cardinal Wolsey's secretary John Cavendish, whose ghost is reputed to appear. Note: the seasonal beers on sale are usually kept under a cask breather. Q ❀ 🍴 ♣ P

# Great Wratting

## Red Lion

School Road ☎ (01440) 783237
11–2.30, 5–11; 11–11 Fri & Sat; 12–2.30, 7–10.30 Sun
**Adnams Mild, Bitter, Old, Extra; Boddingtons Bitter** Ⓗ
Village pub, well-known for its whalebone arch and children's garden. Good, home-cooked food. 🚶 Q ❀ Ⓓ Ⓓ 🍴 P

# Hadleigh

## Cock

89 George Street
☎ (01473) 822879
5 (12 Fri & Sat)–11; 12–3, 7–10.30 Sun
**Tetley Bitter; guest beers** Ⓗ
Large, two-bar town pub with a busy public bar (popular

with the young) and a quieter, large, split-level lounge. The landlord has transformed the trade. Mauldons house beer.
🏠 Q ❄ ☀ 🍴 👜 ♣ P ✗

## Haverhill

### Queen's Head
Queen Street ☎ (01440) 702026
11–11; 12–3, 7–10.30 Sun
**Courage Best Bitter, Directors; Nethergate Bitter, Umbel Magna; Ruddles Best Bitter** 🅗
15th-century, Grade II listed free house with a friendly atmosphere. 🏠 Q ◖ 🍴 ♣ P

## Hawkedon

### Queen's Head
Rede Road ☎ (01284) 789218
12–2.30, 5–11; 12–11 Sat; 12–4, 7–10.30 Sun
**Mauldons Best Bitter; Woodforde's Wherry; guest beers** 🅗
Classic village pub near the church; off the beaten track but well worth finding. Dating in part from the 14th century, it has low ceilings, heavily carved beams and a large inglenook. Home-made meals from a changing blackboard menu. 🏠 Q ❄ 🍴 ◖ ◗ P

## Holton

### Lord Nelson
Mill Road ☎ (01986) 873275
11.30–3, 6.30–11; 12–4, 7–10.30 Sun
**Flowers IPA; Ind Coope Burton Ale; Tetley Bitter; guest beer** (summer) 🅗
Ex-Brent Walker house now transformed into a busy and friendly local with a lounge bar and a public bar with games. Good food. Petanque played.
Q ❄ 🍴 ◖ ◗ A ♣ P 🍺

## Horringer

### Six Bells
The Street ☎ (01284) 735551
11.30–2.30, 6 (7 Sat)–11; 12–2.30, 7–10.30 Sun
**Greene King XX Mild** (summer), **IPA** 🅗, **Abbot** 🅖, **seasonal beers** 🅗
Welcoming, traditional red-brick local in a picturesque village close to Ickworth Park (NT). Good value, home-made pies. 🏠 Q ❄ ◖ ♣ P

## Ipswich

### Brewery Tap
Cliffe Road ☎ (01473) 281508
11–3, 5–11; 11–11 Fri & summer; 12–3, 7–10.30 Sun
**Tolly Cobbold Mild, Bitter, Original, Tollyshooter, seasonal beers** 🅗
Pub on the riverside – the Tolly

Cobbold tap. Comfortable furniture, lots of pictures and old price lists are features. All beers are served through swan necks so ask to have the sparkler removed. Eve meals Tue–Sat.
🏠 Q ❄ ☀ ◖◗ 👜 ♣ P ✗

### Dales
Dales Road ☎ (01473) 250024
11–3, 5–11; 12–3, 7–10.30 Sun
**Adnams Bitter; Draught Bass; Tolly Cobbold Mild, Bitter** 🅗
Modern, two-bar pub situated on a quiet housing estate. Patio access is via the comfortable lounge or the car park. Now a free house. Q ❄ ◖ 🍴 ♣ P

### Grand Old Duke of York
212 Woodbridge Road
☎ (01473) 257115
11–3, 5–11; 12–3, 7–10.30 Sun
**Adnams Bitter, Broadside, Old; Boddingtons Bitter; guest beers** 🅗
Popular pub: a single, large room with an L-shaped bar. No meals Sun eve. Wheelchair WC. Q ❄ ◖ ◗ 👜 P

### Greyhound
Henley Road ☎ (01473) 252105
11–2.30, 5–11; 11–11 Sat; 12–3, 7–10.30 Sun
**Adnams Mild, Bitter, Old, Extra, Broadside; guest beers** 🅗
Attractive, busy, two-roomed pub, popular for food (no eve meals Sun). Q ❄ ◖ ◗ 🍴 ♣ P

### Plough
2 Dog's Head Street
☎ (01473) 288005
11–3, 5–11; 11–11 Fri & Sat; 7–10.30 Sun, closed Sun lunch
**Marston's Bitter; Morland Old Speckled Hen; guest beers** 🅗
Good conversation is assured in this prominent, large (but friendly) town-centre pub which offers an impressive beer and cider range (ten handpumps). House beer from Ushers. Convenient for Ipswich Town FC but pricey for the area.
☀ ◖ 👜 ☁ ✗

### Tap & Spile (Dove)
76 St Helens Street (near Suffolk College)
☎ (01473) 211270
11–3, 5–11; 11–11 Thu–Sat; 12–3, 7–10.30 Sun
**Beer range varies** 🅗
Good, honest ale house: a student pub lunchtimes which welcomes a cross-section of drinkers at night. Don't miss the Sun night quiz. No meals Sun. Cider varies. Wheelchair WC. 🏠 Q ❄ ☀ ◖ 👜 ☁ P

### Woolpack
1 Tuddenham Road
☎ (01473) 253059

11–2.30 (3 Sat), 5–11; 12–3, 7–10.30 Sun
**Draught Bass; Tolly Cobbold Bitter, IPA, Old Strong, Tollyshooter; guest beer** 🅗
16th-century, brick-built country-style pub next to Christchurch Park, with a warm welcome in a lounge bar, a snug bar and a smoke room plus a games room with bar billiards. 🏠 Q ◖ ♣ P

## Ixworth

### Greyhound
High Street ☎ (01359) 230887
11–3, 6–11; 12–3, 7–10.30 Sun
**Greene King XX Mild, IPA, Abbot, seasonal beers** 🅗
Largish pub which has benefited from an excellent refurbishment. It retains two spacious bars with a super little snug between. Lively, with local games teams. No food Sun.
Q ❄ ☀ A ♣ P

## Kennett

### Bell
Bury Road ☎ (01638) 750286
11–2.30, 6.30–11; 12–3, 7–10.30 Sun
**Greene King IPA, Rayments Special, Abbot; guest beers** 🅗
Heavily-beamed pub, circa 15th century; well-known for food and beers, always well served. 🏠 🍴 ◖ ◗ 🍲 ⚖ P 🍺

## Kentford

### Cock
Bury Road ☎ (01638) 750360
12–3, 5.30–11; 12–3, 7–10.30 Sun
**Greene King IPA, Abbot, seasonal beers** 🅗
Large country pub dating partly from the 1600s with three bars (one used as a restaurant). Good for families, with a large play area.
🏠 Q ❄ ◖ ◗ 🍴 A P

## Lakenheath

### Half Moon
4 High Street ☎ (01842) 861484
11–2.30 (3 Sat), 6–11; 12–3, 7–10.30 Sun
**Greene King XX Mild, IPA, seasonal beers** 🅗
Fine local on the outskirts of the village: a super, flint-faced building (pity about the toilet block). It retains an off-sales window between its two bars. Excellent home-made food at reasonable prices – Mexican dishes a speciality. Note: Abbot Ale is kept under a cask breather. 🏠 Q ❄ ◖ ◗ 🍴 ♣ P

### Plough
Mill Road ☎ (01842) 860285
11–2.30, 6–11; 11–11 Sat; 12–4, 6–10.30 Sun

**Greene King IPA, Abbot** Ⓗ
Popular pub at the centre of a busy village. A fine 19th-century flint exterior conceals spacious bars for clientele of all ages! Bank hol barbecues and occasional music nights with a folk/country flavour. Note: mild is kept under a cask breather. ❀ ⊞ ♣ P

## Lavenham

### Angel
Market Place ☎ (01787) 247388
11–11; 12–10.30 Sun
**Adnams Bitter; Mauldons White Adder; Nethergate Bitter; guest beer** Ⓗ
15th-century inn overlooking the Guildhall. The restaurant and bar have a pleasant, relaxed atmosphere and serve good quality food. Accommodation is of a high standard. Guest beers are often from local breweries.
🏚 Q ❀ 🛏 ◑ ▶ ♣ P ⅙

### Cock
Church Street
☎ (01787) 247407
11–11; 12–10.30 (12–4, 7–10.30 winter) Sun
**Greene King XX Mild, IPA; guest beer** Ⓗ
Traditional three-roomer opposite an impressive church: a beamed bar with a stone floor, a lounge and a garden room which is licensed for families. Large safe gardens (play area). A Mauldons beer is sometimes stocked.
🏚 Q ⌚ ❀ ◑ ▶ ⊞ ♣ ⌂ P ⅙

## Laxfield

### King's Head/ ☆
Lowhouse
Gorams Mill Lane (off B1117, by Guildhall)
☎ (01986) 798395
11–3, 7–11; 12–3, 7–10.30 Sun
**Adnams Mild, Bitter, Extra, Broadside, seasonal beers; Greene King IPA** Ⓗ
Classic, 15th-century pub with a tap room, no bar counter, and high-backed settles in the front room. Worth seeking out as a rare example of an unchanged rural pub – a little gem. Noted for its home-cooked food and excellent puddings.
🏚 Q ⌚ ❀ ◑ ▶ ⊞ ⌂ P

## Lidgate

### Star
The Street ☎ (01638) 500275
11–3, 5 (6 Sat)–11; 12–3, 7–10.30 Sun
**Greene King IPA, Abbot, seasonal beers** Ⓗ
Busy, 400-year-old village pub. Note the unusual, bar-level handpumps. The food is

mostly Continental and Mediterranean in flavour. Bar billiards played.
🏚 Q ❀ ◑ ▶ ♣ ⌂ P

## Long Melford

### George & Dragon
Hall Street ☎ (01787) 371285
11.30–11; 12–10.30 Sun
**Greene King IPA, Abbot, seasonal beers** Ⓗ
Family-run, former coaching inn with a lounge-style, single bar and a restaurant with an interesting menu. Still a good drinking pub with live music (folk and blues) Wed eves. The overnight accommodation caters for guests with disabilities. 🏚 ❀ 🛏 ◑ ▶ & P

## Lowestoft

### Factory Arms
Raglan Street ☎ (01502) 574523
11–11; 12–4, 7–10.30 Sun
**Courage Directors; Wells Bombardier; Woodforde's Wherry; guest beers** Ⓗ
Single-room, backstreet local where pool and darts dominate. Guest beers from independent brewers. ♣

### Triangle Tavern
29 St Peters Street
☎ (01502) 582711
10.30–11; 12–10.30 Sun
**Green Jack Bitter, Best Bitter, Golden Sickle, Norfolk Wolf Porter, Lurcher, seasonal beers; Woodforde's Wherry; guest beers** Ⓗ
Basic, town-centre local with a main front bar area and a small pool room. One of Green Jack's two tied pubs, also selling at least three beers from micro- and independent breweries.
🏚 ⊞ ♣ ⌂

### Welcome
182–184 London Road
☎ (01502) 585500
10.30–4, 7.30–11; 12–3, 7–10.30 Sun
**Adnams Bitter, Old, Broadside (summer); Greene King IPA, Abbot; Worthington Bitter** Ⓗ
Town local living up to its name. It can get smoky. ≈ ♣

## Martlesham

### Blacktiles
Main Road ☎ (01473) 610298
.11–11; 12–10.30 Sun
**Adnams Bitter, Broadside; Boddingtons Bitter; guest beer** Ⓗ
Originally a tea room next to the historic RAF station, now a popular food house. Recently refurbished and extended. Food is served all day Sat and Sun. 🏚 Q ⌚ ❀ ◑ ▶ ⊞ & P ⊟

## Middleton

### Bell Inn
The Street ☎ (01728) 648286
11–3.30, 6.30–11; 12–3.30, 7–10.30 Sun
**Adnams Mild (summer), Bitter, Old, Broadside** Ⓗ
Partly thatched pub with an old-style, basic, tap room and a lounge. Regular folk music.
🏚 Q ❀ ◑ ▶ ⊞ & ▲ ♣ P

## Newbourne

### Fox Inn
The Street ☎ (01473) 736307
11–3, 6–11; 11–11 Fri, Sat & summer; 12–5, 7–10.30 Sun
**Flowers IPA; Tolly Cobbold IPA; guest beer (summer)** Ⓖ
Characterful, timber-framed pub. Excellent food (fresh fish). Handy for the nature reserve. Skittle alley.
🏚 Q ⌚ ❀ ◑ ▶ & ▲ ♣ P

## Newmarket

### Five Bells
16 St Mary's Square
11–3 (4 Sat), 6–11; 12–3, 7–10.30 Sun
**Greene King IPA, Abbot, seasonal beers** Ⓗ
Typical locals' pub with many games. Swimming pool in the enclosed garden, plus children's amusements. Note: mild is kept under a cask breather. 🏚 ❀ ♣ P

### Waggon & Horses
High Street ☎ (01638) 662479
11–11; 12–10.30 Sun
**Adnams Bitter, Broadside; Flowers Original; Marston's Pedigree; Whitbread Abroad Cooper** Ⓗ**; guest beers** Ⓗ/Ⓖ
16th-century coaching inn: one long bar with a large open fire at one end. Full details of beers and prices are well displayed.
🏚 ❀ ◑ ▶ & ♣ ⌂ P

## Offton

### Limeburners
Willisham Road
☎ (01473) 658318
12–2.30 (not Mon), 5–11; 12–11 Sat; 12–3, 7–10.30 Sun
**Adnams Bitter; Wells Eagle; guest beer** Ⓗ
Two-bar local with a large garden; named after a lime kiln in the quarry opposite. No food Mon eve. Q ❀ ◑ ▶ ⊞ P

## Pin Mill

### Butt & Oyster ☆
The Quay ☎ (01473) 780764
11–3, 7–11 (11–11 Sat & summer); 12–3, 7–10.30 (12–10.30 summer) Sun
**Tolly Cobbold Mild, Bitter** Ⓖ/Ⓗ**, Original,**

Tollyshooter; guest beers H
Classic riverside pub, CAMRA regional *Pub of the Year* 1992.
🏠 Q ✿ ❀ ◑ ▶ ♣ P ⊁

## Polstead

### Brewers Arms
Bower House Tye (A1071)
☎ (01787) 210441
11–3, 6–11; 12–3, 7–10.30 Sun (may vary)
Greene King IPA; guest beers H
Modernised, large, open-plan pub with an outdoor children's play area. Two guest ales from independents, usually local.
🏠 ✿ ⌂ ◑ ▶ ♣ P ⊟

## Rumburgh

### Buck ☆
Mill Road ☎ (01986) 785257
11–11; 12–3, 7–10.30 Sun
Adnams Bitter; Greene King IPA; guest beer H
Splendid, characterful pub, originally the guest house for a medieval priory: a long, narrow front bar and a games room, plus tastefully extended back rooms and dining areas. Guest beer from independent brewers. 🏠 ✿ ◑ ▶ ⊞ ▲ ♣ P

## Sibton

### White Horse
Halesworth Road
☎ (01728) 660337
11.30–2.30, 7–11; 12–3, 7–10.30 Sun
Adnams Bitter, Old, Broadside; guest beer (occasional) H
Beamed village local with a raised gallery where well-behaved children are welcome. The large garden has a play area. No meals Sun eve or Mon lunch. 🏠 ✿ ⌂ ◑ ▶ ♧ ♣ P

## Snape

### Golden Key
Priory Road ☎ (01728) 688510
11–3, 6–11; 12–3, 7–10.30 Sun
Adnams Bitter, Old, Broadside (summer), Tally Ho H
17th-century village pub serving excellent food.
🏠 Q ✿ ⌂ ◑ ▶ ♧ ▲ P

## Southwold

### Lord Nelson
East Street ☎ (01502) 722079
10.30–11; 12–10.30 Sun
Adnams Mild, Bitter, Old, Extra (summer), Broadside H
Late 18th-century inn, now a popular town pub close to the sea. 🏠 Q ✿ ✿ ◑ ▶ ▲ ♣ ⊟

### Red Lion
East Green ☎ (01502) 722385
11–11; 12–10.30 Sun

Adnams Mild, Bitter, Old, Extra (summer), Broadside, Tally Ho H
Late 17th-century pub, extended in the early 20th century. Formerly a fisherman's pub, it is popular with families in summer. Fresh local fish is a speciality. 🏠 Q ✿ ✿ ⌂ ◑ ▶ ♧ ▲ ♣ P ⊟

### Sole Bay Inn
7 East Green ☎ (01502) 723736
11–11; 12–10.30 Sun
Adnams Mild (summer), Bitter, Old, Broadside H
Small, one-bar local, next to Adnams Brewery. The building is early Victorian, the subject of many paintings, and is overlooked by the lighthouse. Bar snacks include smoked sprats. Q ✿ ⌂ ▲ ♣

## Stowmarket

### Royal William
Union Street East (up Stowupland St from station, 2nd right) ☎ (01449) 674553
11–3, 6–11; 12–3, 7–10.30 Sun
Greene King XX Mild, IPA, Abbot, seasonal beers G
Good example of a small town, backstreet local which still serves its ales from a room behind the bar by gravity. Eve meals on request. ◑ ⇌ ♣

## Stradbroke

### Queen's Head
Queen Street (B118)
☎ (01379) 384384
11.30–3, 6.30–11; 12–3.30, 7–10.30 Sun
Adnams Bitter; Greene King IPA, Abbot; guest beers (weekend) H
Listed building, heavily timbered. Micro-brewery guest beers. 🏠 ✿ ◑ ▶ P

## Theberton

### Lion Inn
On B1122 ☎ (01728) 830185
11–3 (may extend), 6–11; 12–3, 7–10.30 Sun
Adnams Bitter; guest beers H
Popular village local serving three guest beers, often from East Anglia's smaller breweries. Pool room.
🏠 ✿ ◑ ▶ ♧ ▲ ♣ P

## Tostock

### Gardeners Arms
Church Road
☎ (01359) 270460
11.30–3, 7–11; 12–3, 7–10.30 Sun
Greene King IPA, Abbot, seasonal beers H
Fine old building boasting beams and a large fire in the lounge. The good, basic public bar has church pews and a

tiled floor. Good value food in the restaurant (Mon–Sat lunch, Wed–Sun eves).
🏠 ✿ ◑ ▶ ⊞ ♣ P

## Wangford

### Plough Inn
London Road (A12, N of village) ☎ (01502) 578239
11–3, 7–11; 12–3, 7–10.30 Sun
Adnams Bitter G, Old H, Extra G
Old inn with a ghost, a snug and a small dining room. The beer is served from cooling cabinets. 🏠 ✿ ◑ ▶ ♧ ♣ P

## Wenhaston

### Star
Hall Road ☎ (01502) 478240
11–3, 6–11; 12–3, 7–10.30 Sun
Adnams Bitter, Old G
Victorian village local with three bars and a large garden.
🏠 Q ✿ ✿ ◑ ♧ ▲ ♣ ⊟

## Wickhambrook

### Greyhound
Meeting Green
☎ (01440) 820548
11–2.30, 5.30–11; 12–3, 7–10.30 Sun
Greene King XX Mild, IPA, Abbot, seasonal beers H
Excellent, busy, but hard to find, country pub.
Q ✿ ◑ ▶ ⊞ ▲ ♣ P ⊟

## Wickham Market

### George
High Street ☎ (01728) 746306
Tolly Cobbold Mild, Bitter H
Homely local with two main drinking areas – one with pool, the other more relaxed. Ramblers and cyclists are given a welcome. One other beer from Tolly Cobbold is also sold. 🏠 ▲ ♣ P

## Woodbridge

### Bell & Steelyard
New Street ☎ (01394) 382933
11.30–3, 5.30–11; 12–3, 7–10.30 Sun
Greene King XX Mild (summer), IPA, Abbot, seasonal beers H
Traditional local claiming to be the 12th oldest pub in the country. The old steelyard can be seen at the front.
🏠 Q ✿ ✿ ◑ ▶ ♧ ⇌ ♣ ⊁

### King's Head
Market Hill ☎ (01394) 387750
11–3, 7–11; 12–3, 7–10.30 Sun
Adnams Mild, Bitter, Old, Extra, Broadside; Boddingtons Bitter H
Possibly the oldest building in Woodbridge has added a new dining area in the style of the original pub. Extensive menu.
🏠 Q ✿ ◑ ▶ ♧ ▲ ⇌ ♣ P

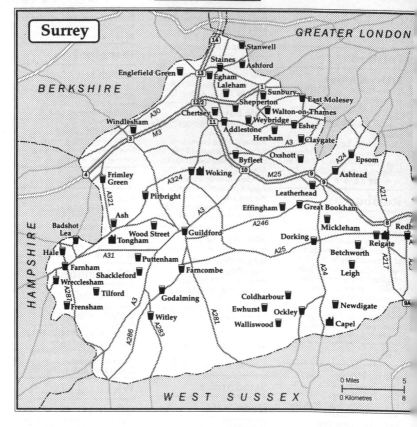

## Surrey

GREATER LONDON

BERKSHIRE

HAMPSHIRE

WEST SUSSEX

0 Miles 5
0 Kilometres 8

---

## Addlestone

### Magnet
21 Station Road (B3121)
☎ (01932) 847908
11–11; 12–4.30, 7–10.30 Sun
**Greene King IPA, Abbot, seasonal beers** H
Small local dating back to 1863.
🏮 ❀ ⇌ ♣ P

## Ash

### Dover Arms
31 Guildford Road (A321/A323 jct) ☎ (01252) 26025
11–3, 6 (7 Sat)–11; 12–4, 7–10.30 Sun
**Marston's Pedigree; Wadworth 6X; guest beers** H
Excellent two-bar pub on a busy roundabout. Plates, brasses and glasses adorn the main bar. Good, home-cooked food. Families welcome.
🏮 ❀ ◑ ▶ ⇌ ♣ P ⅃

## Ashford

### District Arms
180 Woodthorpe Road
☎ (01784) 252160
11–11; 12–3, 7–10.30 Sun

---

**Courage Best Bitter, Directors; Greene King Abbot; John Smith's Bitter; guest beer** H
Welcoming, single-bar local serving excellent home-cooked lunches, Mon–Fri. Large function room.
🏮 Q ❀ ◑ ♿ ⇌ P ⊟

## Ashtead

### Brewery Inn
15 The Street (A24)
☎ (01372) 272405
11–11; 12–10.30 Sun
**Friary Meux BB; Hardy Royal Oak; Ind Coope Burton Ale; King & Barnes Sussex; Marston's Pedigree; Tetley Bitter** H
Large, 19th-century pub on the site of Sayer's Ashtead Brewery. It is busy around the bar, but the raised lounge area is more sedate. Happy 'hour' 5–7.30 Mon–Fri.
🌤 ❀ ◑ ▶ ♣ P

## Badshot Lea

### Crown
Pine View Close (opp. garden centre, off A324)

---

☎ (01252) 20453
10.30–11; 12–10.30 Sun
**Fuller's London Pride, ESB, seasonal beers** H
Sidestreet local serving good value food, including Balti meals. Sun lunch is popular (booking advised). ❀ ◑ ▶ P

## Betchworth

### Dolphin Inn
The Street
☎ (01737) 842288
11–3, 5.30–11; 12–3, 7–10.30 Sun
**Young's Bitter, Special, Ram Rod, Winter Warmer, seasonal beers** H
Attractive, popular inn opposite a church featured in *Four Weddings and a Funeral*. Good food.
🏮 Q ❀ ◑ ▶ ♣ P

## Bletchingley

### William IV
Little Common Lane (off A25, N of village) ☎ (01883) 743278
11–3, 6–11; 12–3, 7–10.30 Sun
**Draught Bass; Fuller's London Pride; Harveys BB; Pilgrim Progress; Shepherd Neame**

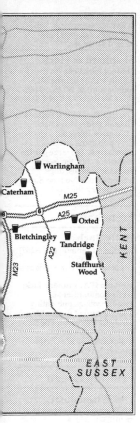

are served from a single bar.
No food Sun.
🏨 ❀ ◑ ♣ P ⊬

## Chertsey

### Coach & Horses

14 St Ann's Road (B375)
☎ (01932) 563085
11–11; 12–3, 7–10.30 Sun
**Fuller's Chiswick, London
Pride, ESB** Ⓗ
Welcoming pub dating from
around 1860, with an
interesting frontage. No meals
Sun eve. Handy for Chertsey
Town FC. 🏨 🛏 ◑ ▶ ▲ ♣ P

### Town Hall Tavern

20 London Street (B375, opp.
the old town hall)
☎ (01932) 563045
11–3, 5–11; 11–11 Thu–Sat; 12–3,
7–10.30 Sun
**Fuller's London Pride; guest
beers** Ⓗ
The only true free house in
Chertsey. First licensed in 1865,
this friendly, one-roomed pub
offers a constantly changing
range of beers. Excellent food
(no lunches Sat/Sun).
🏨 ❀ 🛏 ◑ ▶ ▲ ⇌ P

## Claygate

### Foley Arms

Foley Road ☎ (01372) 463431
11–3, 5.30–11; 11–11 Fri & Sat; 12–
3.30, 7–10.30 (12–10.30 summer) Sun
**Young's Bitter, Special, Ram
Rod, seasonal beers** Ⓗ
Comfortable, two-bar Victorian
village pub, named after local
landowners. Folk music in a
separate room Fri eve. The
large garden has a children's
play area. Barbecues Sat in
summer. No food Sun.
🏨 Q ❀ ◑ 🍺 ⇌ ♣ P

## Coldharbour

### Plough Inn

Coldharbour Lane (road to
Leith Hill from Dorking)
OS152441 ☎ (01306) 711793
11.30–3, 6 (6.30 winter)–11; 12–3,
7–10.30 Sun
**Adnams Broadside; Badger
Dorset Best, Tanglefoot;
North Downs Old Cocky;
Ringwood Old Thumper;
Wadworth 6X; guest beers** Ⓗ
Friendly, family-run pub on
the slopes of Leith Hill. Nine
ales and a cider are always
available. It may open all day
on summer weekends. Family
room weekends and summer
lunchtimes.
🏨 ⏰ ❀ 🛏 ◑ ▶ ♣ ⏺

## Dorking

### Cricketers

81 South Street (A25, one-way
system) ☎ (01306) 889938
12–11; 12–3, 7–10.30 Sun

**Fuller's Chiswick, London
Pride, ESB, seasonal beers** Ⓗ
Pub with bare-brick walls, one
with a large etched mirror
depicting a cricketer. Pleasant,
sheltered patio garden. No
food Sun. ❀ ◑ ♣

### King's Arms

45 West Street (A25, one-way
system) ☎ (01306) 883361
11–11; 12–3, 7–10.30 Sun
**King & Barnes Sussex;
Marston's Pedigree;
Ringwood Best Bitter; Tetley
Bitter; Wadworth 6X; guest
beer** Ⓗ
400-year-old building with
several linked drinking areas.
The guest beer changes weekly
and is from an independent
brewery. Sun night live music.
Eve meals served Tue–Sat.
❀ ◑ ▶ P

### Queen's Head

Horsham Road (A25, one-way
system) ☎ (01306) 883041
11–11; 12–10.30 Sun
**Fuller's Chiswick, London
Pride, ESB** Ⓗ
Family-run, one-bar pub with
keen pool and darts teams.
Happy hours 6–8. No food
Sun. Limited parking.
❀ ◑ ♣ P

## East Molesey

### Europa

171 Walton Road (B369)
☎ (0181) 979 8838
11–11; 12–10.30 Sun
**Courage Best Bitter,
Directors** Ⓗ
Friendly local with a lively
public, a quiet snug and a
comfortable lounge. Happy
'hour' 5–7 Mon–Fri, 12–1 and
7–8 Sun. Eve food and a car
park are planned. No food Sun
lunch. Q ❀ ◑ 🍺 ♣

## Effingham

### Plough

Orestan Lane
☎ (01372) 458121
11–2.45, 6–11; 12–3, 7–10.30 Sun
**Young's Bitter, Special,
Winter Warmer** Ⓗ
Excellent food and
Wandsworth beers make this
Young's outpost always busy.
Early eve diners dominate but
drinkers soon take over.
Q ❀ ◑ ▶ P ⊬

---

## INDEPENDENT BREWERIES

| | |
|---|---|
| **Hogs Back:** | Tongham |
| **North Downs:** | Capel |
| **Pilgrim:** | Reigate |
| **Planets:** | Woking |

---

Master Brew Bitter; guest
beer Ⓗ
Unaltered pub with three small
bars, one used as a restaurant.
The two front bars are alive
with conversation.
Q ❀ ◑ ▶ P

## Byfleet

### Plough

104 High Road (off A245)
☎ (01932) 353257
11–11; 12–3, 7–10.30 Sun
**Courage Best Bitter; guest
beers** Ⓗ
Free house of distinction
offering variety to this choice-
starved area. A real ale
drinkers' pub with a constantly
changing range of beers.
🏨 Q ❀ ◑ ♣ P

## Caterham

### King & Queen

34 High Street (B2030)
☎ (01883) 345438
11–3, 5–11; 11–11 Sat; 12–4, 7–10.30
Sun
**Fuller's Chiswick, London
Pride, ESB, seasonal beers** Ⓗ
400-year-old building, a pub
for 150 years. Three distinct
drinking areas (one for darts)

## Egham

### Crown
38 High Street
☎ (01784) 432608
11–3, 5.30 (6 Sat)–11; 12–3, 7–10.30 Sun
**Fuller's London Pride; guest beers** H
Traditional and friendly, 1930s pub with an attractive secluded garden. A genuine free house offering a constantly changing selection of seven guest ales from regional, and occasionally smaller, breweries. No lunches Sun.
❀ ◖ ⊕ ≢ ♣ P

### Eclipse
Egham Hill (A30, bottom of hill) ☎ (01784) 432989
11–3, 5.30–11; 12–3, 7–10.30 Sun
**Boddingtons Bitter; Courage Best Bitter, Directors; Fuller's London Pride; John Smith's Bitter** H
Pub dating originally from the 1700s but rebuilt in 1936: clean, tidy and comfortably furnished. The former public bar is now used as a dining area lunchtimes and for children eves. ❀ ◖ ≢ ♣ P

## Englefield Green

### Beehive
34 Middle Hill (off A30)
☎ (01784) 431621
12–11; 12–10.30 Sun
**Gale's Best Bitter, IPA, HSB; guest beers** H
Small, friendly, one-bar pub, especially popular in summer. Guest beers are from independent breweries. Cider in summer.
♨ ❀ ◖ ♣ ◔ P

## Epsom

### Barley Mow
12 Pikes Hill (off Upper High St, A2022) ☎ (01372) 721044
11–3, 5.30–11; 12–3, 7–10.30 Sun
**Fuller's Chiswick, London Pride, ESB** H
Splendid backstreet local with a conservatory at the rear where children are allowed in until 8pm. Genuine, home-cooked specials; barbecues summer eves. Q ➻ ◖ ◗ ♿ ♣

### King's Arms
144 East Street (A24)
☎ (01372) 723892
11–3, 5–11; 12–3, 7–10.30 Sun
**Young's Bitter, Special, Winter Warmer** H
Large, Victorian roadside inn catering for more mature drinkers. Daily specials are cooked to order. Darts team and golf society.
Q ❀ ◖ ⊕ ♣ P

## Esher

### Albert Arms
82 High Street (A307)
☎ (01372) 465290
10.30–11; 12–10.30 Sun
**Draught Bass; Boddingtons Bitter; Brakspear Special; Marston's Pedigree; Young's Bitter; guest beer** (summer) H
Popular, two-bar local frequented by well-known sports personalities. No piped music; occasional live piano or guitar. Bar and bistro meals are all home-cooked (no food Sun eve). ◖ ◗ ♣

## Ewhurst

### Windmill Inn
Pitch Hill OS080424
☎ (01483) 277566
12–3, 6–11; 12–11 Sat & summer;
12–10.30 Sun
**Courage Best Bitter; Harveys Pale Ale; guest beers** H
Smart, isolated free house in good walking country, offering panoramic views from the large terraced garden. Three varying guest beers; occasional beer festivals at bank hols. Popular with diners.
♨ ➻ ❀ ◖ ♿ P

## Farncombe

### Cricketers
37 Nightingale Road
☎ (01483) 420273
12–3 (4 Fri & Sat), 5.30–11; 12–4, 7–10.30 Sun
**Fuller's Chiswick, London Pride, ESB, seasonal beers** H
Large amounts of beer are consumed in this busy local, consisting of several drinking areas around a central bar. Cricketing memorabilia abounds. ❀ ◖ ◗ ≢ ♣ ✂

## Farnham

### Lamb
43 Abbey Street
☎ (01252) 714133
11–2.30, 5–11; 11–11 Fri & Sat; 12–10.30 Sun
**Shepherd Neame Master Brew Bitter, Best Bitter, Spitfire, Bishops Finger** H
Proper beer drinkers' pub in a side street. A small bar and a low ceiling contribute to its friendly appeal.
♨ ❀ ◖ ≢ ♣

### Queen's Head
9 The Borough (A325)
☎ (01252) 726524
11–11; 12–3, 7–10.30 Sun
**Gale's Butser, Best Bitter, HSB, seasonal beers; guest beer** H
Classic town-centre pub with a mostly original, 16th-century structure. Busy, it entertains a

cosmopolitan mix of customers in its contrasting bars. Sun night quiz. No food Sun.
♨ ❀ ◖ ⊕ ≢ ♣

### Shepherd & Flock
22 Moor Park Lane (in the middle of A31 Bourne Mill roundabout) ☎ (01252) 716675
11–3, 5.30–11; 11–11 Sat; 12–3, 7–10.30 Sun
**Courage Best Bitter; Fuller's London Pride; Hogs Back TEA; guest beers** H
Cosy pub in the middle of a roundabout. The large garden is ideal for children (some domestic animals; dogs welcome, too). No food Sun. Quiet during the week.
Q ❀ ◖ P

## Frensham

### Holly Bush
Shortfield Common (off A287)
☎ (01252) 793593
11–2.30 (4 Sat), 6–11; 12–4, 7–10.30 Sun
**Morland IPA, Tanner's Jack; Wells Bombardier** H
Two-bar village pub dating from the turn of the century; handy for Frensham Ponds. Thriving games teams. Children's play area in the garden. No food Sun eve.
❀ ◖ ◗ ♣ P

## Frimley Green

### Old Wheatsheaf
205 Frimley Green Road (A321)
☎ (01252) 835074
11–3, 5–11; 11–11 Fri & Sat; 12–4, 7–10.30 Sun
**Morland Original, Old Masters, Old Speckled Hen; guest beers** H
Popular, 100-year-old village local with a low-beamed ceiling and panelled alcoves. Good service at all times. The bookable skittle alley becomes a family room on Sun. No food Sun. ❀ ◖ ♿ ♣ P

## Godalming

### Old Wharf
5 Wharf Street (off A3100)
☎ (01483) 419543
11–11; 12–10.30 Sun
**Boddingtons Bitter; Flowers IPA, Original; Fuller's London Pride; Marston's Pedigree; Whitbread Abroad Cooper** H; **guest beers** H/G
New, barn-style, Hogshead beer emporium. Many guests overshadow a dull basic range. Free tasters! Busy weekday lunchtimes; relaxed eves and weekends. Friendly, attentive service. ♨ ◖ ≢ ◔

### Red Lion
1 Mill Lane ☎ (01483) 415207
11–11; 11–3, 6.30–11 Sat; 12–3, 7–10.30 Sun

Courage Best Bitter, Directors;
Wadworth 6X; guest beers H
Two-bar, town-centre local,
featuring a large games-
oriented public and a smaller,
comfortable lounge.
Imaginative guest beers; lined
glasses on request. No food
Sun eve.
Q ❀ ◑ ◖ ▶ ⌂ ᕈ ᵹ ⇌ ♣ ☐

## Sun

1 Wharf Street (off A3100)
☎ (01483) 415505
11–11; 12–10.30 Sun
Badger Dorset Best,
Tanglefoot; Wadworth 6X H
One-bar, street-corner local,
tastefully furnished. Variety of
games; daily newspapers. Eve
meals on request.
❀ ◑ ⇌ ♣ P

## Great Bookham

### Anchor

161 Lower Road (off A246, via
Eastwick Rd) ☎ (01372) 452429
11–3, 5.30–11; 12–3, 7–10.30 Sun
Courage Best Bitter, Directors;
guest beer H
500-year-old local with
exposed brickwork, oak beams,
a large inglenook and a
pleasant patio. It enjoys a rustic
feel, despite the surrounding
suburbia. No food Sun.
ᴁ Q ❀ ◑ ♣ P

## Guildford

### King's Head

27 Kings Road (A320)
☎ (01483) 568957
11–3, 5–11; 11–11 Sat; 12–3.30, 7–10.30
Sun
Fuller's Chiswick, London
Pride, ESB, seasonal beers H
Popular, multi-roomed pub on
the edge of the town centre,
featuring bare board flooring
and a no-smoking dining area.
Good value beer and food.
ᴁ ❀ ◑ ▶ ⇌ (London Rd) P

### Plough

16 Park Street (one-way
system) ☎ (01483) 570167
11–11; 12–10.30 Sun
Harveys BB; Tetley Bitter;
Young's Special; guest beer H
Small, single-bar pub near the
main station, with one
changing guest beer. Photos of
old Guildford adorn the walls.
◑ ⇌ ♣

### Sanford Arms

58 Epsom Road (A246)
☎ (01483) 572551
11 (11.45 Mon)–3, 5.30–11; 11.30–3.30,
6–11 Sat; 12–3, 7–10.30 Sun
Courage Best Bitter; Marston's
Pedigree; guest beers H
Quiet, friendly local: two,
wood-panelled bars and a
small conservatory. The guest
beer (from independent
breweries) changes regularly.
The pleasant garden features

an aviary, fish pond and
swings. No food Thu and Sun
eves.
Q ❀ ◑ ▶ ⇌ (London Rd)

## Hale

### Ball & Wicket

104 Upper Hale Road (A3106)
☎ (01252) 735278
12–11; 12–3, 7–10.30 Sun
B&T Dragonslayer; Greene
King IPA; Wadworth 6X;
guest beer H
Cosy, 200-year-old pub
opposite the cricket ground. A
brewery and meals are
planned. ᴁ ♣ ⌂ P

## Hersham

### Bricklayers Arms

6–8 Queens Road (off A317)
☎ (01932) 220936
11–11; 12–10.30 Sun
Badger Tanglefoot;
Boddingtons Bitter; Brakspear
Bitter; Flowers IPA; Fuller's
London Pride; Whitbread
seasonal beers H
Friendly local with a
comfortable saloon and a large
public, where the emphasis is
on pool. Spectacular floral
displays in summer. Parking is
difficult. No food Sat and Sun
eves. Q ❀ ⇔ ◑ ▶ ᕈ ♣

## Laleham

### Feathers

The Broadway (B377, 2 miles
S of Staines)
☎ (01784) 453561
11–11; 12–10.30 Sun
Courage Best Bitter; Fuller's
London Pride; Morland Old
Speckled Hen; guest beers H
Popular village pub with two
drinking areas and a log fire.
Quiz nights Mon and Fri.
Regular beer festivals.
ᴁ ❀ ◑ ▶ ⅊ ▲ ♣ P

## Leatherhead

### Plough

93 Kingston Road
☎ (01372) 377608
11–3, 5.30–11; 11–11 Sat; 12–3, 7–10.30
Sun
Hogs Back TEA; Tetley
Bitter H
Pub with two wood-panelled
bars and a conservatory.
Games in the public;
conversation in the saloon. No
food Sun eve.
❀ ◑ ▶ ᕈ ⇌ P ⅋

## Leigh

### Plough

Church Road
☎ (01306) 611348
11–3, 5–11; 12–3, 7–10.30 Sun

King & Barnes Sussex,
Broadwood, Old, Festive,
seasonal beers H
Two-bar country village inn.
The Victorian public features
many games (see menu); the
lounge is 15th-century,
popular with diners and has an
attached restaurant.
Q ❀ ◑ ▶ ᕈ ♣ P

## Mickleham

### King William IV

Byttom Hill (off A24
southbound) OS174538
☎ (01372) 372590
11–3, 6–11; 12–3, 7–10.30 Sun
Adnams Bitter; Badger Dorset
Best; Hogs Back TEA, Hop
Garden Gold (summer); guest
beer H
Charming pub, hidden up a
steep rocky track. The popular
garden offers views across to
Norbury Park. The award-
winning food includes a good
choice for vegetarians. No food
Mon eve. ᴁ Q ⅌ ❀ ◑ ▶ P

## Newdigate

### Surrey Oaks

Parkgate Road, Parkgate
OS205436 ☎ (01306) 631200
11.30–2.30, 5.30–11; 11.30–3, 6–11 Sat;
12–3, 7–10.30 Sun
Young's Bitter; guest beers H
Lovely old country pub with a
stone-flagged bar. The
restaurant features home-made
specials, often with an Asian
bias. Large, attractive garden.
Over 200 different guest beers
a year. Surrey CAMRA Pub of
the Year 1995–6. No food Sun
eve. ᴁ ❀ ◑ ▶ ♣ P

## Ockley

### Cricketers Arms

Stane Street (A29)
☎ (01306) 627205
11–3, 6–11; 12–3, 7–10.30 Sun
Draught Bass; Fuller's London
Pride; Ringwood Best Bitter;
guest beer (occasional) H
Pub dating from the 16th
century, with local flagstones
on the floor and roof. The
garden features a fishpond.
ᴁ ❀ ◑ ▶ ♣ P

## Oxshott

### Bear

Leatherhead Road (A244)
☎ (01372) 842747
11–3, 5.30–11; 12–3, 7–10.30 Sun
Young's Bitter, Special, Ram
Rod, Winter Warmer H
Comfortable, open-plan pub
with a large conservatory and
an extensive menu of home-
cooked food (no meals Sun
eve). Large teddy bear
collection. ᴁ Q ❀ ◑ ▶ P

## Oxted

### George Inn

52 High Street, Old Oxted (off A25)
☎ (01883) 713453
11–11; 12–10.30 Sun
**Adnams Bitter; Draught Bass; Boddingtons Bitter; Fuller's London Pride; Harveys BB; Wadworth 6X** Ⓗ
Well-renovated, 500-year-old pub, well known for its wide choice of food (separate restaurant). Over 200 pictures adorn the walls.
🏚 Q ✿ ◖ ▶ P

## Pirbright

### Royal Oak

Aldershot Road (A324)
☎ (01483) 232466
11–3, 5.30–11; 11–11 Sat; 12–10.30 Sun
**Boddingtons Bitter; Flowers Original; guest beers** Ⓗ
Olde-worlde pub with low beams, good food and a large garden beside a stream.
Q ✿ ◖ ▶ P

## Puttenham

### Good Intent

62 The Street (off B3000 near church)
☎ (01483) 810387
11–3, 6–11; 11–11 Sat; 12–3, 7–10.30 Sun
**Courage Best Bitter; Wadworth 6X; guest beers** Ⓗ
Deservedly popular old village local: three distinct drinking areas. An independent guest beer complements Inch's cider and almost 50 whiskies. Eve meals Tue–Sat, including fish and chips in newspaper Wed.
🏚 Q ✿ ◖ ▶ ⌂ P

## Redhill

### Garland

5 Brighton Road (A23 south)
☎ (01737) 760377
11–11; 12–10.30 Sun
**Harveys XX Mild, Pale Ale, BB, Old, Armada, seasonal beers** Ⓗ
19th-century corner local, Surrey's first Harveys pub. It can be busy early eve. Great collection of clowns behind the bar! Eve meals Wed–Sun.
Q ╰ ✿ ◖ ▶ ⇌ ♣ ⌂

### Home Cottage

3 Redstone Hill (A25, behind station)
☎ (01737) 762771
10.30–11; 12–3, 7–10.30 Sun
**Young's Bitter, Special, Winter Warmer, seasonal beers** Ⓗ
Large, lively pub with an impressive set of handpumps in the front bar.
🏚 ✿ ◖ ▶ ⇌ ♣ P

## Reigate

### Nutley Hall

8 Nutley Lane (behind car park on one-way road at W end of town)
☎ (01737) 241741
11–11; 12–10.30 Sun
**King & Barnes Sussex, Broadwood, Old, Festive, seasonal beers** Ⓗ
Busy drinkers' pub with a quieter rear bar. Various teams make this a great social pub.
🏚 Q ╰ ✿ ◖ ⇌ ♣ ⌂ P

### Tap & Spile

96 High Street (A25, W end of one-way system)
☎ (01737) 243955
11–11; 12–10.30 Sun
**Black Sheep Special; Pilgrim Crusader; guest beers** Ⓗ
Formerly the Red Cross; Reigate's oldest pub, now very comfortable, offers an ever-changing range of beers (usually at least one from Pilgrim Brewery across the road). No food weekends.
🏚 Q ✿ ◖ ▶ ⇌ ♣ ⌂

### Yew Tree

99 Reigate Hill (A217)
☎ (01737) 244944
11–11; 12–10.30 Sun
**Courage Best Bitter; Morland Old Speckled Hen; Wadworth 6X; Young's Bitter** Ⓗ
Local landmark halfway down Reigate Hill: one comfortable wood-panelled bar, very popular for steaks.
🏚 ◖ ▶ P ⎕

## Shackleford

### Cyder House Inn

Peperharow Lane OS935453
☎ (01483) 810360
11–3, 5.30–11; 11–11 Sat; 12–10.30 Sun
**Badger Dorset Best, Tanglefoot; Wadworth 6X; guest beers** Ⓗ
Six beers are usually available in this pleasant free house, where the emphasis is on food. Brewing has now moved to its sister pub at Baynards. Small garden. 🏚 Q ✿ ◖ ▶ ⌂ P

## Shepperton

### Barley Mow

67 Watersplash Road (off B376 at Shepperton Green)
OS073682 ☎ (01932) 225580
11–11; 12–10.30 Sun
**Adnams Broadside; Young's Ram Rod, Winter Warmer; guest beers** Ⓗ
Popular, single-bar pub with several drinking areas, close to Shepperton Studios. Food is highly recommended.
╰ ✿ ◖ ♣ P

## Staffhurst Wood

### Royal Oak

Caterfield Lane (2½ miles S of A25 at Limpsfield) OS407485
☎ (01883) 722207
12–3, 7–10.30 Sun
**Adnams Bitter, Broadside; Larkins Bitter, guest beer** (occasional) Ⓗ
Pub set in good walking country, with views towards Kent and Sussex from the garden. Good food with a French influence. Eve meals Tue–Sat. 🏚 ✿ ◖ ▶ P

## Staines

### Angel Hotel

24 High Street (A308)
☎ (01784) 452509
11–11; 12–10.30 Sun
**Courage Best Bitter; Hogs Back TEA; Pilgrim seasonal beers; John Smith's Bitter; guest beer** Ⓗ
Popular, friendly, town-centre 'home from home'. An inn has stood on this site since 1309. Pleasant conservatory eating area. ✿ 🛏 ◖ ▶ ♿ ⇌ P ⚥

### Beehive

35 Edgell Road (off B376)
☎ (01784) 452663
11–11; 12–10.30 Sun
**Courage Best Bitter; Pilgrim Surrey; guest beers** Ⓗ
Unspoilt, community, three-bar pub just south of the town centre and close to the Thames. Guest beers are mainly from small breweries.
🏚 Q ✿ 🛏 ◖ ▶ ⬚ ⇌ ⌂

## Stanwell

### Wheatsheaf

Town Lane (B378)
☎ (01784) 253372
11–11; 12–4, 7–10.30 Sun
**Courage Best Bitter, Directors; Marston's Pedigree; guest beer** Ⓗ
Cosy, friendly, two-bar local: a 1749 tripe-house which became a pub in 1849. Q ✿ ◖ ♣ P

## Sunbury

### Magpie

64 Thames Street (B376, 1 mile S of Sunbury Cross)
☎ (01932) 782024
11–11; 12–6, 7–10.30 Sun
**Gibbs Mew Overlord, Salisbury, Deacon, Wake Ale, Bishop's Tipple; guest beers** Ⓗ/Ⓖ
Attractive, two-bar riverside pub with a patio and landing stage. Excellent food in the upstairs bar (snacks only Sun eve). Wheelchair access via the patio. Q ✿ ◖ ▶ ♿ ⚥

## Tandridge

### Barley Mow
Tandridge Lane (off A25)
☎ (01883) 713770
11–3, 6–11; 12–3, 7–10.30 Sun
**North Downs Old Cocky;
Pilgrim Progress; Shepherd
Neame Master Brew Bitter,
Spitfire, Bishops Finger** G
Traditional country inn with a
pleasant bar and a restaurant
(good Italian cooking). No food
Sun eve. Three comfortable en
suite rooms.
🏚 Q ✿ 🛏 ◖ ➍ ♣ P

## Tilford

### Duke of Cambridge
Tilford Road ☎ (01252) 792236
11–11; 12–10.30 Sun
**Courage Best Bitter; Greene
King IPA; Hogs Back TEA;
guest beers** H
Friendly roadside free house in
good walking country. Five
beers are usually available,
often including interesting
guests. Children's play area in
the large garden. Meals all day.
✿ ◖ ➍ ౬ P

## Walliswood

### Scarlett Arms
Walliswood Green Road
OS119382 ☎ (01306) 627243
11–2.30, 5.30–11; 12–3, 7–10.30 Sun
**King & Barnes Mild, Sussex,
Broadwood, Old, Festive,
seasonal beers** H
17th-century building; a pub
since 1907. The main stone-
flagged bar features an
inglenook. Separate games
room. A classic country pub.
🏚 Q ✿ ◖ ➍ P

## Walton-on-Thames

### Bear
30 Bridge Street (off A3050)
☎ (01932) 253420
11–11; 12–10.30 Sun
**Greene King IPA; Theakston
Best Bitter; guest beers** H
Friendly backstreet local which
can get crowded. Handy for
the Thames. Breakfasts from
8am. ✿ ◖ ♣ P

### Regent
19 Church Street (A3050)
☎ (01932) 243980
11–11; 12–10.30 Sun
**Courage Directors; Theakston
Best Bitter; Younger Scotch;**

**guest beers** H
Friendly, medium-sized, town-
centre Wetherspoons pub. The
decor relates to local
connections with the film
industry. Meals all day.
◖ ➍ ౬ ⏁ ✕

## Warlingham

### Hare & Hounds
Limpsfield Road (B269)
☎ (01883) 623952
11–11; 12–3, 7–10.30 Sun
**Fuller's London Pride; Greene
King IPA; Highgate Dark** H
Lively local on the edge of
town: a rare outlet for real mild
in these parts. No food Sun.
🏚 ✿ ◖ ♣ P

## Weybridge

### Old Crown
83 Thames Street (off A317)
☎ (01932) 842844
10.30–11; 12–3, 7–10.30 Sun
**Courage Best Bitter, Directors;
Young's Special; guest beer** H
Grade II listed, 16th-century,
riverside pub with a
weatherboarded facade. Its
several rooms have differing
atmospheres. Home-cooked
food. Children's certificate.
Q ⛵ ✿ ◖ ➍ ♣ P

## Windlesham

### Windmill
London Road (A30/B3020 jct)
☎ (01276) 472281
11–11; 12–10.30 Sun
**Beer range varies** H
Large, roadside pub in beer
exhibition style, with an ever-
changing range of 12 beers.
Good food. Large garden.
Cider in summer.
Q ✿ ◖ ➍ ⏁ P

## Witley

### White Hart
Petworth Road (A283)
☎ (01428) 683695
11–2.30, 5.30–11; 11–11 Sat; 12–10.30
(12–3, 7–10.30 winter) Sun
**Shepherd Neame Master
Brew Bitter, Spitfire, Bishops
Finger, seasonal beers** H
14th-century pub: a public bar,
lounge and a restaurant. The
large, enclosed garden has a
play area (children also
welcome in the restaurant).
Haunted by two ghosts, it
claims to hold England's
longest continuous licence.

Wheelchair access via the
restaurant.
🏚 ✿ ◖ ➍ ◨ ౬ ♣ P

## Woking

### Wetherspoons
Chertsey Road
☎ (01483) 722818
11–11; 12–10.30 Sun
**Courage Directors; Theakston
Best Bitter, XB; Younger
Scotch; guest beers** H
Superb addition to the limited
repertoire of Woking pubs.
Typical Wetherspoons decor;
two (often unusual) guest
beers. It can get very busy
weekend eves. Occasional beer
festivals. Q ◖ ➍ ౬ ⇌ ✕

## Wood Street

### Royal Oak
89 Oak Hill ☎ (01483) 235137
11–2.30, 5–11; 12–3, 7–10.30 Sun
**Hogs Back TEA; Morland
IPA; guest beers** H
Village local rejuvenated by an
enterprising landlord. Four
guest beers from independent
breweries. Outside gents';
large garden. No food Sun.
✿ ◖ ♣ P

## Wrecclesham

### Bat & Ball
Bat and Ball Lane OS833444
☎ (01252) 794564
12–11; 12–10.30 Sun
**Boddingtons Bitter; Brakspear
Bitter; Fuller's London Pride;
Young's Special; guest
beers** H
Hard to find pub, decorated in
a variety of styles, with an
unusual brick bar. Often busy,
the garden and conservatory
cater for families. Varied and
interesting food (no meals Sun
eve). Q ⛵ ✿ ◖ ➍ ౬ P

### Sandrock
Sandrock Hill Road
☎ (01252) 715865
11–11; 12–10.30 Sun
**Batham Mild, Best Bitter;
Boddingtons Bitter; Brakspear
Bitter; Enville Ale, Simpkiss
Bitter; guest beers** H
The Black Country comes to
Surrey! As well as unusual
regular beers, this simple free
house sells an impressive
range of guest beers (eight
usually). The landlord now
runs his own beer agency. Not
to be missed. No food Sun.
🏚 Q ✿ ◖

---

For further details of all the beers listed in the above entries,
check the breweries section at the back of the book.

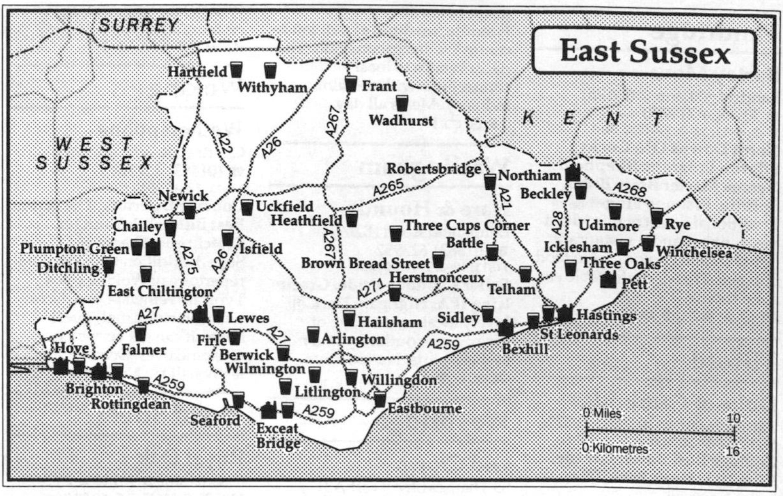


## East Sussex

## Arlington

### Old Oak

Cane Heath (opp. Abbots Wood) ☎ (01323) 482072
11–3, 6–11; 12–3, 7–10.30 Sun
**Badger Dorset Best; Harveys BB; guest beers** G
Ancient pub with low ceilings and log fires: a comfortable lounge and a separate restaurant. Cooler jackets are used on the gravity beers.
Q P

## Battle

### Kings Head

37 Mount Street (just off High St on Whatlington road)
☎ (01424) 772317
10.30–3, 5–11; 12–3, 7–10.30 Sun
**Archers Village; Courage Best Bitter, Directors; Harveys BB; John Smith's Bitter** H
15th-century inn at the top end of town with award-winning floral displays in summer. Its inglenook and low beams make it the sort of pub you would expect in such an historic town.

**Try also: Royal Oak,** Whatlington (Free)

## Beckley

### Rose & Crown

Northiam Road (B2188/B2165 jct) ☎ (01797) 252161
11–3, 5–11; 11–11 Sat; 12–4, 7–10.30 Sun
**Adnams Bitter; Greene King Abbot; Harveys BB; Rother Valley Level Best; guest beers** H
Spacious, welcoming family pub with fine views from the garden. Up to seven beers available. Camping by arrangement. Q P

## Berwick

### Cricketer's Arms ☆

Just off A27, 100 yds W of Drusillas roundabout
☎ (01323) 870469
11–3, 6–11 (11–11 summer Sat); 12–3, 6.30–10.30 (12–10.30 summer) Sun
**Harveys BB, seasonal beers** G
Time has almost stood still in these two old cottages which were converted to a pub ages ago. Quarry tiles in the public bar render the pub suitable for walkers. Value for money food.
Q P

## Brighton

### Basketmaker's Arms

12 Gloucester Road
☎ (01273) 689006
11–3, 5.30 (5 Wed & Thu)–11; 11–11 Fri & Sat; 12–10.30 Sun
**Gale's Butser, Best Bitter, HSB, Festival Mild; guest beers** H
A *Guide* regular, and deservedly so; winner of Gale's cellar awards, this corner pub is often busy. Roasts served Sun, with a vegetarian option. Sympathetically extended in 1995 – can you see the join?

### Bugle

24 St Martin's Street (off Lewes Rd) ☎ (01273) 607753
11–3, 6–11; 11–11 Sat; 12–10.30 Sun
**Courage Best Bitter, Directors; Harveys BB; Marston's Pedigree; Morland Old Speckled Hen; Young's Special** H
Traditional Irish local with a large drinking area around the bar. An alcove away from the bar is devoted to Irish memorabilia. Heavy student influence.

### Cobbler's Thumb

10 New England Road (100 yds W of A23/A270 jct)
☎ (01273) 605636
11–3, 6–11; 11–11 Thu–Sat; 12–10.30 Sun
**Badger Tanglefoot; Fuller's London Pride; Harveys BB, Old; guest beers** H
Unspoilt, two-bar corner local popular with all ages. One bar is used for pool. The pub was under threat of closure for many years, thus no internal changes have taken place and original decor and seating

**INDEPENDENT BREWERIES**

**Cuckmere Haven:** Exceat Bridge
**Dark Star:** Brighton
**First In, Last Out:** Hastings
**Harveys:** Lewes
**Hedgehog & Hogshead:** Hove
**Kemptown:** Brighton
**Old Forge:** Pett
**Rectory:** Plumpton Green
**Rother Valley:** Northiam
**Skinner's:** Brighton
**White:** Bexhill

remain. Interesting collection of carpentry tools. Wheelchair access is via the garden.

🔍 ✿ ◗ ⑤ ⇌ ♣ ▭

## Dover Castle

43 Southover Street
☎ (01273) 889808
11–11; 12–3.30, 7–10.30 Sun
**Shepherd Neame Best Bitter, Spitfire** H
Basic, street-corner local with a strong, welcoming family atmosphere. The accent is on pub games. TV for major sporting events only.
⑤ ♣ ▯

## Evening Star

55–56 Surrey Street (200 yds S of station) ☎ (01273) 328931
12 (11 Sat)–11; 12–10.30 Sun
**Beer range varies** H
Good, down to earth brew pub which holds occasional theme nights with live music. Eleven pumps dispense an ever-changing choice of in-house and rare guest beers, including exclusive one-offs; over 1600 different beers have been sold in four years as a free house.
✿ ◗ ⇌ ♣ ▭

## Greys

105 Southover Street
☎ (01273) 680734
11–3, 5–11; 11–11 Sat; 12–10.30 Sun
**Adnams Bitter; Flowers Original; guest beer** H
Compact, single-bar pub stocking a range of bottled Belgian beers. Frequent live music; imaginative food (no lunches Sun; eve meals Tue and Wed only). ✿ ◗ ▶

## Hand in Hand

33 Upper St James Street
☎ (01273) 602521
11–11; 12–10.30 Sun
**Badger Dorset Best, Tanglefoot; Kemptown Budget, Bitter, Olde Trout, SID** H
Compact home of Kemptown Brewery, with very unusual decor: walls are covered with extracts from old newspapers, and historic local pictures and tiles adorn the ceiling.
◗ ▭

## Lamb & Flag

9 Cranbourne Street
☎ (01273) 326415
10.30–11; closed Sun
**Kemptown Budget; Greene King IPA, Abbot** H
Popular, friendly, town-centre bar, offering well-priced beer in an expensive town. Well-situated for shoppers, office staff and passing visitors.
Q ◗ ⇌

## Prince Arthur

38 Dean Street (off Western Rd)
☎ (01273) 203472
11–11; 12–10.30 Sun

**Adnams Bitter; Flowers Original; Fuller's London Pride; Harveys BB; Morland Old Speckled Hen; Young's Special** H
One of the few unspoilt pubs in the main shopping area. The main bar area is wood-panelled; small, conservatory-like bar at the rear.
⑤ ✿ ◗

## Pump House

46 Market Street
☎ (01273) 326864
11–11; 12–10.30 Sun
**Draught Bass; Fuller's London Pride; Harveys BB; Worthington Bitter; guest beers** H
Busy, well-situated pub in the Lanes area of town; built on the site of the town pump. The cellars are from medieval times. Q ◗ ▶

## Sir Charles Napier

50 Southover Street
☎ (01273) 601413
12–3, 6–11; 12–11 Sat; 12–4, 7–10.30 Sun
**Gale's Butser, Best Bitter, IPA, HSB; guest beer** H
Victorian, backstreet local adorned with items of memorabilia, some of unique interest. The sheltered garden at the rear, with an abundance of flowers, features a George V post box. All food is home-made, including vegetarian options. ✿ ◗ ▶

## Sussex Yeoman

7 Guildford Road (100 yds W of station) ☎ (01273) 327985
11–3, 5–11; 11–11 Sat; 12–10.30 Sun
**Beer range varies** H
Friendly, comfortable and popular, single-bar, corner pub where a warm welcome is guaranteed. Selection of eight ales; large speciality sausage menu. The landlord performs magic tricks Mon and Tue eves. ◗ ▶ ⇌ ♣

## Tap & Spile

67A Upper Gloucester Road
☎ (01273) 327075
11–11; 12–10.30 Sun
**Tap & Spile Premium; guest beers** H
Formerly the Edinburgh, this corner house was taken into the Tap & Spile chain in 1995. It has been tastefully tarted-down to the standard bare-boards look. Up to seven changing beers. ◗ ▶ ⇌ ♣ ▭

Try also: **Nelson**, Trafalgar St (Harveys)

# Brown Bread Street

## Ash Tree Inn

On by-road off lane signed 'Ashburnham' from A271
OS675149 ☎ (01424) 892104

12–3, 7–11; closed Mon except bank hols; 12–3, 7–10.30 Sun
**Harveys BB; Morland Old Speckled Hen; guest beer** H
Cosy, 400-year-old building with three areas, replete with beams: an ale house for 200 years. The public bar was originally the village hall (1902). Two family rooms. Quality food.
🔍 Q ⑤ ✿ ◗ ▶ ▭ ♣

# Chailey

## Horns Lodge

South Street, South Chailey (A275)
☎ (01273) 400422
11–3, 6–11; 12–3, 7–10.30 Sun
**Courage Directors; Harveys BB; Wadworth 6X; guest beer** H
Family-run, single-bar pub with a separate dining area. The large garden is popular with locals and travellers. Winner of many pub games trophies. No eve meals Sun.
🔍 ⑤ ✿ ◗ ▶ ♣ P

# Ditchling

## White Horse

16 West Street
☎ (01273) 842006
11–11; 12–3, 7–10.30 Sun
**Harveys BB; guest beers** H
Welcoming, single-bar village pub close to the church and Anne of Cleves's house. A good range of food includes vegetarian options. The cellar is reputedly haunted.
🔍 ✿ ◗ ▶ ▭

# Eastbourne

## Alexandra Arms

453 Seaside (A259, 3 miles E of centre, near 'Seaside Roundabout')
☎ (01323) 772913
11–3, 5.30–11; 12–3, 7–10.30 Sun
**Beards Best Bitter; Fuller's London Pride; Theakston Old Peculier; guest beers** H
Two-bar local with a friendly welcome. Good bar food with daily specials. Local press *Town Pub of the Year* 1995.
🔍 ✿ ◗ ▭ ♣ P

## Hogshead

South Street (100 yds from station along Gildredge Rd)
☎ (01323) 723107
11–11; 12–10.30 Sun
**Boddingtons Bitter; Flowers Original** H**;Harveys BB** G**; Marston's Pedigree; Wadworth 6X** H**; guest beers** H/G
Large, boisterous, youngsters' pub in the theme mould. Jugs available at discounted prices on selected beers. ◗ ⇌ ▭

### Hurst Arms

76 Willingdon Road (A22, 1½
miles N of centre)
☎ (01323) 721762
11–11; 12–10.30 Sun
**Harveys BB, Armada, seasonal
beers** H
In the *Guide* since 1978: a large
Victorian building holds a
huge public bar and a cosy
lounge. Its name comes from
the local landowner family
prior to incorporation into the
borough of Eastbourne.
Q ❀ ◖

### Lamb

High Street, Old Town (A259
Seaford road, W of centre)
☎ (01323) 720545
10.30–3, 10.30–11; 10.30–11 Fri & Sat;
12–4, 7–10.30 Sun
**Harveys XX Mild, Pale Ale,
BB, Armada, seasonal beers** H
Beamed Harveys show house
with three distinctively
different bar areas – each on a
different level. Parts date from
1290 and a passage (now
blocked) leads from the pub to
the church next door. Cellar
tours by arrangement.
Q ❀ ◖ ▶ ዬ ⇌ P

## East Chiltington

### Jolly Sportsman

Chapel Lane (off B2116)
OS372153
☎ (01273) 890400
11.30–2.30, 6 (7 winter)–11; closed
Mon; 12–3, 7–10.30 Sun
**King & Barnes Sussex; John
Smith's Bitter; Young's
Special** H
Nestling under the South
Downs, this community pub is
located close to a 13th-century
church and commands good
views across the Sussex Weald.
The bar is small, but there are
separate rooms for dining and
pool. Well off the beaten track,
but worth seeking out. No eve
meals Tue or Sun.
❀ ◖ ▶ ♣ P

## Exceat Bridge

### Golden Galleon

Off A259 ☎ (01323) 892247
11–3, 6–11; 12–3, 7–10.30 (12–10.30
summer) Sun
**Cuckmere Haven Best Bitter,
Saxon King, Guv'ner; Greene
King Abbot; Harveys Armada;
guest beers** H
Home of Cuckmere Haven
Brewery. The large bar has a
heavy emphasis on food.
Good-size garden with scenic
views of Cuckmere Haven
Valley and the English
Channel. At least eight beers
(up to 14); good selection of
micro-breweries' ales. No eve
meals in winter.
🏠 ⏁ ❀ ◖ ▶ Å ♣ ⏃ P

## Falmer

### Swan

Middle Street, North Falmer
☎ (01273) 681842
11–3, 6–11; 12–3, 7–10.30 Sun
**Gibbs Mew Premium,
Bishop's Tipple; Palmers IPA;
guest beers** H
Newly renovated, village local
run by the landlord's family
since 1903. Three bars: one
no-smoking, one games-
oriented. The interesting decor
features breweriana and
pictures of village life. Good
collection of bottled beers. A
house beer is also sold.
🏠 ❀ ◖ ⊞ ⇌ P ⮾

## Firle

### Ram

Off A27
☎ (01273) 858222
11.30–3, 7–11; 12–3, 7–10.30 Sun
**Harveys BB; Otter Bitter;
guest beers** H
Pub dating from 1542, with a
Georgian courtyard. One large
bar with two adjacent bars.
Note the interesting pictures of
Firle and its bonfire society.
Good food. 🏠 Q ❀ ⛺ ◖ ▶

## Frant

### Abergavenny Arms

Frant Road (A267)
☎ (01892) 750233
11–11; 12–3, 7–10.30 Sun
**Beer range varies** H/G
Large old country free house
on two levels. There has been
an ale house on this site since
1450. Constantly changing
range of beers, frequently from
distant or micro-breweries.
Good quality food, too.
🏠 Q ❀ ◖ ▶ ዬ ♣ P ⮾

## Hailsham

### Grenadier

High Street (N end)
☎ (01323) 842152
11–11; 12–3, 7–10.30 Sun
**Harveys XX Mild, BB, Old,
Armada, seasonal beers** H
Popular, two-bar town pub: an
imposing building with a
tastefully renovated interior –
particularly the public and
private bars. Spot the original
gas lamp fittings. In the same
family for over 40 years; close
to the Cuckoo Trail foot- and
cycle-path. ❀ ◖ ⊞ ዬ ♣

## Hartfield

### Anchor Inn

Church Street (look for sign on
the main road)
☎ (01892) 770424
11–11; 12–10.30 Sun

**Boddingtons Bitter; Flowers
Original; Fremlins Bitter;
Harveys BB; Marston's
Pedigree; Wadworth 6X; guest
beer** H
Hidden slightly behind the
natural building line, this
friendly local, built circa 1465
(a pub since 1745), features a
superb verandah and loads of
beams. Some rebuilding work
taking place will not alter the
character.
🏠 Q ⏁ ❀ ⛺ ◖ ▶ ዬ ♣ P ⮾

## Hastings

### Carlisle

24 Pelham Street (seafront)
☎ (01424) 420193
11–11; 12–10.30 Sun
**Old Forge Brothers Best, Pett
Progress; guest beers** H
Busy, loud, 'bikers'-type pub
with three bars: the main
(front) bar has live music
several times a week; quieter
bars at the rear. Music and beer
festival in summer.
⏁ ዬ ⇌ ♣

### First In, Last Out

14 High Street (Old Town)
☎ (01424) 425079
11–11; 12–10.30 Sun
**FILO Crofter, Cardinal; guest
beer** H
Home of the FILO Brewery,
featuring alcove seating and
central heating with a
difference – an open central
fireplace complete with flue.
Busy eves and weekends.
🏠 Q ❀ ◖ ዬ ♣ ⏃

### Royal George

Devonshire Road (50 yds from
station) ☎ (01424) 443685
11–11; 12–3, 7–10.30 Sun
**Harveys BB; guest beers** H
Recently re-opened and
renovated two-bar pub. Up to
four guest beers.
🏠 ◖ ⇌ ♣

### Stag

All Saints Street (just off The
Bourne, Old Town, near
church) ☎ (01424) 425734
12–3, 6–11; 11–11 Sat; 12–10.30 Sun
**Shepherd Neame Master
Brew Bitter, Best Bitter,
Spitfire *or* Porter, Bishops
Finger** H
Ancient smugglers' pub in the
picturesque Old Town.
Features include its own pub
game, 'Loggits', and a
collection of mummified cats!
Annual mini-beer festival.
🏠 ⏁ ❀ ⇌ ◖ ▶ Å ♣

## Heathfield

### Prince of Wales

Station Road (by traffic lights
on Horam road, S of town)
☎ (01435) 862919
11–3, 5–11; 11–11 Sat; 12–10.30 Sun

Brewery on Sea Rain Dance;
Greene King Abbot; Harveys
BB; guest beers 🅷
Excellent corner local: popular,
often crowded and with a
good value carvery restaurant
as well as a traditional
public bar.
🏨 ❀ ◖ ▶ 🍴 👟 ♣ P

## Herstmonceux

### Brewer's Arms
Gardner Street (A271)
☎ (01323) 832226
11–3, 6–11; 12–3, 6–10.30 Sun
Adnams Broadside; Beards
Best Bitter; Harveys BB; guest
beers 🅷
Traditional country village pub
with an olde-worlde
atmosphere and many
antiques. Beers from distant
breweries are frequently
available. No eve meals Tue.
🏨 Q ❀ ◖ ▶ ♣ P ⌿

### Welcome Stranger
Chapel Row (100 yds S of
A271, on road to church)
☎ (01323) 832119
7–11; 12–2.30, 7–11 Sat; 12–3, 7–10.30
Sun
Harveys BB, Old 🅷
Fine example of an unspoilt
country ale house, the last in
Sussex to obtain a full licence;
known locally as the 'Kicking
Donkey' and in the same
family since 1908. Beer is
served through a hatch into the
main room. Limited pub food
lunchtime (sandwiches/
ploughmans).
🏨 Q ❀ ♣ P 🍺

## Hove

### Eclipse
33 Montgomery Street
☎ (01273) 272212
11–3, 6–11; 11–11 Sat; 12–4, 7–10.30
Sun
Harveys XX Mild, BB,
Armada, seasonal beers 🅷
Formerly a Charrington house,
this pub has been well restored
by Harveys into a comfortable
local. Note the painted
mouldings on the exterior –
the pub has a connection with
the turf. Upstairs function
room.
❀ ◖ 🚋 ♣

### Farm Tavern
13 Farm Road (off Western Rd)
☎ (01273) 325902
11–11; 12–3, 7–10.30 Sun
Bateman XB; Beards Best
Bitter; Harveys BB; guest
beers 🅷
True backstreet local – small,
cosy, and well worth finding.
Note the impressive coat of
arms above the fireplace. Good
food.
❀ ◖ ♣ 🍺

## Icklesham

### Queen's Head
Parsonage Lane (off A259
nearly opp. church)
☎ (01424) 814552
11–11; 12–5, 7–10.30 Sun
Beer range varies 🅷
Tile-hung country pub in a
rural setting, with a
magnificent mahogany bar.
Superb views from the garden;
warm, friendly atmosphere.
Usually four or five beers
available. Excellent food.
🏨 ❀ ◖ ▶ ▲ ♣ ⌣ P ⌿

## Isfield

### Laughing Fish
Station Road (½ mile W of A26)
☎ (01825) 750349
11–3, 6–11; 12–3, 7–10.30 Sun
Beards Best Bitter; Harveys
BB; guest beers 🅷
Friendly village local next to
the Lavender Line, which runs
generally at weekends: a main
bar plus two rooms at the back.
No eve meals Mon.
🏨 🚋 ❀ ◖ ▶ ♣ P

## Lewes

### Black Horse
55 Western Road
☎ (01273) 473653
11–2.30, 5.30 (6 Sat)–11; 12–2.30,
7–10.30 Sun
Beards Best Bitter; Brakspear
Bitter; Harveys BB, guest
beers 🅷
Originally a coaching inn, this
Beards pub now features two
bars, one with a fascinating
collection of photos of old
Lewes pubs. No lunches Sun.
❀ 🛏 ◖ ♣

### Dorset Arms
22 Malling Street (400 yds E of
Harveys Brewery)
☎ (01273) 477110
11–3, 6–11; 12–4, 7–10.30 Sun
Harveys Pale Ale, BB,
Armada, seasonal beers 🅷
The Harveys brewery tap: a
large, plush, two-bar pub with
a restaurant. No-smoking
family room. No eve meals
Sun/Mon.
🏨 🚋 ❀ ◖ ▶ 👟 🚋 ♣ P ⌿

### Elephant & Castle
White Hill (A2029, 100 yds W
of police station)
☎ (01273) 473797
11.30–11; 12–10.30 Sun
Harveys BB, seasonal beers;
guest beers 🅷
Large, unspoilt, friendly two-
bar local with a real fire in each
bar. Interesting decor includes
a large collection of ornaments.
Separate room for table
football. The pub has its own
rugby club. 🏨 🚋 ◖ 🚋 ♣

## Gardeners Arms
46 Cliffe High Street (close to
Harveys brewery)
☎ (01273) 474808
11–3, 5.30–11; 11–11 Sat; 12–3, 7–10.30
Sun
Harveys BB; guest beers 🅷
Basic, friendly, two-bar free
house featuring a constantly
changing range of ales; sister
pub of Brighton's Evening Star,
featuring Skinner's and Dark
Star beers in the range. Bar
snacks served. 🚋 ♣ ⌣

### Royal Oak
3 Station Street
☎ (01273) 474803
11–3, 5 (6.30 Sat)–11; 12–3, 7–10.30
Sun
Beards Best Bitter; Courage
Directors; Harveys BB; guest
beers 🅷
In business since 1812, the pub
takes its name from the tree in
which Charles II hid after the
Battle of Worcester – an early
landlord was descended from
the family that saved the King.
A comfortable pub with an
extensive menu and a room for
functions. ❀ ◖ ▶ 🚋 ♣

### Snowdrop
119 South Street
☎ (01273) 471018
11–11; 12–10.30 Sun
Harveys BB; Hop Back
Summer Lightning; Shepherd
Neame Spitfire; guest beers 🅷
Popular, two-storey pub aimed
at local youth. Interesting wall
murals; pool table. Brewery on
Sea Avalanche is a house beer.
Good selection of organic and
vegetarian food. ❀ ◖ ▶

## Litlington

### Plough & Harrow
On Exceat–Wilmington by-
road ☎ (01323) 870632
11–2.30, 7–11 (11–11 summer);
12–3.15, 7–10.30 Sun
Badger Dorset Best,
Tanglefoot; Harveys BB;
Wells Bombardier; guest
beers 🅷
Attractive pub catering for a
wide-ranging clientele. Good
beer selection for the area;
separate restaurant. Full of
Southern Railway
memorabilia. Very busy at
weekends. Q ❀ ◖ ▶ ♣ P

## Newick

### Crown Inn
Church Road (S off A272 at
green) ☎ (01825) 723293
11–11; 12–3, 7–10.30 Sun
Adnams Bitter; Beards Best
Bitter; Greene King Abbot;
Harveys BB; guest beers 🅷
One-bar village local hosting
regular quizzes, games, etc.
The sun trap courtyard

through the archway was originally for coaches.
🏮 ✸ ◖ ♣ P

## Plumpton Green

### Fountain
Station Road ☎ (01273) 890294
10.30–3, 6–11; 12–3, 7–10.30 Sun (may vary)
**Young's Bitter, Special, Winter Warmer** Ⓗ
This most southerly of all Young's houses has its origins in a bakehouse. A popular, single-bar, award-winning pub, it has appeared in every *Good Beer Guide*. 🏮 ✸ ◖ ♣ P

## Robertsbridge

### Seven Stars
High Street
☎ (01580) 880333
11–3, 5–11; 11–11 Sat; 12–10.30 Sun
**Courage Best Bitter, Directors; Greene King Abbot; Harveys BB; guest beers** Ⓗ
Warm, oak-beamed pub in the village centre; home of the famed 'Red Monk' ghost and a pub since 1500. Usually between seven and ten beers are available, including brews from Old Forge Brewery. Occasional live music.
🏮 Q ☜ ✸ 🏠 ◖ ▶ ≈ ♣ P

## Rottingdean

### Black Horse
65 High Street
☎ (01273) 302581
10.30–2.30, 6–11; 12–3, 7–10.30 Sun
**Beards Best Bitter; Harveys BB; Mansfield Old Baily; guest beers** Ⓗ
Popular village local with two bars plus a snug (where children are welcome). It is believed to date back to 1531.
☜ ◖ 🏠 ♣

## Rye

### Ypres Castle
Gun Garden (rear of Ypres Tower)
☎ (01797) 223248
11–11; 12–10.30 Sun
**Hook Norton Best Bitter, Old Hooky; guest beers** Ⓗ
Not immediately obvious, this unspoilt pub is well worth seeking out. Access on foot only! Superb view of Rye Harbour; safe garden; near Rye's most picturesque parts. Fresh fish, local lamb and poultry are specialities.
🏮 Q ☜ ✸ ◖ ▶ ♣

## St Leonards

### Dripping Spring
34 Tower Road (just off A2100, 1 mile from seafront)
☎ (01424) 434055

11–3, 6–11; 11–11 Fri & Sat; 12–3, 7–10.30 Sun
**Friary Meux BB; Fuller's London Pride; Wells Bombardier; guest beers** Ⓗ
Formerly the New George & Dragon; a friendly backstreet pub in the Bohemia area of St Leonards. Usually six beers available, one from Old Forge.
✸ ♿ ♣

## Seaford

### Wellington
Steyne Road
☎ (01323) 890032
11–11; 11–2.30, 5.30–11 Tue & Wed; 12–3, 7–10.30 Sun
**Adnams Extra; Beards Best Bitter; Fuller's London Pride; Greene King IPA; Harveys BB; Wadworth 6X; guest beers** Ⓗ
Popular, friendly local with a comfortable U-shaped bar. Note the motto of the day. Quiz Mon. No food Sun.
◖ ≈

### White Lion
74 Claremont Road
☎ (01323) 892473
11–2.30, 6–11; 11–11 Sat; 12–10.30 Sun
**Fuller's London Pride; Harveys BB; guest beers** Ⓗ
Hotel with a U-shaped bar plus a games bar. Good selection of food. No eve bar meals Sun.
✸ 🏠 ◖ ▶ ≈ ♣ P

## Sidley

### Rose & Crown
Turkey Road
☎ (01424) 214625
11–3, 6–11; 11–11 Sat; 12–5, 7–10.30 Sun
**Beards Best Bitter; Courage Directors; Harveys BB; guest beers** Ⓗ
Large, 1930s-style estate pub set back from the road, taken over by Beards who have done a great restoration job. A worthy newcomer to the *Guide*, serving three or four guest beers. 🏮 ✸ ◖ ▶ ♿ ♣ P ⚥

## Telham

### Black Horse
Hastings Road (A2100)
☎ (01424) 773109
11–3, 5–11; 12–3, 7–10.30 Sun
**Shepherd Neame Master Brew Bitter, Best Bitter, Spitfire, Bishops Finger** Ⓗ
A good stop between Battle and Hastings. Note the very unusual skittle alley – in the attic! Boules played in summer. Live music weekend every Spring Bank Hol – special brews are often supplied for the event. Occasional folk music in the bar.
🏮 ✸ ◖ ▲ ♣ P

## Three Cups Corner

### Three Cups
On B2096 ☎ (01435) 830252
11–3, 6.30–11; 12–3, 7–10.30 Sun
**Arkell's 3B; Beards Best Bitter; Harveys BB** Ⓗ**; guest beers** Ⓗ/Ⓖ
Old country local with an inglenook in its cosy interior. Pub games addicts will not be disappointed. Local press *Country Pub of the Year* 1995. Camping by arrangement.
🏮 Q ☜ ✸ ◖ ▲ ♣ P ⚥

## Three Oaks

### Three Oaks
Butchers Lane (by station)
☎ (01424) 813303
12–3, 7–11; 12–3, 7–10.30 Sun
**Harveys BB; King & Barnes Sussex; Rother Valley Level Best; guest beers** Ⓗ
Pleasant country pub with plenty of atmosphere. Home-cooked food. A good base for walking.
🏮 Q ✸ ◖ ▲ ≈ ♣ P 🍴

## Uckfield

### Alma Arms
Framfield Road (B2102 E of centre) ☎ (01825) 762232
11–2.30, 6–11; 12–2, 7–10.30 Sun
**Harveys XX Mild, Pale Ale, BB, Old, Armada, seasonal beers** Ⓗ
Traditional town pub with a comfortable saloon bar, in the same family for generations. An oasis in a poor area for drinking. Small garden area.
Q ☜ ✸ ◖ 🏠 ♿ ≈ ♣ P ⚥

## Udimore

### King's Head
Udimore Road (B2089, W of village) ☎ (01424) 882349
11–4, 5.30–11; 12–3, 7–10.30 Sun
**Arundel Best Bitter; Harveys BB; Rother Valley Level Best; guest beers** Ⓗ
1535 traditional village ale house, with beams and open fires, wood floors, a family room, a skittle room and boules but no cellar. Home-cooked food. A centre for scenic walks.
🏮 Q ☜ ✸ ◖ ▶ ♣ ⚥

## Wadhurst

### Greyhound
St James Square
☎ (01892) 783224
11–2.30, 6–11; 11–11 Sat; 12–3, 7–10.30 Sun
**Draught Bass; Harveys BB; Ruddles County; Young's Bitter; guest beers** Ⓗ
Fine old inn with lots of character and a friendly

atmosphere, set in a Wealden village. Good food; separate restaurant.

🏚 Q ⚘ 🛏 ◗ ◖ ⟊ ♣ P 🍺

## Willingdon

### Red Lion

99 Wish Hill
☎ (01323) 502062
11–2.30, 5.30–11; 12–2.30, 7–10.30 Sun
**King & Barnes Sussex, Broadwood, Festive, seasonal beers** 🇭
One of very few tied K&B houses in E Sussex, set in an attractive by-passed (A22) village. Busy lunchtimes and weekends; good value food. An ideal place to call if walking from the Downs.
Q ⚘ ◗ ◗ ♣ P ⅄

## Wilmington

### Giant's Rest

☎ (01323) 870207
11–2.30, 6–11; 12–3, 7–10.30 Sun
**Harveys BB; Taylor Landlord; Hop Back Summer Lightning; guest beer** 🇭
Fine Edwardian building sympathetically transformed into a cosy village free house. Log fire in winter. The good selection of food does not predominate.
🏚 Q ⛄ ⚘ ◗ ◗ ⌣ P

## Winchelsea

### New Inn

German Street
☎ (01797) 226252
11–3, 6 (7 Mon & Tue)–11; 12–3, 7–10.30 Sun
**Adnams Extra; Beards Best Bitter; Harveys Pale Ale; guest beer** 🇭
Set in the centre of England's smallest town (one of the Cinque Ports), this comfy local is well run by a young couple. A new addition this year, well worth a visit and possibly a stay.
🏚 Q ⚘ 🛏 ◗ ◗ ♣ P ⅄

## Withyham

### Dorset Arms

☎ (01892) 770278
11–3, 5.30 (6 Sat)–11; 12–3, 7–10.30 Sun
**Harveys XX Mild, Pale Ale, BB, seasonal beers** 🇭
16th-century building with interesting architectural features, including a cosy Wealden oak-floored bar with a log fire. Spot the Wealden Ironworks fire backplate, bearing witness to the days when this area was the centre of the English iron industry. Good food; quality separate restaurant.
🏚 Q ⚘ ◗ ◗ ⛁ ♣ P

## Aldwick

### Ship Inn

Aldwick Street
☎ (01243) 865334
11–11; 12–10.30 Sun
**Harveys BB** 🇬**; Ruddles Best Bitter; guest beers** 🇭
Relaxed, two-bar pub away from the town centre, with a good mix of customers. Selection of games. Casks for the Harveys are behind the bar.
⚘ ◗ ◗ ⛁ ◖ ⌣ P ⅄

## Arundel

### King's Arms

36 Tarrant Street
☎ (01903) 882312
11–3, 6–11; 11–11 Sat & summer Fri; 12–3, 7–10.30 (12–10.30 summer) Sun
**Fuller's London Pride; Young's Special; guest beers** 🇭
Small, cosy, two-bar local in a pleasant street just below the RC cathedral and the castle, seat of the Dukes of Norfolk. Note: Addlestones Cider is served with gas pressure.
⚘ ⛁ 🅰 ⇌ ♣

### Swan Hotel

27–29 High Street
☎ (01903) 882314
11–11; 12–10.30 Sun
**Arundel Best Bitter, Gold, ASB, Old Knucker; Fuller's London Pride; guest beers** 🇭
Arundel Brewery's first house, centrally located at the bottom of the High St, close to the Castle. The framed, but ageing, picture of a swan in the bar is actually the previous pub sign, made of beaten brass and dating from 1850. 🛏 ◗ ◗ ⇌

## Balcombe

### Cowdray Arms

London Road (B2036/B2110 jct) ☎ (01444) 811280
11–3, 5.30–11 (11–11 summer Sat); 12–3, 7–10.30 Sun
**Adnams Extra; Harveys BB; guest beers** 🇭
Popular roadhouse with ample parking and a good selection of guest ales. Adnams is sold as Balcombe Best Bitter. The conservatory is a no-smoking eating area. Children's certificate. Q ⛄ ⚘ ◗ ◗ ♣ P

## Balls Cross

### Stag

Kirdford Road (2 miles NE of Petworth, off A283) OS987263
☎ (01403) 820241
11–3, 6–11; 12–3, 7–10.30 Sun
**King & Barnes Sussex, Old, seasonal beers** 🇭

16th-century pub with an original stone floor and an inglenook, sited on an old coaching route. Used as a polling station for elections. No eve meals Sun. Beware: Festive is sometimes on a cask breather.
🏚 Q ⛄ ⚘ ◗ ◗ ⛁ ♣ P

## Binsted

### Black Horse

Binsted Lane (off A27/B2132)
OS980064 ☎ (01243) 551213
11–3, 6–11; 12–3, 7–10.30 Sun
**Arundel Best Bitter; Gale's HSB; Harveys BB; Hop Back Summer Lightning; Wadworth 6X** 🇭
Pub off the beaten track, but worth finding, boasting fine views across the valley from the garden. Excellent food in the bar or the conservatory/ restaurant.
🏚 Q ⚘ ◗ ◗ ⛁ ♣ P

## Bognor Regis

### Lamb Inn

36 Steyne Street
☎ (01243) 868215
10.30–3, 6–11; 11–11 Fri & Sat; 12–10.30 Sun
**Flowers IPA, Original; Greene King Abbot; guest beers** 🇭
Comfortable, friendly backstreet local. One beer is usually at a special low price. The TV in the public bar is only used for sporting events. No eve meals Sun/Mon. Town-centre car park close by.
🏚 ⚘ ◗ ◗ ⛁ ⇌ ♣

## Byworth

### Black Horse Inn

Off A283 ☎ (01798) 342424
11–3, 6–11; 12–3, 7–10.30 Sun
**Flowers Original; Fuller's London Pride; Young's Bitter; guest beers** 🇭
Traditional, welcoming pub with original wood panelling, exposed beams and floorboards. Families welcome in the separate eating areas. The menu features fresh local produce (no eve meals Sun Jan–Feb). The garden overlooks Shimmings Valley. Elizabethan function/dining room upstairs.
🏚 Q ⚘ ◗ ◗ ♣ P

## Chichester

### Jackson's Cellar

3 Little London (N off East St)
☎ (01243) 771771
11–11; closed Sun
**Harveys Armada; Hop Back Summer Lightning; Thwaites Bitter; Young's Bitter; guest beers** 🇬
True free house in three interlinked, vaulted cellars

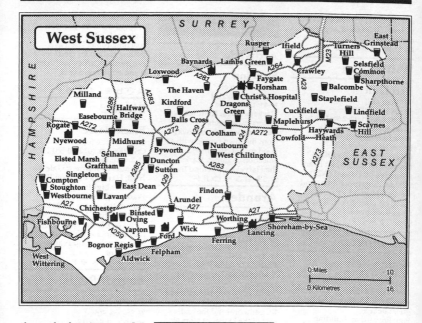

**West Sussex**

close to the shopping centre. It has a restaurant area and a good range of bottled and draught Belgian beers. Independents' guest beers. Public car parks nearby.

## Christ's Hospital

### Bax Castle
Two Mile Ash Road (road from Southwater) OS148273
☎ (01403) 730369
12 (11 Fri)–2.30 (11–3 Sat), 6–11; 12–3, 7–10.30 Sun
**Draught Bass; Brakspear Bitter; Fuller's London Pride; John Smith's Bitter; guest beer** Ⓗ
Pub situated behind a former railway bridge on a T-junction to Barns Green and Christ's Hospital; originally one small bar but recent alterations have increased the seating areas. Popular with walkers on the Downs Link.

### INDEPENDENT BREWERIES

| | |
|---|---|
| **Arundel:** Ford | |
| **Ballard's:** Nyewood | |
| **Baynards:** Baynards | |
| **Brewery on Sea:** Lancing | |
| **Gribble:** Oving | |
| **King & Barnes:** Horsham | |

## Compton

### Coach & Horses
The Square (B2146)
☎ (01705) 631228
11–2.30, 6–11; 12–3, 7–10.30 Sun
**Cheriton Pots Ale; Fuller's ESB; Hook Norton Best Bitter; guest beers** Ⓗ
16th-century pub in a charming downland village, with two bars, a restaurant and a skittle alley. The public bar has old-fashioned shutters and a Victorian fireplace. A good base for walks.

## Coolham

### Selsey Arms
At crossroads (A272)
☎ (01403) 741537
11–3, 5.30–11; 12–3, 6–10.30 Sun
**King & Barnes Sussex; Strong Country Bitter; Wadworth 6X; guest beer** Ⓗ
Basic, one-bar pub with three separate rooms for drinking, each with its own fire. A sociable mix from surrounding villages provides life.

## Cowfold

### Hare & Hounds
Henfield Road (A281)
☎ (01403) 865354
11.30–3, 6–11; 12–3, 7–10.30 Sun
**Friary Meux BB; Harveys BB; King & Barnes Sussex** Ⓗ
Victorian building refurbished with timber obtained from hurricane-damaged trees in nearby Leonardslee Gardens. Good food.

## Crawley

### Snooty Fox
Haslett Avenue, Three Bridges (opp. station)
☎ (01293) 619759
11–11; 12–10.30 Sun
**Friary Meux BB; Ind Coope Burton Ale; Tetley Bitter; guest beers** Ⓗ
New, purpose-built pub where food is available lunch and eve in a separate dining room. The guest beers are mainly from Carlsberg-Tetley.
❀ ≉ (Three Bridges) P

### White Hart
High Street ☎ (01293) 520033
10–11; 12–10.30 Sun
**Harveys BB, Pale Ale, Old, seasonal beers** Ⓗ
Popular, two-bar pub occasionally hosting live music. No meals Sun.

## Cuckfield

### White Harte
South Street ☎ (01444) 413454
11–3, 6–11; 12–3, 7–10.30 Sun
**King & Barnes Sussex, Broadwood, Old, Festive, seasonal beers** Ⓗ
Two-bar village pub situated on a double bend. The saloon bar has genuine beams and an inglenook, in contrast to the more spartan public bar. Family room in summer.

## Dragons Green

### George & Dragon
OS140235
☎ (01403) 741320
11–3, 6–11; 11–11 Sat; 12–10.30 Sun
**King & Barnes Sussex, Broadwood, Festive, seasonal beers** Ⓗ
Delightful, 16th-century pub with an abundance of low beams and a huge inglenook. A gravestone in the front garden belongs to a long-past licensee's son. The excellent home-cooked food is served in generous portions.
🏚 🌟 ◖▶ ♣ P

## Duncton

### Cricketers
Main road (A283)
☎ (01798) 342473
11–3, 6–11; 12–3, 7–10.30 Sun (may vary in summer)
**Archers Golden; Friary Meux BB; Greene King IPA; Ind Coope Burton Ale; guest beer** (summer) Ⓗ
Fine, welcoming hostelry steeped in history. The cosy bar features a large inglenook; separate, split-level eating areas, attractive gardens (barbecues in summer) and a skittle alley. No food Sun/Mon eves in winter. Cider in summer.
🏚 Q 🌟 ◖▶ ♣ ○ P

## Easebourne

### White Horse
Easebourne Street (off A272)
☎ (01730) 813521
11–11; 12–10.30 Sun
**Greene King IPA, Abbot, seasonal beers** Ⓗ
Popular village local on the fringe of the Cowdray Park estate. Two bars cater for a varied clientele, but the overall atmosphere is rural.
🏚 🌟 ◖▶ ♣ ὄ ♣ P

## East Dean

### Hurdlemakers
☎ (01243) 811318
11–2.30 (3 Sat), 6–11; 12–3, 7–10.30 Sun
**Ballard's Wassail; Ruddles Best Bitter; Wadworth 6X; guest beers** Ⓗ
Flint-built free house in a South Downs village near a duck pond. Walkers and cyclists welcome. Good food. The garden has a covered patio. Convenient for Goodwood Racecourse and Singleton Open Air Museum. Wheelchair access is via the garden.
🏚 Q ὄ 🌟 🚗 ◖▶ ♿ ♠ ♣ P

## East Grinstead

### Dunnings Mill
Dunnings Mill Road
☎ (01342) 326341
11–3, 5.30–11; 12–3, 7–10.30 Sun
**Harveys XX Mild** (summer), **BB, Old, Armada** Ⓗ
Attractive, 17th-century pub astride a stream, with four bars on three levels. A cellar bar is open eves Tue–Sat, with fresh seafood as a speciality. 🏚 Q 🌟 ◖▶ P

## Elsted Marsh

### Elsted Inn
Off A272 OS834207
☎ (01730) 813662
11–3, 5.30–11; 12–3, 7–10.30 Sun
**Ballard's Trotton, Best Bitter, Wild, Wassail; Fuller's London Pride** Ⓗ
Welcoming, tastefully refurbished Victorian pub, the former home of Ballard's Brewery. Note the unusual window shutters. Excellent, home-cooked food.
🏚 Q 🌟 🚗 ◖▶ ♣ P

## Faygate

### Cherry Tree
Crawley Road (A264)
☎ (01293) 851305
11–3 (3.30 Sat), 6–11; 12–3, 7–10.30 Sun
**King & Barnes Sussex, Broadwood, Festive, seasonal beers** Ⓗ
Two cottages, built in 1660, became this pub in 1870. Two open fires, an inglenook and original beams are features. Warm atmosphere; good value meals. 🏚 Q 🌟 ◖▶ ♣ P

## Felpham

### Old Barn
42 Felpham Road
☎ (01243) 821564
11–11; 12–10.30 Sun
**Arundel Best Bitter; Fuller's ESB; Gale's Best Bitter; Hop Back Summer Lightning; Ringwood Best Bitter; guest beers** Ⓗ
Single-bar pub equidistant from the village centre and Southcoast World (Butlins); popular with visitors and locals. Quiz and music nights. At least two guest ales.
🌟 ◖▶ ♿ ♣ P

## Ferring

### Tudor Close
Ferringham Lane
☎ (01903) 243155
11–2.30 (3 Sat), 6–11; 12–3, 7–10.30 Sun
**Courage Best Bitter; Flowers Original; Ind Coope Burton Ale; guest beer** Ⓗ

12th-century Sussex barn in the village centre with a separate bar, restaurant and gallery. Note the intricately carved fireplace. Popular with local people and visitors. The large car park at the rear incorporates a boules area. Note: Addlestones Cider is served under gas pressure.
Q 🌟 ◖♿ ♣ A P

## Findon

### Village House
Horsham Road
☎ (01903) 873350
10.30–11; 12–3, 7–10.30 Sun
**Harveys BB; King & Barnes Sussex; Wadworth 6X; Young's Special; guest beers** Ⓗ
Fine, 16th-century village inn. The bar is decorated with racing silks from local stables.
🏚 Q 🌟 🚗 ◖▶ P

## Fishbourne

### Bull's Head
99 Fishbourne Road (A259)
☎ (01243) 785707
11–3, 5.30–11; 11–11 Sat; 12–10.30 Sun
**Gale's Butser, Winter Brew, HSB; Yates Bitter; guest beers** Ⓗ
Large, comfortable pub with a restaurant specialising in fish in summer and game in winter – all meals home-made from fresh produce (no eve meals Sun). Function room/skittle alley. Access to the car park is off Mill Lane. Guest beers. Cider in summer.
🏚 ὄ 🌟 ◖▶ ⇌ ♣ ○ P ✄

## Graffham

### Forester's Arms
N end of village
☎ (01798) 867202
11–2.30, 5.30–11; 12–3, 7.30–10.30 Sun
**Courage Directors; Harveys Pale Ale, seasonal beers; guest beers** Ⓗ
Heavily beamed, 17th-century inn in good walking country, close to the South Downs Way. The restaurant and bar menus feature English farmhouse fare with an emphasis on game.
🏚 Q 🌟 ◖▶ ♿ A ♣ P

## Halfway Bridge

### Halfway Bridge Inn
On A272 ☎ (01798) 861281
11–3, 6–11; 12–3, 7–10.30 Sun (closed winter Sun eve)
**Cheriton Pots Ale; Gale's HSB; guest beers** Ⓗ
Comfortable roadside inn with a traditional rural atmosphere. The emphasis is on food, which is of a high standard. The many interconnecting rooms all have real fires. 🏚 Q 🌟 ◖▶ ♣ ○ P

## The Haven

### Blue Ship

500 yds down a lane W of A281
at Bucks Green OS084306
☎ (01403) 822709
11–3, 6–11; 12–4, 7–10.30 Sun
**King & Barnes Sussex,
Broadwood, Old, seasonal
beers** Ⓖ
Pub in a time warp with four
small bars; the main room has
no bar but a stable door
through which the gravity
beers are served. Most meals
are home-produced and very
good value. A children's menu
is also provided. No food Sun
or Mon.
♨ Q ♣ ✿ ❍ ◐ ▣ ♣ P

## Haywards Heath

### Star

1 The Broadway
☎ (01444) 413267
11–11; 12–10.30 Sun
**Boddingtons Bitter; Brakspear
Bitter; Marston's Pedigree;
Morland Old Speckled Hen;
Wadworth 6X; guest beers** Ⓗ
Large, L-shaped building in
the middle of a busy one-way
road scheme; a Whitbread
Hogshead house, often with a
guest from a small
independent brewer. Thirteen
handpumps ensure choice is
maintained. Many bottled
beers available.
✿ ❍ ◐ ♣ ◔ P

## Horsham

### Dog & Bacon

North Parade (B2237, 800 yds
from A24 jct)
☎ (01403) 252176
11–3, 6–11; 12–3, 7–10.30 Sun
**King & Barnes Sussex,
Broadwood, Old, seasonal
beers** Ⓗ
Popular pub in the suburbs,
attracting a good cross-section
of the local populace.
Occasional food theme eves
(no eve meals Sun or Mon).
No-smoking family room at
the front.
♣ ✿ ❍ ◐ ▣ ♣ P ✕

### Norfolk Arms

Crawley Road, Roffey (A264)
☎ (01403) 264913
11.30–3, 5.30–11; 11.30–11 Sat;
12–10.30 Sun
**King & Barnes Sussex,
Festive, seasonal beers** Ⓗ
Main road, two-bar pub with a
comfortable lounge. Darts and
games in the public bar. Quiz
Sun eve.
♨ Q ✿ ❍ ◐ ▣ ♧ ♣ P

### Stout House

29 Carfax (opp. bandstand)
☎ (01403) 267777
10–4, 7.30–11; closed Tue eve; 12–3,
7.30–10.30 Sun

**King & Barnes Mild, Sussex,
Old, Festive** Ⓗ
Extremely popular town-centre
pub which concentrates on
beer, with food confined to
snacks; recently tastefully
refurbished, with the two
former bars now joined as one.
Regulars lament the loss of the
outside toilets! ⇄ ♣

## Ifield

### Plough

Ifield Street ☎ (01293) 525404
11–3 (4 Fri & Sat), 7–11; 12–4, 7–10.30
Sun
**King & Barnes Sussex,
Festive, seasonal beers** Ⓗ
Traditional village local, now
on the edge of Crawley town,
next to the church and Ifield
Barn Theatre; ten mins' from
Ifield station. An excellent
get-away from the busy town.
No food Sun. Q ❍ ◐ ▣ ♣

## Kirdford

### Forester's Arms

☎ (01403) 820205
11–3, 6–11; 11–11 Sat; 12–3, 7–10.30
Sun
**King & Barnes Sussex, Old,
Festive, seasonal beers** Ⓗ
Typical, old, low-beamed,
stone-floor pub with an
inglenook, attractively
positioned at the rear of the
village green. Eve meals Wed–
Sat. ♨ ✿ ❍ ◐ ▣ ♣ P

## Lambs Green

### Lamb Inn

Off A264 at Faygate
roundabout OS220368
☎ (01293) 871336
11–11; 12–10.30 Sun
**North Downs Old Cocky** Ⓗ;
**Young's Bitter, Special** Ⓖ,
**seasonal beers; guest beers** Ⓗ
Extended country pub built in
the 15th century. Diners enjoy
a large separate area which
features a creeping vine.
♨ ✿ ❍ ◐ P

## Lavant

### Earl of March

Lavant Road (A286)
☎ (01243) 774751
10.30–3, 6–11; 12–3, 7–10.30 Sun
**Gibbs Mew Salisbury;
Mansfield Riding Bitter;
Ringwood Fortyniner, Old
Thumper; guest beers** Ⓗ
Welcoming roadside hostelry
with fine views of the Downs
from the garden. Good food
(large, home-cooked portions)
with game prominent; live
music. Good value for the area,
with three guest beers, a
children's certificate and secure
cycle parking. Dogs welcome.
✿ ❍ ◐ ♧ ♣ ◔ P

## Lindfield

### Linden Tree

47 High Street (B2028)
☎ (01444) 482995
11–3, 6–11; 12–3, 7–10.30 Sun
**Arundel Best Bitter; Marston's
Pedigree; Ringwood Old
Thumper; Taylor Landlord;
Wadworth 6X; guest beers** Ⓗ
Small, friendly free house in an
attractive village. Remains of
an old brewery may be seen at
the rear. Two guest beers. No
food Sun. Wheelchair access at
the rear. ♨ Q ✿ ❦ ♧

**Try also: Snowdrop**,
Snowdrop Lane (King &
Barnes)

## Loxwood

### Sir Roger Tichbourne

Billingshurst Road, Alfold Bars
(B2123) ☎ (01403) 752377
12–2.30, 6–11; 12–2.30, 6–10.30 Sun
(closed Sun eve Oct–Easter)
**King & Barnes Sussex, Old,
seasonal beers** Ⓗ
Typical rural, low-beamed pub
with a quiet saloon on the right
and a busier, stone/brick-
floored bar on the left with an
inglenook; set back from the
main road and easily missed
on dark eves. Eve meals Fri
and Sat. Note: Festive may be
on a cask breather.
♨ Q ✿ ❍ ◐ ▲ ♣ P

## Maplehurst

### White Horse

Park Lane (between A281 and
A272, S of Nuthurst)
☎ (01403) 891208
12–2.30 (3 Sat), 6–11; 12–3, 7–10.30
Sun
**Brakspear Bitter; Harveys BB;
King & Barnes Sussex; guest
beers** Ⓗ
Pub whose landlord is a classic
car fanatic. Fruit machines and
jukeboxes are forbidden. Note
the extremely wide bar.
♨ Q ✿ ❍ ◐ ♣ P

## Midhurst

### Crown

Edinburgh Square (behind old
fire station, near church)
☎ (01730) 813462
11–11; 12–10.30 Sun
**Ballard's Best Bitter; Cheriton
Pots Ale; Fuller's London
Pride, ESB** Ⓗ; **guest beers** Ⓖ
Welcoming, traditional old
pub where superb hospitality
makes it justifiably popular.
An ever-changing range of
guest beers is served by gravity
from a new bar-level cellar.
The rear function hall is used
by live bands Tue eve. Cider in
summer.
♨ ✿ ⛺ ❍ ◐ ♣ ◔ P

## Swan Inn

Red Lion Street, Market Square
☎ (01730) 812853
11–2.30, 5.30–11; 12–10.30 Sun
**Harveys Pale Ale, BB, seasonal beers** ⓗ
15th-century, split-level inn in the centre of the old town. A supper licence gives an extra hour's drinking to diners Fri–Sun eves. Public parking nearby. Note: Addlestones Cider is served under gas pressure.
🏚 Q ✿ 🛏 ◖▮ ◖ 🍴 ♣

**Try also: Wheatsheaf**, Wool Lane (King & Barnes)

## Milland

### Black Fox Inn

Portsmouth Road (B2070, old A3, ½ mile NW of centre)
☎ (01428) 723218
11–3, 6–11; 12–3, 7–10.30 Sun
**Ballard's Best Bitter; Draught Bass; Wadworth 6X; guest beer**
Large and comfortable inn built in 1905 and said to be haunted, but not by the genuine black fox whose stuffed body is displayed in the bar. Large function room.
🏚 ✿ 🛏 ◖▮ & ♣ P ✄

## Nutbourne

### Rising Sun

☎ (01798) 812191
11–3, 6–11; 12–10.30 Sun
**Fuller's London Pride; guest beers** ⓗ
Unspoilt village local in a rural location, popular with walkers. Two contrasting bars: bare boards and an open fire in the friendly Village Bar; quieter, more restrained, atmosphere in the saloon. Up to five guest beers.
🏚 🛏 ✿ ◖▮ ♣

## Oving

### Gribble Inn

Gribble Lane
☎ (01243) 786893
11–2.30 (3 Sat), 6–11; 12–3, 7–10.30 Sun
**Gribble Ale, Reg's Tipple, Plucking Pheasant, Black Adder II, Pig's Ear, Wobbler** ⓗ
Thatched, 16th-century village local set in a fine garden. A compact brewhouse adjoining the skittle alley (view the process) produces the popular home-brewed ales. A deceptively spacious pub, with an extended family room, but mind the low beams. Good food. Quiz Sun eve.
🏚 Q 🛏 ✿ ◖▮ & ♣ 🍴 P ✄

## Rogate

### Wyndham Arms

On A272 ☎ (01730) 821315
11.30–2.30 (3 Sat), 6–11; 12–3, 6–10.30 (12–10.30 summer) Sun
**Ballard's Best Bitter, Wassail; Cheriton Pots Ale; Ringwood Fortyniner, Old Thumper** (winter); **guest beers** ⓖ
Cosy, friendly, 16th-century inn opposite the church and reputedly haunted. Beer stillages can be viewed via a glass panel from the bar. Annual midsummer beer festival. CAMRA Sussex *Pub of the Year 1996*.
🏚 Q ✿ 🛏 ◖▮ ♣ 🍴 P

## Rusper

### Plough

High Street ☎ (01293) 871215
11–2.30 (3 Sat), 6–11; 12–3, 7–10.30 Sun
**Courage Directors; Fuller's London Pride, ESB; guest beers** ⓗ
Popular village pub with a reinstated stone floor in front of the bar and low beams. Parts date back to the 15th century. Good food. 🏚 Q ✿ ◖▮ ♣

### Royal Oak

Friday Street (signed from A24) ☎ (01293) 871393
11–3, 6–11; 12–3, 7–10.30 Sun
**King & Barnes Sussex, Broadwood, Old, Festive, seasonal beers** ⓗ
Compact rural local, a mile west of the village. The bar is long and narrow, with two smaller rooms at each end. No eve meals Sun/Mon.
🏚 Q ✿ ◖▮ ♣ P

## Scaynes Hill

### Sloop Inn

Sloop Lane, Freshfield Lock (1½ miles N of A272 via Church Lane) OS384244
☎ (01444) 831219
11–3, 6–11; 12–3, 7–10.30 Sun
**Beards Best Bitter; Harveys BB; guest beer** ⓗ
Cosy, riverside inn close to the Bluebell Railway; popular with walkers and anglers. Good, home-cooked food. A Beards pub with the same tenant for 12 years.
🏚 Q ✿ ◖▮ 🕭 & 🅰 P

## Selham

### Three Moles

1 mile S of A272, midway between Midhurst and Petworth OS935206
☎ (01798) 861303
11.30–2.30, 5.30–11; 11.30–11 Sat; 12–10.30 Sun
**King & Barnes Mild, Sussex, Festive, seasonal beers** ⓗ
Small pub, well off the beaten track in fine countryside; formerly a station hotel, it is now a haven of good beer, traditional games and quiet conversation. A K&B house beer is also sold. Cider in summer. CAMRA regional *Pub of the Year 1995*.
🏚 Q ✿ ♣ 🍴 P

## Selsfield Common

### White Hart

Ardingly Road, West Hoathly (B2028 between Ardingly and Turners Hill)
☎ (01342) 715217
11–11; 12–10.30 Sun
**Harveys BB; guest beers** ⓗ
Olde-worlde building with oak beams and an inglenook. Two rooms: one is used mainly for eating. There is also a tithe barn which is used as a restaurant proper. Tasty, home-cooked food. Cider in summer. A pub to seek out.
🏚 Q 🕭 ✿ ◖▮ ♣ 🍴 P

## Sharpthorne

### Vinols Cross

8 Top Road (2 miles E of B2028) OS368325
☎ (01342) 810644
12–3, 6–11; 12–11 Sat; 12–3, 6–10.30 Sun
**Harveys BB; Wadworth 6X; guest beers** ⓗ
Welcoming country pub near the recently extended Bluebell Railway. Wide-ranging selection of ales.
🏚 ✿ ◖▮ 🅰 P

## Shoreham-by-Sea

### Lazy Toad

88A High Street
☎ (01273) 441622
11–3, 5.30–11; 11–11 Fri & Sat, 12–10.30 Sun
**Badger Dorset Best, Tanglefoot; Shepherd Neame Bishops Finger; guest beers** ⓖ
Single-bar free house converted from a wine bar. The guest beers (at least three) are regularly changed. Gravity dispense is rare for the area. No food Sun. Occasional cider.
◖ ➤ 🍴

### Marlipins

38 High Street (next to Marlipins Museum)
☎ (01273) 453369
10–11; 12–3.30, 7–10.30 Sun
**Draught Bass; Fuller's London Pride; Harveys BB; Worthington Bitter** ⓗ
16th-century, one-bar pub with low beams and a conservatory and patio at the rear. Good food: full menu of home-made meals and sandwiches.
Q ✿ ◖▮ ➤

## Red Lion Inn

Old Shoreham Road
☎ (01273) 453171
11.30–3, 6–11; 12–4, 7–10.30 Sun
**Arundel Best Bitter; Brewery on Sea Spinnaker Bitter; Courage Directors; King & Barnes Sussex; Marston's Pedigree; Wadworth 6X; guest beers** Ⓗ
Ever-popular, 16th-century coaching inn with low beams and an inglenook. Regular beer festivals; live music. Good food is always available. The front drinking area looks out over the old tollbridge.
🏨 Q ✿ 🚮 ◑ ▶ ✂

Try also: Crabtree, Buckingham Rd (Gale's)

# Singleton

## Horse & Groom

On A286 ☎ (01243) 811455
11–3, 6 (5 summer Fri)–11 (closed winter Tue eve); 12–10.30 Sun
**Ballard's Best Bitter; Cheriton Pots Ale; Courage Best Bitter; Ringwood Fortyniner** Ⓗ
Convivial village free house close to the Downland Museum and Goodwood. Accommodation will be available in mid 1997. The enclosed rear garden has swingboats and a trampoline. Home-made food; separate cosy restaurant (special food eves Thu). No eve meals winter Mon. Family room lunchtime.
🏨 🛏 ✿ 🚮 ◑ ▲ ♣ P

## Staplefield

### Jolly Tanners

Handcross Road
☎ (01444) 400335
11–3, 5.30–11; 11–11 Sat; 12–3, 7–10.30 Sun
**Fuller's Chiswick, London Pride; Thwaites Best Mild; Wadworth 6X; guest beer** Ⓗ
Very pleasant pub on the edge of the village, not far from the cricket field. Reputation for high quality meals (separate dining room for parties).
🏨 Q ✿ ◑ ▶ 🍴 ♣ P

## Stoughton

### Hare & Hounds

Off B2146, through Walderton
OS803115 ☎ (01705) 631433
11–3, 6–11; 12–4, 7–10.30 Sun
**Gale's HSB; Harveys BB; Taylor Landlord; guest beers** Ⓗ
Fine example of a Sussex flint-faced building in a secluded South Downs setting; popular and lively, with a good local trade. Good value food (fresh local seafood and game). Three strong guest beers from independents. Twenty-two

years in the *Guide.*
🏨 ✿ ◑ ▶ ♣ P

# Sutton

## White Horse Inn

The Street ☎ (01798) 869221
11–3, 6–11; 12–3, 7–10.30 Sun
**Arundel Best Bitter; Bateman XB; Courage Best Bitter; Young's Bitter; guest beer** Ⓗ
250-year-old Georgian inn in an attractive downland village, close to Stane Street and the Bignor Roman villa. Excellent food and accommodation. The bare-floored village bar is popular with locals and walkers.
🏨 Q ✿ 🚮 ◑ ▶ 🍴 ♣ P

# Turners Hill

## Red Lion

Lion Lane (off B2028)
☎ (01342) 715416
11–3, 6–11; 12–4, 7–10.30 Sun
**Harveys XX Mild, Pale Ale, BB, Old** Ⓗ
Unchanging village pub with an interesting collection of bottled beers; its 22nd entry in the *Guide.* Pool room upstairs. Jazz day near Midsummer's Day. Folk club Sat eve. No food Sun. 🏨 Q ✿ ◑ ♣ P

# Westbourne

## Good Intent

North Street (200 yds from B2147) ☎ (01243) 372656
10.30–2.30 (3 Sat), 6–11; 12–3, 7–10.30 Sun
**Ansells Mild; Friary Meux BB; Ind Coope Burton Ale; guest beer** Ⓗ
16th-century, two-bar town pub boasting a log fire in winter in the lounge. A rare outlet for mild in the area. The guest beer is from Carlsberg-Tetley. Good value food.
🏨 ✿ ◑ ▶ ♣ P

# West Chiltington

## Five Bells

Smock Alley ☎ (01798) 812143
11–3, 6–11; 12–3, 7–10.30 Sun
**King & Barnes Sussex; guest beers** Ⓗ
Attractive, one-bar pub with a log fire at one end and a conservatory restaurant with a stove at the other. Over 300 different beers have been sold in the last six years. No food Sun eve. Space is reserved for slot car racing.
🏨 Q ✿ ◑ ▶ ♣ 🍴 P

# West Wittering

## Lamb Inn

Chichester Road (B2179)
☎ (01243) 511105
11–2.30, 6–11; 12–3, 7–10.30 Sun

**Ballard's Best Bitter, Wassail; Bunces Benchmark, Best Bitter; Ringwood Fortyniner; guest beers** Ⓗ
Handy for a sailing centre and beaches; an old convivial roadside inn, with a wide range of good, home-cooked food and still room for drinkers in the eve. No meals Sun eve in winter. Local small breweries are well represented.
🏨 Q ✿ ◑ ▶ 🍴 ♠ P

# Wick

## Locomotive

74 Lyminster Road (S of railway gates)
☎ (01903) 716658
11–3, 6–11; 12–3, 7–10.30 Sun
**Ansells Mild; Greene King Abbot; Hardy Country; Harveys Armada; King & Barnes Sussex; guest beer** Ⓗ
Friendly, one-bar local offering good food and a well-appointed family room. Patio, children's activity area and two boules pitches outside. Cider in summer.
🏨 🛏 ✿ ◑ ▶ 🍴 ♣ 🍷 P

# Worthing

## Alexandra

28 Lyndhurst Road (near hospital) ☎ (01903) 234833
11–11; 12–3, 7–10.30 Sun
**Draught Bass; Fuller's London Pride; Harveys BB; Highgate Dark; King & Barnes seasonal beers** Ⓗ
Friendly, two-bar local with a games room. So far, it has avoided being 'improved'. The accent remains on service.
🏨 Q ✿ 🚰 ♣

## Cricketers

66 Broadwater Street West
☎ (01903) 233369
11–3, 6–11; 11–11 Fri & Sat; 12–10.30 Sun
**Draught Bass; Fuller's London Pride; Greene King IPA; Harveys BB; guest beers** Ⓗ
Pub situated on a corner of Broadwater Green and home to the local cricket club. The eastern end of the L-shaped bar has all the tradition of the public bar it once was; the other end is a comfortable saloon leading to a dining area. No eve meals Sun or Mon.
Q ✿ ◑ ♣ 🍴

## Hogshead

25 Warwick Street (E of clock tower) ☎ (01903) 206088
10.30–11; 12–10.30 Sun
**Boddingtons Bitter; Flowers Original** Ⓗ**; Gibbs Mew Bishop's Tipple; Hop Back Summer Lightning** Ⓖ**; guest beers** Ⓗ/Ⓖ
Popular central-town pub with bare floorboards in its

1930s-style interior. The one bar is long, narrow and friendly, with a good mix of people. Excellent range of bar food (available at all times except Fri and Sat eves).
◑ ▶ ⌂

### John Selden

Halfmoon Lane, Durrington (200 yds S off A27)
☎ (01903) 264986
10.30–2.30, 5.30–11; 11–11 Sat; 12–3, 7–10.30 Sun
**Ansells Bitter; Draught Bass; Friary Meux BB; Ind Coope Burton Ale; Tetley Bitter; guest beer** Ⓗ
Traditional, two-bar pub with a large function room, popular with locals in both bars; shove-ha'penny played. Extensive full menu (except Sun).
♨ Q ✿ ◑ ▶ ⊞ � ♣ P

### Old House at Home

77 Broadwater Street East (off A24) ☎ (01903) 232661
11.30–2.30, 6–11; 12–3, 7–10.30 Sun
**Draught Bass; Fuller's London Pride; guest beer** Ⓗ
Popular, two-bar, wood-panelled village pub in traditional Sussex style with a flint-covered exterior. Coal/wood fires in both bars with a plate collection and other curios. Large garden, patio and play area. ♨ ✿ ◑ ⊞ ⅙ ♣ P

### Vine

27–29 High Street, Tarring
☎ (01903) 202891
11–2.30 (3 Sat), 6–11; 12–3, 7–10.30 Sun
**Badger Dorset Best; Ballard's Best Bitter; Harveys BB; Hop Back Summer Lightning** Ⓗ; **guest beers** Ⓗ/Ⓖ
Popular local in a well-preserved village street, attracting a wide cross-section of customers; vibrant and often noisy late eves. The former Parsons Brewery stands at the rear. Beer festival Oct; house beer from Brewery on Sea. No food Sun.
✿ ◑ ≠ (West) P

## Yapton

### Lamb Inn

Bilsham Road (B2132, S of village) ☎ (01243) 551232

11–3, 5.30 (5 Fri, 6 Sat)–11; 12–4.30, 6.30–10.30 Sun
**Fuller's London Pride; Marston's Pedigree; Tisbury Best Bitter; guest beer** Ⓗ
Traditional, friendly country pub serving home-made food. Large garden with children's play area. Ample parking. French boules played.
♨ Q ✿ ◑ ▶ ⊞ ⅙ Ⓐ ♣ P

### Maypole

Maypole Lane (off B2132, ½ mile N of village) OS977041
☎ (01243) 551417
11–2.30, 5.30–11; 12–3, 7–10.30 Sun
**Flowers Original; Ringwood Best Bitter; Younger IPA; guest beers** Ⓗ
Family-run pub with a rural atmosphere, tucked away down a lane away from the village centre: a cosy lounge with two log fires, a large public bar (children's certificate) and a skittle alley. Bank hol beer festivals (Easter and summer). Four guest beers change regularly. No eve meals Tue or Sun.
♨ Q ✿ ◑ ▶ ⊞ ⅙ ♣ P

# Tyne & Wear

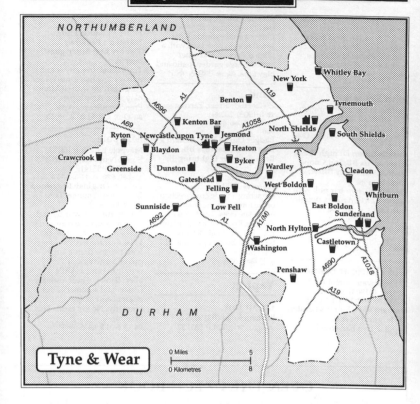

## Benton

### Benton Ale House
Front Street
☎ (0191) 266 1512
11–11; 12–10.30 Sun
**Banks's Bitter; Camerons Bitter, Strongarm; Marston's Pedigree; guest beers** Ⓗ
Formerly the Sun, now splendidly refurbished by Camerons. Good choice of frequently changed guest beers; warm, friendly welcome. Lined glasses guarantee full measures.
◖ & ⊖ (Four Lane Ends) P ⊟

## Blaydon

### Black Bull
Bridge Street
☎ (0191) 414 2846
4–11; 12–3, 6–11 Sat; 12–3, 7–10.30 Sun
**Camerons Bitter, Strongarm; Castle Eden Ale; Ind Coope Burton Ale; guest beers** Ⓗ
Very friendly, well-run pub with a good local clientele. A fine collection of photos shows the decline of Blaydon. The recently renovated lounge hosts weekly blues and jazz.
🏚 Q ✿ ⇌ ♣ P

## Byker

### Free Trade Inn
St Lawrence Road
☎ (0191) 265 5764
11–11; 12–10.30 Sun
**Mordue Five Bridge, Geordie Pride, Workie Ticket; Theakston Best Bitter, XB; guest beers** Ⓗ
Split-level, basic pub, overlooking the river and its bridges, which prides itself on offering all of the local Mordue Brewery's products. Nothing flash, but good company. 🏚 ✿

### Tyne
1 Maling Street (under Glasshouse Bridge)
☎ (0191) 265 2550
12–11; 12–10.30 Sun
**Boddingtons Bitter; Castle Eden Ale; Marston's Pedigree; guest beers** Ⓗ
Large, single-roomed bar, near the mouth of the Ouseburn, offering guest beers from local independent brewers. Excellent, free jukebox. ✿

Try also: **Glendale**, Potts St (Bass); **Ship Inn**, Stepney Bank (Whitbread)

## Castletown

### Wessington
Wessington Way
☎ (0191) 548 9384
11–11; 12–10.30 Sun
**Boddingtons Bitter; Castle Eden Ale; guest beer** Ⓗ
Large motel by a busy main road: an extensive restaurant with a small bar area in typical Brewer's Fayre style. Children's play area. Meals are served all day, but are quite expensive for the area.
🏕 ✿ ⇔ ◖ ▶ & P

---

### 🏠 INDEPENDENT BREWERIES

**Big Lamp:** Newcastle upon Tyne

**Darwin:** Sunderland

**Federation:** Dunston

**Hadrian:** Newcastle upon Tyne

**Mordue:** North Shields

**Vaux:** Sunderland

## Cleadon

### Cottage Tavern
North Street (A1018)
☎ (0191) 536 7883
12–11; 12–10.30 Sun
**Vaux Samson, Double Maxim** Ⓗ
Comfortable village pub with a warm and welcoming feel (created by subdued lighting and Vaux flowery decor), served by a long, semi-circular bar. It can get quite busy.
❀ ♣

## Crawcrook

### Rising Sun Inn
Bank Top ☎ (0191) 413 3316
11.30–11; 12–10.30 Sun
**Boddingtons Bitter; Castle Eden Ale; Marston's Pedigree; guest beers** Ⓗ
Comfortable, recently expanded pub offering a pleasant atmosphere and a varying choice of beers. It caters for the ale drinker whilst not neglecting the needs of families. Good range of home-cooked food.
Q ❀ ◖ ▶ P

## East Boldon

### Grey Horse
14 Front Street
☎ (0191) 536 4186
11–11; 12–10.30 Sun
**Vaux Samson, Waggle Dance; guest beer** Ⓗ
Traditional village pub, dating from the 17th century. The spacious lounge has a dusky, convivial atmosphere created by mock beams and plaster walls. Excellent function room; first-rate service. No meals Sun eve. Q ❀ ◖ ▶ ⊟ ♿ ⇋ ♣ P

## Felling

### Old Fox
Carlisle Street
☎ (0191) 420 0357
11–4, 6–11; 11–11 Fri & Sat; 12–10.30 Sun
**Bateman XB; Fuller's London Pride; guest beers** Ⓗ
Comfortable local with a mixed clientele. A pool table and musical events ensure a wide following; a fast turnover of guest beers ensures quality.
🏠 ㅂ ◖ ⊖

### Wheatsheaf
26 Carlisle Street
☎ (0191) 420 0659
12–3, 6–11; 11–11 Fri & Sat; 12–10.30 Sun
**Big Lamp Bitter, Prince Bishop, Mulligan's Stout; guest beers** Ⓗ
Hospitable, largely unspoilt local which retains much of its

Edwardian charm. Tied to the local Big Lamp brewery, its success is a tribute to the importance of the tied house system. 🏠 ⊖

## Gateshead

### Borough Arms
80–82 Bensham Road (150 yds from Gateshead Metro)
☎ (0191) 478 1323
12–3 (4 Fri), 6–11; 12–11 Sat; 12–3, 7–10.30 Sun
**Draught Bass; Stones Bitter; guest beers** Ⓗ
Welcoming two-roomer; popular with locals and visitors. 🏠 ❀ ◖ ♿ ⊖ P

## Greenside

### White Swan
Main Street ☎ (0191) 413 4255
11–11; 12–10.30 Sun
**Banks's Bitter; Camerons Bitter, Strongarm** Ⓗ
Refurbished, friendly village pub with many rooms.
🏠 Q ♿ ❀ ⊟ P

## Heaton

### Chillingham
Chillingham Road
☎ (0191) 265 5915
11–3, 6–11; 11–11 Sat; 12–10.30 Sun
**Draught Bass; Courage Directors; Theakston Best Bitter, XB; guest beers** Ⓗ
Two equally well fitted and furnished rooms attract their own regulars in this fine roadside pub. Lovely home-made food and an excellent atmosphere make it popular with students in term time.
◖ ⊟ ♿ (Chillingham Rd) ⊖ P

## Jesmond

### Archer
Archbold Terrace
☎ (0191) 281 3010
11–11; 12–10.30 Sun
**Black Sheep Best Bitter; Hexhamshire Shire Bitter; Stones Bitter; Tetley Bitter; guest beers** Ⓗ
An inspiring choice of beers in an uninspiring building – grey 1960s concrete outside, but a pleasant atmosphere inside. An unobtrusive pool room provides entertainment, as do very loud live music events.
◖ ⊖

## Kenton Bar

### Crofters Lodge
Kenton Lane
☎ (0191) 286 9394
11–11; 12–10.30 Sun
**Vaux Samson, Waggle Dance; Ward's Thorne BB, Best Bitter; guest beers** Ⓗ

Pleasant, well-run outlet furnished in traditional Vaux style: a traditional public bar and a conservatory used by diners. Good value food (book eve). Disabled parking available. Children's certificate.
🛏 ◖ ▶ ⊟ ♿ ♿ P ⌿

## Low Fell

### Aletaster
706 Durham Road
☎ (0191) 487 0770
11–11; 12–10.30 Sun
**McEwan 80/-; Marston's Pedigree; Morland Old Speckled Hen; Theakston Old Peculier; Younger No. 3; guest beers** Ⓗ
The large, L-shaped bar in T&J Bernard's flagship pub boasts 16 handpumps, which include one regular and two changing guest ale pumps. ❀ ♿ P

## Newcastle upon Tyne

### Alewrx
14–16 Newgate Street
☎ (0191) 232 6914
11–11; 12–10.30 Sun
**Draught Bass; Stones Bitter; Worthington Bitter; guest beers** Ⓗ
Eccentric decor and furnishings provide a visual treat in this city-centre pub where three drinking areas are served from one bar and can be busy at weekends. Guest beers come from Hadrian Brewery and the Bass portfolio.
◖ ♿ ⇋ ⊖ (Central/Monument)

### Bodega
125 Westgate Road
☎ (0191) 221 1552
11–11; 12–3, 7–10.30 Sun
**Butterknowle Conciliation Ale; Newcastle Exhibition; Theakston Best Bitter; guest beers** Ⓗ
Sympathetically refurbished to a very high standard, the Bodega retains many original features, including two magnificent stained-glass domes. Slightly out of the city centre, it offers a range of six local beers (Mordue No 9 is the brewery's Geordie Pride). No meals Sun.
◖ ⇋ (Central) ⊖

### Cooperage
32 The Close, Quayside
☎ (0191) 232 8286
11–11; 12–10.30 Sun
**Ind Coope Burton Ale; Marston's Owd Rodger; Tetley Bitter; guest beers** Ⓗ
Traditional pub in one of the oldest buildings in Newcastle – always worth visiting, but it can get very busy at weekends. The bare wood and stone is all

original and adds to the comfortable atmosphere. The house beer is Hadrian High Level. ⬧ ⬧ ⬧ ⬧

## Crown Posada ☆
31 Side ☎ (0191) 232 1269
11–11; 12–4, 7–10.30 Sun
**Draught Bass; Butterknowle Conciliation Ale; Jennings Bitter; Theakston XB; guest beers** H
One of the finest pubs around: the original stained-glass windows are beautiful and, with the unusual ceiling, provide the visitor with a treat for the eyes. Ideally situated for exploring the quayside. Q

## Head of Steam
Neville Street (opp. Central station) ☎ (0191) 232 4379
11–11; 12–10.30 Sun
**Draught Bass; Border Special; Highgate Dark; Shepherd Neame Spitfire; guest beers** H
Formerly the Express Bar, and the Green Dolphin, now one of the national Head of Steam chain, but not overstocked with railway memorabilia. The downstairs room, open Thu, Fri and Sat eves, can get very busy. ⬧ ⬧ (Central) ⬧

## Newcastle Arms
57 St Andrews Street
☎ (0191) 232 3567
11–11; 7–10.30 Sun, closed Sun lunch
**Ind Coope Burton Ale; Taylor Landlord; Tetley Bitter; guest beers** H
On the fringe of Newcastle's thriving Chinatown, and very handy for the football ground, this single-roomed pub offers an interesting selection of guest beers. Occasional mini-beer festivals. ⬧ ⬧ (St James)

## Tap & Spile
Nun Street
☎ (0191) 232 0026
11–11; 7–10.30 Sun, closed Sun lunch
**Beer range varies** H
Welcoming pub in the historic market area. The bar is for standing and sampling the fine range of beers, with a comfortable area for sitting in one corner. The cellar bar is used for live entertainment.
⬧ ⬧ (Central) ⬧
(Monument) ⬧

## Tilley's
Westgate Road
☎ (0191) 232 0692
11.30–11; 7–10.30 Sun, closed Sun lunch
**Jennings Bitter, Cumberland Ale, Cocker Hoop, Sneck Lifter** H
Pub standing next to the Tyne Theatre, very popular with students, actors and diners on their way to the Chinatown area. The small, mirrored side

bar is particularly comfortable, while the main bar is busier.
⬧ ⬧ ⬧ (Central) ⬧

# New York

## Shiremoor House Farm
Middle Engine Lane
☎ (0191) 257 6302
11–11; 12–10.30 Sun
**Theakston Best Bitter, Old Peculier; guest beers** H
Award-winning Fitzgerald's outlet, well known for excellent food. Guest beers often come from local micro-breweries. Q ⬧ ⬧ ⬧ P

# North Hylton

## Shipwrights
Ferryboat Lane
☎ (0191) 549 5139
11–3.30, 5–11; 12–3.30, 7–10.30 Sun
**Vaux Samson, Waggle Dance; Ward's Best Bitter; guest beer** H
Haven of tranquillity on the banks of the River Wear, under the hustle and bustle of the A19; now celebrating its 20th consecutive year in the *Guide*. Wooden beams, brass fittings, plenty of bric-a-brac and subtle decor enhance a relaxed drinking atmosphere.
⬧ ⬧ ⬧ ⬧ P

# North Shields

## Bell & Bucket
37 Norfolk Street
☎ (0191) 257 4634
11–3, 7–11; 11–11 Wed–Sat; 12–3, 7–10.30 Sun
**Banks's Bitter; Camerons Strongarm; Marston's Pedigree; guest beers** H
Welcoming, two-level bar, recently refurbished – an interesting conversion from a redundant fire station.
⬧ ⬧ ⬧

## Magnesia Bank
1 Camden Street
☎ (0191) 257 4831
11–11; 12–10.30 Sun
**Butterknowle Conciliation Ale; Mordue Five Bridge, Workie Ticket; Taylor Landlord; Tetley Bitter; guest beers** H
Three times winner of local CAMRA *Pub of the Year* and the brewery tap for Mordue (but other local micro-breweries are regularly featured). Comedy, music and quiz nights staged. Children's certificate.
⬧ ⬧ ⬧ ⬧ ⬧ ⬧ ⬧

## Porthole
11 New Quay
☎ (0191) 257 6645
11–11; 12–10.30 Sun
**Boddingtons Bitter; Village White Boar; guest beers** H

1834 free house with a nautical theme, on the banks of the Tyne. Live music sessions and a changing range of three guest beers keep it thriving and popular. ⬧ ⬧ ⬧ ⬧ P

## Tap & Spile
184 Tynemouth Road
☎ (0191) 257 2523
11.30–11; 12–10.30 Sun
**Beer range varies** H
An excellent choice of ten guest beers is sold at this busy, lively Tap & Spile where there's always a warm welcome.
⬧ ⬧ ⬧ ⬧

# Penshaw

## Grey Horse
Village Green, Old Penshaw
☎ (0191) 584 4882
11–3 (4 Sat), 6–11; 12–4, 7–10.30 Sun
**Tetley Bitter** H
Warm, friendly local, with a village atmosphere, nestling under the shadow of Penshaw Monument, a local landmark. Long-standing licensees; a *Guide* regular for 16 years. No food Sun. ⬧ ⬧ ⬧ P

## Prospect
Victoria Terrace, Old Penshaw
☎ (0191) 584 4001
11–11; 12–10.30 Sun
**Vaux Samson, Waggle Dance; guest beer** H
Popular, two-roomed roadside pub. The large public bar has been refurbished in the usual Vaux style; plush lounge to the side. Beware: the car park is across a very busy road.
⬧ ⬧ ⬧ ⬧ P

# Ryton

## Old Cross
11–3, 7–11; 11–11 Fri & Sat; 12–10.30 Sun
**Vaux Samson; Ward's Best Bitter; guest beers** H
Large, popular pub by the village green in an award-winning *Britain in Bloom* village. Known for good food.
⬧ ⬧

# South Shields

## Alum Ale House
River Drive (by ferry landing)
☎ (0191) 427 7245
11–11; 12–3, 7–10.30 Sun
**Banks's Bitter; Camerons Strongarm; Marston's Pedigree; guest beer** H
One of the oldest pubs in town (William Wood's brewery tap 1763–1936). Panelled walls, a bare wood floor and an unusual, copper-clad bar offer a warm and friendly homeliness in which to enjoy a quiet drink. Cellar bar folk nights. Q ⬧ ⬧

## Bamburgh

175 Bamburgh Avenue
☎ (0191) 454 1899
11–11; 12–10.30 Sun
**Boddingtons Bitter; Castle
Eden Ale; guest beer** Ⓗ
Large, split-level, open-plan
Berni Inn on the coast road,
overlooking the leas and the
finishing line of The Great
North Run. A spacious games
area, with large screen TV,
extensive seating areas and a
small, intimate restaurant offer
something for everyone.
❀ ◖ ▷ & ♣ P ⊬

## Dolly Peel

137 Commercial Road, Laygate
☎ (0191) 427 1441
11–11; 12–3, 7–10.30 Sun
**Courage Directors; Taylor
Landlord; Theakston XB;
Younger No. 3; guest beer** Ⓗ
Unimposing roadside pub
(named after a famous 18th-
century fishwife and smuggler)
hiding an unexpected oasis
behind its Victorian facade. A
perfect environment for the
discerning drinker, with its
friendly landlord and pleasant
atmosphere.
Q ♣ P

## Holborn Rose &
## Crown

East Holborn (opp. Middle
Dock Gate) ☎ (0191) 455 2379
11–11; 12–10.30 Sun
**Jennings Cumberland Ale;
Theakston XB; Younger No. 3;
guest beer** Ⓗ
Olde-worlde gem, off the
beaten track, serving an ever-
changing array of guest ales.
Most of the original bar fittings
have been retained and are
interspersed with antique
brewing memorabilia, giving
the pub a much-used feel.
❀ ♣

## Riverside

3 Commercial Road
☎ (0191) 455 2328
12–11; 12–3, 7–10.30 Sun
**Boddingtons Bitter; Taylor
Landlord; Flowers Original;
guest beer** Ⓗ
Small, deservedly popular
street-corner free house, handy
for the Customs House.
Traditional in style, it is fast
gaining a reputation for
offering smaller independent
brewers' ales and a warm
welcome from smart, efficient
staff. ❀ ⊖

## Steamboat

51 Coronation Street
☎ (0191) 454 0134
12–11; 12–10.30 Sun
**Vaux Samson, Double Maxim,
Waggle Dance; guest beer** Ⓗ
Popular pub near the Customs
House. The wood-panelled
walls are adorned with
shipping artefacts, flags and

other bric-a-brac, giving it a
cosy nautical atmosphere.
⊖

# Sunderland: *North*

## Harbour View

Harbour View
☎ (0191) 567 1402
11–11; 12–10.30 Sun
**Draught Bass; Worthington
Bitter; guest beer** Ⓗ
Modern, one-roomed pub,
designed in the fashion of an
old-style, traditional ale house.
It overlooks the river where
new life is being breathed into
the former North Sands
shipbuilding area. Handy for
Roker Park and especially busy
on match days. ❀

## Smugglers

Marine Walk
☎ (0191) 514 3844
11.30–3, 5–11; 11–11 Sat; 12–10.30 Sun
**Butterknowle Banner Bitter;
Vaux Double Maxim; guest
beer** Ⓗ
Excellent, friendly, family
beach pub overlooking Roker
Cove, offering good quality
food and a Fri eve 'Kid's
Pirates Club'. Nautical
paraphernalia and soft lighting
create a cosy feel. Very popular
burger menu on match days.
🏠 ❀ ◖ ▷

# Sunderland: *South*

## Borough

1 Vine Place ☎ (0191) 567 7909
11–11; 7–10.30 Sun, closed Sun lunch
**Vaux Lorimer's Best Scotch,
Samson, Double Maxim,
Waggle Dance; guest beer** Ⓗ
Busy, two-storey pub with a
laid-back atmosphere, offering
real ale only in the downstairs
bar – served from a large,
ornate central counter. Live
music most weekends. Named
after the old Borough Town
Hall, featured on the pub sign.
⊞ ⇌ ♤

## Brewery Tap

9 Dunning Street
☎ (0191) 567 7472
11–11; 12–10.30 Sun
**Vaux Samson, Double Maxim;
guest beer** Ⓗ
Former Whitbread pub
acquired by Vaux several years
ago due to its proximity to the
brewery. A basic bar, wood-
panelled corridor and a cosy
lounge all sport pictures of old
Sunderland. It has a roomy
feel, although it does get busy
at weekends.
🏠 ⊞ ⇌ ♣

## Chesters

Chester Road
☎ (0191) 565 9952
11–11; 12–10.30 Sun

**Vaux Samson; Ward's Best
Bitter; guest beer** Ⓗ
Former vicarage, converted by
Vaux in 1954, on the main road
leading into the city; close
enough to enjoy the city
atmosphere but seldom
packed. The traditional decor
and use of partitions help to
break up the open-plan layout.
❀ ◖ & ♣ P

## Fitzgerald's

10–12 Green Terrace
☎ (0191) 567 0852
11–11; 12–3, 7–10.30 Sun
**Draught Bass; Theakston Best
Bitter, XB; Worthington Bitter;
guest beer** Ⓗ
Very popular circuit pub near
the university, with a
traditional wood-clad bar area
and a plush, split-level lounge
featuring expensive
furnishings and subtle lighting.
Annual beer festival. Door staff
are employed.
◖ ⊞ ⇌

## Ivy House

6 Worcester Street (behind
Park Lane bus station)
☎ (0191) 567 3399
11–11; 12–10.30 Sun
**Vaux Samson, Double Maxim,
Waggle Dance; Ward's Best
Bitter** Ⓗ
Pub hidden in a back street;
quiet and relaxing during the
day, loud and raucous at night
– much favoured by students
and young people. A large
crescent-shaped bar serves a
small bar/games area and a
larger dimly lit lounge. Large-
screen TV for sporting events.
◖ ⊞ ⇌ ♣

## Lansdowne

32 Deptford Road, Millfield
☎ (0191) 567 1886
11–11; 12–10.30 Sun
**Vaux Lorimer's Best Scotch,
Samson, Double Maxim;
guest beer** Ⓗ
Old-fashioned and welcoming
traditional ale house in a quiet
area, just out of the city centre;
recently refurbished and
reverted back to its original
name. A choice of cask-only
ales in a pleasant setting.
♣

## Tap & Spile

Salem Street, Hendon
☎ (0191) 514 2810
11–3, 5.30–11; 12–3, 7–10.30 Sun
**Beer range varies** Ⓗ
A drinkers' paradise, a short
stroll from the city centre,
offering up to nine ales and
three ciders. It has several
rooms with bare floors and
panelled walls and hosts an
annual (Nov) beer festival.
Local CAMRA *Pub of the Year*
1993–97.
🏠 ◖ ⇌ ♣ ♤

## Sunniside

### Potters Wheel
Sun Street ☎ (0191) 488 3628
11.30–3 (4 Fri), 5.30–11; 11.30–11 Sat;
12–3, 7–10.30 Sun
**Theakston Best Bitter; guest beers** Ⓗ
Very smart pub with a number of drinking and seating areas, served from a central bar. Up to four guest beers, good food and a cheery welcome.
◖ & P

## Tynemouth

### Fitzpatrick's
29 Front Street
☎ (0191) 257 8956
11–11; 12–10.30 Sun
**Theakston Best Bitter, XB; guest beers** Ⓗ
Long, beautifully furnished pub with a raised seating area and a small, cosy snug. Four beers, served from the single, long bar, and good value food, mean that the pub is well used at lunchtime (eve meals in summer). Q ◖ ▶ ⊖

### Tynemouth Lodge Hotel
Tynemouth Road
☎ (0191) 257 7565
11–11; 12–10.30 Sun
**Draught Bass; Belhaven 80/-; Black Sheep Best Bitter** Ⓗ
Welcoming 18th-century, unspoilt free house where full measures are assured. It serves the best Bass in the area, and is the only permanent outlet for Belhaven in the north of England. No children, no hot food, no dogs, no music and no pub games.
🏚 Q ❀ ⊖ P

## Wardley

### Green
White Mare Pool
☎ (0191) 495 0171
11–11; 12–10.30 Sun
**Draught Bass; Theakston Best Bitter; guest beers** Ⓗ
Busy roadside pub frequented post-match by local sportsmen. This large, two-roomed pub

and restaurant offers good food and facilities. Mini-beer festivals held.
◖ ▶ ⊞

## Washington

### Sandpiper
Easby Road, Biddick
☎ (0191) 416 0038
11–11; 12–10.30 Sun
**Boddingtons Bitter; Castle Eden Ale; guest beer** Ⓗ
Modern estate pub styled as a comfortable, traditional village pub. The stone-flagged lounge is strategically adorned with brewing paraphernalia and there is a modern games room-cum-bar. Up to seven ales.
❀ ◖ ⊞ & ♣ P

### Three Horse Shoes
Washington Road, Usworth (opp. Nissan factory)
☎ (0191) 536 4183
12–3, 6.30–11; 11–11 Fri & Sat; 12–3, 7–10.30 Sun
**Vaux Lorimer's Best Scotch, Samson, Double Maxim; guest beer** Ⓗ
Large roadside pub near the Aircraft Museum, in what was once Usworth village. It caters for families in the open-plan lounge, with a more traditional bar and pool room for the discerning drinker. Annual beer festival. No meals Sun eve. Q ❀ ◖ ▶ ⊞ ♣ P

## West Boldon

### Black Horse
Rectory Bank
☎ (0191) 536 1814
11–3, 7–11; 12–3, 7–10.30 Sun
**Boddingtons Bitter; Fuller's London Pride; Mordue Workie Ticket; Morland Old Speckled Hen; guest beer** Ⓗ
Food-dominated, family-run pub, close to the ancient parish church. A large 'restaurant' serves a wide selection of quality meals, while the small bar stocks a choice of guest ales (the range varies with the season). No food Sun. Limited parking.
Q ❀ ◖ ▶ ♣ P

## Whitburn

### Jolly Sailor
1 East Street ☎ (0191) 529 3221
11–11; 12–10.30 Sun
**Draught Bass; Stones Bitter; Worthington Bitter; guest beer (occasional)** Ⓗ
Unspoilt, 18th-century inn next to the village green, reputedly haunted by a former barmaid. There is a jumble of downstairs rooms and an upper bar (open weekends). Popular with visitors to the picturesque village. No food Sun.
🏚 Q ⌂ ❀ ◖ ⊞ ♣

## Whitley Bay

### Briar Dene
The Links ☎ (0191) 252 0926
11–11; 12–10.30 Sun
**Stones Bitter; Theakston Best Bitter, XB, Old Peculier; guest beers** Ⓗ
Large, attractive Fitzgerald's house with several drinking areas. The splendid bar boasts seaviews out over the links, and an ever-changing range of guest beers. Mini-beer festivals held. Q ⌂ ❀ ◖ ▶ & ♣ P

### Fitzgerald's
2 South Parade
☎ (0191) 251 1255
11–11; 12–10.30 Sun
**Newcastle Exhibition; Theakston Best Bitter, XB; guest beers** Ⓗ
Beautiful pub with a well deserved reputation for fine food. The large lounge features back-lit stained-glass panels set into the ceiling above the bar. The Chart Room is smaller, with a nautical theme. Three guest beers. ◖ ⊖

### Tap & Spile
278 Whitley Road
☎ (0191) 251 3852
11–11; 12–10.30 Sun
**Beer range varies** Ⓗ
At the end of the main shopping street: a provider of a large number of fine beers in the Tap & Spile tradition. The shape of the busy bar allows plenty of room for customers.
◖ ⊖ ♣ ⌂

---

# GOOD PUB FOOD

For many pub enthusiasts, a good meal is as important as a good pint. In recognition of this, CAMRA publishes its own guide to *Good Pub Food*. Compiled by award-winning writer Susan Nowak, the fourth edition features around 500 pubs serving the finest pub cooking, with not a microwaved lasagne in sight. Priced £9.99, it is available in bookshops or direct and post-free from CAMRA.

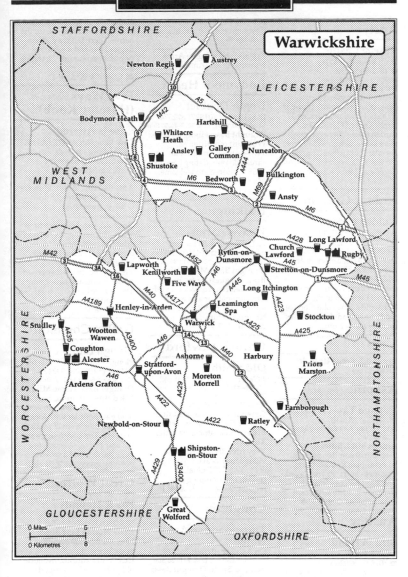

## Warwickshire

*Map showing locations including:*

STAFFORDSHIRE

LEICESTERSHIRE

Newton Regis · Austrey

Bodymoor Heath · Hartshill

Whitacre Heath · Ansley · Galley Common · Nuneaton

Shustoke · Bedworth · Bulkington

WEST MIDLANDS

Ansty

Long Lawford · Church Lawford · Rugby

Lapworth · Ryton-on-Dunsmore · Stretton-on-Dunsmore

Kenilworth · Five Ways · Long Itchington

Henley-in-Arden · Leamington Spa · Stockton

Studley · Wootton Wawen · Warwick

Coughton · Alcester · Ashorne · Harbury · Priors Marston

Ardens Grafton · Stratford-upon-Avon · Moreton Morrell

Farnborough

Newbold-on-Stour · Ratley

Shipston-on-Stour

WORCESTERSHIRE

NORTHAMPTONSHIRE

GLOUCESTERSHIRE · Great Wolford · OXFORDSHIRE

0 Miles 5
0 Kilometres 8

---

## Alcester

### Three Tuns

34 High Street
☎ (01789) 766550
11–11; 12–10.30 Sun
**Goff's Jouster; Hobsons Best Bitter; Fuller's London Pride; Wyre Piddle Piddle in the Hole; guest beers** Ⓗ
Pub which started brewing on the premises in 1996, offering up to eight ales, plus regular festivals. Q ♿ ▲ ♣

**Try also: Holly Bush Hotel,** Henley St (Bass)

---

## Ansley

### Lord Nelson

Birmingham Road (B4112)
☎ (01203) 392305
12–2.30 (3 Sat), 6.30 (6 Sat)–11; 12–10.30 Sun
**Draught Bass; Tetley Bitter; guest beers** Ⓗ
Large roadside pub with a nautical theme; a friendly local decorated with naval artefacts. The sloping bar makes darts an uphill struggle. A separate restaurant is also

available.
♨ Q ❀ ◑ ▶ ⊟ ♣ P

**Try also: Wagon Load of Lime,** Ansley Lane, Old Arley (Enterprise)

---

 **INDEPENDENT BREWERIES**

**Bull's Head:** Alcester

**Church End:** Shustoke

**Feldon:** Shipston-on-Stour

**Judges:** Rugby

**Warwickshire:** Kenilworth

---

## Ansty

### Rose & Castle

Main Road (B4065)
☎ (01203) 612822
12–3, 6–11; 12–10.30 Sun
**Draught Bass; HP&D Entire;
Tetley Bitter; guest beer** H
One-room restaurant-cum-bar
on a split level near Bridge 17
on the Oxford Canal. The
garden (moorings available)
has a safe children's play area.
Popular for business lunches in
the week. Guest beers are from
Carlsberg Tetley's Tapster's
Choice list. Q ❀ ◁ ▷ P

## Ardens Grafton

### Golden Cross

Wixford Road OS114538
☎ (01789) 772420
11–2.30, 6–11; 12–2.30, 7–10.30 Sun
**Draught Bass; Tetley Bitter;
guest beers** H
Old, stone-built pub
commanding views over the
Vale of Evesham to the
Cotswolds. Fine collections of
teddy bears and dolls; always
six ales, many from
independent brewers.
❀ ◁ ▷ & P

**Try also: Queens Head**, Iron
Cross (Free)

## Ashorne

### Cottage Tavern

☎ (01926) 651410
7–11; 12–2.30, 7–11 Sat; 12–2.30,
7–10.30 Sun
**Ansells Mild, Bitter** H
Traditional country pub with
an open-plan lounge. Darts,
dominoes and crib are played.
Weekend lunches (closed
weekday lunchtimes except
bank hols). ❀ Q ❀ ◁ ▷ ♣

## Austrey

### Bird in Hand

Church Road
☎ (01827) 830260
6.30–11; 12–3, 6.30–11 Fri, & Tue–Thu
in summer; 12–4, 6.30–11 Sat; 12–4,
7–10.30 Sun
**Bateman Mild; Marston's
Pedigree, HBC** H
Popular village local with a
thatched roof and a separate
restaurant. Local CAMRA *Pub
of the Year* three times.
❀ ◁ ▷ ⊞ P

## Bedworth

### White Swan

All Saints Square
☎ (01203) 312164
11–11; 12–3, 7–10.30 Sun
**Mansfield Riding Mild; Wells
Eagle, Bombardier** H
Large, bustling, town-centre
pub, popular with shoppers;

near the new market
development. No lunches Sun.
◁ ⊞ ⇌ ♣

**Try also: Newdigate Arms**,
Newdigate Rd (Ansells)

## Bodymoor Heath

### Dog & Doublet

Dog Lane ☎ (01827) 872374
11.30–2.30, 6–11; 12–3, 7–10.30 Sun
**Draught Bass; Highgate Dark;
Worthington Bitter** H
Two-roomed, traditional
canalside pub, dating back to
1789. Children are welcome.
Marquee for private functions.
❀ ➤ P

## Bulkington

### Weavers Arms

12 Long Street, Ryton (off
Wolvey Rd) ☎ (01203) 314415
12–3.30, 5.30–11; 12–3, 7–10.30 Sun
**Draught Bass; M&B Mild,
Brew XI; guest beers** H
Secluded two-room local with
a traditional bar and a cosy
lounge: a gem not to be missed.
No lunches Sun.
❀ Q ❀ ◁ ⊞ ♣

## Church Lawford

### Old Smithy

1 Green Lane ☎ (01203) 542333
11–3, 5–11; 11–11 Sat; 12–4, 7–10.30
Sun
**Ansells Mild, Bitter;
Greenalls Shipstone's Bitter;
Judges Gavelbender; Tetley
Bitter; Theakston Best Bitter,
XB** H
Very friendly, improved
village inn, local CAMRA *Pub
of the Year* 1994. Quality
restaurant. Camping on
request. ❀ ❀ ◁ ▷ & ▲ ♣

## Coughton

### Throckmorton Arms Hotel

On A435 ☎ (01789) 762879
11–3, 5 (6 Sat)–11; 12–3, 7–10.30 Sun
**Banks's Bitter; Draught Bass;
M&B Brew XI** H
Spacious, main road pub
almost opposite NT's
Coughton Court, with
comfortable lounges where
good, home-cooked food is
served. Separate restaurant.
❀ Q ❀ ➤ ◁ ▷ & ♣ P

## Farnborough

### Butcher's Arms

☎ (01295) 690615
12–3, 7–11; 12–11 Sat; 12–10.30 Sun
**Draught Bass; Boddingtons
Bitter; guest beer** H
Stone pub, originally thatched,
that was an ale house in the
Civil War and only obtained a
full licence in the 1950s. The

outbuildings were once used as
a slaughter-house – hence the
name. There is a cosy, stone
flagged bar and a separate,
popular restaurant. Changing
guest beer.
❀ Q ❀ ◁ ▷ & ▲ ♣ P

## Five Ways (Haseley Knob)

### Case is Altered ☆

Case Lane (off A4177 / A4141
roundabout towards
Rowington) OS228697
☎ (01926) 484206
11.30–2.30, 6–11; 12–2, 7–10.30 Sun
**Ansells Mild, Bitter; Flowers
Original** G**; Samuel Smith
OBB** H**; guest beer**
(weekends) G
Unspoilt, rural pub in a time
warp, displaying a collection of
artefacts from former local
breweries. The bar billiards
table takes old 6d pieces.
'Gravity' beers are dispensed
through unusual cask pumps.
The lounge bar is open Fri–Sun
eves and Sun lunch.
❀ Q ❀ ♣ P

## Galley Common

### Plough Inn

Plough Hill Road (½ mile off
B4114) ☎ (01203) 392425
12–3 (4 Sat), 6–11; 12–3, 7–10.30 Sun
**Draught Bass; Home Mild;
M&B Brew XI; guest beer** H
Prominent roadside inn with a
tiled bar, popular with locals
and featuring a small room to
one side. The cosy lounge at
the rear provides access to a
large garden and a crown
bowling green. ❀ ❀ ⊞ ♣ P

## Great Wolford

### Fox & Hounds

☎ (01608) 674220
12–3, 7–11; 12–3, 7–10.30 Sun
**Hook Norton Best Bitter;
Shepherd Neame Spitfire;
guest beers** H
Excellently-run, atmospheric
old pub, offering a superb
range of beers, interesting,
good value food and many
malt whiskies. It can be
difficult to find first time, but
people keep coming back.
❀ Q ❀ ➤ ◁ ▷ & ▲ ♣ P

## Harbury

### Crown

Crown Street ☎ (01926) 612283
12–3, 5–11; 12–11 Fri & Sat; 12–5,
7–10.30 Sun
**Flowers IPA; Theakston Best
Bitter; Whitbread seasonal
beers; guest beer** H
Old farmhouse made of local
white lias limestone, believed
to be the oldest pub in the
village. The lounge is

dominated by TV, which draws a crowd for sport. The guest beer changes regularly. No meals Thu eve or Sun.
🏠 🌼 ◑ ▶ ♣ ⊖ P

## Hartshill

### Royal Oak Inn
56 Oldbury Road
☎ (01203) 392260
11–4, 7–11; 11–11 Sat; 12–10.30 Sun
**M&B Brew XI; Mansfield Riding Mild; Wells Eagle** Ⓗ
Fine, rare example of a North Warwickshire local, complete with outdoor gents'! Nicely furnished; the quiet lounge is offset by a larger, bustling, tiled-floor locals' bar with games. Q 🌼 ♣

## Henley-in-Arden

### White Swan Hotel
100 High Street
☎ (01564) 792623
11–11; 12–10.30 Sun
**Ansells Bitter; Everards Tiger; Tetley Bitter; guest beers** Ⓗ
Large, busy pub with ever-changing guest beers. Separate, spacious restaurant (vegetarian meals a speciality).
🌼 🛏 ◑ ▶ 🍴 ≈ ♣ P 🚽

## Kenilworth

### Clarendon Arms
44 Castle Hill (opp. castle)
☎ (01926) 852017
11–3, 5.30–11; 12–10.30 Sun
**Ansells Mild; Marston's Pedigree; Morland Old Speckled Hen; John Smith's Bitter; guest beer** Ⓗ
Colloquially known as the 'Top Clad', this pub is always busy and, although food-oriented, caters well for drinkers.
Q 🛏 🌼 ◑ ▶ & ⌇

### Clarendon House Hotel
High Street (A429/A452 jct)
☎ (01926) 857668
11.30–2.30 (3 Sat), 6–11; 12–3, 7–10.30 Sun
**Boddingtons Bitter; Flowers IPA, Original; Hook Norton Best Bitter; guest beers** Ⓗ
Well-appointed hotel which maintains a friendly atmosphere. Restaurant meals available eves. Q 🛏 ◑ P

### Earl Clarendon
127 Warwick Road (A452)
☎ (01926) 854643
11–11; 12–4, 7–10.30 Sun
**Marston's Bitter, Pedigree** Ⓗ
The 'Bottom Clad': a friendly, community pub on the main street. No meals Sun.
Q 🌼 ◑ ♣

### Virgins & Castle
7 High Street (A429/A452 jct)
☎ (01926) 853737

12–11; 12–10.30 Sun
**Draught Bass; Greenalls Davenports Bitter, Original; Wadworth 6X; guest beer** Ⓗ
Medieval pub with low beams and many rooms served from a small, central bar. The unusual name is derived from the visit of Elizabeth I to Kenilworth Castle. Cosmopolitan clientele, but especially popular with students. No eve meals Sun/Mon. 🏠 Q 🛏 🌼 ◑ ▶ ♣

## Lapworth

### Navigation
Old Warwick Road (B4439)
☎ (01564) 783337
11–2.30, 5.30–11; 11–11 Sat; 12–10.30 Sun
**Draught Bass; Highgate Dark; M&B Brew XI; guest beers** Ⓗ
Welcoming pub with a stone floor and an open fire in the main bar, sympathetically extended to preserve the cosy atmosphere. Home-cooked food. Pump clips testify to the variety of guest beers served. Local CAMRA *Pub of the Year* 1994–5.
🏠 Q 🌼 ◑ ▶ ▲ ≈ ♣ ⊖ P ⌇

**Try also: Punchbowl,** Mill Lane (Banks's)

## Leamington Spa

### Hope & Anchor
41 Hill Street ☎ (01926) 423031
11–11; 12–10.30 Sun
**Ansells Mild, Bitter; guest beer** Ⓗ
Popular, street-corner pub near the town centre; comfortably furnished and welcoming. Satellite TV sport sessions.
♣

### Red House
113 Radford Road (eastern edge of town, towards Radford Semele) ☎ (01926) 881725
11.30–2.30, 5–11; 11–11 Fri & Sat; 12–3, 7–10.30 Sun
**Adnams Extra; Draught Bass; Worthington Bitter** Ⓗ
Victorian pub serving the local community which has Irish connections. The relaxed atmosphere is conducive to conversation. The only regular local outlet for Adnams Extra.
Q 🌼 ♣

### Somerville Arms
4 Campion Terrace
☎ (01926) 426746
11–2.30 (3 Fri), 5.30–11; 11–11 Sat; 12–3, 7–10.30 Sun
**Ansells Mild, Bitter; Ind Coope Burton Ale; Marston's Pedigree; Tetley Bitter; guest beer** Ⓗ
Friendly Victorian local now in the *Guide* for 20 consecutive years: a busy front bar and a cosy lounge at the rear. Evidence of the landlord's

humour abounds. The guest beer is from the Tapster's Choice range.
Q 🍴 ♣

## Long Itchington

### Harvester
6 Church Road
☎ (01926) 812698
11–3, 6–11; 12–3, 7–10.30 Sun
**Hook Norton Best Bitter, Old Hooky; guest beer** Ⓗ
Friendly country pub with a separate restaurant; a regular *Guide* entry.
Q 🌼 ◑ ▶ 🍴 ▲ P

## Long Lawford

### Sheaf & Sickle
Coventry Road
☎ (01788) 544622
12–2.30, 6–11; 11–11 Sat; 12–10.30 Sun
**Ansells Mild, Bitter; guest beers** Ⓗ
Popular village local, twice local CAMRA *Pub of the Year*. Attractively furnished throughout, it has a cosy bar and a separate restaurant, providing excellent, good value meals.
🏠 🌼 ◑ ▶ 🍴 & ▲ ♣ P

## Moreton Morrell

### Black Horse
2 miles from M40 jct 12
☎ (01926) 651231
11.30–3, 7–11; 12–3, 7–10.30 Sun
**Hook Norton Best Bitter; guest beers** Ⓗ
Welcoming, unpretentious village pub with a games area in the back bar; popular with locals and students from the nearby agricultural college. A pleasant garden offers fine countryside views. Rolls are good value and recommended.
🌼 ▲

## Newbold-on-Stour

### Bird in Hand
☎ (01789) 450253
12–3, 6–11; 12–3, 7–10.30 Sun
**Hook Norton Best Bitter, Old Hooky, seasonal beers; guest beers**
Friendly village local and roadside inn, taking pride in its food.
🏠 Q 🌼 🛏 ◑ ▶ 🍴 ♣ P

## Newton Regis

### Queen's Head
Main Road ☎ (01827) 830271
12–3, 7–11 (11–11 summer); 12–3, 7–10.30 Sun
**Draught Bass; M&B Brew XI; Marston's Pedigree** Ⓗ
Comfortable village local, serving good bar meals. Busy at weekends in summer. Watch out for the ducks!
Q 🌼 ◑ ▶ P

## Nuneaton

### Fox Inn
11A The Square, Attleborough
☎ (01203) 383290
11–11; 12–3, 7–10.30 Sun
**Draught Bass; M&B Mild, Brew XI** Ⓗ
Welcoming, tastefully extended, two-room local with a large friendly bar and a well-appointed lounge. ✿ Ⓓ &

### Oddfellows Arms
Upper Abbey Street
☎ (01203) 385437
12–11; 12–4, 7–10.30 Sun
**M&B Brew XI; Mansfield Riding Mild; Wells Bombardier** Ⓗ
Situated just outside the ring road, off the old A47 (now B4114): a popular, friendly pub with a large bar and a lounge rolled into one. Small, cosy snug to the rear. ✿ ♣

Try also: **Pig & Whistle**, Abbey St (Enterprise)

## Priors Marston

### Holly Bush Inn
Holly Bush Lane
☎ (01327) 260934
12–3, 5.30 (7 Sat)–11; 12–3, 7–10.30 Sun
**Draught Bass; Hook Norton Best Bitter; Marston's Pedigree; guest beer** Ⓗ
Stone-built pub with many varied drinking areas, featuring exposed beams and a large inglenook. This old farmhouse was a bakehouse 100 years ago. It became a beerhouse in 1927 and was fully licensed in 1947.
🏚 Q ✿ 🛏 Ⓓ & P

## Ratley

### Rose & Crown
☎ (01295) 678148
12–2.30 (3 Sat), 6–11; 12–3, 7–10.30 Sun
**Badger Tanglefoot; Wells Eagle, Bombardier** Ⓗ
Superb, stone-built pub in a quiet, secluded village. A welcoming, family-run local, it attracts people from near and far and is reputedly haunted by a Roundhead ghost from the nearby Battle of Edgehill. Families welcome. Food is recommended. Aunt Sally played. 🏚 Q ✿ Ⓓ & ♠ ♣

Try also: **Castle**, Edgehill (Hook Norton)

## Rugby

### Fitchew & Firkin
Sheep Street ☎ (01788) 543023
11–11; 12–10.30 Sun
**Firkin Weasel, Fitchew, Pole, Dogbolter; guest beer** Ⓗ

Medium-sized, L-shaped pub with lots of distressed wood giving a 'back to basics' feel. Food and drink promotions most nights of the week. Good mix of clientele. Music is not as loud as in some other pubs nearby. Wheelchair WC.
Ⓓ ♠ &

### Half Moon
28–30 Lawford Road
☎ (01788) 574420
1 (12 Fri & Sat)–11; 12–10.30 Sun
**Ansells Mild, Bitter; Ind Coope Burton Ale; guest beers** Ⓗ
Basic, mid-terrace boozer featuring real fires and no distracting loud music. Convenient for visitors to Rugby School.
🏚 & ♣

### Quigleys PMC
Albert Street (next to main Post Office) ☎ (01788) 571315
6–11; 12–3, 6–11 Fri; 12–11 Sat; 12–10.30 Sun
**Vaux Samson; guest beers** Ⓗ
Irish-style bar hosting live music five nights a week.
Q ≋ ♣

### Raglan Arms
Dunchurch Road (opp. Rugby School)
☎ (01788) 544441
12 (11 Sat)–3, 7–11; 12–3, 7–10.30 Sun
**Exmoor Gold; Fuller's London Pride; Greene King Abbot; Marston's Bitter, Pedigree, HBC; guest beers** Ⓗ
Deceptively large, terraced pub to sit and sup in, with beers at very reasonable prices. No food or music.
Q ♣ P

### Three Horse Shoes Hotel
Sheep Street
☎ (01788) 544585
11–3, 5.30–11; 11–11 Sat; 12–3, 7–10.30 Sun
**Boddingtons Bitter; Judges Old Gavel Bender; Whitbread seasonal beers; guest beers** Ⓗ
Plush old coaching inn providing a quiet haven from the neighbouring disco pubs. Warm welcome from friendly staff. The only town-centre outlet for Judges beers, except for clubs.
🏚 ⛺ 🛏 Ⓓ ♣ ✂

### Victoria
1 Lower Hillmorton Road
☎ (01788) 544374
12–2.30 (4 Sat), 7–11; 12–3, 7–10.30 Sun
**Draught Bass; M&B Brew XI; guest beers** Ⓗ
Victorian corner pub with original fittings, near the town centre: a basic bar and an impressively refurbished lounge. Trad jazz Mon eve. Weekday lunches.
Q Ⓓ 🍺 ≋ ♣

## Ryton-on-Dunsmore

### Old Bull & Butcher
Oxford Road (A423)
☎ (01203) 301400
11–11; 12–10.30 Sun
**Ansells Mild; Ind Coope Burton Ale; Tetley Bitter** Ⓗ
Old coaching inn on the old Oxford/Banbury road, just outside the Coventry boundary; comfortable and cosy. 🏚 ✿ Ⓓ ♣ P

## Shipston-on-Stour

### Black Horse
Station Road (off A3400)
☎ (01608) 661617
12–3, 7–11; 12–10.30 Sun
**Home Bitter; Ruddles Best Bitter; Theakston XB; Webster's Yorkshire Bitter** Ⓗ
Thatched pub dating back to the 12th century; originally a row of cottages for Cotswold sheep farmers. A rambling interior leads to a children's room across the yard and to the garden. Special offer meals Mon–Thu.
🏚 ⛺ ✿ Ⓓ 🍺 & ♣ P

## Shustoke

### Griffin Inn
Church End (B4116, sharp bend between Coleshill and Atherstone) ☎ (01675) 481205
12–2.30, 7–11; 12–2.30, 7–10.30 Sun
**Marston's Pedigree; guest beers** Ⓗ
Old country village inn full of charm, with a low-beamed ceiling and log fires. Church End Brewery is next door and its beers are on sale. Food lunchtime Mon–Sat. No bare chests in summer!
🏚 Q ⛺ ✿ Ⓓ & ♠ P

## Stockton

### Crown
High Street ☎ (01926) 812255
12–3 (5 Sat), 7–11; 12–5, 7–10.30 Sun
**Ansells Mild, Bitter; guest beers** Ⓗ
Purpose-built brick pub from 1720, once used as a stopover by farmers driving their stock to markets. Small bar; cosy lounge with comfy chairs and a settee. Up to four guest beers available but a price banding policy can make some expensive. No eve meals Sun.
🏚 ✿ Ⓓ 🍺 & ♠ P

## Stratford-upon-Avon

### Garrick
25 High Street
☎ (01789) 292186
11–11; 12–10.30 Sun

**Boddingtons Bitter; Flowers Original; guest beers** Ⓗ
Listed building built in 1595, in a town centre location.
🏠 🛏 🕻 🍴 ≋

## Queen's Head

Ely Street ☎ (01789) 204914
11.30–11; 12–10.30 Sun
**Draught Bass; Hancock's HB; M&B Brew XI; guest beers** Ⓗ
Popular, 18th-century town-centre pub with exposed beams in an L-shaped bar. A house ale named after the dog is occasionally obtained. A wide range of guest ales comes mostly from small breweries. Eve meals Fri and Sat.
🏠 ✿ 🕻 🍴 ≋ 🕙

## Stretton-on-Dunsmore

### Shoulder of Mutton

8–11; 12–3, 8–11 Fri & Sat; 12–3, 8–10.30 Sun
**Draught Bass; M&B Mild, Brew XI** Ⓗ
Wonderfully unspoilt pub caught in two time zones – the original 19th-century snug and a 'modern' early 1950s extension where period records to suit the surroundings are played. No food, but you are welcome to bring your own sandwiches.
🏠 🏬 ⊟ ⅙ ♣ P

## Studley

### Railway Inn

64 Station Road (B4092, 1 mile from Studley)
☎ (01527) 857715
12–3, 5–11; 12–11 Fri & Sat; 12–4, 7–10.30 Sun
**Ansells Mild, Bitter; Everards Tiger; Tetley Bitter; guest beer** Ⓗ
Recently refurbished, friendly pub serving home-cooked, very reasonably priced meals and sandwiches. Live entertainment Sat/Sun eves.
✿ 🕻 🍴 ♣ P

## Warwick

### Cape of Good Hope

66 Lower Cape (at Cape Top Lock, off Cape Rd)
☎ (01926) 498138
12–2.30 (3 Sat), 6 (7 Sat)–11; 12–3, 7–10.30 Sun
**Boddingtons Bitter** Ⓗ; **guest beers** Ⓗ/Ⓖ
Opened soon after the canal in 1800, the Cape has given its name to the locks, streets and district around. Warm welcome in the waterside public bar or in the recently extended rear lounge. One guest beer is usually from a Warwickshire brewery. Limited parking.
✿ 🕻 🍴 ⊟ ♣ P

### Old Fourpenny Shop

27 Crompton Street (off Henley Rd, near racecourse)
☎ (01926) 491360
12–2.30 (3 Fri & Sat), 5.30 (5 Fri, 6 Sat)–11; 12–2.30, 7–10.30 Sun
**M&B Brew XI; guest beers** Ⓗ
Pub offering five ever-changing guest beers (one usually a mild or stout and most lasting only a day) in a comfortable, split-level bar. The separate restaurant serves high class food Mon–Sat lunch and eve. Bar meals lunchtimes. Small car park.
✿ 🛏 🕻 P

### Ricochet Inn

6 Castle Street
☎ (01926) 491232
11–3, 7–11; closed Sun
**Hook Norton Best Bitter; Wadworth 6X; guest beer** Ⓗ
18th-century, timber-framed pub with a Georgian stone front, transformed a few years ago from the neglected Gold Cup pub into a posh, upmarket wine bar. However, drinkers are welcome. The nearest pub to the town exit of Warwick Castle.
🕻 🍴

## Rose & Crown

30 Market Place
☎ (01926) 492876
11–11; 12–10.30 Sun
**Draught Bass; Highgate Dark; M&B Brew XI; guest beer** Ⓗ
Extensive redecoration, which has added lots of character, has made this a busy town pub once more. Look for the unusual decorations suspended from the ceiling. Behind the bar is a small snug. A back room is used for functions and lunches (meals till 5.30). 🕻 ♣

## Whitacre Heath

### Swan

Station Road
☎ (01675) 462181
12–3, 6 (5.30 Wed & Thu, 5 Fri)–11; 12–3, 7–10.30 Sun
**Draught Bass; M&B Mild, Brew XI; guest beer** Ⓗ
Large, two-roomed local, extended to cater for a growing food trade while maintaining a separate public bar for drinkers. The very large garden can be busy in summer.
Q ✿ 🕻 🍴 ⊟ P

## Wootton Wawen

### Bull's Head

Stratford Road (A3400/B4089 jct)
☎ (01564) 792511
12–3.30, 7–11; 12–3.30, 7–10.30 Sun
**Adnams Bitter; Fuller's London Pride; Marston's Bitter, Pedigree, HBC; Morland Old Speckled Hen; Wadworth 6X** Ⓗ
Historic (dated 1387 outside) pub, full of character. Its excellent food attracts customers from near and far. The small, attractive, rustic public bar can get rather smoky on occasions. Handy for moorings on the Stratford Canal. Cider in summer.
🏠 Q ✿ 🕻 🍴 ≋ 🕙 P

---

# SPOT THE INDEPENDENT BREWER

Only one of the following is an independent brewery: Flowers, Strong, Wethered, Bentley's, Fremlins, Higsons, Castle Eden, Boddingtons, Home, Matthew Brown, McEwan, Younger, Theakston, Webster's, Wilson's, John Smith's, Ansells, Aylesbury, Dartmoor, Peter Walker, Friary Meux, Benskins, Ind Coope, Hancock's, Worthington and Highgate. Did you spot it? The answer is Highgate, which was bought from Bass in 1995. The others are all now trading divisions of the national brewers, though you'd never know so from their advertising or point of sale material, which allows them to pass off as 'guest beers' in many nationals' pubs. For details of who really owns whom, see page 131.

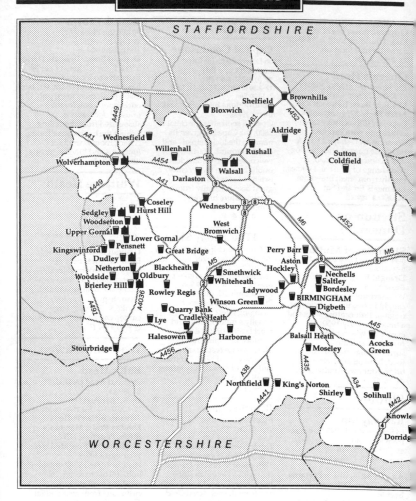

## Aldridge

### Lazy Hill
196 Walsall Wood Road
(1 mile from centre)
☎ (01922) 52040
12–2.30, 6–11; 12–2.30, 7–10.30 Sun
**Ansells Mild; HP&D Entire;
Ind Coope Burton Ale; Tetley
Bitter; guest beer** ⌶
Spacious, friendly, 16th-
century pub with three
adjoining rooms and a function
room. Busy at weekends. The
guest beer is usually Marston's
Pedigree. ⚏ P

## Barston

### Bull's Head
Barston Lane ☎ (01675) 442830
11–2.30, 5.30 (6 Sat)–11; 12–3, 7–10.30
Sun
**Draught Bass; M&B Brew XI;
Tetley Bitter** ⌶

Beamed country pub: the
centre of village life, partly
dating back to 1490. No meals
Wed eve or Sun.
⚏ Q ❀ ◑ ▶ P

## Birmingham:
### *Acocks Green*

### Bernie's Real Ale
### Off-Licence
908 Warwick Road
☎ (0121) 708 1664
5.30 (4 Sat)–10; 7–10 Sun
**Beer range varies** ⌶/Ⓔ
Off-licence serving a constantly
changing range of ales.

## *Aston*

### Manor Tavern
6 Portland Street
☎ (0121) 326 8780
12–2.30, 5.30 (7 Sat)–11; 12–3, 7–10.30
Sun

**Ansells Mild, Bitter; Tetley
Bitter** ⌶
Pub situated within the
Heartlands; a two-roomed
local popular with workers
lunchtimes. Photos of old
Birmingham decorate the
walls.
◑ 🍺 ⇌

## *Balsall Heath*

### Old Moseley Arms
53 Tindal Street
☎ (0121) 440 1954
3 (12 Fri, 1.30 Sat)–11; 12–10.30 Sun
**Ansells Mild, Bitter; HP&D
Entire; Marston's Pedigree** ⌶
Small, two-roomed pub with
a 1930s oak-panelled interior.
The clientele ranges from local
workers to students and
environmentalists. Panoramic
view of Birmingham city
centre outside.
Q ❀ 🍺 ♣

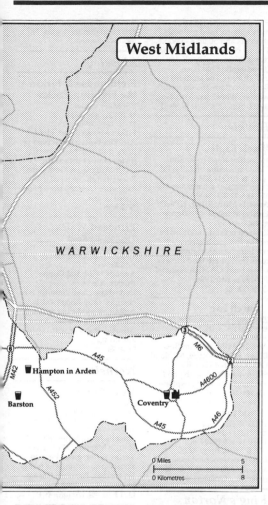

## West Midlands

WARWICKSHIRE

Hampton in Arden

Barston

Coventry

0 Miles 5
0 Kilometres 8

### Prince of Wales

84 Cambridge Street (behind
convention centre)
☎ (0121) 643 9460
11–3.30, 5 (6 Sat)–11; 12–3.30, 7–10.30
Sun
**Ansells Mild, Bitter; Ind
Coope Burton Ale; Marston's
Pedigree; Tetley Bitter** H
Two-roomed pub popular with
both actors and theatre-goers.
Bar at the front; small lounge at
the back.
Q ◖ ⊟ ᵫ ≷ (Snow Hill)

### Village

152 Hurst Street
☎ (0121) 622 4742
11–11; 12–3, 7–10.30 Sun
**Banks's Bitter; Camerons
Strongarm; Marston's
Pedigree** H
Tastefully decorated, open-
plan gay pub with excellent
accommodation.
ᴴ ≷ (New St)

### Wellington

37 Bennetts Hill
☎ (0121) 233 2439
11–11; closed Sun
**Courage Best Bitter, Directors;
guest beer** H
Popular pub with students and
business people, decorated in
the theme of its name.
◖ ≷ (New St/Snow Hill)

## Digbeth

### Adam & Eve

701 Bradford Street
☎ (0121) 693 1500
12–11; 12–10.30 Sun
**HP&D Entire; Ind Coope
Burton Ale; Marston's
Pedigree; Tetley Bitter** H
Pub with a large lounge
(hosting bands regularly), and
a small bar which houses a
pool table. ◖ ⊟ ᵫ

### Anchor

308 Bradford Street (rear of
coach station)
☎ (0121) 622 4516
11–11; 12–10.30 Sun
**Ansells Mild; Tetley Bitter;
guest beers** H
Old corner pub with three
rooms, all served from one bar.
Very friendly atmosphere. Two

## Bordesley

### Rose Tavern

47 Henry Street, Sparkbrook
☎ (0121) 771 4600
10.30–11; 12–10.30 Sun
**Ansells Mild, Bitter** E
Friendly backstreet local with a
lively front bar (pool) and a
rear lounge (large screen TV).
◖ ▶ ⊟ ᵫ P ⊟

## City Centre

### Flapper & Firkin

Cambrian Wharf/Kingston
Row ☎ (0121) 236 2421
12–11; 12–10.30 Sun
**Firkin Flapper, Dogbolter;
guest beers** H
Canalside pub, boasting
upstairs and downstairs
rooms, popular with students
and visitors to the NIA. Live
music downstairs most nights.
❀ ◖ ▶ ♣

### Gunmaker's Arms

92 Bath Street
(in Gun Quarter)
11–3, 5 (7 Sat)–11; 12–3, 7–10.30 Sun
**Draught Bass; M&B Mild** H
Two-roomed pub with a
display of gun manufacturing
objets d'art in the
lounge.
❀ ◖ ⊟ ≷ (Snow Hill) ♣

### Old Contemptibles

176 Edmund Street (right from
Snow Hill station, then 1st
right)
☎ (0121) 236 5264
12–11; 12–3.30, 7–11 Sat; closed Sun
**Draught Bass; Highgate Dark;
M&B Brew XI; guest beers** H
Popular pub which attracts a
mixed clientele; built in the
1800s (note the high
ceiling) but never opened as
such. A local CAMRA *Pub of
the Year* 1993–94. Beer festivals
regularly held.
Q ◖ ▶ ≷ (Snow Hill/New St)

| 🍺 INDEPENDENT BREWERIES | |
| --- | --- |
| **Banks's:** Wolverhampton | |
| **Batham:** Brierley Hill | |
| **Britannia:** Upper Gornal | |
| **British Oak:** Dudley | |
| **Highgate:** Walsall | |
| **Holden's:** Woodsetton | |
| **Hughes:** Sedgley | |
| **Rainbow:** Coventry | |

303

pool teams; regular beer festivals and themed weeks.
❀ ◑ ▶ ⇌ (New St/Moor St) ♣

### Horans Tavern
92 Floodgate Street
☎ (0121) 643 3851
11–10.30 (6 Sat); 12–3 Sun, closed Sun eve
**Ansells Mild; Courage Directors; Flowers IPA; guest beer** Ⓗ
Friendly, quiet, two-roomed backstreet local.
◑ ▶ ⇌ (New St/Moor St) ♣

### Lamp Tavern
157 Barford Street, Highgate
☎ (0121) 622 2599
12–11; 12–3, 7–10.30 Sun
**Bateman Mild; Boddingtons Bitter; Marston's Pedigree; Stanway Stanney Bitter; Wadworth 6X; guest beer (weekends)** Ⓗ
Very popular pub with a wide ranging clientele and an excellent choice of ales (the only regular local outlet for Stanway beers). Live music in the back room. Birmingham CAMRA *Pub of the Year* 1994–95.
◑ ⇌ (New St/Moor St)

### White Swan
276 Bradford Street
☎ (0121) 622 2586
11–3, 5.30–11; 12–3, 7–10.30 Sun
**Ansells Mild; Tetley Bitter** Ⓗ
Outstanding undiscovered Victorian gem, renowned for mild. ◑ ⇌ (Moor St/New St)

### Woodman
106 Albert Street
☎ (0121) 643 1959
11–11; 12–4 Sun, closed Sun eve
**Ansells Mild; Tetley Bitter; guest beer** Ⓗ
Beautifully tiled, Victorian pub that attracts local factory workers, opposite the original Birmingham station.
◑ 🍺

## Harborne

### Junction
212 High Street
☎ (0121) 426 1838
11–11; 12–3, 7–10.30 Sun
**Draught Bass; Highgate Dark; M&B Brew XI; guest beers** Ⓗ
Refurbished pub transformed into a Bass 'Ale Shrine', serving up to seven ales. Some fixtures are originals from the Bass Museum. Guest beers from the Caskmasters range. A house beer, Junction Joker, is brewed at the Bass Museum. No meals Sun eve. ❀ ◑ ▶ ♿ ♣

### New Inn
74 Vivian Road
☎ (0121) 427 5062
11–3.30, 5.30–11; 12–3, 7–10.30 Sun
**Banks's Mild, Bitter, seasonal beers; Camerons Strongarm** Ⓗ

Popular, village-type pub in a busy suburb, used by locals, students and business people. The six crown green bowling teams can now play all day (floodlighting has been introduced). The landlord is a Banks's cellarmanship award-winner. Wheelchair WC. No meals Sun. Q ❀ ◑ ▶ ♿ ♣ 🍴

## Hockley

### Black Eagle
16 Factory Road (near Soho House museum, off Soho Rd, A41) ☎ (0121) 523 4008
11.30 (12.30 Sat)–3, 5.30 (7 Sat)–11; 11–11 Fri; 12–3, 7–10.30 Sun
**Ansells Mild, Bitter; HP&D Entire; Marston's Pedigree; guest beer** Ⓗ
Relaxed pub on the site of an earlier inn and brewery, retaining many original features. Superb food (no eve meals Sun). CAMRA regional *Pub of the Year* 1994.
Q ❀ ◑ ▶ 🍺

### Church Inn
22 Great Hampton Street
☎ (0121) 515 1851
11–11; 12–3, 7–10.30 Sun
**Ansells Mild; Batham Best Bitter; HP&D Entire; Morland Old Speckled Hen** Ⓗ
Single-room pub with good food and a good atmosphere.
◑ ▶ ⇌ (Snow Hill)

### Woodman
11–12 Well Street
☎ (0121) 523 0590
11–11; 12–3, 7–10.30 Sun
**M&B Mild, Brew XI** Ⓗ
Lively, two-roomed local with an L-shaped bar. Q ◑ 🍺 ⇌ (Jewellery Quarter) ♣

## King's Norton

### Navigation Inn
Wharf Road (off Redditch Rd)
☎ (0121) 458 1652
11–11; 12–3, 7–10.30 Sun
**Banks's Mild; Draught Bass; Greenalls Original; Tetley Bitter; guest beer** Ⓗ
105-year-old pub which adopted its name from the Irish workers who worked on the local canal, featuring a very large lounge and a smallish bar. All food is home made. Popular with students.
❀ ◑ ▶ 🍺 ♿ ⇌ ♣ P

## Ladywood

### Vine Inn
Rawlins Street
☎ (0121) 454 7943
11–3, 5.30 (7 Sat)–11; 12–3, 7–10.30 Sun
**Ansells Mild; Ind Coope Burton Ale; Marston's Pedigree; Tetley Bitter** Ⓗ

Wooden-floored pub with darts and domino teams. No food weekends. ◑

## Moseley

### Fieldmouse & Firkin at the Fighting Cocks
1 St Mary's Row
☎ (0121) 449 0811
12–11; 12–10.30 Sun
**Firkin Mouse Bitter, Field Ale, Dogbolter; guest beer** Ⓗ
Brew pub with two names (listed status protects the original name), reflecting the Bohemian character of the local area. Vast assortment of board games.
❀ ◑ ▶ ♣

### Prince of Wales
118 Alcester Road
☎ (0121) 449 4198
11–3 (3.30 Sat), 5.30 (6 Sat)–11; 12–3, 7–10.30 Sun
**Ansells Mild; Ind Coope Burton Ale** Ⓗ
Pub whose classic interior has changed little since 1900. It contains a public bar and two smoke rooms and just oozes cosiness. Popular with a wide age group.
Q ❀ 🍺

## Nechells

### Villa Tavern
307 Nechells Park Road
☎ (0121) 328 9831
11–2.30, 5.30–11; 11–11 Fri & Sat; 12–3, 7–10.30 Sun
**Ansells Mild, Bitter; HP&D Entire; Marston's Pedigree; Tetley Bitter; guest beer** Ⓗ
Locals' pub serving eve meals Fri and Sat. Tapster's Choice guest beer
Q ◑ ▶ 🍺 ⇌ (Aston) ♣ P

## Northfield

### Old Mill
31 West Heath Road
☎ (0121) 475 1337
12–3, 6–11; 12–3, 7–10.30 Sun
**Ansells Mild, Bitter; Tetley Bitter** Ⓗ
Large, two-roomed pub, popular with locals. Nicely decorated lounge. Live music at weekends.
❀ ◑ 🍺 ⇌ ♣ P

## Perry Bar

### Seventh Trap
81 Regina Drive (A34)
☎ (0121) 356 2092
11–11; 12–10.30 Sun
**Banks's Mild, Bitter, seasonal beers; Camerons Strongarm** Ⓔ
Attractive, two-room Banks's pub. Watch greyhounds being chased by a hare (mechanical!)
❀ ▶ 🍺 ♿ ⇌ ♣ P 🍴

## Saltley

### Havelock Tavern

28 Havelock Road
☎ (0121) 472 0054
11–11; 12–10.30 Sun
**M&B Mild** Ⓗ, **Brew XI** Ⓔ
Three-room pub with china
decorating the lounge.
Ⓠ ♣

## Winson Green

### Queen's Arms

286 Heath Street, Smethwick
☎ (0121) 558 4577
12–11; 12–10.30 Sun
**Blackbeard Stairway to
Heaven; guest beers** Ⓗ
Welcoming, tile-fronted, two-
room pub with a partitioned
pool table area in the lounge.
One or two guest beers.
❀ 🛏 Ⓠ ♣

## Blackheath

### Hawthorns

162 Ross ☎ (0121) 561 2276
12–2.30 (3 Sat), 7–11; 12–3, 7–10.30
Sun
**Ansells Mild; Tetley Bitter;
guest beer** Ⓗ
Backstreet local with a small,
cosy bar and a homely lounge
with a real fire. The dispensers
are all in the lounge. No food
Sun. 🛏 ❀ Ⓓ ▸ Ⓠ ≈ (Rowley
Regis) P

### Waterfall

132 Waterfall Lane
☎ (0121) 561 3499
12–3, 5–11; 12–11 Fri & Sat; 12–10.30
Sun
**Batham Best Bitter; Enville
Ale; Holden's Special; Hook
Norton Old Hooky; Marston's
Pedigree; guest beers** Ⓗ
Busy, two-room pub on a steep
hill, well worth the ten mins'
walk down from the town.
Regular musical eves; good
food. Function room. Cider in
summer.
❀ Ⓓ ▸ ≈ (Old Hill) ♣ ⌂ P

## Bloxwich

### Knave of Hearts

Lichfield Road
☎ (01922) 405576
12–2.30 (3 Fri & Sat), 6 (5 Thu & Fri,
6.30 Sat)–11; 12–3, 7–10.30 Sun
**HP&D Mild, Entire; Tetley
Bitter** Ⓗ
Large, pleasant, two-roomed
pub with mock Victoriana.
Live music Sun eve.
❀ Ⓓ ▸ Ⓠ ♣ P

### Romping Cat

97 Elmore Green Road (off A34
near A4124/B4210 jct)
☎ (01922) 475041
12–11; 12–3, 7–10.30 Sun
**Banks's Mild, Bitter** Ⓔ

Superb example of a street-
corner local: a very friendly,
three-roomed pub with etched
windows. ♿ Ⓠ ≈ ♣ ⏸

### Royal Exchange

Stafford Road
☎ (01922) 479618
12–3, 5–11; 12–11 Sat; 12–3, 7–10.30
Sun
**Banks's Mild; Marston's
Bitter, Pedigree, HBC** Ⓗ
Pleasant, 270-year-old local
with a Grade II listed former
brewery at the rear. The small
bar has sporting memorabilia:
the lounge has a quiet corner
nook. Live music Wed and Sun
eves. ❀ Ⓓ ♣ P

## Brierley Hill

### Black Horse

52 Delph Road (B4172)
☎ (01384) 79142
12–11; 12–3, 7–10.30 Sun
**Enville Ale, Gothic; Ruddles
County** Ⓗ
Cosy, one-roomed pub in the
middle of the famous Delph
Run, handy for Merry Hill
shopping centre. Good food all
day. ❀ Ⓓ ▸ ♣ P

### Blue Brick Tap House

153 Dudley Road (A461)
☎ (01384) 78418
11–11; 12–10.30 Sun
**Banks's Hanson's Mild, Mild,
Bitter; Camerons Bitter,
Strongarm; Marston's
Pedigree; guest beers** Ⓗ
Large pub with a number of
linked rooms, most gas-lit.
Hanson's Mild and Camerons
Bitter are sold as house beers.
🛏 ❀ Ⓓ ♣ P ⏸

### Vine (Bull & Bladder)

10 Delph Road (B4172)
☎ (01384) 78293
12–11; 12–4, 7–10.30 Sun
**Batham Mild, Best Bitter** Ⓗ
Famous, multi-roomed pub at
the top of the Delph Run, the
Batham brewery tap. The front
room has been extended into
the old brewery office. Handy
for Merry Hill shopping centre.
♿ ❀ Ⓓ ♣ P

## Brownhills

### Prince of Wales

98 Watling Street
☎ (01543) 372551
7.30–11; 12–3, 7.30–11 Sat; 12–2.30,
7.30–10.30 Sun
**Ansells Bitter; Gray's Mild** Ⓗ
Small, homely single-roomed
local. 🛏 Q ❀ ♣

### Royal Oak

Chester Road, Shire Oak
☎ (01543) 452089
12–3, 6–11; 12–3, 7–10.30 Sun
**Ansells Mild, Bitter; Ind
Coope Burton Ale; guest
beers** Ⓗ

Known as the 'Middle Oak': an
excellent, friendly 1930s local.
Booking is advised for Fri/Sat
eve meals. Beers from Church
End are regularly available.
❀ Ⓓ ▸ Ⓠ ⅋ ♣ P ⏸

## Coseley

### White House

1 Daisy Street
☎ (01902) 402703
11–3, 6–11; 12–3, 7–10.30 Sun
**HP&D Mild, Bitter, Entire;
guest beers** Ⓗ
Cosy, two-roomed free house
offering good food and two
ever-changing guest ales. Hot
pork sandwiches Sat eve; no
food Sun.
🛏 Ⓓ ▸ ≈ ♣

## Coventry

### Biggin Hall Hotel

214 Binley Road, Copsewood
(A428, 3 miles E of centre)
☎ (01203) 451046
10.30–11; 10.30–3.30, 6–11 Sat; 12–3,
7–10.30 Sun
**Banks's Mild; Marston's
Bitter, Pedigree, Owd Rodger;
guest beers** Ⓗ
Pub built in 1923 in mock
Tudor style and virtually
unchanged: a smart bar and a
plush lounge boasting a large,
central oak table. Children
welcome in the games room.
Good food.
🛏 Q ♿ ❀ Ⓓ Ⓠ ♣ P

### Black Horse

Spon End (B4101 near inner
ring road jct 7)
☎ (01203) 677360
10–11; 12–3, 7–10.30 Sun
**Draught Bass; M&B Mild,
Brew XI** Ⓗ
Traditional drinking pub with
separate rooms. Attractive
panelling in the lounge.
🛏 Q ♿ Ⓠ ♣ P

### Boat Inn

108 Blackhorse Road, Exhall
☎ (01203) 367438
12–3, 7–11; 12–3, 7–10.30 Sun
**Ansells Mild, Bitter; Draught
Bass; Tetley Bitter; guest
beers** Ⓗ
Pleasant, 18th-century pub,
renovated, but full of character,
close to the canal (Sutton Stop).
🛏 Q ❀ Ⓠ ♣ P

### Fowl & Firkin

1–2 The Butts (near technical
college, off Albany Rd)
☎ (01203) 221622
11 (12 Sat)–11; 12–10.30 Sun
**Firkin Pullet Bitter, Fowl
Bitter, Cockerel Ale,
Dogbolter** Ⓗ
Spacious, one-roomed brew
pub refurbished in Firkin style.
The brewery is visible through
a viewing window. Occasional
specials are brewed. Young,

friendly clientele. Live music some weekends.

❀ ◖ ㅤ ⇌ ♣

### Gatehouse Tavern

46 Hill Street (just off ring road on edge of centre)
☎ (01203) 256769
11–3, 5–11; 11–11 Fri; 12–4, 7–10.30 Sun
**Draught Bass; M&B Mild, Brew XI; guest beers** Ⓗ
One-room pub built from scratch by the licensee in the old gatehouse of a city-centre mill – a very tasteful conversion. Q ❀ ◖

### Greyhound

118 Much Park Street (between art gallery and ring road, near crown court) ☎ (01203) 221274
12–11; 12–10.30 Sun
**Mansfield Riding Mild; Wells Eagle, Bombardier** Ⓗ
Friendly, one-room, city-centre pub offering a well-priced menu (no meals Sun). Popular with local professionals and students at lunchtime.
❀ ◖ ⇌ ♣

### Jolly Collier

Woodway Lane, Walsgrave-on-Sowe (Sowe Common)
☎ (01203) 612904
12–4, 7–11; 12–3, 7–10.30 Sun
**Draught Bass; Marston's Pedigree; John Smith's Bitter** Ⓗ
Small, friendly locals' pub close to the motorway and canal: a cosy lounge with an adjoining bar. The large rear garden has a play area.
Q ❀ ♣ P

### Malt Shovel

93 Spon End (¼ mile from inner ring road jct 7)
☎ (01203) 220204
12–2.30 (3 Sat), 7–11; 12–3, 7–10.30 Sun
**Ansells Mild, Bitter; Tetley Bitter; guest beer** Ⓗ
Popular, three-roomed pub served from a central bar. Good selection of guest beers. Meals weekday lunchtimes.
🍴 Q ❀ ◖ ♣ P

### New Inn

Bull's Head Lane (off A427, 1½ miles from centre)
☎ (01203) 453764
12–11; 11–11 Fri & Sat; 12–10.30 Sun
**Morland Old Speckled Hen; Ruddles County; guest beers** Ⓗ
Comfortable, two-roomed pub with a bright blue exterior; just a six away from the cricket ground. ❀ Ⓖ ♣ P

### Nursery Tavern

38–39 Lord Street, Chapelfields (1 mile W of centre)
☎ (01203) 674530
11–11; 12–10.30 Sun
**Courage Best Bitter; John Smith's Bitter; guest beers** Ⓗ

Lively, three-roomed pub offering lots of events. Good variety of guest beers, including a mild.
Q 👓 ❀ ◖ Ⓖ ♣ ◠

### Old Windmill

22 Spon Street (¼ mile W of city centre, inside ring road)
☎ (01203) 252183
11–3, 6 (6.30 Sat)–11; 12–3, 7–10.30 Sun
**Banks's Mild; Courage Directors; Marston's Pedigree; Morland Old Speckled Hen; Webster's Yorkshire Bitter; guest beer** Ⓗ
Medieval, multi-roomed pub in a restored 16th-century street next to the shopping centre. Attractive wood panelling in the original bar areas; disused brewhouse in a back room. Popular lunches daily. 🍴 ◖ ㅤ ⇌ ◠

### Rainbow Inn

73 Birmingham Road, Allesley
☎ (01203) 402888
11–11; 12–10.30 Sun
**Courage Best Bitter, Directors; Rainbow Belchers Wood, Firecracker** Ⓗ
17th-century coaching inn, retaining the feel of a village pub although now within the city. Popular for bar meals (lunches Mon–Sat; eve meals Tue–Fri till 8.30), it started brewing in 1994 and became a true free house in 1996.
Q ❀ ◖ ◗ P

### Royal Oak

28 Earlsdon Street, Earlsdon
☎ (01203) 674140
5–11; 12–3, 7–10.30 Sun
**ABC Best Bitter; Ansells Mild; Draught Bass; Tetley Bitter; guest beers** Ⓗ
Very popular pub with table service throughout; both sexes made welcome. The back room's fireplace is based on an original at Oranjeboom Brewery. 🍴 Q ❀

## Cradley Heath

### Little Sausage & Porter

78 St Anne's Road (off A4100 near Five Ways)
☎ (01384) 635494
11.30–3, 6–11; 12–3, 7–10.30 Sun
**HP&D Entire; guest beers** Ⓗ
Typical, basic, 'pig and porter'-decorated pub of the Mad O'Rourke chain. Live folk music Thu. 🍴 ❀ ◖ ⇌ ♣

### Plough & Harrow

82 Corngreaves Road (off A4100) ☎ (01384) 560377
11–3, 7–11; 11–11 Fri; 12–3, 7–10.30 Sun
**Banks's Mild, Bitter** Ⓔ
Traditional Black Country local, popular with local residents and workers.

Children are welcome, but not in the public bar.
❀ ⇌ ♣ P 🍴

### Waggon & Horses

100 Reddal Hill Road (A4100)
☎ (01384) 350130
11–3, 7–11; 12–3, 7–10.30 Sun
**Banks's Mild, Bitter** Ⓔ
Boisterous local with miscellaneous artefacts and sporting prints in the bar; comfortable lounge.
👓 ❀ Ⓖ ⇌ ♣ P

## Darlaston

### Fallings Heath Tavern

Walsall Road (A4038)
☎ (0121) 526 3403
12–2.30 (3 if busy), 7.30–11; 12–2.30, 7.15–10.30 Sun
**Ansells Mild, Bitter; Tetley Bitter; guest beers** (weekends) Ⓗ
Friendly 1930s local. The bar has a large collection of pigs brought in by locals; cosy lounge.
👓 ❀ Ⓖ ♣ P 🍴

### Horse & Jockey

88 Walsall Road (A4038)
☎ (0121) 526 4553
11–11; 12–3, 7–10.30 Sun
**Banks's Mild, Bitter** Ⓔ
A basic bar and a cosy, quiet lounge make this a busy, but friendly, local, popular with games players. ❀ Ⓖ ♣ P 🍴

## Dorridge

### Railway Inn

Grange Road ☎ (01564) 773531
11–3, 4.30–11; 11–11 Wed, Fri & Sat; 12–3, 7–10.30 Sun
**Draught Bass; M&B Mild, Brew XI; guest beer** Ⓗ
Family-run pub popular with locals and retaining a separate bar. Excellent value, home-made food.
🍴 Q ❀ ◖ ◗ Ⓖ ㅤ ⇌ ♣ P

## Dudley

### Fellows

Castle Hill ☎ (01384) 237303
11–11; 12–2.30 Sun, 7–10.30 Sun
**Boddingtons Mild; Castle Eden Ale; Flowers Original; Marston's Pedigree; guest beers** Ⓗ
Former gatehouse of Dudley Zoo now a large, one-roomed bar with a separate restaurant (Beefeater). The car park is controlled by traffic lights.
❀ ◖ ◗ ㅤ P

## Great Bridge

### Port 'n' Ale

178 Horseley Heath (A461)
☎ (0121) 557 7249
12–3, 5–11; 12–11 Sat & summer; 12–3, 7–10.30 Sun

Batham Best Bitter;
Blackbeard Stairway to
Heaven; guest beers H
Three-roomed free house
stocking half a dozen, wide-
ranging guest beers. ✿ ◗ & ⇌
(Dudley Port) ♣ P ᛒ

## Halesowen

### Fairfield

Fairfield Road, Hurst Green
☎ (0121) 422 8289
11–3 (3.30 Sat), 5.30–11; 12–3, 7–10.30
Sun
Banks's Hanson's Mild, Mild,
Bitter E; Marston's
Pedigree H
Popular roadhouse with two
large rooms – a lively bar and a
smart, busy lounge. No food
Sun. ✿ ◗ ▮ ▤ & ♣ P ᛒ

### Hare & Hounds

252 Hagley Road, Hasbury
☎ (0121) 550 1264
11.30–2.30, 5.30–11; 12–3, 6–11 Sat;
12–3, 7–10.30 Sun
Banks's Mild; Greenalls
Original; Tetley Bitter; guest
beers H
Pub with one large room with
two distinct areas, both served
from one bar. Popular for food
(no meals Sun eve) and the
'Guest Beer of the Week'.
✿ ◗ & ᚱ

### Rose & Crown at Hasbury

Hagley Road, Hasbury
☎ (0121) 550 2757
12–2.30 (3 Sat), 5.30 (6 Sat)–11; 12–3,
7–10.30 Sun
HP&D Mild, Entire; Tetley
Bitter H
Large one-room local with
various drinking areas
radiating from a central bar.
No meals Sun. Wheelchair
access at the rear.
▥ ✿ ◗ ▮ & ♣ P

### Waggon & Horses

21 Stourbridge Road (A458,
just outside centre)
☎ (0121) 550 4989
12–11; 12–10.30 Sun
Batham Best Bitter; Enville
Simpkiss Bitter; guest beers H
Friendly pub attracting
customers from far and near,
mainly to try the ever-
changing range of 14 ales. The
house beer, Waggoners, is
brewed by Enville.
♣ ○

### Whitley

Stourbridge Road (A458)
☎ (0121) 550 1056
12–3 (4 Sat), 6–11; 12–3, 7–10.30 Sun
Banks's Mild; Greenalls
Davenports Bitter, Original H
Pub catering for both local and
passing trade in a comfortable
lounge and a games-oriented
bar. No food Sun.
✿ ◗ ▮ ▤ ♣ P

## Hampton in Arden

### White Lion

High Street ☎ (01675) 442833
12–11; 12–3, 7–10.30 Sun
Draught Bass; M&B Brew
XI H
Small, friendly local with a
restaurant. The public bar has
not changed for 50 years.
Handy for the NEC. No eve
meals Sun.
▥ Q ▱ ◗ ▮ ▤ ⇌ ♣ P

## Hurst Hill

### Hurst Hill Tavern

Caddick Street
☎ (01902) 880318
1 (12 Sat)–5, 7–11; 12–3.30, 7–10.30
Sun
Banks's Hanson's Mild, Mild,
Bitter E
Popular backstreet local in a
pleasant, semi-rural setting.
▥ Q ✿ ♣ P ᛒ

## Kingswinford

### Park Tavern

182 Cot Lane (500 yds from
A4101) ☎ (01384) 287178
12–11; 12–3, 7–10.30 Sun
Ansells Bitter; Batham Best
Bitter; Tetley Bitter H
Comfortable, friendly local
with a bustling bar and a
quieter lounge; close to
Broadfield House Glass
Museum. ✿ ▮ ♣ P

### Union

Water Street (off A4101 at end
of Cottage St)
☎ (01384) 830668
12–3 (3.30 Thu & Fri, 4 Sat), 6 (7
Sat)–11; 12–3.30, 7–10.30 Sun
Banks's Mild, Bitter E,
seasonal beers H
Small, traditional backstreet
local in the same family for
over 60 years. Look for the
Rolinson's Brewery window.
✿ ♣ P ᛒ

## Knowle

### Vaults

St John's Close
☎ (01564) 773656
12–2.30, 5 (6 Sat)–11; 12–3, 7–10.30
Sun
Ansells Mild; HP&D Bitter;
Ind Coope Burton Ale; Tetley
Bitter; guest beers H
Three-level pub adjoining a
nightclub in a picturesque
village. A former local
CAMRA *Pub of the Year*.
◗ ♣

## Lower Gornal

### Fountain Real Ale Bar

8 Temple Street (off A459)
☎ (01384) 242777
7 (6 summer)–11; 12–3, 6–11 Sat; 12–3,
7–10.30 Sun

Adnams Broadside; Badger
Tanglefoot; Blackbeard
Stairway to Heaven; Everards
Tiger; guest beers H
Popular free house which was
the last known brewhouse
in Lower Gornal. Seasonal
beer festivals; good range of
guest beers. Irish music
Wed eve.
▥ Q ✿ ♣ ○

## Lye

### Fox

8 Green Lane (off A4036, near
A458 jct)
☎ (01384) 827808
11–11; 12–3, 7–10.30 Sun
Banks's Mild, Bitter E
Small, two-room Black
Country local in a
narrow sidestreet: a quiet,
comfortable lounge and a busy
bar popular with darts-playing
locals.
✿ ▮ ⇌ ♣ P ᛒ

## Netherton

### Dry Dock

21 Windmill End (off St Peter's
Rd)
☎ (01384) 235369
11–3, 6–11 (11–11 bank hol Mon); 12–3,
7–10.30 Sun
HP&D Entire; guest beers H
Mad O'Rourke house, noted
for food, at a famous canal
junction. The central bar in the
one room is part of an ex-
working narrowboat. Live Irish
folk music Mon. Lumphammer
house beer; Tapster's Choice
guest beers.
▥ ✿ ◗ P

## Oldbury

### Waggon & Horses

Church Street (off A4034 in
town centre)
☎ (0121) 552 5467
11–2.30, 5 (6 Sat)–11; 12–2.30, 7–10.30
Sun
Adnams Bitter; Batham Best
Bitter; Everards Mild, Tiger,
Old Original; Marston's
Pedigree; guest beers H
Grade II listed Victorian pub
serving up to 12 beers and a
variety of home-cooked meals
(many vegetarian).
▥ ✿ ◗ ▮ ⇌ (Sandwell &
Dudley)

## Pensnett

### Holly Bush Inn

Bell Street (off A4101)
☎ (01384) 78711
12 (1 winter)–4 (4.30 Sat), 7–11; 12–4,
7–10.30 Sun
Batham Mild, Best Bitter,
seasonal beers H
Basic, one-roomed, estate local
where mild outsells bitter.
♣ P

## Quarry Bank

### Sun Inn

218 High Street
☎ (01384) 566254
11.30–3, 6–11; 12–3, 7–10.30 Sun
**Banks's Mild, Bitter** Ⓔ/Ⓗ,
**seasonal beers** Ⓗ
Large roadhouse, popular with
locals but also handy for Merry
Hill shoppers. Live
entertainment Sun eve. Good
value food; no meals Mon or
Tue eves, or Sun (other eves till
8.30). ✿ ◖ ▶ ও ♣ P ☐

## Rowley Regis

### Sir Robert Peel

1 Rowley Village (B4171)
☎ (0121) 559 2835
12–4, 7–11; 12–4, 7–10.30 Sun
**Ansells Mild, Bitter; Ind
Coope Burton Ale; Morland
Old Speckled Hen** Ⓗ
The oldest building in Rowley
Village: a traditional, three-
roomed pub licensed since
1840. One servery is in the
entrance passage.
ﷺ Q ✿ ≠ ♣ ♣

## Rushall

### Manor Arms

Park Road ☎ (01922) 24491
12–2.30, 6 (5 Fri)–11; 12–11 Sat; 12–3,
7–10.30 Sun
**Banks's Mild, Bitter;
Marston's Pedigree** Ⓗ
The oldest pub in the area,
with an excellent, Grade II
listed interior; known as 'the
pub with no bar'. Eve meals
Wed–Sat till 8.45. ✿ ◖ ▶ ⊞ P

## Sedgley

### Beacon Hotel ☆

129 Bilston Street
☎ (01902) 883380
12–2.30, 5.30–10.45 (11 Fri); 11–3, 6–11
Sat; 12–3, 7–10.30 Sun
**Hook Norton Best Bitter;
Hughes Sedgley Surprise,
Ruby Mild; M&B Mild; guest
beer** Ⓗ
Sprawling, multi-roomed
Victorian brewery tap which
retains many original features.
One changing guest ale
(usually a mid-gravity bitter).
Q ☎ ✿ ♣ P

### Mount Pleasant

144 High Street
☎ (01902) 887383
12–2.30 (11.30–3.45 Sat), 7–11;
12–2.30, 7–10.30 Sun
**Banks's Mild; HP&D Entire;
Tetley Bitter** Ⓗ
Often referred to as 'the
Stump', this pub has a small,
basic bar and a long,
comfortable lounge.
✿ ⊞ ♣

## Shelfield

### Four Crosses

1 Green Lane (off A461)
☎ (01922) 682518
12–4, 6–11; 11–11 Fri; 11.30–4, 7–11
Sat; 12–3, 7–10.30 Sun
**Banks's Mild, Bitter** Ⓔ;
**Marston's Pedigree; guest
beer** Ⓗ
Pleasant, two-roomed, cottage-
style free house.
✿ ◖ ▶ P

## Shirley

### Bernie's Real Ale
### Off-Licence

266 Cranmore Boulevard (off
A34)
☎ (0121) 744 2827
12–2 (not Mon), 5.30–10; 12–2, 7–9.45
Sun
**Adnams Extra; Hook Norton
Best Bitter; Titanic Premium;
guest beers** Ⓗ
Off-licence where real ale takes
precedence; three guest beers.
Sampling cups for the
indecisive. ও

### Red Lion

Stratford Road
☎ (0121) 744 1030
11–2.30 (3 Sat), 6.30–11; 12–3, 7–10.30
Sun
**ABC Best Bitter; Ansells Mild;
Friary Meux BB; Marston's
Pedigree; Tetley Bitter; guest
beer** Ⓗ
Main road pub, part of a
shopping complex. The lounge
has three distinct areas; the old
bar at the back is now the pool
room. No high gravity beer
served. Two milds on tap at
most times.
◖ ♣ ⅍

## Smethwick

### Ivy Bush

218 St Paul's Road (B4160)
☎ (0121) 565 0929
11–11; 12–10.30 Sun
**Holden's Mild, Bitter,
Special** Ⓗ
Basic, street-corner local.
Curries Fri lunch; summer
barbecues Fri and Sat eves.
ও ⊞ ও ≠ (Galton Bridge) ♣

## Solihull

### Old Colonial

Damson Lane (near A45)
11.30–11; 11–3, 6.30–11 Sat; 12–3,
7–10.30 Sun
**Draught Bass** Ⓗ; **M&B Mild,
Brew XI** Ⓔ; **guest beer** Ⓗ
Modern, single-room pub with
seven areas; the central area
has a sliding roof. Family
indoor courtyard till 7. Eve
meals Mon–Fri till 7.30;
lunches Mon–Sat.
ও ✿ ◖ ▶ ও ♣ P ⅍

## Stourbridge

### Crown

208 Hagley Road, Oldswinford
☎ (01384) 394777
12–11; 12–3, 7–10.30 Sun
**Ansells Mild, Bitter; Batham
Best Bitter; Tetley Bitter** Ⓗ
Pub with one room around a
large, U-shaped bar.
Particularly popular early eve
with homeward-bound
workers. The car park is at the
rear on the B4187. No meals
Sun. ﷺ ✿ ◖ ≠ (Junction) P

### Old White Horse

South Road, Norton
(A451/B4186 jct)
☎ (01384) 394258
11–3, 5–11; 11–11 Fri & Sat; 12–10.30
Sun
**Draught Bass; M&B Brew XI;
Stones Bitter; guest beers** Ⓗ
Pub popular with families
(play equipment in the
garden). The large lounge has
various areas served from one
bar. Bar food, plus Harvester
restaurant. Wheelchair WC.
✿ ◖ ▶ ও P

### Plough

154 Bridgnorth Road,
Wollaston ☎ (01384) 393414
12–2.30 (3 Sat), 6–11; 12–3, 7–10.30
Sun
**Draught Bass; M&B Mild;
Stones Bitter; guest beers** Ⓗ
Highly decorated old coaching
house with original windows.
A keen sporting pub, it has a
boules piste. The lounge is
busy lunch and early eve
(excellent food). Varied
entertainment.
✿ ◖ ▶ ⊞ ও ♣ P

### Royal Exchange

75 Enville Street
☎ (01384) 396726
12–11; 12–4, 7–10.30 (may be 12–10.30
summer) Sun
**Batham Mild, Best Bitter** Ⓗ
Ever-popular terraced pub on a
busy road; a small, quiet
lounge to the rear and a lively
bar. Public car park across the
road. Eve meals end at 7.30 (no
eve meals Sun).
Q ✿ ◖ ▶ ⊞ ♣

### Seven Stars

Brook Road, Oldswinford
☎ (01384) 394483
11–11; 12–10.30 Sun
**Batham Best Bitter; Theakston
Best Bitter, XB; guest beers** Ⓗ
Bustling pub, full of character.
Look for the ornate tiling and
the beautiful carved-wood
back bar fitting. Two large
rooms plus a restaurant.
✿ ◖ ▶ ≠ (Junction) P

### Shrubbery Cottage

28 Heath Lane, Oldswinford
☎ (01384) 377598
12–2.30, 6–11; 12–3, 7–10.30 Sun

Holden's Mild, Bitter, Special;
guest beers Ⓗ
Small, one-room local, a
popular drinkers' pub with a
regular lunchtime trade and a
lively, friendly eve crowd.
❀ ◖ ⇌ (Junction) P

## Sutton Coldfield

### Blake Barn
Shelley Drive (off Blake St by
station)
☎ (0121) 308 8421
11–3, 5–11; 11–11 Sat; 12–4, 7–10.30
Sun
Banks's Mild, Bitter Ⓔ;
Camerons Strongarm;
Marston's Pedigree Ⓗ
Large, modern estate pub with
typical Banks's rustic decor.
Food prepared at a large
indoor grill is a speciality (no
meals Sun eve). Families
welcome.
❀ ◖ ▶ ঙ ⇌ (Blake St) P ⌀ ⊟

### Duke Inn
12 Duke Street (off
Birmingham Rd)
☎ (0121) 355 1767
11.30–3, 5.30–11; 12–3, 7–10.30 Sun
Ansells Mild, Bitter; Ind
Coope Burton Ale; Tetley
Bitter Ⓗ
Excellent, traditional pub
near the town centre, with
two rooms and a fine
mahogany back bar.
Q ❀ ♣ P

### Falstaff & Firkin
High Street ☎ (0121) 355 2996
11 (12 Sat)–11; 12–10.30 Sun
Firkin Fal Ale, Staff,
Dogbolter; guest beer Ⓗ
Listed coaching inn famous for
a ghost and a cobbled passage
separating refurbished bars.
Occasional landlord-led beer
festivals.
Q ❀ ◖ ঙ ⇌ ♣ ⌓ P

### Laurel Wines
63 Westwood Road (off
Chester Rd opp. Sutton Park)
☎ (0121) 353 0399
12–2, 5.30–10.30 (11 Fri & Sat); 12–2,
7–10.30 Sun
Adnams Extra; Batham Best
Bitter; Burton Bridge Festival
Ale; Shepherd Neame Spitfire;
guest beers Ⓖ
Friendly off-licence with a
wide range of real ales and
bottled beers. ⌓

### Parson & Clerk
Chester Road North (opp.
Sutton Park)
☎ (0121) 353 7785
11.30–2.30 (3 Sat), 5.30–11; 12–3
Sun
Ansells Mild; Ind Coope
Burton Ale; Tetley Bitter Ⓗ
Pub with four bars plus a
function room. It dates back to
the 1850s when it was the
Royal Oak.
❀ ⇰ ◖ ▶ ঙ ♣ P

## Upper Gornal

### Britannia
109 Kent Street (A459)
☎ (01902) 883253
7–11; 12–3, 7–10.30 Sun
Britannia Sally Perry Mild,
Wally Williams Bitter,
seasonal beers; Courage
Directors; Ruddles County;
guest beers Ⓗ
Pub built in 1780, with an
untouched late-19th-century
tap room where beer is served
from handpumps against the
wall. The original brewery at
the rear has been restored and
is brewing again.
♨ Q ❀ ♣ ᗡ

## Walsall

### Hamemaker's Arms
87 Blue Lane West (A454)
☎ (01922) 28083
11.30–3, 6–11; 11–11 Sat; 12–3, 6–10.30
Sun
Banks's Mild, Bitter Ⓔ;
Camerons Strongarm Ⓗ
Pleasantly modernised, 1930s
pub with a well-laid-out bar
and a warm, bright,
comfortable lounge. The
emphasis is on conversation.
The name refers to the brass
collar hames worn by
carthorses, product of a bygone
local industry. No eve meals
Sun. Q ❀ ◖ ▶ ঙ ⇌ ♣ P ᗡ

### Katz
23 Lower Rushall Street (near
Safeway) ☎ (01922) 725848
12–3, 5.30 (7 Sat)–11; closed Sun
HP&D Entire; Ind Coope
Burton Ale; Marston's
Pedigree; Tetley Bitter; guest
beers Ⓗ
Friendly, two-roomed pub
with a varied clientele.
Interesting guest beers
(sometimes three at a time
Fri/Sat). No food Sat eve.
♨ ❀ ◖ ▶ ⇌

### King Arthur
Liskeard Road (by Park Hall
shopping centre)
☎ (01922) 31400
12–3, 5.30–11; 12–11 Fri & Sat;
12–10.30 Sun
Boddingtons Bitter; Courage
Directors; Highgate Dark;
Ruddles Best Bitter, County;
John Smith's Bitter Ⓗ
Friendly pub with two
substantial rooms in which
families are welcome. Superb
food (not served Sun); Indian/
Balti a speciality. ❀ ◖ ▶ P

### New Fullbrook
West Bromwich Road
☎ (01922) 21761
11.30 (11 Sat)–11; 12–10.30 Sun
Banks's Mild; Highgate Dark,
Saddlers; M&B Brew XI Ⓔ
1930s roadhouse with a large
and popular bar, a games room

and a small, comfortable
lounge. No food Sun. ❀ ◖ ঙ
⇌ (Bescot Stadium) ♣ P ᗡ

### Oak Inn
336 Green Lane
☎ (01922) 645758
12–2.30 (11.45–3 Sat), 7–11; 8–10.30
Sun, closed Sun lunch
Flowers IPA; Whitbread
Fuggles IPA, seasonal beers;
guest beers Ⓗ
Popular pub close to the town
centre with an island bar and a
collection of china mugs. No
eve meals Sun, Tue or Sat.
♨ ❀ ◖ ▶ ⇌ ♣ P ᗡ

### Royal Oak
81 Lord Street, Palfrey (off ring
road) ☎ (01922) 645913
12–4, 7–11; 12–11 Sat; 12–4, 7–10.30
Sun
Banks's Mild Ⓔ; Highgate
Dark, Saddlers; M&B Brew
XI; guest beers Ⓗ
Large 1920s pub where the bar
displays an impressive
collection of darts trophies.
Quiet smoke room; large,
comfortable lounge; off-sales
area which can be crowded
early eve! Eve meals on
request. Q ❀ ◖ ঙ ⇌ (Bescot
Stadium) ♣

### Tap & Spile
5 John Street (off Stafford St)
☎ (01922) 27660
12–3, 5.30–11; 12–11 Thu–Sat; 12–3,
7–10.30 Sun
Wells Eagle; guest beers Ⓗ
Formerly the Pretty Bricks: a
friendly, two-bar pub near the
town centre with ever-
changing guest beers.
Occasional bands; good food
(no food Sun, or Mon eve).
♨ ❀ ◖ ▶ ⇌ ♣

## Wednesbury

### Old Blue Ball
19 Hall End (off A462)
☎ (0121) 556 0197
12–3, 5–11; 11.15–4.30, 7–11 Sat; 12–3,
7–10.30 Sun
Highgate Dark; Stones Bitter;
Worthington Bitter Ⓔ; guest
beers Ⓗ
Deservedly popular backstreet
local, with a small bar, lively
smoke room and a lounge. No
toddlers requested.
Q ⛾ ❀ ঙ ♣

### Star
Wood Green Road (A461, 300
yds from M6 jct 9)
☎ (0121) 502 2218
12–3 (not Sat), 7–11; 12–4, 7–10.30 Sun
Banks's Mild, Bitter Ⓔ;
Marston's Pedigree; guest
beer Ⓗ
Smart roadside food pub with
a new restaurant (varied
menu; no meals Sun eve).
Separate drinking area.
Q ◖ ▶ ঙ P

## Wednesfield

### Broadway

Lichfield Road (A4124)
☎ (01922) 405872
12–11; 12–10.30 Sun
**Ansells Mild, Bitter; Ind Coope Burton Ale; Tetley Bitter** Ⓗ
Pub recently redesigned into one large room with an eating area and a children's play area. The loss of the bar and games has changed the character.
ち ❀ ◖ ▶ P

### Pyle Cock

Rookery Street (A4124)
☎ (01902) 732125
10.30–11; 12–4, 7–10.30 Sun
**Banks's Mild, Bitter** Ⓗ
Excellent locals' boozer with lovely etched windows depicting a pyle cock. The family room is quite basic, the traditional bar always busy.
ち ⊞ ♣ P ⌷

### Vine

35 Lichfield Road
☎ (01902) 733529
11–3 (4 Fri, 5 Sat), 6 (7 Sat)–11; 12–3, 7–10.30 Sun
**Boddingtons Bitter; Thwaites Bitter; guest beers** Ⓗ
Revitalised, friendly, multi-roomed local always stocking a mild. Blackbeard beers often feature. Good value food (eve meals end at 8.30).
♨ ❀ ◖ ▶ ⊞ ♣ ⌷ P

## West Bromwich

### Churchfield Tavern

18 Little Lane (next to Sandwell General Hospital)
☎ (0121) 588 5468
11–11; 12–10.30 Sun
**Banks's Hanson's Mild, Bitter; Camerons Bitter** Ⓔ, **Strongarm** Ⓗ
Popular, three-roomed local, boasting a garden with a children's play area and a floodlit crown bowling green.
♨ ち ❀ ◖ ▶ ♣

### Old Crown

56 Sandwell Road
☎ (0121) 525 4600
12–4, 5–11; 12–3.30, 7–10.30 Sun
**M&B Mild, Brew XI** Ⓔ; **guest beers** Ⓗ
Pleasantly refurbished, backstreet local, brought back from the dead by an enterprising landlord. Home made Baltis/curries are increasingly popular. Two ever-changing guest beers (Cottage and Church End feature regularly). No lunches Sat/Sun. ◖ ▶ ⌷

### Vine

Roebuck Street
☎ (0121) 553 2866

11.30–3, 5–11; 11–11 Fri & Sat; 12–3, 7–10.30 Sun
**M&B Mild, Brew XI** Ⓔ; **guest beers** Ⓗ
Tiny corner house ingeniously extended into its own back-yard; renowned chiefly for its home-made Baltis and curries (no lunches Sat/Sun). One changing guest beer from a micro or other independent.
◖ ▶ ⇌ (Smethwick, Galton Bridge)

### Wheatsheaf

379 High Street
☎ (0121) 553 4221
11–11; 12–3, 7–10.30 Sun
**Holden's Mild** Ⓔ, **Bitter** Ⓗ/Ⓔ, **Special** Ⓗ
Busy pub with a mixed clientele: a basic locals' bar and a newly extended and renovated lounge. Q ◖ ⊞ ♣

## Whiteheath

### Whiteheath Tavern

400 Birchfield Lane (A4034, near M5 jct 2)
☎ (0121) 552 3603
12–4 (3.30 Sat; not Tue–Fri), 7.30–11; 12–3.30, 7.30–10.30 Sun
**Ansells Mild, Bitter** Ⓗ; **Banks's Mild** Ⓔ
Friendly local with a games-oriented bar and a comfortable lounge. The licensees have been here for over a decade.
⊞ ⇌ (Rowley Regis) ♣

## Willenhall

### Brewers Droop

44 Wolverhampton Street (behind Lock Museum)
☎ (01902) 607827
12–3, 6–11; 12–3, 7–10.30 Sun
**Batham Best Bitter; Enville Ale; Hook Norton Old Hooky; guest beers** Ⓗ
Pub with interesting artefacts and an adventurous beer range. Note the three classic motor bikes parked half way up one wall! Good food (no eve meals Sun–Wed). ♨ ◖ ▶ ♣ ♣

### Falcon

Gomer Street West (behind Lock Museum)
☎ (01902) 633378
12–11; 12–10.30 Sun
**Banks's Mild, Bitter; Greene King Abbot; Highgate Dark; Samuel Smith OBB; guest beers** Ⓗ
Quiet pub with a very adventurous guest beer policy (over 500 beers so far).
❀ ⊞ ♣ ⌷

### Robin Hood

54 The Crescent
☎ (01902) 608006
12–3, 7–11; 12–2.30, 7–10.30 Sun
**Ansells Mild; Ind Coope Burton Ale; Tetley Bitter; guest beer** Ⓗ
Very welcoming local with one

U-shaped room: a previous local CAMRA *Pub of the Year* for three consecutive years. Still everything a small pub should be. ❀ ♣ P

### Woolpack

Coltham Road, Short Heath
☎ (01922) 405806
12–3, 7–11; 12–11 Sat; 12–3, 7–10.30 Sun
**Burtonwood Mild, Bitter, Top Hat, seasonal beers** Ⓗ
Dramatically improved former Ansells pub, bought by Burtonwood five years ago. Four rooms include a large lounge and a smaller adjoining room. The snug has been converted to a family room.
Q ち ◖ ▶ ⊞ ♣ ♣ P

## Wolverhampton

### Chindit

113 Merridale Road (½ mile from Chapel Ash towards Bantock Park) ☎ (01902) 25582
12–3, 5–11; 12–11 Sat; 12–3, 7–10.30 Sun
**Highgate Dark; Worthington Bitter; guest beers** Ⓗ
Basic, street-corner local with a public bar and a lounge; named after soldiers of the 1st South Staffs Regiment who fought in Burma in 1944. Guest beers from Whitbread.
⊞ ♣

### Clarendon Hotel

38 Chapel Ash (A41)
☎ (01902) 20587
11–11; 12–3, 7–10.30 Sun
**Banks's Mild, Bitter** Ⓔ, **seasonal beers; Camerons Strongarm** Ⓗ
Popular brewery tap with a large, split-level lounge. The smaller smoke room has its own bar and can be quieter. Improved lunchtime menu (not served Sat); interesting new sandwich bar.
◖ P ⌷

### Exchange Vaults

Cheapside (off Queens Sq)
10.30–11; 12–3, 7–10.30 Sun
**Banks's Mild, Bitter** Ⓔ
Pub whose vaulted design is unusual in the area; popular lunchtimes and weekend eves with concert-goers. Basic bar; more comfy lounge.
◖ ⊞ ⇌

### Feline & Firkin

Princess Street
☎ (01902) 28806
11–11; 6–10.30 Sun, closed Sun lunch
**Firkin Stoker's FSB, Feline Bitter, Pussy Ale, Dogbolter; guest beers** Ⓗ
Smallish, split-level boozer with a dominant cat theme. It boasts its own video hire facility and an amazing range of unusual games. No meals Sun. Newspapers always

available. The beers are not brewed on site. ❀ ◖▶ ⇌ ♣

## Fox & Goose

420 Penn Road
☎ (01902) 332191
11.30–3 (4 Sat), 5.30–11; 12–4.30,
7–10.30 Sun
**Ansells Mild; HP&D Entire;
Tetley Bitter; guest beer** Ⓗ
Pub with a food-oriented large room and a bar showing TV sports. Children welcome if dining. ◖▶ & P

## Great Western

Sun Street (behind station)
☎ (01902) 351090
11–11; 12–3, 7–10.30 Sun
**Batham Best Bitter; Holden's
Mild, Bitter, Special** Ⓗ
A new conservatory has added space to the excellent surroundings of this pub which displays GWR memorabilia. Good value food. Next to the old low level station (soon to be a new leisure complex).
🚶 ❀ ◖▶ ⇌ ♣ P

## Homestead

Lodge Road, Oxley (off A449 at Goodyear roundabout)
☎ (01902) 787357
12–3, 6–11; 12–3, 7–10.30 Sun
**Ansells Bitter; Banks's Mild;
Marston's Pedigree; guest
beer** Ⓗ
Large, two-bar suburban pub. Children welcome (large outdoor play area). Good, home-cooked food. The smaller public bar has a dartboard. ❀ 🛏 ◖▶ 🍴 ♣ P

## Mitre Inn

Lower Green, Tettenhall (near A41/Lower St jct)
☎ (01902) 753487
12–2.30 (3 Sat), 6–11 (12–11 summer Sat); 12–3, 7–10.30 (12–10.30 summer) Sun
**Draught Bass; M&B Brew XI;
Stones Bitter; Worthington
Bitter; guest beer** Ⓗ
Surprisingly spacious, two-room pub, popular with locals, in a pleasant location opposite the Lower Green. The lounge has been refurbished and enlarged, but at the expense of a lost snug. The small patio at the front is busy in summer.
❀ ◖▶ 🍴 ♣

## Moon Under Water

Lichfield Street (opp. Grand Theatre) ☎ (01902) 22447
10–11; 12–10.30 Sun

**Banks's Mild; Courage
Directors; Marston's Pedigree;
Theakston Best Bitter, XB;
Younger Scotch; guest beers** Ⓗ
Large, open-plan Wetherspoons pub with a U-shaped bar. Heritage information and local art are featured on the wood-panelled walls – note the tree sculpture. Extensive food menu; good value specials.
Q ◖▶ & ⇌ ✗

## Newhampton Inn

Riches Street, Whitmore Reans (off A41) ☎ (01902) 745773
11–11; 12–10.30 Sun
**Courage Best Bitter, Directors;
Marston's Pedigree; Ruddles
County; John Smith's Bitter;
guest beer** Ⓗ
Busy, street-corner local attracting a wide-ranging clientele to four distinctly different rooms and a large garden with a bowling green. A function room is used for music. No-smoking room lunchtimes.
🚶 Q ❀ ◖▶ ♣ ⌚ ✗ 🍴

## Old Stag's Head

Penwood Lane, Penn Common
☎ (01902) 341023
11.30–2.30, 6–11; 11.30–11 Sat; 12–3, 7–10.30 Sun
**Banks's Mild, Bitter** Ⓔ
Characterful pub on the edge of the common. The small bar is frequented by locals (dogs welcome). The large lounge welcomes children if eating (play area in the garden).
❀ ◖▶ 🍴 ♣ P 🍴

## Posada

Lichfield Street (opp. art gallery) ☎ (01902) 710738
12–3, 5–11; 12–11 Fri & Sat; 12–3, 7–10.30 Sun
**HP&D Entire; Tetley Bitter;
guest beers** Ⓗ
Small, one-roomed, town-centre hostelry, popular with students and enjoying a good lunchtime trade. Good value food (no meals weekends). Regular live music. The ornate frontage is a notable feature.
◖ ⇌

## Red Lion

252 Bilston Road, Monmore Green ☎ (01902) 454511
12–3, 5–11; 12–11 Fri & Sat; 12–4, 7–10.30 Sun
**Banks's Mild, Bitter** Ⓔ
Basic pub on the outskirts of town with a bar, snug and pool room. Asian bar snacks;

barbecues in summer.
🐕 P

## Stamford Arms

Lime Street, Penn Fields (off Lea Rd) ☎ (01902) 24172
12–3.30, 7–11; 12–11 Sat; 12–5, 7–10.30 Sun
**Banks's Mild, Bitter** Ⓔ
Welcoming, street-corner local with notable exterior tiling. The three unspoilt rooms are served by a single bar with a hatch. A hidden gem in an old residential area. Q ❀ 🍴 ♣

## Stile

23 Harrow Street (off Newhampton Rd East)
☎ (01902) 21595
12–3, 6–11; 11–11 Sat; 12–3, 7–10.30 Sun
**Banks's Mild, Bitter** Ⓔ
Imposing, one-bar, street-corner local with a bowling green. Wooden floor and bench seats in the bar; small, quiet snug; large smoke room with a pool table. Handy for Wolves home games. Q ❀ ♣

## Swan

Bridgnorth Road, Compton (A454) ☎ (01902) 754736
11–3, 5–11; 11–11 Sat; 12–10.30 Sun
**Banks's Mild, Bitter** Ⓔ
A newly refurbished lounge adds taste to an original Victorian pub with a small public bar and a snug.
🚶 Q ❀ 🍴 ♣ P

# Woodsetton

## Park Inn

George Street (off A457, ¼ mile from A4123) ☎ (01902) 882843
11–11; 12–4, 7–10.30 Sun
**Holden's Mild, Bitter, Lucy B,
Special, seasonal beers** Ⓗ
The Holden's brewery tap: a friendly local frequented by all ages. All weather barbecues Fri–Sun in the conservatory (except winter).
🚶 🐕 ❀ ◖▶ & ♣ P

# Woodside

## Railway

39 Buxton Road (off A4036)
☎ (01384) 573483
2–11; 12–4.30, 7–11 Sat; 12–3, 7–10.30 Sun
**Banks's Hanson's Mild,
Bitter** Ⓔ
Cosy, one-roomed local, handy for Merry Hill centre.
❀ ♣ P 🍴

---

Find out more about CAMRA and its campaigning work by taking advantage of three-months' free trial membership. See page 543.

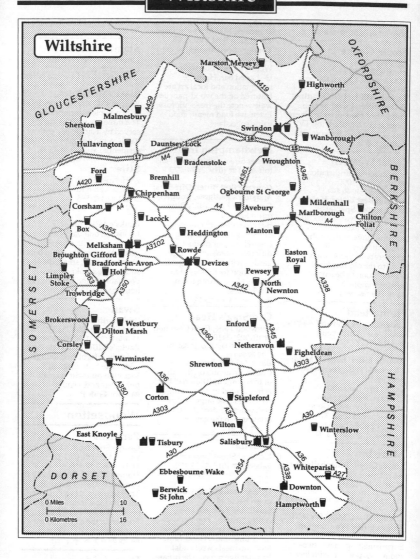

Wiltshire

Marston Meysey
Highworth
GLOUCESTERSHIRE
OXFORDSHIRE
Sherston
Malmesbury
Hullavington
Dauntsey Lock
Swindon
Wanborough
Ford
Bradenstoke
Wroughton
Bremhill
Chippenham
Ogbourne St George
Mildenhall
Corsham
Lacock
Avebury
Marlborough
Box
Heddington
Manton
Chilton Foliat
BERKSHIRE
Melksham
Rowde
Broughton Gifford
Bradford-on-Avon
Devizes
Easton Royal
Holt
Pewsey
Limpley Stoke
North Newnton
Trowbridge
Brokerswood
Westbury
Enford
Dilton Marsh
Netheravon
Corsley
Figheldean
Warminster
Shrewton
SOMERSET
Corton
Stapleford
Wilton
Winterslow
East Knoyle
Tisbury
Salisbury
HAMPSHIRE
Ebbesbourne Wake
Whiteparish
DORSET
Berwick St John
Downton
Hamptworth

0 Miles 10
0 Kilometres 16

## Avebury

### Red Lion
High Street
☎ (01672) 537266
11–11; 12–10.30 Sun
**Boddingtons Bitter; Flowers IPA; Wadworth 6X; Whitbread Fuggles IPA; guest beers** H
Touristy pub and restaurant, set in the middle of an ancient stone circle.
Q ☎ ❀ 🛏 ◖▶ ♿ P

## Berwick St John

### Talbot
The Cross ☎ (01747) 828222
11.30–2.30, 7–11; 12–2.30 Sun, closed Sun eve

**Adnams Bitter, Broadside; Draught Bass; Wadworth 6X** H**, Old Timer** G
Unspoilt village pub: a 400-year-old building with an inglenook. No food Sun.
🏨 Q ❀ ◖▶ ♿ P

## Box

### Quarryman's Arms
Box Hill (300 yds S of A4)
OS834693 ☎ (01225) 743569
11–11; 12–4, 6.30–10.30 Sun

### 🏰 INDEPENDENT BREWERIES

| | |
|---|---|
| **Archers:** Swindon | **Mole's:** Melksham |
| **Arkell's:** Swindon | **Tisbury:** Tisbury |
| **Bunces:** Netheravon | **Ushers:** Trowbridge |
| **Foxley:** Mildenhall | **Wadworth:** Devizes |
| **Gibbs Mew:** Salisbury | **Wylye Valley:** Corton |
| **Hop Back:** Downton | |

Butcombe Bitter; Wadworth 6X; Wickwar Brand Oak Ⓗ; guest beer Ⓖ
Open-plan pub with superb views over the valley; well hidden in a maze of lanes, yet only a short distance from the A4. Phone for directions! Cider in summer. ♨ ☜ ⊛ ⏢ ◖ ▶ ⊞
Å ♣ ⏚ P ⅛

## Bradenstoke

### Cross Keys
65 Bradenstoke
☎ (01249) 890279
7–11; 12–3, 7–11 Fri & Sat; 12–3, 7–10.30 Sun
Archers Best Bitter; Greene King IPA; Wadworth 6X; guest beers Ⓗ
Traditional, 200-year-old, two-bar pub in a quiet pretty village. ♨ ⊛ ◖ ▶ ⊞ ♣ P

## Bradford-on-Avon

### Beehive
263 Trowbridge Road
☎ (01225) 863620
11.30–2.30, 7–11; 12–3.30, 7–10.30 Sun
Butcombe Bitter Ⓗ; guest beer Ⓗ/Ⓖ
Friendly, canalside pub with an excellent and ever-changing range of ales, four dispensed by gravity. No food Sun eve.
♨ Q ⊛ ◖ ▶ ♣ P

### Masons Arms
52 Newtown ☎ (01225) 863435
11–11; 12–3.30, 7–10.30 Sun
Courage Best Bitter; Ushers Best Bitter, seasonal beers Ⓗ
Old-fashioned, unpretentious local high above the main part of town. Ask for oversized glasses. ⊛ ⊞ ♣ ⏪

### Swan Hotel
1 Church Street (A363)
☎ (01225) 868686
11–11; 12–10.30 Sun
Draught Bass; Butcombe Bitter; Gibbs Mew Salisbury; Ushers Founders; Wadworth 6X Ⓗ
Early 16th-century, town-centre building, well modernised, with a friendly atmosphere.
Q ⊛ ⏢ ◖ ▶ ⅚ ⇌ P

## Bremhill

### Dumb Post
Dumb Post Hill (off A4, W of Calne) OS975727
☎ (01249) 813192
12–3 (not Wed), 7–11; 12–3, 7–10.30 Sun
Archers Best Bitter, ASB; Wadworth 6X Ⓗ
Excellent country free house serving good, home-cooked food. Fine views over to Cherhill. The cantankerous parrot is still in residence.
♨ Q ☜ ⊛ ◖ ▶ ♣ P

## Brokerswood

### Kicking Donkey
Follow signs to Woodland Park from A36 or A350 OS833520
☎ (01373) 823250
11.30–2.30, 6 (6.30 Sat)–11; 12–3, 7–10.30 Sun
Smiles Best Bitter; Wadworth 6X Ⓗ; guest beer Ⓗ
17th-century country inn with exposed beams and brasses, divided into three drinking areas and a restaurant. The popular garden has seating for 200. No Sun eve meals Jan–Feb.
☜ ⊛ ◖ ▶ Å ⏚ P

## Broughton Gifford

### Bell on the Common
The Common (near B3107)
☎ (01225) 782309
11–3, 6.30–11; 11–11 Sat; 12–2.30, 7–10.30 Sun
Wadworth IPA, 6X, Old Timer Ⓗ
Handsome old pub overlooking the village common. The large garden is excellent for families.
♨ ⊛ ◖ ▶ ⊞ ♣ P

## Chilton Foliat

### Wheatsheaf
On B4192 ☎ (01488) 682391
11–3, 6–11; 12–4, 7–10.30 Sun
Morland Original, Old Masters, Old Speckled Hen; guest beer Ⓗ
Most welcoming, thatched pub with snug bars. Interesting stained-glass windows.
♨ Q ☜ ⊛ ◖ ▶ ⊞ Å ♣ P ⏪

## Chippenham

### Little George
29 New Road
☎ (01225) 652136
11–2.30, 6–11; 12–3 (not winter), 7–10.30 Sun
Butcombe Bitter; Courage Best Bitter; Marston's Pedigree; Wadworth 6X; guest beers Ⓗ
Large, busy, town-centre pub with mock Victorian and Edwardian decor in the bars. Popular lunchtime with nearby trading estate workers. Guest beers are changed regularly.
⊛ ⏢ ◖ ⊞ ⇌ ♣ P

## Corsham

### Two Pigs
38 Pickwick ☎ (01249) 712515
7–11; 12–2.30, 7–10.30 Sun
Bunces Pigswill; guest beers Ⓗ
Lively pub stocking an ever-changing range of at least three guest beers and catering for over-21s only. Twice local CAMRA *Pub of the Year*. Closed lunchtime, except Sun. ♨ ⊛

## Corsley

### Cross Keys
Lye's Green (½ mile N of A362 at Royal Oak jct) OS821462
☎ (01373) 832406
6.30 (7 Mon)–11; 12–3, 6.30–11 Wed; 12–3, 7–11 Sat; 12–3, 7–10.30 Sun
Draught Bass; Butcombe Bitter; Mole's Best Bitter; guest beer (occasional) Ⓗ
Welcoming free house of character; a popular, spacious pub with a splendid fireplace. Lunches served Wed and Sat.
♨ ⊛ ◖ ▶ ♣ ⏚ P

## Dauntsey Lock

### Peterborough Arms
On B4069 ☎ (01249) 890409
11.30–2.30 (3 Sat), 6–11 (11.30–11 summer); 12–3, 7–10.30 (12–10.30 summer) Sun
Archers Best Bitter; Smiles Brewery Bitter; Wadworth 6X; guest beers Ⓗ
Friendly, roadside free house with a cosy lounge and a log fire. Children welcome in the skittle alley. The large garden is perfect for summer eves. Good range of food. Campsite for Caravan Club caravans.
♨ Q ⊛ ◖ ▶ ♣ P

## Devizes

### Bear Hotel
Market Place ☎ (01380) 722444
11–3, 7–11; 12–10.30 Sun
Wadworth IPA, 6X; guest beers Ⓗ
A welcome return to the *Guide* for Devizes's premier hotel, an interesting and historic building which has shown a renewed interest in cask ale.
Q ⏢ ◖ ▶ ⊞

### Bell by the Green
Estcourt Street
☎ (01380) 723746
11–2, 6–11; 12–3, 7–10.30 Sun
Wadworth IPA, 6X Ⓗ
Comfortable pub overlooking the Crammer. Good menu; good value Sun lunches.
⊛ ⏢ ◖ ▶ ⅚ ♣ P

### British Lion
9 Estcourt Street
☎ (01380) 720665
11–11; 12–10.30 Sun
Beer range varies Ⓗ
Regularly changing guest beers have made this pub a *Guide* regular. House beer from Ash Vine.
⊛ ♣ ⏚ P ⏪

### Hare & Hounds
Hare & Hounds Street
☎ (01380) 723231
11–2.30, 7–11; 12–3, 7–10.30 Sun
Wadworth 6X Ⓗ
Yet another *Guide* entry for this popular, relaxed local.
♨ ⊛ ◖ ♣ P

### Lamb
St John's Street (behind Town Hall) ☎ (01380) 725426
12–3, 7–11; 12–3, 7–10.30 Sun
**Wadworth IPA, 6X; guest beers** (occasional) [H]
Town pub where the interior is basic, but has plenty of original character, unaltered for many years. ♣

### Queen's Head
Dunkirk Hill (A342 Chippenham road) ☎ (01380) 723726
11–3, 7–11; 12–3, 7–10.30 Sun
**Wadworth IPA, 6X** [H]
Pub concentrating more on good food, but retaining its reputation for its beer. ◐ ◗ P

## Dilton Marsh

### Prince of Wales
High Street
☎ (01373) 865487
12–2.30 (4 Sat), 6–11; 12–4, 7–10.30 Sun
**Fuller's London Pride; Smiles Brewery Bitter; Wadworth 6X; Worthington Bitter; guest beer** [H]
Simple, well-run, friendly, open-plan local. ❀ ♣ P

## East Knoyle

### Fox & Hounds
The Green (½ mile S of A303 at Willoughby Hedge) OS873315
☎ (01747) 830573
11–2.30 (3 Sat), 6–11; 12–3.30, 7–10.30 Sun
**Marston's Pedigree; Smiles Brewery Bitter; Wadworth 6X; guest beers** [H]
Remote, 14th-century, thatched inn in a hamlet at the top of a hill, away from the main village, with panoramic views towards Dorset: three bars, a children's room and a skittle alley. Good food.
♨ Q ☺ ❀ ◐ ◗ ♣ ⌒ P

## Easton Royal

### Bruce Arms ☆
On B3087 ☎ (01672) 810216
11–3, 6–11; 12–3, 7–10.30 Sun
**Strong Country Bitter; Wadworth 6X** [H]
Unspoilt rural gem with wooden benches, scrubbed tables, an open fire and a tiled floor. Caravan Club site in the grounds. Cider in summer.
♨ Q ☺ ❀ ⊞ ▲ ♣ ⌒ P

## Ebbesbourne Wake

### Horseshoe
Hanley Street
☎ (01722) 780474
11.30–3, 6.30–11; 12–4, 7–10.30 Sun
**Adnams Broadside; Ringwood Best Bitter; Wadworth 6X; guest beer** [G]
Wonderful pub, adorned with country artefacts. It has never given in to modernity hence its 'proper' village atmosphere. A must. No food Mon eve.
♨ Q ☺ ❀ ▭ ◐ ◗ ⊞ ▲ ♣ P

## Enford

### Swan
Longstreet ☎ (01980) 670338
12–3, 7–11; 12–3, 7–10.30 Sun
**Hop Back Special; guest beers** [H]
True village pub: a popular, friendly, cosy, unspoilt, thatched free house with a great atmosphere, whether you're drinking or dining (curries a speciality). Children welcome in the small bar. Note the unusual gantry sign. Many guest beers. ♨ ❀ ◐ ◗ ♣ ⌒ P

## Figheldean

### Wheatsheaf
High Street ☎ (01980) 670357
12–3 (not winter Mon–Thu), 7–11; 12–3, 7–10.30 Sun
**Draught Bass; Hop Back Special; guest beers** [H]
Friendly, single-bar pub with a large open fire and alcoves. Good food (not served Mon). Large family room and garden.
♨ ☺ ❀ ◐ ◗ ♣ P

## Ford

### White Hart
Off A420 ☎ (01249) 782213
11–2.30, 5–11; 12–3, 7–10.30 Sun
**Beer range varies** [H]
Lovely village pub – a superb watering hole. Normally ten ales, award-winning food, plus ten quality bedrooms.
Q ❀ ◐ ◗ ♿ ▲ P

## Hamptworth

### Cuckoo Inn
Hamptworth Road (1 mile off A36 at Landford turning)
☎ (01794) 390302
11.30–2.30, 6–11; 11.30–11 Sat; 12–10.30 Sun
**Badger Tanglefoot; Draught Bass; Cheriton Pots Ale; Hop Back GFB, Summer Lightning; Wadworth 6X** [G]
Grand, rustic thatched pub on the edge of the New Forest: four small public bar-type rooms with a genuine, friendly, local feel. Simple snack menu. The good garden has caged birds, a play house and petanque. ♨ Q ☺ ❀ ▲ ♣ P

## Heddington

### Ivy
Off A3102/A4
☎ (01380) 850276
12–3, 6.30–11; 12–11 Sat; 12–10.30 Sun
**Wadworth IPA, 6X, seasonal beers** [G]
Popular, thatched, village local. The building originates from the 15th century. Good home-cooked food (eve meals Fri and Sat).
♨ Q ❀ ◐ ◗ ♣ P

## Highworth

### Wine Cellar
High Street ☎ (01793) 763828
7 (1 Fri)–11; 12–4.30, 7–11 Sat; 12–5, 7–10.30 Sun
**Archers Village, Best Bitter; guest beers** [G]
A stairway between shop fronts leads down to a single bar in a stone-walled, Georgian cellar. Good selections of wines and whiskies. Q ♣ ⌒

## Holt

### Old Ham Tree
Ham Green
☎ (01225) 782581
11.15–3, 6.30–11; 12–3.30, 7–10.30 Sun
**Marston's Pedigree; Robinson's Best Bitter; Wadworth 6X; guest beer** [H]
18th-century coaching inn of character with a comfortable lounge/restaurant which contrasts with the simple locals' bar. Good variety of meals with generous portions.
Q ❀ ▭ ◐ ◗ ⊞ ♣ ⌒ P

## Hullavington

### Queen's Head
The Street ☎ (01666) 837221
12–2, 7–11; 12–2, 7–10.30 Sun
**Archers Village; Wadworth 6X; guest beers** [H]
Homely local with open fires and a skittle alley. No food Sun. Local CAMRA *Pub of the Year* 1994. ♨ Q ❀ ▭ ⊞ ♣ ⌒

## Lacock

### Bell Inn
Bowden Hill (1 mile E of Abbey) ☎ (01249) 730308
11–2.30, 6 (7 winter)–11; 12–3, 7–10.30 Sun
**Badger Tanglefoot; Foxley Best Bitter; Smiles Best Bitter; Wadworth 6X** [H]
Pleasant, roadside pub with a large garden, near the NT village. Good food; garden with livestock. ☺ ❀ ▭ ◐ ◗ P

## Limpley Stoke

### Hop Pole Inn
Woods Hill (off A36) OS782612
☎ (01225) 723134
11–2.30 (3 Sat), 6–11; 12–2.30, 7–10.30 Sun
**Draught Bass; Butcombe Bitter; Courage Best Bitter; Ushers Founders** [H]
Comfortable, authentic village pub with a beautiful, dark, oak-panelled public bar. A

large garden overlooks the
Avon Valley, near the Kennet
and Avon Canal. ❀ ◖ ▶ ❶ P

## Malmesbury

### Red Bull
Sherston Road (B4040, W of
town) ☎ (01666) 822108
11–2.30 (3.30 Sat), 6.30–11; 12–3,
7–10.30 Sun
**Draught Bass; Boddingtons
Bitter; Whitbread WCPA;
guest beers** H
Popular family pub with a
skittle alley/children's room.
🏚 ⛻ ❀ ◖ ▲ & P

### Smoking Dog
High Street ☎ (01666) 825823
11.30–11; 12–10.30 Sun
**Archers Best Bitter** G;
**Marston's Bitter, Pedigree;
Wadworth 6X; guest beers** H
Lively, friendly, drinkers' pub.
Home-made food (not served
Sun eve). Families welcome.
🏚 ❀ ◖ ▲ ♣

## Manton

### Oddfellows Arms
High Street ☎ (01672) 512352
12–2.30, 6–11, 12–3, 7–10.30 Sun
**Wadworth IPA, 6X; guest
beer** H
Cosy little local with a friendly
atmosphere, secluded garden
and a games room. Good food
(not served Sun eve).
🏚 Q ❀ ◖ ▶ & ➾ P ⚥

## Marlborough

### Lamb
The Parade ☎ (01672) 512068
11–11; 12–10.30 Sun
**Wadworth IPA, 6X; guest
beer** G
Excellent, noisy, cheerful town
pub. 🏚 ❀ ◖ & ♣

## Marston Meysey

### Old Spotted Cow
2½ miles from A419 OS129969
☎ (01285) 810264
11–3, 6–11; 12–3, 7–10.30 Sun
**Hook Norton Best Bitter;
Wadworth 6X; guest beer** H
Cotswold stone building, once
a farmhouse, serving good
food in the bar and restaurant.
🏚 Q ❀ ⛵ ◖ ▶ & ▲ ♣ P

## Melksham

### Red Lion
The City ☎ (01225) 702960
11–3, 5 (6 Sat)–11; 11–11 Fri; 12–3,
7–10.30 Sun
**Draught Bass; Highgate Dark;
Oakhill Best Bitter; guest
beer** H
13th-century, stone pub of
character: a rare local outlet for
mild. 1995 local CAMRA *Pub of
the Year*. Lunchtime snacks.
Q ❀ ♣ P

## North Newnton

### Woodbridge Inn
On A345 ☎ (01980) 630266
11–11; 12–3, 7–10.30 (12–10.30
summer) Sun
**Wadworth IPA, 6X, Farmers
Glory; guest beer** H
Excellent, welcoming pub on
the Avon: a regular food and
wine award-winner. The
riverside garden has petanque
pistes and trout fishing.
❀ ⛵ ◖ ▶ ▲ ♣ P

## Ogbourne St George

### Old Crown
☎ (01672) 841445
11.30–3, 6–11; 12–3, 7–10.30 Sun
**Wadworth 6X; guest beer** H
Food-oriented, village pub,
popular with locals.
Wheelchair ramp on request.
Q ❀ ⛵ ◖ ▶ ❶ & ▲ ♣ P

## Pewsey

### Coopers Arms
Ball Road ☎ (01672) 563525
11.30–2, 7–11; 12–3, 7–10.30 Sun
**Gale's HSB; Wadworth 6X;
guest beers** H
Pub of great character, hidden
away in a side road: low
ceilings, bare boards and
agricultural artefacts feature.
Live bands at weekends. Cider
in summer. 🏚 ⛻ ❀ ▲ ♣ P

## Rowde

### George & Dragon
High Street ☎ (01380) 723053
12–3, 7–11; 12–3, 7–10.30 Sun
**Wadworth IPA, 6X** H
Welcoming village pub,
popular with locals. Good
reputation for food – booking
advisable (restaurant open
Tue–Sat, 8–11).
🏚 Q ❀ ▲ ♣ P

## Salisbury

### Deacons Alms
118 Fisherton Street
☎ (01722) 336409
11–3, 6–11; 12–3, 7–10.30 Sun
**Boddingtons Bitter; Hop Back
GFB, Summer Lightning;
Wadworth 6X; guest beers** H
Busy town pub, popular with
theatre-goers. A small bar at
the front leads to a larger area
at the rear. Good food.
🏚 ⛵ ◖ ▶ ▲ ➾

### Royal George
17 Bedwin Street (off Castle St)
☎ (01722) 327782
11–3, 6–11; 12–3, 7–10.30 Sun
**Gibbs Mew Salisbury,
Deacon, Wake Ale** H
Grade II listed pub near the
arts centre, with low beams –

one from the *Royal George* ship
– plus brassware and nautical
pictures. Friendly and lively.
No food Sun. Q ❀ ◖ ▲ ♣ P

### Village
33 Wilton Road (A36)
☎ (01722) 329707
11–11; 12–10.30 Sun
**Cottage Southern Bitter, Our
Ken; Hampshire King
Alfred's; Oakhill Best
Bitter** H; **guest beer** G
Convivial pub, popular with
rail enthusiasts and locals. It
specialises in beers unavailable
in the rest of the city. Time is
called with class 33 loco horns.
◖ ▶ ▲ ➾ ♣

### Wig & Quill
New Street ☎ (01722) 335665
11–3, 5–11; 11–11 Sat; 12–10.30 Sun
**Wadworth IPA, 6X, Farmers
Glory, seasonal beers; guest
beers** G
16th-century city pub formerly
known as Burke's Bar &
Buttery and once an antique
shop. Now it caters for
discerning drinkers and is very
friendly. Good quality food.
🏚 ❀ ◖ ♣

### Wyndham Arms
Estcourt Road (off inner ring
road) ☎ (01722) 331026
4.30 (3 Fri, 12 Sat)–11; 12–10.30 Sun
**Hop Back Mild *or* Entire
Stout, Special, Thunderstorm,
Summer Lightning** H
A must for ale visitors to the
city – a welcoming, no-frills
local. One-time home of Hop
Back Brewery, it has one long
narrow bar and two small
drinking rooms. An excellent
boozer. ⛻ ♣

## Sherston

### Rattlebones
Church Street (B4042)
☎ (01666) 840871
11.30–3, 5.30–11; 11.30–11 Sat; 12–3,
7–10.30 Sun
**Draught Bass; Smiles Best
Bitter; Wadworth 6X; guest
beer** H
Old, friendly pub named after
a local hero, featuring skittles
and an unusual six-sided pool
table. Rattlebone SPA is
brewed by Archers. 🏚 Q ⛻ ❀
⛵ ◖ ▶ ❶ & ▲ ♣ ↺ P

## Shrewton

### George Inn
London Road (B3806)
☎ (01980) 620341
11–3, 6–11; 11–11 Sat; 12–3.30, 7–10.30
Sun
**Ringwood Best Bitter; Ushers
Best Bitter; Wadworth 6X;
guest beer** H
17th-century chalk and flint
building, once a brewery, now
an unspoilt village pub. Beer is

sold in pitchers. Good food.
🏚 Q 🕸 🖤 ◑ ▶ P

## Stapleford

### Pelican

☎ (01722) 790241
11–2.30 (3 Sat), 6–11; 12–2.30, 7 (6
summer)–10.30 Sun
**Otter Bitter; Ringwood Best
Bitter, Fortyniner; guest
beers** Ⓗ
Welcoming, 18th-century
former coaching inn. The
restaurant (good food) was the
former stables and mortuary.
Large garden. 🏚 🕸 ◑ ▶ P

## Swindon

### Clifton Hotel

Clifton Street, Old Town
☎ (01793) 523162
11–2.30, 7–11; 12–2.30, 7–10.30 Sun
**Arkell's Bitter, 3B, seasonal
beers** Ⓗ
This reputedly haunted local is
hard to find, but worth the
effort. 🕸 ◑ ▶ ♣ P

### Duke of Wellington

27 Eastcott Hill, Old Town
☎ (01793) 534180
12–2.30, 7–11; 12–3, 7–10.30 Sun
**Arkell's Bitter, 3B** Ⓖ
Small, two-bar pub where
Arkell's is unusually served
from the barrel. The snug is
very small, but comfortable.
Friendly. 🏚 Q 🕸 ◑ ▶ 🥤 ♣

### Famous Ale House

Redcliffe Street, Even Swindon
☎ (01793) 522503
11–2.30, 6–11; 11–11 Fri & Sat;
12–10.30 Sun
**Draught Bass; John Smith's
Bitter; guest beers** Ⓗ
Popular pub, set in a Victorian
building. Good food and beer
range (eight guests). No food
weekends. 🕸 ◑ ▶ ♣ P

### Glue Pot

Emlyn Square
☎ (01793) 523835
11–11; 12–10.30 Sun
**Archers Village, Best Bitter,
Black Jack, Golden, ASB** Ⓗ
The Archers brewery tap, in
Brunel's Railway Village: a
one-bar pub with high-backed
booths. Tables on the patio.
Lunches Mon–Fri.
🕸 ◑ 🥤 ♣

### King's Arms Hotel

Wood Street, Old Town
☎ (01793) 522156
11–2.30, 7–11; 12–2, 7–10.30 Sun
**Arkell's Bitter, 3B,
Kingsdown, seasonal beers** Ⓗ
Large, one-bar hotel, very busy
Fri and Sat. 🛏 ◑ ▶ ♿ P

### Rising Sun

6 Albert Street, Old Town
☎ (01793) 529916

11–11; 12–10.30 Sun
**Courage Best Bitter; Ushers
Best Bitter, Founders, seasonal
beers** Ⓗ
Busy, backstreet boozer – a real
oasis in Swindon's Old Town.
It boasts many local CAMRA
awards, including *Friendliest
Bar Staff*. ◑ ▶ ♣ 🥤 🍺

### Wheatsheaf

Newport Street
☎ (01793) 523188
11–2.30, 5 (6 Sat)–11; 12–2.30, 7–10.30
Sun
**Adnams Bitter; Wadworth
IPA, 6X, Farmers Glory, Old
Timer; guest beers** Ⓗ
Extended and refurbished pub.
The larger back bar is busy Fri
and Sat eves. Meals Mon–Thu.
🕸 🛏 ◑ ▶ 🍺

## Tisbury

### Crown

Church Street
☎ (01747) 870221
11–2.30, 7–11; 12–3, 7–10.30 Sun
**Gibbs Mew Wiltshire,
Salisbury, Wake Ale, Deacon**
(summer) Ⓗ
Former coaching inn: one large
bar with nooks. Good food
(special price lunches for
pensioners). No lunches Mon.
🏚 🕸 ◑ ▶ ♿ ⇌ ♣ 🥤 P

## Wanborough

### Black Horse

On crossroads, S end of village
☎ (01793) 790305
11–3, 5.30–11; 11–11 Sat; 12–4.30, 7–11
Sun
**Arkell's Bitter, 3B, seasonal
beers** Ⓗ
A little gem; a genuine local.
The garden offers pets, an
aviary and views. Past
CAMRA regional *Pub of the
Year*. No food Sun.
🏚 🕸 ◑ 🍺 ♠ P

### Plough

High Street ☎ (01793) 790523
12–2.30, 5–11; 12–11 Fri & Sat; 12–3,
7–10.30 Sun
**Archers Village; Draught
Bass; Boddingtons Bitter;
Wadworth 6X; guest beers** Ⓗ
Listed, thatched pub with cosy,
beamed, stone-walled bars and
log fires. Above-average food.
🏚 Q 🕸 ◑ ▶ 🍺 ♣ P 🍺

## Warminster

### Yew Tree

174 Boreham Road
☎ (01985) 212335
12–2 (4 Sat), 6.30–11; 12–4, 7–10.30
Sun
**Ringwood Best Bitter, XXXX
Porter; guest beer** Ⓗ
On the outskirts of town: an
18th-century former coaching
inn. 🕸 🛏 ◑ ▶ ♣ P

## Westbury

### Crown Inn

Market Place ☎ (01373) 822828
11–2.30, 5.30 (6 Sat)–11; 12–2.30,
7–10.30 Sun
**Wadworth IPA, 6X; guest
beer** Ⓗ
Welcoming, well-appointed
local. Lunches Mon–Sat; eve
meals Fri–Sat. 🕸 ◑ ▶ 🍺 ♣ 🥤 P

### Oak Inn

Warminster Road (A350)
☎ (01373) 823169
5.30 (12 Sat)–11; 12–3, 7–10.30 Sun
**Draught Bass; Ringwood Best
Bitter; guest beer** Ⓗ
A mock-Tudor exterior fronts a
16th-century inn with more
recent additions. Beer festivals
in the skittle alley. Lunches
Sat–Sun; eve meals Sat only.
🏚 🕸 ◑ 🍺 ♣ P

## Whiteparish

### Parish Lantern

Romsey Road
☎ (01794) 884392
11.30–3, 6.30–11; 12–3, 7–10.30 Sun
**Ringwood Best Bitter; guest
beers** Ⓗ
Large, friendly pub just out of
the main village. House beer
from Hampshire Brewery.
🏚 🕸 ▶ ♿ ♣ P

## Wilton

### Bear Inn

West Street ☎ (01722) 742398
11–2.30 (3 Sat), 5 (6 Sat)–11; 12–3,
7–10.30 Sun
**Badger Dorset Best** Ⓗ
16th-century, one-bar inn near
the market square. 🏚 🕸 ♣

## Winterslow

### Lion's Head

The Common, Middleton Road
☎ (01980) 862234
12–2.30, 7–11; 12–3, 7–10.30 Sun
**Courage Directors; Flowers
Original; Ringwood Best
Bitter; Webster's Yorkshire Bitter** Ⓗ
Family-run, village pub,
popular with walkers: a choice
of quiet or lively bars.
Q 🕸 🕸 ◑ ▶ 🍺 ♿ ♠ ♣ P

## Wroughton

### Carters Rest

High Street ☎ (01793) 812288
11–2.30, 5–11; 11–11 Sat; 12–3, 7–10.30
Sun
**Archers Village, Best Bitter,
Golden; Fuller's London
Pride; Marston's Owd Rodger;
Morland Old Speckled Hen;
guest beers** Ⓗ
Edwardian building, tastefully
refurbished. Good food (not
served Sun). Cider in summer.
🏚 Q 🕸 ◑ 🍺 ♣ 🥤 P

# Worcestershire

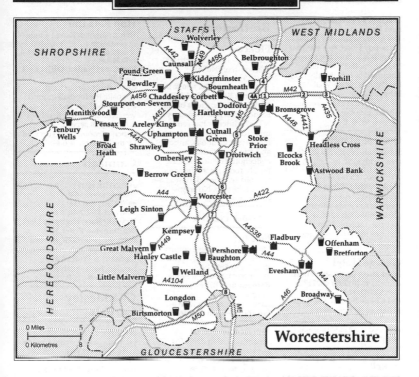

**Worcestershire**

## Areley Kings

### Kings Arms
19 Redhouse Road (off B4196)
☎ (01299) 827132
12–3, 6–11; 12–11 Fri & Sat; 12–3,
7–10.30 Sun
**Banks's Mild** Ⓔ/Ⓗ, **Bitter** Ⓔ;
**guest beer** Ⓗ
L-shaped, single-roomed pub
where the guest beers usually
come from Banks's Festival of
Beers scheme. As well as a
garden, the pub has a bowling
green.
❀ ◑ ▮ ᵫ ▲ ♣ P ♉

## Astwood Bank

### Why Not Inn
The Ridgeway (A441, 1 mile S
of village)
☎ (01527) 893566
11–2.30, 6–11; 12–3, 7–10.30 Sun
**Boddingtons Mild, Bitter;
Flowers IPA; Marston's
Pedigree** Ⓗ
Comfortable and friendly,
roadside pub popular with
locals and tourists. Excellent,
good value food, from
sandwiches to full meals, is
served in all parts, including a
no-smoking dining area and a
pleasant public bar (no meals
Sun eve). ❀ ◑ ▮ ⊞ ♣ P

Try also: Oddfellows,
Foregate St (M&B)

## Baughton

### Jockey Inn
On A4104
☎ (01684) 592153
11.30–3, 6.30–11; 12–3, 7–10.30 Sun;
closed Mon, except bank hols
**Adnams Bitter** Ⓗ; **Banks's
Bitter** Ⓔ; **Hook Norton Best
Bitter; Wood Parish; guest
beers** Ⓖ
Quiet, pleasant village pub
with a small garden in front;
popular for its good value
range of food. The beers
from the above breweries
may vary.
♨ Q ❀ ◑ ▮ ♣ P ♉

## Belbroughton

### Queens
Queens Hill (B4188)
☎ (01562) 730276
11.30–3, 5.30 (6 Sat)–11; 12–3.30,
7–10.30 Sun
**Bateman Mild;
Marston's Bitter, Pedigree,
HBC** Ⓗ
Popular, smart village inn
near a pretty brook. A single
bar serves three lounge
areas. Restaurant quality
food.
❀ ◑ ▮ ᵫ P

Try also: Holly Bush,
Stourbridge Rd (Free)

## Berrow Green

### Admiral Rodney
On B4197, 2 miles N of
Knightwick ☎ (01886) 821375
12–3 (not winter Mon; may extend
summer) 7–11; 12–3, 7–10.30 Sun
**Blackbeard Stairway to
Heaven; Hook Norton Best
Bitter; guest beers** (summer) Ⓗ
Friendly pub set in rolling
countryside, with separate
areas for bar, lounge and pool.
Limited menu Sun; no meals
Mon eve. Q ❀ ◑ ▮ ▲ ♣ P

## Bewdley

### Black Boy
50 Wyre Hill (follow Sandy
Bank off B4194 at Welch Gate)
☎ (01299) 403523
12–3, 7–11; 12–3, 7–10.30 Sun
**Banks's Mild** Ⓔ, **Bitter** Ⓔ/Ⓗ;

**INDEPENDENT
BREWERIES**

**Brandy Cask:** Pershore

**Cannon Royall:**
Uphampton

**Evesham:** Evesham

**Red Cross:** Bromsgrove

**Wyre Piddle:** Fladbury

317

**Marston's Pedigree; guest beer** Ⓗ
Not to be confused with the Black Boy Hotel, this 400-year-old pub is a short, but steep, climb from the town centre. The guest beer is usually from the Banks's range. Well-behaved children may be allowed in the games room when it is not in use.
♛ Q ❀ ⊞ ♣ Ū

### Cock & Magpie
Severnside North (50 yds from river bridge) ☎ (01299) 403748
11–3, 6–11; 11–11 Sat & summer; 12–4, 7–10.30 (12–10.30 summer) Sun
**Banks's Mild, Bitter** Ⓔ
Traditional, two-roomed, friendly riverside pub in a pleasantly cobbled street with cast iron railings. Note the pictures in the bar of winter floods. Q ⊞ ⇌ (SVR) ♣ Ū

### George Hotel
Load Street (main street near church) ☎ (01299) 402117
11–3, 5.30–11; 12–4, 7–10.30 Sun
**Ind Coope Burton Ale; Tetley Bitter; guest beer** Ⓗ
Hotel with a popular bar, accessed via a side passage. The guest beer comes from a variety of breweries.
♛ Q ♘ ❀ 🛏 ◖ ◗ ♿ ⇌ (SVR) P

## Birtsmorton

### Farmer's Arms
Birts Street (signed off B4208) OS792363 ☎ (01684) 833308
11–2.30, 6–11 (11–11 summer Sat); 12–2.30, 7–10.30 (12–10.30 summer) Sun
**Hook Norton Best Bitter, Old Hooky; guest beer** (weekends) Ⓗ
Black and white country pub, tucked away down a lane: a small lounge with a very low, beamed ceiling plus a larger, more basic, bar with darts and games. The large garden, with swings, has a fine view towards the Malvern Hills. Holiday cottage to let.
♛ Q ❀ ◖ ◗ ♿ ♣ P

## Bournheath

### Gate
Dodford Road
☎ (01527) 878169
11–2.30, 6–10.30 (11 Fri & Sat); 12–3, 6–10.30 Sun
**Boddingtons Bitter; Smiles Best Bitter, Exhibition; guest beer** Ⓗ
Popular village pub aimed at diners (booking advised); the restaurant and conservatory specialise in Mexican/Cajun options. Balti night Mon. Special prices on beer and food 6–7 and 12–1. A rare outlet for Smiles ales. ♛ ❀ ◖ ◗ ♿ P

## Bretforton

### Fleece ☆
The Cross (near church, 100 yds south of B4035)
☎ (01386) 831173
11–2.30, 6–11; 12–2.30, 7–10.30 Sun
**Everards Beacon; M&B Brew XI; Uley Bitter; guest beers** Ⓗ
Famous old pub owned by the NT. The interior has remained untouched for many years and includes inglenooks, antiques and a world-famous pewter collection. The no-smoking family room offers the same fine old accommodation as the rest of the pub. No crisps!
♛ Q ♘ ❀ ◖ ◗ ⊞ ♣ 🍏 ⊬

## Broad Heath

### Fox Inn
On B4204 between Tenbury Wells and Clifton-on-Teme
☎ (01886) 853219
12–3, 6.30–11; 12–3, 7–10.30 Sun
**Batham Best Bitter; guest beer** Ⓗ
Large country pub with a farmhouse-style exterior and some beams dating back to the 16th century. Special accommodation deals for anglers. The restaurant has a late supper licence.
♛ Q ❀ 🛏 ◖ ◗ ⊞ ♣ P

## Broadway

### Crown & Trumpet
Church Street (Snowshill road, just off W end of village green)
☎ (01386) 853202
11–3, 5–11; 11–11 Sat; 12–3, 6–10.30 (12–10.30 summer) Sun
**Boddingtons Bitter; Flowers IPA; Morland Old Speckled Hen; Stanway Stanney Bitter; Wadworth 6X** Ⓗ
Fine, 17th-century, Cotswold stone inn, complete with oak beams and log fires in its comfortable interior. Deservedly popular with locals, tourists and walkers. Small car park.
♛ ❀ 🛏 ◖ ◗ ▲ ♣ 🍏 P

## Bromsgrove

### Golden Cross
20 High Street
☎ (01527) 870005
11–11; 12–10.30 Sun
**Banks's Mild; Courage Directors; Morland Old Speckled Hen; Theakston Best Bitter, XB; Younger Scotch; guest beer** Ⓗ
Large, modern, open-plan Wetherspoons pub, popular with young people, especially weekend eves (strictly no under-18s). Meals available up to one hour before closing. Wheelchair WC.
Q ❀ ◖ ◗ ♿ 🍏 ⊬

### Hop Pole Inn
78 Birmingham Road (½ mile N of centre) ☎ (01527) 870100
12–2.30, 5.30–11; 12–3, 7–11 Sat; 12–3, 7–10.30 Sun
**Red Cross Nailers OBJ; guest beer** Ⓗ
Cosy, street-corner local opposite the football ground: an L-shaped bar and a welcoming lounge. Excellent lunches (not served Sun). Function room. OBJ is brewed by the licensee. ❀ ◖ ⊬

## Caunsall

### Anchor Inn
600 yds from A449
☎ (01562) 850254
12–4, 7–11; 12–3, 7–10.30 Sun
**Draught Bass; Highgate Dark; Worthington Bitter** Ⓗ
Pleasant, two-room pub in a small village, a short walk from the Staffs & Worcs Canal. Sandwiches available.
♘ ❀ ♿ ▲ ♣ 🍏 P

## Chaddesley Corbett

### Swan
High Street ☎ (01562) 777302
11–11; 12–3, 7–10.30 (12–10.30 summer) Sun
**Batham Mild, Best Bitter, XXX** Ⓗ
Pleasant country pub built in 1606, with a popular bar, an attractively renovated, large lounge and a separate restaurant. Variety of bar meals available (not Sun lunch); restaurant open every day (except Sun eve). Barbecues in summer. Jazz Thu.
♛ ❀ ◖ ◗ ⊞ ♿ ♣ 🍏 P

## Cutnall Green

### New Inn
On A442 ☎ (01299) 851202
12–3, 5.30 (6 Sat)–11; 12–3, 7–10.30 Sun
**Banks's Mild; Marston's Bitter, Pedigree, HBC** Ⓗ
Friendly, traditional village local with a dining area (accompanied children welcome). Good range of home-cooked food; late supper licence. ♛ Q ❀ ◖ ◗ P

## Dodford

### Dodford Inn
Whinfield Road (off A448, near Bournheath) OS939726
☎ (01527) 832470
12–3, 7–11 (11–11 summer Sat); 12–3, 7–10.30 (12–10.30 summer) Sun
**Greenalls Bitter; guest beers** Ⓗ
Superb, out of the way, friendly pub set in rolling countryside, popular with ramblers. The single bar serves

up to three guest beers. Good value, home-made food. Children's certificate. Cider in summer.
🏺 ⊛ ◖ ▶ ⟁ ▲ ♣ ◔ P ⊱

## Droitwich

### Red Lion
Worcester Road (old A38, 1 mile S of centre)
☎ (01905) 772119
11.30–11; 12–10.30 Sun
**Banks's Hanson's Mild, Bitter; Marston's Pedigree** ⊞
Warm, friendly, two-roomed traditional drinking pub with an extensive lunchtime menu, plus snacks served till 6. The 'Lion'-sized beef cobs are a must. ⊛ ◖ ⊟ ♣ P ⊟

**Try also: Old Cock**, Friar St (Marston's)

## Elcocks Brook

### Brook Inn
Callowhill Lane (off Windmill Lane, Headless Cross)
☎ (01527) 543209
12–3, 6–11; 12–3, 7–10.30 Sun
**Banks's Mild; Marston's Bitter, Pedigree** ⊞
Popular and friendly country pub with a spacious, well-appointed, single lounge bar. Wide variety of home-cooked food lunchtime. Pleasant outside drinking area.
🏺 Q ⊛ ◖ ▲ P

## Evesham

### Green Dragon
Oat Street (just off High St, near library) ☎ (01386) 446337
11–3, 7–11 (midnight Thu–Sat); 12–3, 7–10.30 Sun
**Courage Directors; Evesham Asum Ale, Asum Gold; guest beers** ⊞
A cosy lounge, an extensive bar and a large function room make up this large town pub, complete with its own brewery. ⊛ ◖ ▲ ⥤ ♣

### Trumpet Inn
Merstow Green (just off S end of High St) ☎ (01386) 446227
11–11; 12–10.30 Sun
**Banks's Bitter; Draught Bass; Camerons Strongarm; guest beers** ⊞
Family-run, central pub serving a good mix of townspeople. It has long represented (sometimes single-handedly) Evesham in this guide. ⊛ ◖ ▲ ⥤ ♣ ⊟

## Forhill

### Peacock
Icknield Street (2 miles from A441/Redhill road jct, towards Wythall) OS054755
☎ (01564) 823232

12–11; 12–10.30 Sun
**Banks's Mild, Bitter; Enville Bitter; Judges Old Gavel Bender, Solicitor's Ruin; guest beers** ⊞
Excellent country pub with a very large lounge, sectioned into three areas. Oak beams and flagstone floors feature throughout; large woodburning stove. Good, chatty atmosphere. Bar billiards played. Sun lunches served till 8 (booking advised).
🏺 Q ⊱ ⊛ ◖ ▶ ⊟ ♣ P ⊱

**Try also: Coach & Horses**, Weatheroak (Free)

## Great Malvern

### Foley Arms Hotel
14 Worcester Road
☎ (01684) 573397
12–2.30, 5.30–11; 12–11 Sat; 12–3, 7–10.30 Sun
**Draught Bass; guest beers** ⊞
Popular 1810 coaching inn in the centre with magnificent views across the Severn Valley from the bar and the terrace. Non-smokers are allowed to retreat to the hotel lounge. Two interesting guest beers, one low, one high, gravity. Eve meals end at 8.30 Sat and 7 Sun.
⊛ ⊨ ◖ ▶ ⥤ ♣ P ⊱

**Try also: Unicorn Inn**, Worcester Rd (Whitbread)

## Hanley Castle

### Three Kings ☆
Church End (signed off B4211)
☎ (01684) 592686
11–3 (may vary), 7–11; 12–3, 7–10.30 Sun
**Butcombe Bitter; Thwaites Bitter; guest beers** ⊞
Marvellous, unspoilt village pub, 80 years in the same family: a tiny bar with an inglenook plus a larger 'Nell's Bar' and family room. Occasional live music; great welcome and character. CAMRA national *Pub of the Year 1993*; local CAMRA *Pub of the Year 1995*. No eve meals Sun.
🏺 Q ⊱ ⊛ ⊨ ◖ ▶ ⊟ ♣ ◔

## Hartlebury

### White Hart
Rectory Lane
☎ (01299) 250286
11–3, 6–11; 11–11 Sat; 12–3, 7–10.30 Sun
**Banks's Mild; M&B Brew XI; guest beer** ⊞
Lively village pub with a large, L-shaped lounge and a separate, functional bar room. Live music certain nights. No food Mon eve or Sun.
⊛ ◖ ▶ ⊟ ▲ ♣ P

## Headless Cross

### Seven Stars
75 Birchfield Road
☎ (01527) 402138
12–11; 12–4, 7–10.30 Sun
**Marston's Pedigree; Ruddles Best Bitter; Webster's Yorkshire Bitter** ⊞
Traditional local with a small bar and a lounge with a games area leading off. A friendly town pub with parking close by. ⊛ ⊟ ♣ ◔

## Kempsey

### Walter de Cantelupe Inn
Main Road (A38)
☎ (01905) 820572
12–2.30 (not Mon), 5.30 (7 Mon)–11; 12–2.30, 7–10.30 Sun
**Marston's Bitter; Taylor Landlord; guest beer** ⊞
Village pub with a cosy, welcoming atmosphere. Beer price discount for CAMRA members (show card). Small, restaurant area (good food). Lunches Tue–Sun; eve meals Tue–Sat. 🏺 Q ⊛ ◖ ▶ ▲ P

## Kidderminster

### Hare & Hounds
140 Stourbridge Road, Broadwaters (A449, ¾ mile N of town) ☎ (01562) 751819
3 (12 Fri & Sat)–11; 12–3, 7–10.30 Sun
**Batham Mild, Best Bitter** ⊞
Two-room pub with a comfortable, split-level lounge, a locals' bar and a small pool room (free Wed).
⊛ ⊟ ♣ P

### King & Castle
SVR Station, Comberton Hill
☎ (01562) 747505
11–3 (4 Sat), 5 (6 Sat)–11 (11–11 on days when trains run); 12–10.30 Sun
**Draught Bass; Batham Best Bitter; Highgate Dark; guest beers** ⊞
Friendly, single-bar pub, part of the Severn Valley Railway southern terminus. Children allowed in up to 9pm. Full station facilities (e.g. wheelchair toilets) available when trains are operating. No eve meals Mon–Wed.
🏺 Q ⊛ ◖ ▶ ⟁ ⥤ ♣ P

### Red Man
92 Blackwell Street (N of centre, just inside ring road)
☎ (01562) 67555
10–11; 12–3.30, 7–10.30 (12–10.30 summer) Sun
**Ansells Bitter; HP&D Mild, Entire; Ind Coope Burton Ale; Marston's Pedigree; Tetley Bitter** ⊞
Pub just out on the edge of town, very good for family lunches (wood-chipped play area in the

garden, conservatory for not-so-dry days). A forthcoming guest beers list is displayed. Eve meals end at 7.30.
☎ ❀ ◖▮ ❦ ♣ P

### Station Inn
7 Fairfield (off Comberton Hill)
☎ (01562) 822764
12–3, 6–11; 12–11 Fri & Sat; 12–3, 7–10.30 Sun
**Greenalls Davenports Bitter, Original; Tetley Bitter** Ⓗ
Hidden in a quiet street just above the stations, this welcoming pub has a public bar, a comfortable lounge and a pleasant, safe garden. Good food. Q ❀ ◖▮ ≥ ♣ P

## Leigh Sinton

### Royal Oak
Malvern Road (A4103/B4503 jct) ☎ (01886) 832664
11–3, 6–11; 12–3, 7–10.30 Sun
**Marston's Bitter, Pedigree** Ⓗ
Friendly, two-roomed, cosy village local with lots of low beams and an impressive collection of implements, brasses and other knick-knacks. The Irish landlord ensures that conversation is lively. Good range of food.
🏛 Q ❀ ◖▮ ▲ ♣ P

## Little Malvern

### Malvern Hills Hotel
Wynds Point (A449/B4232 jct)
☎ (01684) 540237
11–3, 7–10 (11–11 summer); 12–3, 7–10 (12–10.30 summer) Sun
**Draught Bass; Hobsons Best Bitter; Otter Ale; Wood Parish** Ⓗ
Comfortable lounge bar in an upmarket weekend retreat on the ridge of the Malvern Hills. Walkers are welcome but are requested to remove their boots before entering. The separate restaurant offers a full à la carte menu but definitely no chips. 🏛 Q ❀ ⛴ ◖▮ P

## Longdon

### Plough
On B4211 ☎ (01684) 833767
12–3 (not winter Mon–Fri), 6.30–11; 12–3, 7–10.30 Sun
**Hardington Best Bitter; Hook Norton Best Bitter; Tetley Bitter; guest beers** (summer) Ⓗ
Large, open, rambling country pub with a games room (children welcome) and a skittle alley. Good value food.
🏛 ❀ ◖▮ ♣ P ⊟

## Menithwood

### Cross Keys Inn
1 mile off B4202
☎ (01584) 881425
11–3, 6–11; 12–4, 7–10.30 Sun

**Marston's Bitter, Pedigree; guest beer** Ⓗ
Friendly country local with a single bar and various drinking areas around. Worth finding.
🏛 Q ❀ ⛴ ◖▮ ▲ ♣ P

## Offenham

### Bridge
Boat Lane (follow signs to the river) ☎ (01386) 446565
11–11; 12–10.30 Sun
**Theakston Best Bitter, XB; Younger Best Bitter; guest beers** Ⓗ
Ancient riverside inn with its own moorings. Thriving local trade; warm welcome for visitors. Guest beers are usually from local independent brewers. ❀ ◖▮ ▮ ♣ P

## Ombersley

### Crown & Sandys Arms
Main Road (A4133)
☎ (01905) 620252
11–3, 5.30–11; 12–3, 7–10.30 Sun
**Hook Norton Best Bitter, Old Hooky; guest beers** Ⓗ
Smart country pub with a wonderful fireplace, in a very pretty village. Excellent, home-made food (vegetarian options); grill room and restaurant (booking advised).
🏛 Q ❀ ⛴ ◖▮ P ⊬

## Pensax

### Bell
On B4202 ☎ (01299) 896677
12–3 (not Mon except bank hols), 6.30–11; 12–3, 6.30–10.30 Sun
**Hook Norton Best Bitter; Taylor Landlord; guest beers** Ⓗ
Popular country pub with various drinking areas, serving five ales (about 60 guests a year from nearly as many breweries). The restaurant serves good, British food.
🏛 Q ☎ ❀ ◖▮ ♣ ⊙ P

## Pershore

### Brandy Cask
Bridge Street (A44)
☎ (01386) 552602
11.30–2.30 (3 Sat), 7–11; 12–3, 7–10.30 Sun (may extend in summer and on special days)
**Brandy Cask Brandy Snapper, John Baker's; Ruddles Best Bitter, County; guest beers** Ⓗ
Popular, town-centre brew pub with a riverside garden. Good range of rotating guest beers. Beer Festival Aug Bank Hol Mon. 🏛 ❀ ◖▮ ▲ ♣

### Miller's Arms
8 Bridge Street (A44)
☎ (01386) 553864
11–3.30 (5 Sat), 7–11; 12–3, 7–10.30 Sun

**Badger Tanglefoot; Morland Old Speckled Hen; Wadworth IPA, 6X, Farmers Glory; guest beer** Ⓗ
Busy, town-centre pub of character, popular with the young. Fortnightly guest beer; monthly folk and quiz nights. Eve meals in summer (finishing early). ❀ ◖▮ ♣ ⊙

## Pound Green

### New Inn
Off B4194 at Buttonoak; 1 mile up hill from Arley station
☎ (01299) 401271
7–11; 12–3, 7–11 Sat; 12–3, 7–10.30 Sun
**Banks's Mild; Draught Bass; guest beers** Ⓗ
One-bar pub with several different drinking areas and a restaurant. Two guest ales in summer. Piano and accordion players are always made welcome.
🏛 Q ☎ ❀ ◖▮ ▲ ♣ P ⊬

## Shrawley

### New Inn
New Inn Lane
☎ (01299) 822701
12–2.30 (11.30–3 Sat), 6–11; 12–3, 7–10.30 Sun
**Banks's Mild; Marston's Bitter, Pedigree, HBC** Ⓗ
Cosy village pub with a welcoming atmosphere in its small lounge, separate family dining room and restaurant. No meals Mon in winter.
🏛 Q ☎ ❀ ◖▮ ▲ ♣ P

## Stoke Prior

### Navigation Inn
Hanbury Road (B4091)
☎ (01527) 870194
11–11; 12–10.30 Sun
**Greenalls Davenports Bitter, Original; Tetley Bitter** Ⓗ
Pub near Lock 23 on the Worcester–Birmingham Canal. The large lounge, with olde-worlde style decor, has plenty of bric-a-brac, is comfortably furnished and has been extended at the rear to create a separate dining area. The large sparsely furnished bar has a pool table and machines. No meals Sun. ❀ ◖▮ ▮ ♣ P

## Stourport-on-Severn

### Bird in Hand
Holly Road (off Baldwin Rd, follow signs) ☎ (01299) 822385
11–3, 5.30–11; 11–11 Sat; 12–10.30 Sun
**Banks's Mild; Boddingtons Bitter; Flowers IPA, Original; guest beer** Ⓗ
Traditional, canalside local with links to the canal working past. Varied guest beer; outside

drinking by the towpath (easy mooring for boats).
🏔 ❀ 🛏 ◑ ▶ ⊟ ♣ P

## Wheatsheaf

39 High Street
☎ (01299) 822613
10.30–11; 12–10.30 Sun
**Banks's Hanson's Mild, Mild, Bitter Ⓔ; Marston's Pedigree** Ⓗ
Two-room, town-centre pub with a typical locals' bar and a popular lounge; close to the historic canal basin and the riverside.
❀ ◑ ▶ ⊟ ▲ ♣ P ⎕

## Tenbury Wells

### Ship Inn

Teme Street
☎ (01584) 810269
11–2.30, 7–11; 12–3, 7–10.30 Sun
**Ansells Bitter; guest beer** Ⓗ
Well-furnished, food-oriented pub with some character, a separate restaurant and a large garden. The emphasis is on quality rather than quantity, hence only two real ales.
❀ 🛏 ◑ ▶

## Uphampton

### Fruiterer's Arms

Uphampton Lane (N of Ombersley; off A449 at Reindeer pub) OS839649
☎ (01905) 620305
12.30–2.30 (3 Sat), 7–11; 12–3, 7–10.30 Sun
**Cannon Royall Fruiterer's Mild, Arrowfield, Buckshot; John Smith's Bitter** Ⓗ
Country pub built in 1848, still owned by the May family: a cosy, quiet, wood-panelled lounge, with a large woodburning stove, and a good-sized, plain bar with a pool table. Cannon Royall Brewery is sited at the rear. Local CAMRA *Pub of the Year* 1996. Caravan park adjacent. No food Sun.
🏔 Q ❀ ◑ ▶ ⊟ ♣ ⌂ P

## Welland

### Anchor Inn

Drakes Street (just off A4104)
☎ (01684) 592317
12–3, 7–11; 12–3, 7–10.30 Sun (closed winter Sun eve)
**Draught Bass; Black Sheep Best Bitter; guest beers** Ⓗ
Comfortable, beamed country pub with an extensive bar food board and a separate, cosy restaurant. Children are welcome in the large garden but check before taking under-14s into the bar. Camping is in a field next to the pub. 'Anchor' house ale comes from a small brewer.
🏔 Q ❀ ◑ ▶ ⚅ ▲ ♣ P

## Wolverley

### Lock Inn

Wolverley Road (B4189 by canal bridge) ☎ (01562) 850581
11.30–3, 5.30–11; 11–11 Sat & summer; 12–4, 7–10.30 (12–10.30 summer) Sun
**Banks's Mild, Bitter Ⓔ; Camerons Strongarm** (summer) Ⓗ
Welcoming canalside pub with real fires, a comfortable lounge and a public bar (games played). Good food. Large children's play area.
🏔 Q 🐎 ❀ ◑ ▶ ⊟ ⚅ ▲ ♣ P ⎕

## Worcester

### Alma Tavern

74 Droitwich Road
☎ (01905) 28103
11.30–2.30 (11–3 Sat), 6–11; 12–4, 7–10.30 Sun
**Ansells Bitter; Banks's Mild; Tetley Bitter** Ⓗ
One-roomed, one-bar local; popular Sun lunchtimes with diners (segregated dining area). Piped gentle music.
🏔 ❀ ◑ ▶ ⚅ ♣

### Bell Inn

35 St John's ☎ (01905) 424570
11–3 (4 Sat), 7–11; 12–3, 7–10.30 Sun
**M&B Mild, Brew XI; guest beer** Ⓗ
Popular local with bags of history. The front door opens into a Victorian tiled passageway. Two old shops now form small rooms suitable for families. The main bar has black and white timbered walls, plus some beams dating back to the 16th century. Note the Hunt Edmunds sign by the door. Q 🐎 ❀ ♣ P

### Crown & Anchor

233 Hylton Road
☎ (01905) 421481
12–3, 5–11; 12–11 Wed–Sat; 12–10.30 Sun
**Banks's Mild; Marston's Bitter, Pedigree, HBC** Ⓗ
Friendly pub popular with locals and students alike. The separate bar has a strong emphasis on games. The skittle alley doubles as a function room. Book Sun lunch.
❀ ◑ ⚅ ♣

### Dragon

51 The Tything
☎ (01905) 25845
11–11; 7–10.30 Sun, closed Sun lunch
**Marston's Bitter, HBC; Taylor Landlord; guest beers** Ⓗ
Locals' pub just outside the city centre: a one-roomed, one-bar *Guide* regular. Live music Sun eve; folk eve Wed. Snacks available. Guest beers include seasonal ales from Wood and Wye Valley.
❀ ⚅ ▲ ⚞ (Foregate St) ⌂

## Glover's Needle

Windermere Drive, Warndon
☎ (01905) 452191
11–11; 12–4.30, 7–10.30 Sun
**Draught Bass; Boddingtons Bitter; Whitbread Fuggles IPA; guest beers** Ⓗ
Large estate pub catering for all ages, with separate rooms for pool and (full-size) snooker. The main bar has a large screen TV. The skittle alley can be used for functions. Live music Tue; quiz Sun. ❀ ⚅ ♣ P

## Plumber's Arms

76 Wylds Lane (300 yds from London Rd) ☎ (01905) 767592
11.30 (12 Mon)–2.30, 4.30–11; 11–11 Fri & Sat; 12–10.30 Sun
**Draught Bass; M&B Brew XI; guest beers** Ⓗ
Welcoming, Victorian terraced local with a traditional bar, not far from the city centre. Up to three guest beers are usually available. Food is served in a quiet area; no meals Mon, or Sun eve. No-smoking area mealtimes. Quiz Wed.
❀ ◑ ▶ ⚞ (Shrub Hill) ♣ ✂

## Swan Inn

81 St John's
☎ (01905) 421241
11–2.30 (3.30 Sat), 6.30–11; 12–3, 7–10.30 Sun
**Ind Coope Burton Ale; Tetley Bitter; guest beer** Ⓗ
Free house with a listed frontage and a wonderful window. Inside, other interesting features include an unusual skylight. No set menu but food is available on request. ❀ 🛏 ◑ ▶ ♣ ⌂ P

## Tap & Spile

35 St Nicholas Street
☎ (01905) 22344
12–3, 6.30–11; 12–11 Sat; 12–3, 7–10.30 Sun
**Beer range varies** Ⓗ
Busy, city-centre pub catering for all ages. No food Mon; quiz Tue. Dress restrictions Fri and Sat eves.
🛏 ◑ ⚞ (Foregate St) ♣ ⌂

## Virgin Tavern

Tolladine Road
☎ (01905) 23988
11–3, 5.30–11; 11–11 Sat; 12–4, 7–10.30 Sun
**Marston's Bitter, Pedigree, HBC** Ⓗ
Large, single-room pub popular with a wide range of people. The food menu is in two parts – standard Marston's fare and the pub's own daily specials, all home-cooked (no meals Sun eve). The award-winning garden contains play equipment; barbecues in summer. ❀ ◑ ▶ ♣ P

**Try also: Swan With Two Nicks**, New St (Free)

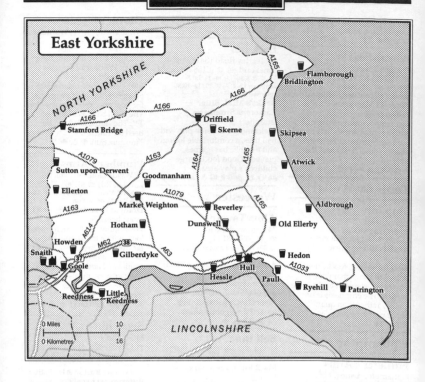

## East Yorkshire

---

### Aldbrough

#### Double Dutch
Cliff Top (1 mile from village on the coast)
☎ (01964) 527786
7–11; 12–3, 7–11 Fri, Sat & summer; 12–3, 7–10.30 Sun
**Old Mill Bitter; John Smith's Bitter; Whitbread Trophy; guest beer (summer)** Ⓗ
Beamed ceilings and York stone give this sea-lashed pub a traditional feel. The roaring log fire divides the bar and intimate restaurant. Next to caravan parks.
🚶 🏠 ◖ ▶ ▲ P

---

### Atwick

#### Black Horse
☎ (01964) 532691
11–4, 7–11; 11–11 Sat; 12–10.30 Sun
**John Smith's Bitter; guest beers** Ⓗ
Super village local dating from c1750, overlooking the green. Three, comfortable drinking areas. Food is served in both restaurant and bar areas. Guest ales change almost daily.
🏠 ◖ ▶ ♿ P

---

### Beverley

#### Queen's Head
Wednesday Market
☎ (01482) 867363
11–11; 12–10.30 Sun
**Vaux Mild, Waggle Dance; Ward's Thorne BB; guest beer** Ⓗ
Pub with a brewers' Tudor exterior overlooking the smaller market place. Tastefully refurbished in 1996, it was opened out into a modern extension which forms a lounge and games area. Eve meals end at 8. ◖ ▶ ≉

#### Rose & Crown
North Bar Without
☎ (01482) 862532
11–3, 5–11; 12–10.30 Sun
**Vaux Double Maxim, Waggle Dance; Ward's Thorne BB, Best Bitter; guest beer** Ⓗ
Substantial brewers' Tudor pub next to the historic North Bar, Westwood and racecourse. Popular for home-made food in the comfortable lounge and smoke room.
Q 🏠 ◖ ▶ 🍺 ♣ P

#### Royal Standard Inn
30 North Bar Within
☎ (01482) 882434
12–4, 6.30–11; 12–6.30, 7–10.30 Sun
**Vaux Mild, Double Maxim; Ward's Thorne BB** Ⓗ
Two-roomed town local with original 1920s bentwood seating in the front bar, which features an etched Darley's window. Well-furnished lounge at the rear. 🏠 🍺

#### Tap & Spile (Sun Inn)
1 Flemingate ☎ (01482) 881547
12–11; 11–11 Sat; 12–10.30 Sun
**Beer range varies** Ⓗ
Sympathetic restoration of a medieval timber-framed building: Beverley's oldest pub, set opposite the Minster. The eight guest beers have transformed the local drinking scene. 🏠 ◖ ♣ ⌂ ⌦

#### White Horse Inn (Nellie's) ☆
22 Hengate ☎ (01482) 861973
11–11; 12–10.30 Sun
**Samuel Smith OBB** Ⓗ
One of Beverley's landmarks, this historic inn offers a multi-roomed interior with gas lighting, stone-flagged floors, coal fires and home cooking. Folk, jazz and blues eves upstairs. No food Mon.
🚶 Q 🏠 ◖ 🍺 ♣ P ⌦

---

> 🏭 **INDEPENDENT BREWERIES**
>
> **Hull:** Hull
>
> **Old Mill:** Snaith

### Woolpack Inn
37 Westwood Road (near Westwood Hospital)
☎ (01482) 867095
12–3 (not Mon), 5 (7 Mon)–11; 12–11 Fri & Sat; 12–10.30 Sun
**Burtonwood Bitter, Top Hat, Buccaneer, seasonal beers** Ⓗ
Superbly located pub in a residential street near the Westwood, built c1830 from a pair of cottages – read its history in the no-smoking snug. Eve meals 5–7 Tue–Thu.
❀ ◖ ▶ ⊬

## Bridlington

### Bull & Sun
11 Baylegate ☎ (01262) 676105
11–11; 12–3, 7–10.30 Sun
**Vaux Mild, Samson, Waggle Dance; Ward's Thorne BB; guest beers**
Former millinery shop near the historic Baylegate and priory in the old town; recently refurbished from two rooms into one. Eve meals Easter–Christmas. ◖ ▶

### New Crown
158 Quay Road
☎ (01262) 604370
11–11; 12–10.30 Sun
**Vaux Waggle Dance; Ward's Thorne BB** Ⓗ
Substantial Victorian pub between the old town and the harbour. The large bar/games room, with its wooden floor, is popular with all ages. Spacious, comfortable lounge.
❀ ⇔ ≈ ♣

### Old Ship Inn
90 St John Street
☎ (01262) 670466
11–11; 12–10.30 Sun
**Vaux Samson, Waggle Dance; Ward's Thorne BB; guest beers** Ⓗ
Thriving local by the old town with a traditional atmosphere, comfortable separate drinking areas and a pool table in the large bar. Outdoor play area for children. Sun lunches in summer only. Q ❀ ◖ ♣

### Pack Horse Inn
7 Market Place
☎ (01262) 675701
11–3 (may extend in summer), 7–11; 12–3, 7–10.30 Sun
**Burtonwood Bitter, Top Hat** Ⓗ
Listed building thought to be 300 years old. The upper windows give an impression of three storeys but the pub is in fact only two (a relic from Day Light Tax days). Inside there is an open-plan lounge and a pool room. ⇔ ❀ ◖ ♣

### Seabirds
6 Fortyfoot ☎ (01262) 674174
11–11; 12–10.30 Sun
**Camerons Bitter, Strongarm; guest beers** Ⓗ

Large, attractively extended pub: a comfortable bar with a pool table and a well-furnished lounge displaying sailing items. Children's play area outside. ❀ ◖ ▶ ♣ P ⊟

## Driffield

### Bell Hotel
Market Place ☎ (01377) 256661
10–2.30, 6–11; 10–11 Thu; 12–3, 7–10.30 Sun
**Cropton Two Pints** or **Hambleton Stallion** or **Malton Double Chance; Younger Scotch** Ⓗ
Historic coaching inn with a wood-panelled bar serving up to four beers and 250 whiskies. Leather seating, substantial fireplaces and antiques lend a quality feel. Separate hotel and restaurant. Q ❀ ⇔ ◖ ▶ ⓗ P

### Mariner's Arms
47 Eastgate (near cattle market)
☎ (01377) 253708
3 (11.45 Sat)–11; 12–10.30 Sun
**Burtonwood Mild, Bitter, seasonal beers** Ⓗ
Traditional market town, street-corner local with two drinking areas.
❀ ⊞ ≈ ♣ P

## Dunswell

### Ship Inn
Beverley Road (A1174)
☎ (01482) 859160
11–11; 12–10.30 Sun
**Hull Mild; Ind Coope Burton Ale; Tetley Bitter** Ⓗ
Welcoming pub where two log fires warm the interior, part of which is a restaurant area with church pew seating. Tasty, home-cooked food served 11–7 (3 Sun). ⇔ ◖ ▶ ♣ P

## Ellerton

### Boot & Shoe
Main Street ☎ (01757) 288346
12–3, 6–11; 12–3, 7–10.30 Sun
**Old Mill Bitter; John Smith's Bitter** Ⓗ
Dating back 400 years, this popular, cosy village local has three separate drinking areas and authentic low beams. A gem. ⇔ Q ❀ ◖ ▶ ♣ P

## Flamborough

### Rose & Crown
High Street ☎ (01262) 850455
11–3, 7–11; 12–3, 7–10.30 Sun
**Camerons Bitter; Tetley Bitter** Ⓗ
Pub frequented by local fishermen. The L-shaped room has a beamed ceiling and walls decorated with local scenes. The pool table is nicely tucked away. Meals in summer only.
◖ ▲ ♣ P

## Gilberdyke

### Cross Keys Inn
Main Road ☎ (01430) 440310
12–11; 12–10.30 Sun
**Boddingtons Bitter; John Smith's Bitter; Tetley Bitter; guest beers** Ⓗ
Traditional village pub with a strong local following of all ages who appreciate the emphasis on traditional beer and games. Separate pool room. Three rotating guest beers. ⇔ ❀ ⓗ ≈ ♣ P

## Goodmanham

### Goodmanham Arms
Main Street ☎ (01430) 873849
7 (12 Sat)–11; 12–3, 7–10.30 Sun
**Black Sheep Best Bitter; Theakston Best Bitter; guest beer** Ⓗ
Homely rural pub with no music or machines, just a pleasant welcome; situated on the Wolds Way footpath and now converted into two rooms both with open fires. The gents' is in the car park.
⇔ Q ❀ ⇔ ⊞ ▲ ♣ P

## Goole

### Macintosh Arms
11 Aire Street
☎ (01405) 763850
11–11; 12–10.30 Sun
**John Smith's Bitter; Tetley Dark Mild, Bitter; guest beer** Ⓗ
Former courthouse, built around 1830, often overlooked by ships in the nearby docks. Popular with locals and foreign seamen. Bikers very welcome. ❀ ⊞ ≈ ♣

### Old George
Market Square
☎ (01405) 763147
11–3, 7–11; 12–3, 7–10.30 Sun
**Draught Bass; John Smith's Bitter; Stones Bitter; Worthington Bitter** Ⓗ
Oddly shaped old building with one room divided into three distinct sections. Good value lunches (not Sun) draw shoppers; eves see younger drinkers. ❀ ◖ ≈ P

Try also: North Eastern, Boothferry Rd (Ward's)

## Hedon

### Shakespeare Inn
9 Baxtergate ☎ (01482) 898371
11–11; 12–10.30 Sun
**Vaux Mild, Samson; Ward's Thorne BB, Best Bitter; guest beer** Ⓗ
The town's own village pub, popular with locals and visitors alike and noted for its food, range of whiskies,

brewery memorabilia and interesting photos of old Hedon. Eve meals end at 7.30; no eve meals Sat/Sun.
🏠 🏵 ◑ ♣ P

# Hessle

## Darleys

Boothferry Road (A1105, near Humber Bridge)
☎ (01482) 643121
11–3, 5.30–11; 11–11 Sat; 12–10.30 Sun
**Vaux Mild, Samson; Ward's Thorne BB, Best Bitter** H
Substantial brewers' Tudor roadhouse on the old western approach to Hull. Built in 1939, it was named after the brewery closed in 1986 and retains its public bar, comfortable lounge, carvery restaurant and family room and has a new function suite. Q ⏁ 🏵 ◑ ⊞ ♣ P

# Hotham

## Hotham Arms

Main Street ☎ (01430) 422939
11–4, 6.30–11; 11–11 Fri; 12–4, 7–10.30 Sun

**Black Sheep Best Bitter; Boddingtons Mild, Bitter; John Smith's Bitter; Tetley Bitter** H
Small village pub dating from 1760, now extended to provide a restaurant in the conservatory at the rear. Separate bar and games room. On the Wolds Way footpath.
Q ◑ ▶ ♣ P

# Howden

## Barnes Wallis

Howden Station (B1228 N of Howden)
☎ (01430) 430639
7–11; 11–3, 7–11 Sat; 12–10.30 Sun
**Badger Dorset Best; Boddingtons Bitter; Flowers IPA; Fuller's London Pride; guest beers** H
Friendly pub, always offering two guest beers. Open-plan layout; welcoming atmosphere.
🏠 Q 🏵 ◑ ⇌ ♣ P

# Hull

## Anlaby Ale House

283–285 Anlaby Road (Coltman St jct)
☎ (01482) 328971
11–11; 12–10.30 Sun
**Banks's Bitter; Camerons Bitter, Strongarm; Marston's Pedigree; guest beers** H
Refurbished Camerons ale house with a large, but cosy, bare brick and wood tap room filled with a myriad of bric-a-brac; games room to the rear. A house beer, Kingston Mild Ale, is brewed by Banks's. Handy for Hull RL. ◑ ♣ 🍺

## Bay Horse

113 Wincolmlee (400 yds N of N Bridge on W bank of River Hull) ☎ (01482) 329227
11–11; 12–4.30, 7–10.30 Sun
**Bateman Mild, XB, XXXB, Victory; Marston's Pedigree** H
Bateman's only tied pub north of the Humber. The wood panelled walls in the bar display local rugby league memorabilia. The spectacular lofty stable bar has a real fire.
🏠 ◑ ▶ ⊞ ♿ ♣ P

## Duke of Wellington

104 Peel Street (N of Spring Bank, NW of centre)
☎ (01482) 329603
12–3, 6–11; 12–10.30 Sun
**Taylor Landlord; Tetley Bitter; guest beers** H
Backstreet, re-styled, Victorian corner pub popular with locals and students. Occasional beer festivals. Home-cooked food until 8pm.
🏵 ◑ ▶ ♿ ♣ P

## Gardeners Arms

35 Cottingham Road
☎ (01482) 342396
11–11; 12–10.30 Sun
**Marston's Pedigree; Tetley Mild, Bitter; guest beers** H
Tetley Festival Alehouse, close to the university. The front room is popular with locals and students, with its dark wood, bare brick walls and original matchboard ceiling. Mr Q's games room at the rear.
🏵 ◑ ▶ ♿ P

## King William

41 Market Place, Old Town
☎ (01482) 227013
11–11; 12–10.30 Sun
**Courage Directors; Cropton King Billy; Old Mill Mild; Marston's Pedigree; John Smith's Bitter** H
Large, recently-built pub on the site of the old King William hotel. It features a wood-panelled lounge and a local sporting heroes hall of fame. It can be busy at weekends. Eve food 5–7 Mon–Fri.
🏵 ◑ ▶ ♣

## Minerva

Nelson Street (near marina and Victoria Pier)
☎ (01482) 326909
11–11; 12–3, 7–10.30 (12–10.30 summer) Sun
**Tetley Bitter; guest beers** H
Friendly, multi-roomed, 19th-century pub overlooking the Humber. The walls are adorned with memorabilia of the old town and the rich maritime history of the area. Pilots Pride, brewed in the adjoining mini-brewery, is kept under mixed gas.
🏠 ⏁ ◑ ▶ ♣

## Mission

11–14 Posterngate (next to Princes Quay shopping centre)
☎ (01482) 221187
11–11; 12–10.30 Sun
**Old Mill Mild, Nellie Dene, Bitter, Old Curiosity, Bullion** H
Old Mill's first Hull pub is a converted seaman's mission. Very large, with a baronial feel, it includes a minstrel's gallery and a deconsecrated chapel. Very busy at weekends.
◑ ▶ ♿ (Paragon) ♣

## New Clarence

77 Charles Street
☎ (01482) 320327
11–11; 12–10.30 Sun
**Marston's Pedigree; Tetley Mild, Bitter; guest beers** H
Tetley Festival Alehouse off Kingston Square, near the New Theatre. Open-plan, it is dimly lit, with wooden partitions. Four guest beers; Belgian bottled beers. Eve meals till 7.30 (not Sun).
◑ ▶ ⇌ (Paragon) ♣ 🍺

## Olde Black Boy

150 High Street, Old Town
☎ (01482) 326516
12–3, 7–11; 12–11 Fri; 12–3, 7–10.30 Sun
**Beer range varies** H
On the medieval High Street; the Black Boy's name echoes the nearby Wilberforce Slavery Museum. Sympathetically refurbished as an unbadged Tap & Spile, it retains a separate bar, a wood-panelled 'Tudor' room, an upstairs bar and a dining room. The interior merits protection.
🏠 Q ◑ ⊞ ♣ 🍺

## Red Lion

Clarence Street (400 yds E of Drypool Bridge)
☎ (01482) 324773
12–11; 12–5, 7–11 Sat; 12–10.30 Sun
**Hull Mild, Ellwood's Best Bitter, Bitter, Amber Ale, Governor; guest beers** H
Pub built in 1939 for Moors & Robsons; the first tied house for the present Hull Brewery owner. An island unto itself, it is bordered by four streets and still retains two separate rooms. Concerts in the wood panelled lounge at weekends. A Bateman beer is one of the two guests. 🏵 ⊞

## St John's Hotel

10 Queens Road
☎ (01482) 343669
12–11; 12–10.30 Sun
**Mansfield Riding Mild, Riding Bitter, Old Baily, seasonal beers** H
Victorian pub which epitomises what a street-corner local is all about. Well loved by regulars and friendly to visitors, 'Johnnies' is an

unpretentious multi-roomer.
Q ⟱ ⊛ ⚒ ♣ P

## Spring Bank Tavern

29 Spring Bank
☎ (01482) 581879
11–11; 12–3, 7–10.30 Sun
**Mansfield Riding Mild, Riding Bitter, Bitter, Old Baily, seasonal beers; guest beers** Ⓗ
Mansfield's first cask ale house, sympathetically refurbished as a street-corner local on the edge of the city centre. Three guest beers.
◖ ⇌ (Paragon)

## Tap & Spile (Eagle)

169–171 Spring Bank (500 yds W of centre) ☎ (01482) 323518
12–11; 12–10.30 Sun
**Beer range varies** Ⓗ
1994 conversion and extension of a street-corner local into a large ale house serving 12 guest beers and two ciders. It can be very busy but the service is invariably good. Eve meals finish at 7 (no eve meals Sun). ◖ ▶ ⚒ ♣ ⌂ P ✂

## Whalebone Inn

165 Wincolmlee
☎ (01482) 327980
12–4, 7–11; 12–11 Wed–Sat; 12–4, 7–10.30 Sun
**Tetley Mild, Bitter** Ⓗ
Popular, no-frills drinkers' local on the west side of the River Hull, between Scott St and Sculcoates Bridges. The old industrial area nearby used to include whale processing plants, which gave this pub its name. ♣

## Little Reedness

## Ferry House Inn

Main Street ☎ (01405) 704330
12–2 (not Mon–Wed; may extend), 8–11; 12–4, 7.30–10.30 Sun
**Mansfield Riding Bitter, Bitter; guest beer** (occasional) Ⓗ
Spacious, 500-year-old village local overlooking the River Ouse, near Blacktoft Sands RSPB reserve. Huge log fire in winter. Eve meals Wed–Sat.
⚌ ⊛ ⇝ ◖ ▶ ♣ P

## Market Weighton

## Carpenters Arms

56 Southgate (A1034)
☎ (01430) 873446
11 (12 Sat)–11; 12–3, 7–10.30 Sun
**Vaux Samson; Ward's Thorne BB; guest beer** Ⓗ
Extensive modernisation has left one large room at this listed building and it now caters for a younger clientele. Strong darts following. ♣ P

## Half Moon Inn

39 High Street
☎ (01430) 872247

11–11; 12–10.30 Sun
**Burtonwood Bitter, Buccaneer** Ⓗ
Small, friendly market town pub. A single room serves as a bar and lounge, one at either end. Strong pool following.
⊛ ◖ ▶ ♣ P

## Old Ellerby

## Blue Bell Inn

On old Hull–Hornsea road
☎ (01964) 562364
7–11 (11–3, 7–11 Wed–Fri in summer); 12 (11 summer)–5, 7–11 Sat; 12–5, 7–10.30 Sun
**Ind Coope Burton Ale; Tetley Mild, Bitter; guest beers** Ⓗ
Cosy village local with plenty of character. Alcoves for quiet drinking; two superb real fires in winter; family play area in summer. Bowling green planned. ⚌ ⊛ ⚒ ▲ P

## Patrington

## Hildyard Arms

Market Place
☎ (01964) 630234
11–11; 12–10.30 Sun
**Tetley Mild, Bitter; guest beers** Ⓗ
Former Georgian coaching inn, which also served as a corn exchange for local farmers; now an extended family pub with four rooms. Two rotating guest beers. Eve meals end at 8.30. ⚌ ⟱ ⊛ ◖ ▶ ♣ P

## Paull

## Humber Tavern

Main Street
☎ (01482) 899347
12–3, 5–11; 12–11 Sat & summer; 12–10.30 Sun
**Tetley Bitter; guest beer** Ⓗ
Victorian, multi-roomed local on the banks of the Humber estuary, a Victorian reconstruction of an earlier building. Excellent views of the Humber Bridge and river traffic. Eve meals 5–8, Mon–Fri.
⚌ ⟱ ⊛ ◖ ▶ ♣

## Royal Oak

Main Street
☎ (01482) 897678
12–3, 7–11 (varies summer); 12–4, 7–10.30 Sun
**Ward's Thorne BB; guest beer** (summer) Ⓗ
Well-run, multi-roomed local on the banks of the Humber estuary with views of the bridge and Lincolnshire from the patio and family room.
⚌ ⟱ ⊛ ⇝ ◖ ▶ ♣ P

## Reedness

## Half Moon Inn

Main Street
☎ (01405) 704484
12–3 (not winter Mon–Fri), 7–11; 12–10.30 Sun

**Bentley's Yorkshire Bitter; Boddingtons Bitter; Chester's Mild; Marston's Pedigree; guest beer** Ⓗ
Traditional, very clean and polished local with a caravan and campsite behind and Blacktoft Sands RSPB reserve nearby. Good food.
⚌ ⊛ ◖ ▶ ▲ ♣ P ⛫

## Ryehill

## Crooked Billet

Pitt Lane (400 yds from A1033)
☎ (01964) 622303
12–2 (not Wed), 5–11; 12–4, 7–10.30 Sun
**Burtonwood Mild, Bitter** Ⓗ
Busy village pub with an attractive beamed ceiling. The lounge features a stone-floored lower level. Interesting display of old cameras. No meals Wed.
⚌ ⊛ ◖ ▶ ♣ P

## Skerne

## Eagle Inn ☆

Wansford Road
☎ (01377) 252178
7–11; 12–2, 7–11 Sat; 12–3, 7–10.30 Sun
**Camerons Bitter** Ⓗ
Classic, unspoilt village local with a basic bar and a front parlour. Drinks are served to your table from a small cellar off the entrance corridor. Beer is dispensed from a Victorian cash register beer engine. Outside toilets.
⚌ Q ⊛ ⊟ ♣ P

## Skipsea

## Board Inn

Back Street
☎ (01262) 468342
7 (11 summer)–11; 11–4, 7–11 (11 summer) Sat; 12–4, 7–10.30 (12–10.30 summer) Sun
**Burtonwood Bitter, Forshaw's, seasonal beers** Ⓗ
Nicely renovated building mainly catering for holidaymakers from nearby camps. Two separate bars plus a restaurant.
⚌ ⊛ ◖ ▶ ⊟ ▲ P ✂

## Snaith

## Brewers Arms

10 Pontefract Road (A645, 200 yds from centre)
☎ (01405) 862404
11–3, 6–11; 12–4, 7–10.30 Sun
**Old Mill Mild, Bitter, Old Curiosity, Blackjack, Bullion, seasonal beers** Ⓗ
Grade II listed building converted to a pub in 1988. The single large room has alcoves and original beams. Friendly atmosphere; good selection of food. ⊛ ⇝ ◖ ▶ ⇌ (limited service) P

## Stamford Bridge

### Swordsman
Front Street (A166)
☎ (01759) 371307
12–11; 12–3, 7–10.30 Sun
**Samuel Smith OBB** H
Friendly local, busy in summer with caravanners and fishermen. The large bar and lounge feature stuffed animals.
🐎 ❀ ◐ ▲ P

## Sutton upon Derwent

### St Vincent Arms
Main Street ☎ (01904) 608349
11.30–3, 6–11; 12–3, 7–10.30 Sun
**Adnams Extra; Fuller's Chiswick, London Pride, ESB; Taylor Landlord; Wells Bombardier; guest beers** H
Welcoming, multi-roomed pub enjoying an excellent reputation for food. The wide selection of beers and the hospitality make it a must, especially in winter (open fire).
♛ Q ❀ ◐◑ P ⊓

## North Yorkshire

## Acklam

### Coronation at Acklam
Acklam Road (A1032/A1130 jct) ☎ (01642) 817599
11–11.30; 11–11 Sat; 12–10.30 Sun
**Banks's Bitter; Camerons Strongarm** H
Inter-war, brick-built pub, recently refurbished as a Wolverhampton & Dudley house with a bar, lounge and function room. Q ◐ ⊞ ♣ P ⊓

## Aldborough

### Ship Inn
Low Road ☎ (01423) 322749
11–3, 5.30–11; 12–3, 7–10.30 Sun
**John Smith's Bitter; Tetley Bitter; Theakston Best Bitter** H
Busy, 14th-century village inn in an historic setting. Well-known for good food.
♛ ❀ 🛏 ◐◑ ♣ P ⊓

## Appletreewick

### New Inn
☎ (01756) 720252
12–3 (not Mon), 7–11; 12–3, 7–10.30 Sun
**Daleside Nightjar; John Smith's Bitter; guest beer** H
Friendly inn close to the Dales Way, with spectacular views of river and moorland: one main, L-shaped room with a separate room across the hall. Large range of foreign bottled beers.
♛ Q 🐎 ❀ 🛏 ◐ ▲ ♣ ⌓ P

## Barlby

### Bay Horse
York Road (A19)
☎ (01757) 703878
3.30 (11Sat)–11; 12–3, 7–10.30 Sun
**Morland Old Speckled Hen; John Smith's Bitter; Wilson's Mild** H
Small, friendly village pub with knocked through bars but still separate rooms. Keen darts team; various entertainments.
Q ❀ ♣ P

## Barton

### King William IV
1 Silver Street
☎ (01325) 377256
12–3 (not Mon or Tue; may extend; 11.30–4 Sat), 6.30 (5 Thu & Fri)–11; 12–3, 7–10.30 Sun
**John Smith's Bitter, Magnet** H
Recently enlarged roadside local with a number of separate spaces clustered around a single serving area. Excellent garden with play equipment. Thai meals are a speciality. Good wheelchair access but no adapted toilet. No meals Mon/Tue. ♛ ❀ ◐◑ ♿ ♣ P ⊓

## Beck Hole

### Birch Hall Inn ☆
☎ (01947) 896245
11–3, 7.30–11 (11–11 summer; closed Mon eve in winter); 12–3, 7.30–10.30 (12–10.30 summer) Sun
**Black Sheep Best Bitter; Theakston Best Bitter, XB; guest beer** H
Tiny, two-room time warp pub in a charming village in TV's *Heartbeat* country. The pub also contains a small shop and offers teas. Popular with walkers and near Goathland and the N York Moors Railway. Cleveland CAMRA *Pub of the Year* 1994. Not to be missed. ♛ Q ❀ ⊞ ♣

## Bishop Monkton

### Lamb & Flag
Boroughbridge Road
☎ (01765) 677322
12–3, 5.30–11; 12–3, 7–10.30 Sun
**Black Sheep Best Bitter; Tetley Bitter; Theakston Best Bitter** H
Friendly, welcoming, country inn in an attractive village. Good local trade.
♛ Q ❀ ◐◑ ♣ P

## Bishopthorpe

### Ebor Inn
Main Street ☎ (01904) 706190
11–11; 12–10.30 Sun
**Samuel Smith OBB** H
Pub where a front lounge bar leads to a back bar used for meals. Lots of brass, plates and winners' certificates from *York in Bloom* competitions. Separate public bar and games room.
❀ ◐◑ ⊞ ▲ P ⚡

## Boroughbridge

### Black Bull
6 St James Square
☎ (01423) 322413
11–11; 12–10.30 Sun
**Black Sheep Best Bitter; Old Mill Bitter; John Smith's Bitter** H
Fine old inn with a welcoming snug bar and lounge, and a well-known restaurant at the rear. ♛ 🐎 🛏 ◐◑ ⊞

### Three Horse Shoes ☆
Bridge Street ☎ (01423) 322314
11–3, 5–11; 12–10.30 Sun
**Theakston Best Bitter** H**; Vaux Samson** E
Welcoming, small town inn with unchanged 1930s decor; in the same family since 1900.
♛ Q 🐎 🛏 ◐◑ ⊞ ♿ ♣ P

## Bradley

### Slaters Arms
Crag Lane (back road to Farnhill) ☎ (01535) 632179
11–3, 6–11; 12–3, 7–10.30 Sun
**Commercial Alesman; John Smith's Bitter; Webster's Green Label** H
Olde-worlde, small, pleasant local, close to a canal and good walking areas. Food is excellent (book Sun lunch) and reasonably priced. The beer range may change when the new Scottish Courage list is available, although the Alesman is a firm favourite.
♛ Q ❀ ◐◑ ♣ P

## Brearton

### Malt Shovel
Off B6165 ☎ (01423) 862929
12–3, 6.30–11; closed Mon; 12–3, 7–10.30 Sun
**Daleside Nightjar; Old Mill Bitter; Theakston Best Bitter; guest beer** H
Welcoming, unspoilt 16th-century village pub with exposed beams and stonework. Good, home-cooked food (not served Sun eve). Cider in summer.
♛ Q 🐎 ❀ ◐◑ ♣ ⌓ P

## Brompton (Northallerton)

### Three Horseshoes
Station Road ☎ (01609) 773591
12–3 (4 Sat), 6 (6.30 Sat)–11; 12–4, 7–10.30 Sun
**Camerons Strongarm; guest beers** H
Two-roomed village local offering several beer festivals

each year. Function room available. A Theakston beer is also sold. 🏾 Q 🍴 ⊟ ♣ ⊟

**Try also: Crown**, Station Rd (Scottish Courage)

## Brompton by Sawdon

### Cayley Arms
On A170
☎ (01723) 859372
11.30–2.30 (not Mon), 4.30–11; 12–3, 7–10.30 Sun
**Tetley Bitter; Theakston Best Bitter, XB; guest beer** Ⓗ
Prominent roadside pub named after a local aviation pioneer. Excellent food; extensive range of malt whiskies. Children's play area.
🏾 Q ⚲ ☀ 🍴 ♿ ⏰ ♣ ➠ P ⅙

## Brotton

### Malt & Hop
High Street
☎ (01287) 678300
12–4, 7–11; 12–11 Sat; 12–10.30 Sun
**Camerons Bitter, Strongarm; Tetley Mild, Bitter; guest beer** Ⓗ
Small terraced pub in a former ironstone mining village with a strong local patronage. Quiet rear snug; separate pool room. Children allowed in the snug.
Q 🍴 ♣

**Try also: Green Tree**, High St (Pubmaster)

## Burton Salmon

### Plough
Main Street
☎ (01977) 672422
12–3 (not winter Mon–Thu), 6–11; 12–3, 7–10.30 Sun
**Boddingtons Bitter; John Smith's Bitter; guest beers** Ⓗ
Friendly village pub with a spacious bar and a large garden: a free house with an excellent guest beer policy. The separate dining room serves super home-made food.
🏾 Q ☀ 🍴 ♿ ♣ P

## Carlton in Cleveland

### Blackwell Ox
Off A172
☎ (01642) 712287
11.30–3, 5.30 (6.30 winter)–11 (11–11 summer Sat); 12–10.30 Sun
**John Smith's Bitter, Magnet; guest beers** Ⓗ
The only pub in the village: a tastefully refurbished, central bar surrounded by seating areas at different levels. Thai cooking is a speciality. Popular with walkers and campers.
🏾 Q ⚲ ☀ 🍴 ⏰ ♣ P ⅙

## Cawood

### Ferry
King Street (upstream of swing bridge)
☎ (01757) 268515
12–4, 6.30–11 (may be 11–11 summer Sat); 12–3, 7–10.30 Sun
**Adnams Bitter, Broadside; Mansfield Riding Mild, Riding Bitter, Old Baily; Morland Old Speckled Hen; guest beers** Ⓗ
Quiet pub on the west bank of the River Ouse with historic connections with Cardinal Wolsey, who lived at Cawood Castle. Low, timbered ceilings and a wood-burning stove help create a friendly atmosphere.
🏾 Q ⚲ ☀ 🍴 ⏰ ♿ ⏰ P ⅙

## Chapel Haddlesey

### Jug
Main Street
☎ (01757) 270307
12–3, 7–11; 11–11 Sat; 12–10.30 Sun
**Marston's Bitter, Pedigree; John Smith's Bitter; guest beers** Ⓗ
250-year-old, small village pub, once also a blacksmith's shop, on the north bank of the River Aire. Welcoming atmosphere; friendly ghost; renowned Desperate Dan Cow Pies. Note the large collection of jugs.
🏾 Q ☀ 🍴 ⏰ ♿ ⏰ ♣ P

## Chapel-le-Dale

### Hill Inn
On B6255
☎ (0152 42) 41256
12–3, 6.30–11; 11.30–11 Sat; 12–10.30 Sun
**Black Sheep Best Bitter; Dent Bitter; Tetley Bitter; Theakston Best Bitter, XB, Old Peculier; guest beers** Ⓗ
Well-known, isolated pub on the Three Peaks Walk, with bare floorboards and exposed stonework. Pool room and food bar (children welcome). Music Sat night; folk Sun lunch. The house brew, Black Shiver, is from Hesket Newmarket brewery.
🏾 ☀ 🍴 ⏰ ♣ P

## Clapham

### New Inn
☎ (0152 42) 51203
11.30–3, 7–11; 11.30–11 Sat; 12–10.30 Sun
**Courage Directors; Dent Bitter; Tetley Bitter; Theakston Best Bitter; guest beers** Ⓗ
Large coaching inn, dated 1776: two lounge bars with oak panelling (1990 vintage) and cycling and caving pictures. Separate restaurant (no-smoking; children welcome).
🏾 ☀ 🍴 ⏰ ♣ P

## Cloughton

### Blacksmith's Arms
High Street
☎ (01723) 870244
11–2.30, 6 (6.30 winter)–11; 12–3, 6–10.30 Sun
**Tetley Bitter; Worthington Bitter** Ⓗ
Classic, two-roomed village pub with a cosy, subdued lounge at the front and a bright, lively bar, popular with the locals, at the back.
🏾 Q 🍴 ⏰ ♿ ♣ P

## Cray

### White Lion Inn
☎ (01756) 760262
11–2.30, 6–11 (11–11 summer); 12–3, 6–10.30 (12–10.30 summer) Sun
**Moorhouse's Premier; Pendle Witches Brew; Tetley Bitter; guest beer** Ⓗ
Traditional, cosy dales inn, nestling beneath Buckden Pike: the highest inn in Wharfedale, with an original beamed ceiling and a stone-flagged floor. The barn has been converted into excellent accommodation. Ring the Bull played.
🏾 Q ⚲ ☀ 🍴 ⏰ ♿ ♣ P ⅙

## Cridling Stubbs

### Ancient Shepherd
Wrights Lane (2 miles from A19 at Whitley)
☎ (01977) 673316
12–3 (not Sat), 7–11; 12–3, 7–10.30 Sun
**Boddingtons Bitter; guest beer** Ⓗ
Welcoming pub with a Victorian-style interior. Excellent food in the bar or separate restaurant.
☀ 🍴 ♿ ♣ P

## Cropton

### New Inn
☎ (01751) 417330
11.30–3, 6.30–11; 11–11 Sat; 12–10.30 Sun
**Cropton King Billy, Two Pints, Scoresby Stout, Backwoods Bitter, Special; Tetley Bitter** Ⓗ
Popular free house at the top of a steep hill, serving beers from its own brewery – now with a visitor centre. Nearby campsites make this an ideal place for a short break. 🏾 Q ⚲ ☀ 🍴 ⏰ ♿ ♣ P ⅙⊟

## Cross Hills

### Old White Bear
6 Keighley Road
☎ (01535) 632115
11.30–3, 5–11; 11.30–11 Fri & Sat; 12–10.30 Sun

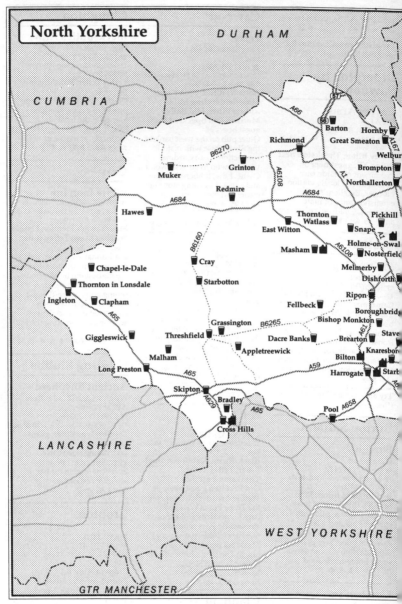

## North Yorkshire

DURHAM

CUMBRIA

Barton
Hornby
Richmond
Great Smeaton
Welbur
Brompton
Grinton
Northallerton
Muker
Redmire
Pickhill
Hawes
Thornton Watlass
Snape
East Witton
Holme-on-Swal
Masham
Nosterfiel
Chapel-le-Dale
Cray
Melmerby
Dishforth
Starbotton
Thornton in Lonsdale
Ripon
Clapham
Fellbeck
Ingleton
Boroughbrid
Grassington
Bishop Monkton
Giggleswick
Threshfield
Dacre Banks
Stave
Appletreewick
Brearton
Malham
Knaresbor
Bilton
Long Preston
Starb
Harrogate
Skipton
Bradley
Pool
Cross Hills

LANCASHIRE

WEST YORKSHIRE

GTR MANCHESTER

## INDEPENDENT BREWERIES

**Black Sheep:** Masham

**Cropton:** Cropton

**Daleside:** Starbeck

**Easingwold:** Easingwold

**Franklin's:** Bilton

**Hambleton:** Holme-on-Swale

**Malton:** Malton

**Marston Moor:** Kirk Hammerton

**North Yorkshire:** Middlesborough

**Old Bear:** Cross Hills

**Rooster's:** Harrogate

**Rudgate:** Tockwith

**Selby:** Selby

**Samuel Smith:** Tadcaster

**Whitby's:** Whitby

**York:** York

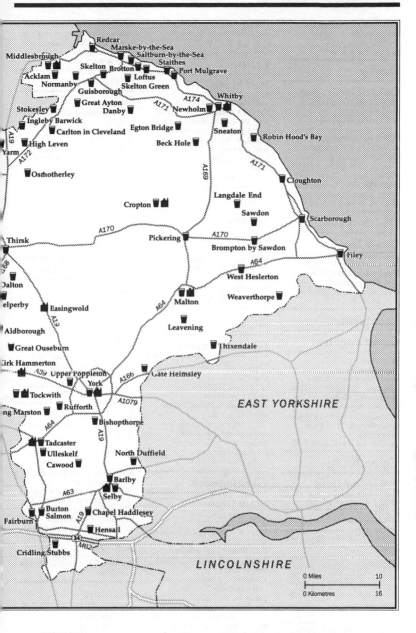

Map of North Yorkshire showing towns and villages including: Redcar, Marske-by-the-Sea, Saltburn-by-the-Sea, Staithes, Middlesbrough, Skelton, Brotton, Loftus, Port Mulgrave, Acklam, Normanby, Guisborough, Skelton Green, Great Ayton, Danby, Whitby, Newholm, Stokesley, Ingleby Barwick, Carlton in Cleveland, Egton Bridge, Sneaton, High Leven, Beck Hole, Robin Hood's Bay, Yarm, Osmotherley, Cloughton, Cropton, Langdale End, Sawdon, Scarborough, Thirsk, Pickering, Brompton by Sawdon, Filey, Dalton, West Heslerton, Elperby, Easingwold, Malton, Weaverthorpe, Aldborough, Leavening, Great Ouseburn, Thixendale, Kirk Hammerton, Upper Poppleton, Gate Helmsley, York, Tockwith, EAST YORKSHIRE, Long Marston, Rufforth, Bishopthorpe, Tadcaster, Ulleskelf, North Duffield, Cawood, Barlby, Selby, Burton Salmon, Chapel Haddlesey, Fairburn, Hensall, Cridling Stubbs, LINCOLNSHIRE.

Roads: A19, A174, A171, A169, A170, A64, A168, A1079, A166, A63, A61, M62, A172.

0 Miles 10
0 Kilometres 16

Boddingtons Bitter; Castle Eden Ale (occasional); Old Bear Bitter, seasonal beers Ⓗ
Large, old (1735) inn on the main road through the village, now extremely popular thanks to beer from the adjoining brewery and to the restaurant. Three distinct drinking areas, plus a games room at the rear. No meals Sun eve, or Mon.
♨ ⊛ ◑ ▶ ♣ P

## Dacre Banks

### Royal Oak
☎ (01423) 780200
12–3, 6–11; 12–3, 7–10.30 Sun
Black Sheep Best Bitter; Tetley Bitter; Theakston Black Bull Ⓗ
18th-century coaching inn with oak panelling, beams and pleasant views over Nidderdale. Interesting quotes on the walls. Dacre Gem house

beer is produced by Daleside Brewery.
♨ Q ⛄ ⊛ ◑ ▶ ♣ P

## Dalton

### Jolly Farmers of Olden Times
☎ (01845) 577359
8.30–11; 12–3, 8–10.30 Sun (closed most lunchtimes)
Courage Directors; John Smith's Bitter; guest beers Ⓗ

18th-century, modernised village pub with a good sociable atmosphere.
🏨 Q ✿ 🛏 ♿ ▲ ♣ P

## Danby

### Duke of Wellington

2 West Lane (at crossroads)
☎ (01287) 660351
11–3, 7–11 (11–11 summer); 12–3, 7–10.30 (12–10.30 summer) Sun
**Camerons Strongarm; Ruddles Best Bitter; John Smith's Magnet; guest beer** H
Coaching inn dating from 1732, popular with walkers, families and locals alike. Good for bar meals, it also has a restaurant.
🏨 Q ☕ ✿ 🛏 ◖ ▶ ▲ 🍴 ♣ P

## Dishforth

### Crown Inn

Main Street ☎ (01845) 577398
12–3, 6.30–11; 12–3, 7–10.30 Sun
**Hambleton Bitter; Robinson's Best Bitter; guest beers** H
Friendly, welcoming village pub. 🏨 ♣ P

## East Witton

### Coverbridge Inn

On Middleham–Masham road
☎ (01969) 623250
11–11; 12–10.30 Sun
**Black Sheep Best Bitter; Morland Old Speckled Hen; John Smith's Bitter; Theakston Best Bitter** H
Unspoiled gem of a local with a welcoming fire and good hospitality.
🏨 Q ✿ 🛏 ◖ ▶ ♿ ▲ ♣ P ⊟

## Egton Bridge

### Horseshoe Hotel

¼ mile from station, over river bridge ☎ (01947) 895245
11.30 (11 summer)–3.30, 6.30–11; 12–3.30, 7–10.30 Sun
**Tetley Bitter; Theakston Best Bitter, XB, Old Peculier; guest beer** H
Former 18th-century country house, set in beautiful grounds adjacent to the River Esk. The bar has wooden pews and a good fire. Bar and restaurant meals served.
🏨 Q ☕ ✿ 🛏 ◖ ▶ ♿ 🍴 ♣ P

Try also: **Postgate**, by station (Free)

## Fairburn

### Waggon & Horses

Great North Road (by A1)
☎ (01977) 675459
12–3, 5.30 (7 Tue)–11; 12–3, 7–10.30 Sun
**Samuel Smith OBB** H
Local where the long bar room has comfortable wall seating. Darts at one end; separate pool room. The friendly landlord

even opens on Christmas Day night. No meals Sun or Tue.
Q ✿ ◖ ▶ 🛏 ♣ P

## Fellbeck

### Half Moon

☎ (01423) 711560
12–3, 6.30–11; 12–3, 7–10.30 Sun
**Taylor Landlord; Theakston Best Bitter; Younger Scotch** H
Good roadside pub close to Brimham Rocks: a large sunny lounge and a small back bar. Self-catering cottage to let.
🏨 Q ☕ 🛏 ◖ ▶ 🛏 ▲ ♣ P

## Filey

### Imperial

20 Hope Street
☎ (01723) 512185
12–11; 12–10.30 Sun
**Boddingtons Bitter; John Smith's Bitter; Whitbread Trophy; guest beers** H
Busy, two-roomed pub popular with locals and tourists; about to be extended. Meals until 6pm in summer.
🛏 ◖ ♿ ▲ ♣

## Gate Helmsley

### Duke of York

Main Street
☎ (01759) 372429
11–11; 12–10.30 Sun
**John Smith's Bitter; Tetley Mild, Bitter** H
Pub with a small public bar and a larger restaurant/lounge: a popular eating establishment for both locals and visitors. ✿ ◖ ▶ 🛏 P

## Giggleswick

### Black Horse

Church Street
☎ (01729) 822506
12–3, 6.30–11 (may vary in summer); 12–3, 7–10.30 Sun
**Holt Bitter; Tetley Bitter; Theakston Best Bitter; guest beer** (summer) H
17th-century, village-centre pub adjoining the church. Smart stained-glass, mullioned windows and chamfered corners are features. The well-upholstered, one-room interior includes much woodwork. Attractive open fireplace.
🏨 Q ✿ 🛏 ◖ ▲ ♣ P

## Grassington

### Black Horse

Garrs Lane ☎ (01756) 752770
11–11; 12–10.30 Sun
**Black Sheep Best Bitter; Taylor Landlord; Tetley Mild, Bitter; guest beer** H
Popular, old coaching inn in the centre of the village,

serving excellent food in the separate dining room and bar meals in the open lounge, with its large fireplace.
🏨 Q ✿ 🛏 ◖ ▶ ♣

## Great Ayton

### Buck

1 West Terrace (A173 near bridge)
☎ (01642) 722242
11–11; 12–10.30 Sun
**Boddingtons Bitter; Flowers Original; Whitbread Trophy; guest beers** H
Riverside coaching inn dating from the 1700s, in Captain Cook's village. Beer festivals held; friendly atmosphere; strong local patronage. Good bar meals. Q ☕ ✿ ◖ ▶ ♣ P

Try also: **Royal Oak**, High Green (Scottish Courage)

## Great Ouseburn

### Crown

Main Street ☎ (01423) 330430
5 (11 Sat)–11; 12–10.30 Sun
**Black Sheep Best Bitter; John Smith's Bitter; Theakston Best Bitter; guest beers** H
Deceptively large village pub with a good local trade and many original features. Reputedly haunted! Note: closed weekday lunchtimes. Good food. 🏨 Q ☕ ✿ ◖ ▶ P

## Great Smeaton

### Bay Horse

On A167
☎ (01609) 881466
12–3, 6.30–11; 12–3, 7–10.30 Sun
**Ruddles County; John Smith's Bitter; guest beer** H
Small free house in the middle of a row of roadside cottages, with two linked rooms: a soft-furnished lounge and a bustling little bar with a pool room attached.
🏨 ✿ ◖ ▶ 🛏 ♣

Try also: **Chequers**, Dalton-on-Tees (Free)

## Grinton

### Bridge Inn

☎ (01748) 884224
11–3, 6–11 (11–11 Sat & summer); 12–3, 7–10.30 (12–10.30 summer) Sun
**Black Sheep Best Bitter, Special; John Smith's Bitter; Tetley Bitter; Theakston Old Peculier; guest beer** H
Hospitable pub with a warm and attractive bar, on the River Swale in a peaceful setting, with spectacular views of hills and moors. Excellent snacks, bar meals and restaurant fare. Very good accommodation. Families well catered for. 🏨 Q ☕ ✿ 🛏 ◖ ▶ 🛏 ♿ ▲ ♣ P ✂

## Guisborough

### Abbey Inn
37 Redcar Road (300 yds N of town cross)
☎ (01287) 632802
12–4, 7–11; 12–3, 7–10.30 Sun
**Samuel Smith OBB** H
Small, friendly end-of-terrace pub with two bars.
🏨 Q ᵬ ♣ 🗍

## Harrogate

### Prince of Wales
49 High Street, Starbeck
☎ (01423) 884235
11–11; 12–10.30 Sun
**John Smith's Bitter** H
Very strong community pub with a mixed clientele, supporting various sports teams. Large children's play area; function room.
ᵬ ❀ ◁ ◗ ᵬ ᵬ ♣ P

### Tap & Spile
Tower Street (200 yds from West Park Stray)
☎ (01423) 526785
11–11; 12–10.30 Sun
**Beer range varies** H
Comfortable, mixed-clientele pub with exposed brick and wood panelling. The three rooms inter-connect around a central bar. No eve meals Sun.
Q ◁ ◗ ⇌ ᗝ

## Hawes

### Board Hotel
Market Place (W end of village)
☎ (01969) 667223
11–4, 6.30–11; 12–3, 7–10.30 Sun
**Tetley Bitter; Webster's Yorkshire Bitter; guest beer** H
Market pub with a mid-19th-century stone frontage and a recently modernised, but unpretentious, interior.
🏨 ❀ 🏚 ◁ ◗ ▲ ♣ ᗝ

## Helperby

### Golden Lion
Main Street
☎ (01423) 360870
6 (12 Sat)–11; 12–3, 7–10.30 Sun
**Taylor Best Bitter; Tetley Bitter; guest beers** H
The home of the Helperby beer festival continues to attract punters from far and wide, with the best selection of guest beers for miles. 🏨 ❀ ◗ ♣

## Hensall

### Railway Tavern
Station Road
☎ (01977) 661478
7 (12 Sat)–11; 12–3, 7–10.30 Sun
**Tetley Bitter; guest beers** H

Typical village local with a lounge bar and separate games room. There has been a pub on this site for 200 years. 🏨 ❀ ⇌ (very limited service) ♣ P

## High Leven

### Fox Covert
Low Lane (A1044, between Yarm and Thornaby)
☎ (01642) 760033
11.30–3, 5–11; 12–3, 7–10.30 Sun
**Vaux Samson, Double Maxim** H
Formerly known as the Half Moon, this whitewashed pub dominates its rural crossroads setting and betrays its origins as a farmhouse. Q ❀ ◁ ◗ ♣ P

## Hornby

### Grange Arms
☎ (01609) 881249
12–3, 7–11; 12–3, 7–10.30 Sun; closed Mon, except bank hols
**John Smith's Magnet; Theakston XB, Old Peculier; guest beer** H
Pleasant whitewashed and red-pantiled village pub with a snug little bar and a dining room. 🏨 ❀ ◁ ◗ 🏚 ♣ P

## Ingleby Barwick

### Teal Arms
Lowfields Avenue
☎ (01642) 750064
11–11; 12–10.30 Sun
**Tetley Bitter** H
Family local, open-plan in layout, in the centre of the Ingleby Barwick development.
ᵬ ❀ ◁ ᵬ P

## Ingleton

### Bridge
New Road (A65)
☎ (0152 42) 41183
11–11 (11–3, 6–11 winter); 12–3, 7–10.30 Sun
**Black Sheep Best Bitter; John Smith's Bitter; Webster's Yorkshire Bitter; guest beer** H
Former main road hotel now converted to a spacious pub/ restaurant. Children's play area outside. Live bands and discos in summer.
🏨 ❀ 🏚 ◁ ◗ ᵬ ▲ ♣ P

### Wheatsheaf
High Street ☎ (0152 42) 41275
11 (12 winter)–11; 12–10.30 Sun
**Black Sheep Best Bitter, Special; Moorhouse's Premier; Tetley Bitter; Theakston Best Bitter** H
Pub with a single, long, cosy bar, handy for the finish of the Waterfalls Walk (walkers with muddy boots catered for). No-smoking restaurant. The beer range is smaller in winter.
❀ 🏚 ◁ ▲ ♣ P

## Knaresborough

### Blind Jacks
Market Place ☎ (01423) 869148
11.30 (5.30 Mon)–11; 12–10.30 Sun
**Beer range varies** H
CAMRA's *Best New Pub* 1992, this intimate gem exudes warmth and hospitality. A regular outlet for Village Brewer beers. Q ◁ ◗ ⇌ ᗝ

### Half Moon
Abbey Road ☎ (01423) 862663
5.30–11; 12–11 Sat; 12–10.30 Sun
**Mansfield Riding Bitter, Old Baily** H
Comfortable, one-room pub staging an annual (Boxing Day) Tug of War contest with the pub on the opposite side of the river. Note: closed weekday lunchtimes. ◁ ◗ ▲ ♣

### Marquis of Granby
York Place (A59, towards York) ☎ (01423) 862207
11–3, 6–11; 11–11 Wed & Sat; 12–10.30 Sun
**Samuel Smith OBB** H
Smartly furnished, twin-roomed Victorian-style pub, displaying prints of old Knaresborough in the lounge.
◁ 🏚 P

## Langdale End

### Moorcock Inn
OS938913 ☎ (01723) 882268
11–3, 6 (7 Mon & Tue)–11 (may vary; 11–11 summer); 12–3, 7–10.30 Sun
**Daleside Nightjar; Highwood Tom Wood; Malton Double Chance; guest beers** H
Sympathetically renovated, remote pub, often busy in summer with those who appreciate idyllic surroundings and in winter with those who enjoy a roaring log fire.
🏨 Q ❀ ◁ ◗ 🏚 ▲ ♣ P ⌫

## Leavening

### Jolly Farmer
Main Street ☎ (01653) 658276
12–3, 7–11; 12–3, 7–10.30 Sun
**Hambleton Stallion; John Smith's Bitter; Tetley Bitter; guest beers** H
Unspoilt, friendly, 17th-century village local serving guest beers (usually from local independent breweries) and excellent, reasonably priced food, including locally caught game dishes (separate dining room).
🏨 ❀ ◁ ◗ P

## Loftus

### Murphy's Bar
65 High Street
☎ (01287) 640612
12–11; 12–10.30 Sun

**John Smith's Magnet; guest beer** H
Small pub in a terrace on the High Street, once known as the Britannia but now named after the current owner and licensee. Strong local patronage.
❀ ♣ P 🏠

## Long Marston

### Sun Inn
York Road ☎ (01904) 738258
11–3, 5.30–11; 11–11 Sat; 12–10.30 Sun
**Samuel Smith OBB** H
Friendly village pub in Sam Smith's panelled fashion, which serves community needs as well as catering for visitors. Q ◑ ▮ ❧ ♣ P

## Long Preston

### Maypole Inn
☎ (01729) 840219
11–3, 6–11; 11–11 Sat; 12–10.30 Sun
**Boddingtons Bitter; Castle Eden Ale; Commercial Alesman; Taylor Landlord; guest beer** (occasional) H
Welcoming pub facing the village green and maypole: two comfortable rooms, each with an open fire. Meals served in the bar or dining room. Good, en suite accommodation. Cider in summer. ⌂ Q ❀ ▮ ◑ ▮ ♣ P

## Malham

### Lister Arms Hotel
Right over bridge opp. post office ☎ (01729) 830330
12–3 (2 winter), 7–11; 12–3, 7–10.30 Sun
**Black Sheep Best Bitter; Ind Coope Burton Ale; Younger Scotch; guest beers** H
Popular, three-room pub, partly dating from 1702, with an original large inglenook complete with fireside cat. Good quality food (separate dining room); large selection of whiskies. Cider in summer. ⌂ ❀ 🏠 ◑ ▲ ♣ ♁ P

## Malton

### Crown Hotel (Suddaby's)
Wheelgate ☎ (01653) 692038
11–3, 5.30–11; 11–11 Fri & summer; 10.30–4, 7–11 Sat; 12–3, 7–10.30 Sun
**Malton Pale Ale, Double Chance, Pickwick's Porter, Crown Bitter, Owd Bob; guest beer** (occasional) H
Busy town-centre pub with a conservatory eating area. Local horse racing mementoes are displayed. Malton Brewery is situated at the rear. No lunches Tue or Sun.
⌂ Q ☸ ❀ 🏠 ◑ ▮ ❧ ♣ P

### King's Head
Market Place ☎ (01653) 692289
10.30–2.30 (extends in summer), 7–11; 12–3, 7–10.30 Sun
**Marston's Bitter, Pedigree; guest beers** H
Imposing, ivy-clad pub overlooking the Market Place, popular with locals and visitors. Excellent food is reasonably priced. Scarborough CAMRA *Rural Pub of the Year* 1995. Three guest beers.
Q ◑ ▮ ▲ ❧ P ✂ 🏠

## Marske-by-the-Sea

### Zetland
9 High Street ☎ (01642) 483973
12–11; 12–4, 7–10.30 Sun
**Vaux Samson, Double Maxim; guest beers** H
Old, established hotel, consisting of a bar, a recently renovated lounge, a games room and an upstairs function room. Varied entertainment most nights. Snacks available.
🏠 ▮ ♣ P 🏠

Try also: **Ship Inn**, High St (Scottish Courage)

## Masham

### White Bear
Wellgarth ☎ (01765) 689319
11–11; 12–3, 7–10.30 Sun
**Theakston Mild, Best Bitter, XB, Old Peculier, seasonal beers** H
Two-roomed stone inn with a friendly welcome: a popular locals' bar and a plush lounge. Excellent food (eve meals weekdays). Live music most Sat eves.
⌂ ❀ 🏠 ◑ ▮ ▮ ♣ P

## Melmerby

### George & Dragon
Main Street ☎ (01765) 640303
11–3, 5–11 (11–11 summer); 12–3, 7–10.30 Sun
**Franklin's Bitter; Theakston Best Bitter; guest beer** H
Traditional, three-roomed village inn with log fires in each room. Local micro-breweries are promoted; a rare outlet for Franklin's beer (usually available).
⌂ Q 🏠 ◑ ▮ ♣ P ✂

## Middlesbrough

### Star & Garter
14 Southfield Road ☎ (01642) 245307
11–11; 12–10.30 Sun
**Draught Bass; Boddingtons Bitter; Theakston XB; Worthington Bitter; guest beers** H
This pub won a CAMRA *Pub Preservation Award* for its conversion from a club and boasts a fine Victorian-style bar. The large, L-shaped lounge has a quiet eating area. Regular beer festivals. Popular with students. ❀ ◑ ▮ ♣ P

### Tap 'n' Barrel
86 Newport Road (near bus station) ☎ (01642) 219995
11–11; 12–3, 7–10.30 Sun
**Beer range varies** H
Cosy pub with a Victorian-style bar illuminated by real gas lamps. Function room upstairs. No meals Sun; eve meals Mon–Fri till 7.
◑ ▮ ❧ ♣

### Tavern
228 Linthorpe Road ☎ (01642) 242589
11–11; 12–10.30 Sun
**Boddingtons Bitter; Castle Eden Ale; guest beers** H
Large pub with a continually changing list of guest beers (14) from Whitbread's portfolio. Function room upstairs; separate games room. Popular with students.
❀ 🏠 ◑ ▮ ♣ ♁

## Muker

### Farmer's Arms
☎ (01748) 886297
11–3, 7–11; 12–3, 7–10.30 Sun
**Butterknowle Bitter; Theakston Best Bitter, Old Peculier** H
Village-centre pub, handy for the Pennine Way and Coast to Coast walks. The inside retains traditional character, with wooden seating and flagged floors.
⌂ Q ☸ ❀ 🏠 ◑ ▮ ♣ P

## Newholm

### Old Beehive Inn
Off A171 ☎ (01947) 602703
11.30–3, 7–11; 12–3, 7–10.30 Sun
**McEwan 80/-; Theakston Mild, Best Bitter, Old Peculier** H
Ancient, family-run village pub, full of character, with oak beams and a pub sign written in verse.
⌂ Q ☸ ❀ 🏠 ◑ ▮ ▮ ▲ ♣ P 🏠

## Normanby

### Poverina
High Street ☎ (01642) 440521
11–11; 12–10.30 Sun
**Banks's Bitter; Camerons Strongarm; guest beer** H
Old roadhouse, taking its name from a racehorse. Furnished in typical Wolverhampton & Dudley style, it has a strong local patronage. Function room. ❀ ◑ ▮ ♣ P 🏠

Try also: **Norman Conquest**, Flatts Lane (Scottish Courage)

## Northallerton

### Tanner Hop

2A Friarage Street (50 yds E of town hall roundabout)
☎ (01609) 778482
11–3, 5.30–11; 11–11 Sat; 12–10.30 Sun
**Black Sheep Best Bitter; Hambleton Stud; North Yorkshire Fool's Gold; John Smith's Bitter; guest beers** Ⓗ
Traditional, friendly, 1940s-style pub: a popular live music venue. The top floor is for music and functions. Many guest beers. ◖ & ⌣

Try also: **Tap & Spile**, High St

## North Duffield

### King's Arms

Main Street
☎ (01757) 288492
4–11 (12–2, 4–11 summer); 12–10.30 Sun
**Hambleton Stallion; John Smith's Bitter; guest beers** Ⓗ
18th-century village free house close to an attractive green and duck pond. Constantly changing range of guest ales; beer festivals held. No eve meals Sun–Tue. Cider in summer. 🚶 ❀ ◖ ◗ ♣ ⌣ P

## Nosterfield

### Freemason's Arms

On B6267 ☎ (01677) 470548
12–3 (not Mon), 6 (7 Mon)–11; 12–3, 7–10.30 Sun
**Black Sheep Best Bitter; Theakston Best Bitter; guest beer** (occasional) Ⓗ
Friendly country inn with a flagstoned bar and an interesting collection of wartime memorabilia. Well-regarded meals make it often very busy. Cider in summer. 🚶 Q ◖ ◗ ⌣ P

## Osmotherley

### Pied Piper

Clack Lane End (A684)
☎ (01609) 883436
12–11; 12–10.30 Sun
**Draught Bass; Theakston Best Bitter, XB, Old Peculier; guest beers** Ⓗ
Popular, 17th-century inn with a warm welcome. Live bands every Sun; 60s/70s disco Fri. Separate pool room and restaurant. Children's certificate.
🚶 ❀ 🛏 ◖ ◗ 🍴 ♣ P

## Pickering

### Black Swan

18 Birdgate ☎ (01751) 472286
10.30–11.30; 12–3.30, 7–10.30 (12–10.30 summer) Sun
**Courage Directors; Ruddles County; John Smith's Bitter** Ⓗ
Former coaching inn, heavily beamed. One long bar with distinct drinking areas, popular with locals and visitors. Large car park to the rear. Busy on market days.
🚶 Q 🛏 ◖ ◗ ♣ P

## Pickhill

### Nag's Head

1½ miles E of A1
☎ (01845) 567391
11–11; 12–10.30 Sun
**Hambleton Best Bitter; John Smith's Bitter; Theakston Best Bitter, XB, Old Peculier; guest beers** Ⓗ
Run by the same family for many years, this comfortable village pub is renowned for its food and beer. It features a small lounge and traditional bar, and a separate no-smoking restaurant. Refurbished en suite bedrooms.
🚶 Q ❀ 🛏 ◖ ◗ 🍴 A ♣ P

## Pool

### Hunter's Inn

Harrogate Road (A658)
☎ (0113) 284 1090
11–11; 12–10.30 Sun
**Tetley Bitter; Theakston Best Bitter; guest beers** Ⓗ
Pub with a mixed clientele and a real fire for cold days. Seven guest ales; Hunters Chase house beer is brewed by Daleside. Pool table.
🚶 ❀ ◖ ♣ P

## Port Mulgrave

### Ship

20 Rosedale Lane (signed off A174 at Hinderwell) OS793188
☎ (01947) 840303
11–11; 12–10.30 Sun
**Tetley Bitter; Theakston Black Bull; Younger No. 3; guest beer** Ⓗ
Family-run local near high cliffs, close to the Cleveland Way. Comfortably furnished, with a nautical theme, it is well worth finding.
🚶 Q 🛏 ◖ ◗ & A ♣ P 🍴

## Redcar

### Pig & Whistle

West Dyke Road
☎ (01642) 482697
11–11; 12–10.30 Sun
**Courage Directors; Marston's Pedigree; Morland Old Speckled Hen; John Smith's Magnet; guest beer** Ⓗ
100-year-old, traditional town-centre pub, displaying a collection of over 2500 pigs from all over the world. Separate games room; new upstairs function room.
🛒 🛏 A 🚆 (Central) ♣ 🍴

## Turners Mill

Greenstones Road
☎ (01642) 475895
11–11; 12–4.30, 7–10.30 Sun
**Draught Bass; Worthington Bitter; guest beers** Ⓗ
New Bass estate pub, tastefully decorated throughout. The separate restaurant features Turner family pictures. Children's certificate.
❀ ◖ ◗ 🛏 & ♣ P ⅄

Try also: **Hop & Grape**, High St (John Smith's); **Yorkshire Coble**, West Dyke Rd (Samuel Smith)

## Redmire

### King's Arms

☎ (01969) 22316
11–3, 5.30–11; 11–11 Sat; 12–3, 7–10.30 Sun
**Black Sheep Special; John Smith's Bitter; Theakston XB; guest beer** Ⓗ
Cosy village inn with an enthusiasm for guest beers. Popular for home-cooked food. Views of Wensleydale from the patio. 🚶 ❀ 🛏 ◖ A ♣ P

## Richmond

### Black Lion

12 Finkle Street (off Market Place) ☎ (01748) 823121
11–11; 11–2.30, 6–10.30 Sun
**Camerons Strongarm; Flowers Original; Tetley Bitter; guest beers** Ⓗ
Old, residential coaching inn. Its traditional bars and homely atmosphere are popular with locals and guests.
🚶 Q 🛏 ◖ ◗ ♣ P ⅄ 🍴

### Holly Hill Inn

Holly Hill, Sleegill (Hudswell road)
☎ (01748) 822192
12–11; 12–10.30 Sun
**Theakston Mild, Best Bitter, XB; guest beers** Ⓗ
Country pub on the edge of town: a busy public bar with an adjoining games room, plus a quiet lounge. The garden leads to fields with panoramic views over Richmond. Animals for children. Good food.
Q 🛒 ❀ 🛏 ◖ ◗ 🛏 & A ♣ P 🍴

## Ripon

### Golden Lion

69 Allhallowgate
☎ (01765) 602598
11–3, 7–11; 12–3, 7–10.30 Sun
**Black Sheep Best Bitter; Hambleton Goldfield; John Smith's Bitter; Theakston Best Bitter; guest beer** (summer) Ⓗ
Recently refurbished but still friendly pub with interesting naval memorabilia. Excellent food. 🛒 🛏 ◖ ◗ ♣

## One Eyed Rat

51 Allhallowgate
☎ (01765) 607704
6–11; 12–2, 5.30–11 Fri; 12–3, 6–11 Sat;
12–3, 7–10.30 Sun
**Boddingtons Bitter; Tetley
Bitter; guest beers** Ⓗ
Unspoilt, popular, terraced
pub close to the town centre.
Excellent guest beers.
🏚 Q ✿ ♣

## Water Rat

24 Bondgate Green (off
Boroughbridge Rd)
☎ (01765) 602251
12–4, 7–11; 12–4, 7–10.30 Sun
**Vaux Samson, Double
Maxim, Waggle Dance;
Ward's Best Bitter; guest
beer** Ⓗ
Pleasant pub with an outdoor
drinking area overlooking the
River Skell.
✿ ◖ ▶ ♣ ⦗

## Wheatsheaf

Harrogate Road (S end of
new bypass)
☎ (01765) 602410
12–3 (not Mon or Tue), 7 (6.30 Sat)–11
(extends in summer); 12–3, 7–10.30
Sun
**Vaux Samson; Ward's Best
Bitter; guest beers** Ⓗ
Friendly old inn on the edge of
the city. Carved sections of an
18th-century bed behind the
bar are of particular interest.
Sunken garden at the rear.
✿ ▲ P

# Robin Hood's Bay

## Victoria Hotel

Station Road
☎ (01947) 880205
11–3, 6.30–11; 11–11 Fri, Sat &
summer; 12–3, 7–10.30 (12–10.30
summer) Sun
**Camerons Bitter, Strongarm;
guest beers** Ⓗ
Large hotel built in 1897 on the
cliff top, with magnificent
views over the bay and this
quaint village where all pubs
sell real ale. The family room
has a pool table.
🏚 Q ⚲ ✿ 🛏 ◖ ▶ ♣

**Try also: Laurel Inn**, The Bank
(Free)

# Rufforth

## Tankard

Wetherby Road (B1224)
☎ (01904) 738621
11–3, 6–11; 11–11 Sat; 12–3, 7–10.30
Sun
**Samuel Smith OBB** Ⓗ
Two-roomed village local with
1930s decor, wood panelling
and old village prints. The
large garden has a children's
play area. No food Sun eve or
Mon lunch.
🏚 Q ✿ ◖ ▶ ⊟ ♣ P

# Saltburn-by-the-Sea

## Saltburn Cricket, Bowls & Tennis Club

Marske Mill Lane
(opp. sports centre)
☎ (01287) 622761
8 (7 summer, 12 summer Sat)–11;
12–3, 8–10.30 Sun
**Tetley Bitter; guest beers** Ⓗ
Club with a lounge and games
room off a single bar. Snacks
available. Open noon on
cricket days. Casual visitors
welcome. ✿ ▲ ⥱ ♣ P ⦗

**Try also: Victoria**, Dundas St
(Tetley)

# Sawdon

## Anvil Inn

Main Street
☎ (01723) 859896
11–11; 12–10.30 Sun
**Theakston Best Bitter;
Younger Scotch; guest beers** Ⓗ
Sympathetically renovated
blacksmith's shop, friendly
and welcoming. Excellent
value meals. Worth the
detour.
🏚 Q ⚲ ✿ 🛏 ◖ ▲ ⥳ P ⦗

# Scarborough

## Alma Inn

1 Alma Parade (near Northway
traffic lights, behind Barclays
Bank) ☎ (01723) 375587
11.30–2.30 (3 Thu), 7–11; 11.30–11 Fri
& Sat; 12–3, 7–10.30 Sun
**Tetley Bitter; Theakston Best
Bitter, XB; Younger Scotch,
No. 3; guest beers** Ⓗ
Busy pub just off the main
shopping precinct: two rooms
with a large and varied
collection of memorabilia.
Good value meals (no food
Sun). ✿ ◖ ⊟ ঌ ⥱ ♣

## Angel

46 North Street
☎ (01723) 365504
11–11; 12–10.30 Sun
**Camerons Bitter; Tetley
Bitter** Ⓗ
Recently extended pub which
has not lost character or
atmosphere; just off the
pedestrian precinct. Rugby
league mementoes are on
show. Q ◖ ঌ ⥱ ♣

## Hole in the Wall

26 Vernon Road
☎ (01723) 373746
11.30–2.30 (3 Sat), 7–11; 12–3, 7–10.30
Sun
**Brakspear Bitter; Fuller's ESB;
Malton Double Chance,
Crown Bitter; guest beers** Ⓗ
Friendly, busy pub just off the
town centre, towards the spa.
Excellent guest beers;

extensive, home-cooked menu
(vegetarian specialities). No
meals Sun. Large collection of
beermats. Scarborough
CAMRA *Town Pub of the Year*
1995. Q ◖ ⥱ ♣ ⥀

## Leeds Arms

26 St Marys Street (200 yds
from seafront across Princess
Sq) ☎ (01723) 361699
11.30–3.30, 7–11; 11.30–11 Fri & Sat;
12–10.30 Sun
**Draught Bass; Highgate Dark;
Worthington Bitter; guest
beer** Ⓗ
Small, unspoilt, one-roomed
pub worth seeking out.
Connections with the fishing
industry and lifeboats are
reflected in the nautical
pictures. 🏚 Q ▲ ⥱ ♣

## Prince of Wales

2 Castle Road (off town centre)
☎ (01723) 373517
11–11; 12–4, 7–10.30 Sun
**Tetley Mild, Bitter, Imperial;
guest beers** (occasional) Ⓗ
Unspoilt, two-room pub with a
friendly atmosphere. Popular
with locals and visitors.
Q ⥱ ♣

## Scalby Mills Hotel

Scalby Mills Road (by Sea Life
Centre)
☎ (01723) 500449
11–3, 7–11; 12–3.30, 7–10.30 Sun
(extends in summer)
**Cropton Two Pints; Tetley
Bitter; guest beers** Ⓗ
Traditional pub on the
Cleveland Way, with views
across the bay. Busy in
summer. Children's certificate.
Q ✿ ◖ ▲

## Scarborough Arms

1 North Terrace (near Castle
Rd / Auborough St jct)
☎ (01723) 373575
11–11; 12–10.30 Sun
**Banks's Mild; Camerons
Bitter; Marston's Pedigree;
guest beer** Ⓗ
Extensively renovated two-
roomed pub based on a
medieval theme; very popular.
Excellent food menu,
reasonably priced.
✿ ◖ ▶ ঌ ⥱ ♣ ⦗

## Talbot Inn

13 Queen Street (near Market
Hall)
☎ (01723) 364723
11.30–11; 12–10.30 Sun
**Theakston Best Bitter, XB;
guest beers** Ⓗ
17th-century coaching inn and
Grade II listed building
incorporating three separate
bars: a concert room (with live
jazz, folk, etc.), a large, airy
lounge with a dartboard and a
period snug with a Yorkshire
range. Belgian beer on draught.
No eve meals weekends.
🏚 ◖ ▶ ⥱ ♣ P

## Selby

### Albion Vaults

New Street (town side of River
Ouse swing bridge)
☎ (01757) 213817
11–11; 11–4.30, 7–11 Tue–Thu;
12–10.30 Sun
**Old Mill Mild, Bitter,
seasonal beers** Ⓗ
Reputed to be the oldest pub in
Selby, with comfortable
traditional furnishings. The
rear bar has a pool table, darts
and Sky TV.
Q ⊛ ⓓ ⓠ & ⇌ ♠

### Blackamoor

Finkle Street (N side of Market
Place) ☎ (01757) 702987
11–11; 12–10.30 Sun
**Tetley Bitter; guest beers** Ⓗ
Pub with an Edwardian style,
open-plan interior with a
raised area. Popular with a
young crowd at weekends.
Enthusiastic football team.
Guest beers are from
Carlsberg-Tetley's Tapster's
Choice range. ⇌ ♠

### Cricketers

Market Place ☎ (01757) 202120
11–11; 11–3.30, 5.30–11 Tue & Wed;
12–10.30 Sun
**Samuel Smith OBB** Ⓗ
Town pub with partitioned
seating areas and a cricketing
theme. Wheelchair access is
from the back yard.
⊛ ⓓ & ⇌

## Skelton

### Royal George

North Terrace (A173,
Guisborough end of town)
☎ (01287) 650326
2 (12.30 Sat)–11; 7–3, 7–10.30 Sun
**Beer range varies** Ⓗ
Pub with a strong local
patronage: a small bar to the
front with a large room to the
rear. Three varying guest
beers. ⊛ ⓠ & ♠

## Skelton Green

### Green Inn

Boosbeck Road
☎ (01287) 650475
12–4, 7–11; 12–3, 7–10.30 Sun
**Camerons Strongarm; guest
beer** Ⓗ
Small, terraced pub in a former
mining village. Old photos of
the area are displayed.
⊛ & ♠

## Skipton

### Cock & Bottle

30 Swadford Street
☎ (01756) 794734
11–11; 12–10.30 Sun
**Boddingtons Bitter; Castle
Eden Ale; Marston's Pedigree;**

**Whitbread Abroad Cooper,
Fuggles IPA; guest beers** Ⓗ
Busy, friendly, single-bar
Hogshead ale house,
preserving original
18th-century stone walls,
beams and fireplaces. Over 150
different guest beers in less
than two years.
⚏ ⊛ ⓓ ⇌ ♠ ◔

### Royal Shepherd

Canal Street ☎ (01756) 793178
11–11; 12–4, 6.30–10.30 Sun
**Boddingtons Bitter; Cains
Bitter; Castle Eden Ale;
Marston's Pedigree;
Whitbread Trophy** Ⓗ
Quiet, friendly, attractively-
situated canalside pub with
three rooms and an award-
winning garden. The main bar
has photos of old Skipton and
an unusual, canal-themed
stained-glass window. The
snug is full of cricketing
memorabilia. ⚏ Q ⊛ ⓓ ⇌ ♠

## Snape

### Castle Arms Inn

☎ (01677) 470270
12–3, 7 (6 Fri & Sat)–11; 12–3, 7–10.30
Sun
**Black Sheep Best Bitter;
Hambleton Bitter; Tetley
Bitter; guest beers** Ⓗ
Friendly village pub with open
fires in its cosy bar. A separate
restaurant serves excellent
food (theme eve once a month).
No meals Mon.
⚏ Q ⊛ ⌂ ⓓ ♪ & ♠ P

## Sneaton

### Wilson Arms

Beacon Way ☎ (01947) 602557
7–11; 12–3, 7–11 Sat & summer; 12–3,
7–10.30 Sun
**John Smith's Bitter;
Theakston Best Bitter; guest
beers** Ⓗ
Grade II listed large pub with a
function room, reputed to be
haunted. Three guest beers.
⚏ Q ⌇ ⊛ ⌂ ⓓ ♪ ♠ P

## Staithes

### Royal George

High Street ☎ (01947) 841432
11.30–4.30, 7–11; 12–4, 7–10.30 Sun
**Camerons Strongarm; Ind
Coope Burton Ale; Tetley
Bitter; guest beer** (summer) Ⓗ
Three-roomed, terraced local in
a charming fishing village: a
small, atmospheric bar and a
comfortable lounge featuring
local scenes by a local artist. No
vehicular access. Children
welcome before 9.30. Meals
served if booked. Q ⓠ ♪ ♠

## Starbotton

### Fox & Hounds

☎ (01756) 760269

11.30–3, 6.30–11; closed Mon eve in
summer and all day Mon in winter;
12–3, 7–10.30 Sun; closed mid-Jan to
mid-Feb
**Black Sheep Best Bitter;
Theakston Best Bitter, Black
Bull, Old Peculier; guest
beers** Ⓗ
Cosy, welcoming old village
inn with a flagstone-floored
bar and no-smoking dining
room. Excellent, good-value
meals (unusual menu and
good vegetarian choice).
⚏ ⌇ ⊛ ⌂ ⓓ ♪ ♠ P

## Staveley

### Royal Oak

☎ (01423) 340267
11.30–3, 5.30–11; 12–3, 7–10.30 Sun
**Rudgate Viking; John Smith's
Bitter; Tetley Bitter** Ⓗ
Much improved old village
local with a keen darts team.
Good food Tue–Sat.
⚏ Q ⓓ & ♠ P

## Stokesley

### Station

Station Road (1 mile along
Kirby road)
☎ (01642) 710436
12–4, 7–11; 12–4, 7–10.30 Sun
**Ind Coope Burton Ale; Tetley
Bitter, Imperial** Ⓗ
Pub built in 1861 to serve a
now defunct railway: a light
and airy front bar, a small snug
with a fire, and a bar and
function room at the rear
(blues Thu). ⚏ Q ⌂ & ♠ 🖫

### White Swan

1 West End (W end of High St)
☎ (01642) 710263
11.30–3, 5.30 (7 Sat)–11; 12–3, 7–10.30
Sun
**Castle Eden Ale; Younger
No. 3; guest beers** Ⓗ
Cosy, traditional pub where
the oak-panelled lounge bar
displays agricultural
memorabilia. Ploughman's
meals served, with a wide
range of cheeses. Up to
seven ales.
⚏ Q ♠ ◔ 🖫

**Try also: Queen's Head**, High
St (Camerons)

## Tadcaster

### Angel & White Horse

Bridge Street
☎ (01937) 835470
11–2.30, 6 (7 Sat)–11; 12–10.30 Sun
**Samuel Smith OBB** Ⓗ
Large, pleasant town pub
adjacent to Sam Smith's
brewery (seen in photos on the
wood panelled walls). The
brewery's shire horses are
stabled in the yard behind.
Cheap beer.
⚏ Q ⊛ ⓓ

## Thirsk

### Old Three Tuns

13 Finkle Street
☎ (01845) 523291
11–11; 12–10.30 Sun
Tetley Bitter; guest beers Ⓗ
Thirsk's original coaching inn,
still with stables and
outbuildings. Excellent food:
try the Yorkshire puddings 'the
size of a flat cap'.
🏚 ⚲ ❀ ◖ ❋ Å ♣ P

## Thixendale

### Cross Keys

☎ (01937) 835470
12–3 (not winter Mon), 6–11; 12–3,
7–10.30 Sun
Jennings Bitter; Tetley
Bitter Ⓗ
Traditional, one-roomed,
village gem in the heart of the
Yorkshire wolds. Unspoilt and
welcoming, it serves good food
at reasonable prices (no meals
between Christmas and New
Year). The village has a youth
hostel. 🏚 Q ❀ ◖ ❋ Å ♣

## Thornton in Lonsdale

### Marton Arms

Off 'waterfalls' road, ½ mile
from Ingleton
☎ (0152 42) 41281
12–3 (not Mon–Fri in winter); 6 (7
winter)–11; 11–11 Sat; 12–10.30 Sun
Black Sheep Best Bitter; Dent
Bitter; Jennings Bitter;
Theakston Best Bitter; guest
beers Ⓗ
Pre-turnpike coaching inn,
dated 1679: a large,
comfortable, oak-beamed
lounge and a restaurant (food
all day Sun). Up to 15 beers. A
ten-minute walk from the start
of the Waterfalls Walk.
🏚 ❀ ⛵ ◖ ❋ ♣ ⌂ P

## Thornton Watlass

### Buck Inn

☎ (01677) 422461
11–2.30, 6–11; 11–11 Sat; 12–10.30 Sun
Black Sheep Best Bitter Ⓗ,
Riggwelter Ⓖ; John Smith's
Bitter; Tetley Bitter;
Theakston Best Bitter Ⓗ
Quiet village pub with open
log fires in the bar, and a
separate restaurant. It
overlooks the village cricket
green. Excellent reputation for
food. Live music in the large
function room at weekends.
🏚 Q ❀ ⛵ ◖ ❋ ⚹ ♣ P

## Threshfield

### Old Hall Inn

☎ (01756) 752441
11.30–3, 6 (5.30 summer)–11; 12–3,
7–10.30 Sun

Taylor Best Bitter, Landlord;
Theakston Best Bitter; guest
beer Ⓗ
Country inn offering good
quality food (no meals Sun
eve): several rooms, one with a
Yorkshire range. A
conservatory to the side opens
onto a garden. The actual 'old
hall' is a listed building behind.
🏚 Q ⚲ ❀ ⛵ ◖ ❋ ⚹ Å ♣ P

## Tockwith

### Spotted Ox

Westfield Road
☎ (01423) 358387
11–3, 6–11; 11–11 Sat; 12–10.30 Sun
Tetley Bitter; guest beers Ⓗ
Modernised village local,
opened out but with a degree
of partitioning. Changing
selection of guest beers from
distant and local sources.
❀ ◖ ❋ P

## Ulleskelf

### Ulleskelf Arms

Church Fenton Lane (by
station) ☎ (01937) 832136
6–11; 12–3, 6.30–11 Sat; 12–3, 7–10.30
Sun
Black Sheep Best Bitter; Old
Mill Bitter; John Smith's
Bitter; guest beers Ⓗ
The rooms have been opened
up into one bar at this village
local. Entertainment most eves.
Popular at weekends,
especially with fishermen. Eve
bar meals if booked, otherwise
use the restaurant.
❀ ⛵ ◖ ❋ ⇌ ♣ P

## Upper Poppleton

### Lord Collingwood

The Green ☎ (01904) 794388
11.30–3, 5.30–11; 12–3, 7–10.30 Sun
Mansfield Riding Bitter,
Bitter, Old Baily, seasonal
beers Ⓗ
Central pub, overlooking the
green in a commuter village.
Home-cooked food with daily
specials and vegetarian
options. 🏚 ◖ ❋ P

## Weaverthorpe

### Star Inn

☎ (01944) 738273
7–11; 12–4.30, 7–11 Sat; 12–5,
7.30–10.30 Sun
John Smith's Bitter; Tetley
Bitter; guest beers Ⓗ
Popular country pub where
extensive menus offer good
value meals. Game specialities
in season.
🏚 Q ❀ ⛵ ◖ ❋ ⚹ Å ♣ P ⚼

## Welbury

### Duke of Wellington

☎ (01609) 882464
11–3.30 (not Mon or Tue), 7–11;
12–10.30 Sun

John Smith's Bitter, Magnet;
guest beer Ⓗ
Pleasant village pub where an
excellent menu and range of
ales combine with a welcoming
atmosphere. The garden has
tables, slide and a swing. Les
Routiers diplomas displayed.
🏚 ⚲ ❀ ⛵ ◖ ❋ ♣ P ⛚

## West Heslerton

### Dawnay Arms

☎ (01944) 728203
7–11 (11–3, 7–11 summer); 12–3,
7–10.30 Sun
Theakston Best Bitter;
Younger Scotch Ⓗ
Central to the village but also
popular with visitors, this
bright, welcoming, multi-
roomed pub offers something
for everybody.
🏚 Q ❀ ◖ ❋ Å ♣

## Whitby

### Duke of York

Church Street (foot of the
abbey steps)
☎ (01947) 600324
11–11; 12–3.30 Sun, closed Sun eve
Courage Directors; John
Smith's Bitter, Magnet; guest
beer Ⓗ
Busy pub overlooking Whitby
harbour, at the foot of the 199
steps. Popular in folk week.
⛵ ◖ ❋ ♣

### Tap & Spile

New Quay Road (opp. bus and
rail stations) ☎ (01947) 603937
11–11; 12–4.30, 7–10.30 (12–10.30
summer) Sun
Tap & Spile Bitter, Premium;
guest beers Ⓗ
Large, multi-roomed, red brick
pub formerly known as the
Cutty Sark. Eve meals end at 7
(4.30 Sun). Five guest beers.
Q ⚲ ◖ ❋ ⚼ ⇌ ♣ ⌂ ⚹

Try also: Golden Lion, Golden
Lion Bank (Tetley)

## Yarm

### Green Tree

High Street ☎ (01642) 780311
11.30–11; 12–3, 7–10.30 Sun
Camerons Bitter, Strongarm Ⓗ
Refurbished, 300-year-old,
town-centre pub: a single long
room with a central bar. Plenty
of parking in the High St. Sun
lunch served. ❀ ♣ ⛚

### Ketton Ox

High Street ☎ (01642) 788311
11–11; 12–10.30 Sun
Vaux Samson Ⓗ
Magnificent ex-coaching inn
with a fascinating history in a
village conservation area. Oval
windows on the facade reveal a
former cockfighting room.
❀ ◖ ❋ ♣

# York

## Blue Bell ☆
Fossgate ☎ (01904) 654904
12–11; 12–3, 7–10.30 Sun
**Vaux Bitter, Samson, Waggle Dance; Ward's Best Bitter; guest beer** Ⓗ
CAMRA regional *Pub of the Year* 1996: an atmospheric Edwardian pub with few concessions to modernity. Two intimate rooms lead off a drinking corridor. Well-frequented by locals and visitors. ⚑ ♣

## Fox Inn
Holgate Road (A59)
☎ (01904) 798341
11–11; 12–10.30 Sun
**Tetley Bitter; Marston's Pedigree; guest beers** Ⓗ
Lively, welcoming, four-roomed pub of great character, retaining many original features. The railway theme reflects the sadly closed carriageworks nearby. A Tetley Heritage inn.
🏰 Q ❀ ♿ ♣ P

## Golden Lion
9 Church Street
☎ (01904) 620942
11–11; 12–10.30 Sun
**John Smith's Bitter; Theakston Mild, Best Bitter, XB, Old Peculier; guest beers** Ⓗ
Recent conversion to a T&J Bernard's ale house, serving a wide range of guest beers. The tastefully refurbished interior provides a pleasant drinking environment. ◖ ≢

## Grapes
4 King Street ☎ (01904) 670696
11–11; 12–10.30 Sun
**Thwaites Bitter, Craftsman, seasonal beers** Ⓗ
Much altered and extended in late 1995, this pub has suddenly jumped back into the fashionable drinking circuit. Relaxing (especially in the armchairs) by day; noisy and vibrant at night. ◖ ≢

## Lighthorseman
124 Fulford Road
☎ (01904) 624818
11.30–2.30, 5.30–11; 12–3, 7–10.30 Sun
**Thwaites Bitter, Craftsman, seasonal beers** Ⓗ
Late Victorian, multi-roomed pub with a wealth of attractive fittings. Note particularly the ornate hanging light shade in the main, high-ceilinged bar.
❀ ⚑ ◖ P

## Maltings
Tanners Moat (below Lendal Bridge) ☎ (01904) 655387
11–11; 12–10.30 Sun
**Black Sheep Best Bitter; York Stonewall; guest beers** Ⓗ
Pub widely renowned for its exotic guest beers and excellent value food which manages to accommodate all tastes with ease. Live music Mon and Tue. Local CAMRA *Pub of the Year* 1996. ◖ ≢ ➲

## Masons Arms
6 Fishergate ☎ (01904) 646046
11–11; 12–10.30 Sun
**John Smith's Bitter; guest beers** Ⓗ
Classic example of brewers' Tudor architecture, sympathetically maintained and refurbished. The oak panelling and fireplace came from York Castle. The guest beers are mainly from the Bass Caskmasters range.
❀ ◖ ◗ ⚑

## Rose & Crown
13 Lawrence Street
☎ (01904) 636947
11–11, 12–10.30 Sun
**Ind Coope Burton Ale; Malton Double Chance; Marston's Pedigree; Tetley Bitter, Imperial; guest beers** Ⓗ
Tetley Festival Alehouse, just outside the city walls: three large drinking rooms and a central stand-up parlour. Popular with students. Regular beer festivals. ◖ ⚑ ➲ P

## Royal Oak
18 Goodramgate
☎ (01904) 653850
11–11; 12–10.30 Sun
**Castle Eden Ale; Ind Coope Burton Ale; Tetley Bitter** Ⓗ
Small, stylish town pub retaining three separate rooms. Popular with diners for the range of freshly-prepared meals. ◖ ◗ ⚑ ✂

## Three Tuns
12 Coppergate
☎ (01904) 621873
11–11; 12–10.30 Sun
**Mansfield Riding Bitter, Bitter, Old Baily, seasonal beers** Ⓗ
Old pub with a modernised interior (but beware the low beams and sloping floor). Despite its size, it hosts occasional live music and attracts a boisterous crowd at weekends. Adjacent to Coppergate shopping centre.
◖ ◗ ⚑

## Waggon & Horses
48 Gillygate ☎ (01904) 654103
11–11; 12–10.30 Sun
**John Smith's Bitter; guest beers** Ⓗ
Multi-roomed pub with strong rugby league connections, including sponsorship of an Australian team! Excellent, well-priced food. Guest beers tend to appear more at weekends. The house beer is Cropton Knock-on.
❀ 🛏 ◖ ◗ ⚑ P

## Wellington Inn
47 Alma Terrace
☎ (01904) 654642
11–3, 6 (5.30 Sat)–11; 12–3, 7–10.30 Sun
**Samuel Smith OBB** Ⓗ
Classic, mid-terrace local, near the river, a pleasant, one-mile walk from the city centre: three rooms off a central corridor, complete with serving hatch and refurbished bar counter. The cheapest regular beer in York. 🏰 ❀ ⚑

## York Arms
26 High Petergate
☎ (01904) 624508
11–11; 12–10.30 Sun
**Samuel Smith OBB** Ⓗ
Tiny, multi-roomed pub in the shadow of York Minster. A delightful front bar is accessed by a sliding door; the rear room is gaily decorated in Sam's brassy style; the wholly modern lounge is popular with students. 🛏 ◖ ◗ ⚑ ≢

## York Beer Shop
Sandringham Street (off A19/ Fishergate)
☎ (01904) 647136
11 (4 Mon, 10 Sat)–10; 12–2, 6–10 Sun
**Old Mill Bitter; Rooster's Yankee; Taylor Landlord; guest beers** Ⓗ
Off-licence selling draught beer to take out in any quantity, along with fine cheese. Increasing emphasis on British bottles (including most available bottle-conditioned ones). ➲

# Barnby Dun

## Gateway Inn
Station Road
☎ (01302) 882849
12–3 (not Mon), 6–11.30; 12–3, 7–10.30 Sun
**John Smith's Bitter; Barnsley Bitter; guest beer** Ⓗ
Hotel and restaurant (very popular with diners) which has cultivated a warm, friendly pub atmosphere in its bar. Early eve carvery. 🛏 ◖ ◗ P

# Barnsley

## Miners Rest
Palm Street, Old Town (near General Hospital)
☎ (01226) 282339
12–3 (4 Sat), 6 (7 Sat)–11; 12–3, 7–10.30 Sun
**John Smith's Bitter, Magnet** Ⓗ
Victorian local with three comfortable and contrasting rooms. The bowling green at the back gives a country pub atmosphere in the middle of town. ❀ ⚑ ♣ P

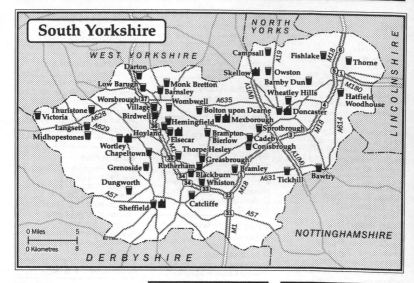

## South Yorkshire

### Shaw Inn

Racecommon Road
☎ (01226) 294021
1 (12 Fri & Sat)–11; 12–4, 7–10.30 Sun
**John Smith's Bitter; guest beers** Ⓗ
Pub just off the 'Bunny Run' and so avoiding the weekend excesses of the town centre; it caters for grown-ups of all ages. A folk club meets here (reflected in the jukebox). Guest beers at reasonable prices from the Whitbread range. Lunches Fri and Sat.
🏧 ❀ ◖ ♣ P

### Bawtry

#### Turnpike

High Street ☎ (01302) 711960
11–3, 6–11; 12–3, 7–10.30 Sun
**Stocks Best Bitter, Select, St Leger Porter; guest beers** Ⓗ
Welcoming pub opposite the market place featuring lots of wood, glass and brick, and a flagstone floor. CAMRA awards adorn the walls. Good value, varied menu (eve meals Tue–Thu). 🏧 ❀ ◖ ◗

**Try also: Crown Hotel**, High St (John Smith's)

### Birdwell

#### Cock Inn

Pilley Hill (off A61 towards Pilley) ☎ (01226) 742155
12–3, 7–11; 12–3, 7–10.30 Sun
**Draught Bass; Boddingtons Bitter** Ⓗ
Popular, 200-year-old village local in Yorkshire stone, with a slate floor, superb fireplace and much brass. Extensive garden with a quality play area. No eve meals Sun.
🏧 ❀ ◖ ◗ 🍺 ♣ P

### Blackburn

#### Sportsman Inn

Blackburn Road
☎ (01709) 551124
11–5, 7–11; 12–3, 7–10.30 Sun
**Barnsley Bitter; Tetley Bitter; guest beer** Ⓗ
Multi-roomed, traditional and friendly local close to the Meadowhall complex. Snooker, pool and darts available. Q 🍺 ♣ P

### Bolton upon Dearne

#### Cross Daggers Inn

Church Street (150 yds off B6098)
☎ (01709) 892299
12–4, 7–11; 12–3, 7–10.30 Sun
**Barnsley Bitter; John Smith's Bitter** Ⓗ
Built in 1923 and virtually unspoiled, a pub with many rooms, including a games room with snooker. A corridor drinking area displays old photos depicting life from the 1920s. 🏧 Q 🍺 ❀ ♿ ⇌ ♣ P

### Bramley

#### Master Brewer

Main Street
☎ (01709) 541103
11–11; 12–10.30 Sun
**Mansfield Riding Mild, Riding Bitter, Old Baily** Ⓗ
13-year-old, two-roomed, brick-built pub. The lounge is softly lit; the bar caters mainly for the younger trade (pool table and TV). The landlady is renowned for her variety of home-made meals (the pies are a must). No food Sun.
❀ ◖ ◗ 🍺 ♿ P

### Brampton Bierlow

#### Brampton Hall

2A Manor Road
☎ (01709) 877488
11–3, 7–11; 12–3, 7–10.30 Sun
**John Smith's Bitter, Magnet** Ⓗ
Converted 17th-century house, full of oak beams and real fires. Excellent lounge bar and restaurant on the top floor. Full menu of home-style cooking.
🏧 Q ❀ ◖ ◗ P 🍴

### Cadeby

#### Cadeby Inn

Main Street ☎ (01709) 864009
11.30–3, 5–11; 11–11 Sat; 12–3, 7–10.30 Sun
**Courage Directors; John Smith's Bitter, Magnet; Samuel Smith OBB; Tetley Bitter; guest beers** Ⓗ
Welcoming, converted farmhouse with a large lounge and a smaller bar. The pleasant front garden is popular with families. Guest beers come from Carlsberg-Tetley's Tapster's Choice range.
🏧 ❀ ◖ ◗ 🍺 ♣ P 🚫

## Campsall

### Old Bells

High Street ☎ (01302) 700423
11–3, 5.30–11; 11.30–4, 7–10.30 Sun
**Barnsley Bitter; Ruddles County; John Smith's Bitter; Tetley Bitter** Ⓗ
At over 850 years old, this, the oldest pub in Doncaster borough, once served Dick Turpin and Oliver Cromwell: a lounge, a small smoke room, a tiny snug and two restaurants. A Tomlinson's house beer is also sold. Q ⚘ ◖ ▶ ⅊ P

## Catcliffe

### Waverley

Brinsworth Road
☎ (01709) 360906
12–3.30, 6–11; 11.30–4.30, 6–11 Sat;
12–4, 7–10.30 Sun
**Beer range varies** Ⓗ
Large, friendly pub with a good family room and garden. Constantly changing range of four ales.
Q ⛄ ⚘ ◖ ▶ 🍴 ⅊ ♣ P 🍺

## Chapeltown

### Prince of Wales

80 Burncross Road (near swimming baths)
☎ (0114) 246 7725
11 (12 Mon)–3 (4 Sat), 5.30 (6 Sat)–11;
11–11 Fri; 12–2.30, 7–10.30 Sun
**Ward's Best Bitter** Ⓔ/Ⓗ
Friendly, welcoming pub with a tap room and a lounge. No food Sat eve or Sun.
Q ⚘ ◖ ▶ ≈ ♣ P

## Conisbrough

### Castle

Minney Moor Hill (off Low Rd via Burcroft Hill)
☎ (01709) 862204
1–4 (not Wed), 7–11; 1–11 Fri; 12–11
Sat; 12–10.30 Sun
**John Smith's Bitter; guest beer** Ⓗ
This local was once a bone mill. It still stands by a stream in the old part of town, five minutes' walk from the castle ruins, and has a quiet, cosy lounge and a long public bar. Quiz nights Thu and Sun.
♨ Q ⚘ 🍴 ≈ ♣ P 🍺

## Darton

### Woolley

Woolley Colliery Road (½ mile from station, up hill through village) ☎ (01226) 382847
11.30–3, 7–11 (11.30–11 summer);
12–4, 7–10.30 Sun
**Barnsley Bitter; John Smith's Bitter; Tetley Bitter, Imperial; guest beer** Ⓗ
Built in the 1920s as the Woolley Miners Welfare Club, this very large pub has a

number of separate drinking areas, plus a sun room. The bowling green can be used by customers, if there is not a match on.
Q ⚘ ◖ ▶ ⅊ ≈ ♣ P

## Doncaster

### Cheswold

Herten Way, Doncaster Leisure Park (next to Warner Bros cinema) ☎ (01302) 533000
11–11; 12–10.30 Sun
**Boddingtons Bitter; Flowers Original; Whitbread Trophy; guest beers** Ⓗ
Pub for families, built in 1994 as part of the leisure park complex: a large restaurant and bar meal area, plus a raised lounge. Large fun park indoors and out for children.
⛄ ⚘ ◖ ▶ ⅊ P

### Corporation Brewery Taps

135 Cleveland Street
☎ (01302) 363715
12–11; 12–10.30 Sun
**Samuel Smith OBB** Ⓗ
Popular, close-to-town centre local with a concert room (blues music Tue and Fri) and a small snug. Sky TV and games in the public bar. ⛄ ≈ ♣

### Hallcross

33–34 Hallgate (next to Odeon cinema) ☎ (01302) 328213
11–11; 11–4, 7–11 Sat; 12–3, 7–10.30
Sun
**Stocks Best Bitter, Select, Old Horizontal, seasonal beers; guest beers** Ⓗ
Comfortable, wood-panelled town pub, the home of Stocks Brewery. Especially good toasted sandwiches. No food Sun. ⚘ ◖

### Leopard

1 West Street ☎ (01302) 363054
11–11; 12–10.30 Sun
**Marston's Pedigree; John Smith's Bitter; guest beers** Ⓗ
Lively, street-corner pub with a superb tiled frontage. Regularly changing guest beers come from all over the country. Live music upstairs. No food Sun. ⚘ ◖ ⅊ ⅋ ≈ ♣ P

### Olde Castle

Market Place ☎ (01302) 360906
10.30–11; 12–3, 7–10.30 Sun
**John Smith's Bitter; Theakston Mild** Ⓗ**, Best Bitter, XB, Old Peculier; guest beer** Ⓗ
Rambling, three-room pub with all the atmosphere and bustle of the market outside. The front room is always busy and has a pianist Tue and Thu afternoons. The back room is a quiet lounge. The only cask mild pub in town.
⚘ 🍴 ⅊ ≈

### Olde Crown

Greyfriars Road (behind church) ☎ (01302) 360096
12–3 (not Mon or Wed in winter), 5–11;
12–11 Sat; 12–3, 7–10.30 Sun
**Barnsley Bitter; Worthington Bitter; guest beers** (occasional) Ⓗ
Welcoming haven just away from the bustle of the town centre, in the shadow of St George's church: an unspoilt bar, separate dining room and a quiet lounge, which features a lending library. Eve meals Mon–Fri till 8.
Q ⚘ ⅊ 🍴 ⅊ ≈ ♣ 🍺

### Plough

8 West Laith Gate
☎ (01302) 738310
11–4, 6.30–11; 11–11 Tue, Fri & Sat;
12–3, 7–10.30 Sun
**Draught Bass; Stones Bitter; guest beer** Ⓗ
Warm, traditional, two-room local, popular with older drinkers and others who shun the fun pub circuit. Old maps of Doncaster show how the town has grown. Possibly the world's smallest beer garden.
Q ⚘ ⅊ ≈ ♣ 🍺

### White Swan

34A Frenchgate
☎ (01302) 366973
11–11; 12–10.30 Sun
**Vaux Waggle Dance; Ward's Best Bitter; guest beer** Ⓗ
Friendly town-centre pub featuring the highest bar in Britain in the front tap room and a tiled passage leading to a comfortable lounge. Karaoke Tue and Sun afternoon/eves. Lunchtime meals (Mon–Sat) are popular with shoppers. The metered Ward's is usually real, but check. ◖ ⅊ ⅊ ≈ ♣

## Dungworth

### Royal Hotel

Main Road (B6076)
☎ (0114) 285 1213
12–3, 7–11; 12–4, 7–10.30 Sun
**Barnsley Bitter; Marston's Pedigree; Stones Bitter; guest beer** Ⓗ
Friendly, village local, popular with walkers in summer.
♨ Q ⛄ ⚘ ◖ ▲ ♣ P

## Elsecar

### Fitzwilliam Arms

Hill Street (50 yds from station)
☎ (01226) 742461
12–3.30 (not Mon), 7–11; 7–10.30 Sun,
closed Sun lunch
**Vaux Samson; Ward's Thorne BB, Best Bitter; guest beer** (occasional) Ⓗ
Friendly, two-roomed local with a central bar. Excellent value lunchtime meals; pie and pea suppers Sat eve. Camping in the grounds.
Q ⚘ ◖ ▲ ≈ ♣ P

## Fishlake

### Old Anchor Inn

Main Street ☎ (01302) 841423
12–3.30, 6 (7 Mon & Tue)–11; 12–3, 7–10.30 Sun
**Ruddles Best Bitter; John Smith's Bitter; guest beer** Ⓗ
Friendly village local serving excellent, home-cooked meals. An occasional beer, 'Natter Watter', is brewed for the pub by Rudgate. No eve meals Mon and Tue. ♨ ❀ ◖ ◗ ♣ P

**Try also: Hare & Hounds,** Church St (Mansfield)

## Greasbrough

### Prince of Wales

Potter Hill ☎ (01709) 551358
11–4 (3 Wed), 7–11; 12–3, 7–10.30 Sun
**Beer range varies** Ⓗ
Popular two-bar village pub with a traditional tap room and a comfortable lounge. Prices below the local average.
❀ ⊟ ♣ ⊔

## Grenoside

### Cow & Calf

Skew Hill Lane (½ mile off A61 towards Oughtibridge)
☎ (0114) 246 8191
11.30–3, 6–11; 11.30–11 Sat; 12–10.30 Sun
**Samuel Smith OBB** Ⓗ
Converted farmhouse with separate drinking areas and a family room. Welcoming atmosphere; plenty of rural charm. No eve meals Sun.
Q 🐴 ❀ ◖ ◗ ♣ P ⊘

## Hatfield Woodhouse

### Green Tree

Bearswood Green (A18/A614 jct) ☎ (01302) 840305
11–11; 12–10.30 Sun
**Ward's Thorne BB; guest beers** Ⓗ
Friendly and welcoming roadside inn, extensively refurbished. Very popular for its excellent food; separate restaurant and function room.
Q 🐴 ❀ 🛏 ◖ ◗ ♿ P

## Hemingfield

### Lundhill Tavern

Beechhouse Road (off A633, ½ mile along Lundhill Lane)
☎ (01226) 752283
12–11; 12–10.30 Sun
**Barnsley Bitter; John Smith's Bitter; Samuel Smith OBB; Stones Bitter; guest beers** Ⓗ
Pub off the beaten track, steeped in local coal mining history. Charity open-air rock festivals on bank hols. Meals served in the pub or in the upstairs function room till 8.30 (no eve meals Sun).
◖ ◗ P

## Hoyland

### Furnace Inn

163 Milton Road (B6097, 400 yds from centre)
☎ (01226) 742000
12–3, 6.30–11; 12–3, 7–10.30 Sun
**Vaux Double Maxim** Ⓗ**; Ward's Thorne BB** Ⓔ**, Best Bitter** Ⓗ/Ⓔ**; guest beers** Ⓗ
Recently refurbished pond-side pub that has retained all its character. A former Ward's *Pub of the Year* and *Ward's in Bloom* award-winner.
Q ❀ ♿ ⇌ (Elsecar) ♣ P ⊔

**Try also: Beggar & Gentleman,** Market St (Whitbread)

## Langsett

### Waggon & Horses

On A616 ☎ (01226) 763147
12–3, 7–11; 12–3, 7–10.30 Sun
**Draught Bass; Theakston Best Bitter; Younger No. 3** Ⓗ
Cosy, friendly roadside pub with an excellent reputation for home-cooked food.
♨ Q ❀ 🛏 ◖ ◗ ⛺ P

## Low Barugh

### Millers Inn

Dearne Hall Road
☎ (01226) 382888
11.30–2.30, 5.30–11; 11.30–11 Fri & Sat; 12–3, 7–10.30 Sun
**Burtonwood Bitter; John Smith's Bitter; Taylor Landlord; guest beers** Ⓗ
Free house backing onto the River Dearne, a meeting place for various clubs. Separate dining area; no eve meals Tue/Sun. Q ❀ ◖ ◗ ♿ ♣ P

## Mexborough

### Concertina Band Club

9A Dolcliffe Road
☎ (01709) 580841
12–4, 7–11; 12–3, 7–10.30 Sun
**Concertina Best Bitter, Bengal Tiger; Mansfield Bitter; John Smith's Bitter; guest beers** Ⓗ
Visitors are welcome at this small, friendly club which is steeped in local history. Brewing on the premises began in 1992, and the choice of Concertina beers varies. Frequent winner of local and national CAMRA awards, including *Regional Club of the Year*. ⇌ ♣ ⊔

### Falcon

12 Main Street
☎ (01709) 571170
11.30–4 (4.30 Fri, 5 Sat), 7–11; 12–3, 7–10.30 Sun
**Old Mill Bitter** Ⓗ
Lively pub: a smart lounge with raised seating areas and a games-oriented tap room. Other beers from the Old Mill range are often available.
❀ ⊟ ⇌ ♣

### George & Dragon

81 Church Street (off A6023, near river)
☎ (01709) 584375
12–4, 7–11; 12–11 Thu–Sat; 12–3, 7–10.30 Sun
**Vaux Samson, Double Maxim; Ward's Best Bitter; guest beers** Ⓗ
Welcoming, cosy pub with a central bar. The pleasant garden at the rear is popular with families. Recent extension and refurbishment have retained its character.
❀ ◖ ♿ P

## Midhopestones

### Midhopestones Arms

400 yds off A616, Stocksbridge bypass
☎ (01226) 762305
12–3, 6–11; 12–10.30 Sun
**Barnsley Bitter; Boddingtons Bitter; Courage Directors; Ruddles County; John Smith's Bitter; Taylor Landlord** Ⓗ
300-year-old village inn popular with walkers. A stone flagged floor, original beams and four real fires are features. Accommodation in summer only.
♨ Q ❀ 🛏 ◖ ◗ ♿ ⛺ ♣ P ⊘

## Monk Bretton

### Sun Inn

Burton Road
☎ (01226) 203621
11–11; 12–2.30, 7–10.30 Sun
**John Smith's Bitter** Ⓗ
Large village pub set back off the main road, with relaxing and comfortable, open-plan drinking areas. A large conservatory leads to an outside drinking area.
❀ ◖ P

## Owston

### Thornhurst Manor

Holme Lane (off A19, 400 yds S of B1220 jct) ☎ (01302) 337799
11–11; 12–10.30 Sun
**Barnsley Bitter; guest beers** Ⓗ
Newly-built pub/golfing complex, hidden behind woods. Restaurant open Tue–Sun (11–11). ♨ ❀ ◖ ◗ ♿ P

## Rotherham

### Belvedere

Moorgate Road
☎ (01709) 374126
11–11; 12–10.30 Sun
**Bentley's Yorkshire Bitter; Boddingtons Bitter; Castle**

Eden Ale; Flowers Original;
Marston's Pedigree H;
Whitbread Trophy E
Spacious pub on the
outskirts of the town centre
with a central wooden bar.
Popular with students.
❀ ◖ ▶ ♣ P

## Charter Arms

Eastwood Lane (high level of
market) ☎ (01709) 373066
10.30–11; 12–10.30 Sun
Mansfield Riding Bitter,
Bitter, Old Baily, seasonal
beers H
Friendly, modern, completely
refurbished pub offering
excellent food, a comfortable
lounge, a function room and a
games room. Very popular
with shoppers. ◖ ⊞ ≢ ♣

## Clifton

105 Clifton Lane (opp. cricket
and rugby ground)
☎ (01709) 372497
12–11; 12–10.30 Sun
Stones Bitter; guest beers H
Traditional early 20th-century
pub: a comfortable lounge and
a tap room. No jukebox.
Q ﾖ ♣ P

## Florence

Moorgate Road
☎ (01709) 360606
11.30–3, 5–11; 12–10.30 Sun
Stones Bitter, Tetley Bitter,
Imperial; guest beer
(occasional) H
Spacious pub near the town
centre, converted from a
nurses' home. The separate
dining area has play space for
children. Eve meals till 8.30.
ﾆ ❀ ◖ ▶ ♣ P

## Moulders Rest

110–112 Masbrough Street,
Masbrough (200 yds from
Millmoor football ground)
☎ (01709) 560095
12–3, 6 (7.30 Sat)–11; 12–3, 7–10.30
Sun
Stones Bitter; guest beer H
Large, main road corner pub: a
busy tap room, a snug and a
through lounge. Big on games.
Good value food (not served at
weekends).
ﾒ ◖ ≢ (Central) ♣ P

## Woodman

Midland Road, Masbrough (off
A629, by bus depot)
☎ (01709) 512128
12–3, 7–11; 12–2, 7–10.30 Sun
Stones Bitter; guest beer H
Friendly, former Bentley's pub
with a traditional tap room, a
snooker room upstairs and a
snug lounge. Built as a local in
1853; almost all the housing
around has since been
demolished. Q ❀ ⊞ ♣

Try also: Tut 'n' Shive,
Wellgate (Whitbread)

# Sheffield: *Central*

## Fat Cat

23 Alma Street
☎ (0114) 249 4801
11–3, 5.30–11; 12–3, 7–10.30 Sun
Kelham Island Bitter;
Marston's Pedigree; Taylor
Landlord; guest beers H
Sheffield's first real ale free
house, opened in 1981. Two
comfortable rooms (one no-
smoking), a corridor drinking
area and an upstairs function
room, used for overspill.
Kelham Island Brewery is
situated in the grounds and
another of its ales is always on
sale. ﾖ Q ❀ ◖ ♣ ⌂ ✄

## Harlequin

26 Johnson Street
☎ (0114) 249 3069
12–4, 7 (8 Sat)–11; 12–11 Fri; 12–3,
8–10.30 Sun
Ward's Best Bitter E
Traditional street-corner local
noted for the pot-bellied stove
in the tap room, which leads
through to a comfortable
lounge. Separate pool room;
corridor drinking area.
ﾖ Q ❀ ⊞ ≢ (Midland) ♣

## Hogshead

25 Orchard Street
☎ (0114) 272 1980
11–11; 12–10.30 Sun
Boddingtons Bitter; Castle
Eden Ale; guest beers H
Whitbread ale house catering
for shoppers during the day
and a mainly young, trendy
clientele in the eve, with a
large, open-plan bar, a small
gallery lounge and a
downstairs dining area,
opening onto the Orchard
Square shopping mall.
❀ ◖ ≢ ⌂

## Lord Nelson

166 Arundel Street
☎ (0114) 272 2650
12–11; 12–5, 7.30–11 Sat; 12–4,
7.30–10.30 Sun
Hardys & Hansons Best Bitter,
Classic; Stones Bitter H
Comfortable, street-corner
local in an area of small
workshops at the edge of the
city centre. Upstairs games/
function room. ◖ ≢ ♣

## Morrissey's Riverside

1 Mowbray Street
☎ (0114) 275 7306
5–11; 12–3, 7–11 Sat; 12–3, 7–10.30
Sun
Adnams Bitter; Boddingtons
Bitter; Fuller's London Pride;
Taylor Landlord, Ram Tam;
guest beers H
Three-roomed, street-corner
pub with an upstairs function
room for entertainment,
including comedy and poetry
nights. A pleasant garden

overlooks the River Don.
Q ❀ ≢ ♣

## Red House

168 Solly Street
☎ (0114) 272 7926
12–3 (4 Sat), 5 (7.30 Sat)–11; 12–3,
7.30–10.30 Sun
Ward's Best Bitter; guest
beers H
Renovated, traditional local,
retaining three drinking areas,
one with darts and pool. Live
music Tue (ceilidh) and Fri
(Appalachian). Quiz Thu. Q ◖ ♣

## Red Lion

109 Charles Street
☎ (0114) 272 4997
11.30–3, 5.30–11; 7–10.30 Sun, closed
Sun lunch
Ward's Best Bitter; guest
beer H
Pub where a large lounge with
raised seating areas adjoins a
conservatory overlooking the
garden. Unusually for the city
centre, it retains a small corner
tap room. ❀ ◖ ⊞ ≢

## Rutland Arms

86 Brown Street
☎ (0114) 272 9003
11.30–3, 5–11; 12–4, 7–11 Sat; 12–3,
8–10.30 Sun
Ind Coope Burton Ale;
Marston's Pedigree; Tetley
Bitter; Younger No. 3 H
City-centre gem in a cultural
quarter. A comfortable lounge
lies behind an impressive
Gilmour's frontage. Eve meals
Mon–Fri till 7.
Q ❀ ﾒ ◖ ▶ ≢ P

## Ship Inn

312 Shalesmoor
☎ (0114) 281 2204
12–3, 6 (5 Fri, 7.30 Sat)–11; 12–3,
7.30–10.30 Sun
Hardys & Hansons Best Bitter;
guest beer H
Community pub with an
impressive Tomlinson's
frontage which opens into a
comfortable, L-shaped lounge
with a pool area at the rear.
♣ P ⊟

## Tap & Spile

42 Waingate ☎ (0114) 272 7042
11.30–3, 5.30 (7 Sat)–11; 7–10.30 Sun,
closed Sun lunch
Beer range varies H
Refurbished, street-corner pub
where the large bar has
exposed brickwork and bare
boards and a smaller side room
has a raised darts area (no-
smoking lunchtime). Folk
music Wed; quiz Thu. Beer
festival Oct. Usually eight
beers on sale.
Q ◖ ≢ ♣ ⌂ ✄

# Sheffield: *East*

## Alma

76 South Street, Mosborough
(behind Eckington Hall)
☎ (0114) 248 4781

11.30–3.30, 6.30 (6.45 winter)–11;
12–3, 7–10.30 Sun
**Vaux Samson** H**; Ward's Best
Bitter** E
Traditional, two-roomed pub
with a central bar. The low,
wood-beamed ceiling in the
lounge provides a cosy
drinking atmosphere. A bit off
the beaten track but worth the
search. Q ⌂ ☞ ♣ ⍾

## Carbrook Hall

537 Attercliffe Common,
Carbrook ☎ (0114) 244 0177
12–3, 5–11; 12–11 Fri & Sat; 12–3,
7–10.30 Sun
**John Smith's Magnet; Stones
Bitter** H
Large, three-roomed,
reputedly haunted pub
retaining many of the hall's
original features. Decor is on a
Civil War theme, due to links
with a local Parliamentarian. It
can be busy lunchtime or when
events are on at the nearby
arena (hours may then be
extended). ♨ ⌂ ☞ ◑ ▶ ⍾
(Carbrook) ♣ P

## Cocked Hat

75 Worksop Road, Attercliffe
☎ (0114) 244 8332
11–11; 11–3, 7–11 Sat & bank hols;
12–2, 7–10.30 Sun
**Marston's Bitter, Pedigree,
HBC** H
Popular Victorian pub by the
Don Valley Stadium: one of the
city's smallest and winner of
many local CAMRA awards.
No meals Sat/Sun.
Q ☞ ◑ ⍾ (Attercliffe) ♣

## Milestone

12 Peaks Mount, Waterthorpe
☎ (0114) 247 1614
11–11; 12–3, 7.30–10.30 Sun
**Banks's Mild, Bitter** E**,
seasonal beers; Camerons
Strongarm** H
Large, modern pub serving
Crystal Peaks shopping centre,
popular with locals in the eve.
Two large rooms, including a
conservatory, are served by a
central bar. Eve meals Mon–
Thu till 8. Wheelchair WC.
☞ ◑ ▶ ⍾ ♿ ⍾ (Crystal Peaks)
P ✁ ⍾

## Red Lion

145 Duke Street
☎ (0114) 272 8296
2–5, 7–11; 12–4, 7–10.30 Sun
**Burtonwood Bitter, Top Hat** H
Unspoilt, traditional pub with
three separate rooms and a
corridor bar/drinking area.
Popular with locals and always
lively.
Q ≢ (Midland) ⍾ (Parkway)

## Sheffield: *North*

## Cask & Cutler

1 Henry Street
☎ (0114) 249 2295

12–2, 5.30–11; 12–11 Fri & Sat; 12–3,
7–10.30 Sun
**Beer range varies** H
Shrine to real ale, serving some
of the lowest priced beers in
the city (six ales). Newly
refurbished no-smoking room;
new outside drinking area. Eve
meals end at 6.30. ♨ Q ☞ ◑ ▶
⍾ ⍾ (Shalesmoor) ♣ ⌂ P ✁
⍾

## Hillsborough Barracks Inn

601 Penistone Road
☎ (0114) 232 2100
11–3, 5–11; 11–11 Sat; 12–3, 7–10.30
Sun
**Barnsley Bitter, IPA, Black
Heart Stout; John Smith's
Magnet; Stones Bitter; guest
beers** H
Ex-Gilmour's house close to
the barracks. Sold by Tetley
into the free trade, it has
become a lively centre for local
drinkers; well refurbished,
with no tat or bare bricks in
sight. Sheffield Steelers meet
their fans here. Q ☞ ☞ ⍾ ◑ ▶
⍾ (Bamforth St) ♣ P ✁

## Morrissey's East House

18 Spital Hill
☎ (0114) 272 6916
12–3, 5–11; 12–3, 7–10.30 Sun
**Boddingtons Bitter; Taylor
Landlord; guest beers** H
Long, narrow pub with a single
bar. Home to climbing and
hiking clubs. Q ♣

## Robin Hood

Greaves Lane, Little Matlock,
Stannington (right turn after
Pinegrove Country Club)
☎ (0114) 234 4565
12–2.30 (3 summer), 7–11; 12–3,
7–10.30 Sun
**Stones Bitter** E
Former coaching inn on a
defunct route to Manchester,
retaining its tap room. Long-
serving licensees.
Q ☞ ◑ ▶ ♣ P ⌂

## Rose & Crown

21 Stour Lane, Wadsley
☎ (0114) 233 7980
11.30–3 (4.30 Sat), 6–11 (may vary in
winter); 12–3, 7–10.30 Sun
**Tetley Bitter** H
Welcoming village local, once a
row of cottages, close to
Wadsley Common beauty spot.
Attractive garden and
children's play area; split-level
bar. No bar food Sun or Mon
eves. ☞ ◑ ▶ ♣ P

## Sheffield: *South*

## Archer Road Beer Stop

57 Archer Road
☎ (0114) 255 1356
11 (10.30 Sat)–10; 12–2, 6–10 Sun
**Bateman XXXB; Taylor
Landlord; guest beers** H

Corner shop-type real ale
off-licence with a wide
selection of bottle-conditioned
and foreign beers.

## Cremorne

185 London Road
☎ (0114) 255 0126
12–11; 12–3.30, 7.30–11 Sat; 12–3.30,
7–10.30 Sun
**Marston's Pedigree; Tetley
Bitter, Imperial; guest beers** H
Tetley Festival Alehouse in the
stone and bare boards
tradition: a large, comfortable
L-shaped drinking area and a
lower level games area with a
pool table. Up to four beer
festivals a year. One of the
better places to drink in an area
awash with pubs. ♣

## Earl of Arundel & Surrey

528 Queens Road
☎ (0114) 255 1006
11–11; 12–10.30 Sun
**Ward's Thorne BB, Best
Bitter** H
Imposing, Victorian, red brick
building, very much games-
oriented, with two snooker
tables. The stables house shire
horses and other visiting
animals. Early eve meals
served weekdays; no lunches
weekends. ☞ ◑ ▶ ⍾ ≢ ♣ P

## Old Mother Redcap

Prospect Road, Bradway
☎ (0114) 236 0179
11.30–3, 5.30–11; 11.30–11 Sat;
12–10.30 Sun
**Samuel Smith OBB** H
Modern farmhouse-style
building at Bradway bus
terminus. The single, L-shaped
lounge attracts a good cross-
section of the community. Eve
meals Thu and Fri only.
☞ ◑ ▶ ≢ (Dore) ♣ P ⌂

## Shakespeare

106 Well Road
☎ (0114) 255 3995
12–3.30 (4 Sat), 5.30 (7 Sat)–11; 12–3,
7–10.30 Sun
**Stones Bitter; Tetley Bitter,
Imperial; guest beers** H
Welcoming, community pub:
one bar, but with separate
drinking areas. Guest beers
come from Carlsberg-Tetley's
Tapster's Choice range. ☞ ♣ P

## White Swan

57 Greenhill Main Road
☎ (0114) 237 7851
11–11; 12–10.30 Sun
**Boddingtons Bitter; Castle
Eden Ale; Marston's Pedigree;
Whitbread Trophy; guest
beer** H
Fine village community pub
with four distinct drinking
areas served from a central bar.
Good, home-cooked food
served every day, except Sun.
The guest beer is from
Whitbread's range.
☞ ◑ ▶ ♣ P ✁

## Sheffield: *West*

### Banner Cross
971 Ecclesall Road
☎ (0114) 266 1479
11.30–11; 12–10.30 Sun
**Ind Coope Burton Ale; Tetley Bitter; guest beer** Ⓗ
Busy local with a panelled lounge, a large, quiet, tap room and an upstairs games room.
Q ✿ ◑ ♣

### Cherry Tree
2 Carterknowle Avenue
☎ (0114) 258 5051
12–11; 12–10.30 Sun
**Draught Bass; Stones Bitter; Worthington Bitter; guest beer** Ⓗ
Friendly estate local built in 1961. The single bar has a raised area. Q ✿ ◑ ♣ P

### Devonshire Arms
118 Ecclesall Road
☎ (0114) 272 2202
11–11; 12–10.30 Sun
**Vaux Waggle Dance; Ward's Best Bitter; guest beers** Ⓗ
Extensively renovated local with several partitioned seating areas and a conservatory. The Ward's brewery tap. Q ✿ ◑ & P

### Lescar
303 Sharrowvale Road
☎ (0114) 266 3857
12–11; 12–10.30 Sun
**Draught Bass; Stones Bitter; Taylor Landlord; guest beer** Ⓗ
Friendly, street-corner local, popular with locals and students: a tap room, a lounge and a function room (used for live bands and for the comedy club Thu eve). Eve meals end at 7. Q ✿ ◑ ▶ ⊞ & ♣ P

### Old Grindstone
3 Crookes
☎ (0114) 266 0322
11–11; 12–10.30 Sun
**Taylor Landlord; Vaux Waggle Dance** Ⓗ**; Ward's Best Bitter** Ⓗ/Ⓔ**; guest beer** Ⓗ
Spacious, busy pub. The Victorian design lounge has a raised area; the oak-panelled games room is based on a gentlemen's club. Eve meals end at 7.30. ✿ ◑ ▶ ♣

### Old Heavygate
114 Matlock Road
☎ (0114) 234 0003
2 (12 Sat)–4, 7–11; 12–3, 7–10.30 Sun
**Hardys & Hansons Best Bitter, Classic** Ⓗ
Pub dating from 1696, previously a cottage and toll house. ✿ ⊞ & ♣ P 🍺

### Sportsman
679 Redmires Road
☎ (0114) 230 1935
11.30–4, 6–11; 12–3, 7–10.30 Sun
**Courage Directors; Ruddles Best Bitter; John Smith's Bitter** Ⓗ
Country pub within the city boundary; family-run, with genuine friendliness. Note the curious corner mirrored cabinets. No meals Sun.
Q ✿ ◑ & ▲ ♣ P 🍺

## Sprotbrough

### Boat Inn
Nursery Lane, Lower Sprotbrough
☎ (01302) 857188
11–3, 6–11 (may extend summer); 11–11 Sat; 12–10.30 Sun
**Courage Directors; John Smith's Bitter, Magnet** Ⓗ
17th-century former coaching house where Sir Walter Scott wrote *Ivanhoe*, attractively set beside the River Don. It reopened in 1985 after use as a farm. Restaurant and bar meals served; no bar meals Sat/Sun eves. ✿ ◑ ▶ & P

## Thorne

### John Bull
Waterside (out of town, past M18 jct 6)
☎ (01405) 814677
12–2, 7 (6 summer)–11; 12–3, 7–10.30 Sun
**Old Mill Bitter; John Smith's Bitter** Ⓗ
A tavern since the 16th century; open-plan but with separate drinking areas. The emphasis is on food.
Q ◑ ▶ & ⇌ (North) ♣ P

## Thorpe Hesley

### Masons Arms
Thorpe Street
☎ (0114) 246 8079
11.30–3, 6–11; 12–3, 7–10.30 Sun
**John Smith's Bitter; Theakston Best Bitter, Old Peculier; Younger IPA** Ⓗ
Welcoming, early 19th-century pub with one bar and three rooms on a split level. No food Sun. ✿ ◑ ▶ P

## Thurlstone

### Huntsman
136 Manchester Road (A628, 1½ miles W of Penistone)
☎ (01226) 762278
6–11; 12–4, 7–11 Sat; 12–3, 7–10.30 Sun
**Bateman XB; Boddingtons Bitter; Castle Eden Ale; Marston's Pedigree; Taylor Landlord; guest beer** Ⓗ
Charming, old terraced pub. A working Yorkshire range at one end provides respite from the Pennine winters. Stunning views from the garden. No food Sun. ⚌ ✿ 🍴 ▶ ▲

## Tickhill

### Carpenters Arms
Westgate ☎ (01302) 742839
11–3.30, 6–11; 12–3, 7–10.30 Sun
**Vaux Samson; Ward's Best Bitter; guest beers** Ⓗ
Appealing pub with a lounge, a bar and a large, no-smoking, family room. Award-winning garden. No food Sun/Mon.
🐾 ✿ ◑ ⊞ ♣ P 🍺

### Scarbrough Arms
Sunderland Street
☎ (01302) 742977
11–3, 6–11; 12–3, 7–10.30 Sun
**Courage Directors; Ruddles County; John Smith's Bitter, Magnet; guest beers** Ⓗ
Popular local with three rooms of differing character. Guest beers, from independent breweries, vary weekly. Home-made lunches (no food Sun).
⚌ Q ✿ ◑ ⊞ ♣ P 🍺

Try also: Royal Oak, Northgate (Whitbread)

## Victoria

### Victoria Inn
Huddersfield Road (A616, near pipe works) ☎ (01484) 682785
7–11; 12–2, 7–11 Fri & Sat; 12–2, 7–10.30 Sun
**Tetley Bitter; Theakston Best Bitter** Ⓗ
Barnsley area's longest standing *Guide* entry, with possibly the longest serving licensees (since 1956). Good welcome (but children not allowed in). Try a toasty from the antique grill.
⚌ Q ✿ ♣ P

## Wheatley Hills

### Wheatley Hotel
Thorne Road ☎ (01302) 364092
11–11; 12–3, 7–10.30 Sun
**John Smith's Bitter, Magnet; Theakston XB** Ⓗ
Large, friendly hotel with a comfortable lounge, divided by impressive wood/leaded glass sliding doors. Well-equipped children's play area. The restaurant (closed Sun eve) serves excellent value home cooking.
🐾 ✿ 🛏 ◑ ▶ P

## Whiston

### Golden Ball
Turner Lane ☎ (01709) 378200
11.45–11; 12–10.30 Sun
**Ind Coope Burton Ale; Marston's Pedigree; Taylor Landlord; Tetley Bitter; guest beer** Ⓗ
Picture postcard pub offering a pleasant outside drinking area. Full of olde-worlde charm, it

offers an extensive bar menu, a restaurant and two real fires.
🏠 ✿ ◖ ▶ P ⊁

# Wombwell

## Royal Oak
13 Church Street
☎ (01226) 210900
11–11; 12–10.30 Sun
**Boddingtons Bitter; John Smith's Bitter; guest beers** H
Attractive, town-centre pub with old Clarkson's Brewery windows. Live music Sat/Sun; a popular meeting place for clubs. Eve meals finish early.
🏠 ◖ ▶ ⊞ ⇌ ♣

# Worsbrough Village

## Edmunds Arms
25 Worsbrough Village (off A61)
☎ (01226) 206865
11–3, 6–11; 12–4, 7–10.30 Sun
**Samuel Smith OBB** H
Splendid inn opposite an historic church: a lounge, tap room and a restaurant, offering good value food. No eve meals Sun/Mon. ✿ ◖ ▶ ♿ ♣ P

# Wortley

## Wortley Arms Hotel
Halifax Road
☎ (0114) 288 2245
12–2.30, 5.30–11; 12–3, 7–10.30 Sun
**Stones Bitter; Wortley Earls Bitter, Countess; Younger IPA, No. 3; guest beers** H
16th-century coaching house in a picturesque village, ideally placed for walkers. Very large feature fireplace in the lounge; upstairs function room. Wortley beers are brewed in the cellar. 🏠 Q ♿ 🏠 ◖ ▶ ⊞ ♿
▲ ♣ P ⊁ 🍺

### West Yorkshire

# Airedale

## Airedale Hotel
197 Hollywell Lane
☎ (01977) 553497
11–11; 11–10.30 Sun
**Tetley Bitter, Imperial; guest beers** H
Large, open-plan, two-roomed pub around a central bar with a separate games area. Popular with locals. Live music Mon; quizzes Tue and Thu.
🏠 🏠 ◖ ⊞ ♣ P

# Bingley

## Ferrands Arms
Queen Street
☎ (01274) 563949
11.30–11; 12–10.30 Sun

**Taylor Golden Best, Best Bitter, Landlord; Tetley Bitter** H
Spacious pub, close to the arts centre, very rarely found empty. The lunchtime menu (not served Sun) is popular with local workers. Upstairs function room. Easy parking nearby. ⇌

# Bradford

## Blue Pig
Fagley Road, Lower Fagley (lane at end of Fagley Rd)
☎ (0113) 256 2738
3–11; 11–10.30 Fri & Sat; 12–10.30 Sun
**Taylor Landlord; Tetley Bitter; Theakston Best Bitter; guest beers** H
Split-level pub on the Leeds Country Way. Good atmosphere; quiz most nights. Excellent family room. Snacks available afternoons.
♿ ✿ ♣ P

## Cartwright Hotel
308 Manningham Lane, Manningham (A650)
☎ (01274) 499908
11–11; 12–10.30 Sun
**Taylor Landlord; Theakston Mild, Best Bitter; guest beers** (occasional) H
Hotel situated near Lister Park and Cartwright Museum and Art Gallery. Nicely decorated conservatory; high-class restaurant (English and Indian cuisine). Eve meals end at 8.30; no meals weekends.
✿ 🏠 ◖ ▶ P

## Castle
20 Grattan Road (200 yds from centre, off Westgate)
☎ (01274) 393166
11.30–11; closed Sun
**Mansfield Riding Mild, Riding Bitter, Bitter; guest beers** H
Popular city-centre house, built in 1898. The single room has been partitioned to provide a drinking area away from the main bar. Bradford CAMRA *Pub of the Year* 1995. Free food Fri lunchtime. Car park open eves and weekends. Q ◖
⇌ (Exchange/Forster Sq) P

## Corn Dolly
110 Bolton Road (bottom end of city centre)
☎ (01274) 720219
11.30–11; 12–10.30 Sun
**Black Sheep Best Bitter; Moorhouse's Premier; Theakston Best Bitter; Younger No. 3; guest beers** H
Bradford CAMRA *Pub of the Year* 1994, serving up to 12 guest beers every week (over 800 pumpclips on display). Comfortable and friendly.
🏠 ✿ ◖ ♿ ⇌ (Forster Sq) ♣ P

## Fighting Cock
21–23 Preston Street (between Thornton and Lister Hill Rds)
☎ (01274) 726907
11.30–11; 12–10.30 Sun
**Black Sheep Special; Old Mill Bitter; Samuel Smith OBB; Taylor Landlord; Theakston Old Peculier; guest beers** H
Down to earth, bare-boarded drinkers' haven in an industrial area. At least 11 beers on sale. The menu (not served Sun) consists of a famous chilli and docker's wedge sandwiches. Live bands. ◖ ⌂

## Idle Cock
1190 Bolton Road (A6176, 2 miles from centre)
☎ (01274) 639491
11.30–11; 12–10.30 Sun
**Black Sheep Best Bitter; Old Mill Bitter; Taylor Landlord; Tetley Bitter; Vaux Samson; guest beers** H
Excellent, two-roomed free house, frequented by locals.
✿ ◖

## Malt Kiln
129 Idle Road, Undercliffe
☎ (01274) 630035
11–11; 12–10.30 Sun
**Ind Coope Burton Ale; Marston's Pedigree; Tetley Bitter; guest beers** H
Cosy, inter-war pub, built by Whitaker's with some of the profits from the sale of their brewery; now a Tetley Festival Alehouse. The jukebox can be loud. ✿ P

## Melborn
104 White Abbey Road (B6144, ½ mile from centre)
☎ (01274) 726867
12–11; 12–10.30 Sun
**Commercial Alesman, Wild Boar; Tetley Bitter; guest beers** H
Friendly, down to earth pub with music most eves: three rooms adorned with breweriana and musical instruments. ✿ 🏠 ⊞ ♣ P

## New Beehive ☆
171 Westgate
☎ (01274) 721784
11–11 (11am Fri & Sat); 12–10.30 Sun
**Commercial Worth BB; Mitchell's Lancaster Bomber; Taylor Landlord; guest beers** H
Built by the local council in 1901 to replace pubs lost to road widening and bought by an ancestor of the present licensee. Gas-lit and multi-roomed, it has a new cellar bar.
🏠 Q ✿ 🏠 ◖ ♣ ⌂ P

## Prospect of Bradford
527 Bolton Road (½ mile from centre) ☎ (01274) 727018
7–11; 3–5, 7–11 Sat; 12–4, 7–10.30 Sun

**Tetley Bitter; Theakston Best Bitter** H
Victorian building with extensive views of Bradford. Organ music and sing-alongs at weekends. Function room available. The eat in or take-home curries are recommended. ♨ ▶ ♣ P

## Queen Ale House
863 Thornton Road, Fairweather Green
☎ (01274) 542898
12–11; 12–10.30 Sun
**Boddingtons Bitter; Castle Eden Ale; Flowers Original; guest beers** H
Busy, two-roomed free house with an ever-changing guest beer range. Local stone and slate flooring add to the character. No meals Sun.
❀ ◖ ⊟ ♣ P

## Rams Revenge
1–3 Upper Millergate (opp. Arndale Centre at Kirkgate jct)
☎ (01274) 720283
11.30–11; 11.30–5.30, 7–11.30 Sat; 12–6 Sun
**Moorhouse's Pendle Witches Brew; Taylor Landlord; Tetley Bitter; Theakston XB; guest beer** H
Single-room, split-level, city-centre ale house on the site of a former toll booth and court house, the dungeon of which is now the pub cellar. The adjoining Cobbles Bar opens 11.30–3 Mon–Sat and 7.30–11 Fri–Sat. ◖ ⇌ (Forster Sq/ Interchange) ♣

## Red Lion
589 Thornton Road, Girlington (B6145) ☎ (01274) 498664
11–3 (3.30 Thu), 5.30–11; 11–11 Fri & Sat; 12–3, 7–10.30 Sun
**Samuel Smith OBB** H
Small, friendly local with a large lounge and a small tap room. Many social activities. No food Sun. ❀ ◖ ♣ P

## Shoulder of Mutton
28 Kirkgate ☎ (01274) 726038
11–11; 12–2, 7–10.30 Sun
**Samuel Smith OBB** H
The 18th consecutive entry for this small, multi-room, city-centre pub dating from 1825. A cross-section of clients enjoy the home-made lunches (not served Sun) and the large, award-winning suntrap garden. Q ☎ ❀ ◖ ⇌ (Interchange/Forster Sq)

## Steve Biko Bar
Bradford University: D Floor, Richmond Building (off Gt Horton Rd) ☎ (01274) 383257
11 (12 Sat)–11; 7–10.30 Sun, closed Sun lunch
**Castle Eden Ale; Courage Directors; John Smith's Bitter; Taylor Landlord; Theakston XB; guest beers** H

Lively student bar, very busy at times. Live bands Thu eve.
◖ ♣ ⌂ P

## Castleford

### Crimea Tavern
Savile Road (300 yds from centre on right bank of River Aire) ☎ (01977) 557868
11–11; 12–10.30 Sun
**John Smith's Bitter; Tetley Bitter; guest beers** H
Two-roomed local, often very busy Fri and Sat eves. Up to four guest beers, including one or two from local brewers.
⇌ ♣ P

## Churwell

### Commercial Inn
Elland Road ☎ (0113) 253 2776
11.30–3 (4 Sat), 6–11; 12–3, 7–10.30 Sun
**John Smith's Bitter; Tetley Mild, Bitter** H
Known as 'Top 'Ole', a pleasantly refurbished pub that has kept its separate drinking areas. Family room until 8pm. No lunches Sat/ Sun. ☎ ❀ ◖ ♣ P

## Cleckheaton

### Marsh Hotel
28 Bradford Road (200 yds from bus station)
☎ (01274) 872104
11.45–3, 7–11; 12–5, 7–10.30 Sun
**Old Mill Mild, Bitter, Bullion, seasonal beers** H
Good local with a friendly welcome. Its layout includes a quiet dais and a games area.
♿ ♣ P

## Crossroads

### Quarry House Inn
Bingley Road, Lees Moor (½ mile from A629/A6033 jct)
☎ (01535) 642239
12–3, 7–11; 12–3, 7–10.30 Sun
**Ind Coope Burton Ale; Taylor Landlord; Tetley Bitter; Theakston Best Bitter** H
Family-run, converted farmhouse in open countryside with extensive views. The bar is a former church pulpit and is set in a small, cosy area. Excellent food (especially the mixed grill Wed eve); late supper licence. Children welcome. ♨ ❀ ◖ ▶ ♿ ♠ P

## Dewsbury

### Beer Street
Nowells Yard (off Boothroyd Lane, ¼ mile W of centre)
☎ (01924) 466207
12 (5 Mon & Tue)–11; 12–10.30 Sun
**Bateman Mild, XB; guest beers** H

Multi-roomed pub with a traditional tap room and flagged floors; reopened after a major refit. Quiet and lively areas.
♨ Q ❀ ◖ ▶ ⊟ ⇌ ♣ ⌂

## 'Sir' Geoffrey Boycott OBE
125 High Street, Westtown
☎ (01924) 457610
11–3, 5.30–11; 11–11 Sat; 12–10.30 Sun
**Theakston Best Bitter, XB; guest beers** H
Renovated pub with stone-flagged floors and pictures of the man himself. Excellent meals. Live music Thu/Sun.
❀ ◖ ♿ ♣ ⌂ P

## West Riding Licensed Refreshment Rooms
Railway Station, Wellington Road ☎ (01924) 459193
11–11; 12–10.30 Sun
**Bateman Mild, XB, XXXB; Linfit English Guineas Stout; guest beers** H
Interesting restoration of a mid 19th-century station master's house and rooms into an open, cosy, wood-floored bar. Weekly live bands; popular Wed curry night (meals other eves till 7). Vast numbers of guest ales; annual beer festival.
♨ ❀ ◖ ▶ ♿ ⇌ ♣ ⌂ P ⅍

## Elland

### Golden Fleece
Lindley Road, Blackley (1 mile S of Elland, near M62 jct 24)
☎ (01422) 372704
12–2.30 (not Sat), 7–11; 12–3, 7–10.30 Sun
**Vaux Samson; Ward's Thorne BB** H
Comfortable village inn with brassware and pictures, next to a cricket pitch. The organ is played Thu eve. ❀ ◖ P

*Try also:* **Barge & Barrel**, Park Rd (Free); **Colliers**, Park Rd (Samuel Smith)

## Flanshaw

### Flanshaw Hotel
Flanshaw Lane (500 yds from A638) ☎ (01924) 290830
11.30 (1 Tue)–11; 12–3, 7.30–10.30 Sun
**Tetley Bitter; John Smith's Bitter; guest beers** H
Large, well-renovated estate pub with three rooms. Good range of guest beers at competitive prices. Lunches on request Mon–Sat; Sun lunch served. ◖ ▶ ♣ P ⊟

## Garforth

### Miners Arms
4 Aberford Road
☎ (0113) 286 2105
12–11; 12–10.30 Sun

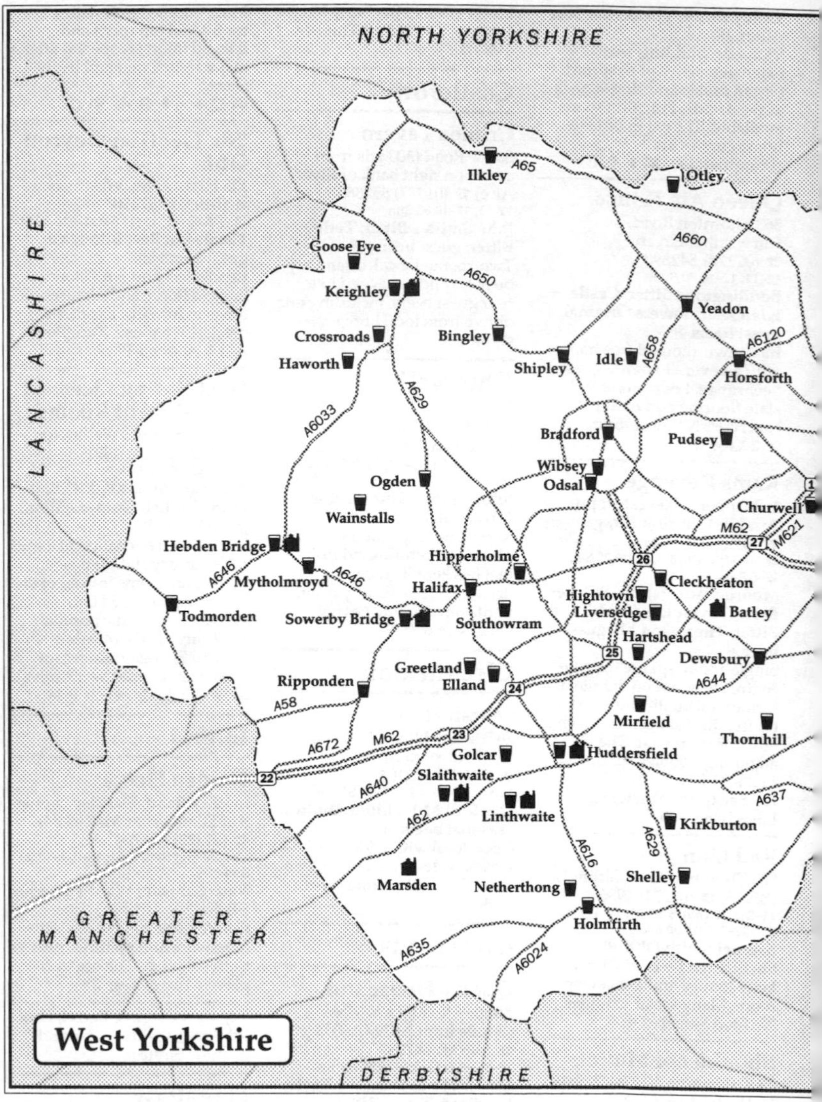


**Ind Coope Burton Ale; Marston's Pedigree; Tetley Mild, Bitter, Imperial** Ⓗ
Tetley Festival Alehouse: a one-bar pub with various drinking areas, attractively refurbished. Mini-beer festivals. Lively at weekends (but no food weekends). Note: an aspirator is used on guest beers.
⛫ Q ❀ ◐ ♿ ⇌ ♣ P ⊬

## Golcar

### Golcar Lily

Slades Road (follow sign for Heath House Mill)
☎ (01484) 659277
12–3, 5.30–11; 12–11 Sat; 12–3, 7–10.30 Sun
**Mansfield Riding Bitter, Bitter, Old Baily; guest beer** Ⓗ
Friendly, light and airy, stone building formerly a Co-op, perched on the side of a hill with panoramic views. Cosy bar; separate restaurant (no food Mon). ❀ ◐ ◑ P

## Goose Eye

### Turkey Inn

☎ (01535) 681339
12–3 (5 Sat; not Mon), 5.30 (7 Sat)–11; 12–3, 7–10.30 Sun
**Goose Eye Bitter; Ind Coope Burton Ale; Tetley Bitter; guest beer** Ⓗ
Village pub with three drinking areas, two decorated with barrel staves and two with open fires. Separate dining area (steaks a specialty). Children welcome till 8pm.
⛫ ❀ ◐ ◑ ⛺ ♣ P

## Greetland

### Greetland Community & Sporting Association

Rochdale Road (B6113, by church)
☎ (01422) 370140
7 (12 Sat)–11; 12–3, 7–11 Wed; 12–10.30 Sun
**Beer range varies** Ⓗ

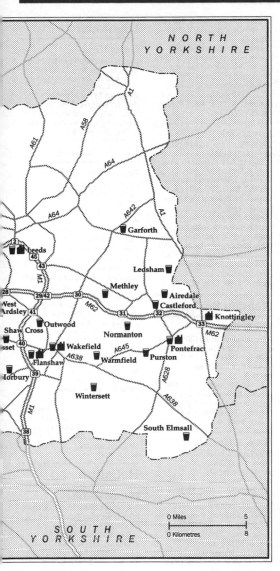

guest beer is from the Vaux
range. 🌣 ♣

## Halifax

### Commercial Inn

23 Lower Skircoat Green (off
A629 1¼ miles S of centre)
☎ (01422) 365078
12–2, 5–11; 12–3, 7–10.30 Sun
**Tetley Bitter; guest beer** H
Small, friendly pub with a
long-serving licensee. The
guest beer may be a house beer
by Coach House. 🌣 ⌸ ♣

### Horse & Jockey

301 Warley Road, Highroad
Well (1½ miles W of centre)
☎ (01422) 361992
12–11; 12–10.30 Sun
**Old Mill Bitter; Ruddles
County; John Smith's Bitter** H
Welcoming, two-roomed pub,
deservedly popular with all
ages. The tap room is always
busy. 🌣 ⌸ ♣ P

### Shears Inn

Paris Gates, Boys Lane (behind
flats off Shaw Hill)
☎ (01422) 362936
11.45–11; 12–10.30 Sun
**Taylor Golden Best, Best
Bitter, Landlord; Younger
Scotch, No. 3; guest beers** H
Hidden in a wooded valley
bottom and overshadowed by
nearby Holdsworth's Mill, this
small, one-roomed pub, is
popular with all ages, and is
home for several sports teams.
The Hebble Trail footpath
passes close by. No meals
weekends. ♨ 🌣 ◑ ♣ P

### Tap & Spile

1 Clare Road ☎ (01422) 353661
11–11; 12–3, 7–10.30 Sun
**Big Lamp Bitter; Tap & Spile
Bitter, Premium; Wells Eagle;
guest beers** H
Mock Tudor extravaganza
built in 1931 as Ramsden's
brewery tap. Sensitive
conversion to a traditional ale
house has retained many
original fittings in its two
drinking areas. Spacious
upstairs function room.
◑ ⇌ ⌂ ⦚

Club which caters for all ages
with a single, friendly bar
serving six cask beers
(normally one from Black
Sheep and one from Taylor).
🌣 ♣ P

### Star

1 Lindwell (off B6113)
☎ (01422) 373164
12–4 (not Tue), 7–11; 12–3, 7–10.30
Sun
**Ward's Thorne BB, Best Bitter;
guest beer** H
Friendly village local: a well-lit,
busy tap room and a cosy
lounge with subdued lighting.
The start/finish of the
Calderdale Way is nearby. The

## 🍺 INDEPENDENT BREWERIES

| | |
|---|---|
| **Black Horse:** Hebden Bridge | **Old Court:** Huddersfield |
| **Blackmoor:** Batley | **Rat & Ratchet:** Huddersfield |
| **Clark's:** Wakefield | **Riverhead:** Marsden |
| **Commercial:** Keighley | **Ryburn:** Sowerby Bridge |
| **Eastwood's:** Huddersfield | **Steam Packet:** Knottingley |
| **Goose Eye:** Keighley | **Taylor:** Keighley |
| **Kitchen:** Huddersfield | **Tigertops:** Flanshaw |
| **Linfit:** Linthwaite | **Tomlinson's:** Pontefract |
| **Merrimans:** Leeds | **Wild's:** Slaithwaite |

## Three Pigeons Ale House

1 Sun Fold, South Parade (left from station, 350 yds)
☎ (01422) 347001
12–3, 5–11; 12–11 Sat; 12–3, 7–10.30 Sun

**Black Sheep Best Bitter; Boddingtons Bitter; Old Mill Bitter; Taylor Best Bitter; Tetley Bitter; guest beer** Ⓗ
Small, friendly and hospitable ale house consisting of an octagonal drinking area (note the mural overhead) with rooms radiating off. House beer from Coach House.
🏠 🛏 ◖ 🌿

## Woodcock

213 Gibbet Street (½ mile W of centre) ☎ (01422) 359906
11–11; 12–4, 7–10.30 Sun
**Bateman XXXB; Black Sheep Special; Boddingtons Bitter; Old Mill Bitter; Wadworth IPA; guest beers** Ⓗ
Ale house-style pub with bare floorboards and pumpclip and bottle collections. Three or four changing guest beers from independent breweries sold. It may open 12–10.30 Sun on rugby match days.
🏠 ◖ ♣ ⟲

**Try also: Lewins**, Bull Green (Bass)

## Hartshead

### New Inn

108 Prospect Road (B6119, ¾ mile from A62)
☎ (01274) 874781
5–11; 11–11 Sat & summer Tue–Fri; 12–10.30 Sun
**Boddingtons Bitter; Tetley Bitter; guest beers** Ⓗ
Village local extended into adjoining cottages with many old and interesting features. Fine views. Frequently changing guest beers (four). No meals Mon. 🏠 🛏 ◖ ▶ ♣

## Haworth

### Fleece

Main Street ☎ (01535) 642172
12 (11.30 summer)–11; 12–10.30 Sun
**Taylor Mild, Golden Best, Best Bitter, Porter, Landlord, Ram Tam** Ⓗ
Former coaching inn with a small, stone-flagged bar area and three drinking areas, including a family room and a games room. A popular local with a welcome for visitors. No wheelchair access to ladies' WC.
🏠 🛏 ◖ 🚻
🚃 (KWVLR) ♣

### Haworth Old Hall

Sun Street (bottom of Main St, opp. park) ☎ (01535) 642709
11–11; 12–10.30 Sun

**Draught Bass; Stones Bitter; Taylor Golden Best; Tetley Bitter** Ⓗ
Three-room, 17th-century Tudor building featuring open stonework, oak beams and mullioned windows. No wheelchair access to ladies' WC. Large garden. Good Sun lunches. 🏠 🛏 🐕 🛏 ◖ ▶ 🅰
🚃 (KWVLR)

### Royal Oak

2 Mill Hey (opp. station)
☎ (01535) 643257
11.30–3.30, 7–11; 11.30–11 Fri & Sat; 12–10.30 Sun
**Courage Directors; John Smith's Bitter; Webster's Yorkshire Bitter; guest beer** (summer) Ⓗ
Former village mortuary and courthouse now featuring a large, open lounge area, with brass and copper decor, and a small family room decorated with railway memorabilia (children welcome till 8).
🏠 🛏 ◖ 🚃 (KWVLR) ♣ P

## Hebden Bridge

### Fox & Goose

9 Heptonstall Road (300 yds W of centre) ☎ (01422) 842649
11.30–3, 7–11; 12–3, 7–10.30 Sun
**Goose Eye Bitter; guest beers** Ⓗ
A haven for sociable people, serving three ever-changing guest beers from independent brewers. No eve meals Tue.
Q 🐕 ◖ ▶ 🚃 ♣

### Hare & Hounds

Billy Lane, Chiserley, Old Town OS005280
☎ (01422) 842671
12–3 (not Mon or Tue except bank hols; not winter Wed), 7–11; 12–10.30 Sun
**Taylor Golden Best, Best Bitter, Landlord, Ram Tam** Ⓗ
Hillside pub known locally as 'Lane Ends'. Families with well-behaved children welcome. It may stay open afternoons if there is demand. No eve meals Mon.
🏠 Q 🐕 ◖ ♣ P

### White Lion Hotel

Bridge Gate ☎ (01422) 842197
11–11; 12–3, 7–10.30 Sun
**Boddingtons Bitter; Castle Eden Ale; Flowers Original; Taylor Landlord; guest beers** Ⓗ
Pleasant, opened-out former coaching inn, offering a mix of styles to a wide-ranging clientele. The garden is by the river. Two changing guest beers (one from Whitbread). Wheelchair WC.
🏠 🛏 🐕 🛏 ◖ ▶ 🚻 🚃 P ⚥

**Try also: Nutclough House**, Keighley Rd (Free)

## Hightown

### Cross Keys

283 Halifax Road (A649, 1 mile from A62 jct) ☎ (01274) 873294
11.30–2.30 (not Mon), 5.30–11; 11–11 Sat; 12–10.30 Sun
**Bateman Mild; Marston's Bitter, Pedigree, HBC** Ⓗ
Refurbished local with a separate games room and an eating area. 🐕 ◖ ▶ P

## Hipperholme

### Brown Horse Inn

Denholme Gate Road, Coley (A644, 1 mile N of centre)
☎ (01422) 202112
11–11; 12–3, 7–10.30 Sun
**Ruddles Best Bitter; John Smith's Bitter; Taylor Landlord; Webster's Yorkshire Bitter** Ⓗ
Yorkshire's only Brown Horse Inn. The site, if not the building, has been an inn since the late 18th century. The interior is comfortably spacious, with interesting displays of collectables. Food is cooked to order. 🐕 ◖ ▶ P

### Dusty Miller Inn

290 Halifax Road, Hove Edge (A644, ¾ mile SE of centre)
☎ (01484) 712390
11–11; 12–10.30 Sun
**Old Mill Bitter; Tetley Bitter** Ⓗ
Pleasant, comfortable, mock Tudor pub serving a wide selection of bar food, including Curry Dish of the Day. Eve meals in summer.
🐕 ◖ ♣ P

## Holmfirth

### Farmers Arms

2–4 Liphill Bank Road, Burnlee (down Burnlee Rd, A635; turn by Compo's Café, then 2nd right) ☎ (01484) 683713
6 (12 Sat)–11; 12–10.30 Sun
**Black Sheep Best Bitter; Taylor Best Bitter; Tetley Mild, Bitter; guest beers** Ⓗ
Cosy, friendly pub on a secluded road on the edge of Holmfirth with three low-ceilinged rooms.
Q 🐕 🛏 ♣ ⟲ P

### Rose & Crown (Nook)

Victoria Square (down alley behind Barclays Bank)
☎ (01484) 683960
11.30–11; 12–10.30 Sun
**Samuel Smith OBB; Stones Bitter; Taylor Best Bitter, Landlord, Ram Tam; Tetley Mild; guest beers** Ⓗ
Traditional boozer that has been in the *Guide* for more than 21 years, with the same jovial landlord. Loyal locals.
🏠 🛏 🐕 ♣

## Horbury

### Calder Vale Hotel

Millfield Road, Horbury junction (400 yds from A642)
☎ (01924) 275351
12–3.30, 6.15–11; 12–3, 7–10.30 Sun
**John Smith's Bitter; Magnet; guest beer** (occasional) H
Victorian, three-roomed local built in 1884 by Fernandes brewery. Friendly and welcoming, it is located away from the town centre. Large function room. Q ❀ ◑ ▶ ♣ P

## Horsforth

### Old Kings Arms

The Green ☎ (0113) 258 1189
11–11; 12–10.30 Sun
**Tetley Mild, Bitter** H
Stone-built Victorian pub. The tap room is an oasis of calm, separate from the main room. Note: guest beers may be on an aspirator. ❀ ◑ ⊞ P

## Huddersfield

### Clarence

Towngate, Newsome (near shops, 1 mile S of centre)
☎ (01484) 513699
11–11; 12–3.30, 7–10.30 Sun
**Burtonwood Forshaw's, seasonal beers** H
Former keg local fielding various games teams. Handpumps also in the party room. ♣ P

### Electricians Arms

159–161 Manchester Road, Longroyd Bridge (A62, ½ mile from centre) ☎ (01484) 429779
12–1 (2 Fri), 7.30–11; 11.30–11 Sat; 12–3, 7.30–10.30 Sun
**Mitchell's Lancaster Bomber; John Smith's Bitter; Theakston XB, Old Peculier; guest beers** H
Long, stone-built pub specialising in premium strength beers. Distinctive artwork adorns the table tops; spot the beer names on the woodwork. Everyone welcome including bikers. Lunches at weekends. ♨ ◑ ♣

### Marsh Liberal Club

Glenfield, 31 New Hey Road, Marsh (A640, 1½ miles from centre) ☎ (01484) 420152
12–2 (not Mon), 7–11; 12–11 Sat; 12–10.30 Sun
**Black Sheep Best Bitter; Taylor Best Bitter; Theakston Mild, Best Bitter; Wild's Wild Blonde; guest beers** H
Vibrant club with an imposing frontage. The beer range goes from strength to strength. Eclectic selection of members' tapes played. Show this guide or a CAMRA membership card at the bar to be signed in.

Families welcome till 9pm. Occasional cider.
♿ ❀ ♣ ⌂ P

### Rat & Ratchet

40 Chapel Hill (A616, near ring road) ☎ (01484) 516734
12–11; 12–4, 7–10.30 Sun
**Adnams Bitter; Banks's Mild; Black Sheep Special; Morland Old Speckled Hen; Taylor Best Bitter; Wadworth 6X; guest beers** H
No-nonsense drinkers' pub normally selling a Rat beer brewed on the premises as well as 14 different ales (ever-changing cast of guests). Lunches Wed–Sat.
❀ ◑ ⇌ ♣ ⌂ P

### Shoulder of Mutton

11 Neale Road, Lockwood (off B6108, near A616 jct, 1 mile S of centre) ☎ (01484) 424835
7 (3 Sat)–11; 12–3.30, 7–10.30 Sun
**Black Sheep Special; Boddingtons Bitter; Taylor Best Bitter, Landlord; Tetley Mild, Bitter; guest beers** H
Tucked away at the head of a cobbled street, this genuine free house has charm, a cosy atmosphere and a legendary jukebox.
❀ ⇌ (Lockwood) ♣

### Zeneca Club

509 Leeds Road (A62, 1½ miles NE of centre) ☎ (01484) 421784
11–11; 12–10.30 Sun
**Taylor Golden Best, Best Bitter; Tetley Mild, Bitter; guest beers** H
Twice-winner of CAMRA's *Club of the Year* award: a large club with three lounges, two bars, eight snooker tables, bowls, tennis, croquet, etc. Show this guide or CAMRA membership to be signed in. No meals weekends.
♿ ❀ ◑ ♣ P ⌦

## Idle

### Brewery Tap

51 Albion Road
☎ (01274) 613936
11.30–3 (4 Sat), 6.30–11; 12–3, 7–10.30 Sun
**Castle Eden Ale; Flowers IPA; Tetley Bitter** H
Pub converted from a bakery by the now defunct Trough Brewery, featuring wood panelled walls, a stone-flagged floor and a large central bar. Live rock music Tue and Sat; quizzes Thu and Sun.
❀ ♿ ♣

### Idle Workingmen's Club

23 High Street
☎ (01274) 613602
12–3 (4 Sat; not Tue–Thu), 7.30 (7 Thu–Sat)–11; 12–3, 7–10.30 Sun
**Tetley Bitter; guest beers** H

Club known nationwide because of its name! Reasonably priced guest beers (usually a different beer available in the downstairs games room). Concerts Sat/Sun eves. Show CAMRA membership or this guide to be signed in at the door.
♿ ♿ ♣

### Springfield

179 Bradford Road
☎ (01274) 612710
12–11; 12–10.30 Sun
**Vaux Samson** H
Roadside local on the edge of a large housing estate, featuring two small rooms: a lounge with pool and a tap room popular with darts players. Like the car park, it is often not big enough. Happy 'hour' Sun 1–3.
⊞ ♣ P

## Ilkley

### Ilkley Moor Vaults

Stockeld Road
☎ (01943) 607012
12–11; 12–10.30 Sun
**Taylor Best Bitter, Landlord; Tetley Bitter; guest beers** H
Tetley Festival Alehouse very near the River Wharfe. Its stone floors and wood attract a wide range of customers. The small snug-like room is warm and welcoming.
♨ Q ❀ ◑ ▶ ♿ ▲ ⇌ ♣ P

### Midland

Station Road ☎ (01943) 607433
11–11; 12–10.30 Sun
**Marston's Pedigree; John Smith's Bitter; guest beers** H
Convenient for bus and train stations; a pub with two rooms, both with fine wooden bar backs and glasswork. Comfortable and well run, with lots of pictures of old Ilkley and railway items.
Q ◑ ⊞ ▲ ⇌ ♣ P

## Keighley

### Albert Hotel

13 Bridge Street
☎ (01535) 602306
11–5, 7–11; 11–11 Fri & Sat; Sun hours vary
**Taylor Golden Best, Best Bitter, Landlord** (summer), **Ram Tam** (winter) H
Large Victorian (ex-)hotel, generally busy in its large, open bar area and separate pool room (which features a motorbike sculpture on the wall). Prices are very reasonable. It can be noisy at weekends. ⇌ ♣

### Boltmakers Arms

117 East Parade
☎ (01535) 661936
11.30–11; 11–4.30, 7–11 Sat; 12–4, 7–10.30 Sun

Taylor Golden Best, Best
Bitter, Landlord; Tetley
Bitter Ⓗ
Split-level, one-roomed, town-
centre gem, more than ten
successive years in the *Guide*. A
popular pub not to be missed.
➤ ♣

## Cricketers Arms

Coney Lane
☎ (01535) 669912
11–11; 12–10.30 Sun
Taylor Golden Best, Best
Bitter, Landlord Ⓗ
Small, comfortable local
wedged between mills, a short
walk from the town centre.
Snacks at all times.
& ➤ ♣

## Eastwood Tavern

37 Bradford Road (right from
station) ☎ (01535) 604849
11.30–11; 12–5, 7–10.30 Sun
Taylor Golden Best, Best
Bitter, Landlord, Ram Tam
(winter) Ⓗ
Friendly, mainly quiet local
split into a main bar, a games
room (mostly taken up by a
pool table) and a small front
room with a real fire.
Interesting old brewery prints
and posters. ♨ ❀ ♣ ♠

## Red Pig

Church Street
☎ (01535) 604383
12–3, 7–11; 12–11 Fri & Sat; 7–10.30
Sun, closed Sun lunch
Commercial Alesman, Neary's
Stout; Taylor Golden Best,
Landlord; guest beers Ⓗ
Interesting and idiosyncratic
town-centre pub which
features local artists' works –
several for sale. Much of the
interior is stripped back to
underlying brickwork. The
only regular outlet for
Commercial beers in Keighley.
No dogs. ♨ ➤ ♣

## Volunteer Arms

Lawkholme Lane (behind the
Cavendish pub in Cavendish
St) ☎ (01535) 600173
11–11; 12–10.30 Sun
Taylor Golden Best, Best
Bitter Ⓗ
Compact local with two rooms,
the smaller one used mainly
for games. ➤ ♣

# Keighley to Oxenhope and Back

## Keighley and Worth Valley Buffet Car

Stations at Keighley, Ingrow
West, Oakworth, Haworth and
Oxenhope ☎ (01535) 645214;
talking timetable (01535) 647777
Trains run Sat, Sun & bank hols,
Mar–Oct
Beer range varies Ⓗ

Volunteer-run railway buffet
car giving changing views of
the Worth Valley.
Q ♠ (Marsh/Oxenhope) ➤
(Keighley) P (Keighley/
Ingrow West/Oxenhope) ⚡ ▯

# Kirkburton

## Royal

64 North Road (B6116)
☎ (01484) 602521
11.30–3 (not Mon), 5–11; 11.30–11 Sat;
12–10.30 Sun
Ind Coope Burton Ale; Taylor
Landlord; Tetley Mild, Bitter;
guest beers (occasional) Ⓗ
Welcoming Victorian pub
serving excellent quality and
value food; a refurbished
lounge, separate tap room and
an upstairs function room. No
jukebox. Eve meals Tue–Fri.
♨ ◑ ♣ P

## Spring Grove Tavern

20 Penistone Road
(A629/B6116 jct)
☎ (01484) 605826
4 (12 Fri & Sat)–11; 12–10.30 Sun
Barnsley Bitter; Tetley Bitter;
guest beers Ⓗ
The constantly changing beer
range in this roadside pub
ensures its popularity with ale
aficionados of all ages. One
large, opened out lounge,
tastefully decorated, with a
collection of jugs and pictures.
❀ P

# Ledsham

## Chequers

Claypit Lane (off Selby fork of
A1)
☎ (01977) 683135
11–3, 5.30–11; 11–11 Sat; closed Sun
John Smith's Bitter;
Theakston Best Bitter;
Younger Scotch, No. 3 Ⓗ
Unspoilt, timeless gem where
small rooms, low ceilings and
open fires make for a warm
welcome. The restaurant
upstairs serves an excellent
range of food, including
vegetarian. Closed Sun (due to
the laws of the local manor).
♨ Q ❀ ◑ ▶ ♣ P

# Leeds: *City*

## Courtyard

25–37 Cookridge Street
☎ (0113) 242 7588
11–11; 12–3, 7–10.30 Sun
Draught Bass; Stones Bitter;
Taylor Best Bitter;
Worthington Bitter Ⓗ
Tasteful conversion of old
office space that preserves the
calm oasis of the Georgian
courtyard: joint winner of
CAMRA/English Heritage's
award for conversion to pub
use. The decor and style is
distinctly modern – exposed
air conditioning ducts, et al.

Meals end at 6.30.
❀ ◑ ▶ & ➤

## Duck & Drake

43 Kirkgate (between parish
church and markets)
☎ (0113) 246 5806
11–11; 12–10.30 Sun
Old Mill Bitter; Taylor
Landlord; Theakston Best
Bitter, XB, Old Peculier;
Younger No. 3; guest beers Ⓗ
Leeds's original 'back to basics'
ale house, once owned by the
Fighting Cock chain but now in
the hands of Scottish Courage.
However, the wide range of
guest ales has continued, many
from distant breweries. Live
music from local rock and
blues bands Tue, Thu and Sat
eves. ♨ ⊕ & ➤ ♣ ♨

## Horse & Trumpet

The Headrow
☎ (0113) 243 0338
11–11; 12–10.30 Sun
Marston's Pedigree; Tetley
Bitter, Imperial; guest beers Ⓗ
Tetley Festival Alehouse with a
fine Victorian facade giving
way to an opened out and
altered interior. Up to four
independent guest beers.
Smart dress – checked by
doormen – at weekends. No
food Sun. ◑ & ➤

## Londoner

Lovell Park Road
☎ (0113) 245 3666
11–11; 12–3, 7–10.30 Sun
Marston's Pedigree; Tetley
Bitter, Imperial; guest beers Ⓗ
Bare boards, flickering electric
lights and sepia-stained walls
provide the decor at this Tetley
Festival Alehouse. Though
open-plan, it retains a games
area and partitioned cubby
holes. Four guest beers a week.
❀ ◑ ♣ P

## Palace

Kirkgate (next to parish
church) ☎ (0113) 244 5882
11–11; 12–10.30 Sun
Ind Coope Burton Ale;
Marston's Pedigree; Tetley
Mild, Bitter, Imperial; guest
beers Ⓗ
Tetley Festival Alehouse
offering up to six guest beers
from independent brewers
which usually include a stout
or porter. No eve meals Sun;
other eves until 8. ❀ ◑ ▶

## Prince of Wales

Mill Hill ☎ (0113) 245 2434
11–11; 12–10.30 Sun
Black Sheep Best Bitter;
McEwan 80/-; Morland Old
Speckled Hen; John Smith's
Bitter; Younger No. 3 Ⓗ
Pub with a comfy lounge (note
the brass decorations) and a
separate pool area. Interesting
etched windows.
🛏 ◑ ➤ ♣

## Tap & Spile

Georgian Arcade, Merrion Centre

☎ (0113) 244 5355

11–11; closed Sun

**Beer range varies** Ⓗ

Leeds CAMRA's *Pub of the Year* 1995, serving up to eight beers and real ciders. Regular beer festivals with a theme (autumn ales, etc.).

◑ ♣ ○

## Viaduct

11 Lower Briggate

☎ (0113) 246 9178

11–11; 12–3, 7–10.30 Sun

**Ind Coope Burton Ale; Marston's Pedigree; Tetley Dark Mild, Bitter, Imperial; guest beer** Ⓗ

Tasteful refurbishment has transformed this basic boozer but the wooden panels have thankfully been saved. A warm welcome in pleasant surroundings.

❀ ◑ & ≈ ⁄

## West Yorkshire Playhouse

Quarry Hill Mount

☎ (0113) 244 2141

12–2.30, 5.30–11 (open all day Sat if there's a matinee)

**Ind Coope Burton Ale; Tetley Bitter; guest beer** Ⓗ

Spacious modern bar within the theatre complex. A good sense of timing is essential – it gets very busy during show intervals. Above average prices. Q ◑ ▶ & P

## Whitelocks ☆

Turks Head Yard (off Briggate)

☎ (0113) 245 3950

11–11; 12–10.30 Sun

**McEwan 80/-; Theakston Best Bitter; Younger Scotch, IPA, No. 3** Ⓗ

A feast of brass and glass, including long lost brewery mirrors, adorns this oasis of stability in an area of refurbished theme bars. Large outdoor drinking area in the passage. Eve meals end at 8 (7.30 Fri and Sat).

Q ❀ ◑ ▶ ≈

## Leeds: *East*

## Beer Paradise

Unit 11, Riverside Place, Bridgwater Road, Cross Green (off South Accommodation Rd)

☎ (0113) 235 9082

12–4; 11–7 Thu & Fri; 10–5.30 Sat; 11–4 Sun

Huge beer emporium specialising in Belgian/ foreign beers but with a good range of bottle-conditioned British beers. CAMRA members are automatic members (take your membership card).

& ○ P

## Leeds: *North*

### Bricklayers Arms

St Mark's Road, Woodhouse

☎ (0113) 245 8277

11–3, 5–11 (11–11 termtime); 12–4, 7–10.30 (12–10.30 termtime) Sun

**Courage Directors; Marston's Pedigree; Morland Old Speckled Hen; John Smith's Magnet; guest beers** Ⓗ

Thriving local/university pub in amidst St Mark's flats, which, although technically open-plan, still retains the feel of many rooms. Eve meals end at 7. ❀ ◑ ▶ ♣ P

### Chemic Tavern

Johnston Street, Woodhouse

☎ (0113) 244 0092

11–3, 5.30–11 (11–11 bank hol Mons); 11.30–11 Sat; 12–10.30 Sun

**Ind Coope Burton Ale; Tetley Bitter; guest beers** Ⓗ

Two-roomed, 'village' local in the midst of old back to back terraces, featuring low beams, mirrors and wallplates. No jukebox. Quizzes Mon/Thu. Toasted sandwiches lunchtime.

Q ⊞ ♣ P

### City of Mabgate

45 Mabgate (under motorway flyover, 400 yds from bus station)

☎ (0113) 245 7789

12–11; 12–4, 7–10.30 Sun

**Black Sheep Special; Boddingtons Bitter; Marston's Pedigree; Morland Old Speckled Hen; Whitbread Trophy; guest beers** Ⓗ

Cosy, backstreet pub popular with locals and real ale fans alike. The rugby league-keen landlord always has three guest beers and runs occasional beer festivals. No food Sat/Sun. ⚒ ❀ ◑ ⊞ ♣

### Eagle Tavern

North Street, Sheepscar

☎ (0113) 245 7146

11–3, 5.30–11; 12–3, 7–10.30 Sun

**Taylor Mild, Golden Best, Best Bitter, Landlord, Ram Tam; guest beers** Ⓗ

The days of excellence at this legendary Leeds alehouse may be numbered, so go whilst you still can. Ever-changing guest beers are served in a clean, basic tap room and comfy lounge. Jazz Sun lunch.

❀ ⛴ ◑ ♣ ○ P

### Feast & Firkin

229 Woodhouse Lane (next to university) ☎ (0113) 245 3669

11–11; 12–10.30 Sun

**Firkin Fuzz Bitter, Feast Bitter, Dogbolter, seasonal beers; guest beers** Ⓗ

Pub opened in 1994 but built in 1901 as a fire station/police station and library. Well-priced food. Wheelchair WC.

Children not allowed in.

◑ & ○ P

### Nag's Head

20 Town Street, Chapel Allerton ☎ (0113) 262 4938

11–11; 12–10.30 Sun

**Samuel Smith OBB** Ⓗ

White-painted, 17th-century pub in Georgian manor house style, with a large lounge, no-smoking room and a busy tap room. No food Sat.

⛄ ❀ ◑ ⊞ ♣ P ⁄

### New Roscoe

Benson Street, Sheepscar

☎ (0113) 246 0778

11.30–11; 12–10.30 Sun

**Ruddles County; John Smith's Bitter; Tetley Bitter; guest beers** Ⓗ

Fine conversion from a former club into a smart large pub, taking its name from the original Roscoe 200 yards away, which fell to the bulldozers in 1982. The landlord was the last tenant in the old Roscoe, so many artefacts of the old pub are on display. Moorhouse's house beer. No food Sat/Sun.

❀ ◑ ⊞ & ♣ P

## Leeds: *South*

### Adelphi ☆

1–5 Hunslet Road

☎ (0113) 245 6377

11.30–3, 5 (7.30 Sat)–11; 11.30–11 Fri; 12–3, 7–10.30 Sun

**Tetley Mild, Bitter, Imperial** Ⓗ

The most ornate pub in the city: a listed Edwardian feast of engraved glass, patterned tiles and elaborate joinery. The tap for Tetley Brewery, which can be seen from the garden at the rear. ❀ ◑ ⊞ ≈ ♣ ⁄

### Grove

Back Row, Holbeck

☎ (0113) 243 9254

12–11; 12–4, 7–11 Sat; 12–4, 7–10.30 Sun

**Draught Bass; Courage Directors; Ruddles Best Bitter; John Smith's Bitter, Magnet; guest beer** Ⓗ

Classic, inter-war pub with intact fixtures and fittings, including four separate rooms, pew seats, an excellent Yorkshire corridor and tiles inside and out. Jam sessions, folk club meetings and all manner of live music. Barbecues in summer.

Q ❀ ◑ ⊞ ≈ ♣ ⁄

## Leeds: *West*

### Cardigan Arms

364 Kirkstall Road

☎ (0113) 274 2000

12–11; 12–10.30 Sun

**Marston's Pedigree; Tetley Mild, Bitter** Ⓗ

Tetley Heritage pub also Grade II listed. An increasing rarity: a delightful, many-roomed boozer. No meals Sat/Sun.
☾ ⊟ ♿ ♣ P

### Fox & Newt
Burley Street, Burley
☎ (0113) 243 2612
11–11; 12–10.30 Sun
**Castle Eden Ale; Fox & Newt Diesel, Cushtie, Black and Amber, Ghostbuster** [H]
Basic brew pub with bare boards, popular with students. Chips and chili available all day. Sun lunches served; no lunches Sat. Not all the beers may be on sale. ☾ ♿

### Old Vic
17 Whitecote Hill, Bramley (just off Bramley Town St, on the Rodley road)
☎ (0113) 256 1207
11–3 (4 Sat), 7 (6.30 Sat)–11; 12–3, 7–10.30 Sun
**Black Sheep Best Bitter; Taylor Golden Best, Landlord; Tetley Bitter; guest beers** [H]
Formerly a vicarage, this popular free house is set back from the road in its own grounds. Two lounges and a tap/games room are served from a central bar.
♨ Q ☾ ♿ ♣ P

### Sun Inn
153 Town Street, Stanningley (by railway viaduct)
☎ (0113) 257 4894
11.30–3 (4 Sat), 6 (7 Sat)–11; 1–5, 7–10.30 Sun
**Tetley Bitter; guest beers** [H]
Large, stone-built, Victorian multi-roomed local, with a tap room, snug and separate lounges. A house beer is also on sale. Q ❀ ☾ ◗ ♣ P

### White Horse
87 Town Street
☎ (0113) 231 1667
11–11; 12–10.30 Sun
**Boddingtons Bitter; Flowers Original; John Smith's Bitter; Taylor Landlord; Whitbread Trophy; guest beers** [H]
Bustling, three-roomed local which is home to football teams, sporting and other memorabilia, and a collection of 200 teapots and water jugs. It used to have a brewhouse many years ago (brewing Medal Ales), traces of which are still visible in the cellar.
❀ ☾ ◗ ⊟ ♣

## Linthwaite

### Sair Inn
139 Lane Top, Hoyle Ing (off A62) ☎ (01484) 842370
7–11; 12–4, 7–11 Sat; 12–4, 7–10.30 Sun
**Linfit Mild, Bitter, Special, Janet Street Porter, Autumn Gold, Old Eli** [H]
Former 19th-century brewhouse brewing again since 1982. Stone flagged floors and real fires feature in several of the rooms. Historical connections are revealed in a replica of Enoch's Hammer, as used by the Luddites. Popular with environmental groups.
♨ ☋ ▲ ♣ ⊖ ⚟

## Liversedge

### Black Bull
37 Halifax Road (A649, 400 yds N of A62) ☎ (01924) 403779
12–4 (5 Sat), 5.30 (7 Sat)–11; 12–5, 7–10.30 Sun
**Stones Bitter; Tetley Bitter; guest beers** [H]
Good local which caters for all ages in a pool room with music plus quieter rooms leading off. Good range of changing guest beers. P

## Methley

### New Bay Horse
Main Street, Mickletown
☎ (01977) 553557
12–4, 6–11; 12–3, 7–10.30 Sun
**Friary Meux BB; Tetley Bitter; guest beer** [H]
Refurbished and expanded pub with further expansion planned to cope with demand. Leeds CAMRA *Pub of the Year* 1994. One of the few genuinely free houses in the area. No eve meals Sun.
Q ☋ ❀ ☾ ◗ ♿ ♣ P ⚟

## Mirfield

### Railway
212 Huddersfield Road (A644, on edge of centre)
☎ (01924) 480868
12–11; 12–3.30, 7–10.30 Sun
**Bass Toby Cask, Draught Bass; Stones Bitter; Worthington Bitter; guest beers** [H]
Comfortable local: a recent winner of the *Bass in Bloom* award. The lounge features an open fire and seasonal displays in its alcoves. No eve meals Sun. ♨ ❀ ☾ ◗ ⇌ ♣ P

## Mytholmroyd

### Shoulder of Mutton
38 New Road (B6138)
☎ (01422) 883165
11.30–3, 7–11; 11.30–11 Sat; 12–3, 7–10.30 Sun
**Black Sheep Best Bitter; Boddingtons Bitter; Castle Eden Ale; Flowers IPA; Robinson's Hartleys XB; guest beers** [H]
Popular roadside local with a fine display of Toby jugs and china. Whitbread guest beers. No eve meals Tue.
☾ ◗ ⇌ ♣ P

## Netherthong

### Clothiers' Arms
106 School Street (off A6024; up hill behind Royal Oak)
☎ (01484) 683480
12–4 (not Mon), 7–11; 12–11 Fri & Sat; 12–10.30 Sun
**Black Sheep Best Bitter; Boddingtons Bitter; Old Mill Bitter; Tetley Mild, Bitter; guest beers** [H]
Genuine free house serving the village community well with a good atmosphere, good quality and good prices. Brewery memorabilia is a feature.
Q ☾ ♣

## Normanton

### Huntsman
84 Dalefield Road (500 yds from A655, Wakefield road)
☎ (01924) 892212
12–4 (not Thu), 7–11; 12–11 Fri & Sat; 4–11 Wed; 12–10.30 Sun
**Burtonwood Bitter, Forshaw's** [H]
Community pub originally built as a club in the 1950s, although never used as one. The only Burtonwood tied house in Normanton.
❀ ⊟ ♿ ♣ P

## Odsal

### Mail Coach
32 Huddersfield Road (200 yds from Odsal Stadium)
☎ (01274) 671857
7 (12 Sat)–11; 12–10.30 Sun
**Vaux Bitter, Samson** [H]
Inter-war pub still largely intact, with three distinct rooms which can get very busy when Bradford are at home.
☋ ⊟ ♣ P

## Ogden

### Moorlands Inn
Keighley Road (A629)
☎ (01422) 248943
11–11; 12–10.30 Sun
**Black Sheep Special; Taylor Landlord; Tetley Bitter; guest beers** [H]
Large pub at the edge of a built-up area. The main room is L-shaped and is punctuated by raised areas and a fireplace. Food at all times; three quiz nights per week. Guest beers include a house beer (by Moorhouse's) on Thu.
❀ ⊨ ☾ ◗ ♣ P

## Ossett

### Brewer's Pride
Low Mill Road (bottom of Healey Rd) ☎ (01924) 273865
12–3, 5.30–11; 12–11 Fri & Sat; 12–3, 7–10.30 Sun
**Taylor Landlord; guest beers** [H]

Despite its location, this is a deservedly popular true free house. Four ever-changing guest beers (including a mild), Biddenden cider, a range of Belgian beers, log fires and an unspoilt interior make this a must for visitors. No food Sun. ⚲ Q ❀ ◖ ♣ ♢

## Commercial Inn

1 Dewsbury Road, Flushdyke (near M1 jct 40)
☎ (01924) 274197
12–11; 12–4, 7–10.30 Sun
**Highgate Dark; Stones Bitter; guest beer** (occasional) Ⓗ
Friendly and popular, three-roomed local with a separate games room. Live music once a week. Home-cooked food (eve meals March–Sept till 7.30). Children's playground in the garden. Barbecue Sun lunch in summer. ❀ ◖ ▶ ♣ P

## George

Bank Street ☎ (01924) 264754
12–3, 7–11; 11.30–11 Fri & Sat; 12–3, 7–10.30 Sun
**Ind Coope Burton Ale; Taylor Landlord; Tetley Mild, Bitter, Imperial** Ⓗ
Popular, town-centre pub next to the award-winning police station. A comfortable main bar and traditional tap room cater for most clientele. Eve meals Mon only.
❀ ◖ ዼ ♣ P

## Little Bull

99 Teall Street (¼ mile from Queens Drive)
☎ (01924) 273569
12–3, 6–11; 12–3, 7–10.30 Sun
**Thwaites Best Mild, Bitter, Craftsman, seasonal beers** Ⓗ
Very friendly, popular local, with a comfortable, L-shaped lounge and a small, but lively, tap room. Regular games and quiz nights. Reasonable prices.
⚲ Q 🝙 ♣ P

## Otley

### Bay Horse

Market Place ☎ (01943) 461122
11–11; 12–10.30 Sun
**Tetley Mild, Bitter; guest beers** Ⓗ
Tiny pub with stained-glass windows, sandwiched between shops. The small tap room is served through a hatchway; linked spaces make up the main lounge. Good sandwiches. ❀ 🝙 ♣

### Junction

44 Bondgate ☎ (01943) 463233
11–11; 12–5, 7–10.30 Sun
**Taylor Best Bitter, Landlord; Theakston XB, Old Peculier; guest beer** Ⓗ
Single-room, stone-built pub on a prominent corner. Lively, young atmosphere. A public

car park is close by.
⚲ ◖ ♣

## White Swan

Boroughgate ☎ (01943) 463138
11–11; 12–10.30 Sun
**Black Sheep Best Bitter; Stones Bitter** Ⓗ
Partially opened out, lively, thriving local, noted for having bought many Guide Dogs for the Blind. ⚲ ❀ ዼ ♣ P

## Outwood

### Kirklands Hotel

605 Leeds Road
☎ (01924) 826666
11–11; 12–3, 7–10.30 Sun
**Old Mill Mild, Bitter, Bullion, seasonal beers** Ⓗ
Large, three-star hotel tied to Old Mill Brewery. Spacious comfortable bars; busy local trade; reasonable prices. Home-cooked food. Children welcome until 9pm.
Q ❀ 🛏 ◖ ▶ ⇌ P

### Nightingale

Newton Lane (400 yds from A61, Leeds road)
☎ (01924) 824101
11–11; 12–4, 7–10.30 Sun
**John Smith's Bitter; guest beers** Ⓗ
Busy, friendly village local offering pub games, quiz nights and a disco (Sun). Free snacks Sun lunch. Q ❀ ♣ P

## Pontefract

### Counting House

Swales Yard (N of centre, opp. war memorial)
☎ (01977) 600388
11–3, 6.30–11; 12–3, 7–10.30 Sun
**Tetley Bitter** Ⓗ
14th-century, listed building converted to a pub after extensive renovation. The open-plan bar has a stone floor and old church seats; separate no-smoking room. A large upstairs room is open weekends.
❀ ◖ ⇌ (Tanshelf) ♣ ✂

### Greyhound

13 Front Street (50 yds N of centre) ☎ (01977) 791571
12–4, 7–11; 12–11 Sat; 12–10.30 Sun
**Ruddles Best Bitter; John Smith's Bitter; Theakston XB; Tomlinson's Sessions** Ⓗ; **Wilson's Bitter** Ⓔ
Busy, lively pub hosting live music Fri.
⚲ 🝙 ⇌ (Tanshelf) ♣

### Liquorice Bush

8 Market Place (close to bus station) ☎ (01977) 703843
11–4, 7–11; 12–10.30 Sun
**Tomlinson's Sessions; Vaux Double Maxim; Ward's Thorne BB; guest beers** Ⓗ
Large, one-roomed pub with an alcove at each end. Busy

weekday lunchtimes (wide range of meals). No food Sun. ◖ ዼ ⇌ (Baghill/Monkhill/ Tanshelf) ♣

## Pudsey

### Butchers Arms

Church Lane (main shopping street) ☎ (0113) 256 4313
11–11; 12–10.30 Sun
**Samuel Smith OBB** Ⓗ
Busy, central pub with an open interior and 1980s furniture and decor. Separate dining area. ❀ ◖ ♣

### Mason's Arms

Lowtown (main street)
☎ (0113) 257 7857
11–11; 12–10.30 Sun
**Boddingtons Bitter; Flowers Original; Whitbread Trophy** Ⓗ
Fine example of a Victorian pub in the Yorkshire house style. Nice Bentley's windows front an unaltered interior of three rooms. 🝙 ♣ P

## Purston

### White House

257 Pontefract Road
☎ (01977) 791878
11–4, 7–11; 12–3, 7–10.30 Sun
**Samuel Smith OBB** Ⓗ
Large roadside pub comprising one room with a central bar adorned with rugby and football pictures. Friendly clientele. A well deserved 20th appearance in the *Guide*. Reasonable prices.
❀ ♣ P

## Ripponden

### Blue Ball

Blue Ball Lane, Soyland (off A58, near Baitings Reservoir)
OS011192 ☎ (01422) 823603
12–3 (not Tue), 7–11; 12–3, 7–10.30 Sun
**Draught Bass; Taylor Golden Best, Landlord; Theakston Old Peculier; guest beers** Ⓗ
Cosy, welcoming moorland inn dating from 1672, with panoramic views over the upper Ryburn Valley. Regular folk music, sing-alongs and live jazz. Four guest beers.
⚲ Q ❀ ◖ ▶ P

### Griffin Inn

Stainland Road, Barkisland (400 yds downhill from A6025 jct) ☎ (01422) 823873
11.30–3, 7–11; 12–3, 7–10.30 Sun
**Draught Bass; Black Sheep Best Bitter; Ryburn Best Bitter; Stones Bitter; Worthington Bitter** Ⓗ
Busy village inn dating from 1642, serving good value, home-cooked food.
❀ ◖ ▶ ♣ P

## Old Bridge Inn

Priest Lane (off A58 near B6113 jct) ☎ (01422) 822595
11.30–3, 5.30–11; 12–11.30 Sat; 12–10.30 Sun

**Black Sheep Special; Ryburn Best Bitter; Taylor Golden Best, Best Bitter; guest beers** Ⓗ
Possibly Yorkshire's oldest pub (recorded as early as 1307), in a picturesque setting by a packhorse bridge. Only the guest beer pumps are labelled. Ten continuous years in the *Guide*. ᕫ Q ✿ ◑ ▶ P

## Shaw Cross

### Huntsman

1 Walker Cottages, Chidswell Lane (400 yds NE of A653/B6128 jct) ☎ (01924) 275700
12–3 (not Mon), 7–11; 12–3, 7–10.30 Sun

**Black Sheep Special; John Smith's Bitter; Stones Bitter; Taylor Landlord; guest beers** Ⓗ
Guns on walls, horse brasses on beams and a Yorkshire range enhance the rural feel of this friendly pub (originally two 17th-century cottages), quietly set amidst fields. No lunches Sun. ᕫ ✿ ◑ P

## Shelley

### Three Acres Inn

Roydhouse (off B6116 near Emley Moor mast) ☎ (01484) 602606
12.30–3 (not Sat), 7–11; 12.30–3, 7–10.30 Sun

**Mansfield Riding Bitter, Bitter; Morland Old Speckled Hen; Taylor Best Bitter; guest beers** Ⓗ
Attractively set pub with the emphasis on wining and dining. Twenty en suite bedrooms. Resident pianist. ᕫ ✿ ⌂ ◑ ▶ P

## Shipley

### Branch

Bradford Road (Otley Rd jct) ☎ (01274) 584495
11–11; 12–10.30 Sun

**Ind Coope Burton Ale; Marston's Pedigree; Tetley Bitter, Imperial; guest beers** Ⓗ
Well-refurbished Festival Alehouse with a varied clientele and a friendly atmosphere. Children allowed in for meals. Five guest beers. ✿ ◑ P ⚊

### Shipley Pride

1 Saltaire Road ☎ (01274) 585341
11.30 (11 Sat)–11; 12–3, 7–10.30 Sun

**Clark's Festival; Tetley Bitter; Old Bear Bitter; guest beers** (occasional) Ⓗ
Friendly, two-roomed pub popular with locals and passing trade. No food weekends. ◑ ➾ ♣ P

### Victoria Hotel

192 Saltaire Road
☎ (01274) 585642
11.30–11; 12–10.30 Sun

**Boddingtons Bitter; Whitbread Trophy; guest beers** Ⓗ
Friendly local with Victorian-style decor (stained-glass and wood), the nearest pub to the historic village of Saltaire and its tourist attractions. Eve meals end at 8; no food Sat/Sun. Q ◑ ▶ ➾ (Saltaire) P

## Slaithwaite

### Pack Horse Hotel

Carr Lane ☎ (01484) 844690
11–11; 12–10.30 Sun

**Black Sheep Best Bitter; guest beers** Ⓗ
Former Co-op converted into a hotel. A games room sits in the V of a wedge, with two lounges on higher levels. Function room.
⌂ ➾ ♣ P ⚊

## South Elmsall

### Barnsley Oak

Mill Lane (½ mile from A638/B6428 jct)
☎ (01977) 643427
12–3.30 (5 Sat), 7–11; 12–3, 7–10.30 Sun

**John Smith's Bitter; Webster's Yorkshire Bitter** Ⓗ
1960s estate pub on the edge of a mining village, offering panoramic views of the Elms Valley from the conservatory. Free sausages, scallops, etc. Sun eve. ᗞ ◑ ➾ ᕫ ♣ P

## Southowram

### Shoulder of Mutton

14 Cain Lane ☎ (01422) 361101
11.30–3, 6–11; 11.30–11 Sat; 12–10.30 Sun (may close for an hour if quiet)

**Marston's Pedigree; Ruddles County; John Smith's Bitter; guest beers** Ⓗ
Village local with changing independent guest beers. ᕫ ♣

## Sowerby Bridge

### Navigation Inn

47 Chapel Lane (downhill at turning by A58/A6026 jct)
☎ (01422) 831636
11–11; 12–10.30 Sun

**Black Sheep Best Bitter; guest beers** Ⓗ
17th-century house converted to cottages and a weaving shop, then a pub. Its location, beside the Calder and Hebble Navigation, close to Sowerby Bridge basin, is reflected in the decor. Two house beers: Moorhouse's Navvy Bitter and Eastwood's Calderd Ale.
ᗞ ✿ ⌂ ◑ ➾ ⌂ P

### Ram's Head

26 Wakefield Road (A6026, ¼ mile from centre)
☎ (01422) 835876
7 (12 Sat)–11; 12–3, 7–10.30 Sun

**Ryburn Mild, Best Bitter, Rydale, Luddite, Stabbers, Coiners** Ⓗ
Cottage-style pub which has been gradually extended into adjoining property. Exposed stonework and four open fireplaces provide interior features. Ryburn Brewery's only tied house. Sing-alongs Sat/Sun nights. ᕫ ✿ ⚅ ♣ P

### William IV

80–82 Wharf Street
☎ (01422) 833584
11.30–11; 12–4, 7–10.30 Sun

**Boddingtons Bitter; Tetley Bitter; guest beers** Ⓗ
Having origins as a beer house and shop, this pub was closed by Whitbread in 1969 only to reopen a few years later as a free house. Small and well appointed, its emphasis is on beer. IVth Rite Ale is a house beer from Coach House.
Q ✿ ◑ ➾ ♣ P

## Thornhill

### Savile Arms

12 Church Lane (B6117)
☎ (01924) 463738
5–11; 12–3, 7.30–11 Sat; 12–3, 8–10.30 Sun (may vary in summer)

**Black Sheep Best Bitter; Old Mill Bitter; Tetley Bitter; guest beers** Ⓗ
Next to a fine 15th-century church (full of Savile family monuments), this 600-year-old pub, known as the Church House, has kept its character. One of the four rooms houses paintings by local artists. Lunches served Sat. Q ✿ ♣ P

## Todmorden

### Bramsche Bar

31 Rochdale Road (opp. library) ☎ (01706) 815117
11–11; 12–10.30 Sun

**Taylor Landlord; Theakston Best Bitter; guest beer** Ⓗ
Basic, bare-floored pub close to the Rochdale Canal; named after Todmorden's twin town. ✿ ◑ ➾

### White Hart

White Hart Fold, Station Road
☎ (01706) 812198
11.30–3.30, 7–11; 11–11 Fri & Sat; 12–10.30 Sun

**Tetley Mild, Bitter; guest beers** Ⓗ
Imposing brewers' Tudor pub close to the station: a single, large lounge. Two guests (one always from Moorhouse's). ✿ ◑ ➾ ♣ P

## Wainstalls

### Cat i'th'Well Inn
Wainstalls Lane, Lower Saltonstall (¼ mile W of Wainstalls) OS042285
☎ (01422) 244841
7 (5.30 Fri)–11; 12–4, 7–11 Sat; 12–4, 7–10.30 Sun
**Boddingtons Bitter; Castle Eden Ale; Taylor Golden Best, Best Bitter, Landlord** H
Cosy, oak-panelled free house, delightfully situated in a wooded valley. The panelling came from the demolished Victorian 'castle' in beautiful Luddenden Dene nearby.
❀ ◐ ▲ P

**Try also: Withens Hotel**, Cold Edge Rd (Free)

## Wakefield

### Albion
94 Stanley Road (follow Peterson Rd from Kirkgate roundabout)
☎ (01924) 876206
11–4 (5 Sat), 7–11; 12–5, 7–10.30 Sun
**Samuel Smith OBB** H
Impressive, 1930s local at the edge of the town centre. Popular lunchtimes for good value, home-cooked food. No lunches Wed. A collection of teapots adorns the lounge.
❀ ◐ ⊞ ⇌ (Kirkgate) ♣ P

### Black Rock
19 Cross Square (bottom of Wood St) ☎ (01924) 375550
11–11; 12–10.30 Sun
**Tetley Mild, Bitter** H
Victorian drinking house: a cosy, one-room pub full of pictures of old Wakefield.
⇌ (Westgate)

### Elephant & Castle
109 Westgate (opp. station)
☎ (01924) 376610
11–11; 12–5, 7–10.30 Sun
**Courage Directors; John Smith's Bitter; guest beers** H
Very friendly, town-centre local with a pool room at the back. Note the impressive, tiled Warwick's of Boroughbridge frontage. Old photos and brewery mirrors add to the interest.
⛰ ⛟ ◐ ◑ ⇌ (Westgate) ♣

### Redoubt ☆
28 Horbury Road (next to St Michael's church)
☎ (01924) 377085
11–11; 12–3, 7–10.30 Sun
**Taylor Landlord; Tetley Mild, Bitter** H
Unspoiled Tetley Heritage pub with four small rooms adorned with rugby league photographs. The tap room and small front snug are gems.
Q ❀ ⊞ ⇌ (Westgate) ♣ P

### Talbot & Falcon
56 Northgate (near bus station)
☎ (01924) 201693
11–11; 12–10.30 Sun
**Marston's Pedigree; Tetley Mild, Bitter; Theakston Best Bitter; guest beers** H
Long, narrow Tetley Festive Alehouse with a central bar, catering for a very varied clientele. Up to five guest beers. ◐

### Wakefield Labour Club
18 Vicarage Street (near Market Hall) ☎ (01924) 215626
7–11; 11–3, 7–11 Sat; 12–3 Sun, closed Sun eve
**Taylor Golden Best; guest beers** H
Friendly, welcoming club offering an interesting range of guest beers from small breweries at reasonable prices. Yorkshire *Club of the Year*, it is the town centre's last true free house. Large range of bottled Belgian beers; occasional cider. Visitors must be signed in.
Q ⛀ ❀ ♿ ⇌ (Westgate/ Kirkgate) ♣ ⌓ P ⊡

**Try also: Henry Boon's**, Westgate (Clark's)

## Warmfield

### Plough Inn
45 Warmfield Lane (400 yds from A655) ☎ (01924) 892007
12–2, 7–11 (12–11 summer); 12–10.30 Sun
**Barnsley Bitter; Theakston Best Bitter, XB, Old Peculier; guest beers** H
Unspoilt, 18th-century country inn overlooking the lower Calder Valley, with low, beamed ceilings and a small corner bar. Lively piano sing-alongs Sat eve. Good bar meals – try the Old Peculier Pie. Barbecues in summer. Eve meals on request.
❀ ⛟ ◐ ◑ P

## West Ardsley

### British Oak
407 Westerton Road
☎ (0113) 253 4792
12–3, 6–11; 12–3, 7–10.30 Sun
**Boddingtons Bitter; Castle Eden Ale; Flowers Original; guest beers** H
Excellent local staging live music and quiz nights. Ever-changing, usually small independent, guest beers (over 400 in five years). ❀ ◐ ♿ P

## Wibsey

### Gaping Goose
5–6 Black Bottom Road (off Buttershaw Lane)
☎ (01274) 601701
12–3, 7–11; 12–3, 7–10.30 Sun
**Black Sheep Best Bitter; Taylor Landlord; Tetley Bitter; Theakston Old Peculier; Whitbread Trophy** H
Intimate and friendly, true village local, recently extended to offer much needed extra room. Brassware features in the lounge. ❀ ♿ ♣ P

## Wintersett

### Anglers Retreat
Ferry Top Lane OS382157
☎ (01924) 862370
12–3, 7–11; 12–3, 7–10.30 Sun
**Tetley Bitter; Theakston Best Bitter, XB; guest beers** (summer) H
Cosy rural pub between the villages of Ryhill and Crofton, handy for anglers and birdwatchers using Wintersett Reservoir. Biker friendly.
⛰ Q ❀ ♿ P

## Yeadon

### New Inn
Albert Square
☎ (0113) 250 3220
11–11; 12–4, 7–10.30 Sun
**John Smith's Bitter, Magnet; guest beer** H
Friendly, 18th-century stone pub, much altered but with a rustic interior.
⛰ ❀ ◐ ⊞ ♣ ⌓

## WEBSTER'S RIP

It may have mainly been the home of copycat Wilson's beers and of one of the great national blands, Webster's Yorkshire Bitter, but the decision by Scottish Courage to close the Webster's brewery in Halifax is much lamented none the less. Its demise means a loss of 170 jobs and 150 years of Yorkshire brewing heritage.

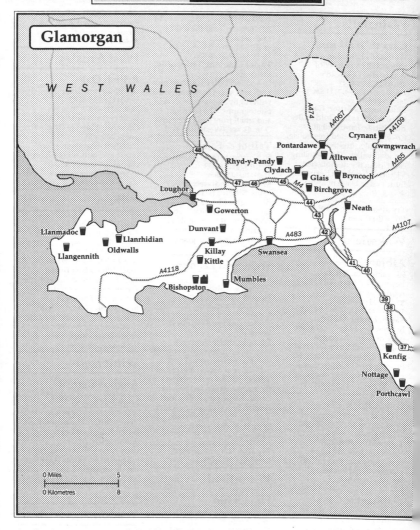

## Glamorgan

*Authority areas covered: Bridgend UA, Caerphilly UA, Cardiff UA, Merthyr Tydfil UA, Neath & Port Talbot UA, Rhondda, Cynon, Taff UA, Swansea UA, Vale of Glamorgan UA*

## Aberaman

### Blaengwawr Inn
Cardiff Road
☎ (01685) 871706
12–4.30, 6.30–11; 12–11 Fri & Sat; 12–10.30 Sun
**Cains Bitter; Worthington Bitter; guest beer** H
Pleasant, single-bar pub with a good community atmosphere.
♣

### Temple Bar
Cardiff Road ☎ (01685) 876137
12–4, 6.30–11 (may vary); 12–3, 7–10.30 Sun
**Bullmastiff Best Bitter;**
Felinfoel Bitter; Hancock's HB H
Small, friendly single-bar pub with a notable history. In the same family for over 100 years.
🏠 Q ♣ P

## Abercarn

### Old Swan
58 Commercial Road
☎ (01495) 243161
12–11; 12–10.30 Sun
**Courage Best Bitter; Ushers Founders, seasonal beers** H
Comfortable, friendly valleys local with games and pool rooms. Snuff available; good value food; real cider in summer. Reputedly haunted.
🏠 ◑ ▷ ▲ ♣ ⌂

## Aberdare

### Gadlys Arms
26 Bridge Street, Robertstown (off A4059)
☎ (01685) 876055
12–3, 7–11; 12–3, 7–10.30 Sun
**Brains Dark; Marston's Pedigree; Tetley Bitter; Worthington Bitter; guest beer** H
Comfortable house with a village pub atmosphere, adorned with golfing

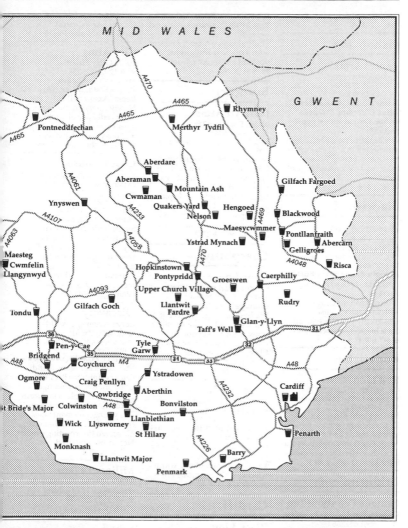

memorabilia. Popular
restaurant and extensive bar
menu. ✿ ◖ ▶ P

## Aberthin

### Hare & Hounds
On A4222 ☎ (01446) 774892
11.30–11; 12–10.30 Sun
**Draught Bass** G; **Hancock's
HB** H; **Worthington Bitter** G
Small, friendly community pub
with an extended family and
games room, plus a safe garden
play area. Limited parking.
Meals in summer only.
🏰 Q ⛟ ✿ ◖ ♣ P

## Alltwen

### Butchers Arms
Alltwen Hill (off A474)
☎ (01792) 863100
12–3, 6.30–11; 12–3, 7–10.30 Sun

**Courage Directors; Everards
Old Original; John Smith's
Bitter; Wadworth 6X; guest
beer** H
Hillside gem serving guest ales
from independent brewers.
The restaurant is closed Sun
eve. 🏰 Q ✿ ◖ ▶ P

## Barry

### Old College
Buttrills, Barry Road
☎ (01446) 700580
11.30–11; 12–10.30 Sun
**Banks's Bitter** E; **Marston's
Pedigree** H
One of the few Banks's houses
in the area, an open-plan, long
bar extends from the public
drinking area to a lounge (used
as a lounge when food is
not being served).
✿ ◖ ▶ P ⛁

## Birchgrove

### Bridgend Inn
265 Birchgrove Road (off M4
jct 44) ☎ (01792) 321878
11–11; 12–10.30 Sun
**Brains Dark; Marston's
Pedigree; John Smith's Bitter;
Wadworth 6X; guest beers** H
Local with a bar, a pool room
and a quiet, comfortable
lounge (families welcome). Eve
meals are cooked to order.
Weekly guest beer. Open from

**INDEPENDENT
BREWERIES**

**Brains:** Cardiff

**Bullmastiff:** Cardiff

**Swansea:** Bishopston

357

9am for breakfast, Mon–Sat.
Q ❀ ◑ ◗ ♿ ♣ P

## Bishopston

### Joiners Arms
50 Bishopston Road
☎ (01792) 232658
11–11; 12–10.30 Sun
**Brains Dark; Courage Best Bitter, Directors; Swansea Bishops Wood Bitter; guest beers** Ⓗ
Excellent free house offering a wide selection of beers and its own micro-brewery. Good value food for a wide range of tastes.
❀ ◑ ◗ ♣ P

## Blackwood

### Masons Arms
Bridge Street
☎ (01495) 227979
12–4, 7–11; 11–11 Sat & summer; 12–10.30 Sun
**Draught Bass; Crown Buckley Dark; Hancock's HB; guest beers** Ⓗ
Spacious well-appointed pub with a friendly licensee. Deservedly popular with all ages. Interesting guest beers.
❀ ◑ ◗ P

## Bonvilston

### Red Lion
On A48 ☎ (01446) 781208
11.30–3, 5–11; 11–11 Sat & summer; 12–2, 7–10.30 Sun
**Brains Dark, Bitter, SA** Ⓗ
Roadside pub with a separate area for eating and a darts room. Good mix of visitors and local characters. No eve meals Sun/Mon. Q ❀ ◑ ◗ ♣ P

## Bridgend

### Famous Penybont Inn
Derwen Road
☎ (01656) 652266
11.30–11; 12–10.30 Sun
**Brains SA; Greenalls Bitter; Marston's Pedigree; Wadworth 6X; guest beers** Ⓗ
Popular town-centre pub with a cosy atmosphere and much railway memorabilia.
◑ ◗ ♿ ⇌

### Five Bells Inn
Ewenny Road
☎ (01656) 668188
11.30–4, 6–11; 11.30–11 Thu–Sat; 12–10.30 Sun
**Draught Bass; Worthington Bitter** Ⓗ
Spacious, comfortable bar with an adjoining games area. A quiet lounge is housed on an upper level. ◑ ⊞ ♿ ⇌ P

### Victoria Hotel
7 Adare Street
☎ (01656) 659802
11–11; 12–10.30 Sun
**John Smith's Bitter; Ushers Best Bitter, Founders, seasonal beers** Ⓗ
Traditional town-centre boozer with a popular restaurant upstairs and a roof garden.
❀ ◑ ♿ ⇌

## Bryncoch

### Dyffryn Arms
Neath Road (A474)
☎ (01639) 636184
12–3, 7–11; 12–3, 7 (8 winter)–10.30 Sun
**Boddingtons Bitter; Brains SA; Fuller's London Pride** Ⓗ
Families are welcome at this well-run rural pub where a large comfortable bar displays local historical photographs. The separate restaurant has a late supper licence; no meals Sun eve. ❀ ◑ ◗ P

## Caerphilly

### Courthouse
Cardiff Road ☎ (01222) 888120
11–11; 12–5, 7–10.30 Sun
**Courage Best Bitter; Wadworth 6X; guest beer** Ⓗ
14th-century longhouse with a conservatory overlooking Caerphilly Castle. Caerphilly Cheese is made on the premises. No meals Sun.
Q ❀ ◑ ◗ ⇌

### Green Lady
Pontygwindy Road
☎ (01222) 851510
11–11; 12–3, 7–10.30 Sun
**Banks's Mild, Bitter, seasonal beers; Camerons Strongarm** Ⓗ
Good example of how a newly-built pub can have a good atmosphere and offer a warm welcome. No eve meals Fri–Sun. ❀ ◑ ◗ ♿ P

## Cardiff

### Black Lion
Cardiff Road, Llandaff (A4119/High St jct)
☎ (01222) 567312
11–11; 12–3, 7–10.30 Sun
**Brains Dark, Bitter, SA; guest beers** (occasional) Ⓗ
Traditional Brains house on a busy road near Llandaff Cathedral. Spacious lounge. A Brains cellarmanship award-winner.
Q ◑ ◗ ⊞ ⇌ (Fairwater) ♣

### Butchers Arms
29 Llandaff Road, Canton (1 mile W of centre)
☎ (01222) 227927
11–11; 12–3, 7–10.30 Sun
**Brains Dark, Bitter, SA** Ⓗ
Friendly, traditional, corner pub with a small lounge and a no-frills bar. Brains *Best-Kept Cellar* awards are on show. Occasional back room poetry and folk music (close to Chapter Arts Centre).
⊞ ⇌ (Ninian Pk) ♣

### City Arms
10–12 Quay Street
☎ (01222) 225258
11–11; 12–3, 7–10.30 Sun
**Brains Dark, Bitter, SA; guest beers** (occasional) Ⓗ
Newly extended pub, deservedly popular with all ages. Close to the Arms Park and busy on match days.
Q ◑ ⊞ ♿ ⇌ (Central) ♣

### Coach House
Station Terrace, Ely Industrial Estate (near A48/A4161 jct)
☎ (01222) 555573
12–2.30 (not Mon or Sat), 8 (7 Thu–Sat)–11; 12–3, 7–10.30 Sun
**Hancock's HB; guest beer** Ⓗ
Single building at the end of a cul-de-sac, near the former Ely/Rhymney brewery. The welcoming single bar has no jukebox, TV or noisy games. Popular with local workers. No meals Sun. Q ❀ ◑ ◗ ⇌ (Waungron Rd) P

### Discovery
Celyn Avenue, Lakeside
☎ (01222) 755015
11–3, 5.30–11; 11–11 Fri & Sat; 12–3, 7–10.30 Sun
**Courage Best Bitter, Directors; Marston's Pedigree; Ruddles County; John Smith's Bitter** Ⓗ
Comfortable, two-lounge, 1960s pub in a pleasant North Cardiff location near a lake. The younger element takes over one bar, which has a large TV screen (for sporting events). Neat dress preferred.
Q ◑ ⊞ ♿ ♣ P

### Millers Tavern
3 Brook Street, Riverside (10 mins' walk W of centre)
☎ (01222) 237605
11–11; 12–10.30 Sun
**Brains Dark, SA; Tetley Bitter** Ⓗ
Imposing, semi-circular building comprising a bar plus a lounge. Live music every Fri. The house beer, Millers Bitter, is brewed by Carlsberg-Tetley. No food Sun. ❀ ◑ ⊞ ♣

### Roath Cottage
Plasnewydd Road, Roath (off City Road via Cyfarthfa St)
☎ (01222) 487490
11–11; 12–10.30 Sun
**Brains Dark, Bitter** Ⓗ
Basic, friendly, two-roomed, end of terrace local; difficult to find. ⊞ ♣

### Royal Oak
200 Broadway, Roath (Newport Rd jct)
☎ (01222) 473984
11–11; 12–10.30 Sun
**Brains Dark, Bitter** Ⓗ, **SA** Ⓖ; **guest beers** (occasional) Ⓗ/Ⓖ

Large, street-corner local with
lots of sporting memorabilia.
The bar is a shrine to peerless
Jim Driscoll. Frequent live
music. ❀ ⊞ ♣

### Three Horseshoes
Merthyr Road, Gabalfa (400
yds N of A48/A470 jct)
☎ (01222) 625703
11–11; 12–10.30 Sun
**Brains Dark, Bitter, SA; guest
beers** (occasional) ⊞
Pub of rather unremarkable
appearance but with a friendly
welcome and good food (Mon–
Fri only). Built in 1968 to
replace the previous Three
Horseshoes, which was
demolished to make way for
the A470. Q ❀ ◑ ⊞ ♣ P

### Traders Tavern
6–8 David Street
☎ (01222) 238795
11–11 (midnight on International
Arena concert nights); closed Sun
**Brains Bitter; Tetley Bitter;
guest beer** ⊞
Single-bar, comfortable,
welcoming pub just south of
the main shopping area. The
guest beer is from Carlsberg-
Tetley's Tapster's Choice
range. Eve meals end at 7.30.
◑ ▶ ⇌ (Central/Queen St)

### Vulcan Hotel
10 Adam Street (A4160 behind
the prison) ☎ (01222) 461580
11–8 (11 Fri & Sat); 11–6 Sun
**Brains Dark, Bitter** ⊞
Built to last in 1853, this is the
oldest Cardiff pub with its
name unchanged. Down-to-
earth public bar; excellent
value lunches in the lounge.
Urinal connoisseurs should
pay a visit to the gents'.
◑ ⊞ ⇌ (Queen St) ♣

### White Hart
James Street Docks
☎ (01222) 472561
11–11; 12–6 Sun
**Brains Dark, Bitter** ⊞
Single-bar, basic but
refurbished, Brains tenanted
house, winner of a *Best-Kept
Cellar* award. It may close early
during quiet periods but a tap
on the window should secure
entry. ⇌ (Bay) ♣

*Try also:* **Cottage**, St Mary St
(Brains); **Newt & Cucumber**,
Wharton St (Morland);
**Romilly**, Romilly Rd (Brains)

## Clydach

### Carpenters Arms
High Street ☎ (01792) 843333
11–11; 12–10.30 Sun
**Ansells Mild; Everards Old
Original; Wadworth 6X;
Worthington Bitter** ⊞
Pleasant village pub with a
large dining area.
❀ ◑ ▶ ⊞ ♣ P

### New Inn
The Lone ☎ (01792) 842839
11–4, 6–11; 11–11 Fri & Sat; 12–3,
7–10.30 Sun
**Flowers Original; Greene
King Abbot; Morland Old
Speckled Hen; Whitbread
Fuggles IPA; Worthington
Bitter; guest beers** ⊞
Very friendly, olde-worlde
country pub with three bars
and a pool room. Popular with
locals and walkers (on the edge
of an RSPB reserve). Children's
certificate; good food.
🏨 Q ❀ ◑ ▶ ⊞ ♿ ♣ P

## Colwinston

### Sycamore Tree
Off A48 ☎ (01656) 652827
12–3 (not Mon or Tue, Oct–Easter), 6
(6.30 winter)–11; 12–3, 7–10.30 Sun
**Draught Bass; Hancock's HB;
guest beer** (summer) ⊞
An attractive old interior and a
very friendly licensee make
this village inn a joy to visit.
Superb home-produced fare
(the dining room is no-
smoking). Families welcome in
the lounge. Ask for games.
🏨 Q ❀ ◑ ▶ ⊞ ♿ ♠ ♣ P

## Cowbridge

### Edmondes Arms
High Street ☎ (01446) 773192
3 (12 Sat)–11; 12–10.30 Sun
**Hancock's HB** ⊞
Lively, street-corner local,
popular with all ages.
🏨 ⊞ ♣

## Coychurch

### Prince of Wales
Main Road
☎ (01656) 860600
12–11; 12–3, 7–10.30 Sun
**Banks's Mild, Bitter;
Marston's Pedigree** ⊞
Pleasant village local with
exposed stone walls and
flagstone floors, a rare Banks's
outlet for the area.
Q ❀ ⊞ ♿ P

### White Horse
Main Road ☎ (01656) 652583
11–4, 5.30–11; 11–11 Fri & Sat; 12–
3.30, 7–10.30 Sun
**Brains Dark, Bitter, SA; guest
beers** (occasional) ⊞
Pub featuring a plush,
restaurant-style lounge and a
comfortable public bar.
❀ ◑ ▶ ⊞ ♿ P

## Craig Penllyn

### Barley Mow
1½ miles N of A48 OS978773
☎ (01446) 772558
12–3, 6–11; 12–3, 7–10.30 Sun
**Hancock's HB; Worthington
Bitter; guest beer** ⊞
Deservedly popular village
pub with fine food and a warm

welcome. No food Sun eve.
🏨 Q ❀ ◑ ▶ ⊞ ♣ P

## Crynant

### Kingfisher
On Ystradgynlais road
OS791064 ☎ (01639) 750040
11–3, 5.30–11 (11–11 summer);
12–10.30 Sun (may vary winter)
**Courage Best Bitter; Ushers
Best Bitter** ⊞
Pub with a small locals' bar
complemented by a very
homely lounge dedicated to
good food. Q ❀ 🏨 ◑ ▶ ⊞ ♣ P

## Cwmaman

### Falcon Inn
1 Incline Row (off B4275)
OS008998 ☎ (01685) 873758
11–11; 12–10.30 Sun
**Beer range varies** ⊞
Remote, but welcoming, pub
well worth finding. Outside
bar in summer. ❀ ◑ ▶ P

## Cwmfelin

### Cross Inn
Maesteg Road
☎ (01656) 732476
11.45–11; 12–10.30 Sun
**Brains Bitter, SA; Morland
Old Speckled Hen** ⊞
Friendly local on a busy road,
boasting a traditional benched
public bar and a smart lounge.
⊞ ♿ ⇌ (Garth) P

## Cwmgwrach

### Star
17 Glannant Place (off A465 at
Glynneath) ☎ (01639) 720365
12–3, 7–11; 12–11 Fri & Sat; 12–10.30
Sun
**Crown Buckley CPA, Best
Bitter** ⊞
Friendly local comprising a
bar, bar-lounge and a small
children's area in a typical
valley house built over 100
years ago. ❀ ♣ P

## Dunvant

### Found Out
8 Killan Road (400 yds up hill
from the square)
☎ (01792) 203596
11–11; 12–10.30 Sun
**Flowers Original; guest
beer** ⊞
Friendly local with a bar and a
lounge, offering pool, darts,
quiz nights and good quality
lunches. ❀ ◑ ⊞ ♿ ♣ P

## Gelligroes

### Halfway House
Upper Gelligroes
☎ (01495) 220255
12–3, 6–11; 11–11 Sat; 12–10.30 Sun
**Hancock's HB; Worthington
Bitter; guest beers** ⊞

Comfortable, multi-level pub with lots of bric-a-brac and memorabilia, situated up a lane off a bypass. Good selection of meals. ◑ ▶ P

## Gilfach Fargoed

### Capel
Park Place ☎ (01443) 830272
12–4, 7–11; 12–11 Fri & Sat; 12–10.30 Sun
**Brains SA; Courage Best Bitter; John Smith's Bitter; guest beer**
Large, traditional valleys pub with lots of interesting features.
Q ☎ ❀ ◑ ⚑ ≈ ♣ P

## Gilfach Goch

### Griffin Inn
Hendreforgan (600 yds S of A4093) OS988875
☎ (01443) 672247
7–11; 12–4.30, 7–11 Sat; 12–3.30, 7–10.30 Sun
**Brains SA; guest beer** Ⓗ
Traditional local, situated in a small valley bottom, featuring interesting bric-a-brac and hunting trophies. Hard to find, but worth the effort.
Q ❀ P

## Glais

### Old Glais Inn
Glais Road ☎ (01792) 843316
12–3, 6–11; 12–3, 6–10.30 Sun
**Courage Directors; Ruddles Best Bitter; John Smith's Bitter; Webster's Yorkshire Bitter; guest beers** Ⓗ
Pub where a comfortable lounge offers a fine display of cheese dishes and plates. Excellent food in the adjoining restaurant. ❀ ◑ ▶ ⚑ ♿ ♣ P

## Glan-y-Llyn

### Fagin's Ale & Chop House
8 Cardiff Road
☎ (01222) 811800
12–11; 12–10.30 Sun
**Brains Bitter; Felinfoel Double Dragon; Hardington Best Bitter** Ⓗ**; Morland Old Speckled Hen; guest beers** Ⓖ
Popular ale house serving up to 12 ales. Its wooden beams display 'Wenglish' sayings. A former regional CAMRA *Pub of the Year*. No lunches Sat; no eve meals Sun.
❀ ◑ ▶ ≈ (Taff's Well)

## Gowerton

### Welcome to Gower
2 Mount Street
☎ (01792) 872611
11.30–3, 7–11; 12–3, 7–10.30 Sun
**Crown Buckley Best Bitter, Rev. James** Ⓗ

Wood panelling and diffuse lighting make for a relaxed atmosphere in this well appointed pub at the 'Gateway to Gower'. One other Crown Buckley beer is also sold.
Q ❀ ◑ ▶ ≈ P

## Groeswen

### White Cross Inn
OS128870 ☎ (01222) 851332
12–3.30, 6–11; 11–11 Sat (supper licence); 12–3.30, 6–10.30 Sun
**Flowers IPA; Hancock's HB; Wadworth 6X; guest beer** Ⓗ
Cosy pub with a small bar and two additional rooms, the larger allowing live entertainment. The patio has a view of Caerphilly Castle. Children welcome (grassed play area).
🏛 Q ❀ ◑ ▶ ▲ ♣ P

## Hengoed

### Junction Inn
9 Kings Hill ☎ (01443) 812192
12–4 (4.30 Fri & Sat), 7–11; 12–3, 7–10.30 Sun
**Hancock's HB; Worthington Bitter** Ⓗ
Immaculately appointed local featuring railway memorabilia, on the western side of Hengoed viaduct.
◑ ▶ ⚑ ≈ ♣

## Hopkinstown

### Hollybush
Tŷ Mawr Road (main road to Rhondda) ☎ (01443) 402325
11.30–4.30, 6.30–11; 12–3, 7–10.30 Sun
**Hancock's HB; Worthington Bitter; guest beer** Ⓗ
Terrace pub with a small bar dedicated to sports, both physical and mental. The comfortable lounge doubles as an eating area.
◑ ▶ ⚑ ♿ ♣ P 🍴

## Kenfig

### Prince of Wales
Maudlam OS804818
☎ (01656) 740356
11.30–4, 6–11; 12–10.30 Sun (varies)
**Draught Bass; Worthington Bitter; guest beers** Ⓖ
Historic pub with exposed stone walls and large open fireplace. The former town hall of the lost town of Kenfig.
🏛 Q ❀ ◑ ▶ ♿ ▲ P

## Killay

### Railway Inn
555 Gower Road, Upper Killay
☎ (01792) 203946
12–11; 12–10.30 Sun
**Crown Buckley Dark, Best Bitter, Rev. James** Ⓗ
Former station house with three rooms, sporting railway

paraphernalia throughout. Handy for walkers using the Clyne Valley Line.
❀ ⚑ ♣ P

## Kittle

### Beaufort Arms
18 Pennard Road
☎ (01792) 234521
11.30–11; 12–10.30 Sun
**Crown Buckley Best Bitter, Rev. James** Ⓗ
Comfortable village pub with an adjoining restaurant offering good value meals. Large play area outside. A third Crown Buckley beer is also sold. ❀ ◑ ▶ ♣ P

## Llanblethian

### Cross Inn
On B4270 ☎ (01446) 772995
12–2.30, 6–11 (supper licence); 12–10.30 Sun
**Cains Bitter; Hancock's HB; guest beer** Ⓗ
Busy roadside pub greatly improved and offering competitive prices for beer and food. Open for breakfast at 8.30. Families welcome in the dining room.
🏛 Q ❀ ◑ ▶ ⚑ ▲ ♣ P

## Llangennith

### King's Head
☎ (01792) 386212
11–11; 12–10.30 Sun
**Crown Buckley Best Bitter, Rev. James** Ⓗ
Springs rise on the village green opposite this intimate, stone-walled pub. Good view of Rhossili Bay, which is within walking distance for the energetic. Separate games room. Another Crown Buckley beer is occasionally sold. Food served all day. ❀ ◑ ▶ ▲ ♣ P

## Llangynwyd

### Corner House
OS858889 ☎ (01656) 732393
11–11; 12–10.30 Sun
**Tetley Bitter; Worthington Bitter; guest beers** Ⓗ
Ancient, characterful building with an excellent range of beers. No eve meals Sun. No wheelchair access to the ladies' WC. 🏛 Q ☎ ❀ ◑ ▶ ⚑ ♿ P ⚥

### Old House (Yr Hen Dŷ)
OS858889 ☎ (01656) 733310
11–11; 12–10.30 Sun
**Flowers Original; guest beers** Ⓗ
One of Wales's oldest pubs (1147): a thatched house with bags of atmosphere. Extremely popular, its restaurant is well known.
🏛 Q ❀ ◑ ▶ ⚑ ♿ P

## Llanmadoc

### Britannia
Cheriton
☎ (01792) 386624
12–3.30, 6–11 (12–11 summer; closed Tue & Wed eves in winter); 12–10.30 Sun
**Marston's Pedigree; guest beer** Ⓗ
Pleasant, stone-walled pub/restaurant tucked away on the North Gower coast; handy for wildfowl watchers. Extra guest beers in summer.
❀ 🛏 ◖ ▶ ♣ P

## Llanrhidian

### Welcome to Town
Off B4295
☎ (01792) 390015
12–3, 7–11; closed Mon eve; 12–3, 7–10.30 Sun
**Wadworth 6X** Ⓗ
Low ceilings create a cosy atmosphere in this friendly village pub. Open for morning coffee, it is handy for visitors to Llanrhidian Marsh and Pony Centre. Family garden.
❀ ◖ ▶ ♣ P

## Llantwit Fardre

### Bush Inn
Bryn Terrace
☎ (01443) 203958
11–11; 12–10.30 Sun
**Hancock's HB; guest beers** Ⓗ
Welcoming village local offering ever changing selection of guest ales. Pre-match breakfasts are a house speciality. Q ❀ P

## Llantwit Major

### Old White Hart
Wine Street
☎ (01446) 793549
11–11; 12–10.30 Sun
**Worthington Bitter** Ⓗ
Friendly pub, a row of three converted 14th-century yeomen's cottages. Pictures of old Llantwit adorn the walls. Food is served all day. The garden has a children's play area. ♨ ⛺ ❀ ◖ ⊞ ♠ ♣

## Llysworney

### Carne Arms
On B4268
☎ (01446) 775553
12–3, 6–11; 12–3, 7–10.30 Sun
**Draught Bass; Flowers Original; Hancock's HB** Ⓗ
Attractive roadside hostelry serving good value food. A good range of whiskies and an inglenook provide warmth in winter. Children's farm in the garden. Bass occasionally makes way for a guest beer.
♨ Q ❀ ◖ ⊞ ♠ ♣ P

## Loughor

### Reverend James
180 Borough Road
☎ (01792) 892943
12–11; 12–10.30 Sun
**Crown Buckley Dark, Best Bitter, Rev. James** Ⓗ
Friendly local with a comfortable lounge and an adjoining restaurant. Note the story of the pub's name on the wall. Taking a pew is recommended.
❀ ◖ ▶ ⊞ ♿ ♣ P

## Maesteg

### Sawyer's Arms
4 Commercial Street
☎ (01656) 734500
11–11; 12–3, 7–10.30 Sun
**Boddingtons Bitter; Brains Bitter, SA** Ⓗ
An oasis: a popular, traditional public bar plus a smart lounge offering quizzes and live music at times. Eve meals by arrangement; no lunches Sun.
◖ ⊞ ♿ ⇌

## Maesycwmmer

### Maesycwmmer Inn
Main Road ☎ (01443) 814385
12–4, 7–11, 12–3, 7–10.30 Sun
**Brains SA; Hancock's HB** Ⓗ
A small bar and a comfortable lounge in a pub on the eastern side of the Hengoed viaduct. No lunches Sat.
Q ❀ ◖ ⊞ ⇌ (Hengoed) ♣ P

## Merthyr Tydfil

### Lantern
Bethesda Street, Georgetown
☎ (01685) 382551
11.30–3.30, 5–11; 11–11 Sat; 12–3, 7–10.30 Sun
**Crown Buckley Best Bitter, Rev. James, seasonal beers** Ⓗ
200-year-old town pub. Its horseshoe-shaped bar has a raised dining area. ◖ ▶ ⇌

## Monknash

### Plough & Harrow
Off B4265 ☎ (01656) 890209
12 (6 Mon)–11; 12–10.30 Sun
**Draught Bass** Ⓖ**; Hancock's HB; Worthington Bitter** Ⓗ**; guest beers** Ⓖ
Stone-built, lively, two-bar pub near the Coastal Heritage Path: local CAMRA *Pub of the Year*. Live music Sun; eve meals Fri only. Excellent range of guest beers, plus a house beer from Castle Eden. ♨ ❀ ◖ ⊞ ♠ ♣ P

## Mountain Ash

### Jeffreys Arms
Jeffrey Street ☎ (01443) 472976
7 (12 Fri & Sat)–11; 12–10.30 Sun

**Draught Bass; Worthington Bitter; guest beers** Ⓗ
Large, friendly pub with a good atmosphere. ♣

## Mumbles

### Park Inn
23 Park Street (turn right opposite Boot's; first left)
☎ (01792) 366738
12–3 (not Mon), 5.30–11; 12–10.30 Sun
**Marston's Pedigree; Ruddles County; Worthington Bitter; guest beers** Ⓗ
19th-century local, a popular, cosy free house offering a wide variety of ales and home cooked food in its single lounge/bar. Beer festival Nov.
♨ Q ◖ ♿

### Vincent's
580 Mumbles Road
☎ (01792) 368308
2–11; 12–3.30, 7.30–10.30 Sun
**Draught Bass; Worthington Bitter; guest beer** Ⓗ
Seafront pub with a Spanish theme, offering an extensive tapas menu until 8pm. Regularly changed guest ale.
◖

## Neath

### Highlander
2 Lewis Road, Melyn (at Stockham's Corner)
☎ (01639) 633586
12–2.30, 6–11; 12–11 Sat; 12–3, 7–10.30 Sun
**Worthington Bitter; guest beers** Ⓗ
Welcoming, pleasantly furnished free house serving good value, quality meals (late supper licence in the restaurant). No meals Sun eve. Live music Sun, Tue and Thu in the bar. ◖ ▶ ⇌

### Star
Penydre (near Gnoll rugby ground) ☎ (01639) 637745
12.30–4.30, 6–11; 12.30–11 Sat; 12–2.30, 7–10.30 Sun
**Draught Bass; Hancock's HB; Worthington Dark** Ⓗ
Traditional, friendly local with two rooms, one of which is a snug. Mature clientele; favoured by rugby fans on match days. Snacks served. Q P

## Nelson

### Dynevor Arms
Commercial Street
☎ (01443) 450295
11–11; 11.30–4.30, 6–11 Tue & Thu; 12–10.30 Sun
**Brains Bitter; Hancock's HB; Worthington Bitter** Ⓗ
Former brew pub (and mortuary), over 200 years old, with a busy public bar.
⊞ ♣ P

## Nottage

### Rose & Crown

Heol-y-Capel
☎ (01656) 784880
11.30–11; 12–10.30 Sun
**Ruddles Best Bitter; County;
John Smith's Bitter;
Theakston Best Bitter;
Webster's Yorkshire
Bitter** Ⓗ
Smartly kept old pub,
pleasantly modernised.
Q ✿ 🛏 ◖ ▶ ⌂ ᗚ & Ⓐ

## Ogmore

### Pelican

Ewenny Road (B4524)
☎ (01656) 880049
11–11 (11.30–3, 6–11 winter); 12–10.30
(12–3, winter) Sun
**Marston's Pedigree; John
Smith's Bitter; Wadworth 6X;
guest beers** Ⓗ
Welcoming roadside tavern,
opposite a ruined castle. Guest
beers are changed regularly.
Excellent, home-made food at
good prices. Spot the last
working bar billiards table in
the Vale. Families welcome
in the lounge. Cider in
summer.
🛏 Q ✿ ◖ ▶ & ♣ ⌂ P

## Oldwalls

### Greyhound

☎ (01792) 391027
12–11; 12–10.30 Sun
**Draught Bass; guest beers** Ⓗ
Large rural inn on the North
Gower road. Plenty of room
outside for children to play
and enjoy the countryside.
Fish is a speciality in the
restaurant.
🛏 Q ᗚ ✿ ◖ ▶ ⌂ P

## Penarth

### Golden Lion

69 Glebe Street
☎ (01222) 701574
12.30–11; 12–4, 7–10.30 Sun
**Cains Bitter; Hancock's
HB** Ⓗ
Cosy, two-bar terraced pub, a
short walk from the town
centre: a comfortable local with
good value Cains, but it can be
smoky.
Q ✿ ⌂ ≠ (Dingle Rd) ♣

### Merrie Harrier

Penlan Road, Llandough (at
A4055/B4267 jct)
☎ (01222) 707706
12–11; 12–10.30 Sun
**Brains Dark, Bitter, SA** Ⓗ
Large prominent pub on a
busy road junction, popular
with hospital staff lunchtimes.
Comfortable rooms with
wide local appeal. No food
Sun.
Q ✿ ◖ ⌂ ≠ (Cogan) ♣ P

## Penmark

### Six Bells

☎ (01446) 710229
12–11; 12–10.30 Sun
**Hancock's HB; guest beer**
(occasional) Ⓗ
The village local: a bar and a
separate lounge/restaurant
offering a high standard of
comfort. Close to Cardiff
Airport. Q ✿ ▶ ⌂ P

## Pen-y-Cae

### Tŷ'r Isha

Off A4061/A4063, Bridgend
side of M4 services OS903827
☎ (01656) 725287
12–4, 6–11; 12–11 Fri, Sat & summer;
12–10.30 Sun
**Draught Bass; Worthington
Bitter** Ⓗ
Popular, converted
15th-century farmhouse, once a
court-house. There are benches
and a children's play area on
the surrounding lawns. Disco
Sat. 🛏 Q ✿ ◖ ▶ & P

## Pontardawe

### Pontardawe Inn

Herbert Street (A474)
☎ (01792) 830791
12–11; 12–10.30 Sun
**Crown Buckley CPA, Best
Bitter, Rev. James, seasonal
beers** Ⓗ
17th-century coaching inn
known as the Gwachel. Home
to Pontardawe International
Music Festival and Old Tom,
the resident ghost. Live music
Thu and Sat. Local industrial
exhibits are displayed in the
bar. Sun lunches served.
✿ ◖ ♣ P

## Pontllanfraith

### Crown

The Bryn (near A472/A4049
jct) ☎ (01495) 223404
12–3, 5–11; 12–11 Fri & Sat; 12–3 (may
extend), 7–10.30 Sun
**Courage Best Bitter; Felinfoel
Double Dragon; John Smith's
Bitter** Ⓗ
Two-roomed pub with a basic
public bar and a spacious
lounge, popular with diners
(good varied menu). Outdoor
amusements for children. A
haven for local golfers.
✿ ◖ ▶ ⌂ ≠ ✂

## Pontneddfechan

### Angel

On B4242 ☎ (01639) 722013
11.30–4, 6.30–11 (11–11 summer);
12–3, 7–10.30 Sun
**Draught Bass; Boddingtons
Bitter** Ⓗ
Pub with a large lounge and a
comfortable, low-ceilinged bar

in the heart of waterfall
country. Q ᗚ ✿ ◖ ▶ P

## Pontypridd

### Greyhound Hotel

1 Broadway (opp. station)
☎ (01443) 402350
11–11; 12–10.30 Sun
**Bass Toby Light, Draught
Bass; Hancock's HB;
Worthington Bitter** Ⓗ
Friendly local uniting the
generations. ✿ ⌂ ≠ ♣

### Llanover Arms

Bridge Street ☎ (01443) 403215
11–11; 12–3, 7–10.30 Sun
**Brains Dark, Bitter, SA;
Worthington Bitter; guest
beer** Ⓗ
Bustling town pub brimming
with character(s).
Q ✿ ⌂ ≠ ♣ P

### Market Tavern

Market Square
☎ (01443) 485331
11–11; 12–3, 7–10.30 Sun
**Courage Directors; Hancock's
HB; John Smith's Bitter;
Wadworth 6X; Worthington
Bitter** Ⓗ
Town-centre local with a cellar
bar for younger clientele. It
also features a restaurant and
comfortable accommodation.
🛏 ◖ ▶ ≠

## Porthcawl

### Royal Oak

South Road ☎ (01656) 782684
11.30–11; 12–10.30 Sun
**Draught Bass; Worthington
Bitter; guest beers** Ⓗ
Pleasant pub full of character
and characters: a cosy public
bar and a smart lounge. No
meals Sun eve.
Q ✿ ◖ ▶ ⌂ & Ⓐ P

## Quakers Yard

### Glantaff Inn

Cardiff Road ☎ (01443) 410822
12–4, 7–11; 12–4, 7–10.30 Sun
**Courage Best Bitter, Directors;
Ruddles Best Bitter; John
Smith's Bitter; guest beer** Ⓗ
Comfortable inn with a warm
atmosphere and a good
collection of water jugs.
Upstairs restaurant. No meals
Sun eve. Q ✿ ◖ ▶ & P

## Rhyd-y-Pandy

### Masons Arms

Rhyd-y-Pandy Road (N of M4
jct 46) ☎ (01792) 842535
12–11; 12–10.30 Sun
**Courage Best Bitter; Marston's
Pedigree; guest beer** Ⓗ
Two-roomed, 17th-century inn,
a mile NW of Morriston. Tricky
to find but worth the effort.
🛏 Q ✿ ◖ ▶ ⌂ P 🍺

## Rhymney

### Farmers Arms
Brewery Row
☎ (01685) 840257
12–11; 12–3, 7–10.30 Sun
**Boddingtons Bitter; Brains Bitter; guest beers** Ⓗ
Friendly, spacious and comfortable pub with a separate restaurant; traditionally furnished with interesting bric-a-brac, including Rhymney Brewery memorabilia. ◧ ▶ ⇌ ♠

## Risca

### Exchange Inn
52 St Mary Street
☎ (01633) 612716
11–11; 12–10.30 Sun
**Crown Buckley Best Bitter, SBB, Rev. James; guest beer** Ⓗ
Small but lively pub on the main road. The public bar features many trophy cabinets and Hancock's prints.
❀ ◧ ⊕ ♠ P

## Rudry

### Maenllwyd Inn
☎ (01222) 888505
11–3.30, 6–11; 11–11 Sat; 12–10.30 Sun
**Theakston XB; Younger Scotch** Ⓗ
Characterful old country inn with low ceilings and discrete drinking and eating areas.
♨ Q ❀ ◧ ▶ P

## St Bride's Major

### Farmers Arms
Wick Road (B4265)
☎ (01656) 880224
12–3, 6–11; 12–3, 7–10.30 Sun
**Courage Best Bitter; John Smith's Bitter; Ushers Best Bitter, Founders, seasonal beers** Ⓗ
Busy village pub opposite the pond. Popular for its food and children's garden play area.
♨ Q ❀ ◧ ▶ P

### Fox & Hounds
Ewenny Road (B4265)
☎ (01656) 880285
5.30 (2 Fri, 12 Sat)–11; 12–10.30 Sun
**Brains Bitter; Wadworth 6X; guest beers** Ⓗ
16th-century local in a pretty village, the centre of local activity. Rugby league memorabilia adorns one of the beams in the bar. Families welcome in the lounge, dogs welcome in the bar. Lunches weekends only; no food Sun eve. Q ❀ ◧ ▶ ⅊ ♠ P

## St Hilary

### Bush Inn
¾ mile S of A48
☎ (01446) 772745
11–11; 12–10.30 Sun
**Draught Bass** Ⓖ**; Hancock's HB** Ⓗ**; Morland Old Speckled Hen** Ⓖ
Friendly, traditional, 14th-century thatched inn in an exclusive part of the Vale. The ghost of a highwayman resides in a bedroom. Families welcome; help is provided for guests with disabilities. The food is excellent (no meals Sun eve). Cider in summer.
♨ Q ❀ ⌂ ◧ ▶ ⊕ ♠ ⇲ P

## Swansea

### Bryn-y-Mor Hotel
Bryn-y-Mor Road
☎ (01792) 466650
11–11; 12–10.30 Sun
**Ansells Bitter; Ind Coope Burton Ale; Tetley Bitter; guest beers** Ⓗ
Friendly local with a bar and a lounge; handy for rugby and cricket at St Helens. Live music Wed and Sun. ❀ ◧ ▶ ⊕ ♠

### Cross Keys
12 St Mary's Street
☎ (01792) 473417
11–11; 12–10.30 Sun
**Hancock's HB; Worthington Bitter** Ⓗ
Well appointed, city-centre pub and restaurant catering for a variety of tastes. ❀ ◧ ▶ ⇌

### Eli Jenkins Alehouse
24 Oxford Street (near station)
☎ (01792) 465289
11–11; 7–10.30 Sun, closed Sun lunch
**Draught Bass; Worthington Bitter; guest beers** Ⓗ
Pub named after the reverend from *Under Milkwood*, refurbished as a 'trad' ale house with a flagstone floor, decorative wooden alcoves, nooks and prints of historic Swansea. ◧ ▶ ⅙ ⇌

### O'Brien's Exchange
10 The Strand (off Wind St down Green Dragon Lane)
☎ (01792) 645345
12–11; closed Sun
**Brains Bitter, SA** Ⓗ
Pub worth visiting for its unique furniture and fittings, friendly atmosphere and superb collection of jazz photographs. Q ◧ ⇌

### Queens Hotel
Gloucester Place
☎ (01792) 643460
11–11; 12–10.30 Sun
**Crown Buckley Best Bitter; Theakston Mild, Best Bitter, Old Peculier** Ⓗ
One-roomed lounge bar on the edge of the marina; its numerous pictures reveal the maritime history of the area. Excellent lunches. Quiz nights Sun/Wed. ❀ ◧ ⅙ ⇌

### St George
30 Walter Road
☎ (01792) 469317
11.30–11; 12–10.30 Sun
**Felinfoel Double Dragon; Hancock's HB; Worthington Bitter** Ⓗ
Large, one-roomed pub on the edge of the city centre. Live music Sun eve; quiz Tue. The only outlet in the city for Felinfoel (unavailable in high summer). ◧ ⅙

### Singleton
Singleton Street
☎ (01792) 655987
11–11; 12–10.30 Sun
**Brains SA; Courage Best Bitter** Ⓗ
Very welcoming, smart city bar with some relaxing areas. ◧

### Vivian Arms
Vivian Road, Sketty
☎ (01792) 203015
12–11; 12–10.30 Sun
**Brains Dark, Bitter, SA** Ⓗ
Two-tiered bar with a comfortable lounge. Excellent value lunches. ❀ ◧ ⊕ ♠

### Westbourne Hotel
1 Bryn-y-Mor Road
☎ (01792) 459054
12–11; 12–3, 7–10.30 Sun
**Draught Bass; Hancock's HB; Worthington Dark; guest beers** Ⓗ
Striking corner pub, near the Guildhall. The imposing slate plaque in the bar is of uncertain age. Mind the steps in the bar. Eve meals end at 8; no-smoking lounge till 9pm.
❀ ◧ ▶ ⊕ ⅌

### Wig & Pen
134–136 St Helens Road
☎ (01792) 466519
11.30–11; 12–10.30 Sun
**Boddingtons Bitter; Morland IPA, Old Speckled Hen; Theakston XB; guest beers** Ⓗ
Pub next to the Guildhall, with sectioned seating areas. Plaques depict the industrial and cultural history of Swansea. ◧ ▶ ♠

## Taff's Well

### Anchor Hotel
Cardiff Road ☎ (01222) 810104
12 (11 Sat)–11; 12–3, 7–10.30 Sun
**Brains Bitter; Marston's Pedigree; Wadworth 6X** Ⓗ
Comfortable, nautically-themed pub with a restaurant specialising in Mongolian cuisine. ◧ ▶ ⊕ ⇌ ♠ P

### Taff's Well Inn
Cardiff Road ☎ (01222) 810324
12–11; 12–3, 7–10.30 Sun
**Tetley Bitter; guest beer** Ⓗ
Comfortable roadside inn adjacent to a bowling green and an ancient well.
❀ ◧ ▶ ⇌ P

## Tondu

### Llynfi Arms
Maesteg Road
☎ (01656) 720010
11 (12 Fri & Sat)–4, 6.30–11; 12–3,
6.30–10.30 Sun
Hancock's HB; Worthington
Bitter; guest beer Ⓗ
Roadside pub with a lively bar
and a comfy lounge. Lunches
Sat/Sun only; eve meals Thu–
Sat. Q ◖ ▶ 🖶 🚳 ♿ ⇌

## Tyle Garw

### Boar's Head
Coed Cae Lane
☎ (01443) 225400
12–4, 7–11; 12–10.30 Sun
Beer range varies Ⓗ
Small, welcoming, unspoilt
local, simply furnished. Forest
walks opposite. Q ❀ ♣

## Upper Church Village

### Farmers Arms
St Illtyds Road
☎ (01443) 205766
11–11; 12–10.30 Sun

Draught Bass; Hancock's HB;
guest beer Ⓗ
Bustling village pub with a
strong local atmosphere and a
varied clientele. Occasional
male voice choir events. No
food Sun. ❀ ◖ P

## Wick

### Star Inn
On B4265
☎ (01656) 890519
12–3, 5–11 (11–11 summer); 12–5.30,
7–10.30 Sun
Hancock's HB; Worthington
Bitter; guest beer Ⓗ
Friendly, sympathetically
refurbished pub, re-opened in
1994 after being closed for
years. No food Sun eve.
🏚 Q ❀ 🚗 ◖ ▶ 🚳 ♣ P 🚬

## Ynyswen

### Crown Hotel
Ynyswen Road
☎ (01443) 772805
4 (2.30 summer)–11; 12–10.30 Sun
Courage Directors; guest
beers Ⓗ
Popular, main road pub, where
the public bar features a red

phone box and coal-mining
memorabilia. Separate lounge.
🏚 🍴 ⇌ ♣

## Ystrad Mynach

### Royal Oak
Commercial Street
☎ (01443) 814196
12–3, 5.30–11; 12–11 Sat; 12–3,
5.30–10.30 Sun
Draught Bass; Hancock's HB;
Worthington Bitter Ⓗ
Unmistakable brewers' Tudor
pub with a busy public bar.
Good food.
Q ❀ ◖ ▶ 🍴 🚳 ⇌ ♣ P

## Ystradowen

### White Lion
On A4222 ☎ (01446) 772540
12–3, 6.30–11; 11–11 Sat; 12–4.30,
7–10.30 Sun
John Smith's Bitter; Ushers
Best Bitter Ⓗ
Cosy roadside inn, one of the
new Ushers outlets in the area:
two rooms, low wooden-
beamed ceilings and an
attractive open fireplace. Good
quality food from a varied
menu (no meals Sun eve).
🏚 Q ❀ ◖ ▶ P

---

# SHOW US YOUR PRICES!

It is the law that all licensed premises must prominently display a
representative sample of their drink prices. Sadly, as the latest
CAMRA prices survey reveals, over nine per cent of pubs do not
comply.

Do they think drinkers are not interested in how much their beer
costs?

Next come the second division of price list dodgers, those pubs
which do have a price list but one which is taped to the back of the
bar, so far away that its small print is illegible.

These retailers surely wouldn't put up with the same treatment at
their local supermarket, or petrol station, so why do they expect
drinkers to shop in ignorance?

Everyone knows that the social practice of buying drinks in rounds
obscures the cost of individual drinks. Everyone knows that, when a
pub is busy, the customer gets little chance to question staff about
pricing policy. Try working out the cost of three pints of bitter, a gin
and tonic and a glass of lager shandy when the queue at the bar is
three-deep on a Friday night. Without a price list as a guide, it's a stiff
challenge even for a *Krypton Factor* champion.

Beer prices are high enough as it is without drinkers running the risk
of being ripped off by unscrupulous bar staff, so it's time for pubs to
come clean.

Come on publicans. Show us your prices — what have you got to
hide?

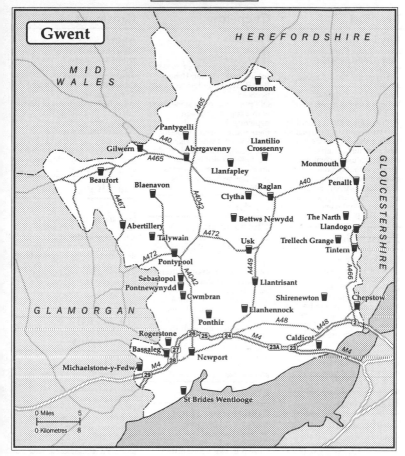

*Authority areas covered: Blaenau Gwent UA, Monmouthshire UA, Newport UA, Torfaen UA*

## Abergavenny

### Somerset Arms
Victoria Street (Merthyr Rd jct)
☎ (01873) 852158
7–11; 12–3.30, 7–11 Sat; 12–3, 7–10.30 Sun
**Draught Bass; Felinfoel Bitter; guest beer** Ⓗ
The wonderful, cosy public bar is an integral part of the charm of this pub, which is just outside the central area of town. Note: closed lunchtime during the week. Good value food and accommodation.
🏚 Q 🛏 ◑ ▶ ⊞ ♣

### Station
37 Brecon Road
☎ (01873) 854759
5–11; 12–11 Fri & Sat; 12–3, 7–10.30 Sun
**Draught Bass; Freeminer Bitter; Tetley Bitter; guest beer** Ⓗ
Frequently changing, excellent value guest beers, in addition to providing an outlet for Freeminer (rare in the area), help to explain the popularity of this pub, which caters for a wide variety of folk.
🏚 ⊞ ♣ P

Try also: **Coach & Horses**, Cross St (Free)

## Abertillery

### Clynmawr Hotel
Tŷ Bryn Road (off A467)
☎ (01495) 212323
2 (1 Sat)–11; 12–3, 7–10.30 Sun
**Crown Buckley Best Bitter; guest beer** (occasional) Ⓗ
Unspoilt local where the public bar features pictures of past pub sports teams and is adjoined by a skittle alley. Comfortable lounge and upstairs family room. The enclosed garden has children's climbing apparatus.
🛏 🏚 ⊞ ♣

## Bassaleg

### Tredegar Arms
4 Caerphilly Road (off M4 jct 28) ☎ (01633) 893247
11–11; 12–10.30 Sun
**Boddingtons Bitter; Brains Bitter; Flowers Original; Fuller's London Pride; Greene King Abbot; guest beers** Ⓖ/Ⓗ
Large cask ale house offering a wide and varied range of beers. The interior, comprising a cosy lounge and a bar/dining area, features old brewery-style notices and wooden casks. Recently added family area, plus a garden with play apparatus. Cider in summer.
🏚 🛏 🏚 ◑ ▶ ⊞ ♣ ⏚ P ⦸

365

## Beaufort

### Rhyd-y-Blew

Rassau Road, Carmeltown
(near A4046/A4047 jct)
☎ (01495) 308935
12–3 (11.30–3.30 Sat), 6 (6.30 Mon, Tue
& Thu)–11; 12–3, 7–10.30 Sun
**Flowers IPA, Original;
Fuller's London Pride; guest
beer** H
With a name meaning 'Ford of
the Hairs', and a sign depicting
two horses being washed in a
ford, this pub's multi-level
interior features a comfortable
lounge, a dining room, and a
games room. Impressive array
of pumpclips from past guest
ales. No food Sat/Sun. Live
entertainment Fri eve.
🏚 ❀ ◖ ♣ P

## Bettws Newydd

### Black Bear

Off B4598 OS361062
☎ (01873) 880701
12–3 (not Mon), 6–11.30; 12–11 Sun
**Beer range varies** G
17th-century village pub
serving excellent food (fish
dishes a speciality; half-
portions for children) and a
constantly changing beer
selection. Live folk music Sun,
2–6. Use of a map is strongly
advised for first time visitors.
🏚 ❀ ◖ ▲ ⎔ P

## Blaenavon

### Cambrian Inn

Cambrian Row (off Llanover
Rd) ☎ (01495) 790327
6 (1 Fri, 12 Sat)–11; 12–3, 7–10.30 Sun
**Draught Bass; Brains Dark,
Bitter, SA; guest beer** H
Friendly, traditional street-
corner pub where sporting and
local history photos and
humorous notices decorate the
bar. A cosy lounge and a
games room complete the
interior. Interesting guest ales.
Q ⊞ ♣

## Caldicot

### Cross Inn

Newport Road
☎ (01291) 420692
11–4, 7 (6.30 Fri)–11; 11–11 Sat; 12–3,
7–10.30 Sun
**Brains Dark; Courage Best
Bitter; Ruddles County; John
Smith's Bitter; Wadworth 6X;
guest beer** H
Popular pub in the shopping
centre, by main road bus stops.
The lounge has seating centred
around a fireplace, also a
cabinet display of pumpclips.
The public bar features various
games. Fifteen mins' stroll
from the railway station.
❀ ⊞ ♣ ⎔ P

## Chepstow

### Five Alls

Hocker Hill Street
☎ (01291) 622528
11–5, 7 (6.30 Fri)–11; 12–4, 7–10.30 Sun
**John Smith's Bitter; Ushers
Best Bitter, Founders, seasonal
beers** H
Old pub on a cobblestone street
with a superb pub sign
depicting the 'Five Alls';
there's also a set of stocks for
customers who misbehave!
The L-shaped bar displays old
local photos and framed
theatrical posters. Ten mins
from bus and rail stations.
❀ ♣

## Clytha

### Clytha Arms

On B4598, old Abergavenny–
Raglan road ☎ (01873) 840206
11.30–3.30 (not Mon), 6–11; 11–11 Sat;
12–3, 7–10.30 Sun
**Draught Bass; Brains Bitter;
Hook Norton Best Bitter;
guest beers** H
Winner of many CAMRA
awards, this former dower-
house has been converted into
a fine country inn with an
enviable reputation for
excellent food (no meals Mon).
Very friendly staff and
atmosphere.
🏚 Q ❀ 🚌 ◖ ♣ ⎔ P ⊟

## Cwmbran

### Commodore Hotel

Mill Lane, Llanyravon
☎ (01633) 484091
11–3, 5–11; 12–3, 7–10.30 Sun
**Crown Buckley Best Bitter,
SBB; guest beer** H
Friendly, family-run plush
hotel. Cask ales are served in
the Pilliners Lounge, a pleasant
room with a relaxing dark
decor. Good value bar meals
and snacks. High-standard
accommodation and restaurant
facilities. ❀ 🚌 ◖ ▶ P

## Gilwern

### Corn Exchange Inn

Crickhowell Road
☎ (01873) 830337
12–4, 6 (5 Fri)–11; 12–11 Sat; 12–10.30
Sun
**Draught Bass; Hancock's HB;
Worthington Bitter; guest
beer** H
Pub with a convivial
atmosphere in its pleasant bar
and lounge, plus attractive
summer floral displays. A
worthwhile stop after
exploring the beautiful
Clydach Gorge. Book Sun
lunch.
❀ ◖ ▶ ⊞ ♣ P

**Try also: Bridgend Inn**, Main
Rd (Felinfoel)

## Grosmont

### Angel

Main Street (off A465)
☎ (01981) 240646
12–2.30, 7–11; 12–3, 7–10.30 Sun
(varies summer weekends)
**Crown Buckley Best Bitter,
Rev. James** H
Pub which is the focus of life in
this charming village that
nestles among hills. An
excellent base for walkers on
the 18-mile Three Castles Walk
or for visitors to the impressive
castle remains and church.
🏚 Q ❀ 🚌 ◖ ▶ ♣

## Llandogo

### Sloop Inn

On A466 ☎ (01594) 530291
12–2.30, 6–11; 12–3, 7–10.30 Sun
**Beer range varies** H
18th-century inn which takes
its name from the barges which
once traded on the River Wye:
a traditional public bar and a
comfortable lounge. An
excellent base from which to
explore the area. Very good
accommodation.
🏚 ❀ 🚌 ◖ ▶ ⊞ ▲ ♣ P

## Llanfapley

### Red Hart

On B4233 ☎ (01600) 780227
12–3, 6–11; 12–3, 6–10.30 Sun
**Beer range varies** H
Village pub serving three
changing guest beers. Families
welcome in the games room.
Interesting food includes
various chilis.
🏚 Q ❀ 🐕 ❀ ◖ ▶ ♣ P

## Llanhennock

### Wheatsheaf Inn

1st right off the Usk road, from
Caerleon OS353929
☎ (01633) 420468
11–3, 5.30–11; 11–11 Sat; 12–3, 7–10.30
Sun
**Draught Bass; Worthington
Bitter; guest beers** H
Popular country pub,
unchanged for many years.
Very popular in summer for its
delightful surroundings.
Boules has a strong following.
🏚 Q ❀ ◖ ⊞ ♣ P

## Llantilio Crossenny

### Hostry Inn

On B4233 ☎ (01600) 780278
12–3, 6.30–11; 12–3, 7–10.30 Sun
**Wye Valley Bitter, Supreme** H
15th-century village pub
featuring a crisp-eating Irish
wolfhound, a large garden, a
function hall and a skittle alley.
The good range of food
includes vegetarian options
and Sun lunch.
❀ 🚌 ◖ ▶ ▲ ♣ ⌇

## Llantrisant

### Greyhound Inn

3 miles S of Usk, by A449 (no
access) ☎ (01291) 672505
11–3, 6–11; 12–3, 6–10.30 Sun
**Flowers Original; Marston's
Pedigree; Morland Old
Speckled Hen; guest beer** Ⓗ
Charming country pub,
originally a 17th-century
farmhouse. Excellent
accommodation in the recently
converted stone stable block.
Good selection of meals. Pine
shop on site.
🏚 Q ⑤ ❀ 🛏 ◁ ▷ 🍴 P

## Michaelstone-y-Fedw

### Cefn Mably Arms

Off A48 at Castleton (follow
signs) ☎ (01633) 680347
12–3 (not Mon), 6.30–11; 12–3, 7–10.30
Sun
**Hancock's HB; Marston's
Pedigree; Tetley Bitter** Ⓗ
Popular, traditional pub in a
beautiful rural location. The
decor is dominated by timber
and copper and the food is
hard to resist (no meals Sun
eve or Mon). ❀ ◁ ▷ P

## Monmouth

### Green Dragon

St Thomas Square
☎ (01600) 712561
11–11; 12–3, 7–10.30 Sun
**Hancock's HB; Marston's
Bitter, Pedigree; guest beers** Ⓗ
Pub with an excellent range of
beers (up to three guests).
Comfortably furnished
throughout, it features many
pictures and mirrors while the
cartoon gallery in the loos is a
must for visitors! Varied range
of light bites and main meals.
Q ❀ ◁ ▷ 🍴 🍴

## The Narth

### Trekkers

OS525064 ☎ (01600) 860367
11–3.30, 6–11; 12–10.30 Sun
**Felinfoel Bitter; Freeminer
Bitter; guest beers** Ⓗ
Welcoming log cabin-styled
country pub with an extensive
garden and a bandstand. The
central fireplace is a feature of
the bar/restaurant area. The
landlady provides a distinctive
menu to suit discerning diners.
🏚 Q ❀ 🛏 ◁ ▷ ♿ 🍴 P

## Newport

### Hornblower

126 Commercial Street
☎ (01633) 267575
11–11; 12–10.30 Sun
**Ansells Mild; Tetley Bitter;
guest beers** Ⓗ

Loud and lively bikers' pub
serving five real ales. It can get
busy at weekends. Chess is
often played at quieter times!
🚄

### Lyceum Tavern

110 Malpas Road (near M4 jct
26) ☎ (01633) 858636
11.30–11 (varies in winter); 12–3.30,
7–10.30 Sun
**Marston's Pedigree; John
Smith's Bitter; guest beer** Ⓗ
Busy town pub offering nightly
events including live music,
plus a function room. Book Sun
lunch. ❀ ◁ ▷

### Olde Murenger House

53 High Street
☎ (01633) 263977
11.30–3.30, 5.30–11; 11–11 Fri & Sat;
12–3, 7–10.30 Sun
**Samuel Smith OBB** Ⓗ
Popular town-centre pub close
to the station. The building
dates from the 16th-century
and is Sam Smith's only pub in
Wales. Home-cooked bar
lunches served (except Sun).
Very busy Fri/Sat eves.
◁ 🚄 ♣

### Red Lion

47 Stow Hill ☎ (01633) 264398
12–11; 12–10.30 Sun
**John Smith's Bitter; Ushers
Best Bitter, Founders, seasonal
beers** Ⓗ
Recently modernised corner
pub which proudly tells its
customers that the menu (no
meals Sun) is a Linda
McCartney-free zone! Live
music Fri. A pub with
character which is gaining
popularity. 🏚 ◁ ▷ 🚄 ♣ ○

### St Julian Inn

Caerleon Road
☎ (01633) 258663
11.30–11; 12–10.30 Sun
**Courage Best Bitter; Ruddles
Best Bitter; John Smith's
Bitter; guest beers** Ⓗ
Large, refurbished pub
popular with all ages. Very
busy in summer due to its
location on the River Usk. A
good place to stop when
visiting Caerleon's Roman
sites. Excellent range of guest
beers. Regional CAMRA *Pub of
the Year* 1995. Eve meals end at
8.30. Occasional cider.
❀ ◁ ▷ ♣ ○ P

**Try also: Wetherspoons,
Cambrian Centre**

## Pantygelli

### Crown Inn

Old Hereford Road (off A465)
☎ (01873) 853314
11.30–2.30, 7–11; 12–4, 7–10.30 Sun
**Draught Bass; Felinfoel
Double Dragon; guest beer** Ⓗ
Large, semi-open-plan pub
with a separate dining area

(families welcome), situated at
the gateway to the Black
Mountains – the countryside is
wonderful. The flower-decked
patio has lovely views over the
Skirrid mountain.
🏚 ❀ 🛏 ◁ ▷ P

## Penallt

### Boat Inn

Lone Lane (off A466; access by
footbridge from Redbrook)
☎ (01600) 712615
11–3, 6–11; 12–4, 6.30–10.30 Sun
**Butcombe Bitter; Freeminer
Bitter; Fuller's London Pride;
Hook Norton Old Hooky;
Theakston Old Peculier; guest
beers** Ⓖ
Extremely popular riverside
pub, particularly in summer.
The largely stone interior has
two rooms. Beers (up to ten,
plus cider, in summer) are
served from a stillage behind
the bar. Tasty, fresh food from
an appetising menu. Live
music Tue and Thu. Park at
Redbrook AFC.
🏚 ❀ ◁ ▷ 🍴 ○

## Ponthir

### Ponthir House Inn

Caerleon Road (B4236, 1 mile
NW of Caerleon)
☎ (01633) 420479
11.30–11; 12–3, 7–10.30 Sun
**Hancock's HB; M&B Brew XI;
Worthington Bitter; guest
beer** Ⓗ
Spacious country pub with
linked areas and separate space
for diners. The attractive,
stonework interior is tastefully
decorated. 🏚 Q ❀ ◁ ▷ ♣ P

## Pontnewynydd

### Horseshoe Inn

Hill Street ☎ (01495) 762188
12–11; 12–4, 7–10.30 Sun
**John Smith's Bitter; Ushers
Best Bitter, Founders, seasonal
beers** Ⓗ
Popular pub of Georgian origin
with an attached restaurant.
The small, cosy lounge features
horseshoes and sketched local
scenes. The public bar gives
access to an upstairs games
room and a family room. Book
Sun lunch. 🚼 ❀ ◁ ▷ 🍴 ♣

## Pontypool

### George

Commercial Street
☎ (01495) 764734
11.30–11; 12–3, 7–10.30 Sun
**John Smith's Bitter; guest
beer** Ⓗ
Edwardian-style bar with
wooden floorboards and a
picture gallery linked to the
name of George. Two high-
mounted tables with coloured

lamps are an attractive feature. Popular with younger folk in the eve. The upstairs restaurant is used Sun lunchtime (book). ⌐

### Pontypool RFC Clubhouse

Elm House, Park Road
☎ (01495) 762524
12–3 (not Mon–Thu), 6–11; 12–3, 7–10.30 Sun
**Hancock's HB; guest beer** Ⓗ
Comfortable bar and lounge featuring many reminders in pictures and trophies of a great rugby union tradition. Real ale is firmly established thanks to the steward's efforts. Near the Eastern Valley Heritage Museum and a short stroll from Pontypool Park. Access at steward's discretion.
Q ⊞ ♣

## Raglan

### Ship Inn

High Street ☎ (01291) 690635
11.30–11; 12–10.30 Sun
**Draught Bass; Hancock's HB; Worthington Bitter; guest beer** Ⓗ
16th-century coaching inn with a cobbled forecourt which features an old waterpump. The low-beamed interior comprises adjoining bars, a separate dining room, and a pool room. Within walking distance (15 mins) of Raglan Castle. ♨ Q ❀ ◖ ▶ ⊞ ♣

## Rogerstone

### Old Globe

1 St John's Crescent
☎ (01633) 897154
12–3, 5.30 (6 Sat)–11; 12–2.30, 7–10.30 Sun
**Hancock's HB; guest beers** Ⓗ
Friendly and comfortable pub, popular with locals. The open lounge features a pool table. Small meeting room available.
❀ ♣ P

## St Brides Wentlooge

### Church House Inn

Church Road (B4239)
☎ (01633) 681289
11–4, 7–11 (11–11 summer); 12–4, 7–10.30 Sun
**Brains Dark, Bitter, SA** Ⓗ
Traditional, two-bar Brains pub. A quiet local in winter during which it features one log and two coal fires; very busy in summer. A good pub to visit with a family (large

garden). A bistro is open eves.
♨ Q ❀ ◖ ▶ ⊞ ♣ P

## Sebastopol

### Open Hearth

Wern Road (off South St)
☎ (01495) 763752
11–3 (4 Sat), 6–11; 12–3, 7–10.30 Sun
**Archers Golden; Boddingtons Bitter; Brains SA; Hancock's HB; guest beers** Ⓗ
Gwent CAMRA *Pub of the Year* 1995 and a long-time favourite. The handpumps are dotted around its three rooms but a blackboard lists the beer menu. A good range of tasty food includes daily specials. A separate restaurant menu is also available. ❀ ◖ ▶ ⊞ ♣ P

## Shirenewton

### Carpenters Arms

Usk Road ☎ (01291) 641231
11–2.30, 6–11; 12–2.30, 7–10.30 Sun ◄
**Boddingtons Bitter; Fuller's London Pride; Marston's Pedigree, Owd Rodger; Wadworth 6X; guest beer** Ⓗ
Ever-popular country pub just outside the village. The numerous interconnected drinking areas create a warm, cosy atmosphere. Good value meals at all times.
♨ Q ❀ ◖ ▶

### Tredegar Arms

The Square ☎ (01291) 641274
12–3, 6–11; 12–11 Sat; 12–4, 7–10.30 Sun
**Draught Bass; Hancock's HB; Hook Norton Best Bitter; guest beers** Ⓗ
Popular pub in the heart of the village. The bar area is popular with a lively selection of locals; the smart lounge area is used extensively for meals (highly recommended). No food Sun eve. Very good selection of guest beers.
♨ ❀ ◖ ▶ ⊞ ♣ P

## Talywain

### Globe Inn

Commercial Road (B4246)
☎ (01495) 772053
6.30 (11 Sat)–11; 12–3, 7–10.30 Sun
**Brains Dark, Bitter; Hancock's HB; guest beer** Ⓗ
Pleasant roadside pub, an oasis for local cask ale drinkers: a traditional public bar with a fireplace and a comfortable lounge with a games room at the rear. Live music Sat eve. Brains Dark is mainly a winter

visitor. Cider in summer.
♨ ⊞ ♣ ⌣

## Tintern

### Cherry Tree

Devauden Road (off A466)
OS526001 ☎ (01291) 689292
11–2.30 (not winter Mon), 6–11; 12–3, 7–10.30 Sun
**Hancock's HB** Ⓖ
Rare example of a one-roomed village pub: the hub of the community. Beer is served from the cellar. A *Good Beer Guide* ever-present.
♨ Q ❀ ♣ ⌣ P

**Try also: Rose & Crown,** on A466 (Ushers)

## Trellech Grange

### Fountain Inn

Off B4293 OS503011
☎ (01291) 689303
12–3, 6–11; 12–3, 7–10.30 Sun
**Wadworth 6X; guest beer** Ⓗ
Welcoming, 17th-century pub in the Wye Valley, providing a good range of food (Fri night fish and chips a speciality).
♨ ❀ ➤ ◖ ▶ ▲ ♣ P

## Usk

### King's Head Hotel

18 Old Market Street
☎ (01291) 672963
11–11; 12–10.30 Sun
**Badger Tanglefoot; Flowers Original; Fuller's London Pride; Marston's Pedigree** Ⓗ
This pub's public bar is one of the few left in the area but the real ales are in the cosy lounge, which has a mixture of furniture and a welcoming fireplace. Pictures depict local scenes and the landlord's fishing prowess.
♨ Q ➤ ◖ ▶ ⊞ ♣ P

### New Court Hotel

56 Maryport Street
☎ (01291) 673364
11–11; 12–3, 7–10.30 Sun
**Draught Bass; Marston's Pedigree; Tetley Bitter; guest beers** Ⓗ
Pub named after the original courthouse opposite. The long interior is served from a bar adorned with a large collection of ties and hats. Dining area at the rear; well balanced menu. The spacious garden is popular with children. ❀ ➤ ◖ ▶ ♣

**Try also: Greyhound Inn,** Old Chepstow Rd (Bass)

---

See the inside back cover for a map of all the new Welsh regions used in this book.

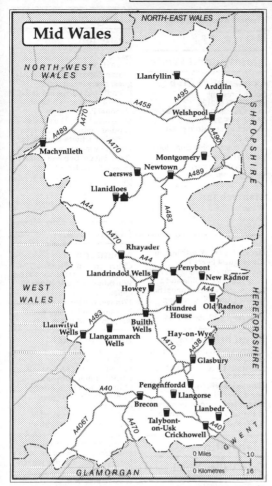

## Mid Wales

NORTH-EAST WALES

NORTH-WEST WALES

Llanfyllin

Arddlîn

Welshpool

Machynlleth

Montgomery

Caersws  Newtown

Llanidloes

Rhayader

Penybont

Llandrindod Wells  New Radnor

WEST WALES  Howey

Hundred House  Old Radnor

Llanwrtyd Wells  Builth Wells

Llangammarch Wells  Hay-on-Wye

Glasbury

Pengenffordd  Llangorse

Brecon  Llanbedr

Talybont-on-Usk  Crickhowell

SHROPSHIRE

HEREFORDSHIRE

GWENT

GLAMORGAN

0 Miles 10
0 Kilometres 16

*Authority areas covered: Powys UA*

## Arddlîn

### Horseshoe
On A483/B4392
☎ (01938) 590318
12–3, 5.30–11; 12–4, 6–10.30 Sun
**Marston's Pedigree; Worthington Bitter** Ⓗ
Welcoming village pub: a traditional public bar with a comfortable lounge/restaurant, serving a wide range of reasonably priced food. Children's play area in the garden. Weston's ciders.
🏠 ⊛ ◑ ▶ ⊟ ♣ ⌂ P

## Brecon

### George Hotel
George Street
☎ (01874) 623421
11–11; 12–10.30 Sun

**Tetley Bitter; Wadworth 6X; guest beers** Ⓗ
Historic, 17th-century inn with warm, comfortable bars, popular with the local business community. Interesting guest beers. Good selection of bar meals at all times.
🍴 ◑ ▶ P

### Old Boar's Head
14 Ship Street
☎ (01874) 622856
11–3, 5.30–11; 11–11 Fri & Sat (& summer Tue); 12–4, 7–10.30 (12–10.30 summer) Sun
**Brains SA; Everards Beacon; Fuller's London Pride, ESB; Thwaites Bitter; guest beers** Ⓗ
Ancient pub by the River Usk; a comfortably modernised public bar and a spacious rear bar with a pool table, popular with the young. A patio-style outdoor drinking area

overlooks the river. Parking limited; public car park nearby.
⊛ ◑ ⊟ ♣ P

**Try also: Bull's Head**, The Struet (Free)

## Builth Wells

### Greyhound
3 Garth Road ☎ (01982) 553255
12–3, 6.30–11; 12–3, 7–10.30 Sun
**Draught Bass; Worthington Bitter** Ⓗ
Attractively decorated hotel, comprising a lounge bar for quiet eating and drinking and a public bar with a pool table.
Q 🏠 ◑ ▶ ⊟ ⅙ P

## Caersws

### Red Lion
3–4 Main Street (off A470)
☎ (01686) 688023
11–11; 12–5, 7–10.30 Sun
**Banks's Mild, Bitter; Marston's Bitter** Ⓗ
Pleasant village local with a warm welcome. 🚃

## Crickhowell

### Bear Hotel
On A40 ☎ (01873) 810408
11–3, 6–11; 12–3, 7–10.30 Sun
**Draught Bass, Ruddles Best Bitter, County; John Smith's Bitter; guest beers** (occasional) Ⓗ
Delightful, historic coaching inn dating from the 15th century, winner of many awards for its bar and cuisine. Very popular with locals, it can get very busy. Limited parking.
🏨 Q 🛏 ⊛ 🏠 ◑ ▶ P

### White Hart Inn
Brecon Road (A40, W side of town) ☎ (01873) 810473
12–3, 6–11; 12–11 Sat; 12–3, 7–10.30 Sun (may extend in summer)
**Brains Bitter; Hancock's HB; Theakston XB; guest beer** Ⓗ
Small, friendly old inn, formerly a toll house (tolls are still displayed on the outside wall). A warm welcome awaits even the most casual visitor. Good range of pub food at reasonable prices (Welsh dishes a speciality).
◑ ▶ P

## Glasbury

### Harp Inn
On B4350, near A438 jct
☎ (01497) 847373
11–3, 6 (6.30 winter)–11; 12–3, 7–10.30 Sun

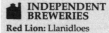

**INDEPENDENT BREWERIES**
**Red Lion:** Llanidloes

Boddingtons Bitter; Flowers
Original; Robinson's Best
Bitter; Thwaites Bitter ⊞
Friendly inn bordering the
River Wye, formerly a 17th-
century cider house. A good
base for the many activities in
the area. Good bar meals at
keen prices.
🏨 Q ❀ 🛏 ◖ ▮ ⊞ ♣ P

# Hay-on-Wye

## Blue Boar
Castle Street ☎ (01497) 820884
11–3, 6–11 (11–11 summer); 12–10.30
Sun
Draught Bass; Flowers IPA,
Original; Wadworth 6X;
Whitbread Fuggles IPA; guest
beer ⊞
Old pub with lots of character,
close to the castle; popular with
locals and visitors to the 'town
of books'. Good bar food (eve
meals in summer). It can get
very busy on market days and
in summer.
🏨 Q ◖ ▮ ⊞

# Howey

## Drover's Arms
Off A483, 1½ miles S of
Llandrindod Wells
☎ (01597) 822508
12–2.30 (not Tue), 7–11; 12–3, 7–10.30
Sun
Fuller's London Pride; Wood
Special; guest beers ⊞
Picturesque, two-bar village
inn on the original drovers'
route, with a 13th-century
cellar. Outside seating at the
front; attractive patio garden
overlooking a brook. The
varied, home-cooked food
incorporates local produce.
🏨 Q ❀ 🛏 ◖ ▮ ⊞ ▲ ♣ P

# Hundred House

## Hundred House Inn
On A481 ☎ (01982) 570231
12 (11 summer)–3, 6.30 (6
summer)–11; 12–3, 7–10.30 Sun
Hancock's HB; Worthington
Bitter; guest beers ⊞
Former drovers' pub set
amongst fine upland scenery.
Five rooms: a pool room,
farmers' bar, lounge, dining-
room and a garden bar.
Families welcome.
🏨 Q ☎ ❀ ◖ ▮ ⊞ ▲ P

# Llanbedr

## Red Lion
☎ (01873) 810754
12–2.30 (not Mon or Tue in winter),
7–11; 12–11 Sat; 12–3, 7–10.30 Sun
(may extend bank hols)
Felinfoel Double Dragon;
Worthington Bitter; guest
beer ⊞
Friendly old village pub next to
a church, lying at the foot of
the Black Mountains. An
additional guest beer is stocked

in summer. Good choice of
vegetarian dishes. Limited
parking.
🏨 Q ☎ 🛏 ◖ ▮ P ✗

# Llandrindod Wells

## Conservative Club
South Crescent
☎ (01597) 822126
11–2, 5.30 (4.30 Fri)–11; 11–11 Sat;
12–2, 7–10.30 Sun
Worthington Bitter; guest
beers ⊞
Quiet, comfortable club, not as
political as its name implies.
Non-members must be signed
in. Q ◖ ⅙ 🕽 ♣

## Llanerch Inn
Waterloo Road (across station
footbridge, 100 yds)
☎ (01597) 822086
11.30–2.30 (3 Sat), 6–11; 12–3, 7–10.30
Sun
Hancock's HB; Worthington
Bitter; guest beers ⊞
16th-century coaching inn with
a low, beamed ceiling and a
large stone hearth. Annual beer
tasting (Aug). No-smoking
area until 8.
Q ◖ 🛏 ◖ ▮ ⊞ ❀ ♣ P ✗

## Royal British Legion
Tremont Road (by fire station)
☎ (01597) 822558
7.30–11; 12–3, 7.30–11 Fri; 11–11 Sat;
12–3, 7–10.30 Sun
Hancock's HB; M&B Brew XI;
guest beer ⊞
Non-members must be signed
in to this British Legion club.
⅙ 🕽 ♣ P

# Llanfyllin

## Cain Valley Hotel
On A490
☎ (01691) 648366
11–11; 12–10.30 Sun
Ansells Bitter; Draught Bass;
Worthington Bitter ⊞
Excellent, 17th-century
coaching inn: a plush lounge
and two basic bars, one with an
imposing stone fireplace.
❀ 🛏 ◖ ▮ ⊞ ♣ P

# Llangammarch
Wells

## Aberceiros Inn
SW end of village
☎ (01591) 620227
6.30–11; 12–3, 6.30–11 Thu–Sat; 12–3,
7–10.30 Sun
Hancock's HB; Worthington
Bitter; guest beer ⊞
A little way out of the village
centre, this pub is worth
finding. It has been in the
licensee's family for 150 years
and has been well modernised,
retaining much of its
character.
🏨 Q ❀ ◖ ▮ ▲ 🕽 ♣ P 🕽

# Llangorse

## Castle Inn
☎ (01874) 658225
12–2.30, 6–11 (extends in summer);
12–3, 7–10.30 Sun
Brains Bitter; Castle Eden Ale;
guest beers (summer) ⊞
Friendly old village inn at the
heart of the Brecon Beacons
National Park, close to
Llangorse Lake. The area is a
popular centre for water sports
and other activities, and gets
very busy in summer. Parking
limited at the pub and in the
village. Good food at keen
prices.
🏨 Q ❀ 🛏 ◖ ▮ ⊞ ▲ ♣ P

Try also: Red Lion Hotel
(Free)

# Llanidloes

## Mount Inn
China Street ☎ (01686) 412247
11–2, 5.30–11; 11–11 Sat; 12–10.30 Sun
Worthington Dark, Bitter ⊞
Quiet, many-roomed,
17th-century inn with a cast
iron stove and a listed floor.
🏨 Q ☎ ❀ 🛏 ◖ ▮ ♣ P 🕽

## Red Lion Hotel
Longbridge Street
☎ (01686) 412270
11–3 (5 Sat), 7–11; 12–5, 7–10.30 Sun
Banks's Bitter; Flowers
Original; Red Lion Blind
Cobbler's Thumb; guest
beers ⊞
Old building, converted to
open plan, popular with all
and offering the widest choice
of real ales for many miles. It
now brews its own beer – one
barrel a week; a barley wine is
also planned.
❀ 🛏 ◖ ▮ ⅙ ♣ P

## Unicorn
Longbridge Street
☎ (01686) 413167
12–2.30, 5.30–11; 12–4, 7–10.30 Sun
Draught Bass; Tetley Mild,
Bitter ⊞
Pub with a raised lounge area:
a rare outlet for Tetley Mild.
Watch the step. 🛏 ◖ ▮

# Llanwrtyd Wells

## Neuadd Arms Hotel
The Square ☎ (01591) 610236
11.30–11 (may close afternoons); 12–3,
7–10.30 Sun
Felinfoel Double Dragon;
Hancock's HB; Worthington
Dark; guest beer ⊞
Georgian hotel, enlarged in the
1860s: an excellent centre for
activities in the surrounding
mountains and forests. A
venue for the Mid Wales Beer
Festival (Nov) and winter ale
festival (Jan).
🏨 Q ❀ 🛏 ◖ ▮ ⊞ ▲ ≢

### Stonecroft Inn
Dolecoed Road
☎ (01591) 610332
12–3, 5–11; 11–11 Sat; 12–10.30 Sun
**Brains SA; Younger Scotch** Ⓗ
Friendly Victorian pub in
Britain's smallest town, amid
beautiful scenery on the
spectacular Heart of Wales
railway line. Large riverside
garden with barbecue patio.
Regular special events and live
music. Children welcome.
Meals at all times. A venue
for the Mid Wales Beer
Festival.
🏠 Q ❀ 🛏 ◑ ▶ & ▲ ≱ ♣
P

## Machynlleth

### White Horse
Maengwyn Street
☎ (01654) 702247
11–3, 6–11; 11–11 Sat; 12–10.30 Sun
**Hancock's HB** Ⓗ
Popular public and lounge bars
in an old coaching inn.
❀ 🛏 ◑ ▶ ♣ P

### Wynnstay Arms Hotel
Maengwyn Street
☎ (01654) 702941
11–11; 12 10.30 Sun
**Boddingtons Bitter; guest
beers** Ⓗ
Small bar serving a number
of rooms in a comfortable
town-centre hotel. Log fire in
the main room. Two guest
beers. Children's menu on
request.
🏠 Q ❀ 🛏 ◑ ▶ ≱ P

## Montgomery

### Dragon Hotel
Off B4385
☎ (01686) 668359
11–11; 12–2, 7–10.30 Sun
**Wood Special; guest beers** Ⓗ
Excellent, comfortable bar in a
former 17th-century coaching
inn. The stone and timber
behind the bar are reputed to
have come from the local
castle. The hotel has an
indoor swimming pool. Two
guest beers.
Q 🛏 ◑ ▶ ♣

**Try also: Cottage**, Pool Rd
(Free)

## New Radnor

### Eagle Hotel
Broad Street (off A44)
☎ (01544) 350208
12–11; 12 10.30 Sun
**Draught Bass; Hook Norton
Best Bitter; guest beer** Ⓗ
Old coaching inn with beamed
bars and lounge. Handy for
local outdoor activities. Menu
specialities include vegetarian
and vegan. Supper licence.
🏠 Q ❀ 🛏 ◑ ▶ & ▲ ♣ ⏚ P
✍

## Newtown

### Cross Guns
32 Park Street (off A483)
☎ (01686) 625546
11–11; 12–10.30 Sun
**Theakston Best Bitter; guest
beer** Ⓗ
Many-roomed, beamed,
friendly pub. Indian meals
on the menu.
🛏 ◑ ▶ 🍴 ≱ P

### Railway Tavern
Old Kerry Road (off A483)
☎ (01686) 626151
11–3.30 (4.30 Tue, Fri & Sat), 6.30–11;
12–4, 7–10.30 Sun
**Draught Bass; Worthington
Bitter; guest beer** Ⓗ
Small, friendly one-bar local.
≱ ♣

### Sportsman
Severn Street (off A483)
☎ (01686) 625885
11–2.30, 5.30–11; 11–11 Fri & Sat;
12–3, 7–10.30 Sun
**Ind Coope Burton Ale; Tetley
Bitter; guest beer** Ⓗ
Friendly, town-centre local,
popular with a wide range of
customers. Traditional music
jam sessions every Tue.
Q ❀ ◑ ▶ ≱ ♣

## Old Radnor

### Harp
1 mile W of A44/B4362
☎ (01544) 350655
11.30–11; 12–3, 7–10.30 Sun
**Hanby Drawwell; Wood
Special; guest beers** Ⓗ
Beautifully restored,
15th-century inn with stone
walls, flagged-floor, beamed
ceilings and antique furniture.
Fine view of Radnor Forest. No
food Mon.
🏠 Q ❀ 🍴 🛏 ◑ ▶ ▲ ♣ P

## Pengenfordd

### Castle Inn
On A479, 3 miles S of Talgarth
☎ (01874) 711353
11–3, 7–11 (11–11 summer Sat & bank
hols); 12–3, 7–10.30 Sun
**Ruddles County; Wadworth
6X; guest beer** (summer) Ⓗ
Friendly, old country pub,
popular with hill-walkers and
pony-trekkers; situated at the
summit of the A479, between
Talgarth and Crickhowell, with
Castell Dinas, the highest
hillfort in Wales, forming a
dramatic backdrop.
🏠 ❀ 🛏 ◑ ▶ 🍴 ▲ ♣ P

## Penybont

### Severn Arms Hotel
At A44/A488 jct
☎ (01597) 851224
11–2.30, 6–11; 12–3, 7–10.30 Sun
**Draught Bass; Tetley Bitter;
Worthington Bitter** Ⓗ
Roadside inn with extensive
gardens sloping down to the
River Ithon (fishing rights): a
large public bar with an open
fire, a games room, a lounge
bar and a restaurant. 🏠 Q ❀
🛏 ◑ ▶ 🍴 ▲ ♣ P

## Rhayader

### Cornhill Inn
West Street
☎ (01597) 810869
7–11; 12–3, 7–11 Sat & summer; 12–3,
7–10.30 Sun
**Marston's Pedigree; Wye
Valley Bitter; guest beers** Ⓗ
Friendly, low-beamed,
400-year-old pub, reputedly
haunted: a single, L-shaped bar
with motorcycling artefacts.
No keg beer. Good food.
🏠 Q 🛏 ◑ ▶ ▲ ♣

### Triangle Inn
Off Bridge Street (B4518),
Cwmdauddwr
☎ (01597) 810537
12–3, 6.30–11; 11–11 Fri & Sat; 12–3,
7–10.30 Sun
**Draught Bass; Hancock's
HB** Ⓗ
Beautiful little weatherboarded
gem, overlooking the River
Wye. The ceilings are so low
that customers have to stand in
a hole to play darts.
❀ ◑ ▶ ♣

## Talybont-on-Usk

### Star Inn
On B4558 ☎ (01874) 676635
11–3, 6–11; 11–11 Sat; 12–10.30 Sun
**Beer range varies** Ⓗ
Canalside pub, extensively
renovated in 1995 after a
disastrous flood, but retaining
its real pub atmosphere.
Popular with walkers.
Excellent beer range (up to 12
ales) and good pub food. The
cider varies. Well worth a visit.
🏠 ❀ 🛏 ◑ ▶ ▲ ⏚

## Welshpool

### Royal Oak Hotel
Severn Street (off A483)
☎ (01938) 552217
11–3, 5.30–11; 11–11 Mon; 12–3,
7–10.30 Sun
**Worthington Bitter; guest
beers** Ⓗ
Plush, 350-year-old coaching
inn; formerly the manor house
of the Earls of Powis, now an
hotel which has been in the
same family for 60 years.
🏠 Q 🛏 ◑ ▶ ≱ P

> Don't forget to check
> neighbouring counties
> for even more pubs
> serving excellent beer.

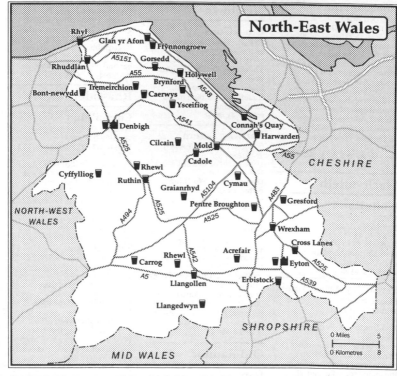

## North-East Wales

*Authority areas covered: Denbighshire UA, Flintshire UA, Wrexham UA*

## Acrefair

### Duke of Wellington
Llangollen Road (A539)
☎ (01978) 820169
7 (12 Sat, 11 Fri & Sat in summer)–11;
12–10.30 Sun (may extend)
**Marston's Bitter, Pedigree** Ⓗ
Intimate and lively, former
coaching inn haunted by a well
suicide. Two small rooms
either side of a central
passageway have walls
decorated by old photos,
adverts and brass. Bar snacks
in summer. Outside loo.
Handy for Pontcysyllte
aqueduct.
🛏 ❀ ♣ P

## Bont-newydd

### Dolben Arms
W of Trefnant OS015705
☎ (01745) 582207
7–11; 12–4, 7–10.30 Sun
**Dyffryn Clwyd Four Thumbs;
Theakston XB** Ⓗ
16th-century, remote country
pub in a picturesque valley
accessible only via narrow
country lanes. One single bar
separates into restaurant,
lounge and games areas.
Q ❀ ♪ ♣ P

## Brynford

### Llyn y Mawn
Brynford Hill (B5121)
☎ (01352) 714367
12–3 (not Mon), 5.30 (6 Sat)–11; 12–3,
7–10.30 Sun
**Crown Buckley Best Bitter;
guest beers** Ⓗ
600-year-old, family-run
former coaching inn,
sympathetically renovated and
extended. Growing reputation
for good, wholesome food (no
meals Sun lunch or Mon eve).
CAMRA *Welsh Pub of the Year*
1995. Quality service.
🛏 ❀ ♪ ♣ P 🍴

## Cadole

### Colomendy Arms
Gwernaffield Road (200 yds
from A494) ☎ (01352) 810217
7 (12 Fri & Sat)–11; 12–10.30 Sun
**Marston's Bitter; guest
beers** Ⓗ
Friendly, unspoilt, two-
roomed pub in a village named
after the local 'Cats Hole' mine.
A footpath leads from the
garden to Loggerheads
Country Park. Pets corner.
🛏 Q ❀ ▲ ♣ P

## Caerwys

### Piccadilly
North Street (B5122, 1 mile N
of A541) ☎ (01352) 720284
12–11; 12–10.30 Sun
**Boddingtons Mild, Bitter;
Theakston Best Bitter; guest
beer** Ⓗ
Very good, popular pub, one of
two in this ancient village.
Recently renovated (after fire
damage); separate restaurant.
No eve meals Mon.
🛏 Q ♪ ♪ ▲ ♣ P

## Carrog

### Grouse Inn
½ mile off A5 ☎ (01490) 430272
12–3 (not winter Mon–Wed), 7–11;
12–3, 7–10.30 Sun
**Lees Bitter** Ⓗ
Quaint, two-room-plus-pool-
room pub, popular with locals
and tourists, close to the
Llangollen steam railway

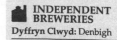

**INDEPENDENT
BREWERIES**
**Dyffryn Clwyd:** Denbigh

**Plassey:** Eyton

station. Fine view across the
River Dee. No food Mon.
🏰 Q ❀ 🚟 ◑ ● ♣ P

## Cilcain

### White Horse
2 miles S of A541 OS177652
☎ (01352) 740142
12–3, 7–11; 12–3, 7–10.30 Sun
**Thwaites Bitter; guest beers** Ⓗ
Attractive village pub close to
Moel Fammau Country Park.
The split-level lounge serves
meals; the separate public bar,
where walkers are welcome,
has a museum piece beer
engine.
🏰 Q ◑ ▶ ❄ ♣ P

## Connah's Quay

### Sir Gawain & the Green Knight
Golftyn Lane ☎ (01244) 812623
12–3, 5.30–11; 12–11 Sat; 12–4, 7–10.30
Sun
**Samuel Smith OBB** Ⓗ
Converted farmhouse with an
aviary, close to Dee Estuary
Bird Sanctuary. Eve meals till
8.30 Mon–Fri; no lunches Sat.
❀ ◑ ▶ ♣ P

## Cross Lanes

### Kiln
On B5130, 250 yds off A525
11–3, 7–11; 12–3, 7–10.30 Sun
**Hanby Drawwell** Ⓗ
Cosy country pub with an
attached farm. A centre for pub
games, in the same family for
100 years. 🏰 Q ❀ ❄ ♣ P

## Cyffylliog

### Red Lion
Off B5105 at Llanfwrog
OS058578 ☎ (01824) 710664
7–11; 11–3, 6–11 Sat & summer; 12–3,
7–10.30 Sun
**Lees GB Mild, Bitter** Ⓗ
Traditional village local with
tasteful decor, log fires and
low-beamed ceilings. Pool
table and jukebox in the bar;
the lounge is divided into three
rooms with antique furniture/
oak dressers. Good food;
accommodation planned.
🏰 Q ◑ ▶ ❄ ▲ P

## Cymau

### Talbot Inn
Cymau Lane ☎ (01978) 761410
12–3 (5 Sat; not Mon–Wed), 7–11;
12–5, 7–10.30 Sun
**Hydes' Anvil Dark Mild,
Bitter** Ⓔ
Friendly country pub next to
Hope Mountain and Country
Park: a games-oriented bar and
a quieter lounge. Extensive
views.
Q 🛏 ❀ ❄ ♣ P 🍴

## Denbigh

### Plough
Bridge Street ☎ (01745) 812961
11–11; 12–10.30 Sun
**Banks's Mild; Marston's
Bitter, Pedigree** Ⓗ
Traditional, friendly, beamed
local with a public bar and a
lounge. Organ sing-along most
weekends. TV, pool table and a
jukebox in the bar.
❀ ◑ ❄ ♣ P

## Erbistock

### Cross Foxes
Overton Bridge (A528)
☎ (01978) 780380
12–3, 6–11; 12–3, 7–10.30 Sun
**Marston's Bitter, Pedigree** Ⓗ
Old pub by the banks of the
River Dee: two bars furnished
in olde-worlde style, one
dominated by a TV. Separate
restaurant. Very pleasant
garden. 🏰 ❀ ▶ ❄ P

## Eyton

### Plassey Leisure Park
Off B5426; signed from A483
Wrexham bypass
11–11; 12–10.30 Sun (Treetops closed
Nov–March; Golf Club may close early
winter eves)
**Plassey Bitter, Cwrw Tudno,
Stout, Dragon's Breath** Ⓗ
Diversified farm with a
camping/caravan park, craft
centre, golf club and brewery.
Treetops bar on the caravan
park; club on the golf course.
The bistro sells Plassey, too, if
you are dining.
Q 🛏 ◑ ▶ ▲ P

## Ffynnongroew

### Railway
Main Road ☎ (01745) 560447
11–11; 12–10.30 Sun
**Vaux Samson, Double Maxim;
guest beers** (occasional) Ⓗ
Basic pub in an ex-mining
village: a locals' bar plus a
lounge. 🏰 ❀ ♣ P

## Glan yr Afon

### White Lion
Glan yr Afon Road (W of A548
at Ffynnongroew) OS118817
☎ (01745) 560280
6–11 (12–2, 6–11 Wed–Sat summer);
12–2, 6–10.30 Sun
**Morland Tanner's Jack;
Ruddles Best Bitter; guest
beers** Ⓗ
Excellent unspoilt pub with
many interesting features
including old farming tools
and a plant-filled conservatory.
Clay pigeon shooting. Well
worth a detour; former home
of actor/writer Emlyn
Williams.
🏰 ❀ ◑ ▶ ❄ ◔ P ✂

## Gorsedd

### Druid Inn
Off A5026 ☎ (01352) 710944
7–11; 12–3, 7–10.30 Sun
**Boddingtons Bitter; Marston's
Pedigree; Taylor Landlord;
guest beers** (summer) Ⓗ
Smart country pub opposite a
church. A selection of
comfortable rooms suit all
tastes; separate restaurant. No
eve meals Sun or Mon; lunches
served Sun only. Supper
license till 12 Mon–Sat.
🏰 🛏 ❀ ◑ ❄ ▲ ♣ P

## Graianrhyd

### Rose & Crown
On B5430 ☎ (01824) 780727
12–11; 12–10.30 Sun
**Boddingtons Bitter; Flowers
IPA; guest beers** (occasional) Ⓗ
Busy, friendly pub. A large
teapot collection hangs from
the ceiling. The clock on the
piano is worth the visit alone.
Good value food.
🏰 ❀ ◑ ▶ ▲ ♣ P

## Gresford

### Griffin
The Green ☎ (01978) 852231
1 (12 Sat)–4.30, 7–11; 1–4, 7–10.30 Sun
**Greenalls Mild, Bitter** Ⓗ
Quiet, friendly oasis unspoilt
by progress; popular with all
ages. The L-shaped drinking
area displays a large amount of
brass. Q ❀ ♣ P

## Hawarden

### Crown & Liver
The Highway (B5125)
☎ (01244) 531182
11–11; 12–10.30 Sun
**Burtonwood Bitter,
Buccaneer** Ⓗ
Pub with a comfortable,
L-shaped lounge tastefully
decorated in olde-worlde style.
The bar is more basic, with Sky
TV. Eclectic jukebox selection
in the lounge. No meals Sat/
Sun. ❀ ◑ ❄ ⅙ ⇌ ♣ P

## Holywell

### Red Lion
High Street ☎ (01352) 710097
11–4, 6–11; 12–4, 7–10.30 Sun
**Tetley Bitter** Ⓗ
Well-established, town-centre
local, with an unspoilt single-
bar interior. House beer by
Carlsberg-Tetley. 🏰 ♣

## Llangedwyn

### Green Inn
☎ (01691) 828234
11–3, 6–11; 12–4, 6.30–10.30 Sun

373

Boddingtons Bitter; guest
beers H
Out of the way pub in the
picturesque Tanat Valley, very
popular with walkers and
families. Always four guest
ales. The cider alternates
between sweet and dry, April–
Oct. Restaurant upstairs
(good food).
🏰 ❀ ◖▮ ✿ ⤴ P

## Llangollen

### Jenny Jones Hotel
Abbey Road (A542, near
station) ☎ (01978) 860653
11–2, 7–11 (may vary); 12–2, 7–10.30
Sun
Tetley Bitter; guest beer H
Pub named after a landlady
who took over the pub with
her husband who fought at the
Battle of Trafalgar. Its history
goes back to 1500. House beer
from Coach House.
❀ ◖▮ ✿ P

### Wynnstay Arms
Bridge Street ☎ (01978) 860710
12–3, 7–11; 11–11 Fri & Sat; 12–3,
7–10.30 Sun
Cains Bitter; Ind Coope
Burton Ale; guest beer H
Victorian town house with a
quiet bar and a welcoming
atmosphere and a large
garden. 🏰 Q ❀ ⇌ ◖▮ P

## Mold

### Boar's Head
17 Chester Street
☎ (01352) 758430
11.30–3 (5 Fri & Sat), 7–11; 12–3,
7–10.30 Sun
Ind Coope Burton Ale; Tetley
Bitter H
Supposedly haunted former
coaching inn with an attractive
black and white exterior. Good
array of pictures and paintings
in the single U-shaped bar. No
meals Sun. ◖ & ✿ P

### Leeswood Arms
67 Wrexham Street
☎ (01352) 753950
11–11; 12–10.30 Sun
Cains Bitter; Castle Eden Ale;
Wilson's Mild; Worthington
Bitter; guest beers H
Former assize court building
displaying horse racing
pictures. Good changing beer
choice; cold snacks at all times.
Family entertainment Sun eve.
Ample parking nearby.
❀ ✿

### Y Pentan
3–5 New Street
☎ (01352) 753772
11–3.30, 6.30–11; 11–11 Fri & Sat;
12–10.30 Sun
Bateman Mild; Marston's
Bitter, Pedigree, HBC; guest
beer H
Lively town centre pub. No

lunches Sun. Car park nearby.
◖ ⇌ & ✿

## Pentre Broughton

### Cross Foxes
High Street ☎ (01978) 755973
4 (12 Sat)–11; 10.30–3, 7–10.30 Sun
Burtonwood Bitter, Top Hat,
Buccaneer H
Open-plan, two-room, friendly
local converted from 19th-
century cottages. Popular with
families. The landlord insists a
ghost occupies the gents'.
🏰 Q ❀ & ▮ ✿ P

## Rhewl (Llangollen)

### Sun
Off B5103 OS178448
☎ (01978) 861043
12–3, 6–11; 12–3, 7–10.30 Sun
Worthington Bitter; guest
beers H
Rural gem: a 14th-century
drovers' pub with stone floors
and low ceilings. A centre for
fishing, walking and fell
running. One guest is normally
from Dyffryn Clwyd Brewery.
Not to be missed.
Q ⛺ ❀ ◖▮ ⇌ ▮ ✿ P

## Rhewl (Ruthin)

### Drovers Arms
☎ (01824) 703163
12–3, 6.30–11; 12–10.30 Sun
Dyffryn Clwyd Four Thumbs;
Ruddles Best Bitter; guest
beer H
Roadside pub popular with
locals and visitors alike. Food
is available in the dining room
at all times. One beer from
Dyffryn Clwyd Brewery is
usually available.
❀ ◖▮ P

## Rhuddlan

### New Inn
High Street (A525)
☎ (01745) 591305
11–3, 5.30–11; 11–11 Fri & Sat; 12–3,
7–10.30 Sun
Theakston Best Bitter, XB;
guest beer H
Popular, comfortable, village
pub: a single bar with several
drinking areas, including a
low-level games room.
Separate dining room (good
food). The guest beer changes
weekly. ❀ ⇌ ◖▮ ✿ P

## Rhyl

### Galley
Vale Road (A525, near station)
☎ (01745) 353432
11–11; 12–3, 7–10.30 Sun
Banks's Mild; Marston's
Bitter, Pedigree H
Popular town local with
lounge and public bars. Good

cask ale range for the town.
❀ ⇌ ▮ ⇌ P

## Ruthin

### Wine Vaults
St Peter's Square
12–11; 12–10.30 Sun
Robinson's Best Bitter H
Unpretentious, unchanging,
gimmick-free regular entry in
the *Guide*. One of a handful of
Robinson's tied pubs in N
Wales. ❀ ⇌ ▮ ✿ P

## Tremeirchion

### Salusbury Arms
Off B5429, next to church
☎ (01745) 710262
11–11 (12.30am Tue, Fri & Sat); 12–3,
7–10.30 Sun
Boddingtons Bitter; Flowers
Original; guest beers H
Pub with three separate bars, a
restaurant attached and a large
garden.
🏰 Q ⛺ ❀ ◖▮ ▮ ✿ P

## Wrexham

### Albion Hotel
1 Pen-y-Bryn (from High St
down Town Hill, along Bridge
St: at top of hill)
☎ (01978) 364969
12–4, 7–11; 12–4, 7–10.30 Sun
Lees Bitter H
Typical, early 20th-century
commercial hotel, largely
unchanged. The only Lees
outlet in town.
Q ⇌ ⇌ (Central)

### Black Horse
Yorke Street ☎ (01978) 352474
11–4, 7–11; 12–4, 7–10.30 Sun (may
vary)
Marston's Bitter, Pedigree,
HBC H
Large, friendly single-roomed
pub with entertainment at
weekends. ❀ ◖▮ P

### Plas Coch
Plas Coch Road
☎ (01978) 261470
11–11; 12–3, 7–10.30 Sun
Banks's Bitter E; Camerons
Strongarm H
Four-year-old Banks's house,
well laid out and comfortably
furnished, near an out of town
shopping development and
college. Close to Wrexham FC.
❀ ◖▮ & P ⌇ 🍴

## Ysceifiog

### Fox
N of A541, W of Mold
OS152715 ☎ (01352) 720241
12–3 (not Wed), 6–11; 12–4, 7–10.30
Sun
Beer range varies H
Classic, unspoilt village pub
with up to four beers. A centre
of village activities. Mild in
winter only. 🏰 Q ❀ ⇌ ✿

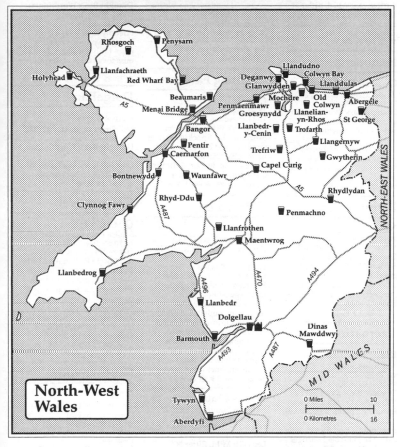

North-West
Wales

*Authority areas covered: Anglesey UA, Conwy UA, Gwynedd UA*

## Aberdyfi

### Penelig Arms
☎ (01654) 767215
11–3, 6–11; 12–4, 6–10.30 Sun
**Ansells Mild; Ind Coope
Burton Ale; Tetley Bitter;
guest beer** H
Bar overlooking the estuary,
popular with the yachting
fraternity. Good food. The
guest beer comes from
Carlsberg-Tetley's Tapster's
Choice. ▲ Q ⇆ ◖ ▶ Å ≱ P

## Abergele

### Bull Hotel
Chapel Street
☎ (01745) 832115
12–3, 6–11; 12–3, 7–10.30 Sun
**Lees GB Mild, Bitter** H
Two-roomed local with a
restaurant and a large, homely
lounge. Transport theme charts
on the walls.
▲ Q ⛐ ⇆ ◖ ▶ ≱ ♣ P

## Bangor

### Belle Vue
Holyhead Road
☎ (01248) 364439
11.30 (12 Sat)–11; 12–10.30 Sun
**Boddingtons Bitter; Flowers
IPA; Marston's Pedigree;
guest beers** H
Popular two-roomed pub
where the bar has Sky Sports
and pool but the lounge area
tends to be quiet. It can get
busy with both locals and
students. Good reputation for
lunches; no food Sat.
Q ✿ ◖ ≱

### Tap & Spile
Garth Road (follow signs to
pier) ☎ (01248) 370835
11–11; 12–10.30 Sun
**Tap & Spile Premium** H;
**guest beers** H/G
Excellent, multi-levelled pub
with a constantly changing
range of beers. One of the few
outlets for real cider (and

occasionally perry) in N Wales.
Very popular. Eve meals end at
8. Q ⇆ ◖ ▶ ♣ ⌂ P

### Union Hotel
Garth Road (near the pier)
☎ (01248) 362462
11–11; 12–4, 7–10.30 Sun
**Burtonwood Bitter, Top Hat,
seasonal beers** H
Friendly, quiet, multi-roomed
pub with a maritime
atmosphere and a garden
overlooking the Menai Straits.
Eve meals end at 8; no lunches
Tue. Q ⇆ ◖ P

## Barmouth

### Tal y Don
High Street ☎ (01341) 280508
11.30–3.30, 6–11; 11.30–11 Sat; 12–
10.30 Sun

**INDEPENDENT
BREWERIES**
**Cambrian:** Dolgellau

**Burtonwood Mild, Bitter** Ⓗ
Recent development has spoilt
this town-centre local, but it
still sells a good pint.
🛲 ⚜ ⋈ ▲ ⇌ ♣

## Beaumaris

### Olde Bull's Head
Castle Street ☎ (01248) 810329
11–11; 12–10.30 Sun
**Draught Bass; Worthington
Bitter; guest beers** Ⓗ
500-year-old coaching inn
featuring oak beams, antiques
and armour. The 60-cover
restaurant has an excellent
reputation. Fifteen very good
letting bedrooms.
🛲 Q ⛄ ⚜ ⋈ ◖▸ ♣ P

## Bontnewydd

### Newborough
☎ (01286) 673126
11–3, 6–11; 11–11 Sat; 12–10.30 Sun
**Draught Bass; Ind Coope
Burton Ale; Tetley Bitter;
guest beer** Ⓗ
Busy, often crowded village
pub, very popular for food.
Friendly staff.
🛲 Q ⛄ ◖▸ ⊟ P

## Caernarfon

### Black Boy Inn
Northgate Street
☎ (01286) 673604
11–11; 12–10.30 Sun
**Draught Bass; guest beer** Ⓗ
Pub within the old town walls,
featuring a public bar, a small
lounge and a separate
restaurant. Open fires in both
bars. The guest beer changes
weekly. 🛲 Q ⚜ ⋈ ◖▸ ⊟

### Y Goron Fach
Hole in the Wall Street/Palace
Street (opp. castle)
☎ (01286) 673338
11–11; 12–10.30 Sun
**Draught Bass; Tetley Bitter;
guest beer** Ⓗ
Long pub with access from two
streets and a bar in the middle.
Part-stone walls and benches
feature in the bar; the lounge is
slightly quieter and more
comfortable, with a large
screen TV for major sporting
events. No wheelchair access to
ladies' WC. Eve meals in
summer. ⚜ ◖▸ ⊟

## Capel Curig

### Cobden's Hotel
☎ (01690) 720243
11–3, 6–11; 11–11 Sat; 12–10.30 Sun
**ABC Best Bitter; Greenalls
Original; Tetley Bitter** Ⓗ
Informal, family-run hotel at
the heart of Snowdonia: a
lounge, a restaurant and a
climbers' bar with a feature
natural rock face. Freshly

prepared food; warm welcome;
very comfortable
accommodation.
🛲 Q ⛄ ⚜ ⋈ ◖▸ ⊟ ♿ ▲ ♣ P

Try also: Ty'n-y-Coed
(Whitbread)

## Clynnog Fawr

### Coach Inn
☎ (01286) 660785
11–11; closed Sun
**Marston's Bitter, Pedigree;
Morland Old Speckled Hen** Ⓗ
Grade I listed building (c1600)
full of character and
overlooking the sea. At its best
during the busy summer
season. 🛲 ⛄ ⚜ ⋈ ◖▸ ♿ P

## Colwyn Bay

### Taylors
Pen-y-Bryn Road, Upper
Colwyn Bay (top of King's Rd,
1 mile from centre)
☎ (01492) 533360
11–3, 5.30–11; 11.30–3, 7–10.30 Sun
**Marston's Pedigree; Tetley
Bitter; guest beer** Ⓗ
Modern free house and
restaurant, built in old brick
with a well-furnished plaster
and natural wood interior.
Panoramic views from the
lounge over the town and bay.
Separate function room and
restaurant (including carvery).
🛲 Q ⛄ ⚜ ◖▸ ⊟ ♿ P

### Wings Club
Imperial Buildings, Station
Square ☎ (01492) 530682
12–3, 6.30–11; 11–11 Sat; 12–3, 7–10.30
Sun
**Lees GB Mild, Bitter** Ⓗ
Club with a large lounge area,
separate billiards and pool and
darts rooms, plus a snug with
TV. Families and all visitors
welcome. ⇌

Try also: Park Hotel, Abergele
Rd (Bass)

## Deganwy

### Deganwy Castle Hotel
Station Road
☎ (01492) 583555
12–3, 5.30–11; 12–11 Sat; varies Sun
**Courage Directors; Ruddles
County; John Smith's Bitter** Ⓗ
Large residential hotel by the
station. 100 yds from the beach.
Many different rooms for
drinking suit all tastes and
ages. Good food; large
gardens. 🛲 Q ⛄ ⚜ ⋈ ◖▸ ♿
⇌ ♣ P ⚲

## Dinas Mawddwy

### Red Lion
Off A470 ☎ (01650) 531247
11–3, 6–11; 11–11 Sat & summer;
12–10.30 Sun

**Draught Bass; Worthington
Dark, Bitter; guest beers**
(occasional) Ⓗ
Friendly local with a large
lounge; a popular meeting
place for hill walkers. Don't
miss the brasses in the public
bar.
🛲 Q ⛄ ⚜ ⋈ ◖▸ ⊟ ♿ ▲ ♣

## Dolgellau

### Cross Keys
Mill Street ☎ (01341) 423342
11–11; 12–10.30 Sun
**Draught Bass; Worthington
Bitter** Ⓗ
Unspoilt town local: a good,
old-fashioned backstreet
tavern. 🛲 ▲ ♣

## Glanwydden

### Queen's Head
3 miles from Llandudno, off
A470 ☎ (01492) 546570
11–3, 6–11; 12–3, 7–10.30 Sun
**Ind Coope Burton Ale; Tetley
Bitter; guest beer** Ⓗ
Old village pub/restaurant
with a cosy atmosphere, well-
patronised by locals and
holidaymakers. Reasonable
dress expected. The guest beer
is from Carlsberg-Tetley's
Tapster's Choice. Excellent
food. 🛲 Q ◖▸ ⊟ ♿ ▲ ⇌
(Llandudno Jct) P

## Groesynydd

### Groes
Ty'n-y-Groes (1 mile from
Conwy on B5106)
☎ (01492) 650545
12–3, 7–11; 12–3, 7–10.30 Sun (ring for
summer hours)
**Ind Coope Burton Ale; Tetley
Bitter** Ⓗ
The first licensed house in
Wales, dating from 1573,
extended during the high
period of coach travel. A pub
with great character. Excellent
meals. 🛲 Q ⚜ ◖▸ P

## Gwytherin

### Lion Inn
☎ (01745) 860244
12–3, 6–11 (12–3, 7–10.30 winter);
12–3, 7–10.30 Sun
**Marston's Bitter** Ⓗ
Two crown (WTB) inn, a
traditional village local
reputed to be over 300 years
old. The present building is a
mixture of old and new,
tastefully refurbished; oak-
beamed ceilings. Off the beaten
track. 🛲 Q ⚜ ⋈ ◖▸ ⊟ ▲ ♣ P

## Holyhead

### 79
79 Market Street
☎ (01407) 763939
11–3.30, 7–11; 12–3, 7–10.30 Sun
**Brains SA; guest beers** Ⓗ

Comfortable town pub, popular with the younger set, particularly at weekends. The dining area overlooks the ferryport. ◖ ≱

Try also: Crown, Bodedern (Burtonwood)

## Llanbedr

### Victoria Hotel

Main Road ☎ (01341) 241213
11–11; 12–10.30 Sun
Robinson's Best Bitter E, Frederics H
Pleasant hotel with three separate drinking areas, built with locally quarried stone.
➳ ⇔ ◖ ♪ ⊕ ♨ ≱ ♣ P

## Llanbedrog

### Ship Inn

Off A499 W of town, towards Mynytho OS321319
☎ (01758) 740270
11–11 (11–3.30, 5.30–11 winter); closed Sun
Burtonwood Mild, Bitter, Forshaw's H
Very friendly local with an interesting layout: a traditional bar, a two-tier lounge/eating area and a recent, unusual 'prow'-shaped extension housing a comfortable family/no-smoking room. Good value food. ♨ Q ➳ ❀ ◖ ♪ ⊕ ♨ ♣ P ⊬

## Llanbedr-y-Cenin

### Bull

½ mile off B5106 at Tal-y-Bont OS761694 ☎ (01492) 660508
12–3, 7–11; 12–3, 7–10.30 Sun
Lees GB Mild, Bitter H
Small hillside pub with splendid views over the Conwy Valley. Excellent food (booking recommended).
♨ Q ❀ ◖ ♪ P

## Llanddulas

### Dulas Arms Hotel

Abergele Road
☎ (01492) 515747
12–11; 12–10.30 Sun (winter hours vary)
Lees GB Mild, Bitter H
Welcoming, six-roomed pub, formerly the 'Railway Hotel': a lounge, snug, games room, quiet front rooms, family room and a restaurant. Children's certificate (very good facilities). The large garden overlooks the sea. Aug bank hol beer festival.
Q ➳ ❀ ❀ ⇔ ◖ ♪ ⊕ ♨ ♣ P ⊬

## Llandudno

### London Hotel

131 Mostyn Street
☎ (01492) 876740
11.30–4 (5 Sat), 7–11; 12–3, 7–10.30 Sun

Burtonwood Bitter, Forshaw's, Top Hat H
Large, friendly town pub, with a collection of jugs and an original red phone box. Family room lunchtime. Ten mins' walk from the station.
➳ ⇔ ◖ ♣

### Links Hotel

Conwy Road (A470)
☎ (01492) 879180
11–11; 12–10.30 Sun
Lees GB Mild, Bitter H
Friendly, family-run pub with ample room and good parking facilities. Consistent local trade; well-patronised by holidaymakers. Near two golf courses. Quiz nights. Good value meals. Children's outdoor play area. ➳ ❀ ⇔ ◖ ♪ ⊕ ♨ ♨ ≱ ♣ P

## Llanelian-yn-Rhos

### White Lion Inn

☎ (01492) 515807
11–3, 6–11; 12–3, 7–10.30 Sun
Burtonwood Buccaneer; Marston's Pedigree; Tetley Bitter; guest beer (summer) H
Olde-worlde, Welsh village inn, with a tasteful extension for diners (large menu). The slate-floored bar, tiny snug and lounge suit all visitors. The oldest part of the building dates back to the 16th century. A true free house, its guest beers often include local Welsh beers. Converted barn en suite accommodation.
♨ Q ⇔ ◖ ♪ ♨ ♨ ♣ P

## Llanfachraeth

### Holland Hotel

On A5025
☎ (01407) 740252
11–3.30, 7–11; 11–11 Sat & summer; 12–3, 7–10.30 Sun
Lees GB Mild, Bitter, Moonraker H
Pleasant little village pub with separate rooms and a passage, all served from a central bar. An ideal base for driving round the island or walking the Anglesey Coastal Path.
❀ ⇔ ◖ ♪ ⊕ ♣ P

## Llanfrothen

### Brondanw Arms

On A4085
☎ (01766) 770555
12–3, 6–11 (12–11 summer); 12–5, 7–10.30 Sun
Robinson's Best Bitter, Hartleys XB H
Hard to find local worth seeking out. Uninspiring from the outside, but the large lounge is popular with locals and hill walkers.
♨ Q ➳ ◖ ♪ ⊕ P

## Llangernyw

### Stag Inn

☎ (01745) 860213
12–3, 6–11; 12–11 Sat; 12–3, 7–10.30 Sun
M&B Brew XI; guest beer H
Classic, 18th-century country inn, in the heart of this beautiful village. The walls and ceiling are literally dripping with brasses and artefacts: an horologist's paradise! Aptly described as 'the old curiosity shop, with fine food and ales'.
♨ Q ➳ ❀ ⇔ ◖ ♪ ♨ ♨ ♣ P

## Maentwrog

### Grapes Hotel

On A496, near A487 jct
☎ (01766) 85208
11–11; 12–10.30 Sun
Draught Bass; Dyffryn Clwyd Four Thumbs; Worthington Bitter; guest beers H
Family-run hotel built in the 13th century, overlooking the Vale of Ffestiniog: a lounge, public bar, verandah, dining room and a downstairs restaurant. Brassware and artefacts adorn the public bar. Good value food; en suite accommodation.
♨ Q ➳ ❀ ⇔ ◖ ♪ ⊕ ♨ ♨ P

## Menai Bridge

### Liverpool Arms

St George's Pier (100 yds from main square)
☎ (01248) 712453
11–4, 5.30–11; 12–3, 7–10.30 Sun
Greenalls Mild, Bitter G, Original H; Tetley Bitter G; guest beers H
150-year-old pub with two bars, nooks and crannies and a conservatory. Popular with the sailing fraternity (close to the slipway) and students. Note the old nautical artefacts. Very good food and accommodation.
Q ➳ ❀ ⇔ ◖ ♪ ♨

### Victoria Hotel

Telford Road (Beaumaris road, 100 yds from suspension bridge) ☎ (01248) 712309
11–11; 12–10.30 Sun
Draught Bass; Hancock's HB H; Stones Bitter E; guest beers H
Attractive, two-bar residential hotel, popular for functions. Live music at least once a week. A lovely garden area overlooks the Menai Straits. Food is highly recommended. Wheelchair access is through the rear conservatory. Comfortable, en suite bedrooms.
♨ ➳ ❀ ⇔ ◖ ♪ ♨ P ⊬

## Mochdre

### Mountain View
7 Old Conwy Road
☎ (01492) 544724
11.30–3, 6–11; 11.30–11 Sat; 12–3,
7–10.30 Sun
**Burtonwood Mild, Bitter, Top
Hat, seasonal beers** Ⓗ
Village local: a large lounge
with a dining area and a
separate bar with a pool table.
Pleasant atmosphere, although
it can be rather noisy. Sadly the
no-smoking area is no more.
🏚 ◑ ▶ 🖴 & ♣ P

## Old Colwyn

### Red Lion
385 Abergele Road
☎ (01492) 515042
5–11; 12–3, 5–11 Sat; 12–3, 7–10.30
Sun
**Boddingtons Bitter; Cains
Mild; M&B Mild; Thwaites
Bitter; guest beers** Ⓗ
Popular, traditional town pub:
a bar and two lounges. A
proper meeting place for locals,
where all are made welcome.
Solid timber doors and
panelled walls are features.
🏚 Q 🏚 🖴 ♣

## Penmachno

### Machno Inn
OS791505 ☎ (01690) 760317
12–3, 6–11; 12–11 Sat; 12–10.30 Sun
**Tetley Bitter; Theakston Mild,
Bitter** *or* **XB; guest beer** Ⓗ
Village pub in a remote valley,
comfortably catering for all
tastes. Extensive menu;
alfresco benches beside a small
stream.
🏚 🏚 ⛺ ◑ ▶ & ♣ P

## Penmaenmawr

### Bron Eryri
Ffordd Bangor
☎ (01492) 623978
12–11; 12–10.30 Sun
**Banks's Mild; Marston's
Bitter, Pedigree** Ⓗ
Old, established, friendly
village pub with first class
hosts. Sandwiches available on
request. 🏚 ≹ ♣

## Pentir

### Vaynol Arms
☎ (01248) 362895
12–3, 6–11; 12–11 Sat; 12–3, 7–10.30
Sun
**Dyffryn Clwyd Four Thumbs;
Tetley Bitter; Theakston Old
Peculier; guest beer** Ⓗ
Pleasant village inn with a
locals' bar and a quiet lounge.
Good reputation for food
(restaurant). One of few outlets
for locally-brewed beer.
🏚 🏚 ◑ ▶ 🖴 P ⅙

## Penysarn

### Y Bedol
Off A5025 ☎ (01407) 832590
12–11; 12–3, 7–10.30 Sun
**Marston's Bitter, Pedigree;
guest beer** Ⓗ
Welcoming, family-run village
pub which has a lounge and a
separate pool/games room.
The guest beer is from the
Marston's list and changes
weekly. Q 🏚 🖴 & A ♣ P

## Red Wharf Bay

### Ship Inn
1½ miles off A5025
☎ (01248) 852568
11–3.30, 7–11 (11–11 summer); 12–3,
7–10.30 (12–10.30 summer) Sun
**Benskins BB; Friary Meux BB;
Ind Coope Burton Ale; Tetley
Mild, Bitter; guest beers** Ⓗ
Nautically-themed,
beautifully-set pub on the
beach with wonderful views.
Lovely fires in winter. Award-
winning food.
🏚 Q ⛺ 🏚 ◑ ▶ & ♣ P ⅙

## Rhosgoch

### Ring
Off B5111 ☎ (01407) 830720
5.30 (12 Sat)–11; 12–10.30 Sun
**Draught Bass** (summer/
Xmas)**; Stones Bitter;
Worthington Bitter** Ⓗ
Off the beaten track, a pub
where a central bar serves
several drinking areas,
including a pool room. Good
outside area for children. A
Caravan Club site adjoins the
pub. 🏚 🏚 ◑ ▶ A ♣ P

## Rhyd-Ddu

### Cwellyn Arms
On A4085 Caernarfon–
Beddgelert road
☎ (01766) 890321
11–11; 12–10.30 Sun
**Draught Bass; Worthington
Bitter; guest beers** Ⓗ
200-year-old family pub at the
foot of Snowdon, on the
proposed route of the Welsh
Highland Railway. Busy in
summer. Children's adventure
playground. Seven guest beers;
extensive menu.
🏚 🏚 🖴 ◑ ▶ & P

## Rhydlydan

### Giler Arms Hotel
On A5, 1 mile E of Pentrefoelas
☎ (01690) 770612
11–3, 6–11; 12–3, 7–10.30 Sun (hours
may vary with the season)
**Tetley Bitter; guest beer** Ⓗ
Friendly country hotel with a
lounge, bar, pool room, and a
restaurant. Situated in seven
acres of grounds with a coarse
fishing lake, a small campsite

and pleasant gardens, beside
the River Merddwr. The guest
beer is from Carlsberg-Tetley's
Tapster's Choice.
🏚 Q 🏚 🖴 ◑ ▶ 🖴 & A ♣ P

## St George

### Kinmel Arms
Off A55 ☎ (01745) 832207
12–3, 7–11; 12–3, 7–10.30 Sun
**Marston's Bitter, Pedigree;
guest beers** Ⓗ
Friendly, olde-worlde pub in a
hillside village, with a
reputation for good food. Very
popular at weekends.
Q 🏚 ◑ ▶ 🖴 ♣ P

## Trefriw

### Fairy Falls Hotel
Opp. Trefriw Mill
☎ (01492) 640250
12–11 (may vary); 12–3, 7–10.30 Sun
**Banks's Mild; Marston's
Bitter, Pedigree** Ⓗ
Pub where the public bar is
home to a TV and games and
the lounge has traditional
seating and original stone
walls. Restaurant to the rear.
🏚 🖴 ◑ ▶ A ♣ P

## Trofarth

### Holland Arms
On B5113 ☎ (01492) 650777
12–2, 7–11; 12–2, 7–10.30 Sun
**Ansells Mild; Tetley Bitter** Ⓗ
Pleasantly furnished,
18th-century coaching house
with a traditional warm Welsh
welcome. Set in a country
landscape, within sight of
Snowdonia, it has bar, lounge
and restaurant areas. Popular
for good meals. Families
welcome till 9pm.
Q 🏚 ◑ ▶ ♣ P

## Tywyn

### Corbett Arms Hotel
High Street ☎ (01654) 710264
11–11; 12–10.30 Sun
**Draught Bass; Hancock's HB;
Worthington Bitter** Ⓗ
Plush, pleasant hotel bar
whose dress code encourages
the over-25s. 🖴 ◑ ▶ A ≹ P

## Waunfawr

### Snowdon Parc
On A4085
☎ (01286) 650218
11–11; 12–10.30 Sun
**Marston's Bitter, Pedigree;
guest beers** Ⓗ
Popular pub with walkers and
climbers, in the heart of
Snowdonia. The proposed
Welsh Highland Railway is to
pass outside. Extensive
campsite breakfasts available;
wide-ranging menu. Live
entertainment Fri and Sat in
season. ⛺ 🏚 ◑ ▶ & A ♣ P

*Guinness back in the real ale fold. Mike Jobson, account director, lifts a glass to the company's new cask-conditioned porter.*

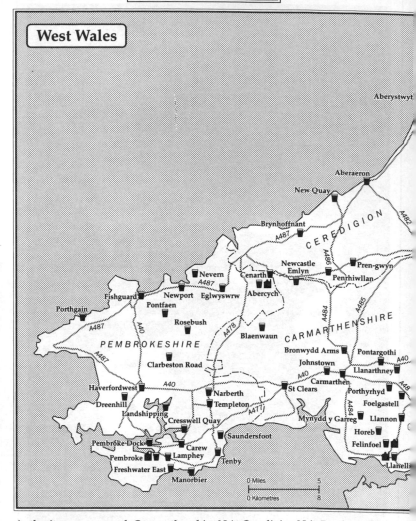

West Wales

Authority areas covered: *Carmarthenshire UA, Ceredigion UA, Pembrokeshire UA*

---

## Carmarthenshire

### Ammanford

**Wernolau Hotel**
31 Pontamman Road
(signed on A474, Glanaman road)
☎ (01269) 594048
5–11; 12–10.30 Sun
**Crown Buckley Best Bitter; guest beers** Ⓗ
Refurbished, converted gentleman's residence in its own grounds. Eve meals Fri and Sat. At least two guest beers.
🏚 Q ❧ ⊛ 🛏 🌙 ➊ Ꮬ ♣ P 🚻

---

### Blaenwaun

**Lamb Inn**
8 miles N of St Clears on Tegryn road OS237271
☎ (01994) 448440
Hours vary
**Young's Bitter** Ⓗ
Small, traditional, country inn in an isolated hamlet.
⊛ ♣ P

---

### Bronwydd Arms

**Holybrook Tavern**
On B4301, Pontarsais road
☎ (01267) 233521
12–3 (school hols only), 5–11; 12–3, 7–10.30 Sun
**Brains Dark; Worthington Bitter; guest beer** Ⓗ
Traditional country pub near a preserved railway (Gwili).
Cider in summer.
🏚 Q ❧ ⊛ 🛏 ➊ Ꮬ ♣ ⌂ P

---

### Caio

**Brunant Arms**
Church Street (1 mile NE of A482) ☎ (01558) 650483
12–3, 6.30–11; 11–11 Sat; 12–3, 7–10.30 Sun
**Boddingtons Mild, Bitter; guest beers** Ⓗ
Friendly pub, full of character, in the centre of the UK's largest parish, close to the Dolaucothi gold mines. Vast number of

**pub games.**
🏚 ❀ 🍴 🌖 ▶ 🚲 ♣ P

## Carmarthen

### Boar's Head
Lammas Street
☎ (01267) 222789
11–11; 12–10.30 Sun
**Felinfoel Bitter, Dark, Double Dragon; guest beer** Ⓗ
Family-run hotel, a refurbished 17th-century coaching inn, serving excellent food.
🍴 🌖 ▶ ≇ P

### Mansel Arms
1 Mansel Street
☎ (01267) 236385
11–11; 12–3, 7–10.30 Sun
**Worthington Dark, Bitter; guest beers** Ⓗ
Lively town pub by the market, popular with shoppers and locals. ❀ 🌖 🚲 ≇

### Queens Hotel
Queens Street
☎ (01267) 231800
11–11; 12–10.30 Sun
**Worthington Bitter; guest beers** Ⓗ
Convivial, town pub, popular with all ages. ❀ 🌖 ⊟

## Cenarth

### Three Horseshoes
On A484 ☎ (01239) 710119
11–11; 12–10.30 Sun (may close afternoons)
**Crown Buckley Dark, Best Bitter** Ⓗ**, Rev. James** Ⓖ**; guest beer** Ⓗ
Cosy, traditional inn with a thatched former brewhouse at the rear. The garden overlooks Cenarth Falls.
🏚 Q ❀ 🌖 ▶ ♣ P

## Cwmann

### Ram Inn
On A482 ☎ (01570) 422556
11–11; 12–10.30 Sun
**Draught Bass; Fuller's London Pride; guest beers** Ⓗ
Dating from the 16th century, a traditional pub with a superb display of Welsh love spoons. Imaginative guest beers.
🏚 Q 🌖 ▶ ♣ P

## Dryslwyn

### New Cross Inn
Off A40 at Dryslwyn crossroads OS551238
☎ (01558) 668276
Hours vary
**Worthington Bitter** *or* **Crown Buckley Best Bitter** Ⓖ
Friendly, family-run pub with a tiny public bar leading into a large restaurant. Good value meals. 🏚 Q ▶ P

## Felinfoel

### Royal Oak
33 Farmers Row (opp. brewery) ☎ (01554) 751140
11–11; 12–4, 7–10.30 Sun
**Felinfoel Bitter, Dark, Double Dragon** Ⓗ
The food is excellent in this very friendly pub (meals Wed–Sun). 🌖 ▶ 🚲

## Ffairfach

### Torbay Inn
Heol Cennen (A483)
☎ (01558) 822029
11–11; 12–10.30 Sun
**Crown Buckley Dark, Best Bitter; Tetley Bitter; Worthington Bitter; guest beers** (occasional) Ⓗ
Popular pub, tending to cater for the more mature customer in a comfortable atmosphere.
🏚 ➷ ❀ 🌖 ▶ ≇ P

## Foelgastell

### Smiths Arms
Off A48 ☎ (01269) 842213
11–11; 12–10.30 Sun
**Boddingtons Mild; Crown Buckley Best Bitter; Flowers Original** Ⓗ**; guest beer** Ⓖ
Country pub with log fires and an open, beamed ceiling. Children welcome. Meals every day – bar food and à la carte.
🏚 ❀ 🍴 🌖 ▶ ⊟ 🚲 ♠ P

## Horeb

### Waunwyllt Inn
Horeb Road (off B4309 at Fiveroads) ☎ (01269) 860209
12–3, 6.30–11; 12–3, 7–10.30 Sun
**Felinfoel Double Dragon; guest beers** Ⓗ
Very friendly, country pub with an extensive bar and restaurant menu (supper licence until midnight). Children welcome. Large garden. Cider in summer.
Q ❀ 🍴 🌖 ▶ ⊟ 🚲 ♠ ⟳ P

## Johnstown

### Friends Arms
St Clears Road
☎ (01267) 234073
11–11; 12–10.30 Sun
**Ansells Mild; Ind Coope Burton Ale; Tetley Bitter** Ⓗ
Old village tavern which once doubled as a blacksmith's; sensibly modernised as a friendly local. ❀ 🚲

## Llanarthney

### Golden Grove
On B4300 ☎ (01558) 668551
12–2.30, 6–11; 12–3, 7–10.30 (12–10.30 summer) Sun
**Crown Buckley Dark, Best Bitter, Rev. James** Ⓗ
Friendly, former coaching inn with an excellent menu.
🏚 Q ➷ ❀ 🍴 🌖 ▶ ♣ P

## Llandeilo

### White Horse Inn
125 Rhosmaen Street (off A483)
☎ (01558) 822424
12–11; 11.30–3.30, 7–10.30 Sun

| 🏭 INDEPENDENT BREWERIES | |
| --- | --- |
| **Crown Buckley:** Llanelli | |
| **Felinfoel:** Felinfoel | |
| **Nag's Head:** Abercych | |
| **Pembroke:** Pembroke | |
| **Tynllidiart Arms:** Capel Bangor | |
| **Watkin:** Llandeilo | |

Wadworth 6X; Wells
Bombardier; Worthington
Bitter; guest beers Ⓗ
Friendly, 17th-century
coaching inn with a courtyard.
Pool table in the family room.
🏚 ⛄ 🌣 ◖ 🍴 ⇌ ◠ P

## Llandovery

### Red Lion ☆

2 Market Square
☎ (01550) 720813
11.30–3 (not Wed), 5.30–10.30; closed
Sun

**Crown Buckley Dark, Best
Bitter** Ⓖ
Ancient, eccentric and
friendly pub with one basic
drinking room; in the same
family for a century.
🏚 Q 🍴 ⇌

## Llandybie

### Red Lion

6 Llandeilo Road (off A483)
☎ (01269) 851202
11.30–3, 6–11; 12–3 Sun, closed Sun
eve

**Boddingtons Bitter; Flowers
Original; guest beers** Ⓗ
Stylish pub offering a good
welcome to families in a
pleasant, bilingual atmosphere.
🏚 Q ⛄ 🌣 🏠 ◖ 🍴 ⇌ ⇌ P
✁

## Llanelli

### Apple Tree

Station Road
☎ (01554) 774562
11–11; 12–10.30 Sun
**Draught Bass; Worthington
Bitter** Ⓗ
Basic pub, full of local
character. ⇌ P

### Lemon Tree

2 Prospect Place (behind
Crown Buckley Brewery)
☎ (01554) 775121
12–11; 12–10.30 Sun
**Crown Buckley CPA, Best
Bitter; guest beer** Ⓗ
Pub with a bowling green at
the back. Chinese meals
available until 7. Good
atmosphere. 🌣 ⇌

## Llannon

### Red Lion

3 Heol y Plas
☎ (01269) 841276
5 (12 Sat)–11; 12–3, 7–10.30 Sun
**Felinfoel Dark, Bitter, Double
Dragon** Ⓗ
Pub dating back to at least the
17th century, rumoured to
have a secret tunnel leading to
the neighbouring church, plus
a ghost, and to have been
visited by Cromwell. It does (in
fact) have a well and a Toby
Jug collection.
🏚 Q ⛄ 🍴 P

## Mynydd y Garreg

### Prince of Wales Inn

1½ miles from Mynydd y
Garreg turn off Kidwelly
bypass ☎ (01554) 890522
5–11; 12–3, 7–10.30 Sun (may vary in
summer)
**Beer range varies** Ⓗ
Attractive, friendly country
pub displaying movie
memorabilia. Extensive range
of beers. A cosy restaurant
caters for all tastes. Sun
lunches served; no eve meals
Sun. No under-14s.
🏚 Q 🌣 🍴 🅰 ⇌ P 🍴

## Newcastle Emlyn

### Coopers Arms

Station Road (A484, E of
centre)
☎ (01239) 710323
12–3.30, 5.30–11; 12–3, 7–10.30 Sun
**Draught Bass; Worthington
Bitter** Ⓗ
Friendly pub, well known for
its excellent food. 🌣 ◖ 🍴 P ✁

## Pontargothi

### Cresselly Arms

On A40
☎ (01267) 290221
12–3, 6.30–11; 12–3, 7–10.30 Sun
**Flowers Original; Marston's
Pedigree; guest beers** Ⓗ
Handsomely furnished,
roadside pub. Both the garden
and the restaurant overlook the
picturesque River Cothi.
🏚 Q 🌣 ◖ 🍴 P

## Porthyrhyd

### Mansel Arms

Banc y Mansel (B4317, off A48)
☎ (01267) 275305
6–11; 12–3, 6–11 Sat; 12–3, 7–10.30
Sun
**Beer varies** Ⓗ
Comfortable and inviting
country pub just a couple of
miles off the busy A48.
Welcoming fires in both the bar
and lounge. The single beer is
usually Marston's Pedigree.
Eve meals Fri and Sat.
🏚 🍴 🅰 ⇌ P

## Rhandirmwyn

### Royal Oak Inn

On road to Llyn Brianne
Reservoir
☎ (01550) 760201
11–11 (may vary in winter); 12–2,
7–10.30 (varies in summer) Sun
**Ind Coope Burton Ale; guest
beers** Ⓗ
Friendly, family-owned
establishment, popular with
locals and visitors. Excellent
views; a good centre for
walkers, campers, cyclists and
ornithologists (RSPB reserve
close by). 🏚 🌣 🍴 ◖ 🅰 ⇌ P

## St Clears

### Corvus Inn

Station Road (B4299)
☎ (01994) 230965
11–11; 12–10.30 Sun
**Beer range varies** Ⓗ
Comfortable pub in a largish
village. The beer range varies
according to the taste of the
regulars; always two ales. The
lounge is set aside for meals.
◖ 🍴 ⇌ ◠ 🍴

## Ceredigion

## Aberaeron

### Royal Oak

30 North Road (A487)
☎ (01545) 570233
11–11 (11–3, 5.30–11 winter); 12–10.30
(12–3, 7–10.30 winter) Sun
**Ind Coope Burton Ale; Tetley
Bitter; guest beer** Ⓗ
Village-centre pub; a Welsh-
speaking house popular for
food. 🏚 Q ◖ 🍴 🍴 🅰

## Aberystwyth

### Cambrian Hotel

Alexandra Road (opp. station)
☎ (01970) 612446
11–11; 12–10.30 Sun
**Draught Bass; Hancock's HB;
guest beers** Ⓗ
Elegant, 106-year-old hotel,
popular with locals, students
and visitors, with a cocktail
lounge and a games room.
Families welcome. The beer is
reliable but expensive.
🍴 ◖ 🅰 ⇌

### Mill Inn

Mill Street ☎ (01970) 612306
11–3, 6–11; 11–11 Fri & Sat; 12–3,
7–10.30 Sun
**Brains Dark; Greenalls
Original; Tetley Bitter; guest
beers** Ⓗ
The longest surviving free
house in Aberystwyth, a very
popular local offering live folk
music (Wed), occasional cider,
plus changing guest beers from
six pumps. 🅰 ⇌ ⇌

## Bow Street

### Rhydypennau Inn

On A487 ☎ (01970) 828308
11–3, 6–11; 11–11 Sat; 12–4, 7–10.30
Sun
**Boddingtons Bitter;
Hancock's HB; guest beers** Ⓗ
White-painted pub offering a
variety of ales from two guest
pumps. It has two bars, with
the accent on food in the
lounge, which adjoins a large
restaurant. No eve meals Sun
or winter Mon.
🏚 Q 🌣 ◖ 🍴 🍴 ⇌ P

## Brynhoffnant

### Brynhoffnant Inn
On A487
☎ (01239) 654413
12 (6 winter)–11; 12–10.30 Sun
**Courage Best Bitter; Ruddles Best Bitter; Webster's Yorkshire Bitter; guest beer (summer)** Ⓗ
Large, one-roomer with a games room attached, popular with locals and tourists. Huge log fire.
🏚 ❀ ◑ ▶ ▲ ♣ P

## Capel Bangor

### Tynllidiart Arms
On A44
☎ (01970) 880248
11–2.30, 6–11; 12–2.30, 7–10.30 Sun (closed winter Sun)
**Boddingtons Bitter; Flowers Original; Tynllidiart Rheidol Reserve; guest beers** Ⓗ
Cottage brew pub with two small bars, dating from 1688. Guest beers are mostly from small brewers. Cider in summer; bottled Belgian beers stocked. 🏚 ◑ ▶ ♣ ♤ ⊓

## Goginan

### Druid Inn
On A44
☎ (01970) 880650
11–3, 5.30–11; closed Sun
**Banks's Bitter; guest beers** Ⓗ
Free house on the hillside in a former lead mining village, offering two changing guest beers, Romanian vodkas and bottled Czech lager. Families welcome.
🏚 ❀ ◑ ▶ ♣ P

## Llanbadarn Fawr

### Black Lion
Off A44
☎ (01970) 623448
11–3, 5.30–11; 11–11 Thu–Sat; 12–10.30 Sun
**Banks's Mild** Ⓗ**, Bitter** Ⓔ**; Marston's Pedigree; guest beer** Ⓗ
Friendly pub, frequented by locals and students. Function room at the rear; garden at the side. Live music weekdays.
❀ ◑ ▲ ♣ P ⊓

## New Quay

### Black Lion
Glanmor Terrace (B4342)
☎ (01545) 560209
12–11 (12–3, 6–11 winter, may vary); 12–10.30 Sun
**Courage Directors; John Smith's Bitter; James Williams IPA** Ⓗ
Popular pub overlooking the beach. Quality food. Good garden for children.
Q ☙ ❀ ⌸ ◑ ▶ ♿ ▲ ♣ P

## Penrhiwllan

### Penrhiwllan Inn
On A475 ☎ (01559) 370394
11–11; 12–10.30 Sun
**Draught Bass; Hancock's HB; Worthington Bitter** Ⓗ
Unspoilt country pub and restaurant with very reasonably priced beer. Transport service provided for customers within a five-mile radius. 🏚 ☙ ❀ ◑ ▶ ♣ P

## Pren-gwyn

### Gwarcefel Arms
On A475 ☎ (01559) 362720
11 (may be 5 Mon)–11; 12–3 Sun, closed Sun eve
**Crown Buckley Best Bitter; guest beer** Ⓗ
Popular pub for meals. Children welcome in the bars and restaurant.
🏚 ❀ ◑ ▶ ▲ P

## Talybont

### Black Lion Hotel
On A487 ☎ (01970) 832335
10.30–11; 12–10.30 Sun
**Ind Coope Burton Ale; Tetley Bitter; guest beer** Ⓗ
Imposing, grey slate, country hotel on the village green, with two lounge bars and a restaurant; popular with the local farming fraternity. It may close afternoons in winter.
❀ ⌸ ◑ ▶ ♣ P

## Pembrokeshire

## Abercych

### Nag's Head
On B4332 ☎ (01239) 841200
3 (11 Sat)–11; 12–10.30 Sun
**Boddingtons Bitter; Flowers Original; Morland Old Speckled Hen; Nag's Head Old Emrys** Ⓗ
Well-restored old smithy with beamed bars, riverside gardens and a micro-brewery.
🏚 Q ☙ ❀ ♿ P

## Carew

### Carew Inn
☎ (01646) 651267
12–2.30, 7.30–11 (11–11 summer); 12–3, 7–10.30 Sun (may extend summer)
**Crown Buckley Rev. James; Worthington Bitter; guest beer** Ⓗ
Unspoilt pub near the castle and monument. ❀ ⌸ ◑ ▶ P

## Clarbeston Road

### Picton Inn
By station ☎ (01437) 731615
11–11; 12–10.30 Sun

**Crown Buckley Rev. James; Worthington Bitter** Ⓗ
Pub with a good, old-fashioned atmosphere.
🏚 Q ❀ ◑ ▶ ⇌ P

## Cresswell Quay

### Cressely Arms
☎ (01646) 621210
11–3, 5–11 (may be 11–11 summer); 12–3, 7–10.30 Sun
**Flowers IPA; guest beer (Mon)** Ⓖ
Famous waterside pub, unaltered since 1900, with beer served in jugs. Popular with all ages. 🏚 Q ❀ P

## Dreenhill

### Denant Mill Inn
B4327 out of Haverfordwest; 1st left at Dreenhill
☎ (01437) 766569
11–11; 12–10.30 Sun (may vary in winter)
**Beer range varies** Ⓗ
16th-century, water-driven cornmill in an idyllic setting. Large garden. Lunchtime snacks. Cider in summer.
🏚 Q ☙ ⌸ ▶ ▲ ♣ ♤ P

## Eglwyswrw

### Butcher's Arms
On A487 ☎ (01239) 891630
11–3, 7–11; 11–11 Sat; 12–3, 7–10.30 Sun
**Crown Buckley Rev. James; Tetley Bitter; Worthington Bitter** Ⓗ
Pub with a cosy bar. Accommodation and meals in summer (food also winter weekends). No-smoking restaurant.
Q ❀ ⌸ ◑ ▶ ♿ ♤

## Fishguard

### Fishguard Arms
Main Street ☎ (01348) 872763
11–3, 6.30–11; 12–3, 7–10.30 Sun
**Worthington Bitter; guest beer** Ⓖ
Unspoilt, two-roomer: an essential visit. 🏚 Q ▲

## Freshwater East

### Freshwater Inn
On B4584 ☎ (01646) 672329
12–3, 7–11 (11–11 summer); 12–3, 7–10.30 Sun
**Worthington Bitter; guest beer** Ⓗ
Attractively modernised clifftop pub with sea views from the restaurant.
🏚 Q ☙ ❀ ⌸ ◑ ▶ ⊞ ▲ P

## Haverfordwest

### King's Arms Hotel
Dew Street ☎ (01437) 763726
11–3, 5.30 (7 Sat)–11; 12–3, 7–10.30 Sun

Theakston Best Bitter; guest
beers H
Pub in the old part of town
which prides itself on its ever-
changing selection of ales. A
local jazz venue.
🏚 ♣ ♠

## Pembroke Yeoman
Hill Street (off St Thomas
Green) ☎ (01437) 762500
11–11; 12–3, 7–10.30 Sun
Draught Bass; Flowers IPA;
Greene King Abbot;
Marston's Pedigree; guest
beers H
Comfortable local attracting all
ages. 🏚 ❀ ◁ ♣ ♠

## Lamphey

### Dial Inn
☎ (01646) 672426
11–3, 6–11; 12–3, 7–10.30 Sun
Draught Bass; Hancock's HB;
Worthington Bitter H
Delightful village pub
serving excellent food
(restaurant).
🏚 Q ☎ ◁ ▶ & ▲ ≈ P

## Landshipping

### Stanley Arms
OS011118 ☎ (01834) 891227
12–3, 6–11; 12–3, 7–10.30 Sun
Worthington Bitter; guest
beers H
Attractive pub near the estuary
in a quiet location. Excellent
choice of beers and food.
🏚 ❀ ◁ ▶ ▲ P

## Manorbier

### Castle Inn
☎ (01834) 871268
11–11; 12–10.30 Sun
Theakston Best Bitter, XB,
Old Peculier; guest beer
(summer) H
Friendly, welcoming pub near
the castle and beach.
Q ☎ ❀ ◁ ▶ ▲

## Narberth

### Angel
High Street
☎ (01834) 860215
11–3, 6–11 (11–11 summer); 12–3,
7–10.30 (12–10.30 summer) Sun
Worthington Bitter; guest
beers H
Attractive pub offering
excellent food and friendly
service. Q ❀ ◁ ▶ ⊞ ▲

### Kirkland Arms
East Gate, St James Street
☎ (01834) 860423
11–3, 5–11; 11–11 Sat; 12–3, 7–10.30
Sun
Felinfoel Bitter, Double
Dragon H
Unspoilt, traditional bar.
❀ ⊞ ▲ P

## Nevern

### Trewern Arms
½ mile off A487, by River Nyfer
☎ (01239) 820395
11–3 (may vary), 6–11; 12–3, 7–10.30
Sun
Castle Eden Ale; Flowers
Original; guest beer H
Ivy-clad, 16th-century inn
popular with visitors to the
coast. The beer range may
vary. 🏚 ❀ 🚲 ◁ ▶ P

## Newport

### Castle Hotel
Bridge Street (A487)
☎ (01239) 820742
11–11; 12–10.30 Sun
Wadworth 6X; Worthington
Bitter; guest beer H
Friendly local with a bar for
darts and games, plus a dining
area. 🏚 ☎ ❀ 🚲 ◁ ▶ ▲ P

## Pembroke

### Castle Inn
Main Street ☎ (01646) 682883
11–11; 12–10.30 Sun
Draught Bass; Tetley Bitter;
Worthington Bitter; guest
beers H
Pub hosting lively music and
retaining many original
features. ❀ ≈ P

### Old Cross Saws
109 Main Street
☎ (01646) 682475
11–11; 12–10.30 Sun
Crown Buckley Best Bitter;
guest beers H
Rugby followers' local – a
friendly pub.
❀ 🚲 ◁ ▶ ≈

## Pembroke Dock

### First & Last
London Road
☎ (01646) 682687
11–11; 12–10.30 Sun
Worthington Bitter; guest
beer H
Lively, friendly local. Guest
beers change regularly. One of
the cheapest places to drink in
the area.
❀ ◁ ▶ ≈ ♣ P

### Station Inn
Dimond Street
☎ (01646) 621255
12–2 (not Mon–Wed), 7–11; 12–2,
7–10.30 Sun (may extend in summer)
Pembroke Darklin, Dimond
Lager, Main Street Bitter,
Golden Hill Ale, Off the
Rails H
Redundant station at the end of
the line, brought back to life as
the tap for Pembroke Brewery;
dedicated to the age of steam.
The beer range may vary.
🏚 Q 🚲 ◁ ▶ ≈ ♣ P

## Pontfaen

### Dyffryn Arms ☆
Off B4313 ☎ (01348) 881305
Hours vary
Draught Bass or Ind Coope
Burton Ale G
1920s front room where time
has stood still. Beer is served
by the jug and conversation is a
must. Set in the Gwaun Valley.
🏚 Q ❀ ▲ ♠

## Porthgain

### Sloop Inn
Off A487 at Croes-goch
☎ (01348) 831449
11.30–3, 6–11 (11–11 summer); 12–3,
7–10.30 (12–10.30 summer) Sun
Brains SA; Felinfoel Double
Dragon; Worthington Bitter H
Old fishing pub featuring
quarrying and shipping
ephemera.
🏚 ❀ ◁ ▶ ♣ P

## Rosebush

### New Inn
At B4329/B4313 jct
☎ (01437) 532542
11–11; 12–4, 7–10.30 Sun
Crown Buckley Best Bitter,
Rev. James; guest beers H
A bar with an open fire and a
choice of bottled continental
beers are features of this pub.
🏚 Q ❀ ◁ ▶ & ♣ ⊂ P

## Saundersfoot

### Royal Oak
Wogans Terrace
☎ (01834) 812546
11–11; 12–10.30 Sun
Draught Bass; Flowers IPA,
Original; Worthington Bitter;
guest beers H
Very attractive old pub with
unusual outside patio heaters
for cooler eves. A popular
eating place. Q ❀ ◁ ▶ ▲

## Templeton

### Boar's Head
☎ (01834) 860286
11–3, 5.30–11; 12–3, 7–10.30 Sun
Ruddles County; Worthington
Bitter H
Traditional pub with two bars,
plus a restaurant/lounge,
decorated with fresh hops
every year. Q ☎ ◁ ▶ ▲ P

## Tenby

### Hope & Anchor
St Julian Street
☎ (01834) 842131
11–11 (11–3, 7–11 winter); 12–10.30
Sun (may close afternoons)
Crown Buckley Rev. James;
Worthington Bitter; guest
beer H
Friendly local, close to the
harbour. Q ❀ ▲ ≈

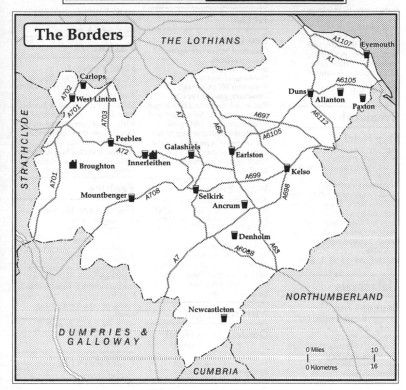

## The Borders

*Authority area covered: The Borders UA*

## Allanton

### Allanton Inn
On B6437
☎ (01890) 818260
12–2.30, 6–11; 12–midnight Sat;
12.30–11 Sun
**Belhaven 80/-, St Andrew's
Ale; guest beer** Ⓗ
Old coaching house with a
restaurant. The unchanged
exterior still boasts iron
hitching rings for horses. Stone
flags surround the bar in a
comfortable, functional
interior. Children's certificate.
Occasional cider.
🏚 Q 🐄 ✿ 🛏 ◁ ▶ ⅋ ♣ ⌂ P

## Ancrum

### Cross Keys Inn ☆
The Green (B6400, off A68)
☎ (01835) 830344
11–2.30, 6–11 (midnight Thu; 5–1am
Fri); 11–midnight Sat; 12.30–11
Sun
**Alloa Arrol's 80/-; Caledonian
Deuchars IPA; guest beer** Ⓗ
Wonderfully unspoilt village
boozer, virtually unaltered
since its 1906 refurbishment!
The games area used to be the
cellar and retains the overhead
tram lines used for moving

heavy casks. A gem – not to be
missed.
🏚 Q ✿ ◁ ▶ 🛏 & ♣ P

## Carlops

### Allan Ramsay Hotel
On A702 ☎ (01968) 660258
11–midnight
**Belhaven Sandy Hunter's Ale,
80/-** Ⓗ
Old coaching inn in a village
high on a shoulder of the
Pentland Hills. Though the bar
has been knocked into a single
eating/drinking area, the
atmosphere has been retained
by dark panelling and log fires.
Children welcome.
🏚 Q ✿ 🛏 ◁ ▶ & P

## Denholm

### Auld Cross Keys Inn
On A698 ☎ (01450) 870305
11–2.30 (not Mon), 6–11 (midnight Thu
& Sat, 1am Fri); 12.30–11 Sun
**Broughton Greenmantle Ale;
guest beer** Ⓗ
Picturesque, 17th-century inn
overlooking the village green.
A low ceiling and a blazing fire
add to the cosy conviviality.
The cheesy eggs at the bar and
high teas in the restaurant are

both famous. No food Mon.
Children's certificate.
🏚 ✿ ◁ ▶ 🛏 & ♣ P

## Duns

### Whip & Saddle
Market Square (off A6105)
☎ (01361) 883215
11 (12.30 Sun)–11.30 (midnight Fri)
**Caledonian Deuchars IPA;
Theakston XB; guest beer** Ⓗ
Town-centre bar, dating from
1790, with a modern interior
offering wood floors and views
over the town square. The
family room is upstairs
(children's certificate). River
Whiteadder angling permits
available. Camping for
caravans. Q 🐄 ◁ ♣

## Earlston

### Black Bull Inn
High Street (A6105, off A68)
☎ (01896) 848170

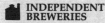

### INDEPENDENT BREWERIES
**Broughton:** Broughton

**Traquair:** Innerleithen

12 (12.30 Sun)–11; 11–midnight
Sat
**Beer varies** Ⓗ
Old coaching inn whose
deeds date from the 16th
century; once part of the
Mellerstain Estate, now a
village local, reflecting
sporting interests.
🏯 ❀ 🍴 ♣ P

## Eyemouth

### Ship Hotel
Harbour Road
☎ (01890) 750224
11–midnight (11.30 winter); 12.30–
11.30 Sun
**Beer range varies** Ⓐ
Family-run hotel, right on the
harbour front. The public bar is
warmed by a coal fire and
there is a vast selection of
rums, as befits a fisherman's
haunt. Limited parking
available.
🏯 ⛵ ❀ 🍴 ◖ 🍴 🍴 ♿ ▲ ♣ P

## Galashiels

### Ladhope Inn
33 High Buckholmside (A7,
½ mile N of centre)
☎ (01896) 752446
11–3, 5–11; 11–11 Wed; 11–midnight
Thu–Sat; 12.30–11 Sun
**Caledonian 80/-; Tetley
Imperial; guest beer** Ⓗ
Well-appointed locals' bar
built into the hillside and
dating from 1792, though
much altered since. Vibrant
Borders atmosphere.
❀ ♣

## Innerleithen

### Traquair Arms Hotel
Traquair Road (B709, off A72)
☎ (01896) 830229
11–11 (midnight Fri & Sat);
12–midnight Sun
**Broughton Greenmantle Ale;
Traquair Bear Ale** Ⓗ
Family-run, 18th-century hotel
with a plush lounge, warmed
by a log fire. Good, home-
cooked food from local
produce. Beware the
Addlestones cider is kept
under $CO_2$, but try the
draught Traquair as this is the
only regular outlet in
Scotland.
🏯 Q ❀ 🍴 ◖ ▲ ♣ P

## Kelso

### Red Lion
Crawford Street (off A6089, N
of town centre)
☎ (01573) 224817
11–midnight (1am Fri); 12.30–11 Sun
**Belhaven 80/-; Courage
Directors; guest beers** Ⓗ
Pub which features a fine wood
and plaster, vaulted ceiling and
wood panelling. Old spirit
barrels decorate the rear of the
bar, on top of a painted gantry
with original mirrors. Two
guest beers. Children welcome.
🏯 🍴 ♿ ♣

### White Swan
Abbey Row (off town square,
near abbey) ☎ (01573) 224348
11–midnight (1am Fri); 12.30–11 Sun
**Alloa Arrol's 80/-; Greenalls
Shipstone's Bitter; Tetley
Bitter; guest beer** Ⓗ
Facing on to the ruins of Kelso
Abbey, a modernised old pub
attracting a good local trade.
Children's certificate.
🏯 ❀ ◖ ♿ ▲ ♣

## Mountbenger

### Gordon Arms Hotel
At A708/B709 crossroads
☎ (01750) 82232
11 (12.30 Sun)–11 (closed winter Tue)
**Broughton Greenmantle Ale,
Oatmeal Stout** Ⓗ
Dating from 1828, this is a cosy,
welcoming hotel of
considerable historic interest,
situated at an isolated
crossroads near St Mary's
Loch. A converted hayloft
accommodates walkers on the
Southern Upland Way which
passes close by. Children's
certificate.
🏯 Q ❀ 🍴 ◖ ♿ ▲ ♣ P

## Newcastleton

### Grapes Hotel
Douglas Square (B6357)
☎ (0138 73) 75245
11 (12 Sun)–11 (1am Fri, midnight Sat)
**Caledonian Deuchars IPA;
Worthington Bitter** Ⓗ
Friendly, family-run village
local with a busy, if rather
basic, public bar and a games
area. Railway buffs will
appreciate the old photos.
Good selection of malt
whiskies and good value

meals. Worthington White
Shield available.
🏯 ❀ 🍴 ◖ ♣

## Paxton

### Hoolit's Nest
Off B6460 ☎ (01289) 386267
11 (12.30 Sun)–2.30 (not Mon), 6.30–11
**Beer range varies** Ⓗ
Village pub with more 'hoolits'
(owls) than you can shake a
stick at – of every shape and
description, they survey the
bar from every nook and
cranny. A stately home, Paxton
House, is nearby. Children's
certificate. ❀ ◖ ♿ ♣ P

## Peebles

### Green Tree Hotel
41 Eastgate (A72)
☎ (01721) 720582
11 (12 Sun)–midnight
**Caledonian 80/-; guest beers** Ⓗ
Bustling hotel bar with
interesting leaded windows.
Very much a local in the front;
the back room is more relaxed.
Children welcome. Two guest
beers. No-smoking dining
room.
🏯 ❀ 🍴 ◖ 🍴 ♿ ▲ ♣ P

## Selkirk

### Cross Keys Inn
Market Place (on A7)
☎ (01750) 21283
11 (12.30 Sun)–11 (midnight Thu–Sat)
**Caledonian 80/-; Tetley
Bitter** Ⓗ
Vibrant, wee, wood-panelled
public bar with steps leading
up to a comfortable lounge;
often packed. Excellent meals
(not served Sat eve). No-
smoking family room.
⛵ ◖ 🍴 ▲ ♣ ⌫

## West Linton

### Gordon Arms Hotel
Dolphinton Road (A702)
☎ (01968) 660208
11 (12 Sun)–midnight
**Alloa Arrol's 80/-; guest
beers** Ⓐ
Excellent public bar with a
blazing fire and settles. An odd
assortment of old phones,
bottles and motoring
paraphernalia provides topics
for conversation. Two guest
beers. Children's certificate.
🏯 ❀ 🍴 ◖ 🍴 ♣ P

---

# A SCOTTISH STAR

The Cross Keys at Ancrum is just one of the many pubs in this
year's *Good Beer Guide* displaying a 'heritage pub' star.

See the feature at the front of this book for details of other 'star' pubs.

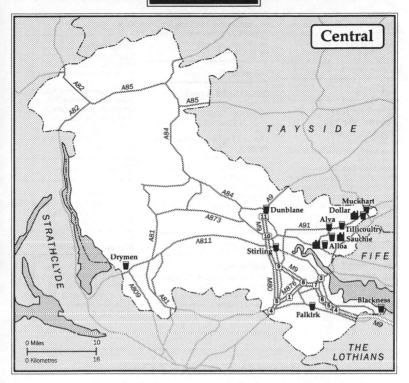

*Authority areas covered: Clackmannan UA, Falkirk UA, Stirling UA*

## Alloa

### Crams Bar
8 Candleriggs
☎ (01259) 219420
11 (12.30 Sun)–11 (midnight Fri & Sat)
**Maclay 80/-** Ⓐ
Traditional, friendly
workingmen's bar in the town
centre. ⅍ ♣

## Alva

### Cross Keys
120 Stirling Street
☎ (01259) 760409
11–11 (midnight Thu, 1am Fri & Sat);
12.30–11 Sun
**Beer range varies** Ⓗ
Comfortable, two-bar local
with a spacious lounge.
Always two Maclay beers
available, plus one guest.
🏚 ◖ ▷ ⌂ ⅍

## Blackness

### Blackness Inn
The Square (B903, off A904)
☎ (01506) 834252
11–2.30, 6–11 (midnight Fri & Sat);
12.30–11 Sun
**Maclay 80/-** Ⓗ
Typical country inn, nicely
situated on the edge of the
River Forth, near Blackness
Castle. A warm welcome is
assured, with real fires in both
bars and award-winning,
home-cooked food (fish a
speciality).
🏚 ❀ 🛏 ◖ ▷ ⌂ ♣ P

## Dollar

### Lorne Tavern
17 Argyll Street
☎ (01259) 743423
11–2.30, 5–11 Mon; 5–11 Tue; 3–11
Wed; 3–midnight Thu; 11–1am Fri &
Sat; 12.30–11 Sun
**Greene King IPA** Ⓐ;
**Harviestoun 70/-,
Ptarmigan** Ⓗ; **guest beer** Ⓐ
Pub with the oldest licence in
Dollar (1850), handy for
walkers from the Ochil Hills.
Lunches Sat and Sun; eve
meals Thu–Sun.
Q ◖ ▷ ⌂ ⅍ ♣ P

## Drymen

### Clachan
The Square ☎ (01360) 60824
11 (12.30 Sun)–11.30 (midnight Sat)
**Belhaven 80/-; Boddingtons
Bitter** Ⓗ
Village local, established in
1734: a cosy public bar with
church pew seats and pictures
of local life around the walls.
The lounge now serves more as
a restaurant. 🏚 ◖ ▷ ⌂

### Winnock Hotel
The Square ☎ (01360) 60245
11 (12 Sun)–midnight (1am Fri & Sat)
**Draught Bass; Broughton
Greenmantle Ale, Merlin's
Ale; Courage Directors** Ⓗ
Whitewashed building along
one side of the village square: a
long bar to the front with
exposed beams, and a
restaurant leading off. There's
a comfortable seating area by
the hotel entrance. Petanque
played. 🏚 Q ⛺ ❀ 🛏 ◖ ▷ ♣

## Dunblane

### Tappit Hen
Kirk Street ☎ (01786) 825226
11 (12.30 Sun)–11.30 (12.30am Fri &
Sat)
**Harviestoun Ptarmigan;
Maclay Kane's Amber Ale,
Wallace; guest beers** Ⓗ

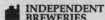

### INDEPENDENT BREWERIES

**Devon:** Sauchie

**Harviestoun:** Dollar

**Maclay:** Alloa

387

Traditional, one-room local opposite the cathedral. Seven handpumps serve an extensive range of guest beers; there's also a good choice of malt whiskies. Local CAMRA *Pub of the Year* 1995. ≷ ♣

## Falkirk

### Eglesbrech at Behind the Wall

14 Melville Street
☎ (01324) 633338
12–midnight (1am Fri & Sat); 12.30–midnight Sun
**Newcastle Exhibition; Theakston XB; guest beers** H
The ale house is on the upper floor of this former Playtex bra factory. Good food is served in all areas (Mexican a speciality). Live music Thu. ❀ ◑ ◗ ≷

## Muckhart

### Muckhart Inn

Pool of Muckhart (A91, 3 miles E of Dollar) ☎ (01259) 781324
11 (12.30 Sun)–11 (midnight Fri & Sat)
**Devon Original, Thick Black, Pride** A
Pub retaining the atmosphere of a traditional coaching inn (1806). Good inexpensive food served all day, until 9.
⛰ ❀ ◑ ◗ ♿ P

## Sauchie

### Mansfield Arms

7 Main Street
☎ (01259) 722020
11–11 (12.30am Fri & Sat); 12.30–11 Sun
**Devon Original, Thick Black, Pride** A
Family-run local in a traditional mining area: a workingmen's bar and a warm, friendly lounge. Good, inexpensive meals all day until 9. CAMRA Forth Valley *Pub of the Year* 1996.
❀ ◑ ◗ ⊞ ♿ P

## Stirling

### Borestone

1 Glasgow Road, St Ninians
☎ (01786) 471023
11–midnight (1am Fri & Sat)
**Maclay Kane's Amber Ale, Wallace** H
Busy, two-roomed local.
⊞ ♿

### Hogshead

2 Baker Street (top of Friar St)
☎ (01786) 448722
11 (12.30 Sun)–midnight (1am Fri & Sat)
**Boddingtons Bitter, Castle Eden Ale; Flowers IPA, Original; guest beers** H
Comfortable, friendly, city-centre local, modernised to look old! Eve meals in summer (till 7). ◑ ◗

## Tillicoultry

### Woolpack Inn

1 Glassford Square (150 yds N of A91 at W End of town)
☎ (01259) 750332
11–midnight (1am Fri & Sat); 12.30–11 Sun
**Beer range varies** H
Traditional old drovers' inn, dating from 1743; a friendly pub with a strong local trade and occasional business from walkers coming off the Ochil Hills. Meals Fri–Sun.
Q ☕ ◑ ◗ ♣

## PULLING A FAST ONE

The handpump is widely recognised as the trademark of real ale and real cider. It indicates a product which is traditionally brewed and conditioned, before being traditionally served without added gas. Shame, therefore, on those brewers and cider makers who look to take advantage of this symbolism by using 'fake' handpumps to dispense keg beers and keg ciders.

These producers are perpetrating a con on the drinking public. Why else would they want to use fake handpumps except to muscle in on the goodwill and respect real beer and cider enjoy and to blur the distinction between real ale and cider and their inferior processed equivalents?

Remember, keg beers and ciders are hugely more profitable than traditional products, so manufacturers have a vested interest in getting drinkers to buy keg rather than real.

CAMRA believes it is time to eradicate this deception once and for all. Consequently, in this guide you won't find any pub which serves keg beer or keg cider through a fake handpump. The *Good Beer Guide*, as a consumer publication, clearly cannot condone such malpractice.

Our campaign is not against the products on sale – after all, one of our driving principles is choice for the customer – but against the method of dispense. These products are also available with standard keg dispensers and we urge all publicans still using fake handpumps to request a change of equipment and so stop helping, however inadvertently, these manufacturers from deliberately confusing the public.

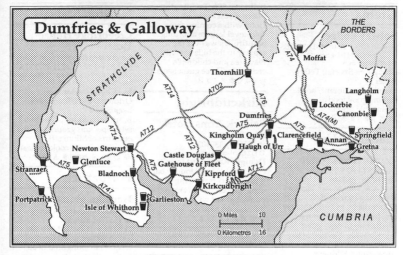

**Dumfries & Galloway**

THE BORDERS

Moffat
Thornhill
Langholm
Lockerbie
Canonbie
Dumfries
Clarencefield
Annan
Springfield
Kingholm Quay
Gretna
Haugh of Urr
Newton Stewart
Castle Douglas
Glenluce
Gatehouse of Fleet
Kippford
Stranraer
Bladnoch
Kirkcudbright
Portpatrick
Garlieston
Isle of Whithorn

STRATHCLYDE

CUMBRIA

0 Miles 10
0 Kilometres 16

*Authority area covered: Dumfries & Galloway UA*

## Annan

### Blue Bell Inn
High Street ☎ (01461) 202385
11 (12.30 Sun)–11 (midnight Thu–Sat)
**Theakston Best Bitter; guest beers** H
Excellent, traditional boozer with impressive wood panelling. Friendly and very popular; local CAMRA *Pub of the Year 1994.* Q ❀ ▲ ⇌ ♣

## Bladnoch

### Bladnoch Inn
On A714, 6 miles S of Newton Stewart ☎ (01988) 402200
11 (12 Sun) 11 (midnight Fri & Sat)
**Theakston XB; guest beers** H
Friendly village local: a rural gem with a comfortable and homely dining area. The wood-panelled bar features hunting dog drawings. Opposite the Bladnoch Distillery Museum.
⚌ Q ⛴ ❀ ⇝ ◑ ▶ P

## Canonbie

### Riverside Inn
☎ (0138 73) 71512
12–3, 6.30–11; 12–3 (not winter), 7–10.30 Sun
**Yates Bitter; guest beer** H
Charming, comfortable, country inn on the River Esk. Good quality food.
⚌ Q ❀ ⇝ ◑ ▶ ⛯ P ⛭

## Castle Douglas

### Royal Hotel
17 King Street (opp. Market Hill car park)
☎ (01556) 502040
11 (12.30 Sun)–midnight

Alloa Arrol's 80/-; Ind Coope Burton Ale; Orkney Dark Island; Tetley Bitter; guest beer H
Town-centre hotel with two comfortable, airy lounges (one with an open fire), decorated with framed beer posters. Games room. Children's certificate. ⚌ Q ⇝ ◑ ▲ ♣

## Clarencefield

### Farmers Arms
Main Street ☎ (01387) 87675
11–2.30, 6–11 (midnight Fri); 11–midnight Sat; 12.30–11 Sun
**Caledonian 70/-, 80/-; guest beers** H
Welcoming, 18th-century inn, once a Temperance hotel.
⚌ ⛴ ❀ ⇝ ◑ ▶ ⚂ ▲ ♣ P

## Dumfries

### Douglas Arms
Friars Vennel ☎ (01387) 56002
11 (12.30 Sun)–11 (midnight Thu–Sat)
**Broughton Greenmantle Ale, Oatmeal Stout, Old Jock; Jennings Cumberland Ale; guest beer** H
Town-centre pub with a cosy snug bar. ⚌ Q ♣

### New Bazaar
38 Whitesands
☎ (01387) 68776
12–midnight; 12.30–11 Sun
**Broughton Greenmantle Ale; McEwan 80/-; Maclay Wallace; guest beers** H
Excellent, traditional bar with Victorian fittings. Varied guest beers. ⚌ Q ♣

### Ship Inn
97 St Michael Street
☎ (01387) 55189

11–2.30, 5–11
**Caledonian Double Amber Ale; McEwan 70/-, 80/-; guest beers** H
Superb, award-winning, traditional pub; a gem, not to be missed. Large selection of guest beers. Q ♣ P

**Try also: Moreig Hotel**, Annan Rd (Free)

## Garlieston

### Queens Arms Hotel
1 High Street ☎ (01988) 600652
11–3, 6–11; 11–11.30 Sat; 12–11 Sun
**Belhaven Festival Gold; guest beers** H
Traditional village hotel, close to the harbour and seafront.
⚌ Q ⛴ ❀ ⇝ ▲

## Gatehouse of Fleet

### Masonic Arms
Ann Street (sidestreet opp. Bank of Scotland)
☎ (01557) 814337
11–2.30, 5–midnight; 12–3, 6–midnight Sun
**Theakston XB** H
Comfortable lounge bar with exposed beams and a large conservatory. Children's certificate. ❀ ◑ ▶ ⚂ ▲ ♣ ⅍

## Glenluce

### Kelvin House Hotel
53 Main Street (off A75)
☎ (01581) 300303
11–11 (midnight Sat & Sun)
**Orkney Red MacGregor; guest beers** H
Small, friendly hotel near Luce Bay in a bypassed village. Excellent, home-cooked meals.
⛴ ❀ ⇝ ◑ ▶ ⚄ ▲ ♣

## Gretna

### Solway Lodge
Annan Road ☎ (01461) 338266
12–11 (midnight Fri & Sat); 12–11
(12–3 winter) Sun
**Broughton Special; Tetley
Bitter** ⊞
Excellent restaurant/hotel
serving good food at
reasonable prices.
⌂ ❀ 🚲 ◖ ◗ & P

## Haugh of Urr

### Laurie Arms Hotel
1 mile S of A75
☎ (01556) 660246
11.45–2.30, 5 (6.30 winter)–midnight
**Beer range varies** ⊞
Comfortable, friendly country
inn, just off the beaten track,
offering up to three guest
beers, a wide selection of bar
meals and an à la carte
restaurant. Children's
certificate. ⌂ ❀ 🚲 ◖ ◗ P

## Isle of Whithorn

### Steam Packet Hotel
Harbour Row (A750)
☎ (01988) 500334
11 (12 Sun)–11
**Theakston XB** ⊞
Quaint harbourside inn, which
has a large stone fireplace in an
unusual stone-clad bar. This
popular sailing centre has the
most southerly real ale in
Scotland.
⌂ Q ❀ 🚲 ◗ ⊟ ♣

## Kingholm Quay

### Swan Hotel
On B726, 1½ miles S of
Dumfries ☎ (01387) 253756
11.30–2.30, 5–11 (midnight Thu–Sun);
(11.30–midnight summer Sun)
**Theakston Best Bitter** ⊞
Attractive and friendly hotel
overlooking the River Nith.
Excellent bar meals.
⌂ Q 🚲 ❀ ◖ ◗ ⊟ & ♣ P ⨪

## Kippford

### Anchor Hotel
Main Street ☎ (01556) 620205
11–midnight; 12.30–11 Sun
**Boddingtons Bitter;
Theakston XB; guest beer** ⊞
Traditional village inn set
opposite a busy yachting
haven. The chef/proprietor
takes pride in his food. The
traditional bar has a great
atmosphere and original
features. Children's certificate.
⌂ 🚲 ◖ ◗ ▲ ♣ P

### Mariner Hotel
Main Street (opp. pier)
☎ (01556) 620206
12–2.30, 6–11 (12–11 summer Sat &
Sun)

**Belhaven 80/-; Boddingtons
Bitter; guest beers** ⊞
Hotel with a comfortable,
split-level lounge affording
beautiful views over the
estuary to the hills beyond.
Play area and children's
certificate. Three guest beers.
❀ 🚲 ◖ ◗ ▲ ◡ P

## Kirkcudbright

### Selkirk Arms Hotel
High Street
☎ (01557) 330402
11 (12 Sun)–midnight
**Draught Bass; guest beer** ⊞
Comfortable hotel lounge bar
where conversation thrives.
Cask ales are not on tap in the
public bar but will be brought
through on request.
Q ❀ 🚲 ◖ ◗ ⊟ ▲

Try also: **Masonic Arms**,
Castle St (Free)

## Langholm

### Crown Hotel
High Street ☎ (0138 73) 80247
11 (12 Sun)–11 (midnight Thu–Sat)
**Beer range varies** ⊞
Comfortable, 18th-century inn
with common riding
connections. High teas served.
⌂ 🚲 🚲 ◖ ◗ ⊟ & ▲ ♣

## Lockerbie

### Somerton House Hotel
35 Carlisle Road
☎ (01576) 202583
11–11 (midnight Thu–Sat)
**Broughton Greenmantle
Ale** ⊞
Deservedly popular, well-
appointed hotel with friendly
service. Excellent meals.
⌂ Q 🚲 ❀ 🚲 ◖ ◗ & ▲ P

## Moffat

### Black Bull Hotel
Church Gate ☎ (01683) 20206
11 (12 Sun)–11 (midnight Thu–Sat)
**McEwan 80/-; Theakston Best
Bitter; guest beers** ⊞
Historic, 16th-century hotel
with Rabbie Burns
connections: a comfortable
lounge and a traditional bar,
decorated with railway
memorabilia.
⌂ 🚲 ❀ 🚲 ◖ ◗ ⊟ ▲ P

### Star Hotel
High Street ☎ (01683) 20156
11 (12 Sun)–11 (midnight Thu–Sat)
**Theakston Best Bitter; guest
beer** (summer) ⊞
Welcoming, family-run hotel;
the narrowest detached hotel
in Britain. High teas served.
Note: real ale is sold in the
lounge only.
🚲 ◖ ◗ ♣

## Newton Stewart

### Creebridge House
Hotel
Creebridge (on old main road,
E of river) ☎ (01671) 402121
11–2.30, 6–11 (11.30 Sat); 12.30–2.30,
7–11 Sun
**Ind Coope Burton Ale;
Orkney Dark Island; guest
beer** ⊞
Beautiful country house hotel
set in spacious grounds on the
outskirts of Minnigaff.
Excellent, home-cooked meals.
⌂ Q 🚲 ❀ 🚲 ◖ ◗ ▲ ♣ P

## Portpatrick

### Harbour House Hotel
53 Main Street (harbour)
☎ (01776) 810456
11 (12 Sun)–11.15 (11.45 Fri & Sat)
**Tetley Bitter; guest beers** ⊞
Open-plan lounge bar in an
hotel looking on to a
picturesque fishing port.
Children's certificate. Two
guest beers.
⌂ ❀ 🚲 ◖ ◗ ▲ P

Try also: **Downshire Arms
Hotel**, Main St (Free)

## Springfield

### Queen's Head
☎ (01461) 37173
12–2.30, 7–11 (midnight Thu–Sat)
**McEwan 70/-, 80/-; Theakston
Mild, Best Bitter** ⊞
Single-room local. ♣ P

## Stranraer

### Rudicott Hotel
London Road (A75)
☎ (01776) 702684
12–2.30, 5–11 (midnight Fri);
12.30–2.30, 6.30–11 Sun
**Beer range varies** ⊞
Small, family-run hotel, handy
for ferry terminals and the
football and rugby grounds.
Note the unusual division of
the bar by low screens. Two
guest beers. Q ❀ 🚲 ◖ ◗ ▲ P

Try also: **George Hotel**,
George St (Free)

## Thornhill

### Buccleugh &
Queensbury Hotel
112 Drumlanrig Street (A76)
☎ (01848) 330215
11–1am (midnight Sun)
**Beer range varies** ⊞
Hotel with a comfortable
lounge where meals are served
all day (breakfast from 7.30 in
the fishing season – late Feb–
Nov). One guest beer all year
with one other in the public bar
in summer.
⌂ Q 🚲 🚲 ◖ ◗ ⊟ & ▲ ♣ P

# Fife

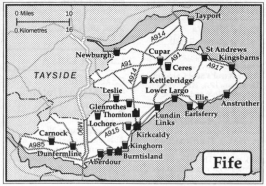

*Authority area covered: Fife UA*

## Aberdour

### Aberdour Hotel

38 High Street (A921)
☎ (01383) 860325
4–11 (11.45 Thu); 11–midnight Fri &
Sat (& Mon–Wed in summer); 12–
11.45 Sun

**Beer range varies** H
Dating from the 17th century,
this friendly family-run old
coaching inn is situated in one
of Fife's picturesque coastal
villages. Through the arch lies
a cobbled yard and stables
where an annual beer festival is
held. Three guest beers are on
tap. Lunches served in
summer. Limited parking
available. Eleven recently
refurbished en suite
bedrooms.
🏨 Q ❀ 🛏 ◐ ▶ ♿ ⇌ P

## Anstruther

### Dreel Tavern

High Street
☎ (01333) 310727
11–midnight

**Alloa Arrol's 80/-; Orkney
Dark Island; guest beers** H
Refurbished, stone-built pub
by a ford over Dreel Burn,
allegedly once used by King
James V. A popular pub for its
food.
🏨 Q ◐ ▶ ♣

## Burntisland

### Crown Tavern

19 Links Place (off High St)
☎ (01592) 873697
4 (12 Fri & Sat, 12.30 Sun)–11

**Belhaven Sandy Hunter's Ale;
guest beer** H
Well-appointed, two-roomed
lounge bar near the beach and
opposite the town's links,
where a summer-long fun fair
is situated. Snacks include
renowned Pillan's Pies.
🍴 ⇌ ♣

## Carnock

### Old Inn

6 Main Street (A907, 4 miles W
of Dunfermline)
☎ (01383) 850381
12–11 (midnight Fri & Sat, & Mon–Thu
in summer); 12.30–11.30 Sun

**Maclay 80/-; guest beers** H
Traditional, cottage-style,
two-bar pub, the centre of
village life and catering for all.
The bar is functional, with a
games area, while the lounge is
pleasantly comfortable. Busy
restaurant for eve meals,
serving good value food. Two
guest beers. Wheelchair WC.
❀ ◐ ▶ 🍴 ♿ ♣ P

## Ceres

### Brands Inn

High Street ☎ (01334) 828325
11.30–3, 5.30–midnight (1am Fri);
11–midnight Sat; 12.30–11.30 Sun

**Beer range varies** H
Pleasantly restored village inn
beside the Folk Museum.
Interesting mirrors, and a
games room where children
are welcome, are features. Two
real ales always available.
🏨 Q ◐ 🍴 ♣

### Ceres Inn

The Cross (B939)
☎ (01334) 828305
11–2.30, 5 (6 Tue)–11 (1am Thu & Fri,
midnight Sat)

**Beer range varies** H
Single bar lined with dark
wooden walls which are
covered with memorabilia.
Pool table in an alcove;
restaurant downstairs. One
Belhaven beer and one guest
beer on sale. ◐ ▶ ♣ P

## Cupar

### Drookit Dug

43 Bonnygate
☎ (01334) 655862

11–1am; 12.30–midnight Sun

**Alloa Arrol's 80/-; guest
beers** H
Lively, noisy, town-centre bar:
one wood-panelled room
drawing a young clientele. Real
ale promotions Sun. 🍴 ◁

## Dunfermline

### City Hotel

18 Bridge Street (opp. city
chambers)
☎ (01383) 722538
11 (12.30 Sun)–11

**Maclay 80/-, Wallace; guest
beers** H
Coaching inn from around
1775, now a prestigious town-
centre hotel. The cask beers are
in the ground floor bar which
is comfortable, if lacking a little
atmosphere. Close to the
Abbey. Children welcome.
Q ☆ 🛏 ◐ ▶ ♿ ⇌ P

### Coady's

16 Pilmuir Street (near bus
station) ☎ (01383) 736057
11–midnight; 12.30–11 Sun

**Theakston Best Bitter; guest
beer** H
Busy, friendly, street-corner
local with wooden floorboards,
a back sitting room and a pool
room upstairs; named after an
Irish painter whose works
adorn the walls. Public car
park opposite. ⇌ ♣

## Earlsferry

### Golf Tavern, 19th Hole

Links Road ☎ (01333) 330610
11–midnight (1am Fri); 12.30–11 Sun
(11–2.30, 5–midnight Oct–April)

**Caledonian Deuchars IPA;
Maclay 80/-; guest beers** H
This traditional bar and lounge
attract locals and visitors alike.
The golf links provide the view
whilst the friendly staff
provide good quality, well-
priced food. Children welcome
until 8. 🏨 Q ☆ ◐ ▶ 🍴 ▲ ♣

## Elie

### Ship Inn

The Toft (by Elie harbour)
☎ (01333) 330246
11–midnight; 12.30–11 Sun

**Belhaven 80/-** H
Pub renovated in traditional
style, with a stone-flagged floor
and original beams. The inn
dates back to 1838 and has
three dining areas and fine
views over the harbour. The
garden is tented over in July

---

🍺 **INDEPENDENT
BREWERIES**

**Backdykes:** Thornton

**Burntisland:** Burntisland

**Fyfe:** Kirkcaldy

391

and Aug and features live jazz.
🏰 Q 🍺 🕭 ◐ ▶ 🍴 ▲ ♣

## Glenrothes

### Glenrothes Snooker Club

Plot 7, Caskieberran Road (off B921) ☎ (01592) 758916
11 (12 Sun)–11 (midnight Thu–Sat)
**Alloa Arrol's 80/-; Ind Coope Burton Ale; guest beer** Ⓗ
Plush lounge bar, more like a pub than a club. The central bar area has leather armchairs and couches and is surrounded by private snooker rooms. No entry restrictions.
♿ ♣ P

## Kettlebridge

### Kettlebridge Inn

9 Cupar Road (A92 Glenrothes road) ☎ (01337) 830232
11.30–2.30, 5–11 (4.30–midnight Fri & Sat); 12.30–11 Sun
**Belhaven Sandy Hunter's Ale, 80/-, St Andrew's Ale; guest beers** Ⓗ
Great little country inn, well refurbished; a small bar, plus a restaurant. Local CAMRA *Pub of the Year* 1994. Eve meals finish at 8.30 (not served Mon).
🏰 Q 🍺 ◐ ▶

## Kinghorn

### Auld Hoose

8 Nethergate (off A921) ☎ (01592) 891074
12 (12.30 Sun)–midnight
**Broughton Greenmantle Ale; guest beers** Ⓐ
Busy sidestreet pub. Pool table in the refurbished public bar; the lounge is peaceful. Handy for the beach. Four guest beers.
🏰 🍺 ♿ ♣ ♣

### Ship Tavern

2 Bruce Street (A921) ☎ (01592) 890655
12 (11 Sat, 12.30 Sun)–midnight
**Caledonian Deuchars IPA; guest beers** Ⓗ
Traditional, wood-panelled gem. Fine bar counter and ornate gantry; the jug bar remains, too, in one of the best surviving pub interiors in the Kingdom. Two guest beers. Meals in summer.
🏰 Q 🍺 ◐ ▶ ♿ 🚃 ♣ P

## Kingsbarns

### Cambo Arms Hotel

5 Main Street ☎ (01334) 880226
11–11 (midnight Fri & Sat); 12.30–11 Sun
**Belhaven 80/-, St Andrew's Ale; guest beer** Ⓗ
Hotel with a traditional, cosy bar and a comfy sitting room. Good food (eve meals in summer).
🏰 Q 🍺 🕭 ◐ ▶ ♣ P

## Kirkcaldy

### Betty Nicol's

297 High Street (E end) ☎ (01592) 642083
11 (12.30 Sun)–11 (midnight Wed–Sat); 12.30–2.30, 6.30–11 winter Sun)
**Alloa Arrol's 80/-; Caledonian Deuchars IPA; Harviestoun Schiehallion; Ind Coope Burton Ale; Tetley Bitter; guest beers** Ⓗ
Two-roomed ale house with restored tiled walls in the public bar. The marvellous back room has a coal fire and folk music (Thu). Try the sarnies – known as 'hoagies'; lunches served Fri and Sat. Two guest beers.
🏰 Q 🕭 ▲ ♣ ⌣

### Harbour Bar

471–473 High Street (opp. harbour) ☎ (01592) 264270
11–2.30, 5–11; 11–midnight Fri & Sat; 12.30–midnight Sun
**Belhaven St Andrew's Ale; Fyfe Auld Alliance; guest beers** Ⓗ
Marvellous, unspoilt boozer with a rare jug bar and lovely etched windows. The public bar has murals depicting the town's whaling past. Home of the Fyfe Brewing Company. Excellent pies; four guest beers.
Q 🍺 ♿ ♣ ♣

## Leslie

### Burn's Tavern

184 High Street (A911) ☎ (01592) 741345
11–11 (midnight Wed–Sat); 12.30–midnight Sun
**Beer range varies** Ⓗ
Busy local with a narrow public bar which leads through to a games area. The lounge has karaoke at weekends. Three guest beers. No food Sun. 🏰 🕭 ♿ 🚽

## Lochore

### Miners' Welfare Society Social Club

1 Lochleven Road (B920) ☎ (01592) 860358
12–3.30, 6–11; 11.30–11.30 Sat; 12.30–11.30 Sun
**Maclay 70/-** Ⓐ
Large club, with a public bar, lounge, two dance halls and an upstairs games room, in what was once part of Fife's thriving coalfield. Non-members must be signed in but are made most welcome.
Q 🍺 ♿ ♿ ♣ P

## Lower Largo

### Railway Inn

The Harbour ☎ (01333) 320239
11–midnight; 12.30–11 Sun

**Beer range varies** Ⓗ
Robinson Crusoe's local: a one-room, low-roofed bar which offers a welcome to all.
Q 🍺 🍺 ▲ ♣

## Lundin Links

### Coachmans (Old Manor Hotel)

Leven Road ☎ (01333) 320368
11–3, 5–11
**Beer range varies** Ⓗ
Although predominantly a restaurant, this inn continues to see good ale as an essential accompaniment to good food. Continually changing guest ales.
Q 🍴 ◐ ▶ P

## Newburgh

### Abbey Inn

East Port, Cupar Road (E end of High St) ☎ (01337) 840761
11 (12.30 Sun)–11 (midnight Thu & Sat, 1am Fri)
**Beer range varies** Ⓗ
Fine village inn with a bar and an attractive lounge, offering four ales in summer, two in winter, and excellent meals.
Q 🍺 🍴 ◐ ▶ ♿ ♣

## St Andrews

### Aikman's (Cellar Bar)

32 Bell Street ☎ (01334) 477425
11–3, 5–midnight; 11–11.45 Sat; 6.30–11 Sun
**Belhaven 80/-; guest beers** Ⓗ
Basement lounge below a bistro, popular with students: a long-standing outpost of quality ale. ◐ ▶

### Whey Pat Tavern

1 Bridge Street (opp. West Port) ☎ (01334) 477740
11–11.30 (11.45 Fri & Sat); 12–11.30 Sun
**Theakston XB; guest beers** Ⓗ
Well-run town pub, popular with students. Named after a pot for making whey brose. Two guest beers. ◐ ♣

## Tayport

### Bell Rock

4–6 Dalgliesh Street (opp. harbour) ☎ (01382) 552388
11 (12.30 Sun)–midnight (1am Thu & Fri)
**Beer range varies** Ⓗ
Busy bar with a strong nautical flavour: a split-level room with a games and function area upstairs. Bargains for pensioners. At least three beers at all times. Children's certificate. Q 🍺 ◐ ▲ ♣

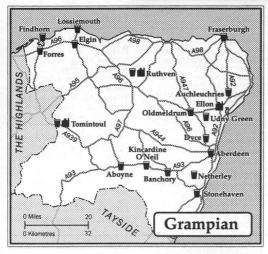

**Grampian**

*Authority areas covered: Aberdeenshire UA, City of Aberdeen UA, Moray UA*

## Aberdeen

### Atholl Hotel
54 Kings Gate (½ mile from ring road) ☎ (01224) 323505
11–2.30, 5–11; 11–2, 5–11.30 Fri & Sat; 12.05–2.30, 6.30–11 Sun
**Courage Directors; Taylor Landlord; guest beers** H
Popular local hotel in an established residential area, enjoying a reputation for good food. Q 🚗 ◑ ▶ P

### Blue Lamp
121–123 Gallowgate
☎ (01224) 647472
11–midnight
**Caledonian Deuchars IPA, 80/-; Theakston Best Bitter** H; **Younger No. 3** A; **guest beers**
Set in a listed building, this pub consists of a small, traditional public bar and a large, modern, sympathetic lounge conversion, popular with students and hosting live bands regularly. Free jukebox. Different beers in each bar. Wheelchair access to the lounge only. ⊕ 㕧

### Carriages
101 Crown Street (below Brentwood Hotel)
☎ (01224) 595440
11–2.30, 5–midnight; 6–11.30 Sun, closed Sun lunch
**Boddingtons Bitter; Caledonian Deuchars IPA; Castle Eden Ale; Courage Directors; Flowers Original; guest beers** H
Very friendly, busy, city-centre bar offering an excellent and varied selection of ales (ten in all), plus bottled Belgian and German Weisse beers. Good food in both the bar and restaurant (open eves). Limited parking. 🚗 ◑ ▶ 㕧 P

### Cocky Hunters
504 Union Street
☎ (01224) 626720
11–midnight; 12.30–11 Sun
**Boddingtons Bitter; Caledonian 80/-; guest beers** H
Very popular, city-centre pub decorated with bric-a-brac. Live music nightly, but the entrance has wooden alcoves offering quieter surroundings. ◑ 㕒

### Donview
2 Ellon Road, Bridge of Don (A92 at River Don bridge, 2½ miles N of centre)
☎ (01224) 703239
11–midnight; 12.30–11 Sun
**Ind Coope Burton Ale; guest beers** H
Pub handy for the beach, riverside walks, and bird and seal watching. Food is served in the lounge bar. Live music Fri eve. 🍻 ◑ ▶ ⊕ P

### Dutch Mill Hotel
7 Queens Road
☎ (01224) 322555
11 (12.30 Sun)–midnight
**Boddingtons Bitter; Courage Directors; McEwan 80/-; guest beer** H
Large lounge bar in a West End hotel, with a conservatory and a small, elevated patio area. A popular venue for TV sports. ❀ 🚗 ◑ ▶ P

### Ferryhill House Hotel
169 Bon Accord Street
☎ (01224) 590867
11–11; 11.30–midnight Fri & Sat; 12.30–11 Sun
**Caledonian 80/-; Taylor Landlord; Theakston Best Bitter; guest beer** H
City-centre hotel with a large garden and outdoor drinking area. The bar features wood panelling and a subdued tartan theme, with an open fireplace. Families welcome. The attractive conservatory is relaxed and comfortable. 🍻 Q ❀ 🚗 ◑ ▶ P

### Globe
13 North Silver Street
☎ (01224) 624528
11–midnight; 12.30–5 Sun
**Boddingtons Bitter; guest beers** H
Pleasant, open, one-roomed pub, popular with office workers and theatre-goers. Try spotting the stars! Booking is advisable for meals; a free buffet is served from 6pm Fri (no eve meals Fri). Open 11.30 Sun for coffee and breakfast. ◑ ▶ 㕒

### Macandrew's
6 Crown Street
☎ (01224) 583724
11–midnight; 12.30–11 Sun
**Broughton Black Douglas; Caledonian Deuchars IPA; Orkney Raven Ale; guest beers** H
Good restoration of a 'people's palace' pub with beautiful ceilings, stocking a wide range of Scottish independent brewery beers. Live bands. ◑ ▶ 㕒

### Mains of Scotstown Inn
1 Jesmond Square East, Bridge of Don ☎ (01224) 825222
11–11 (midnight Thu-Sat)
**Draught Bass; Maclay Wallace** H
A bar, lounge and a restaurant in a popular local with a good food reputation. Darts in the bar. Various regular functions are organised by the owners who work at making this pub popular. ◑ ▶ ⊕ ♣ P

### Moorings
2 Trinity Quay (harbour front)
☎ (01224) 587062
11–midnight; 12.30–11 Sun
**Beer range varies** H
Five guest beers are sold in this haven for heavy rock and real ale. Not for those looking for a quiet pint! ◑ 㕒

| 🍺 INDEPENDENT BREWERIES | | |
| --- | --- | --- |
| **Aberdeenshire:** Ellon | | |
| **Borve:** Ruthven | | |
| **Tomintoul:** Tomintoul | | |

## Old Blackfriars

52 Castle Street
☎ (01224) 581992
11–midnight; 12.30–11 Sun
**Caledonian Deuchars IPA,
80/-; Ind Coope Burton Ale;
Tetley Bitter; guest beers** Ⓗ
Pub where a fine combination
of old and new creates a
warm and welcoming
atmosphere. Imaginative use
of stained-glass displays
behind the bar; plenty of
nooks and crannies. Families
welcome. Coffee served
from 10am.
Q ⓓ ▶ & ⇌

## Olde Frigate

57 Netherkirkgate (near M&S)
☎ (01224) 640505
11 (12.30 Sun)–11
**Beer range varies** Ⓗ
Small, pleasant, recently
refurbished pub (cask beer in
the bar only). A friendly local,
hosting a darts league.
ⓓ ⓔ ⇌ ♣

## Palm Court Hotel

81 Seafield Road (400 yds W of
Anderson Drive, ring road)
☎ (01224) 312707
11 (12 Sun)–11 (midnight Wed–Sat)
**Caledonian Deuchars IPA;
guest beer** Ⓗ
Popular lounge bar in a
refurbished hotel, drawing a
mix of locals and office
workers. Big screen TV sport,
but quiet corners can be found.
Good, home-cooked food
from an extensive menu.
Wheelchair access to the
function suite. 📫 ⓓ ▶ P

## Prince of Wales

5 St Nicholas Lane
☎ (01224) 640597
11–11.45; 12.30–10.45 Sun
**Draught Bass; Caledonian
80/-; Theakston Old Peculier;
Younger No. 3; guest beers** Ⓗ
Friendly, unspoilt city-centre
pub where a long, traditional
bar boasts two fine gantries.
Occasional live music at the
back of the pub. Good,
wholesome lunches (Mon–Sat).
Q ⓓ ⇌ ♣

## Tilted Wig

55 Castle Street (opp. court
house)
☎ (01224) 583248
12–midnight; 7–11 Sun, closed Sun
lunch
**Alloa Arrol's 80/-; Caledonian
Deuchars IPA, 80/-; Ind Coope
Burton Ale; Marston's
Pedigree; Tetley Bitter; guest
beers** Ⓗ
Bar brimming and bouncing
with friendly folk, where legal
eagles and fallen angels mix
and match. Regular quiz
nights. Food till late. The
comfiest bar stools in town.
ⓓ ▶ & ⇌ ♣

# Aboyne

## Boat Inn

Charleston Road (N bank of
River Dee, by road bridge)
☎ (0133 98) 86137
11–2.30, 5–11 (midnight Fri);
11–midnight Sat; 11–11 Sun
**Draught Bass; guest beer** Ⓗ
Old-style, riverside inn with an
emphasis on food in the
lounge. Popular with walkers
and holidaymakers. Children
welcome – ask to see the train-
set. 🚲 Q ⊛ ⓓ ▶ ⓔ Å P

# Auchleuchries

## Halfway House

On A92, Fraserburgh road, 5
miles N of Ellon
☎ (01385) 711229
11–2.30, 5–midnight; 11–midnight Sat;
12.30–11 Sun
**Beer range varies** Ⓗ
Small, friendly, family-run
country pub. Tillie lamps
feature in the lounge. Cask
beer is on tap in the lounge
only. Freshly prepared food.
🚲 ⊛ ⓓ ▶ ⓔ & Å ♣ P

# Banchory

## Ravenswood Club,
## Royal British Legion

Ramsay Road
☎ (01330) 822347
11–2.30, 5–11; 11–midnight Sat; 12–11
Sun
**Beer range varies** Ⓗ
Friendly club offering value for
money. Members are always
on hand to welcome passing
guests (bring this guide).
⊛ 📫 ⓓ ▶ & Å ♣ P

## Scott Skinner's

North Deeside Road (A93)
☎ (01330) 824393
11–3, 5–11.30 (midnight Thu–Fri);
11–midnight Sat; 12–11 Sun
**Draught Bass, guest beers** Ⓗ
Converted croft on the east
side of town which offers a
play area, a games room and a
varied choice of ales.
🚲 ⊛ ⓓ ▶ Å ♣ P

# Dyce

## Tap & Spile

Aberdeen Airport Terminal
(off A96, 6 miles from
Aberdeen centre)
☎ (01224) 722331
8am–10pm (7pm winter Sat); 12.30–10
Sun
**Beer range varies** Ⓗ
Welcoming haven if your flight
is delayed, or a good welcome
home from holidays: a smart,
open lounge bar from which
you can see your luggage
arrive on the carousel. Snacks
available. & ♣ P ✄

# Elgin

## Newmarket Lounge
## Bar

301 High Street
☎ (01343) 548733
11–11 (12.30 Wed, Fri & Sat)
**Theakston Best Bitter;
Younger No. 3; guest beer** Ⓗ
Friendly, refurbished town-
centre pub. Å ⇌ ♣

## Sunninghill Hotel

Hay Street (opp. Moray
College) ☎ (01343) 547799
11–2.30, 5–11
**Boddingtons Bitter; Ind
Coope Burton Ale; guest
beer** Ⓗ
Small, pleasant, friendly
lounge in a family-run hotel.
Limited, but varied, menu and
a good choice of snacks.
⊛ 📫 ⓓ ▶ Å ⇌ P ⛫

# Findhorn

## Crown & Anchor Inn

☎ (01309) 690243
11–11 (11.45 Thu, 12.30am Fri & Sat);
12–11.45 Sun
**Draught Bass; Boddingtons
Bitter; guest beers** Ⓗ
Pub with two beamed bars and
a dining area, situated in the
centre of picturesque Findhorn,
a haven for watersports and
wildlife. Good selection of
three or four guest beers and a
wide variety of good pub food.
Children welcome in the
dining area.
🚲 🛥 ⊛ 📫 ⓓ ▶ ⓔ & Å ♣ P

## Kimberley Inn

☎ (01309) 690492
11–11 (11.45 Thu, 12.30am Fri & Sat);
12.30–11.45 Sun
**Tetley Bitter; guest beers** Ⓗ
Very popular, friendly, one-bar
pub with a pool room. Bay
views from the front patio.
Three guest beers and good
food at reasonable prices.
Children's certificate until 8.
🚲 Q ⊛ ⓓ ▶ Å ♣

# Forres

## Carisbrooke Hotel

Drumduan Road (½ mile off
A96, E end of Forres)
☎ (01309) 672582
11–11 (11.45 Tue & Thu, 12.30 Fri &
Sat)
**Boddingtons Bitter; Marston's
Pedigree; guest beer** Ⓗ
Cosy, two-bar, extended small
hotel on the outskirts of town.
Families welcome.
🚲 ⊛ 📫 ⓓ ▶ & ♣ P

# Fraserburgh

## Crown Bar

125 Shore Street (alley between
Broad St and Shore St)

☎ (01346) 518452
11–11.30 (12.30am Fri, midnight Sat);
12.30–11.30 Sun
**Beer range varies** Ⓗ
Unspoilt, cosy bar overlooking
the harbour; a gem in a real ale
desert. Note the vintage
Guinness font. The lounge bar
(no real ale) opens weekends
only. Its 18th consecutive year
in this guide.
🏠 ♣

## Kincardine O'Neil

### Gordon Arms Hotel
☎ (0133 98) 84236
12 (11.30 Sat & Sun)–midnight
**Beer range varies** Ⓗ
Large inn in an historic
Deeside village offering
excellent food and
accommodation. Salmon
fishing can be arranged.
Children welcome in the
lounge.
🌢 🚗 ◁ ▶ 🏠

## Lossiemouth

### Skerry Brae Hotel
Stotfield Road (near golf course
and RAF station)
☎ (01343) 812040
11–11 (11.45 Wed, 12.30am Thu–Sat)
**Boddingtons Bitter; guest
beer** Ⓗ
Very popular hotel on the
outskirts of the village, with
views over the sea and golf
course, and an extended one-
room bar with a pool table. It
specialises in steak and seafood
meals. Families welcome in the
conservatory.
🏨 🌢 ✿ ◁ ▶ ⅋ ▲ ♣ P

## Netherley

### Lairhillock Inn
On B979 ☎ (01596) 30001
11–midnight; 12.30–3.30, 6.30–11 Sun
**Courage Directors; Flowers
Original; McEwan 80/-** Ⓐ;
**guest beers** Ⓗ

Pub set in rolling countryside –
look out for 'inn' on the roof. A
large central open fire features
in the lounge; the public bar
has two fires and a very
friendly atmosphere.
Marvellous food. Families
welcome in the conservatory.
🏨 Q 🌢 ✿ ◁ ▶ P

## Oldmeldrum

### Redgarth
Kirk Brae (off A947)
☎ (01651) 872353
11 (11.30 Sun)–2.30, 5 (5.30 Sun)–11
(11.45 Fri & Sat)
**Caledonian 80/-; guest
beers** Ⓗ/Ⓖ
Superb guest ales,
imaginatively chosen by a
cheery host, are served in this
comfortable lounge bar. Varied
menu of good value, freshly
home-cooked food (including
vegetarian specialities).
Caledonian 80/- is sold as
Redgarth Ale. Fine views from
the garden.
Q 🌢 ✿ 🚗 ◁ ▶ ⅋ ♣ P

## Ruthven

### Borve Brew House
Off A96, Aberdeen–Keith road,
NE of Huntly OS506469
☎ (01466) 760343
12.30–11 (11.45 Fri & Sat)
**Borve Ale, Tall Ships IPA** Ⓗ
Bar in a converted primary
school with a coal stove and a
pool table. Two handpumps
dispense the pub's own
unusual, smoky beer. If
deserted, call at the house next
door to the brewery. The
cheapest real ale in the district!
🏨 Q ⅋ ♣ P

## Stonehaven

### Marine Hotel
Shorehead (harbourside)
☎ (01569) 762155

11–midnight; 12–11 Sun
**Draught Bass; Taylor
Landlord; guest beers** Ⓗ
Traditional, wood-panelled bar
which always stocks unusual
guest beers. Lined glasses, a
classic jukebox, a pool room
and a picturesque harbourside
location are further
attractions. No children in the
bar; the family room is
upstairs.
🏨 🌢 ✿ 🚗 ◁ ▶ 🏠 ▲ 🔔

## Tomintoul

### Glen Avon Hotel
1 The Square
☎ (01807) 580218
11 (12.30 Sun)–11 (11.45 Fri & Sat)
**Beer range varies** Ⓗ
Cosy and welcoming, village
pub set on the edge of the
Cairngorms, used by walkers
and handy for skiers on the
Lecht. Look out for odes to
locals and an interesting
Drambuie haggis starter.
One beer from Tomintoul
Brewery is always on
sale.
🏨 Q 🚗 ◁ ▶ ⅋ ▲ ♣

## Udny Green

### Udny Green Hotel
On B999, Aberdeen–Tarves
road, 1 mile S of
Pitmedden ☎ (01651) 842337
12–3, 6–11 (1am Fri); 12–3, 5.30–11.45
Sat; 12.30–3, 5.30–11 Sun
**Beer range varies** Ⓗ
200-year-old, Grade II listed
building in a conservation
village. Cask beer is served in
the lounge, which is modern
and makes generous use
of pine. Children's
certificate and garden play
area. One beer on tap in
the winter, two in
summer.
Q 🌢 ✿ ◁ ▶ 🏠 ⅋ ♣ P

---

# HELP US TOP 50,000!

The success of a consumer movement like CAMRA lies in its grass
roots support. Our members are a vital source of information
about the pub and brewing scene in their various parts of the UK.
They help to improve the local drinking environment by ensuring
brewers and publicans are aware of pub-users' concerns – essential
activity which complements national initiatives like the lobbying of
Parliament, the annual prices survey and the publication of the *Good
Beer Guide*. If you share CAMRA's views on the brewing industry,
and believe that choice and quality should be the watchwords in our
pubs, please join us. You may be the person that takes our
membership over 50,000, we're that close! See details at the back of
this book.

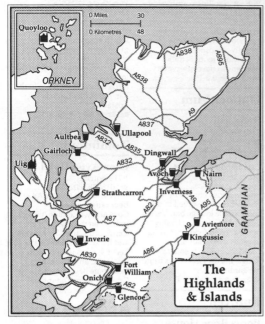

*Authority areas covered: Highland UA, Orkney Islands UA, Shetland Islands UA, Western Isles UA*

## Aultbea

### Drumchork Lodge Hotel
450 yds above A832, at southern edge of village
☎ (01445) 731242
11–11 (1am Fri, 11.30 Sat); 12.30–11 Sun
**Bateman XXXB; guest beers** Ⓗ
Popular, family-run holiday hotel with splendid views over Loch Ewe and of west coast sunsets. Owned by an ex-Lincolnshire publican, this old shooting lodge stands in a lovely walking area; very peaceful. One or two guest beers. 🛏 ◑ ▶ ⊟ ♣ P

## Aviemore

### Winking Owl
Grampian Road (main street)
☎ (01479) 810646
11–midnight; 12.30–11 Sun
**Alloa Arrol's 80/-; Ind Coope Burton Ale; Tetley Bitter; guest beers** Ⓗ
Pub conversion from a farm building many years ago, well-patronised by skiers, hill-walkers and locals. One of the guest beers is from the nearby brewery at Tomintoul.
❀ ◑ ▶ ▲ ⇥ P

## Avoch

### Station Hotel
Bridge Street
☎ (01381) 620246
11–2.30, 5–11 (midnight Fri); 11–11.30 Sat & Sun
**Beer varies** Ⓗ
Busy local in a pleasant Black Isle fishing village, with a friendly atmosphere. Children's play area in the garden. Popular at weekends for good value food, served all day.
❀ ◑ ▶ ♣ P

## Dingwall

### National Hotel
High Street
☎ (01349) 862166
11–midnight (1am Fri, 11 Sun)
**Alloa Arrol's 80/-; Caledonian 80/-; Ind Coope Burton Ale; Orkney Dark Island; guest beers** Ⓗ
Real ale is served in the bar (situated in a modern extension) of this 1930s-style town-centre hotel: comfortable, but utilitarian, with a friendly atmosphere. Mini-beer fests are held occasionally, with up to 20 guest ales.
❀ 🏠 ◑ ▶ ⇥ P

## Fort William

### Alexandra Hotel
The Parade ☎ (01397) 702241
11 (12.30 Sun)–11
**Draught Bass; Caledonian Deuchars IPA, 80/-** Ⓗ
Bright, friendly, lounge bar in the town's main hotel; modern-looking and nicely decorated, although built in the last century. Popular with coach parties. Live music most nights. Good value food in the restaurant next to the bar, which is frequented by hill-walkers.
🛏 ❀ 🏠 ◑ ▶ & ▲ ⇥ P

### Grog & Gruel
66 High Street (pedestrian precinct) ☎ (01397) 705078
11–11.45 (12.45am Thu–Sat)
**Alloa Arrol's 80/-; Ind Coope Burton Ale; Tetley Bitter; guest beers** Ⓗ
Recently refurbished pub, bought by the owners of the famous Clachaig Inn. Church pew seating is a feature. Meals served most of the day in the restaurant upstairs (Tex-Mex food a speciality). Up to six guest beers. ◑ ▶ & ▲

## Gairloch

### Old Inn
The Harbour
☎ (01445) 712006
11 (11.30 Sat)–midnight; 12.30–11 Sun
**Beer range varies** Ⓗ
Small Highland hotel in a picturesque setting by a burn and an old bridge. Popular all year round, with sailors, walkers and climbers; quite busy in the holiday season. Safe garden for children. Beer fest in May.
Q ❀ 🏠 ◑ ▶ ⊟ ▲ ♣ P

## Glencoe

### Clachaig Inn
On old riverside road, at rear of NT centre ☎ (01855) 811252
11 (12.30 Sun)–11 (midnight Fri, 11.30 Sat)
**Alloa Arrol's 80/-; Ind Coope Burton Ale; guest beers** Ⓗ
Busy tourists' pub, flanked by some of Britain's highest mountains. Every day, climbers and hill-walkers descend to slake their thirsts in the public bar. Live folk music. Annual beer festival. Restaurant open 6–8.
🛏 ❀ 🏠 ◑ ▶ & P

---

🍺 **INDEPENDENT BREWERIES**

**Isle of Skye:** Uig

**Orkney:** Quoyloo

### Kings House Hotel
200 yds off A82, 11 miles S of
Glencoe village OS260546
☎ (01855) 851259
11–midnight (1am Wed–Sat)
**Alloa Arrol's 80/-; Caledonian
80/-** H
Welcoming oasis for walkers,
climbers and travellers,
situated in splendid isolation
where the Glencoe Mountains
give way to Rannoch Moor.
Look out for the tame deer in
the car park. 🏚 ❀ ◐ ▶ ▲ P

## Inverie

### Old Forge
Regular ferry from Mallaig; no
connection by road OS766000
☎ (01687) 462267
11–midnight
**Draught Bass; guest beers**
(summer) H
The most remote pub in
Britain, 107 miles from the
nearest city, and one hour by
ferry from the nearest town;
cited in the *Guinness Book of
Records* and extensively used
by yachtsmen and hill-walkers.
Fine views over Loch Nevis.
Food at all hours. Frequent
impromptu folk music
sessions. 🏚 Q ❀ ◐ ▶ 🕹 ▲ ♣

## Inverness

### Blackfriars
93–95 Academy Street
☎ (01463) 233881
11–11 (1am Thu & Fri, 11.45 Sat)
**Marston's Pedigree;
Theakston Best Bitter, Old
Peculier; guest beers** H
Very well-managed, beer
drinkers' pub with a good
selection of foreign beers; one
large bar with snug alcoves.
Speciality pies are available
most of the day. Very loud
music Wed and Thu eves most
weeks. ◐ ▶ ⇌ ♨

### Clachnaharry Inn
17–19 High Street (Beauly
road, western outskirts of
town) ☎ (01463) 239806
11–11 (midnight Thu & Fri, 11.45 Sat);
12.30–11 Sun
**McEwan 80/-; guest beers** H

300-year-old coaching inn
overlooking the railway, the
Beauly Firth and the sea lock of
the Caledonian Canal. The
garden was once the platform
of the old station. Up to three
guest beers.
🏚 ☎ ❀ ◐ ▶ ⊟ ♣ P

### Phoenix
108 Academy Street
☎ (01463) 233685
11–11 (12.30am Thu & Fri, 11.30 Sat);
12.30–11 Sun
**Draught Bass; Worthington
Bitter; guest beers** H
Busy, town-centre pub
drawing a mixed clientele to its
traditional public bar with
sawdust strewn floors and a
rare example of an island bar.
The lounge is due to become a
Scottish theme bar.
☎ ◐ ▶ ⊟ ♨ ▲ ⇌ ✂

## Kingussie

### Royal Hotel
High Street ☎ (01540) 661898
11–midnight (1am Thu–Sat); 12.30–
midnight Sun
**Alloa Arrol's 80/-; Ind Coope
Burton Ale; Tetley Bitter;
guest beers** H
Extended, spacious, old
coaching inn, still popular with
coach parties. The large lounge
bar serves good value food
with music accompaniment at
weekends. Special beer prices
and bargain accommodation
Nov–early Dec. Up to ten guest
beers.
☎ ❀ 🛏 ◐ ▶ ♨ ▲ ⇌ ♣ P ✂

## Nairn

### Claymore House Hotel
Seabank Road (off A96)
☎ (01667) 453731
12–11.30 (12.30am Fri & Sat)
**Boddingtons Bitter; guest beer**
(summer) H
Pleasant, friendly bar with a
cosy fireside dining area,
situated in Nairn's West End,
en route to the golf course and
West Beach: a popular venue
for bar suppers. Children's
certificate. Live jazz Mon.
🏚 Q ❀ 🛏 ◐ ▶ P

### Invernairne Hotel
Thurlow Road (off Seabank
Rd) ☎ (01667) 452039
11–11.30 (12.30am Fri, midnight Sat)
**Isle of Skye Red Cuillin; guest
beer** H
Lovely wood-panelled bar in a
Victorian seaside hotel with a
panoramic view of Moray
Firth. A path through the
garden leads to West Beach
Promenade (alternate route to
town). Traditional high teas are
popular. Children's certificate.
🏚 Q ❀ 🛏 ◐ ▶ ♨ P

## Onich

### Nether Lochaber
By S terminal of Corran ferry,
200 yds off A82
☎ (01855) 821235
11–2.30, 5–11; 12.30–2.30, 6.30–11 Sun
**Draught Bass** H
Delightful, wee, family-run
bar, tucked behind the hotel on
the slipway to the ferry. The
hotel has been owned by the
same family for over 70 years.
Q ❀ 🛏 ◐ ▶ ▲ ♣ P

## Strathcarron

### Strathcarron Hotel
On A890, by the station at the
head of Loch Carron
☎ (01520) 722222
11–11 (may close earlier in winter)
**Theakston Best Bitter; guest
beers** H
Typical hill-walker's pub,
allowing free use of hotel
facilities for campers. Meals
served all day. It enjoys a
spectacular position,
overlooking Loch Carron on
the road to Skye.
🏚 ❀ 🛏 ◐ ▶ ▲ ⇌ ♣ ⌂ P

## Ullapool

### Ferryboat Inn
Shore Street ☎ (01854) 612366
11 (12.30 Sun)–11
**Beer range varies** H
Small, comfortable lounge bar
on the village waterfront, with
open views inland over Loch
Broom. Up to three beers.
🏚 Q ☎ 🛏 ◐ ▶ ▲

---

# CAMRA LOCAL GUIDES

In addition to its national publications, CAMRA also produces a
series of local guides to pubs and real ale. These are compiled and
published by individual CAMRA branches and usually cover every
single real ale pub in a given county or area. Prices range from
around £2.50 up to around £5, depending on the size of the book.

A catalogue of all the latest editions is available from the Products
Secretary at CAMRA, 230 Hatfield Road, St Albans, Hertfordshire
AL1 4LW, tel. (01727) 867201.

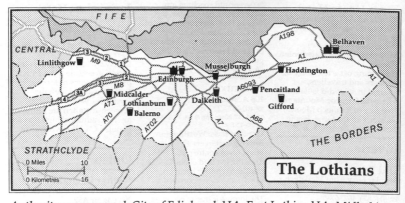

# The Lothians

## The Lothians

*Authority areas covered: City of Edinburgh UA, East Lothian UA, Midlothian UA, West Lothian UA*

## Balerno

### Johnsburn House

64 Johnsburn Road (off A70)
☎ (0131) 449 3847
12–3, 6.30–11.15; 12–12.15am Sat; 12.30–11.15 Sun; closed Mon
**Dent Bitter; Ind Coope Burton Ale; Theakston Best Bitter; guest beers** H
Baronial mansion dating from 1760 and now Grade B listed. Well-deserved reputation for meals. The cosy bar has a convivial atmosphere. Two guest beers. Children welcome.
🏚 Q ✿ ◁ ▶ ₺ ♣ P

## Belhaven

### Mason's Arms

8 High Street (A1087, ½ mile W of Dunbar) ☎ (01368) 863700
11–2.30 (not Wed), 5–11 (1am Fri); 11–midnight Sat; 12.30–5 Sun
**Beer varies** H
Friendly locals' bar close to the brewery, affording fine views to the Lammermuir Hills. Aviary in the back yard. Eve meals Fri and Sat. Q ▶ ⌂ ▲ ♣

## Dalkeith

### Black Bull

1 Lothian Street (off A68 S of shopping precinct)
☎ (0131) 663 2095
11 (12.30 Sun)–midnight
**Caledonian Deuchars IPA, 80/-; guest beers** H
Good example of a 'Gothenburg'; a busy, traditional bar with fine arched windows, cornice work and a well-crafted gantry. Large TV for sport. The quieter lounge is contrastingly modern. Children's certificate. Good facilities for customers with disabilities. Two guest beers.
✿ ◁ ⌂ ₺ ♣

## Edinburgh

### Baron Bailie

2–4 Lauriston Street (West Port off the Grassmarket)
☎ (0131) 229 3201
12 (12.30 Sun)–1am
**Caledonian Deuchars IPA, 80/-; Ind Coope Burton Ale; guest beers** H
Ale house on the fringe of the Old Town, attracting students. The fine selection on the jukebox is unashamedly played loud. Well-used pinball machine. Two guest beers are available.
₺ ♣

### Bow Bar

80 West Bow (between Royal Mile and Grassmarket)
☎ (0131) 226 7667
11–11.15; 7–11 Sun
**Draught Bass; Caledonian Deuchars IPA, 80/-, ERA; Courage Directors; guest beers** A
Traditional, one-room, stand-up bar with efficient, friendly service. Several extinct brewery mirrors and old cigarette ephemera cover the walls. Large selection of malts; four guest beers. Quality hot snacks.
Q

### Cask & Barrel

115 Broughton Street (between Leith Walk and Canonmills)
☎ (0131) 556 3132
11–12.30am (1am Thu–Sat); 12.30–midnight Sun
**Draught Bass; Caledonian Deuchars IPA, 80/-; guest beers** H
Spacious and extremely busy, suburban ale house with an imposing horseshoe bar, wooden floorboards and a splendid cornice. Collection of brewery mirrors (some quite rare). Ten handpumps dispense the beers. Wheelchair WC. ◁ ₺

### Cloisters Bar

26 Brougham Street (between Tollcross and the Meadows)
☎ (0131) 221 9997
11 (12.30 Sun)–midnight (12.30am Fri & Sat)
**Draught Bass; Caledonian Deuchars IPA, 80/-; Courage Directors** A**; guest beers** H
Ale house which reflects its previous use as a parsonage, with bare boards, church pews and a bar and gantry built from wood reclaimed from a redundant church. The walls are decorated with rare old brewery mirrors. Imaginative meals; five guest beers.
Q ◁

### Cumberland Bar

1–3 Cumberland Street (off Dundas St in New Town)
☎ (0131) 558 3134
12–11.30; 4–11 Sun
**Draught Bass; Caledonian Murrays Summer Ale, Deuchars IPA, 80/-** A**; guest beers** A/H
Completely rebuilt New Town bar, turned into a superb public bar with some peripheral seating and a cosy sitting room. Half-wood-panelling and rare old brewery mirrors feature. It is often extremely busy, but the service is fast. Eight guest beers are available.
🏚 Q ✿ ◁ ₺

### Golden Rule
30 Yeaman Place (off Dundee
St, near the S&N factory)
☎ (0131) 229 7399
11–11.30; 12.30–11 Sun
**Draught Bass; Caledonian
Deuchars IPA, 80/-;
Harviestoun Old Manor;
Orkney Dark Island; guest
beers** H
Split-level lounge bar in a
Victorian tenement which can
get extremely busy when Heart
of Midlothian are playing at
home. Five guest beers. Spicy
snacks served all day.
⊕

### Guildford Arms
1 West Register Street (behind
Burger King, at E end of
Princes St) ☎ (0131) 556 4312
11.30 (12.30 Sun)–11 (midnight Fri &
Sat)
**Draught Bass; Belhaven 60/-;
Caledonian Deuchars IPA** H,
**80/-** A; **Harviestoun 70/-;
Orkney Dark Island; guest
beers** H
Pub laid out with ornate
plasterwork and ceilings,
spectacular cornices and
friezes, window arches and
screens, and an unusual,
wood-panelled gallery bar
overlooking the busy main bar.
Five guest beers.
Q ◑ ⊕ ≠ (Waverley)

### Halfway House
24 Fleshmarket Close (between
Cockburn St and Waverley
station rear entrance)
☎ (0131) 225 7101
11 (12.30 Sun)–11.30 (1am Fri & Sat)
**Belhaven 70/-, 80/-; guest
beers** H
Cosy, friendly, wee, L-shaped
howff down an Old Town
close; often crowded and
smoky. Railway memorabilia
features. Two guest beers.
≠ (Waverley) ♣

### Home's Bar
102 Constitution Street
(between foot of Leith Walk
and The Shore)
☎ (0131) 553 7710
12–11 (midnight Thu, 1am Fri & Sat)
**Beer range varies** H
Fine, traditional, one-room
public bar with no frills.
Interesting decor includes
antique tin boxes and a
growing array of pumpclips
(500 guest beers so far). Folk
music Fri and Sat eves. Eight
handpumps. ◑ ♣

### K Jackson's
40–44 Lady Lawson Street
(West Port off the
Grassmarket)
☎ (0131) 228 4284
11–1am; 12.30–midnight Sun
**Draught Bass; Caledonian
Deuchars IPA, 80/-; guest
beers** H

Small, busy, one-room local
with friendly staff. Newly-
redecorated, it has had much-
needed smoke extractors
installed. Five guest beers.
♣ ⌂

### Leslie's Bar
45 Ratcliffe Terrace (between
Newington and The Grange)
☎ (0131) 667 5957
11–11 (11.30 Thu, 12.30am Fri, 11.45
Sat); 12.30–11.30 Sun
**Draught Bass; Belhaven 80/-;
Caledonian Deuchars IPA,
80/-; guest beer** H
Superb, busy, Victorian pub
with one of the finest interiors
in the city. A snob screen
separates the saloon and snug
from the public bar. Snacks
served. ⌖ Q ⊕ ♣

### Malt & Hops
45 The Shore (on the
waterfront at Leith)
☎ (0131) 555 0083
12 (12.30 Sun)–11 (midnight Thu, 1am
Fri & Sat)
**Alloa Arrol's 80/-; Ind Coope
Burton Ale; Marston's
Pedigree; Tetley Bitter; guest
beers** H
One-room public bar dating
from 1749, facing onto the
Water of Leith. It is said to be
haunted by the ghost of a
previous licensee who
drowned when the cellar
flooded. No food Sun. Large
pumpclip collection. Four
guest beers. ⌖ Q ◑ ♣ ⌂

### Navaar House Hotel
12 Mayfield Gardens (A7, 2
miles S of centre)
☎ (0131) 667 2828
12–midnight (1am Fri & Sat)
**Beer range varies** H
19th-century town house
converted into a modern hotel
with a large, comfortable
lounge bar. Jazz Tue eve. Up to
four guest beers.
❀ ⇐ ◑ ▶ ♣ P

### Oxford Bar
8 Young Street (between
George and Queen Sts, at West
End) ☎ (0131) 225 4262
11–1am (12.30am Sun)
**Belhaven 80/-, St Andrew's
Ale; guest beers** H
Tiny, yet vibrant, New Town
drinking shop, retaining signs
of its 19th-century parlour
arrangement. Two guest beers.
Q ♣

### Royal Ettrick Hotel
13 Ettrick Road (behind
Merchiston Tennis and
Bowling Club)
☎ (0131) 228 6413
11–midnight
**Draught Bass; Caledonian
80/-; Maclay Kane's Amber
Ale; guest beers** H
Built as a town house in 1875;
now a splendid, family-run
hotel, set in leafy suburbs. The

lounge bar is comfortably
appointed and the
conservatory is bright and airy.
A new extension is non-
smoking. Excellent meals; five
guest beers. Q ❀ ⇐ ◑ ▶ P ⌇

### Southsider
3–7 West Richmond Street
(near Surgeons' Hall)
☎ (0131) 667 2003
11.30 (11 Sat)–midnight (1am Fri);
12.30–11 Sun
**Maclay 70/-, 80/-, Kane's
Amber Ale, Wallace; guest
beers** H
Busy Southside lounge bar,
popular with discerning locals
and students. The public bar is
a handy refuge if the lounge
gets too smoky. Four guest
beers. ◑ ⊕ ♣ ⌂

### Starbank Inn
64 Laverockbank Road
(between Leith and Granton)
☎ (0131) 552 4141
11 (12.30 Sun)–11 (midnight Thu–Sat)
**Belhaven Sandy Hunter's Ale,
80/-, St Andrew's Ale; Taylor
Landlord; guest beers** H
Bright and airy, bare-boarded
ale house with three separate
areas. Decor includes rare
brewery mirrors, waiters' trays
and water jugs. Six guest beers.
Q ◑ ▶

### Winston's
20 Kirk Loan, Corstorphine (off
St John's Rd, A8)
☎ (0131) 539 7077
11–11.30 (midnight Fri & Sat);
12.30–11 Sun
**Alloa Arrol's 80/-; Caledonian
Deuchars IPA; Ind Coope
Burton Ale; guest beers** H
Not far from Edinburgh Zoo,
this is a smart suburban lounge
bar well favoured by locals.
Golfing and rugby themes play
their part in the decor. Two
guest beers. Q ◑ ⌾

## Gifford

### Tweeddale Arms Hotel
High Street (off B6355)
☎ (01620) 810240
11–11 (midnight Fri & Sat)
**Broughton Greenmantle Ale;
guest beers** H
Referred to in a 1687 deed as
the 'Great Inn of Gifford', this
attractive, whitewashed hotel
looks across the village green
to a 300-year-old avenue of
lime trees. The public bar, with
its large collection of
miniatures, attracts a loyal
local following. Three guest
beers. Children welcome.
⌖ ⇐ ◑ ▶ ⌾ ⌾ ♣

## Haddington

### Pheasant
72 Market Street
☎ (01620) 824428

11–11 (midnight Thu–Sat)
**Alloa Arrol's 80/-; Ind Coope Burton Ale; Tetley Bitter; guest beers** H

Vibrant and sometimes noisy pub attracting younger folk. A long, thin bar snakes through to a games area where Basil (surely a Norwegian Blue) oversees the pool table. Two guest beers. ♣

## Linlithgow

### Black Bitch Tavern
14 West Port (25 yds from A803/A706 jct)
☎ (01506) 842147
11 (12.30 Sun)–midnight
**Beer range varies** H

Established pub with separate bar and lounge, recently modernised. The oldest pub in Linlithgow. One or two beers may be on sale.
Q ❀ 🍴 ⅃ ⅃ ⅃ ♣

### Four Marys
65 High Street
☎ (01506) 842171
12–2.30, 5–11; 5–midnight Fri; 12–midnight Sat; 12.30–2.30, 7–11 Sun
**Belhaven 70/-, 80/-; Caledonian Deuchars IPA; Harviestoun Ptarmigan; guest beers** H

Attractive lounge with antique furniture and items reflecting the town's history. Nine handpumps serve constantly changing guest beers; large range of malt whiskies. No food Sun eve.
🍴 ▶ ⇌

## Lothianburn

### Steading
118 Biggar Road (A702, near dry ski slope)
☎ (0131) 445 1128
11–11.45; 12.30–11 Sun
**Caledonian Deuchars IPA, 80/-; Ind Coope Burton Ale; Orkney Dark Island; Taylor Landlord; guest beer** H

Stone cottages converted into an attractive bar and restaurant, with a conservatory extension: a popular eating establishment but there is still a drinking area where only snacks are served.
🏠 Q ❀ 🍴 ▶ ⅃ P

## Midcalder

### Torphichen Arms
36 Bank Street
☎ (01506) 880020
11 (12.30 Sun)–11 (midnight Thu–Sat)
**Caledonian Deuchars IPA, 80/-; Greenalls Shipstone's Bitter; Ind Coope Burton Ale; Orkney Dark Island; Taylor Landlord** H

Village local, originally several rooms, now one, L-shaped bar with public and lounge areas. Live music at weekends. Occasional beer festivals. Children's certificate.
❀ ▶ ♣ P

## Musselburgh

### Levenhall Arms
10 Ravenshaugh Road (B1348 near racecourse roundabout)
☎ (0131) 665 3220

11.30 (12.30 Sun)–11 (1am Thu–Sat)
**Caledonian Deuchars IPA, 80/-; Ind Coope Burton Ale; guest beer** H

Busy public bar popular with locals and racegoers. The building dates from 1830 and houses a functional three-room pub. A tram terminus once stood outside.
🍴 ⅃ ⅃ ♣ P

### Volunteer Arms (Stagg's)
78–81 High Street (behind Brunton Hall)
☎ (0131) 665 9654
11–2.30, 5–11; 11–11.30 Thu; 11–midnight Fri & Sat; closed Sun
**Caledonian Deuchars IPA, 80/-; guest beers** H

Run by the same family since 1858, this is a busy, traditional bar with dark wood panelling, defunct brewery mirrors and a superb gantry topped with old casks. A comfortable lounge to the rear has no real ale.
❀ ⅃ ⅃ ♣ P

## Pencaitland

### Old Smiddy Inn
On A6093 ☎ (01875) 340368
11.30–11 (midnight Fri & Sat); 12.30–11 Sun
**Caledonian Deuchars IPA, 80/-; guest beer** H

Previously the village smithy and now a friendly country inn with a large, comfortable lounge bar and a noted restaurant. High teas are popular Sun. Well worth seeking out. Glenkinchie distillery is nearby.
Q ❀ ▶ ⅃ ♣ P

---

# ENJOY THE BOTTLED BEER REVIVAL

Most drinkers associate the term 'real ale' with cask-conditioned beers, draught beers which ferment and mature in the cask at the pub until they are served. But some *bottled* beers are real ales, too. 'Bottle-conditioned' beers are not pasteurised or artificially carbonated. They contain yeast, just like cask-conditioned ales, and therefore continue to ferment and mature in a similar way.

In the early days of CAMRA, there were just five regular bottle-conditioned beers: Worthington White Shield, Gale's Prize Old Ale, Eldridge Pope's Thomas Hardy's Ale, Courage Imperial Russian Stout and the now sadly missed Guinness Original. These days around a hundred British bottled real ales, plus others from Belgium, Germany and other parts of the world, can be found, many of them stocked by the major supermarket chains.

So, if you fancy a night in, or are throwing a party, why not make sure you can enjoy the full, fresh flavour of living beer by bringing home some 'real ale in a bottle'? Look for the words 'bottle-conditioned' on the label.

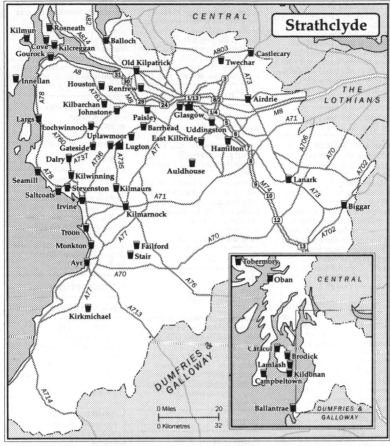

## Strathclyde

Authority areas covered: *Argyll & Bute UA, City of Glasgow UA, Dumbarton & Clydebank UA, East Ayrshire UA, East Dunbartonshire UA, East Renfrewshire UA, Inverclyde UA, North Ayrshire UA, North Lanarkshire UA, Renfrewshire UA, South Ayrshire UA, South Lanarkshire UA*

Note: Licensing laws permit no entry after 11pm to pubs in the following locations: Barrhead, Gourock, Houston, Johnstone, Kilbarchan, Lochwinnoch, Paisley, Renfrew and Uplawmoor

## Airdrie

### Cellar Bar
79 Stirling Street
11–midnight
**Beer range varies** H
Comfortable, split-level, town-centre lounge bar with over 300 whisky bottles on the gantry. Impromptu folk sessions Mon eve. ❀ ≠

## Auldhouse

### Auldhouse Arms
6 Langlands Road (from E Kilbride, right from Strathaven road, follow signs) OS624502
☎ (0135 52) 63242
11 (12.30 Sun)–11 (midnight Thu & Fri)
**Belhaven 80/-** A
Traditional Scottish village pub with several rooms warmed by well-fed fires; recently refurbished, but retaining its original character. The handpump activates an air pressure pump. Book eve meals. ♨ Q ☎ ◖▶ & P

## Ayr

### Burrowfields
13 Beresford Terrace
☎ (01292) 269152
11–12.30; 12.30–midnight Sun

**Theakston Best Bitter; guest beers** H
Pleasant, wood-panelled café/bar in a corner location in the town centre. Formerly an insurance office, it has been well converted in Art Deco style. Very handy for the station.
◖▶ & ≠

## Chestnuts Hotel

52 Racecourse Road (A719, S of centre) ☎ (01292) 264393
11 (12 Sun)–midnight
**Draught Bass; Broughton Special, Ghillie; guest beers** Ⓗ
Comfortable lounge bar with a vaulted ceiling and a collection of over 300 water jugs. Excellent bar meals. Garden play area; conveniently placed for the beach and two golf courses. Children's certificate.
🌢 Q ❀ 🛏 ◑ ▶ P

## Geordie's Byre

103 Main Street (200 yds over river towards Prestwick)
☎ (01292) 264925
11 (11.30 Sun)–11 (midnight Thu–Sat)
**Caledonian Deuchars IPA, 80/-; guest beers** Ⓐ
Excellent, friendly, traditional pub. The back lounge (open weekends) features a collection of Victoriana and bric-a-brac. Three guest beers from anywhere between Orkney and Cornwall. Poems and Pints nights. 1996 Scottish CAMRA *Pub of the Year*. ⊞ & ❀

## Old Racecourse Hotel

2 Victoria Park (A719 jct, S of centre) ☎ (01292) 262873
11–midnight (12.30am Fri & Sat)
**Boddingtons Bitter; guest beer** Ⓗ
Smart hotel lounge bar with an unusual pot still-shaped log fire as a centrepiece and portraits of Ayr Gold Cup winners on the walls. Close to the beach and two golf courses.
🌢 ❀ 🛏 ◑ ▶ & P

## Tam O'Shanter

230 High Street
☎ (01292) 611684
11 (12.30 Sun)–midnight
**Beer range varies** Ⓗ
Small, traditional, town-centre bar which has returned to its original use after years as a Burns Museum. Note the flagstoned floor and thatched roof. The guest beer is rotated on a regular basis. The music can be loud occasionally.
& ❦

## Wellington's

17 Wellington Square (behind seafront) ☎ (01292) 611684
11–12.30am; 12.30–midnight Sun
**Beer range varies** Ⓗ
Basement lounge bar in a Georgian square near the beach. Folk music Sun and Tue eves; quiz Wed eve. Student discount. Good bar meals.
◑ ▶ ❦

## Ballantrae

### King's Arms Hotel

40 Main Street (A77, coast road) ☎ (01465) 831202
11–12.30am; 12–midnight Sun

**Beer range varies** Ⓗ
Comfortable village hotel on the main route between central Scotland and Northern Ireland, close to the seafront. Three guest beers in summer, at least one in winter. Children's certificate. Restaurant open eves (5–9). 🌢 ❀ 🛏 ◑ ▶ & P

## Balloch

### Balloch Hotel

Balloch Road ☎ (01389) 752579
11–11 (midnight Fri, 11.45 Sat)
**Ind Coope Burton Ale; Tetley Bitter; guest beers** Ⓗ
Attractive hotel by the source of the River Leven, also the bonnie banks of Loch Lomond. Beer is on tap in the lounge bar only, but is supplied to the public bar. The landlord is a member of the Ind Coope *Guild of Master Cellarmen*.
🛏 ❀ 🛏 ◑ ▶ ◐ Å ⇌ ❦ P

## Barrhead

### Hurlet

Hurlet Crossroads
☎ (0141) 876 1637
11–11
**Boddingtons Bitter; Flowers Original; Marston's Pedigree; Whitbread Fuggles IPA; guest beers** Ⓗ
Typical Whitbread Brewers' Fayre pub/restaurant with excellent facilities for families. Guest beers from Caledonian. Cream teas a speciality.
❀ & P

## Biggar

### Crown Hotel

109 High Street
☎ (01899) 220116
11.30 (11 Sat)–11 (midnight Thu & Sat, 1am Fri); 12.30–11 Sun
**Beer range varies** Ⓗ
Busy lounge bar in a small hotel opposite a thimble museum. Two guest beers are supplied by Belhaven.
❀ 🛏 ◑ ▶ Å

## Brodick

### Brodick Bar

Alma Road (by post office)
☎ (01770) 302169
11–midnight; closed Sun
**Beer range varies** Ⓗ
Modernised public bar in a single-storey building; there is increasing emphasis on meals in the adjacent lounge. Two beers from the Scottish Courage guest list.
🌢 🛏 ◑ ▶ &

### Duncans Bar

Kingsley Hotel
☎ (01770) 302531
11 (12.30 Fri & Sat)–2.30, 7–midnight; closed Sun (11–midnight Mon–Sun in summer)

**Boddingtons Bitter; Theakston Best Bitter, guest beer** Ⓗ
Comfortable lounge bar to the side of a large seafront hotel. Views across the bay to Goat Fell can be enjoyed from the garden. Regular music eves in summer. Eve meals in summer.
🌢 🛏 ❀ 🛏 ◑ ▶ P

## Ormidale Hotel

Glencloy Road
☎ (01770) 302293
4.30–midnight (12–2.30, 4.30–midnight summer); 12–midnight Sat & Sun
**McEwan 70/-** Ⓐ
Fine sandstone building overlooking the southern end of the golf course. A small, friendly public bar with a conservatory leading off, giving extra space in summer. The original Mackie and Carnegie founts are still in use, mounted on an eccentric boat-shaped bar. Good B&B.
🌢 🛏 ❀ 🛏 ◑ ▶ P

## Campbeltown

### Ardshiel Hotel

Kilkerran Road
☎ (01586) 552133
11–2.30, 5–midnight
**Theakston XB or guest beer** Ⓗ
Family-run hotel serving excellent food. Children are welcomed.
Q 🛏 ❀ 🛏 ◑ ▶ P

### Commercial Inn

Cross Street ☎ (01586) 553703
11 (12.30 Sun)–1am
**Caledonian Deuchars IPA; guest beers** Ⓗ
Superb, friendly, family-run pub, very popular with locals and most welcoming to visitors. Good guest beer range. ⊞

## Castlecary

### Castlecary House Hotel

Main Street (off A80)
☎ (01324) 840233
11 (12.30 Sun)–11 (11.30 Thu–Sat)
**Draught Bass; Belhaven Sandy Hunter's Ale; Broughton Greenmantle Ale; Caledonian Deuchars IPA; guest beers** Ⓗ
Small private hotel with three drinking areas. The village is on the site of one of the major Roman Forts along the Antonine Wall. The Castlecary Arches (a large viaduct carrying the main Glasgow–Edinburgh railway line) are nearby. Most beers are in the Castle Lounge. Booking advised for the restaurant.
Q ❀ 🛏 ◑ ▶ ⊞ P

## Catacol

### Catacol Bay Hotel
☎ (01770) 830231
11–midnight (1am Thu–Sat)
**John Smith's Bitter;
Theakston Best Bitter; guest
beer** Ⓗ
Originally built as a manse in
the 19th century, this seafront
hotel sits next to the
appropriately named 'Twelve
Apostles', a listed row of
former fishermen's houses.
Wheelchair access is via the
garden. ♨ ✿ 🍴 🍺 ⅋ Ḁ P

## Cove

### Knockderry Hotel
204 Shore Road (B833)
☎ (01436) 842283
11–midnight (11 Sun)
**Theakston Best Bitter, XB;
guest beer** Ⓗ
An architectural delight – a
converted Victorian mansion,
situated on the Rosneath
Peninsula. The magnificent,
wood-panelled lounge bar
offers fine views over Loch
Long. Snooker room.
♨ ✿ 🍴 🍺 Ḁ ♣ P

## Dalry

### Greenbank Inn
97 New Street (A737, E of
centre) ☎ (01294) 835522
11–2.30, 5–midnight; 11–1am Fri &
Sat; 12.30–3.30, 6–midnight Sun
**Beer range varies** Ⓗ
Friendly, comfortable bar and
lounge near the station. If the
guest beer is Greenbank Ale,
it's Maclay's Autumn Ale.
Meals Thu–Sat. 🍺 🍴 ⊞ ⇌ ♣

## East Kilbride

### East Kilbride Sports Club
Torrance Avenue, Strathaven
Road ☎ (0135 52) 36001
11–11 (1am Fri & Sat); 12.30–11 Sun
**Beer range varies** Ⓗ
Successful sports club run by
the owner of a beer agency,
which means that the three
handpumps offer some harder
to find beers as well as quality
Scottish beers. Carry this guide
or CAMRA membership card
to be signed in. Regular beer
festivals. Lunches not always
available. Q ✿ 🍺 P

### New Farm
Strathaven Road
☎ (0135 52) 67177
11 (12.30 Sun)–11 (midnight Fri & Sat)
**Boddingtons Bitter;
Caledonian Deuchars IPA,
80/-; Flowers Original; guest
beer** Ⓗ
Large Brewers' Fayre pub with
a commitment to quality cask

ale and helpful, knowledgeable
staff. Occasional beer festivals.
✿ 🍺 🍴 & Ḁ P ⅋

## Failford

### Failford Inn
On B743, Ayr–Mauchline road
☎ (01292) 541674
11–midnight; 12.30–11 Sun
**Belhaven 80/-; guest beer** Ⓗ
Rural gem, set on the banks of
the River Ayr, featuring a
low-ceilinged bar with an old
tiled range. The restaurant
(booking advised) and the
garden overlook the river. A
popular river walk starts
nearby. The guest beer is from
the Belhaven range. Limited
parking. ♨ Q ✿ 🍺 🍴 P

## Gateside

### Gateside Inn
39 Main Road (B777, 1 mile E of
Beith) ☎ (01505) 503362
11–2.30, 5–11; 11–midnight Sat;
12.30–11 Sun
**Broughton Greenmantle
Ale** Ⓗ
Cosy country inn with a
modernised interior, in a small
village near Beith. Eve meals
Thu–Sun. ✿ 🍺 🍴 P ⅋

## Glasgow

### Athena Taverna
780 Pollokshaws Road (next to
Queen's Park)
☎ (0141) 424 0858
11–2.30, 5–11; closed Sun
**Belhaven 80/-; guest beers** Ⓐ
Modern-style, single-bar café
attached to a Greek restaurant,
selling an excellent, ever-
changing range of five guest
ales, plus a large range of
German bottled beers.
Glasgow's answer to a licensed
conservatory, which can be
extremely busy weekend eves.
🍺 🍴 ⇌ (Queen's Pk/
Pollockshields W)

### Babbity Bowster
16–18 Blackfriars Street (off
High St) ☎ (0141) 552 5055
11 (12.30 Sun)–midnight
**Maclay Broadsword, 80/-,
Kane's Amber Ale; guest
beer** Ⓐ
Café bar on the eastern edge of
the city centre with an
individual style of decor. Open
from 8am for food and soft
drinks. ♨ Q ✿ 🍴 🍺 🍴 ⇌
(High St) ♣ ⌂

### Blackfriars
35 Bell Street (off Trongate,
opp. Candleriggs Market)
☎ (0141) 552 5924
11 (12.30 Sun)–midnight
**Alloa Arrol's 80/-; Ind Coope
Burton Ale; Tetley Bitter;
guest beers** Ⓗ

Vibrant bar with a youngish
clientele and live music. Up to
three guest ales, draught
Belgian ale, plus bottled
German and Belgian
traditional beers.
🍺 🍴 ⇌ (High St) ⌂

### Brewery Tap
1055 Sauchiehall Street
☎ (0141) 339 8866
12 (12.30 Sun)–11 (midnight Fri & Sat)
**Alloa Arrol's 80/-; Belhaven
60/-; Ind Coope Burton Ale;
Tetley Bitter** Ⓐ**; guest beers** Ⓗ
Lively two-roomed pub, handy
for public transport. The
friendly and efficient staff can
be stretched, particularly at
weekends when it can get very
busy. Live music; occasional
beer festivals. Good range of
foreign bottled/draught beers.
🍺 ⊖ (Kelvinhall) ⌂ Ḋ

### Hogshead
1397 Argyle Street (opp.
Museum and Art Gallery)
☎ (0141) 334 1831
11 (12.30 Sun)–11 (midnight Fri & Sat)
**Boddingtons Bitter;
Caledonian Deuchars IPA,
80/-; Flowers Original;
Marston's Pedigree;
Whitbread Abroad Cooper;
guest beers** Ⓗ
Traditional ale house, part of
the Whitbread chain. Formerly
the Calypso Bar, it now does a
rumba of beers from
independent brewers. Regular
beer festivals.
🍺 & ⊖ (Kelvinhall)

### Mitre
12–16 Brunswick Street (off
Trongate by Clydesdale Bank)
☎ (0141) 552 7642
11–11 (midnight Fri & Sat); 12.30–10
Sun
**Belhaven 80/-, St Andrew's
Ale; guest beer** Ⓗ
Small, friendly bar providing a
haven off a busy shopping
street: a largely unspoilt
Victorian pub with a mini-
horseshoe bar and a coffin
gantry. The house beer is a
recent addition. Meals served
11–5. 🍺 ⇌ (Argyle St)

### State Bar
148 Holland Street (off
Sauchiehall St, near Charing
Cross) ☎ (0141) 332 2159
11 (12.30 Sun)–midnight
**Belhaven St Andrew's Ale;
Orkney Dark Island;
Theakston Best Bitter; guest
beers** Ⓗ
Modern, city-centre pub
hosting live folk music and
beer festivals, much frequented
by students and business
people. The interesting
stained-glass window was
uncovered during a recent
refurbishment. 🍺 ⇌ (Charing
Cross) ⊖ (Cowcaddens)

## Station Bar

55 Port Dundas Road
☎ (0141) 332 3117
11 (12.30 Sun)–midnight
**Caledonian Deuchars IPA; guest beers** Ⓗ
Well-run, street-corner pub with friendly staff, popular with office workers during the day and musicians eves. The bar boasts a fine McEwan's mirror. Two guest beers. A must. ⇌ (Queen St) ⊖ (Cowcaddens)

## Three Judges

141 Dumbarton Road
☎ (0141) 337 3055
11 (12.30 Sun)–11 (midnight Fri & Sat)
**Maclay Broadsword, 80/-, Wallace; guest beers** Ⓔ
Busy, lively, West End saloon bar, serving over 1000 guest ales in four years! Current holder, and frequent past winner, of local CAMRA *Landlord* and *Pub of the Year* awards. Fast and friendly service. & ⇌ (Partick) ⊖ (Kelvinhall) ⏛

## Gourock

### Spinnaker Hotel

121 Albert Road
☎ (01475) 633107
11–11.30; 12.30–11 Sun
**Belhaven 80/-; guest beer** Ⓗ
Family-run, Clydeside hotel boasting sea views over the Clyde estuary. The welcoming public bar is in one half of this imposing, sandstone building; full à la carte restaurant in the other. Bar snacks and coffee available all day. The guest beer is from Belhaven.
✿ 🛏

## Hamilton

### George

18 Campbell Street
☎ (01698) 424225
11 (6.30 Sun)–11.45; closed winter Sun
**Maclay 80/-; guest beers** Ⓗ
Small, friendly pub, a frequent winner of CAMRA's Lanarkshire *Pub of the Year* award. Although in the town centre, it can be difficult to find, but is well worth the effort. Children's certificate. ⏴ ◑ ▲ (Strathclyde Pk) ⇌ (Central)

## Houston

### Fox & Hounds

South Street ☎ (01505) 612448
11–midnight (1am Fri, 11.45 Sat);
12–midnight Sun
**Beer range varies** Ⓗ
Popular country pub in a rural setting, with today's comforts and the atmosphere of a bygone time. A hunting theme permeates three olde-English-style bars. Four real ales in the

Fox & Vixen lounge; bar meals in the Huntsman lounge upstairs, with a full à la carte restaurant adjacent.
✿ ◑ 🍴 ♣ P ⚥

## Innellan

### Braemar Hotel

Shore Road (A815, 4 miles S of Dunoon) ☎ (01369) 830792
12 (12.30 Sun)–midnight
**Beer range varies** Ⓗ
Built in the 19th century as the superb seaside home of textile magnate JP Coates, this hotel boasts a splendid view over the Firth of Clyde. Large outdoor seating area; children's play area. ⏴ ✿ 🛏 ◑ ▶ & ♣ P

## Irvine

### Marina Inn

110 Harbour Street
☎ (01294) 274079
11–3, 6–midnight (11–midnight summer); 11–1am Fri & Sat; 12.30–midnight Sun
**Belhaven St Andrew's Ale** Ⓗ
Attractive, harbourside lounge bar next to the Magnum Centre and the Scottish Maritime Museum. Emphasis on food at lunchtime and early eve, with an extensive menu, including swordfish steaks. Children's certificate. ✿ ◑ ▶ & ⇌

### Ship Inn

120–122 Harbour Street (next to Magnum Leisure Centre)
☎ (01294) 279722
11–2.30, 5–midnight (1am Fri); 11–1am Sat; 12.30–11 Sun
**Theakston Best Bitter** Ⓗ
Harbourside pub, the oldest licensed premises in town, renowned for its well-cooked and good value meals. Quiet atmosphere lunchtime and early eve, but rather lively later on. See the local scenes drawn on the ceiling. Children's certificate. Q ✿ ◑ ▶ & ⇌

### Turf Hotel

32–34 Eglinton Street
☎ (01294) 275836
11–midnight (1am Fri & Sat); 12.30–11 Sun
**Theakston Best Bitter; guest beer** Ⓗ
Totally unspoilt, traditional Scottish bar, with a lounge to the rear which has its own character (more restricted hours). Quite cosmopolitan at lunchtime, when quality lunches of amazing value are served, it is more of a local at night. ⏴ ◑ ⊞ ♣

## Johnstone

### Coanes

26 High Street
☎ (01505) 322924
11–11.30 (1am Fri, 11.45 Sat); 6.30–11.30 Sun

**Draught Bass; Boddingtons Bitter; Caledonian Deuchars IPA; Orkney Red MacGregor, Dark Island; guest beers** Ⓗ
Friendly, town-centre local offering a warm welcome from the locals: a cosy bar with fake beams and bric-a-brac, and a comfortable, open-plan lounge. Five guest beers. ◑ ⇌

## Kilbarchan

### Trust Inn

8 Low Barholm
☎ (01505) 702401
11–2.30, 5–11; 11–midnight Thu–Sat;
12.30–11 Sun
**Ind Coope Burton Ale; Tetley Bitter; guest beers** Ⓗ
Popular, friendly local with cosy nooks, beamed ceilings and decorative brasses: a comfortable lounge in a one-bar pub, set in a former weaving village. Handy for cyclists on the Irvine–Glasgow cycle path. No food Sun.
◑ ▶ ⇌ (Milliken Pk)

## Kilcreggan

### Kilcreggan Hotel

Argyll Road (100 yds from B833) ☎ (01436) 842243
11–11 (1am Fri & Sat); 12.30–midnight Sun
**Orkney Dark Island; Theakston Best Bitter; Younger No. 3; guest beer** Ⓗ
Friendly, well-run, family hotel offering good views over the Firth of Clyde; only five mins' walk from the Gourock ferry. Children's certificate (toys available). Eve meals finish at 8.45. Beer is on tap in the lounge bar only, but is supplied to the public bar. Local CAMRA 1995 *Pub of the Year*.
🛏 ⏴ ✿ 🛏 ◑ ▶ ⊞ ▲ ♣ P

## Kildonan

### Breadalbane Hotel

On village loop road
☎ (01770) 820284
11–midnight (1am Thu–Sat)
**Draught Bass** Ⓗ
Friendly, seaside hotel in a very quiet corner of Arran. Enjoy the views of the Firth of Clyde from the lounge or the conservatory after a bracing walk along the beach. Self-catering flats available.
🛏 ⏴ ✿ 🛏 ◑ ▶ & ▲ P

## Kilmarnock

### Hunting Lodge

14–16 Glencairn Square (opp. Safeway) ☎ (01563) 522920
11–3, 5–midnight; 11–12.30am Fri & Sat; 12.30–midnight Sun
**Broughton 80/-; Caledonian 80/-; guest beers** Ⓗ

The biggest selection of real ales in the area is served in this pub's attractive Malty Hop lounge. An additional ten handpumps are used for mini-festivals. The venue for the local folk club (Thu), quizzes (Mon) and occasional ceilidhs. Children's certificate.
◑ ◗ ♿ ⚥

## Kilmaurs

### Weston Tavern
27 Main Street (A735)
☎ (01563) 538805
11 (12.30 Sun)–midnight
**Beer range varies** Ⓗ
Originally a manse, school and smithy in an historic area next to the 'Jougs', this pub dates back to circa 1500. The partly-tiled floor is a listed feature; note, too, the craggy stone-worked bar and panelled games area. The rear lounge is for families and meetings. Fishing club. Eve meals on request.
Q ➳ ◑ ◗ ⊞ ♿ ≋ ♣ P ⛟

## Kilmun

### Coylet Inn
Loch Eck (A815, 9 miles N of Dunoon) ☎ (01369) 840426
11 (12.30 Sun)–2.30, 6.30–11 (5–midnight Fri & Sat)
**Caledonian Deuchars IPA; McEwan 80/-; Younger No. 3** Ⓔ
Attractive, inviting lochside bar where you can relax around the open fire after a day's fishing, touring or walking in the hills. The setting for the film *The Blue Boy*. Good bar food. Caravan park nearby.
🏨 ✿ 🛏 ◑ ◗ ♣ P

## Kilwinning

### Claremont Hotel
67 Byres Road (A738)
☎ (01294) 558445
12–2.30, 5–midnight (1am Fri); 12–1am Sat; 12–midnight Sun
**Beer range varies** Ⓗ
Attractive, comfortable lounge in a small hotel right next to the station. Three beers available, two from the Scottish Courage list and one free of tie. The traditional Scottish bar has longer opening hours, but no real ale. Children's certificate.
🛏 ◑ ◗ ⊞ ♿ ≋ P

## Kirkmichael

### Kirkmichael Arms
3 Straiton Road
☎ (01655) 750375
11–2.30, 5–11; 11–11 Fri, Sat & summer; 12.30–11 Sun
**Beer range varies** Ⓗ
Rural gem with low ceilings, set in a conservation village. The comfortable lounge and

small bar are made cosy by a real fire. Good value pub food. Children's certificate.
🏨 Q ➳ ◑ ◗ ⊞ ♣

## Lamlash

### Pier Head Tavern
Shore Road ☎ (01770) 600380
9am–midnight (1am Thu–Sat); 12.30–midnight Sun
**Draught Bass; guest beer** Ⓗ
Large, L-shaped bar situated on the seafront with views across to Holy Island. Known as the PHT, it plays host to the local rugby team.
🏨 ✿ ◑ ◗ ♿ ♠ P

## Lanark

### Horse & Jockey
56 High Street
☎ (01555) 664825
11–11 (1am Fri, 11.45 Sat)
**Beer varies** Ⓗ
Friendly, down-to-earth, town-centre bar. The name and decor are reminders of the town's former racecourse. Real ale in the public bar. ◑ ◗ ⊞ ≋

## Largs

### Clachan
14 Bath Street (B7025, off main street) ☎ (01475) 672224
11–midnight (1am Thu–Sat); 12.30–11 Sun
**Belhaven 80/-, St Andrew's Ale** Ⓐ
Single-bar pub in a sidestreet, close to the seafront and the Cumbrae ferry. Live music Fri. Lunchtime snacks.
♿ ≋ ♣

## Lochwinnoch

### Brown Bull
33 Main Street (off A737, on Largs road) ☎ (01505) 843250
11–11 (midnight Fri, 11.45 Sat)
**Belhaven Sandy Hunter's Ale; Orkney Dark Island; guest beer** Ⓗ
Gem of a pub with a friendly welcome. Step back in time in surroundings of low ceilings, stone walls and a 1930s telephone. Paintings by local artists adorn the walls and hop bines decorate the gantry. A location for TV's *Dr Finlay*. Quiz night Tue; folk night Sun.
🏨 ✿ ♿

### Mossend
Largs Road (200 yds from A737) ☎ (01505) 842672
11–11; 12.30–11 Sun
**Boddingtons Bitter; Flowers Original; guest beers** Ⓗ
Brewers' Fayre pub, ideal for families, with a Charlie Chalk Fun Factory. The garden and play area offer extensive views over the countryside, with a bird sanctuary and loch

(watersports) nearby. One guest beer in winter, three in summer. ✿ ◑ ◗ ♿ ≋ P ⚥

## Lugton

### Paraffin Lamp
1 Beith Road (A736/B777 jct)
☎ (01505) 850510
11 (12.30 Sun)–11
**Boddingtons Bitter; Castle Eden Ale; Flowers Original; Marston's Pedigree; guest beer** Ⓗ
Whitbread Brewers' Fayre country eatery with a separate bar. Food is available all day. The guest beer is from the Whitbread range. Popular with families, as children are well catered for (certificate). Handy for the newly established Lugton Inn Brewery.
Q ✿ ◑ ◗ ♿ ♣ P

## Monkton

### Monkton Lodge
Kilmarnock Road (A77/A78 roundabout) ☎ (01292) 678262
11–11 (midnight Sat)
**Boddingtons Bitter; Castle Eden Ale; Flowers IPA, Original; Marston's Pedigree; Morland Old Speckled Hen; guest beer** Ⓗ
Purpose-built Brewers' Fayre pub close to Prestwick airport. Food is available all day. The real ale choice has been increasing, within the limitations of the Whitbread list. Popular with families (children's certificate). Accommodation is in the adjacent Travel Inn motel.
Q ✿ 🛏 ◑ ◗ ♿ ♠ P

## Oban

### Caledonian Hotel
Station Square
☎ (01631) 563133
10.30–11
**Caledonian 80/-** Ⓗ
Grand Victorian seafront hotel next to the station and the islands ferry terminal. A large, plush, open-plan lounge with an adjacent restaurant. Tiny car park. ✿ 🛏 ♿ ≋ P

## Old Kilpatrick

### Ettrick
159 Dumbarton Road
☎ (01389) 872821
11 (12.30 Sun)–11.30 (midnight Fri & Sat)
**Theakston Best Bitter; Younger No. 3; guest beers** Ⓗ
Lively, late Victorian pub with a traditional horseshoe bar and an island gantry. The comfortable lounge hosts families during the day and entertainment eves; live music Sat. Named after the Ettrick Shepherd, a close friend of

Walter Scott. No-smoking area until 7. ⛺ ❄ ◖ ▶ ⊞ ⇌ (Kilpatrick) P ⊬

## Paisley

### RH Finlay

33 Causeyside Street
☎ (0141) 889 9036
11–midnight (12.45am Fri, 11.45 Sat, 11 Sun)
**Draught Bass; Caledonian Deuchars IPA** Ⓗ
Traditional town-centre pub with two lounge bars. Quality food is served Mon–Sat. An ideal meeting place, where a friendly welcome is assured.
◖ ⇌ (Gilmour St/Canal St)

### Tannahills

100 Nelston Road (opp. South primary school)
☎ (0141) 889 2491
11–11 (midnight Thu & Fri, 11.45 Sat); 12.30–11 Sun
**Caledonian Deuchars IPA** Ⓐ
This pub's unusual bar is in the form of a house, complete with roof tiles. Pictures of old Paisley and the poet Robert Tannahill adorn the wall. It can get very busy. ◖

### Wee Howff

53 High Street
☎ (0141) 889 2095
11–11 (11.30 Fri & Sat); closed Sun
**Caledonian 70/-; Ind Coope Burton Ale; guest beers** Ⓗ
Long, narrow, bar with a mock Tudor interior, popular with university students. The publican was the first Burton *Master Cellarman* in Scotland. The only regular outlet for Caley 70/- in the area.
⇌ (Gilmour St)

## Renfrew

### Ferry Inn

2 Clyde Street (beside slipway of Yoker ferry)
☎ (0141) 886 2104
11–midnight (1am Fri, 11.45 Sat); 12.30–11 Sun
**Belhaven 80/-; guest beers** Ⓗ
L-shaped bar, with an adjoining lounge, in a listed building. The histories of the nearby ferry and Clyde shipbuilding are well represented in the decor. Quiz Wed. ⚌ Q

### Tap & Spile

Terminal Building, Glasgow Airport ☎ (0141) 848 4869
8am–11 (1am Fri, 11.45 Sat); 12.30–11 Sun
**Beer range varies** Ⓗ
Stained-glass enhances this recently extended, busy airport bar. (Expensive) bar snacks and sandwiches available. A price list and the beer range are displayed outside the bar entrance. Tap & Spile

merchandise on display and for sale. ♿ ⊬

## Rosneath

### Rosneath Bistro

Rosneath Castle Caravan Park (1 mile from B833)
☎ (0436) 831333
11–11 (midnight Fri & Sat); 12.30–11 Sun
**Beer range varies** Ⓗ
Popular bistro bar on the picturesque Rosneath Peninsula, providing a superb holiday base for campers and caravanners, and serving a merry-go-round of Harviestoun beers, plus a guest beer (Mar–Oct). Children's certificate. Eve meals finish at 8.45. Q ❄ ◖ ▶ ♿ ♠ P

## Saltcoats

### Hip Flask

13 Winton Street (near seafront) ☎ (01294) 465222
11–midnight (1am Thu–Sat)
**Belhaven St Andrew's Ale; guest beer** Ⓗ
Small, friendly café-bar, well placed for both the town centre and the beach. The raised seating area can double as a small stage; live music and quizzes some eves. Good value food (book eve meals). Newspapers and magazines are supplied. Children's certificate. ❄ ◖ ▶

## Seamill

### Waterside Inn

Ardrossan Road (A78)
☎ (01294) 823238
11 (12 Sun)–11
**Boddingtons Bitter; Flowers IPA, Original; Marston's Pedigree; guest beers** Ⓗ
Brewers' Fayre pub with a bar that has more of a pub feel than others. It sits right on the beach and has wonderful sea views from the restaurant and garden. Summer beer festival in a marquee. Food available all day. Children's certificate. Play areas inside and out.
❄ ◖ ▶ ♿ ♠ P

## Stair

### Stair Inn

On B730, between A70 and B743 ☎ (01292) 591650
11 (12.30 Sun)–11 (1am Fri & Sat)
**Belhaven Sandy Hunter's Ale; guest beer** Ⓗ
Recently refurbished inn, set in the heart of rural Ayrshire in an extremely picturesque location. Beware of the adjacent narrow bridge. The guest beer is from the Belhaven range. ⚌ ❄ ◖ ▶ P

## Stevenston

### Champion Shell Inn

5 Schoolwell Street (just off A738) ☎ (01294) 463055
11 (12.30 Sun)–midnight (1am Thu–Sat)
**Beer range varies** Ⓗ
Refurbished bar/lounge in a listed building – the oldest inhabited building in the 'Three Towns'. Its name comes from an 18th-century competition for drinking mead from a shell. Two guest beers from a variety of sources. Public car park opposite. Award-winning food.
Q ◖ ▶ ♿ ♣

## Tobermory

### Mishnish Hotel

Main Street ☎ (01688) 302009
11–midnight (1am Fri & Sat)
**Boddingtons Bitter; Younger No. 3; guest beer** Ⓗ
Listed seafront building, circa 1860, which has been in the same family for over 100 years. Friendly and efficient service, catering for yachtsmen, divers, sightseers and locals alike. Home-made broth always available. ⚌ ⛺ ⌂ ◖ ▶ ⊞ ♠

## Troon

### Harbour Bar

169 Templehill (B749)
☎ (01292) 312668
11–12.30am; 12.30–midnight Sun
**Broughton Greenmantle Ale; guest beers** Ⓗ
Harbourside local with a public bar and a games room, both served from the same bar. The real ale range may be reduced in winter, but at least one beer is always available.
⊞ ♣ P

### McKay's

69 Portland Street (A759)
☎ (01292) 311079
11–12.30am; 12.30–midnight Sun
**Boddingtons Bitter** Ⓗ**; Maclay 80/-; guest beers** Ⓔ
Friendly, town-centre lounge bar which can get busy at weekends. Regular rotation of guest beers from throughout the UK; four ales are dispensed by electric 'handpump'. Occasional live music Sun.
❄ ◖ ▶ ⇌

### Piersland House Hotel

15 Craigend Road (B749, S of centre) ☎ (01292) 314747
11–midnight
**Broughton Greenmantle Ale; Courage Directors** Ⓗ
Popular, three-star hotel, overlooking Royal Troon golf course. The hotel has a good reputation for its food and the bar prices tend to reflect the

quality of the establishment.
Croquet played.
🏾 Q ❀ 🍴 ⓓ ☖ ♣ P

## Twechar

### Quarry Inn
Main Street ☎ (01236) 821496
11–11.30 (1am Fri); 12.30–11 Sun
**Maclay 70/-, Broadsword;
Tetley Bitter; guest beer** Ⓗ
Excellent, friendly, traditional
village pub in a former mining
community. The public bar is a
gem, with its pot-bellied
stoves, brewery mirrors and
lack of any modernisation.
Annual (Oct) beer festival.
Petanque played. 🏾 🍺 ♣ P

## Uddingston

### Rowan Tree ☆
60 Old Mill Road
☎ (01698) 812678
11–11.45; 12.30–11 Sun
**Maclay 80/-, Wallace; guest
beers** Ⓗ
Vibrant community pub which
features an unspoilt wooden
interior with two fireplaces,
fine brewery mirrors and a
stained-glass phone booth; said
to be haunted by a stable lad
who was kicked by a horse
when it was a coaching inn.
Lanarkshire CAMRA *Pub of the
Year* 1995. 🏾 🍴 ⓓ 🍺 ⇌ P

## Uplawmoor

### Uplawmoor Hotel
66 Neilston Road (off A736,
Barrhead–Irvine road)
☎ (01505) 850565
12–2.30, 5–11 (midnight Fri); 12–
midnight Sat; 12.30–11 Sun
**Draught Bass; Caledonian
80/-** Ⓗ
Village hotel catering for
everyone from the drinker to
the wedding party. Nothing is
too difficult for the efficient
and friendly staff. A bit off the
beaten track, but well worth
the effort of finding.
🏾 🍴 ❀ 🛏 ⓓ ▶ ☖ P

---

# WHAT'S BREWING

There are numerous benefits that members of CAMRA receive for their £14 a year subscription.

Most obvious are the big discounts on products and books like the *Good Beer Guide, Good Pub Food, Room at the Inn* and *The CAMRA Guide to Real Cider*, or reduced price (sometimes free) admission to CAMRA beer festivals, including the Great British Beer Festival. However, probably the most appreciated by members is the delivery to their homes each month – free of charge – of the acclaimed *What's Brewing* newspaper.

*What's Brewing* is the leading national newspaper on beer and pub matters. Edited by award-winning beer writer Roger Protz, it offers up to the minute news of events in the beer and pub world, with sections on new micro-breweries, the latest CAMRA campaigns, trade gossip and brewery boardroom battles.

There are entertaining features by world-renowned beer hunter Michael Jackson, pub food articles by Susan Nowak and cartoons by Bill Tidy. Jackson files a monthly report on his beer travels, fuelling the wanderlust of the armchair tippler, Nowak highlights some of the best food pubs and beer recipes to be found, and Tidy, through his doughty cartoon campaigner, Kegbuster, satirises the issues of the day.

Guest beer writers, CAMRA social diaries, beer festival information, interviews and profiles of breweries big and small also figure prominently in the tabloid paper, with many pages in full colour. Four times a year, the *Cider Press* supplement, compiled by Ted Bruning, focuses on developments in the world of traditional cider. Not least, *What's Brewing* also carries updates to the *Good Beer Guide* in each issue, ensuring that *Guide* users are aware of any major changes to pubs featured.

If you want to keep in touch with events in the fast-changing world of beer, join CAMRA and make sure of your copy of *What's Brewing* every month. Full details of CAMRA membership and how to subscribe can be found on page 543 of this book.

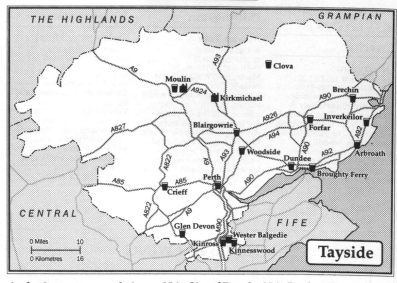

# Tayside

THE HIGHLANDS

GRAMPIAN

Clova

Moulin
A924
Kirkmichael

Brechin

Inverkeilor

Forfar
Blairgowrie

Woodside

Dundee
Arbroath

Broughty Ferry
Perth

Crieff

CENTRAL

FIFE

Glen Devon

Wester Balgedie

**Tayside**

Kinross
Kinnesswood

0 Miles 10
0 Kilometres 16

*Authority areas covered: Angus UA, City of Dundee UA, Perth & Kinross UA*

## Arbroath

### Lochland
14–16 Lochlands Street
☎ (01241) 873286
11–11
**Draught Bass; guest beer** Ⓗ
Busy, friendly, street-corner
local with an active social life.
Keen football support.
Ⓠ ▲ ⇌ ♣

## Blairgowrie

### Stormont Arms
101 Perth Street (SW side of
town on Perth road)
☎ (01250) 873142
11–2.45, 5–11; 11–11 Fri & Sat; 12.30–
2.30, 6.30–11 Sun
**Beer range varies** Ⓗ
Former drovers' inn, now a
busy, town local, a pioneer of
cask ales (three beers).
Ⓠ ♣

## Brechin

### Dalhousie
1 Market Street
☎ (01356) 622096
11 (12.30 Sun)–11
**Beer range varies** Ⓗ
High, wood-panelling lines
this traditional pub with a
horseshoe bar. Small, but often
lively. Ⓠ ♣

## Broughty Ferry

### Fisherman's Tavern
10 Fort Street (by lifeboat
station) ☎ (01382) 775941
11–midnight; 12.30–11 Sun

**Belhaven St Andrew's
Ale; Boddingtons Bitter;
Maclay 80/-; guest
beers** Ⓗ
The only Scottish pub to
feature in every *Good Beer
Guide* since 1975: CAMRA
national *Urban Pub of the
Year* 1993, now with a full
hotel licence. Three guest
beers.
Ⓠ ⬛ ⌂ ◑ ◨ ⇌ (limited
service) ♣

### Old Anchor
48 Gray Street
☎ (01382) 737899
11–11.30 (midnight Wed–Sat);
12.30–11 Sun
**McEwan 80/-; Theakston
Best Bitter, XB; guest
beers** Ⓐ
Traditional-style, partitioned
bar with a nautical flavour.
Occasional beer festivals are
held. Family and no-smoking
areas are available at
lunchtime.
⬛ ◑ ⇌ (limited service) ✁

## Clova

### Clova Hotel
On B955, 15 miles N of
Kirriemuir
☎ (01575) 550222
11–midnight; 12.30–11 Sun
**Orkney Dark Island; guest
beers** Ⓗ
Splendid outpost at the head of
Glen Clova, beloved of
climbers and ramblers.
Arguably the most remote beer
festival is held here each
Easter.
⛺ ⬛ ⌂ ◑ ◨ ▲ P

## Crieff

### Oakbank Inn
Turret Bridge (½ mile S off A85
at Glenturret Distillery)
☎ (01764) 652420
12–3 (not Mon–Thu in winter), 6–11
(11.45 Fri); 12–11.45 Sat; 12–11 Sun
**Beer varies** Ⓗ
Modern pub, contrasting with
500-year-old Eppie Callum's
oak tree nearby. Popular for
family meals (winter eve meals
weekends only). The single
beer comes from Belhaven.
❀ ◑ ◨ ▲ ♣ P

## Dundee

### Hogshead
7–9 Union Street (opp. city
churches, corner of
Nethergate) ☎ (01382) 205037
11–midnight; 12.30–11 Sun
**Caledonian 80/-; Boddingtons
Bitter; Flowers IPA;
Whitbread Abroad Cooper** Ⓗ;
**guest beers** Ⓗ/Ⓖ
New ale house with a single
room cleverly divided into a
bar area and cosy seating
alcoves. Good food, a
welcoming atmosphere and a
wide range of ales. Children
welcome for meals, served
12–7 (12.30–5 Sun).
◑ ◨ ⚋ ⇌ ⌂

---

🏭 **INDEPENDENT
BREWERIES**

**Aldchlappie:** Kirkmichael

**Moulin:** Moulin

### Mickey Coyle's

21–23 Old Hawkhill
☎ (01382) 225871
11–11.30; 7–11 Sun
**Boddingtons Bitter;
Broughton Greenmantle
Ale; Younger No. 3 Ⓐ; guest
beers Ⓐ/Ⓗ**
Old town pub, now an
extension (unofficial!) of the
university. Once in the
*Guinness Book of Records* for the
shortest pub name (MC). Good
food (not served Sun; eve
meals 5–7.45). The car park is at
the rear of the pub.
◁ ▶ & P

### Phoenix

103 Nethergate (near
university campus)
☎ (01382) 200014
11–midnight; 12.30–11 Sun
**Beer range varies Ⓗ**
Lively city-centre bar, a former
CAMRA Dundee *Pub of the
Year*. Refurbished with the bar
gantry salvaged from
demolished Victorian bars.
◁ ▶ ⇌ (Taybridge)

### Planet

161 South Road, Lochee (off
Coupar Angus road/Lochee
bypass, A923)
☎ (01382) 623258
11–11.30 (midnight Fri & Sat);
12.30–11 Sun
**Orkney Dark Island; guest
beer (occasional) Ⓗ**
A 'moon-base' exterior
conceals a friendly, lively local
with a spacious bar and lounge
(ales usually in the bar). Social
activities include a hill-walking
club.
🍺 & P

### Speedwell Bar     ☆
### (Mennie's)

165–167 Perth Road
☎ (01382) 667783
11–midnight; 12.30–11 Sun
**Belhaven 80/- Ⓐ; guest
beers Ⓐ/Ⓗ**
Pub with a quality, listed
Edwardian interior, circa 1903,
boasting mahogany and glass
fittings and excellent Art
Nouveau etched windows.
Now managed by the landlord
of the Fisherman's Tavern,
Broughty Ferry (see entry on
the previous page). Try the
pies.
Q 🍺 & ⤢

## Forfar

### O'Hara's

41 West High Street
☎ (01307) 464350
11–2.30, 5.30–11 (midnight Fri & Sat)
**Beer varies Ⓗ**
Pleasant, welcoming first-floor
bistro serving excellent food.
Traditional music Thu and
occasional blues sessions Sat.
One real ale.
🏨 ◁ ▶

## Glen Devon

### Tormaukin Hotel

On A823 ☎ (01259) 781252
11 (12 Sun)–11
**Harviestoun 80/-; Ind Coope
Burton Ale; guest beer Ⓗ**
Cosy, welcoming, if slightly
upmarket, hotel in a beautiful
setting. Once a drovers' inn,
dating to around 1720, its name
means 'hill of the mountain
hare'. Meals served all day Sun
(12–9.30).
🏨 Q 🛏 🍴 ◁ ▶ ♿ P

## Inverkeilor

### Chance Inn

Main Street ☎ (01241) 830308
12–2.30, 5–11; 12.30–11 Sat, Sun &
summer
**Beer range varies Ⓗ**
Modernised country pub, very
popular for food. The
handpumps are in the rear
lounge, but orders are also
taken in the public bar. Three
beers. ❀ 🍴 ◁ ▶ 🍺 & ♣ P

## Kinnesswood

### Lomond Country Inn

Main Street ☎ (01592) 840253
11–11 (midnight Fri & Sat)
**Draught Bass; Caledonian
Deuchars IPA; Jennings
Bitter Ⓗ**
Modernised village inn with a
picture window view of Loch
Leven from the open-plan
bar/restaurant.
🏨 Q 🛏 ❀ 🍴 ◁ ▶ & P ⤢

## Kinross

### Kirklands Hotel

High Street ☎ (01577) 863313
11–2.30, 5–11 (11.45 Sat); 12.30–11
Sun
**Maclay 80/-; guest beers Ⓗ**
Small hotel with three ales in
the spartan bar and two in the
luxurious lounge.
Q 🍴 ◁ ▶ 🍺 & P ⤢

### Muirs Inn

49 The Muirs (Milnathort road,
N of town) ☎ (01577) 862270
11–2.30, 5–11 (11.45 Fri); 11–11.45 Sun;
12.30–11 Sun
**Belhaven 80/-; Orkney Dark
Island; guest beers Ⓗ**
Inn with a small, panelled bar,
a cosy, intimate lounge and a
restaurant. Up to four guest
ales. Q ❀ 🍺 & ♿ ♣ P

## Moulin

### Moulin Inn

11–13 Kirkmichael Road
(¾ mile NE of Pitlochry on
Kirkmichael road)
☎ (01796) 472196
11–11 (11.45 Fri & Sat); 12–11 Sun

**Boddingtons Bitter; Moulin
Ale of Atholl, Braveheart;
guest beer Ⓗ**
300-year-old inn with much
original character in the bar.
Accommodation is in the hotel
extension.
🏨 🛏 🍴 ◁ ▶ 🍺 & ♿ P

## Perth

### Greyfriars

15 South Street
☎ (01738) 633036
11–10.30 (11 Tue–Thu, 11.45 Fri & Sat);
12.30–11 Sun
**Caledonian Deuchars IPA;
Ind Coope Burton Ale;
Moulin Braveheart; guest
beers Ⓗ**
Tiny, but vibrant, pub near
Queen's Bridge. Restaurant
upstairs (eve meals in
summer).
◁ ▶ &

### Old Ship Inn

Skinnergate (just off High St)
☎ (01738) 624929
11–2.30, 5–11 (11–11.45 Fri & Sat);
closed Sun
**Caledonian Deuchars IPA,
80/-; guest beers Ⓗ**
A haven in the heart of busy
Perth, the city's oldest pub
with its inn sign preserved.
Restaurant upstairs; eve meals
Sat. Q ◁ 🍺 ♣

## Western Balgedie

### Balgedie Toll Tavern

At B919/A911 jct, near Kinross
☎ (01592) 840212
11 (12.30 Sun)–11
**Ind Coope Burton Ale Ⓗ**
Original 1534 toll house
featuring wooden beams and
an open fire. Families welcome.
Private dining room.
🏨 Q ❀ ◁ ▶ & P

## Woodside

### Woodside Inn

Main Street
☎ (01828) 670254
11–11 (11.45 Fri & Sat); 12.30–11 Sun
**Caledonian Deuchars IPA,
80/-; guest beer Ⓗ**
Enterprising, refurbished
village pub at the east end of
Burrelton/Woodside. Children
welcome in the restaurant;
good food.
🏨 ❀ ◁ ▶ & P

---

For a quick guide to
the new geographical
areas used in the
*Good Beer Guide*,
see the Key Map on
the inside back cover.

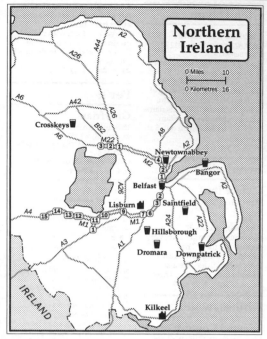

# Northern Ireland

## Bangor

### Jenny Watts
High Street (marina end)
☎ (01247) 270401
11.30–11.30; 12.30–2.30, 7–10 Sun
**Theakston Best Bitter** Ⓗ
Cosy seaside pub, one of the oldest licensed premises in Bangor: a very comfortable single bar/lounge. Live bands play during the week. Children welcome Sun lunch. Good value, varied food.
🏨 ⊛ Ⓓ ▶

## Belfast

### Beaten Docket
48 Great Victoria Street (opp. Europa Hotel)
☎ (01232) 242986
11.30–midnight (1am Thu–Sat);
11–2.30, 7–10 Sun
**Draught Bass; Cains Bitter or Theakston Best Bitter; Caledonian Deuchars IPA; guest beers** Ⓗ
Modern, city-centre bar where the upstairs entertainment/function room has a dance floor. Spacious ground-floor bar with a small snug and a real fire. Meals 12–6 (9 Thu–Sat); 11–2 Sun.
🏨 Ⓓ ▶ ♿ ⇌ (Gt Victoria St)

### Bittles Bar
103 Victoria Street
☎ (01232) 311088

11–midnight; 12–10 Sun
Unusual, triangular-shaped, old city-centre bar offering good food and occasional music nights. Pictures of local landmarks and noted personalities are displayed. No cask ale; Worthington White Shield sold. Q Ⓓ ⇌ (Central)

### Botanic Inn
23–27 Malone Road
☎ (01232) 660460
11.30–11 (12.30am Wed–Sat); 12.30–3, 7–10.30 Sun
**Cains Bitter; Theakston Best Bitter; guest beers** Ⓗ
Large, open-plan pub, recently refurbished with wooden floors and panelling: an extremely popular bar in the Queen's University area. The pub menu varies daily. Children admitted up until 6 and on Sun lunch.
🏨 Ⓓ 🍴 ♿ ⇌ (Botanic)

### Brown's Restaurant
30 Chichester Street (100 yds from City Hall)
☎ (01232) 232100
10–11 (1am Fri & Sat); 11–5.30 Sun
**Hilden Ale** Ⓖ
Friendly, comfortable city-centre restaurant with an upstairs gallery and a developing taste for real ale amongst its customers in the downstairs bar. The best of food, ale and company in one venue. Worthington White Shield sold. Easy listening live music every night. No food Sun eve. Ⓓ ▶ ♿ ⇌ (Central/Gt Victoria St)

### Crown Liquor Saloon ☆
42–44 Great Victoria Street (opp. Europa Hotel)
☎ (01232) 325368
11.30–midnight (1am Fri & Sat); 12–2.30, 7–10.30 Sun
**Draught Bass** Ⓗ
Historic pub owned by the NT and run by Bass with almost museum status. Set in a fine Victorian building, formerly a railway hotel, the bar retains its gas lighting and carved and wood-panelled swing door snugs, with stained-glass windows and mirrors. Try the oysters. No food Sun.
Ⓓ ♿ ⇌ (Gt Victoria St)

### Crow's Nest
22–28 Skipper Street (off High St, near Albert Clock)
☎ (01232) 325491
11.30–11 (1am Tue–Sat); 7–10 Sun
Large, tidy one-bar pub with a wood and tiled floor, and piped and live music. Popular with Belfast's gay community. No food Sun. No cask beer, but Worthington White Shield is sold.
Ⓓ ⇌ (Central)

### Elms Diner Saloon
36 University Road (near Shaftesbury Sq)
☎ (01232) 322106
11.30–1am; 7–10 Sun, closed Sun lunch
City-centre pub with a single large bar which is friendly, young and lively, with live bands on Mon, Thu and Sat; disco Wed. Good value food Mon–Sat, 11.30–6. The cask Worthington Bitter is kept under gas; Worthington White Shield is stocked.
Ⓓ ⇌ (Botanic)

### Errigle Inn
320 Ormeau Road (near Curzon cinema)
☎ (01232) 641410
11.30–11 (8–1am upstairs); 12.30–2.30, 7–10 Sun
**Cains Bitter; Caledonian Deuchars IPA; guest beers** Ⓗ
Large, modern inn with six bars and a restaurant. The Oak Lounge has wood panelling and comfortable seating. Live entertainment Wed–Sat eves in the upstairs bar. Excellent food.
Q Ⓓ ▶ 🍴 ♿

---

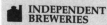

🏠 **INDEPENDENT BREWERIES**

**Hilden:** Lisburn

**Whitewater:** Kilkeel

## Fly

5 Lower Crescent (off
University Rd)
☎ (01232) 246878
11.30–midnight (1am Tue & Thu–Sat);
7–10 Sun, closed Sun lunch
**Cains Bitter, FA; guest
beers** Ⓗ
Lively, friendly town house
pub, where the long, narrow
bar has comfortable seating in
a library setting at the rear;
quiet lounge/function room
upstairs with a real fire. Live
jazz most Sat afternoons. Good
value lunches Mon–Fri.
🏚 Ⓠ Ⓓ ⇌ (Botanic)

## Kitchen & Parlour Bars

16 Victoria Square
☎ (01232) 324901
11–11; 12–3, 7–10 Sun
**Beer range varies** Ⓗ
Traditional, family-run, city
pub with a warm, friendly,
atmosphere. Two long separate
bars offer varying guest beers
and fine Ulster food.
🏚 Ⓓ ⊞ ⇌ (Central)

## Lavery's Gin Palace

12–14 Bradbury Place
☎ (01232) 327159
11.30–1am; 7–10 Sun, closed Sun lunch
**Cains Bitter** Ⓗ
Large, open-plan pub on
Belfast's Golden Mile: a very
popular bar eves (expect to
queue to get in); a cover charge
is paid on the door. Disco
Mon–Sat. Meals served till
5.30pm.
🏚 Ⓓ ⊞ & ⇌ (Botanic)

## Monico Bar

17 Lombard Street (off Castle
Place opp. Corn Market)
☎ (01232) 323211
11.30–11; 12.30–2.30, 7–10 Sun
**Cains Bitter; guest beers** Ⓗ
Comfortable, two-bar, city-
centre pub with a high-beamed
ceiling and alcove seating, plus
a swing-door snug. The lounge
bar has a stable theme and a
coal stove. Simple, good value
food Mon–Sat, 12–6.
🏚 Ⓠ Ⓓ ⊞ ⇌ (Gt Victoria St)

## Nick's Warehouse

35–43 Hill Street
☎ (01232) 439690
11.30–11; 11–5 Mon; 6–11 Sat; closed
Sun
Downstairs the bijou wine bar
serves great meals; upstairs is
an excellent, popular upmarket
restaurant (open 12–3, 6–9;
closed Sun). No cask beers but

bottled wheat beers are
stocked. Ⓠ Ⓓ Ⓓ &

## Crosskeys

### Crosskeys

Grange Road, Toomebridge
(off main road between
Randalstown and Portglenone)
☎ (01648) 50694
11.30–11 (ring for Sun hours)
Listed, thatched building, *the*
pub in rural Ulster: a main
public bar and a small bar in
another room, full of knick-
knacks. Local musicians often
play at weekends. A pub not to
be missed. No cask beer but
Worthington White Shield is
available. 🏚 Ⓠ ❀ P

## Downpatrick

### Denvir's Hotel

14–16 English Street
☎ (01396) 612012
11.30–11.30; 12.30–2.30, 7–10 Sun
**Hilden Ale** Ⓗ
Friendly, family-run, partially
restored coach house, dating
back to 1642. The small, olde-
worlde bar has an original
stone floor and a huge stone
fireplace; the large Stables
function room features open
rafters and stone walls; the
modern lounge has a log
fire. Live music Sat/Sun.
🏚 Ⓠ ⛴ ❀ ⛴ Ⓓ Ⓓ ⊞ & ❀ P

## Dromara

### Stove

6–8 Hillsborough Road (B7,
from Ballynahinch)
☎ (01238) 532700
11.30–11.30; 12.30–2, 7–10.30 Sun
**Cains Bitter** Ⓗ
Comfortable, restored, olde-
worlde village pub with two
bars; the lounge has a huge
inglenook, stone floor, church
pew seating and local
memorabilia. Friendly locals
and staff ensure a warm
welcome. No food Sun.
🏚 Ⓠ Ⓓ ⊞

## Hillsborough

### Hillside

21 Main Street
☎ (01846) 682765
11.30–11; 12–2.30, 7–10 Sun (may vary)
**Beer range varies** Ⓗ
18th-century, country village
pub with a low ceiling, stone

floor and friendly staff. A new
extension under construction
will allow wheelchair access.
Excellent food (not served Sun
eve). 🏚 Ⓠ ⛴ ❀ Ⓓ Ⓓ ❀

### Plough

3 The Square ☎ (01846) 682985
11.30–11; 12–2.30, 7–10 Sun (may
vary)
**Theakston Best Bitter** Ⓗ
Country village pub
(established 1758) with wood-
panelled seats, ceiling beams,
china and memorabilia.
Excellent bar food; restaurant
open 6–9, Tue–Sat. Caledonian
beers are also available.
🏚 Ⓠ ❀ Ⓓ ❀ P

## Newtownabbey

### Crown & Shamrock

584 Antrim Road (A6, 1½ miles
W of Glengormley)
☎ (01232) 832889
11.30–11.30; 7–10.30 Sun, closed Sun
lunch
Family-run, plain, panelled,
low-ceilinged pub with a high
bar adjoining an intimate
sitting room. Occasional
draught beers but always
Worthington White Shield.
🏚 Ⓠ ❀ ⊞ P

### Whittley's

401–403 Ballyclare Road (B56,
at level crossing, 2½ miles NW
of Glengormley)
☎ (01232) 832438
11.30–11; 5–10 Sun, closed Sun lunch
Unspoilt, friendly public bar
dating back to 1840, with a low
ceiling, stone floor and open
fire. A large lounge bar with a
roaring log fire adjoins the
Signal Box, an excellent,
railway-themed restaurant (no
lunch Sun, but high tea 5–8.30).
Worthington White Shield sold
(no cask beer). 🏚 Ⓠ ❀ Ⓓ Ⓓ ⊞ P

## Saintfield

### White Horse Inn

49 Main Street
☎ (01238) 510417
11–11; closed Sun
**Theakston Best Bitter; guest
beers** Ⓗ
Family-run pub and basement
restaurant with friendly staff
and locals and a comfortable
atmosphere. Noted for its
ostrich steaks. The adjoining
off-licence sells ale from the
handpump. 🏚 Ⓠ Ⓓ Ⓓ

---

# CASK IS BACK!

With beers from breweries like Caledonian and Cains joining Bass
and Theakston's in the Province's bars, and a new brewery,
Whitewater, helping Hilden to add local flavour, the Northern Ireland
beer revival continues apace. Here's to another progressive year!

# Channel Islands

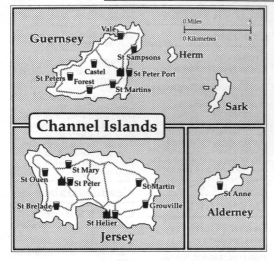

only outlet for cask Randalls in town. ◖ ⊞ ♣

## Rohais Inn
Rohais ☎ (01481) 720060
10–2, 4–11.45; closed Sun
**Guernsey Braye** Ⓖ
Basic, no-frills local, convenient for the island's largest supermarket: a rare outlet for Braye and gravity dispense. Bar billiards. Limited parking. ♣ P

## Ship & Crown
North Pier Steps, North Esplanade ☎ (01481) 721066
10–11.45; 12–3.30, 6–11 Sun
**Guernsey Sunbeam, seasonal beers** Ⓗ
Busy, single-bar town pub, opposite the marina for visiting yachts. Walls are covered with pictures of ships and local shipwrecks. Popular with bankers at lunchtime, and young people eves. Eve meals Sun. ◖ ▮

Try also: **Britannia Inn**, Trinity Sq (Guernsey)

## St Peters

### Longfrie Inn
Route de Longfrie
☎ (01481) 63107
11–2.30, 5.30–11.45; 6.30–9.30 Sun
**Guernsey Sunbeam, seasonal beers** Ⓗ
Food- and family-oriented hostelry, sometimes very busy. A good, varied menu and a well-equipped children's play room are features.
⛺ ❀ ⛴ ◖ ▮ P

## St Sampsons

### Pony Inn
Petites Capelles
☎ (01481) 44374
10.30–11.45; 12–2 (not winter) Sun
**Guernsey Sunbeam** Ⓗ
1960s, purpose-built pub near Oatlands Craft Centre and Guernsey Candles: three quite different bars and a large function room.
❀ ◖ ▮ ⊞ ♣ P

## Vale

### Houmet Tavern
Grande Havre ☎ (01481) 42214
10.30–11.45; closed Sun
**Guernsey Braye** Ⓗ

---

## Alderney

### St Anne

#### Nellie's Garden Bistro
Victoria Street
☎ (01481) 824000
10–12.30am; 10–midnight Sun
**Tipsy Toad Jimmy's Bitter, Horny Toad** Ⓗ
Bistro-style bar and restaurant, set back from the main shopping street, overlooking a large lawn. The ale is collected from Jersey by plane.
❀ ◖ ▮ P

Try also: **Moorings Hotel**, Braye St (Guernsey)

---

## Guernsey

Sunday drinking on Guernsey is only available to customers purchasing a meal to the value of £3 or more.

### Castel

#### Fleur du Jardin
Kings Mills ☎ (01481) 57996
11–3, 6–11.45; 12–2, 7–10.30 Sun
**Guernsey Sunbeam, seasonal beers** Ⓗ
Comfortable, attractive hotel in a pleasant setting, renovated in keeping with its farmhouse origins. The public bar does not open winter lunch. Outdoor play area.
⛺ ❀ ⛴ ◖ ▮ ⊞ P

### Forest

#### Deerhound Inn
Le Bourg ☎ (01481) 38585
10.30–11.45; 12–3.30, 7–11 Sun

**Theakston Old Peculier** Ⓗ
Welcoming bar of a comfortable hotel, handy for the airport. Excellent bar meals (till 7), plus a restaurant (open later). Swimming pool. The beer range may vary.
⛺ Q ❀ ⛴ ◖ ▮ P

### Venture Inn
Rue de la Villiaze (New Road)
☎ (01481) 63211
10–11.45; closed Sun
**Randalls Patois Ale** Ⓗ
Established local, not far from the airport. The functional, sports-oriented bar contrasts with the cosy lounge. Local CAMRA *Pub of the Year* 1995. No food Mon eve, or winter Mon lunch.
⛺ Q ❀ ◖ ▮ ⊞ ♣ P

### St Martins

#### Captain's Hotel
La Fosse ☎ (01481) 38990
10–11.45; closed Sun
**Guernsey Sunbeam, seasonal beers** Ⓗ
Hotel with an attractive, cosy lounge bar boasting an impressive handpump, plus a bistro-type restaurant. Moulin Huet Bay and Pottery are nearby. ❀ ⛴ ◖ ▮ P

Try also: **L'Auberge Divette**, Jerbourg (Guernsey)

### St Peter Port

#### Prince of Wales
Manor Place (Smith Street)
☎ (01481) 721066
10–11.45; closed Sun
**Randalls Patois Ale** Ⓔ
Busy town pub boasting many original Victorian features: the

---

📛 **INDEPENDENT BREWERIES**

**Guernsey:** St Peter Port

**Jersey:** St Helier

**Randalls:** St Peter Port

**Tipsy Toad:** St Helier/St Peter

Busy pub: a large, lively bar and a comfortable lounge with sea views. Excellent food; a rare outlet for cask mild. Eve meals Wed, Fri and Sat.
❀ ◁ ▶ ⊞ ♣ P

## Jersey

## Grouville

### Pembroke
Coast Road ☎ (01534) 855756
9am–11pm; 11–1, 4.30–11 Sun
**Draught Bass; Boddingtons Bitter; Theakston XB; guest beers** Ⓗ
Recently refurbished, large family pub next to the golf course. Food is so popular that it is advisable to book for large groups. No meals Sun lunch. Pub games in the public bar.
🏨 Q ⏰ ❀ ◁ ▶ ⊞ ૐ ♣ P

### Seymour Inn
La Rocque ☎ (01534) 854558
9am–11pm; 11–1, 4.30–11 Sun
**Guernsey Sunbeam; Jersey Old Jersey Ale, Winter Ale** Ⓗ
Friendly coastal pub with a real ale bar and a recently refurbished back lounge. Good food. No meals Sun lunch. Eve meals Tue–Sun summer, Fri–Sat winter. Excellent selection of games; regular live music.
🏨 ⏰ ❀ ◁ ▶ ⊞ ૐ ♣ P

## St Brelade

### Old Court House
St Aubins Harbour
☎ (01534) 46433
10–11; 11–1, 4.30–11 Sun
**Boddingtons Bitter; Marston's Pedigree; Theakston XB** Ⓗ
15th-century pub, famous for its appearances in the *Bergerac* TV series. It boasts a few bars, one in the shape of a ship, plus an upstairs restaurant with a view of the picturesque harbour. Popular patio.
Q ❀ 🍴 ◁

### Old Smugglers Inn
Ouaisne Bay ☎ (01534) 41510
11–11; 11–1, 4.30–11 Sun
**Draught Bass; Theakston Old Peculier; guest beers** Ⓗ
Historic, 17th-century granite pub with a regularly rotating choice of guest beers. The food is excellent. A good venue for a romantic rendezvous. Live folk and blues music Sun eve.
🏨 Q ⏰ ◁ ▶ ♣

## St Helier

### Dog & Sausage
Hilary Street ☎ (01534) 30982
10–11; 11–1, 4.30–11 Sun
**Draught Bass; Boddingtons Bitter** Ⓗ

Small pub in a pedestrian shopping area, fashioned like the inside of a pre-war railway carriage. Unusual array of Charlton Athletic mementoes.
◁

### Lamplighter
Mulcaster Street
☎ (01534) 23119
10–11; 11–1, 4.30–11 Sun
**Draught Bass; Boddingtons Bitter; Marston's Pedigree; guest beers** Ⓗ
The only gaslit pub on Jersey, serving a wide range of beers and good, no-nonsense food. No TV and no music, but still one of the liveliest pubs on Jersey. An amazing collection of memorabilia adorns the dark panelled interior.
Q ◁ ⏰

### Tipsy Toad Town House & Brewery
New Street
☎ (01534) 615000
9.30am–11pm; 11–1, 4.30–11 Sun
**Ringwood Best Bitter, Old Thumper; Tipsy Toad Ale, Jimmy's Bitter, Black Tadger, Horny Toad, Star Drooper; guest beers** Ⓗ
Superb redevelopment of a former warehouse, boasting the largest beer range on the island. The micro-brewery can be viewed through glass windows at the back. Excellent food. ◁ ▶ ૐ ⏰

## St Martin

### Anne Port Bay Hotel
Anne Port Bay
☎ (01534) 852058
11–2.30, 5–11; 11–11 Sat; 11–1, 5–11 Sun
**Draught Bass; Marston's Pedigree; guest beers** Ⓖ
Small, quiet bar in an hotel in the east of the island, popular with locals in the know. Look for guest beers on the blackboard, as they are hidden out the back. Good B&B.
Q ❀ 🍴 ◁ A P

### Royal Hotel
La Grande Route de Faldouet
☎ (01534) 856289
10–11; 11–1, 4.30–11 Sun
**Boddingtons Bitter; Marston's Pedigree; guest beers** Ⓗ
Large, popular, pub next to St Martin's church. A spacious new conservatory and a secluded garden next to an imaginative children's play area provide a fine setting for quality home-cooked food. The restaurant upstairs will serve real ale from the bar on request.
🏨 Q ❀ ◁ ▶ ⊞ ૐ A ♣ P

### Rozel Bay Inn
Rozel ☎ (01534) 863438
10–11; 11–1, 4.30–11 Sun

**Draught Bass; Boddingtons Bitter** Ⓗ
Characteristic, two-bar village pub at the foot of the valley, near a picturesque fishing harbour.
🏨 Q ⏰ ❀ ◁ P

## St Mary

### St Mary's Country Inn
☎ (01534) 481561
11–11; 11–1, 4.30–11 Sun
**Draught Bass; Worthington Bitter** Ⓗ
This 200-year-old farmhouse is now a tranquil pub in a rural setting. Garden with shady trees for the summer; good food. The games room keeps children occupied.
🏨 Q ⏰ ❀ ◁ ▶ A ♣ P ½

## St Ouen

### Moulin de Lecq
Greve de Lecq
☎ (01534) 482818
10–11; 11–1, 4.30–11 Sun
**Guernsey Braye, Sunbeam; Jersey Old Jersey Ale, Winter Ale** Ⓗ
Converted, working, 12th-century watermill with a moving drivewheel behind the bar. Large outdoor barbecue area and landscaped playground. Excellent food (not served Sun).
🏨 Q ⏰ ❀ ◁ ▶ ૐ ♣ P

## St Peter

### Star & Tipsy Toad
La Route de Beaumont
☎ (01534) 485556
10–11; 11–1, 4.30–11 Sun
**Ringwood Best Bitter, Old Thumper; Tipsy Toad Jimmy's Bitter, Black Tadger, Horny Toad; guest beers** Ⓗ
Tipsy Toad brew pub in a spacious, beautifully restored Victorian building. Good food; regular live music; indoor and outdoor children's play areas. Regular rotation of guest beers. Tours of the micro-brewery are available.
🏨 ⏰ ❀ ◁ ▶ ૐ ♣ ⏰ P

# Isle of Man

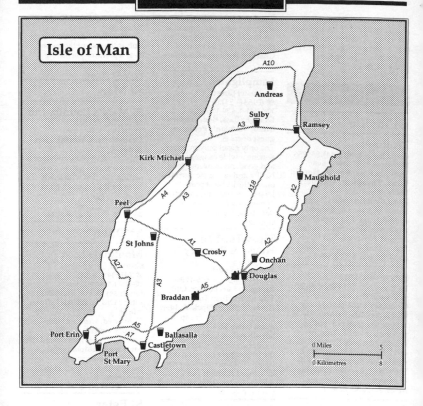

**Isle of Man**

## Andreas

### Grosvenor
☎ (01624) 880227
12–11 (midnight Fri & Sat); 12–3,
7–10.30 Sun
**Cains Bitter; Okells Bitter** Ⓗ
The most northerly island pub,
standing in the centre of the
village.
Q ☆ ◐ ▷ 🍴 & ♣ P

## Ballasalla

### Whitestone Inn
☎ (01624) 822334
12–11 (midnight Fri & Sat); 12–3,
7.30–10.30 Sun
**Okells Bitter** Ⓗ
Very friendly, village pub.
Good food is served in the
lounge; the public bar remains
for those who enjoy a pint
without the smell of cooking.
◐ 🍴 & ⇌ (IMR) ♣ P

## Castletown

### Castle Arms (Gluepot)
Quayside
☎ (01624) 824673
11–11 (midnight Fri & Sat); 12–3,
7.30–10.30 Sun
**Cains Mild, Bitter; Tetley
Bitter; guest beers** Ⓗ

One of the oldest pubs on
the island, on the harbour
opposite Castle Rushen. It
has a strong nautical flavour,
and is much favoured by
locals. Good food (not served
Sun).
🏚 Q ◐ ▷ 🍴 & ▲ ⇌ (IMR) ♣

### Sidings
Victoria Road
☎ (01624) 823282
10.30–11 (midnight Fri & Sat); 12–3,
7.30–10.30 Sun
**Draught Bass; Theakston
Black Bull, Best Bitter, XB;
guest beers** Ⓗ
Popular local with up to seven
ever-changing guest beers;
close to the Isle of Man Steam
Railway and within walking
distance of the harbour and
castle.
Q ☎ ☆ ◐ & ▲ ⇌ (IMR) ♣ P

### Viking
Victoria Road
11–11 (midnight Fri & Sat); 12–3,
7.30–10.30 Sun
**Cains Bitter; John Smith's
Bitter; guest beers** Ⓗ
Very popular, family-run
pub serving good food.
Barbecues are held in the
large garden.
Q ☎ ☆ ◐ ▷ 🍴 & ▲ ⇌ (IMR)
♣ P

## Crosby

### Crosby Hotel
11–11 (midnight Fri & Sat); 12–3,
7.30–10.30 Sun
**Okells Mild, Bitter** Ⓗ
Good pub with a local
atmosphere and friendly staff.
Popular with motorcyclists
during the TT period.
🏚 Q ☆ ☆ 🍴 & ▲ ♣ P

## Douglas

### Albert
Chapel Row (next to bus
station) ☎ (01624) 673632
12–11 (midnight Fri & Sat); 12–3,
7.30–10.30 Sun
**Okells Mild, Bitter; guest
beers** Ⓗ
Good local close to the
harbour, popular with
fishermen: a no-frills, good,
basic drinkers' pub that sells
no keg beer. A house beer,
Jough Ale from Okells, is also
sold. ⇌ (IMR)

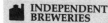

🏠 **INDEPENDENT
BREWERIES**

**Bushy's:** Braddan

**Okells:** Douglas

414

### Foresters Arms

St George's Street (off Athol St, opp. Steam Railway)
☎ (01624) 676509
12–11 (midnight Fri & Sat); 12–3, 7.30–10.30 Sun
**Okells Mild, Bitter** Ⓗ
Workingman's local with a good atmosphere. Baps and toasties are available all day. Well noted for its mild.
♨ ⬚ ⇌ (IMR) ♣

### Manor

Willaston (near the College of Further Education)
☎ (01624) 676957
11.30–11 (midnight Fri & Sat); 12–3, 7.30–10.30 Sun
**Okells Mild, Bitter** Ⓗ
Former private house, situated on a large housing estate and popular with locals.
♨ Q ❀ ⬚ P

### Old Market Inn

Chapel Row (next to bus station) ☎ (01624) 675202
10–11 (midnight Fri & Sat); 7.30–10.30 Sun
**Bushy's Best Bitter; Okells Bitter** Ⓗ
Typical local, next door to the aforementioned Albert. Good homely atmosphere; visitors are always welcome.
♨ ⬚ ⇌ (IMR) ♣

### Rover's Return

Church Street (behind Town Hall) ☎ (01624) 676459
12–11 (midnight Fri & Sat); 12–3, 7.30–10.30 Sun
**Bushy's Mild, Best Bitter, seasonal beers** Ⓗ
One of Bushy's houses: a very popular pub with locals and business people, offering the full range of Bushy's ales. The pub is known as the 'Firemans' – note the fire brigade artefacts. Good food at reasonable prices.
♨ ❀ ⬚ ⬚ ⇌ (IMR)

### Samuel Webb

Marina House, Marina Road (end of main shopping street)
☎ (01624) 675595
11–11 (midnight Fri & Sat); 12–3, 7.30–10.30 Sun
**Courage Directors; Marston's Pedigree; Ruddles County; John Smith's Bitter; Tetley Bitter; Theakston Black Bull; guest beers** Ⓗ
Family-run, popular, traditional pub which offers a fine selection of guest beers. Home-made, freshly cooked meals are served Mon–Sat (very good menu for all tastes).
❀ ⬚ ⬚

### Terminus Tavern

Strathallan Crescent (N end of Douglas Promenade)
☎ (01624) 624312
12–11 (midnight Fri & Sat); 12–3, 7.30–10.30 Sun
**Okells Mild, Bitter** Ⓗ

Elegant Victorian hostelry, built 100 years ago, well-furnished in a style reminiscent of a terminus waiting buffet, and serving clients of the adjacent electric and horse trams. Excellent food. Wheelchair WC. ♨ Q ⬚ ❀ ⬚ ⬚ & ⇌ (MER) ♣ P

### Tramshunters Arms

Sefton Hotel, Harris Promenade ☎ (01624) 626011
11–11 (midnight Fri & Sat); 12–3, 7.30–10.30 Sun
**Boddingtons Bitter; Castle Eden Ale; Flowers IPA, Original; Marston's Pedigree; guest beers** Ⓗ
Popular, town-centre pub with a large range of traditional beers and constantly changing guest beers. ⇌ ⬚ ⬚ & P

### Waterloo

Strand Street (main shopping street) ☎ (01624) 676833
12–11 (midnight Fri & Sat); 12–3, 7.30–10.30 Sun
**Okells Mild, Bitter** Ⓗ
Typical, town-centre pub saved from development: the only basic pub left in the shopping area. Baps and toasties all day. The rear entrance is off Market St.
♣

**Try also: Railway**, Bridge Rd (Okells)

## Kirk Michael

### Mitre

Main Road ☎ (01624) 878244
11–10.45 (midnight Fri & Sat); 12–3, 7.30–10.30 Sun
**Okells Bitter** Ⓗ
The island's oldest inn has been well refurbished, making it a friendly, cosy pub. The rear garden boasts views across the hills; an ideal TT vantage point. Varied menu.
♨ ❀ ⬚ ⬚ ⬚ & ⬚ ♣ P

## Maughold

### Glen Mona

Glen Mona Hotel
☎ (01624) 861263
12–3, 6–11 (midnight Fri & Sat); 12–3, 7.30–10.30 Sun
**Bushy's Bitter; Okells Bitter; Tetley Bitter** Ⓗ
Country inn with views across the hills to the sea. An ideal spot to hop off the electric tram for lunch. The garden has a pets corner for children.
♨ ❀ ⬚ ⬚ ⬚ ⇌ (Glen Mona MER) ♣ P

## Onchan

### Liverpool Arms

Main Road, Baldrine (Laxey road, 1½ miles from Onchan)
☎ (01624) 674787

12–11 (midnight Fri & Sat); 12–3, 7.30–10.30 Sun
**Okells Mild, Bitter** Ⓗ
Old halfway house, still showing its former Castletown Brewery livery, in a pleasant rural setting. Convivial atmosphere; good food.
♨ Q ❀ ⬚ ⬚ & ⇌ (MER) ♣ P

### Manx Arms

Main Road
☎ (01624) 675484
12–11 (midnight Fri & Sat); 12–3, 7.30–10.30 Sun
**Okells Mild, Bitter** Ⓗ
Large, busy pub in the village centre, on the corner of a former car racing circuit (as shown in numerous photos inside). Q ⬚ ❀ ⬚ ♣ P

## Peel

### Royal

Atholl Street
12–11 (midnight Fri & Sat); 12–3, 7.30–10.30 Sun
**Okells Mild, Bitter** Ⓗ
Town-centre pub, opposite the bus station: a small front room, a large rear room and a popular narrow bar.
Q ❀ ⬚

### White House

2 Tynwald Road
☎ (01624) 842252
11–11 (midnight Fri & Sat); 12–3, 7.30–10.30 Sun
**Draught Bass; Bushy's Best Bitter; Flowers Original; Okells Mild, Bitter; guest beers** Ⓗ
Friendly pub with a cosy 'Captain's' snug. Manx music Sat eve. CAMRA IOM *Pub of the Year* 1992 and '94. Lunchtime snacks.
♨ Q ❀ ⬚ ♣ P

## Port Erin

### Falcon's Nest

Near the station
☎ (01624) 834077
11–11 (midnight Fri & Sat); 12–3, 7.30–10.30 Sun
**Castle Eden Ale; Okells Bitter; Tetley Bitter** Ⓗ
Hotel at the centre of Port Erin: a lively bar and a quiet room. The small bar boasts sea views. Good food.
♨ Q ⇌ ⬚ ⬚ ⬚ & ⇌ (IMR) ♣

## Port St Mary

### Albert Hotel

Athol Street (opp. harbour, next to the main bus terminus)
☎ (01624) 832118
11–11 (midnight Fri & Sat); 12–3, 7.30–10.30 Sun
**Bushy's Best Bitter; Cains Mild; Okells Bitter; guest beers** Ⓗ
Traditional fisherman's pub by the harbour; popular with yachtsmen. Pool room.

Children welcome. No meals Sun eve. Limited parking.
🛏 Q 🍴 ◖◗ ⊞ ♣ P

## Ramsey

### Britannia
Waterloo Road
☎ (01624) 816547
12–11 (midnight Fri & Sat); 12–3, 7.30–10.30 Sun
**Okells Mild, Bitter** Ⓗ
Opposite the electric tram terminus: a good locals' bar and a popular lounge.
Q 🚲 ❀ ◖◗ ⊞ ⇌ (MER) ♣

### Swan
Parliament Square
☎ (01624) 814236
12–11 (midnight Fri & Sat); 12–3, 7.30–10.30 Sun
**Okells Mild, Bitter** Ⓗ

---

Town-centre pub on the TT course, popular with motorcyclists during the races: a large lounge and a bar.
❀ ◖◗ ⊞ ♿ ⇌ (MER) ♣

### Trafalgar
West Quay ☎ (01624) 814601
12–11 (midnight Fri & Sat); 12–3, 7.30–10.30 Sun
**Bushy's Best Bitter; Cains Mild, Bitter; guest beers** Ⓗ
Harbourside pub, accessible from the shopping area through any of the many lanes.
◖ ⇌ (MER)

### St Johns

### Farmers Arms
Left off road to St Johns at Tynwald Hill
☎ (01624) 801372

---

11–11 (midnight Fri & Sat); 12–3, 7.30–10.30 Sun
**Bushy's Best Bitter; Cains Bitter; Ind Coope Burton Ale; Tetley Bitter** Ⓗ
Typical rural inn, popular with locals and refurbished in country style. Home-cooking and a friendly atmosphere feature. ❀ ◖◗ P

## Sulby

### Sulby Glen Hotel
Main Road ☎ (01624) 897240
12–11 (midnight Fri & Sat); 12–3, 7.30–10.30 Sun
**Bushy's Best Bitter; Cains Mild; Okells Mild, Bitter; guest beer** Ⓗ
Country inn on a fast stretch of the TT course. Food available all day. Recommended B&B.
🛏 ❀ 🍴 ◖◗ ⊞ ⚓ ♣ P

# CAMRA's Aims

## We aim to

 *maintain consumer rights*

 *promote quality, choice and value for money*

 *support the public house*

 *and campaign for greater appreciation of traditional beers, ciders and perries*

# THE BREWERIES

# THE BREWERIES

A SENSATIONAL 68 – that's the number of new breweries which feature in the breweries section of *Good Beer Guide 1997*. When added to the dozens of new breweries which have arrived in the last few years, this is a remarkable increase in the number of producers. It means that, if you look hard enough, you can discover hundreds of new real ales. With the established brewers also broadening their ranges, through special and seasonal offerings (often one a month), there hasn't been a better variety of British beers for decades.

The national breweries, on the other hand, seem to be moving in reverse. Though there are notable exceptions – Whitbread's limited edition brews and Carlsberg-Tetley's Allsopp's guest beer plant – they are closing breweries and rationalising beer brands. Tetley Walker in Warrington, Webster's in Halifax, Plympton in Devon and Home in Nottingham are the major losses, and though their beer brands are still produced elsewhere, how long this will continue is anyone's guess.

## —— BASS-CARLSBERG? ——

More closures could be on the way, particularly if the Bass-Carlsberg deal is given the go-ahead. The merger of Scottish & Newcastle and Courage into Scottish Courage was bad enough, but the thought of Bass-Carlsberg is alarming. This new company would have over 40 per cent of all UK beer production. Bass-Carlsberg and Scottish Courage, the top two brewers together, would have over 70 per cent of the market. This fact alone should bring the Monopolies and Mergers Commission into play. The threat to jobs and beer choice should, in a sensible world, ensure the Government blocks the deal, but, having seen how Scottish Courage was nodded through, there is little confidence that a heavy hand from above will be forthcoming.

## —— THE CONSEQUENCES ——

Bass-Carlsberg: think of the consequences. One company with two giant breweries in Burton upon Trent – would both survive? One company with numerous competing beer brands – what future is there for Stones or M&B in the same stable as Tetley and Ansells? Draught Bass would surely see off Ind Coope Burton Ale – what a way to go for CAMRA's *Champion Beer of Britain 1990*. The new company would also have control over thousands of pubs. Another question is where does this leave Whitbread, by far the smallest of the national brewers? Would it decide that the game was up, sell up its breweries and brands to Bass-Carlsberg or Scottish Courage, and retire to retailing?

CAMRA will continue to campaign against such concentration in the industry at the same time as it is happily promoting all the new breweries and their beers. All the UK's real ale producers are featured in the new-look breweries section, which contains all the same information as before (indeed more), but in a more concise fashion. See the key opposite for details of the new symbols we have introduced this year. Read on and find out all you need to know about British brewing today.

418

## KEY TO THE BREWERIES SECTION

Breweries are listed in alphabetical order. The Independents (including brew pubs) are listed first, followed by The Nationals. The major Pub Groups (non-brewing pub owning chains) complete the section. Within each brewery listing, beers are listed in increasing order of strength. Beers which are available for less than three months of the year are listed in the main brewery description as 'occasional' or 'seasonal' beers. Bottle-conditioned beers are also mentioned. These are bottled beers which have not been pasteurised and still contain yeast, allowing them to continue to ferment in the bottle just like draught real ale ferments in the cask.

**Symbols:**

A brew pub: a pub which produces beer on the premises.

◆ CAMRA tasting notes (supplied by a trained CAMRA tasting panel). Beer descriptions not preceded by this symbol are based on limited tastings only or have been obtained from other sources. Tasting notes are not provided for brew pub beers which are only available in one or two outlets, nor for other breweries' beers which are available for less than three months of the year.

◨ A *Good Beer Guide Beer of the Year* in the last three years.

◧ One of this year's *Good Beer Guide Beers of the Year*, finalist in the *Champion Beer of Britain* contest held during the Great British Beer Festival at Olympia in August 1996.

**Abbreviations:**

OG stands for Original Gravity, the reading taken before fermentation begins of the amount of fermentable material in the brew. It is a rough indicator of strength. More reliable is the ABV (Alcohol by Volume) rating, which gives the percentage of alcohol in the finished beer. Many breweries now only declare ABV figures, but where OGs are available these have been included.

---

**ABC** See Nationals, Carlsberg-Tetley.

---

## ABERDEENSHIRE
**Aberdeenshire Ales Ltd.,
Mains of Inverebrie,
Drumwhindle, Ellon,
Aberdeenshire AB41 8PX.
☎ / FAX (01358) 761457**

Brewery founded in old farm buildings in May 1995 by Simon and Valerie Lister, who commissioned a hand-made real copper kettle and use Yorkshire square fermenters. The beers are now distributed throughout the UK. Tours by arrangement.

**Buchan Gold** (ABV 4%) A beer with an earthy hop aroma, with ripe citrus fruit, and a rich, firm, malty palate. The finish starts bittersweet and becomes dry with malt, hops and a hint of vanilla.

**Buchan Bronco** (ABV 4.6%) A traditional Scottish ale, with a roast malt nose. Initial sweetness develops into a complex fruitiness and nuttiness, leading to a dry, malty finish.

## ABERYSTWYTH
**Aberystwyth Ales, Llanrhystud, Ceredigion.**

Brewery closed.

## ABINGTON PARK
See Nationals, Scottish Courage.

## ADNAMS
**Adnams and Company PLC,
Sole Bay Brewery, East
Green, Southwold, Suffolk
IP18 6JW. ☎ (01502) 727200
FAX (01502) 727201**

East Anglia's seaside brewery, established in 1890, whose local deliveries are still made by horse drays. Real ale is available in all its 102 pubs, and it also supplies some 650 other outlets direct, with the beers available nationwide via agents. A gradual expansion is planned for the tied estate, 32 ex-Lacon pubs having been acquired from Whitbread in April 1995. Brewery shop open Mon–Fri. Occasional/seasonal beers: Barley Mow (OG

1050, ABV 5%, August–September), Tally Ho (OG 1075, ABV 6.4%, Christmas).

**Mild** (OG 1035, ABV 3.2%) ⬚ ❧ In this fine black/red mild, the aroma is a subtle blend of fruit and malt with a hint of roast. A good balance of malt, roast and hops on a bittersweet base precedes a dry, faintly malty finish.

**Bitter** (OG 1036, ABV 3.7%) ▮ ❧ An excellent drinking beer, with the characteristic Adnams aroma of hops, citrus fruits and sulphur. The flavour is dry and hoppy, with some fruit. The finish is long, dry and hoppy.

**Old Ale** (OG 1041, ABV 4.1%) ⬚ ❧ A rich, dark brown winter beer, a well-balanced blend of grain, roast malt and raisin, on a bittersweet base. The rich fruit aroma has faint roast and grain elements. Dry, faintly fruity aftertaste.

**Extra** (OG 1043, ABV 4.3%) ⬚ ▮ ❧ An aroma of hops and citrus fruit leads through to bitter orange and hops on the palate, before a long dry, finish with some hops and fruit. Noticeably less pungent than in previous years.

**Mayday** (OG 1046, ABV 5%) A spring beer, brewed April–June.

**Broadside** (OG 1049, ABV 4.7%) ❧ Mid-brown beer with a well-balanced flavour of fruit, malt and hops on a bittersweet base. The aroma is fruity, with some underlying malt and hops. Bitter fruit finish.

## ALDCHLAPPIE
**Aldchlappie Hotel, Kirkmichael, Perthshire and Kinross, PH10 7NS.**
☎ **(01250) 881224**

🍺 A new micro-brewery opened alongside this pub in 1996 to produce two beers (a combination of full mash and malt extract) for its clientele of walkers and skiers. The beer names follow a Scottish/English history theme. Special brews may follow. Beers: 1314 (ABV 4.5%), 1707 (ABV 4.5%).

## ALFORD ARMS
See Nationals, Whitbread.

## ALL NATIONS
**All Nations, Coalport Road, Madeley, Telford, Shropshire TF7 5DA.**
☎ **(01952) 585747**

🍺 One of the very few brew pubs left before the new wave. All Nations has, in fact, been brewing for 200 years. Still known as Mrs Lewis's, the inn has been in the same family since 1934. Beer: Pale Ale (OG 1033, ABV 3%).

## ALLIED BREWERIES
See Nationals, Carlsberg-Tetley.

**ALLOA** See Nationals, Carlsberg-Tetley.

## ANCIENT DRUIDS
**Ancient Druids, Napier Street, Cambridge CB1 1HR.** ☎ **(01223) 576324**
FAX **(01223) 576323**

🍺 Brew pub set up in 1984 by Charles Wells, brewing with malt extract. It occasionally supplies one or two other Wells pubs. Tours by arrangement. Beer: Druids' Mild, Pcella (a honey beer), Elle's SB (the ABVs tend to vary).

## ANN STREET See Jersey.

## ANSELLS
See Nationals, Carlsberg-Tetley.

## ARCHERS
**Archers Ales Ltd., Penzance Drive, Churchward, Swindon, Wiltshire SN5 7JL.** ☎ **(01793) 496789**
FAX **(01793) 421598**

Small brewery, set up in 1979 in the old Great Western Railway works. Renovation and reconstruction of an old engine weighing shed, to transform it into a traditional tower brewery, was undertaken in 1996 and a new brewery tap is to be built alongside. This will bring the Archers tied estate up to four houses. Around 200 free trade outlets from Oxford to Bath are also supplied via wholesalers. Shop open 9–5. Tours by arrangement for customers and CAMRA groups.

**Village Bitter** (OG 1035, ABV 3.5%) ❧ A dry, well-balanced beer, with a full body for its gravity. Malty and fruity in the nose, then a fresh, hoppy flavour with balancing malt and a hoppy, fruity finish.

**Best Bitter** (OG 1040, ABV 4%) ❧ Slightly sweeter and rounder than Village, with a malty, fruity aroma and a pronounced bitter finish.

**Black Jack Porter** (OG 1046, ABV 4.6%) ❧ A winter brew: a black beer with intense roast malt dominant on the tongue. The aroma is fruity and there is some sweetness on the palate, but the finish is pure roast grain.

**Golden Bitter** (OG 1046, ABV 4.7%) ❧ A full-bodied, hoppy, straw-coloured brew with an underlying fruity sweetness. Very little aroma, but a strong bitter finish.

**ASB** (OG 1055, ABV 5.5%)

## ARKELL'S
**Arkell's Brewery Ltd., Kingsdown, Swindon, Wiltshire SN2 6RU.**
☎ **(01793) 823026**
FAX **(01793) 828864**

Established in 1843 and now one of the few remaining breweries whose shares are all held by one family, with its managing director, James Arkell, a great-great-grandson of founder John Arkell. A gradual expansion is taking place in the tied estate, mainly along the M4 corridor, and the brewery is committed to a continual programme of upgrading and refurbishment for its pubs. All 85 tied pubs serve real ale, which is also supplied direct to around 200 free trade accounts. Brewery tours by arrangement. Occasional/seasonal beers: Mash Tun Mild (OG 1036, ABV 3.5%, winter), Summer Ale (OG 1042, ABV 4.2%), Yeomanry (OG 1045, ABV 4.5%, spring), Peter's Porter (OG 1049, ABV 4.8%, autumn/winter), Noel Ale (OG 1055, ABV 5.5%, Christmas) – these may not be available in all Arkell's pubs and may need seeking out.

**Bitter** (OG 1032, ABV 3.2%) ◈ Formerly 2B: a hoppy, pale beer with a hint of fruit and honey. A most refreshing lunchtime or session ale, with good body for its OG.

**3B** (OG 1040, ABV 4%) ◈ An unusual and distinctive bitter. The crystal malt gives a nutty taste which persists throughout and combines with bitterness in the aftertaste.

**Kingsdown Ale** (OG 1052, ABV 5%) ◈ 3B's big brother with which it is parti-gyled (derived from the same mash). A powerful roast malt/fruit flavour is followed by a lingering, dry aftertaste.

---

## ARUNDEL

**Arundel Brewery, Unit C7, Ford Airfield Estate, Ford, Arundel, W. Sussex BN18 0BE.**
☎ (01903) 733111
FAX (01903) 733381

Set up in 1992, the town's first brewery in 60 years, Arundel produces beers from authentic Sussex recipes, without the use of additives. Its commitment to this tradition has led to steady growth and the brewery now supplies around 100 outlets, plus its single tied house, the Swan in Arundel. Old Knucker was named after a legendary dragon, Knucker, who terrorised townsfolk before being slain by a local hero. Arundel now also brews for Beards of Sussex (see Pub Groups). Tours by arrangement. Occasional/seasonal beers: Old Conspirator (OG 1050, ABV 5%, October–November), Old Scrooge (OG 1060, ABV 6%, Christmas).

**Best Bitter** (OG 1040, ABV 4%) ◈ A pale tawny beer with fruit and malt noticeable in the aroma. The flavour exhibits a good balance of malt, fruit and hops, with a dry, hoppy finish.

**Gold** (OG 1042, ABV 4.2%) ◈ A light golden 'summer' style ale with a malty character.

**ASB** (OG 1045, ABV 4.5%)

**Summerdaze** (OG 1047, ABV 4.7%)

**Stronghold** (OG 1050, ABV 5%) ◈ A good balance of malt, fruit and hops come through in this rich, malty beer.

**Old Knucker** (OG 1055, ABV 5.5%) ◈ A dark, full-bodied beer. The flavour is a complex blend of sweet fruit and caramel maltiness, which balances a dry roast bitterness. This is mirrored in the aftertaste. Roast malt, fruit, caramel and some hops feature in the aroma. Brewed September–April.

### For Beards:

**Beards Best Bitter** (OG 1040/ABV 4%) ◈ Hints of fruit and hops in the aroma lead into a sweet, malty beer, with a dry, hoppy aftertaste.

---

## ASH VINE

**Ash Vine Brewery (South West) Ltd., The White Hart, Trudoxhill, Frome, Somerset BA11 5DP.**
☎ /FAX (01373) 836344

Brewery set up in 1987 near Taunton, but moved to the White Hart pub in January 1989. Ash Vine acquired its third pub in 1995 and brewing capacity was increased by 50 per cent in the same year. A new beer is now brewed every month, usually to a theme and to a never-repeated recipe. Some 50 free trade outlets are supplied locally. Tours by arrangement. Bottle-conditioned beer: Hop & Glory (OG 1052, ABV 5%).

**Bitter** (OG 1036, ABV 3.5%) ◈ A light gold bitter with a floral hop aroma. A powerful, bitter hoppiness dominates the taste and leads to a dry, and occasionally astringent, finish. An unusual and distinctive brew.

**Challenger** (OG 1043, ABV 4.1%) ◈ A mid-brown beer with a solid malt flavour balanced by a good hoppy bitterness and subtle citrus fruits. It can be sulphurous and slightly metallic.

**Black Bess Porter** (OG 1044, ABV 4.2%) ◈ A dark copper-brown, bitter porter with roast malt, hops and a sweet fruitiness. Roast malt and hop nose; dry, bitter finish.

**Hop & Glory** (OG 1052, ABV 5%) ◈ A copper-coloured beer with a malt, fruit and hop aroma. The taste is bittersweet, with hops in abundance and some citrus fruits. Similar finish. A complex, rich and warming winter ale.

---

## ASTON MANOR

**Aston Manor Brewery Company Ltd., 173 Thimblemill Lane, Aston, Birmingham, W. Midlands B7 5HS.** ☎ (0121) 328 4336
FAX (0121) 328 0139

Aston Manor ceased brewing cask-conditioned beer in 1994, due to lack of free trade outlets in Birmingham. It now concentrates on canned and bottled beers.

---

## AYLESBURY (ABC)

See Nationals, Carlsberg-Tetley.

## B&T

B&T Brewery Ltd., The
Brewery, Shefford,
Bedfordshire SG17 5DZ.
☎ (01462) 815080
FAX (01462) 850841

Banks & Taylor, founded in 1981, fell into receivership in 1994 but was quickly rescued under the name of B&T, with key Banks & Taylor personnel retained to produce the same extensive range of beers, including the monthly special brews. The company now supplies around 60 outlets direct, including two tied pubs of its own. Brewery tours by arrangement. Occasional/seasonal beers: Midsummer Ale (OG 1035, ABV 3.5%), Bedfordshire Clanger (OG 1038, ABV 4%, March), Santa Slayer (OG 1040, ABV, 4%), Madhatter (OG 1042, ABV 4.2%, May), Maiden's Rescue (OG 1042, ABV 4.2%, April), Bodysnatcher (OG 1044, ABV 4.4%, October), Guy Fawkes Bitter (OG 1045, ABV 4.5%, November), Romeo's Ruin (OG 1045, ABV 4.5%, February), Emerald Ale (OG 1050, ABV 5%, March), Juliet's Revenge (OG 1050, ABV 5%, February), Shefford Wheat Beer (OG 1050, ABV 5%, July–August), Frostbite (OG 1055, ABV 5.5%, December–January), Bat out of Hell (OG 1060, ABV 6%, November), Skeleton Special (OG 1060, ABV 6%).

**Shefford Bitter** (OG 1038, ABV 3.8%) ◆ A pleasant, well-balanced session beer with a distinct bitter aftertaste.

**Shefford Mild** (OG 1038, ABV 3.8%) ◆ A dark beer with a well-balanced taste. Sweetish, roast malt aftertaste.

**Dragonslayer** (OG 1045, ABV 4.5%) ◆ A straw-coloured beer, dry, malty and lightly hopped.

**Edwin Taylor's Extra Stout** (OG 1045, ABV 4.5%) ◆ A pleasant, bitter beer with a strong roast malt flavour.

**Shefford Pale Ale (SPA)** (OG 1045, ABV 4.5%) ◆ A well-balanced beer, with hop, fruit and malt flavours. Dry, bitter aftertaste.

**Shefford Old Dark (SOD)** (OG 1050, ABV 5%) ◆ SOS with caramel added for colour. Often sold under house names.

**Shefford Old Strong (SOS)** (OG 1050, ABV 5%) ◆ A malty, fruity beer with a bitter aftertaste.

**Black Bat** (OG 1060, ABV 6%) ◆ A powerful, sweet, fruity and malty beer for winter. Fruity, nutty aroma; strong roast malt aftertaste.

**2XS** (OG 1060, ABV 6%) ◆ A reddish beer with a strong, fruity, hoppy aroma. The taste is full-flavoured and the finish strong and sweetish.

**Old Bat** (OG 1070, ABV 7%) ◆ Powerful-tasting, sweet winter beer, with bitterness

coming through in the aftertaste. Fruit is present in both aroma and taste.

## BACKDYKES

Backdykes Brewing Company, Mid Strathore Farm, Thornton, Fife KY1 4DF.
☎ (01592) 775303

Brewery founded in late 1995 which began production in January 1996. 'Malcolm's Severely Drinkable Ales' are supplied to the local free trade and to outlets further afield.

**Malcolm's Ceilidh** (ABV 3.7%) Sold South of the Border as Session.

**Malcolm's Premium Ale** (ABV 4.3%)

**Malcolm's Help Ma Bob** (ABV 5%)

## BADGER

Hall & Woodhouse Ltd.,
The Badger Brewery,
Blandford St Mary,
Blandford Forum, Dorset
DT11 9LS. ☎ (01258) 452141
FAX (01258) 459953

BADGER

Hall & Woodhouse (established as the Ansty Brewery in 1777) has been known as the Badger Brewery since it moved from Ansty to its present site over 100 years ago. The company has only now adopted this as its trading name, at the same time making alterations to its beer range. Still largely family-run, the brewery continues to broaden its trading area. All 167 of its tied houses take real ale (although some use cask breathers) and a further 500 outlets are supplied direct. The brewery also owns the Gribble Inn in Oving, W. Sussex (see Gribble). Shop open 9–7 Mon–Sat. Tours by arrangement.

**IPA** (OG 1036, ABV 3.6%)

**Dorset Best** (OG 1041, ABV 4.1%) ◆ Formerly Badger Best Bitter. A fine best bitter whose taste is strong in hop and bitterness, with underlying malt and fruit. Hoppy finish with a bitter edge.

**Tanglefoot** (OG 1050, ABV 5.1%) ◆ A pale-coloured beer, with a full fruit character throughout. Some malt and hops are also present in the palate, whilst the finish is bittersweet. Dangerously drinkable.

## BALLARD'S

Ballard's Brewery Ltd.,
Unit C, The Old Sawmill,
Nyewood, Petersfield,
Hampshire GU31 5HA.
☎ (01730) 821301/821362
FAX (01730) 821742

Founded in 1980 at Cumbers Farm, Trotton, Ballard's has been trading at Nyewood (in W. Sussex, despite the postal address) since 1988 and now supplies around 60 free trade outlets. Shop open 8–4 Mon–Fri (Sat by arrangement). Tours by arrangement. Occasional/seasonal beer: a Christmas ale with a gravity to match the number of the year. Bottle-conditioned beers: Wassail (OG 1060, ABV 6%), Divine (OG 1095, ABV 9.6%, formerly known as Off the Wall).

**Midhurst Mild** (OG 1034, ABV 3.5%) A rarely seen, basic dark mild.

**Trotton Bitter** (OG 1035, ABV 3.6%) ◆ Complex for its gravity, this well-balanced beer has an initial maltiness which fades to a hoppy finish.

**Best Bitter** (OG 1042, ABV 4.2%) ◆ A copper-coloured beer with a malty aroma. A good balance of fruit and malt in the flavour gives way to a dry, hoppy aftertaste.

**Golden Bine** (OG 1042, ABV 4.2%) ◆ A refreshing, golden summer brew.

**Wild** (ABV 4.7%) ◆ A dark brown beer, produced by blending Mild with Wassail. Initial hints of fruit give way to a malty flavour and a dry, hoppy aftertaste.

**Wassail** (OG 1060, ABV 6%) ▱ ◆ A strong, full-bodied, fruity beer with a predominance of malt throughout, but also an underlying hoppiness. Tawny red in colour.

**Divine** (OG 1095, ABV 9.6%) Available in winter.

## BANKS & TAYLOR See B&T.

## BANKS'S
**The Wolverhampton & Dudley Breweries PLC, PO Box 26, Park Brewery, Bath Road, Wolverhampton, W. Midlands WV1 4NY.**
☎ (01902) 711811 [FAX] (01902) 29136

*Unspoilt by Progress*

Wolverhampton & Dudley Breweries was formed in 1890 by the amalgamation of three local companies. Hanson's was acquired in 1943, but its Dudley brewery was closed in 1991 and Hanson's Mild is now brewed at Wolverhampton. The 150 Hanson's pubs keep their own livery. In 1992, W&D bought Camerons Brewery and 51 pubs from Brent Walker, bringing the total estate for the whole group up to 950 houses, virtually all serving traditional ales, mostly through electric, metered dispense. There is also extensive free trade throughout the country, in pubs and clubs. Special brews are produced every two months for sale under the Festival Beers banner. Tours by arrangement.

**Hanson's Mild** (OG 1035, ABV 3.2%) ◆ A mid- to dark brown mild with a malty roast flavour and aftertaste.

**Mild** (OG 1036, ABV 3.5%) ◆ Also known as Banks's Ale. A top-selling, amber-coloured, well-balanced, refreshing light mild.

**Bitter** (OG 1039, ABV 3.8%) ◆ A pale brown bitter with a pleasant balance of hops and malt. Hops continue from the taste through to a bittersweet aftertaste.

## BANK TOP
**Bank Top Brewery, Unit 1, Back Lane, off Vernon Street, Bolton, Gtr Manchester BL1 2LD.** ☎ (01204) 528865

John Feeney learned about the brewing business at Sunderland University and then at Thomas McGuiness Brewery. In September 1995, he set up this new brewery with partner Bernard Fallon. Already working to its weekly capacity of ten barrels, the brewery now plans to add another fermentation vessel. Around 40–50 outlets take the beers locally, but they are also available nationwide via wholesalers. Tours by arrangement (reception at the Howcroft Inn, Bolton).

**Bridge Bitter** (ABV 3.8%)

**Fred's Cap** (ABV 4%)

**Samuel Crompton's Ale** (ABV 4.2%)

## BARLEY See Fox & Hounds.

## BARNSLEY
**Barnsley Brewing Co. Ltd., Elsecar Brewery, Wath Road, Elsecar, Barnsley, S. Yorkshire S74 8HJ.**
☎ (01226) 741010
[FAX] (01226) 741009

Established in March 1994 as the South Yorkshire Brewing Company, Barnsley brews with an old yeast culture from the town's long-defunct Oakwell Brewery. Demand continues to grow and the brewery now serves 175 free trade outlets alongside its own three tied houses (there are plans to increase the estate by a dozen pubs by mid-1997). A bottling plant was installed in the spring of 1996. Tours by arrangement. Bottle-conditioned beer: Bitter (ABV 3.8%).

**Bitter** (OG 1037, ABV 3.8%) ▱ ◆ A smooth ruby/mid-brown coloured beer which has little aroma, but an even balance of malt and hops compensates. A distinctive bitter with a lasting aftertaste.

**IPA** (OG 1041, ABV 4.2%) ◆ When tasted in the early days of its production, this beer appeared to be dominated by fruit and hops, leading on to a hoppy finish. Yellowish in colour; flowery aroma.

**Black Heart Stout** (OG 1044, ABV 4.6%) ◆ A black stout with a hoppy aroma, and lots of roasted malt flavour throughout. Chocolatey bitter finish. Hard to find.

**BASS** See Nationals.

## BATEMAN

**George Bateman & Son Ltd., Salem Bridge Brewery, Mill Lane, Wainfleet, Skegness, Lincolnshire PE24 4JE. ☎ (01754) 880317 FAX (01754) 880939**

A family-owned and -run brewery, established in 1874 by a bankrupt farmer, the grandfather of present chairman George Bateman, to serve local landworkers. In the mid-1980s a family dispute threatened the brewery's future, but, after a three-year battle, George secured the brewery's independence and is now steadily expanding its sales area to cover nearly the whole of the UK. Around 200 outlets are supplied direct. Bateman owns 57 houses (three of which are free of tie) and all serve real ale. Shop open 8.45–5 Mon–Fri. Tours by arrangement.

**Dark Mild** (OG 1033, ABV 3%) 🍷 🍺 ✦ A complex ruby/black mild with a mottled brown head and a bitter bite in the taste and beyond. Malt, however, is the predominant factor, backed by some roast malt and caramel features.

**XB** (OG 1037, ABV 3.7%) ✦ Golden brown, light drinking bitter, with a strong, fruity hop aroma and taste. Maltiness is never far behind, but cannot overpower the hop bitterness.

**Valiant** (OG 1043, ABV 4.2%) ✦ Old gold in colour: a bitter and hoppy beer, but with an apple fruit aroma and a malty, slightly banana toffee aftertaste. Difficult to find in the tied trade.

**Salem Porter** (OG 1049, ABV 4.7%) 🍷 ✦ A fruity (rosehips) nose giving way to a deep liquorice taste, ending in a hoppy dryness, only partially describes this complex, black beer. Again, not all that easy to find.

**XXXB** (OG 1049, ABV 4.8%) ✦ Dark amber ale with powerful malt and hops throughout and underlying orange and cinnamon flavours. The malt and hops balance beautifully, but the bitterness always wins through.

**Victory Ale** (OG 1059, ABV 5.7%) ✦ A fruity, powerful, strong beer, malty and sweet to the taste, developing into a lighter, fruity, hoppy and bitter finish, that makes it dangerously drinkable for its strength.

## BATH

**Bath Ales, Gibbs Marsh, Bow Bridge Works, Henstridge Trading Estate, Henstridge, Somerset BA8 0TH. ☎ (01963) 362549**

Brewery founded in September 1995 by two former Smiles Brewery employees, using the same brewing plant as Henstridge Brewery (qv). Around 50 outlets now take the beers from time to time. The aim is to move into

premises in Bath itself at the earliest opportunity.

**Gem** (OG 1041, ABV 4.1%)

**Barnstormer** (OG 1046, ABV 4.5%)

## BATHAM

**Daniel Batham & Son Ltd., Delph Brewery, Delph Road, Brierley Hill, W. Midlands DY5 2TN. ☎ (01384) 77229 FAX (01384) 482292**

Small brewery hidden behind one of the Black Country's most famous pubs, the Vine (or the 'Bull & Bladder', as it is commonly known). Established in 1877 and now in its fifth generation of family ownership, Batham currently supplies 20 free trade outlets. A programme of upgrading and refurbishment in its tied estate (nine houses) is expected to be completed by 1997 and there are plans to acquire more pubs. Tours on Saturdays, at 10am by arrangement (max. ten people).

**Mild Ale** (OG 1037, ABV 3.5%) ✦ A fruity, dark brown mild with a malty sweetness and a roast malt finish.

**Best Bitter** (OG 1044, ABV 4.3%) 🍷 🍺 ✦ A pale yellow, fruity, sweetish bitter, with a dry hoppy finish. A good, light refreshing beer when on form.

**Strong Ale** (OG 1064, ABV 6.3%)

## BAYNARDS

**Baynards Brewhouse, The Thurlow Arms, Baynards, Rudgwick, W. Sussex RH12 3AD. ☎ (01403) 822459 FAX (01403) 822125**

🍺 Brewery established in February 1996, using equipment transferred from the owner's brother's pub, the Cyder House Inn at Shackleford. Apart from the Thurlow Arms, only The Cyder House takes the beer at present. Tours by arrangement. Beers: Station House Brew (OG 1039, ABV 3.8%), Old Shunter (OG 1045, ABV 4.5%), Tunnel Vision (ABV 5.5%, winter).

**BEARDS** See Arundel and Pub Groups.

## BEARTOWN

**Beartown Brewery, Unit 9, Varey Road, Eaton Bank Trading Estate, Congleton, Cheshire CW12 1UW. ☎ (01260) 299964 FAX (01260) 274263**

Congleton's links with brewing can be traced back to 1272, when the town received charter status. Two of its most senior officers at the time were Ale Taster and Bear Warden, hence the name of this new brewery, set up in November 1994 on land which once housed a silk mill. The brewery is constantly being upgraded, with recent additions being a cold store room and new conditioning vessels, while the beer range has also been completely revised. Around 15 free trade outlets take the beers directly. Tours by arrangement.

**Ambeardextrous** (OG 1037, ABV 3.8%) ❧ A mid-brown, well-balanced bitter with coffee and chocolate notes.

**Bearskinful** (OG 1040, ABV 4.2%)

**SB** (OG 1043, ABV 4.2%) ❧ A tawny-coloured, malty beer, with a clean hop finish.

**Bruins Ruin** (OG 1048, ABV 5%)

## BEER ENGINE
**The Beer Engine,
Sweetham, Newton St
Cyres, Exeter, Devon
EX5 5AX. ☎ (01392) 851282**

Brew pub set up in 1983, next to the Barnstaple branch railway line (hence the beer names). One other outlet is supplied regularly and the beers are also distributed via agencies. Tours by arrangement. Occasional beers are brewed for celebrations, anniversaries and other special events.

**Rail Ale** (OG 1037, ABV 3.8%) ❧ An amber-coloured beer with a malty aroma and a fruity, sweet taste.

**Piston Bitter** (OG 1043, ABV 4.3%) ❧ A mid-brown, sweet-tasting beer with a pleasant, bittersweet aftertaste.

**Sleeper Heavy** (OG 1055, ABV 5.4%) ❧ Red-coloured beer with a fruity, sweet taste and a bitter finish.

**BELCHERS** See Hedgehog & Hogshead.

## BELHAVEN
**Belhaven Brewery Co. Ltd.,
Spott Road, Dunbar,
Lothian EH42 1RS.
☎ (01368) 862734
FAX (01368) 864550**

With a tradition of brewing going back almost 800 years, Scotland's oldest brewery has had a chequered recent history. It was bought in 1989 by the London-based Control Securities PLC, but in 1993 its employees successfully engineered a management buyout of the brewery and it was due to be floated on the stock market as we went to press. It continues to produce award-winning beers, supplying 56 of its 65 houses, and a further 400 outlets, with cask beer. Shop open 9–5 Mon–Fri. Tours by arrangement. Occasional beer: 90/- (OG 1070, ABV 7.5%).

**60/- Ale** (OG 1030, ABV 2.9%) 🍴 ❧ A fine, but sadly rare, example of a Scottish light: a reddish-brown beer dominated by malt throughout. Roast is evident, with fruit in the aftertaste. Characteristic Belhaven sulphury nose.

**70/- Ale** (OG 1035, ABV 3.5%) ❧ A malty, bittersweet, pale brown beer in which hops and fruit are increasingly evident in the aftertaste. The Belhaven sulphury nose is noticeable.

**Sandy Hunter's Traditional Ale** (OG 1038, ABV 3.6%) ❧ A distinctive, medium-bodied beer named after a past chairman and head brewer. An aroma of malt, hops and characteristic sulphur greets the nose. A hint of roast combines with the malt and hops to give a bittersweet taste and finish.

**Festival Gold** (OG 1039, ABV 3.8%)

**80/- Ale** (OG 1041, ABV 4.2%) ❧ Incredibly robust, malty beer with the characteristic sulphury aroma. This classic ale has a burst of complex flavours and a rich, bittersweet aftertaste.

**St Andrew's Ale** (OG 1046, ABV 4.9%) ❧ A bittersweet beer with plenty of body. There are malt and fruit in the taste, with a developing hop character leading to an increasingly bitter aftertaste.

## BELVOIR
**Belvoir Brewery, Woodhill,
Nottingham Lane, Old
Dalby, Leicestershire
LE14 3LX.
☎ / FAX (01664) 823455**

Brewery founded at the edge of the Vale of Belvoir by a former Theakston and Shipstone's brewer in summer 1995, with equipment largely obtained from the defunct Shipstone's Brewery. Around 40 local free trade customers take the beer. Tours by arrangement.

**Whippling Golden Bitter** (OG 1037, ABV 3.6%)

**Beaver Bitter** (OG 1044, ABV 4.3%) ❧ A light brown bitter, which starts malty in both aroma and taste, but soon develops a hoppy bitterness. Appreciably fruity.

**Old Dalby Ale** (OG 1053, ABV 5.1%)

## BENSKINS
See Nationals, Carlsberg-Tetley.

**BENTLEY** See Nationals, Whitbread.

## BERKELEY
**Berkeley Brewing Co., The
Brewery, Bucketts Hill
Farm, Berkeley,
Gloucestershire GL13 9NZ.
☎ (01453) 811895**

This small operation was set up in an old farm cider cellar in 1994 and now supplies around a dozen local pubs. Occasional beer: Vale Ale (OG 1044, ABV 4.5%, winter).

**Old Friend** (OG 1039, ABV 3.8%) ❧ A hoppy aroma leads into this fruity, hoppy beer which has a moderately hoppy, bitter finish.

## BERROW

**Berrow Brewery, Coast Road, Berrow, Somerset TA8 2QU. ☎ (01278) 751345**

Brewery founded in June 1982 to supply pubs and clubs locally (about 15 direct free trade outlets). Occasional tours by arrangement.

**Best Bitter (BBBB or 4Bs)** (OG 1038, ABV 3.9%) 🍺 A pleasant, pale brown session beer, with a fruity aroma, a malty, fruity flavour and bitterness in the palate and finish.

**Porter** (OG 1044, ABV 4.4%)

**Topsy Turvy (TT)** (OG 1055, ABV 6%) 🍺 A straw-coloured beer with an aroma of malt and hops, which are also evident in the taste, together with sweetness. The aftertaste is malty. Very easy to drink. Beware!

## BIG END See Daleside.

## BIG LAMP

**Big Lamp Brewers, 1 Summerhill Street, Newcastle upon Tyne, Tyne & Wear NE4 6EJ. ☎ (0191) 261 4227**

Big Lamp was set up in 1982 and changed hands at the end of 1990. The plant was expanded in February 1995, to double the capacity, and Big Lamp currently supplies one tied house and a free trade of about 55 outlets. Occasional/seasonal beers: Old Genie (OG 1070, ABV 7.4%), Blackout (OG 1100, ABV 11%).

**Bitter** (OG 1038, ABV 3.9%) 🍺 An amber bitter with a rich, strong hop character, drying in the aftertaste. Some sweetness and fruit persist; good body.

**Prince Bishop Ale** (OG 1044, ABV 4.8%) 🍺 A deceptively light-coloured beer for its gravity. The aroma and taste are well-balanced, with malt, hops, background fruit and 'spikiness'. A beer full of flavours.

**Summerhill** or **Mulligan's Stout** (OG 1048, ABV 4.8%) 🍺 Another beer with many features, including a rich roast aroma and a malty mouthfeel. Look for a light bitterness and some sweetness.

**Premium** (OG 1046, ABV 5.2%) 🍺 Formerly ESB, a complex beer with a red/amber hue. A mellow taste and noticeably dry finish make this a distinctive and special bitter.

**Winter Warmer** (OG 1048, ABV 5.2%) 🍺 A strong bitter, fortified with roast malt character and rich maltiness. Try it for its mouthfeel and lasting bitterness.

> 🍺 The pub sign indicates a brew pub: a pub which produces beer on the premises.

## BIRD IN HAND

**Wheal Ale Brewery Ltd., Paradise Park, Hayle, Cornwall TR27 4HY. ☎ (01736) 753974**

🍺 Unusual brewery in a bird park, founded in 1980 as Paradise Brewery. Three other pubs are supplied, plus more in summer. Beers: Paradise Bitter (OG 1040, ABV 3.8%), Miller's Ale (OG 1045, ABV 4.3%), Artists Ale (OG 1055, ABV 5.1%), Old Speckled Parrot (ABV 6.3%).

## BISHOPS

**Bishops Brewery, 2 Park Street, Borough Market, London SE1 9AB. ☎ / FAX (0171) 357 8343**

Small brewery established in December 1993 by the former brewer at the Market Porter brew pub. The brewery has grown in strength and reputation and now sells its beers throughout the UK, as well as supplying free trade outlets in Greater London direct. It switched from using malt extract to full mash brews in spring 1996 and expanded the product range. Tours by arrangement.

**Cathedral Bitter** (OG 1037, ABV 3.7%) 🍺 A light golden brown bitter. Crisp hoppiness is present from the aroma through to the finish, with a fruitiness also present. Astringently bitter.

**Thirsty Willies** (ABV 3.7%)

**Mitre Ale** (ABV 4.2%)

**Cardinal Ale** (OG 1047, ABV 4.7%)

**Willies Revenge** (ABV 4.9%)

## BITTER END

**Bitter End, 15 Kirkgate, Cockermouth, Cumbria CA13 9PJ. ☎ (01900) 828993**

🍺 Brew pub opened in August 1995 in a derelict building which was used as a pub until 1974. The one-barrel plant can be viewed from the bar and lounge. A third beer may be added but all brews are only available at the pub itself. Beers: Cockersnoot (OG 1038, ABV 3.8%), Skinners Old Strong (OG 1054, ABV 5.5%).

## BLACKAWTON

**Blackawton Brewery, Washbourne, Totnes, Devon TQ9 7UF. ☎ (01803) 732339 FAX (01803) 732151**

Situated just outside the village of Washbourne, this small family brewery was founded in 1977 and is now the oldest in Devon. It originated in the village of Blackawton, but moved to its present site in 1981 and, although it changed ownership in 1988, it retains a loyal local following, serving around 50 free trade outlets, but having no pubs of its own. Occasional/ seasonal beers: Winter Fuel (ABV 4.1%, Christmas–January), Shepherd's Delight (OG 1044, ABV 4.6%, April).

**Bitter** (OG 1038, ABV 3.8%) 🍂 Tawny in colour, with a bitter/fruity taste and a bitter aftertaste.

**Devon Gold** (OG 1041, ABV 4.1%) A straw-coloured summer brew, available April–October.

**44 Special** (OG 1045, ABV 4.5%) 🍂 A tawny, fruity-flavoured bitter with a slightly sweet taste and finish.

**Headstrong** (OG 1052, ABV 5.2%) 🍂 A mid-brown, strong beer, with a pleasant, fruity, sweet taste and finish.

## BLACKBEARD

See Fox & Hounds, Freeminer and Hanby.

## BLACK BULL

**Black Bull Brewery, Ashes Farm, Ashes Lane, Fenny Bentley, Ashbourne, Derbyshire DE6 1LD.**
**☎ / FAX (01335) 350581**

Brewery opened as a part-time venture by a keen home brewer in 1994. He moved the brewery to a larger, converted building on his farm in summer 1996 to provide greater capacity. Trade has grown steadily, with 50 outlets now taking the beer. Tours by arrangement. Occasional/seasonal beers: Anklecracker (OG 1041, ABV 4.2%, summer), Lover's Leap (OG 1047, ABV 4.8%, February).

**Dovedale Bitter** (OG 1036, ABV 3.6%) Light straw-coloured summer beer, partly hopped with American lager hops.

**Best Bitter** (OG 1040, ABV 4%) A ruby-coloured, well-hopped bitter.

**Raging Bull** (OG 1050, ABV 4.9%) A light copper-coloured beer, similar to the best bitter but stronger.

**Jacobs Ladder (Dovedale Special)** (OG 1051, ABV 5%) A new, stronger version of Dovedale.

**Owd Shrovetide** (OG 1061, ABV 5.9%) A winter warmer, available October–February.

## BLACK HORSE

**Black Horse Brewery, Walkleys Clogs, Mauds Mill, Hebden Bridge, W. Yorkshire HX7 8NH. ☎ (01422) 843097**

Brewery founded in October 1996 at Walkleys Clogs centre, but looking to move to new premises in Halifax (dependent on planning permission). Around 15 outlets are supplied locally.

**Bitter** (OG 1040, ABV 4%)

**Spur** (OG 1044, ABV 4.4%)

**Black Stallion** (OG 1053, ABV 5.3%)

## BLACK HORSE & RAINBOW

See Liverpool.

## BLACKMOOR

**Blackmoor Brewery, Unit 8, Healey Mill, Healey Lane, Batley, W. Yorkshire WF17 5SH. ☎ / FAX (01924) 422400**

Brewery founded in 1994 and now supplying around 50 outlets with an extended range of beers. One-off brews are sold under the title of Exhibitionism Ale.

**Batley Bitter** (OG 1036, ABV 3.6%) 🍂 Clean and well-balanced, golden-coloured session bitter, with a slight hop and malt aroma, and a good hop and malt flavour, with strong bitterness, which lingers in the finish.

**Bog Standard Bitter** (OG 1038, ABV 3.8%) 🍂 A full-bodied, mid-brown bitter, with a light, hoppy aroma and a very bitter, dry taste which is dominated by maltiness with a little sweetness. A very astringent aftertaste follows.

**Pete Cutter** (ABV 4%) A brown ale which replaces Shampayne in the range.

**DOA or Dark Old Ale** (OG 1050, ABV 4.5%) 🍂 A dark brown, sweet, thin-bodied ale, which is again dominated by caramel, with some fruitiness and maltiness in the nose and a lingering caramel finish.

**Banana Madness** (OG 1045, ABV 4.6%) 🍂 An intensely fruity, banana-flavoured beer. Straw-coloured, it has a moderate bitter, dry taste and a strong, fruity, bitter finish.

**Winter's Warmer** (OG 1065, ABV 6.4%) 🍂 A new, dark brown, winter ale with a rich roast and malt flavour, but little aroma. A very complex beer, with little hoppiness and fruitiness, but a good bitter, dry, malty finish.

## BLACK SHEEP

**The Black Sheep Brewery PLC, Wellgarth, Masham, Ripon, N. Yorkshire HG4 4EN. ☎ (01765) 689227 FAX (01765) 689746**

Set up in 1992 by Paul Theakston, a member of Masham's famous brewing family, in the former Wellgarth Maltings, Black Sheep now supplies a free trade of some 300 outlets, but owns no pubs. All the beers are fermented exclusively in Yorkshire slate squares. A new visitor centre opened in May 1996 and incorporates a larger shop (open 10–5 daily), a bistro and a video area. Tours by arrangement.

**Best Bitter** (OG 1039, ABV 3.8%) 🍂 A well-balanced, predominantly bitter, pale brown beer, with underlying fruit and hop tastes before a long, dry finish with bitter overtones.

**Special Bitter** (OG 1046, ABV 4.4%) 🍂 An intensely bitter beer with a fruity aroma and a dry, astringent aftertaste.

**Riggwelter** (OG 1056, ABV 5.9%) ◆ A full-bodied, complex beer, with fruity overtones in the taste and aroma. Quite astringent, leaving a dry, slightly liquorice aftertaste.

## BLEWITTS
**Blewitts Brewery, The Ship & Plough, The Promenade, Kingsbridge, Devon TQ7 1JD.**
☎ (01548) 852485

Brewery established in 1991 which moved for a while to a business park before returning to its original home, the Ship & Plough. New premises are still being sought, however. Beers: Best (OG 1040, ABV 3.8%), Kingsbridge Gold (ABV 4.2%), Wages (OG 1044, ABV 4.2%), Nose (OG 1048, ABV 4.6%, occasional), Head Off (OG 1050, ABV 4.8%), Top (OG 1055, ABV 5.2%, occasional).

## BLUE ANCHOR
**Blue Anchor,
50 Coinagehall Street,
Helston, Cornwall
TR13 8EL.** ☎ (01326) 562821

Historic thatched brew pub, possibly the oldest in the UK, originating as a monks' resting place in the 15th century. It produces powerful ales known locally as 'Spingo' beers. Tours by arrangement. Beers: Middle (OG 1050, ABV 4.9%), Best (OG 1053, ABV 5.4%), Special (OG 1066, ABV 6.3%, brewed to replace Extra Special), Extra Special (OG 1076, ABV 7.3%, winter and Easter).

## BLUE BOAR
**Blue Boar Inn, 28 Oulton Street, Oulton Village, Lowestoft, Suffolk NR32 3BB.**
☎ (01502) 572160

Brewing started at this pub in 1994 but was soon stopped because of problems with the pub's lease. Production, using malt extract, was resumed early in 1996, and currently only the Blue Boar itself is supplied. Beers: Darbys (OG 1042, ABV 3.6%), Welders Armpit (OG 1052, ABV 4.8%), Pheasant Plucker (OG 1060, ABV 5.5%).

## BODDINGTONS
See Nationals, Whitbread.

**BODICOTE** See Plough Inn.

## BORDER
**Border Brewery Company,
The Old Kiln, Brewery
Lane, Tweedmouth,
Berwick-upon-Tweed,
Northumberland
TD15 2AH.** ☎ (01289) 303303
[FAX] (01289) 306115

Do not confuse with the Wrexham brewery taken over and closed by Marston's; this operation opened in 1992 in an old kiln on the site of Berwick's original (defunct)

Border Brewery, which was established in the 17th century. A change in ownership took place in 1994, with the company becoming a partnership. The output is slowly increasing, and the brewery supplies roughly 100 outlets. Some changes have been made to the beer range in the last year. Tours by arrangement. Occasional/seasonal beer: Rudolph's Ruin (OG 1061, ABV 6.5%, Christmas).

**Special Bitter** (OG 1037, ABV 3.8%) 🍺 ◆ A light, dry bitter, with a fruity aroma and moderate, but subdued, bitterness. A drinkable pint with a smooth mouthfeel.

**Noggins Nog** (OG 1041, ABV 4.2%) ◆ An unusual mix of malt and roast malt leaves an impressive chocolate character in the aftertaste of this solidly made beer.

**Rampart** (OG 1047, ABV 4.8%) A session beer with flavours of fruit, malt and hops in the mouth and a smooth aftertaste.

**SOB** (OG 1048, ABV 5%) ◆ A malty ale with a resinous bitterness, finishing with a woody dryness.

## BORVE
**Borve Brew House,
Ruthven, Huntly, Moray
AB54 4SR.**
☎ (01466) 760343

Established in 1983, Borve moved from its original site, on the Isle of Lewis, five years later, taking up residence in a former school on the mainland. The school is now a pub, with the brewhouse adjacent. Tours by arrangement. Beers: Borve Ale (OG 1040, ABV 3.9%), Tall Ships (OG 1050, ABV 4.9%). Bottle-conditioned beers: as cask, plus Extra Strong (OG 1085, ABV 10%).

## BRAINS
**SA Brain & Co. Ltd., The
Old Brewery, 49 St Mary
Street, Cardiff CF1 1SP.**
☎ (01222) 399022
[FAX] (01222) 383127

Traditional brewery which has been in the Brain family since Samuel Brain and his uncle Joseph bought the Old Brewery in 1882. It supplies cask-conditioned beer to all its 125 pubs and many free trade outlets, including clubs. It also runs a guest beer promotion for its pubs, some of the ales being occasional brews by the company itself. Brains beers also feature as guests in many big brewers' outlets in South Wales and beyond, and the company still has interests in hotel and leisure projects in Wales and the West Country. MA (OG 1035, ABV 3.6%, a brewery mix of Dark and Bitter) is usually only available in one pub, the Crown Hotel, Skewen, near Neath. Brewery shop open 9.30–5.45 Mon–Sat. Tours by arrangement.

**Dark** (OG 1035, ABV 3.5%) 🍺 ◆ A dark brown mild, bittersweet, with traces of roast and fruit, followed by a rounded finish.

**Bitter** (OG 1035, ABV 3.7%) ◆ A distinctively bitter beer, pale and somewhat hoppy, with a hint of malt and fruit and a dry finish. Commonly known as 'Light'.

**SA Best Bitter** (OG 1042, ABV 4.2%) 🍺 ◆ A full-bodied, malty, hoppy, premium bitter; well-balanced, with a smooth, dry aftertaste.

## BRAKSPEAR

**WH Brakspear & Sons PLC, The Brewery, New Street, Henley-on-Thames, Oxfordshire RG9 2BU.**
☎ (01491) 573636
[FAX] (01491) 410254

Brewing took place before 1700 on this Henley site, but the Brakspear family involvement only began in 1799, when Robert Brakspear formed a partnership with Richard Hayward. It was Robert's son, William Henry, who greatly expanded the brewery and its trade. Investment continues at the site and a new bottling plant for bottle-conditioned beers is planned. After many years of closing small, unprofitable pubs in the Henley area, Brakspear is now displaying a greater determination to enhance its tied estate of 106 pubs, which boasts many excellent, unspoilt hostelries, all serving traditional ales. Around 310 free trade outlets are supplied direct and trading arrangements with Whitbread and Scottish Courage mean that Brakspear's ales are available throughout southern England. A new shop in the brewery yard is planned (phone for opening times). Tours by arrangement.

**Mild** (OG 1030, ABV 3%) ◆ A thin beer with a red/brown colour and a sweet, malty, fruity aroma. The well-balanced taste of malt, hops and caramel has a faint bitterness, complemented by a sweet, fruity flavour. The main characteristics extend through to the bittersweet finish.

**Bitter** (OG 1035, ABV 3.4%) ◆ Amber in colour, with a good fruit, hop and malt nose. The initial taste of malt and the dry, well-hopped bitterness quickly dissolves into a predominantly bitter, sweet and fruity aftertaste.

**Old Ale** (OG 1043, ABV 4.3%) ◆ Red/brown with good body. The strong, fruity aroma is well complemented by malt, hops and roast caramel. Its pronounced taste of malt, with discernible sweet, roast malt and caramel flavours, gives way to fruitiness. The aftertaste is of bittersweet chocolate, even though chocolate malt is not present.

**Special** (OG 1043, ABV 4.3%) ◆ A tawny/amber beer offering a good, well-balanced aroma with a hint of sweetness. The initial taste is moderately sweet and malty, but is quickly overpowered by the dry bitterness

of the hops, before a slightly sweet fruitiness. A distinct, dry, malty finish.

**OBJ** (OG 1050, ABV 5%) Available November–January. Red/brown in colour, with an intensely fruity/hoppy aroma. An initial sweetish taste, strong in fruit and hops, is followed by bitterness with some malt and a lasting hops/bitter aftertaste.

## BRAMCOTE

**Bramcote Brewing Company, 236 Derby Road, Bramcote, Nottinghamshire NG9 3JN.** ☎ (0115) 939 3930

Philip Darby and Niven Balfour had been brewing non-commercially for over ten years when they decided to go professional in 1996. Response from the free trade has been excellent, and after overcoming some initial problems, they are now supplying 26 local outlets with a wide range of beers. Occasional/seasonal beers: Tickers Tipple (OG 1036, ABV 3.6%), Blonde Bombshell (OG 1042, ABV 4.2%), BBC 1 (OG 1045, ABV 4.5%), BBC 2 (OG 1055, ABV 5%).

**Hemlock Bitter** (OG 1040, ABV 4%) A fruity session ale.

**Bendigo Bitter** (OG 1045, ABV 4.5%) A robust, hoppy beer.

**Elsie Mo** (OG 1045, ABV 4.5%) A pale-coloured premium bitter.

**Broxtowe Bounty** (OG 1049, ABV 4.9%) A ruby-coloured, rich beer.

## BRANDY CASK

**Brandy Cask Brewing Company, 25 Bridge Street, Pershore, Worcestershire WR10 1AJ.**
☎ /[FAX] (01386) 555338

🍺 Brewing started in premises behind the Brandy Cask pub in June 1995, supplying that pub (not tied to the brewery) and 16 other local outlets. Tours by arrangement.

**Brandy Snapper** (OG 1040, ABV 4%) ◆ A pungent nose gives way to a strong, hoppy taste that attacks the tongue before leaving a pleasing aftertaste.

**John Baker's Original** (OG 1046, ABV 4.8%) ◆ A sweet, malty old ale, with roast flavours that leave a fruity taste in the mouth.

## BRANSCOMBE VALE

**The Branscombe Vale Brewery, Great Seaside Farm, Branscombe, Devon EX12 3DP.** ☎ (01297) 680511

Brewery set up in July 1992 in two cowsheds owned by the National Trust, by former dairy workers Paul Dimond and Graham Luxton, who converted the sheds and dug their own well. It currently supplies 40 outlets regularly, but plans to double capacity have been put back to summer 1997. An own label house beer

(OG 1044, ABV 4.6%) is produced for several local pubs in East Devon and beer is also brewed for Lock, Stock and Barrel wholesaling company ☎ (01364) 644124. Tours in winter only, by arrangement. Occasional/seasonal beers: Anniversary Ale (OG 1044, ABV 4.6%, January–February), Yo Ho Ho (OG 1063, ABV 6%, Christmas).

**Branoc** (OG 1037, ABV 3.8%) ◆ An amber-coloured, well-balanced bitter with a hoppy, bitter taste and aftertaste.

**Summa That** (OG 1049, ABV 5%) Brewed May–October.

**Olde Stoker** (OG 1052, ABV 5.4%) ◆ A dark brown, smooth, bittersweet beer, with a bitter finish. Available November–April.

### For Lock, Stock and Barrel:

**Pistol Knight** (OG 1042, ABV 4.3%)

**Pistol Ready** (OG 1049, ABV 5%)

## THE BREWERY See Liverpool.

## BREWERY ON SEA
**The Brewery on Sea Ltd.,
Unit 24, Winston Business
Centre, Chartwell Road,
Lancing, W. Sussex
BN15 8TU.**
☎ / FAX (01903) 851482

Brewery established in 1993. The capacity was increased early in 1995 to around 55 barrels a week, some of which is taken by wholesalers, although an increasing volume is now marketed directly. Beers are also brewed for East-West Ales ☎ (01892) 834040, and the brewery often produces beers for special occasions (Tidal Wave has become so popular at beer festivals that it is now brewed all the time). Tours available for customers only. Occasional/seasonal beers: Spinnaker Shamrock (ABV 4.2%, a green beer for St Patrick's Day), Shell Shock (ABV 4.3%, early spring), Big Fat Santa (ABV 4.2%, December).

**Spinnaker Bitter** (OG 1036, ABV 3.5%) ◆ A hoppy-tasting, smooth, basic ale.

**Spinnaker Mild** or **Lancing Special Dark** (OG 1036, ABV 3.5%) ◆ A traditional mild which is hard to find.

**Spinnaker Classic** (OG 1040, ABV 4%) ◆ The brewery's first beer: copper-coloured, with hints of malt in the aroma, giving way to a fruity flavour.

**Rain Dance** (ABV 4.4%) ◆ A light golden beer, with a strong fruity aroma. The flavour is a complex mixture with a hint of almonds, leading to a bittersweet aftertaste.

**Spinnaker Buzz** (OG 1044, ABV 4.5%) ◆ An amber-coloured, interesting beer, primed with honey, which dominates the aroma. An initial sweetness gives way to an intriguing flavour mix of malt, honey and hops. Hoppy aftertaste.

**Black Rock** (OG 1050, ABV 5.5%) A dark, strong beer with a good measure of roasted barley.

**Special Crew** (OG 1050, ABV 5.5%) A full-bodied, full-strength bitter.

**Spinnaker Ginger** (OG 1050, ABV 5.5%) A ginger beer seen often at festivals.

**Riptide** (OG 1060, ABV 6.5%) A very strong premium beer without too much sweetness.

**Tidal Wave** (OG 1065, ABV 7%) A medium brown strong ale.

### For East-West Ales:

**Winter Widget** (OG 1043, ABV 4.5%)

**Wicked Widget** (OG 1045, ABV 4.7%)

## BRIDGWATER
**Bridgwater Brewing Company, Goathurst, Bridgwater, Somerset.**

Brewery closed.

## BRISTOL BREWHOUSE See Ross.

## BRITANNIA
**The Britannia Ales Brewery,
Britannia Inn, Kent Street,
Upper Gornall,
W. Midlands DY3 1UX.**
☎ (01902) 883253

🍺 Historic brew pub which ceased production in 1959 but began brewing again in May 1995. The two full mash beers are available in the pub itself and occasionally at local beer festivals. Beers: Sally Perry Mild (ABV 3.5%), Wally Williams Bitter (ABV 4.5%), Yule Britannia (ABV 6%, Christmas).

## BRITISH OAK
**British Oak Brewery, Salop
Street, Eve Hill, Dudley,
W. Midlands DY1 3AX.**
☎ (01384) 236297

🍺 British Oak began life as a family-run brew pub in 1988, and now usually only supplies this and a second pub of its own. Tours by arrangement. Beers: Mild (OG 1038, ABV 3.7% ), Eve'ill Bitter (OG 1042, ABV 4%), Colonel Pickering's Porter (OG 1046, ABV 4.6%, occasional), Dungeon Draught (OG 1050, ABV 4.8%, occasional), Old Jones (OG 1062, ABV 6.2%, September–April).

## BROUGHTON
**Broughton Ales Ltd., The
Brewery, Broughton,
Biggar, The Borders
ML12 6HQ.**
☎ (01899) 830345
FAX (01899) 830474

Brewery founded in 1980 by former S&N executive David Younger. The company grew successfully and was taken over in August 1995 by Whim Brewery owner Giles Litchfield who is relaunching existing brands alongside new brews. The beers, both cask and bottled (not bottle-conditioned) should become more widely available under the new ownership, and the number of free trade outlets supplied has already grown to some 600. There is also a single tied house. Group tours by arrangement. Occasional/seasonal beer: Reeket Yill (OG 1048, ABV 4.8%, a smoked winter ale).

**Greenmantle Ale** (OG 1038, ABV 3.9%) ◆ Now a disappointing beer, lacking real character. A predominately malty aroma, a malt taste with hints of fruit and hops, but little aftertaste.

**Special Bitter** (OG 1038, ABV 3.9%) ◆ Greenmantle dry-hopped. An aroma of hop, with malt and fruit, leads into a pleasingly bitter beer, balanced with more malt and fruit, with the bitterness and fruit lasting into the aftertaste. Slightly lacking in body.

**Merlin's Ale** (OG 1042, ABV 4.2%) A deep golden, well-hopped ale.

**80/-** (OG 1042, ABV 4.2%)

**The Ghillie** (OG 1043, ABV 4.5%) ◆ This superb new ale assaults the nose with a strong aroma of hop. Hops continue to dominate the palate, with malt and fruit, and it ends in a hop-dominated, dry finish.

**Scottish Oatmeal Stout** (OG 1045, ABV 4.2%) ◆ A rare pleasure, this wonderfully dry stout has a bitter aftertaste, dominated by roast malt. A distinctive malt aroma is followed by a prominent roast taste, with fruit evident throughout.

**Black Douglas** (OG 1053, ABV 5.2%) A new winter brew, dark ruby in colour..

**Old Jock** (OG 1070, ABV 6.7%) Strong, sweetish and fruity in the finish. Also sold as River Tweed Festival Ale.

## MATTHEW BROWN
See Mansfield and Nationals, Scottish Courage.

## ABEL BROWN'S
**Abel Brown's Brewery, The Stag, 35 Brook Street, Stotfold, Hitchin, Hertfordshire SG5 4LA. ☎ (01462) 730261**

🛇 This pub (which is in Bedfordshire, despite the postal address), began brewing in the spring of 1995, using the name of its first publican, Abel Brown, on the pump clips. Some of the beers take their names from the village's famous traction engines. Special brews are also produced. Beers: Jack of Herts (OG 1040, ABV 4%), Little Billy (OG 1040, ABV 4%), Stotfold Pale Ale (OG 1040, ABV 4%), Pickled Wombat (OG 1052, ABV 5%).

**TOM BROWN'S** See Goldfinch.

## BRUNSWICK
**The Brunswick Brewery Co. Ltd., 1 Railway Terrace, Derby DE1 2RU.**
**☎ (01332) 290677**

🛇 Purpose-built tower brewery attached to the Brunswick Inn, a famous railway hotel partly restored by the Derbyshire Historic Building Trust and bought by the present owners in 1987. Brewing began in 1991 and a viewing area allows pub-users to watch production. The beers are supplied to the Inn and four other outlets directly. Tours by arrangement. Beers: Recession Ale (OG 1033, ABV 3.3%), Best Dark Mild (OG 1035, ABV 3.5%, occasional), First Brew (OG 1036, ABV 3.6%, spring), Recession Extra (OG 1038, ABV 3.8%, occasional), Pain i'th Neck (OG 1039, ABV 3.9%, occasional), Triple Hop (OG 1040, ABV 4%), Light Dinner Ale (OG 1041, ABV 4.1%), Nut Ale (OG 1041, ABV 4.1%, occasional), Second Brew (OG 1042, ABV 4.2%), Railway Porter (OG 1045, ABV 4.3%), Novice's Nog (OG 1046, ABV 4.6%, occasional), Festival Ale (OG 1046, ABV 4.6%, occasional), Old Accidental (OG 1050, ABV 5%), Auld Acquaintance (OG 1050, ABV 5%, winter), Owd Abusive (OG 1066, ABV 6%, winter).

**BUCHANAN** See Federation.

**BUCKLEY** See Crown Buckley.

## BUFFY'S
**Buffy's Brewery, Mardle Hall, Rectory Road, Tivetshall St Mary, Norfolk NR15 2DD.**
**☎ (01379) 676523**

*Buffy's*

Situated alongside a 15th-century house, Buffy's started life as Mardle Hall Brewery in 1993, but was forced to change its name after a complaint from another brewery. Twenty local free houses are supplied with the beer, which is also now available more widely via wholesalers. The new mild has been very well received. Tours by arrangement. Occasional/seasonal beer: Festival 8X (OG 1075, ABV 8%, brewed for CAMRA's Norwich Beer Festival).

**Bitter** (OG 1038, ABV 4%) ◆ Very well-balanced throughout, this is a flavoursome session beer, not at all bland or cloying, with more complexity than its gravity may suggest.

**Polly's Folly** (OG 1041, ABV 4.3%) 🗖 ◆ A well-balanced amber beer with a flowery hop character in its aroma. The palate is clean and bitter, with malt and some citrus notes which die away in the aftertaste to let the hops and bitterness come through.

**Mild** (OG 1042, ABV 4.2%) A stronger than average dark mild.

**Polly's Extra Folly** (OG 1046, ABV 4.9%) ❦ Much like the bitter, only stronger and fuller-bodied. It is just as well-balanced, but with a rounder, fruitier palate. It is also moreish, with a clean, bitter finish.

**Buffy's Ale** (OG 1052, ABV 5.5%) ❦ A pale brown beer which is a smooth and malty, strong bitter throughout. Slightly warming and easy to drink.

**Strong Ale** (OG 1062, ABV 6.5%) ❦ A rich, hearty and complex, darkish brown beer which is full of malt and fruit, with some hoppiness. Very drinkable for its strength.

## BULLMASTIFF

**Bullmastiff Brewery, 14 Bessemer Close, Leckwith, Cardiff CF1 8DL.**
☎ (01222) 665292

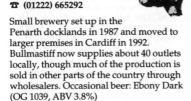

Small brewery set up in the Penarth docklands in 1987 and moved to larger premises in Cardiff in 1992. Bullmastiff now supplies about 40 outlets locally, though much of the production is sold in other parts of the country through wholesalers. Occasional beer: Ebony Dark (OG 1039, ABV 3.8%)

**Gold Brew** (OG 1039, ABV 3.8%)

**Best Bitter** (OG 1042, ABV 4%) ❦ A well-balanced, malty, bitter beer with a balanced, hoppy, fruity finish. Very drinkable.

**Brindle** (OG 1050, ABV 5%)

**Son of a Bitch** (OG 1062, ABV 6%) 🍶 🍺 ❦ A full-bodied, notably hoppy, malty and bitter beer. A powerful, premium bitter with a distinctive aftertaste.

## BULL'S HEAD

**Bull's Head Brewery, The Three Tuns, 34 High Street, Alcester, Warwickshire B49 5AB.** ☎ (01789) 766550

🍶 Brewery founded on a farm at Inkberrow, Worcestershire in 1994 and moved to the rear of the Three Tuns in Alcester, Warwickshire in 1995. It now brews almost entirely for the pub itself, where the beer is no longer kept in cellar tanks with gas but is cask-conditioned. Beer: Genesis (OG 1040, ABV 3.9%).

## BUNCES

**Bunces Brewery, The Old Mill, Mill Road, Netheravon, Salisbury, Wiltshire SP4 9QB.**
☎ /FAX (01980) 670631

Tower brewery housed in a listed building on the Wiltshire Avon, established in 1984 and sold to Danish proprietors in summer 1993. Its cask-conditioned beers are delivered to around 30 free trade outlets within a radius of 50 miles, and a number of wholesalers are also supplied. Shop open 8.30–5.30 Mon–Fri, 10–1 Sat. Tours by arrangement. Occasional/seasonal beer: Rudolph (OG 1050, ABV 5%, Christmas).

**Benchmark** (OG 1035, ABV 3.5%) ❦ A pleasant, bitter ale of remarkable character, which maintains one's interest for a long time. The taste is malty, the aroma subtle and the very long finish is quite dry on the palate.

**Vice Beer** (OG 1038, ABV 3.8%) A wheat beer for summer.

**Pigswill** (OG 1040, ABV 4%) A beer first brewed for the Two Pigs at Corsham, now more widely available.

**Best Bitter** (OG 1042, ABV 4.1%) ❦ A first-rate beer. The piquant aroma introduces a complex, malty and bitter taste with a hint of fruit. Long, fresh, bitter aftertaste.

**Sign of Spring** (OG 1044, ABV 4.6%) Brewed from March–May; a light green spring beer.

**Danish Dynamite** (OG 1050, ABV 5%) A light golden, slightly fruity, dry strong ale with hop and bitter balance.

**Old Smokey** (OG 1050, ABV 5%) ❦ A delightful, warming, dark bitter ale, with a roasted malt taste and a hint of liquorice surrounding a developing bitter flavour. Very appealing to the eye.

**Stig Swig** (OG 1050, ABV 5%) A golden autumn beer brewed with the herb sweet gale, an old Viking beer ingredient.

## BURNTISLAND

**Burntisland Brewery, 83 High Street, Burntisland, Fife KY3 9AA.**
☎ (01592) 873333

Brewery housed behind a delicatessen/off-licence which began operation in October 1995. The shop is open 7–7 (7–2 Wed, 12–3 Sun). A handful of other outlets take the beer. Beers: Alexander's Downfall (ABV 4.4%), Stout (ABV 4.8%).

## BURTON BRIDGE

**Burton Bridge Brewery, 24 Bridge Street, Burton upon Trent, Staffordshire DE14 1SY.** ☎ (01283) 510573

Brewery established in 1982, with one tied outlet at the front and another added in 1996. Conversion of the adjoining premises in a new brewhouse has begun and the pub will eventually be extended into the old brewery buildings. Guest beers are supplied to around 250 outlets virtually nationwide, and Burton Bridge specialises in commemorative bottled beers to order. Tours by arrangement. Occasional/seasonal beers: Spring Ale (OG 1047, ABV 4.7% March–April), Battle Brew (OG 1050, ABV 5%, July–August), Hearty Ale (OG 1050, ABV 5%, December–January). Bottle-conditioned beer: Burton Porter (OG 1045, ABV 4.5%) 🍶, Empire Pale Ale (ABV 7.5%), Tickle Brain (ABV 8.5%).

**Summer Ale** (OG 1038, ABV 3.8%) Only available during British Summer Time. A beer with a strong hop aroma and a dry, bitter finish.

**XL Bitter** (OG 1040, ABV 4%) 🍺 A golden, malty drinking bitter, with a faint, hoppy and fruity aroma. An excellent mix of flavours follows, with fruitiness dominating.

**Bridge Bitter** (OG 1042, ABV 4.2%) 🍺 An amber-coloured, robust and malty beer. The taste is bittersweet with fruit and gives way to a dominating hoppy finish.

**Porter** (OG 1045, ABV 4.5%) 🍺 Ruby red, with a faint aroma. The taste combines moderate liquorice flavour with hops and fruit; slightly sweet. Dry, astringent aftertaste.

**Knot Brown Ale** (OG 1048, ABV 4.8%) An autumn beer.

**Top Dog Stout** (OG 1050, ABV 5%) 🍺 A winter brew with a strong roast malt and fruit mix, developing into a potent malt and roast malt aftertaste.

**Festival Ale** (OG 1055, ABV 5.5%) 🍺 A full-bodied, copper-coloured, strong but sweet beer. The aroma is hoppy, malty and slightly fruity. Malt and hops in the flavour give way to a fruity finish. Tremendous mouthfeel.

**Old Expensive** (OG 1065, ABV 6.7%) A winter warmer, virtually a barley wine. Its wonderful mix of sweetness and fruit certainly hits the throat.

## BURTONWOOD

**Burtonwood Brewery PLC, Bold Lane, Burtonwood, Warrington, Cheshire CH3 8AN. ☎ (01925) 225131 FAX (01925) 224562**

A family-run public company established in 1867 by James Forshaw. In the 1980s, Burtonwood embarked on a £6 million extension plan and a new brewhouse was completed in 1990. Evening tours by arrangement. Real ale is supplied to over 450 of its 500 tied houses (138 of which are on long lease from Allied-Domecq), and to 100 pubs in the free trade. Early in 1996 Burtonwood sold its stake in the Paramount pub chain (to Allied), and bought shares in Vantage Inns from Café Inns. Occasional/seasonal beer: Hoppers (OG 1041, ABV 4.2%, July–August).

**Mild** (OG 1032, ABV 3%) 🍺 A smooth, dark brown, malty mild with a good roast flavour, some caramel taste and a hint of bitterness. Slightly dry finish.

**Bitter** (OG 1036, ABV 3.7%) 🍺 A well-balanced, refreshing, malty bitter, with good hoppiness. Fairly dry aftertaste.

**James Forshaw's Bitter** (OG 1038, ABV 4%) 🍺 A malty and hoppy, well-balanced bitter.

**Tom Thumper** (OG 1044, ABV 4.5%) Available March–May: a malty, full-bodied bitter with a dry-hop aftertaste.

**Top Hat** (OG 1045, ABV 4.8%) 🍺 Soft, nutty, malty and a little sweet. Fairly thin for its gravity.

**Buccaneer** (OG 1052, ABV 5.2%) 🍺 Pale golden, sweet and malty bitter, with subtle hop flavour. Its light taste belies its strength.

### For Whitbread:

**Chester's Best Bitter** (OG 1033, ABV 3.6%) A thin bitter not strong in flavour.

**Oldham Bitter (OB)** (OG 1037, ABV 3.8%) 🍺 Copper-coloured beer with an aroma of malt and fruit. The flavour is malty and bitter, with a bittersweet tinge and a dry, malty finish. A relic of the Oldham Brewery closed by Boddingtons.

## BURTS

**Burts Brewery (Newport) Ltd., 16 Manners View, Dodnor Industrial Estate, Newport, Isle of Wight PO30 5FA. ☎ / FAX (01983) 528098**

Brewery originally founded in 1840, but which went into receivership in 1992. The name and brands were bought by Hampshire soft drinks firm Hartridges, owners of Island Brewery, who now use the Burts name for all their brewing operations, supplying 40 pubs both on the island and the mainland. The first tied house was acquired in March 1995, and the company has since acquired a further four. A brew pub is planned in Sandown. Brewery tours by arrangement.

**Nipper Bitter** (OG 1035, ABV 3.4%)

**Parkhurst Porter** (OG 1038, ABV 3.8%)

**Ventnor Premium Ale** or **VPA** (OG 1041, ABV 4.2%)

**Newport Nobbler** (OG 1044, ABV 4.4%)

**Tanner Bitter** (OG 1047, ABV 4.8%)

**Old Vectis Venom** (OG 1049, ABV 5%)

## BUSHY'S

**The Mount Murray Brewing Co. Ltd., Mount Murray, Castletown Road, Braddan, Isle of Man IM4 1JE. ☎ (01624) 661244 FAX (01624) 611101**

Set up in 1986 as a brew pub, Bushy's moved to its present site in 1990, when demand outgrew capacity. The beers, all brewed to the stipulations of the Manx Brewers' Act of 1874, are supplied to five tied houses (including a new brewery tap) and 25 other outlets. Tours by arrangement. Occasional/seasonal beers: Summer Ale (OG 1038, ABV 3.8%), Old Shunter (OG 1045, ABV 4.2%, summer), Oyster Stout (OG 1045, ABV 4.2%, summer), Piston Brew (OG 1045, ABV 4.5%, for the TT races in May–June), Old Bushy Tail (OG 1045, ABV 4.5%), Lovely Jubbely Christmas Ale (OG 1055, ABV 5.2%).

**Dark Mild** (OG 1035, ABV 3.4%) ◆ With a hoppy aroma, and notes of chocolate and coffee to the malty flavour, this rich, creamy, fruity, very dark brew is reminiscent of a porter.

**Best Bitter** (OG 1038, ABV 3.8%) ◆ An aroma full of pale malt and hops introduces you to a beautifully hoppy, bitter beer. Despite the predominant hop character, malt is also evident. Fresh and clean-tasting.

## BUTCOMBE

Butcombe Brewery Ltd.,
Butcombe, Bristol
BS18 6XQ.
☎ (01275) 472240

One of the most successful of the new wave of breweries, set up in 1978 by a former Courage Western MD, Simon Whitmore. During 1992–93, the brewery virtually doubled in size (for the third time), allowing for an 80-barrel brew and, after 18 years of producing just a single beer, a second ale is now available. Butcombe supplies four tied houses and 350 free trade outlets, most within a 50-mile radius of the brewery, but others further afield via wholesalers. Tours (for trade only) by arrangement.

**Bitter** (OG 1039, ABV 4%) 🍎 ◆ An amber-coloured, malty and notably bitter beer, with subtle peardrop fruit qualities. It has a hoppy, malty aroma and a long, dry, bitter finish. A well-regarded, consistent and refreshing bitter.

**Wilmot's Premium Ale** (ABV 4.8%)

## BUTTERKNOWLE

Butterknowle Brewery, The
Old School House,
Lynesack, Butterknowle,
Bishop Auckland, Co.
Durham DL13 5QF.
☎ (01388) 710109  [FAX] (01388) 710373

Since its launch in August 1990, Butterknowle has continued to prosper and grow by producing award-winning ales. It now supplies almost 200 outlets nationwide on a regular basis. The brewery is situated in Victorian buildings, once home to the Lynesack National School. Occasional beer: West Auckland Mild (OG 1034, ABV 3.3%). Bottle-conditioned beer: Conciliation Ale (OG 1042, ABV 4.3%).

**Bitter** (OG 1036, ABV 3.6%) ◆ A light, fruity pale ale with a good balance of flavours. Fruity aroma with a slight hoppy aftertaste.

**Banner Bitter** (OG 1040, ABV 4%) 🍎 ◆ A pale brown beer with a noticeable malty/hoppy aroma. Slightly fruity aftertaste; bags of flavour. More like the old Conciliation.

**Conciliation Ale** (OG 1042, ABV 4.2%) 🍎 ◆ A mid-brown ale with a decent aroma and hoppy taste, but not the beer it used to be. It lacks the original brew's 'bite' and aftertaste.

**Black Diamond** (OG 1050, ABV 4.8%) ◆ A rich malty/toffee/liquorice taste dominates this deep red/brown ale. Fruity aroma; bitterness complements the initial sweetness.

**Lynesack Porter** (OG 1050, ABV 5%). A dark, traditional porter.

**High Force** (OG 1060, ABV 6.2%) 🍎 ◆ A smooth strong ale, well-hopped, with some fruity sweetness. A good depth of flavour develops in the aftertaste: a multi-dimensional beer.

**Old Ebenezer** (OG 1080, ABV 8%) ◆ A splendid, rich and fruity, seasonal barley wine: liquid Christmas cake with a potent punch. Surprisingly moreish, if only in sips!

## BUTTS

Butts Brewery Ltd.,
Northfield Farm, Great
Shefford, Hungerford,
Berkshire RG17 7DQ.
☎ (01488) 648133
[FAX] (01734) 345860

Brewery set up in converted farm buildings in autumn 1994 with plant acquired from Butcombe. It now supplies 40 outlets, mainly in Berkshire, but also in Oxfordshire, Hampshire and Wiltshire. Jester was added to the range early in 1996.

**Jester** (OG 1035, ABV 3.5%)

**Bitter** (OG 1040, ABV 4%)

## CAINS

Robert Cain & Co. Ltd.,
The Robert Cain Brewery,
Stanhope Street, Liverpool,
Merseyside L8 5XJ.
☎ (0151) 709 8734
[FAX] (0151) 708 8395

Robert Cain's brewery was first established on this site in 1850, but was bought out by Higsons in the 1920s, then by Boddingtons in 1985. Whitbread took control of the Boddingtons breweries in 1990 and closed the site, switching the brewing of Higsons to Sheffield and later Castle Eden. The site was then bought by GB Breweries to brew canned beers, but with enthusiastic staff and CAMRA support, it soon moved on to cask ales. The company is now a division of the Brewery Group Denmark A/S. It won CAMRA's 1994 *Best Refurbishment* award for its first tied house and two further pubs have since been added. Cains supplies 400 outlets in Merseyside and the North-West. A monthly guest beer is brewed. Tours by arrangement. Occasional beer: Superior Stout (OG 1048, ABV 4.8%).

**Dark Mild** (OG 1032, ABV 3.2%) 🍎 ◆ A smooth, dry and roasty, dark mild, with some chocolate and coffee flavours.

**Traditional Bitter** (OG 1039, ABV 4%) ◆ A darkish, full-bodied bitter, with a good, hoppy nose and a dry aftertaste.

**Formidable Ale (FA)** (OG 1048, ABV 5%) ● A bitter and hoppy beer with a good, dry aftertaste. Sharp, clean and dry.

## CALEDONIAN

**The Caledonian Brewing Company Ltd., 42 Slateford Road, Edinburgh EH11 1PH. ☎ (0131) 337 1286 FAX (0131) 313 2370**

Described by Michael Jackson as a 'living, working museum of beer making', Caledonian operates from a Victorian brewhouse, using the last three direct-fired open coppers in Britain, one of which dates back to 1869, when the brewery was started by George Lorimer and Robert Clark. The site was taken over by Vaux of Sunderland in 1919, who continued to brew there until 1987, when, under threat of closure, it was acquired by a management buyout team. A disastrous fire in 1994, which destroyed the historic maltings, necessitated a major rebuild and a new visitors' centre was incorporated. Caledonian has no tied estate, but around 900 free trade outlets are supplied. Some occasional beers are produced. Tours by arrangement.

**60/- Ale** (OG 1032, ABV 3.2%) ● A dark beer with plenty of body for a 'light'. A bittersweet balance of malt, hops, roast and fruit, gives a complex taste, while the aroma and aftertaste are dominated by malt and hop. Sadly, not widely available.

**70/- Ale** (OG 1036, ABV 3.5%) ● A traditional Scottish session beer, with malt to the fore in the aroma. The subtle bittersweet taste has a balance of malt, fruit, hop and roast, with the malt fading in the aftertaste. Can be hard to find.

**Murrays Pale Summer Ale** (OG 1036, ABV 3.6%) ⬛ ● A clean-tasting, thirst quenching, golden session beer, with hop evident throughout. A bitter beer, balanced by malt in the taste and aftertaste.

**Deuchars IPA** (OG 1038, ABV 3.8%) ⬙ ⬛ ● A refreshing, amber-coloured beer. Malt, hops and hints of fruit are evident throughout and lead to a satisfying, hoppy, bitter finish.

**Edinburgh Real Ale** or **ERA** (OG 1042, ABV 4.1%) ● Full-bodied, with hops, malt, fruit and caramel. This bittersweet, dark brown beer retains its character in the aftertaste. Fruity aroma.

**80/- Ale** (OG 1042, ABV 4.1%) ⬛ ● A predominantly malty, copper-coloured beer well-balanced by hop and fruit; a bitter with the characteristics of a Scottish heavy. Complex.

**Porter** (OG 1042, ABV 4.1%) A dry and malty, dark beer, well-balanced with hops. Not easy to find.

**Murrays Heavy** (OG 1044, ABV 4.3%) An amber-coloured ale brewed in the traditional

Scottish style. Clean tasting, with a malty sweetness.

**Campbell, Hope & King's Double Amber Ale** (OG 1045, ABV 4.6%) ● A full-bodied, complex beer, named after an Edinburgh brewery closed by Whitbread in 1970. Mid-brown in colour and dominated by malt and fruit throughout, its bittersweet taste is followed by an interesting finish of hop and roast.

**Golden Promise** (OG 1049, ABV 5%) An organic beer, pale in colour, with a pronounced hop characteristic. Floral and fruity on the nose.

**Merman XXX** (OG 1049, ABV 4.8%) ● A mid-brown beer, based on a Victorian recipe. This rich malty, fruity beer has a thick, initially sweetish, taste which becomes increasingly complex, with roast, hops and a hint of caramel. The finish is similar, but with more bitterness.

**Edinburgh Strong Ale** or **ESA** (OG 1063, ABV 6.4%) A complex mix of malt and hops without the cloying sweetness that beers of this strength can have. Most commonly available in bottles (not bottle-conditioned).

## CAMBRIAN

**Cambrian Brewery Co. Ltd., Units 17–18, Marian Mawr Enterprise Park, Dolgellau, Gwynedd LL40 1UU. ☎ (01341) 421000 FAX (01341) 421111**

Brewery opened by two brothers in June 1996, the first in Dolgellau in nearly 90 years. Tours by arrangement.

**Original** (OG 1037, ABV 3.7%)

**Best Bitter** (OG 1042, ABV 4.2%)

**Premium** (OG 1048, ABV 4.8%)

## CAMERONS

**Camerons Brewery Company, Lion Brewery, Hartlepool TS24 7QS. ☎ (01429) 266666 FAX (01429) 868195**

This major brewer of real ale, established in 1865, went through a period of neglect for some 17 years, when it was owned by non-brewers, including the ill-fated Brent Walker group. In January 1992 it was bought by Wolverhampton & Dudley Breweries, in a deal that included the brewery, 51 pubs and the brands. Now with solid investment and a successful relaunch of the beers, Camerons has turned a corner. The tied estate of 104 pubs (most of which take real ale) is being expanded, and the beers are also sold to 600 other outlets. Tours by arrangement.

**Bitter** (OG 1036, ABV 3.6%) ● A light bitter, but well-balanced, with hops and malt.

**Strongarm** (OG 1041, ABV 4%) ⬛ ● A well-rounded, full-bodied, ruby red ale with a distinctive, tight creamy head and a good balance of malt, hops and bittersweetness throughout.

## CANNON

**Parker & Son Brewers Ltd., The Cannon, Cannon Street, Wellingborough, Northamptonshire NN8 4DJ.**
☎ / FAX (01933) 279629

Brewery founded in 1993, in the old bottle store of the Cannon pub. A family-run business, it supplies the pub and ten other free trade outlets, with most of the production taken by the Flying Firkin wholesaler.

**Light Brigade** (OG 1036, ABV 3.6%) Thin-bodied, amber/gold session beer, with a fruity malt aroma and apple fruitiness on the tongue. Faint, dry bitterness in the aftertaste.

**Pride** (OG 1042, ABV 4.2%) Cascade hops give tart fruitiness to the malt aroma. Hops finally overcome the intense malt of this amber brew into a well-balanced finish.

**Florrie Night-in-Ale** (OG 1048, ABV 4.8%) Hops and malt battle in an astringent fruitiness for dominance on the tongue. The bitter aftertaste finally wins through with dryness building. Light brown, with medium body.

**Fodder** (OG 1055, ABV 5.5%) Mid-brown, very fruity and vinous.

## CANNON ROYALL

**Cannon Royall Brewery, The Fruiterer's Arms, Uphampton, Ombersley, Worcestershire WR9 0JW.**
☎ (01562) 743262

This five-barrel plant was set up in 1993, in a converted cider house behind the Fruiterer's Arms pub, by the former brewer at the Fox & Hounds in Stottesdon. It now brews 12 barrels a week, to supply the Fruiterer's Arms and ten other outlets directly. Tours by arrangement. Occasional beer: Heart of Oak (OG 1054, ABV 5.4%).

**Fruiterers Mild** (OG 1037, ABV 3.7%) 🍺 A fruity, malt aroma introduces the sweet roast flavours of this black mild. Clean, fruity finish.

**Arrowhead** (OG 1039, ABV 3.9%) 🍺 A beer brimming with aromatic hop flavours that attack the tongue before leaving a dry, refreshing aftertaste.

**Buckshot** (OG 1045, ABV 4.5%) 🍺 A wide range of elements in the aroma is balanced by a sweet, hoppy taste which gives way to a fruit aftertaste.

**Olde Merrie** (OG 1060, ABV 6.4%) 🍺 A very malty old ale that is very sweet, both in the mouth and aftertaste. A fruity, malt flavour is dominant throughout.

## CARTMEL

**Cartmel Brewery, Unit 7, Fell View Trading Park, Shap Road, Kendal, Cumbria LA9 6NZ.** ☎ (01539) 724085

Set up by Nick Murray, in a disused barn at the Cavendish Arms, Cartmel in 1994, this new brewery took off so successfully that larger premises were soon required and the plant was moved to nearby Kendal. Around 40 outlets are supplied, mostly in Cumbria and Lancashire, with a few in Scotland. Tours by arrangement.

**Lakeland Gold** (OG 1038, ABV 4%) A golden beer with a light, clean taste, a hoppy aroma and a dry finish.

**Lakeland Sheepdog** (ABV 4.5%) Formerly sold as Westmerian Ale; a ruby-red beer with a positive taste of roast malt balanced by hops.

## CASTLE EDEN
See Nationals, Whitbread.

## CASTLETOWN See Okells.

## CHALK HILL

**Chalk Hill Brewery, Rosary Road, Thorpe Hamlet, Norwich, Norfolk NR1 4DA.**
☎ / FAX (01603) 620703

Run by former Reindeer brew pub owner Bill Thomas and his partners, Chalk Hill began production with a 15-barrel plant in 1993. It supplies around 50 local free trade outlets and the beers are available nationwide via beer agencies. Tours by arrangement.

**Tap Bitter** (OG 1036, ABV 3.6%) 🍺 A simple and unpretentious session beer, hoppy and quite well-balanced, but not strongly flavoured. A gentle, hoppy bitterness lingers in the aftertaste.

**CHB** (OG 1042, ABV 4.3%) 🍺 A fairly well-balanced, mid-brown beer, not very strongly flavoured.

**Porter** (ABV 4.3%) Brewed for autumn/winter.

**Dreadnought** (OG 1049, ABV 4.8%) 🍺 A strong brown bitter which, despite having little aroma, is full-flavoured, well-balanced, rounded and fruity. The aftertaste is similar but short. A beer which is easier to drink than its strength may suggest.

**Old Tackle** (OG 1056, ABV 5.6%) 🍺 A reddish brown beer with little aroma but a fairly full body and a full palate. The taste is complex, with mainly fruit but even hints of liquorice.

## CHARRINGTON See Nationals, Bass.

## CHERITON

**The Cheriton Brewhouse,
Cheriton, Alresford,
Hampshire SO24 0QQ.**
☎ (01962) 771166

Purpose-built brewery, opened at Easter 1993 by the proprietors of the Flower Pots Inn next door and the Tally Ho! at Broughton. With a ten-barrel plant, it supplies around 40 free trade outlets and the Watercress Line steam railway. Cheriton also produces occasional special brews. Tours by arrangement.

**Pots Ale** (OG 1038, ABV 3.8%) 🍺 🍃 Golden in colour, with a hoppy nose, a well-balanced bitter taste and a bitter aftertaste.

**Best Bitter** (OG 1041, ABV 4.2%) Dark, malty and slightly fruity.

**Diggers Gold** (OG 1046, ABV 4.6%) 🍺 Golden, smooth and well-hopped.

## CHESTER'S

See Burtonwood, Everards and Nationals, Whitbread.

## CHILTERN

**The Chiltern Brewery, Nash
Lee Road, Terrick,
Aylesbury,
Buckinghamshire
HP17 0TQ.**
☎ (01296) 613647 FAX (01296) 612419

Set up in 1980 on a small farm, Chiltern specialises in an unusual range of beer-related products, like beer mustards, Old Ale chutneys, cheeses and malt marmalade. These products are available from the brewery shop (open 9–5 Mon–Sat) and also from about 20 other retail outlets. The brewery itself is regularly supplied to up to ten free trade outlets (no tied houses). There is a small museum (recently expanded) and brewery tours are at noon Saturday, or by arrangement. Bottle-conditioned beer: Bodgers Barley Wine (OG 1080, ABV 8%).

**Chiltern Ale** (OG 1038, ABV 3.7%) A distinctive, tangy light bitter.

**Beechwood Bitter** (OG 1043, ABV 4.3%) Full-bodied and nutty.

**Three Hundreds Old Ale** (OG 1050, ABV 4.9%) A strong, rich, deep chestnut-coloured beer.

## CHURCH END

**Church End Brewery Ltd.,
The Griffin Inn, Church
Road, Shustoke,
Warwickshire B46 2LB.**
☎ (01675) 481567

Brewery founded in 1994 in an old coffin workshop next to the Griffin Inn. Brewing about six barrels a week, it produces many guest and special brews to order for its free trade outlets (between 30

and 50). After the successful launch of the honey beer (Pooh Beer), some spice and fruit beers are planned. A beer named after the latest car registration letter is also brewed. Tours by arrangement. Bottle-conditioned beers: Gravediggers (OG 1038, ABV 3.8%), Cracker Ale (OG 1050, ABV 5%), RIP (OG 1070, ABV 7%).

**Cuthberts** (OG 1038, ABV 3.8%) 🍃 A refreshing, hoppy beer, with hints of malt, fruit and caramel taste. Lingering bitter aftertaste.

**Gravediggers** (OG 1038, ABV 3.8%) A premium mild. Dark black and red in colour, with a complex mix of chocolate and roast flavours, it is almost a light porter. Available in spring and summer.

**Wheat-a-Bix** (OG 1042, ABV 4.2%) A wheat beer; clear, malty and very pale, combining German hops and English wheat.

**What the Fox's Hat** (OG 1043, ABV 4.2%) 🍃 A beer with a malty aroma and a hoppy and malty taste with some caramel flavour.

**Pooh Beer** (OG 1044, ABV 4.3%) 🍃 A bright golden beer brewed with honey. Sweet, yet hoppy; moreish.

**Vicar's Ruin** (OG 1044, ABV 4.4%) A straw-coloured best bitter with an initially hoppy, bitter flavour, softening to a delicate malt finish.

**Pews Porter** (OG 1045, ABV 4.5%) A moderately hopped, rich chocolate porter with a dry finish. Available in autumn and winter.

**Old Pal** (OG 1055, ABV 5.5%) A strong, copper-coloured ale, full of rich, malty flavours. Three different types of hops are used; dry finish.

**Rest In Peace (RIP)** (OG 1070, ABV 7%) A light amber-coloured strong bitter, with a malty mouthfeel and a well-balanced sweet finish.

## WILLIAM CLARK

**William Clark Brewing Company,
Scarborough, N. Yorkshire.**

Brewery closed. Its one beer, Thistle Mild (OG 1040, ABV 4%), is contract brewed by an undeclared brewer.

## CLARK'S

**HB Clark & Co.
(Successors) Ltd., Westgate
Brewery, Westgate,
Wakefield,
W. Yorkshire WF2 9SW.**
☎ (01924) 373328 FAX (01924) 372306

Founded in 1905, Clark's ceased brewing during the keg revolution of the 1960s and 1970s, although it continued to operate as a drinks wholesaler. It resumed cask ale production in 1982. It now has four tied houses and Clark's beers are widely available (including in Scotland and

London) either supplied directly from the brewery or via beer agencies. A special brew (OG 1042, ABV 4.2%) is brewed for particular occasions – the name depending on the event. Brewery shop open 8–5 Mon–Fri, 8–1 Sat and Sun. Tours by arrangement.

**Traditional Bitter** (OG 1038, ABV 3.8%) ❧ A copper-coloured, well-balanced smooth beer, with a malty and hoppy aroma, leading to a hoppy, fruity taste and a good, clean, strong malt flavour. Bitterness and dryness linger in the taste and aftertaste.

**Festival Ale** (OG 1042, ABV 4.2%) ❧ A light, fruity, pleasantly hopped premium bitter with a good fruity, hoppy nose. Moderate bitterness follows, with a dry, fruity finish. Gold in colour.

**Burglar Bill** (OG 1044, ABV 4.4%) ❧ A good, hoppy, fruity aroma precedes an enjoyable, strong hoppy and fruity taste, with moderate bitterness and good malt character. A lingering dry, hoppy finish follows. Dark brown in colour.

**Rams Revenge** (OG 1046, ABV 4.6%) ❧ A strong, dark brown ale with good body, a strong malt flavour and some caramel, balanced with a fruit and hop taste which does not linger.

**Hammerhead** (OG 1056, ABV 5.6%) ❧ Rich malt in the mouth, but with hop flavour and bitterness to balance. The malty, hoppy aroma is faint, but the finish is long, malty and dry. A robust, strong bitter.

**Winter Warmer** (OG 1060, ABV 6%) ❧ A dark brown, powerful strong ale. A strong, mouth-filling blend of roast malt, hop flavour, sweetness and fruit notes concludes with a satisfying finish of bittersweet roast malt.

**Old Dreadnought** (OG 1080, ABV 9%) A strong, powerful, mid brown beer, moderately malty with a good hop flavour. Easy to drink for its strength.

## COACH HOUSE

**The Coach House Brewing Company Ltd., Wharf Street, Howley, Warrington, Cheshire WA1 2DQ.**
☎ **(01925) 232800**
[FAX] **(01925) 232700**

Brewery founded in 1991 by four ex-Greenall Whitley employees. In 1995 Coach House increased its brewing capacity to cope with growing demand and it now delivers to outlets throughout England, Wales and Scotland, either direct or via wholesalers. The brewery also produces specially commissioned beers and brews three beers for non-brewing company John Joule of Stone ☎ (01785) 814909. Tours by arrangement. Occasional/seasonal beers: Wizards Wonder Halloween (OG 1042, ABV 4.2% October), Cracker Barrel Bonfire (OG 1046, ABV 4.6% November), Dewi Sant Heritage Ale (OG 1047, ABV 4.7% March), St

Patrick's Leprechaun Ale (OG 1047, ABV 4.7%), Regal Birthday Ale (OG 1047, ABV 4.7% April), St George's Heritage Ale (OG 1047, ABV 4.9% April), Bootleg Valentine Ale (OG 1050, ABV 5%, February), Combine Harvester (OG 1051, ABV 5.1%, late summer), Burns Auld Sleekit (OG 1055, ABV 5.5%, January), Three Kings Christmas Ale (OG 1060, ABV 6%).

**Coachman's Best Bitter** (OG 1037, ABV 3.7%) ❧ A well-hopped, malty bitter, moderately fruity with a hint of sweetness and a peppery nose. Refreshing.

**Gunpowder Strong Mild** (OG 1038, ABV 3.9%) ⬚ ❧ Full-bodied and roasty dark mild with hints of pepper, fruit and liquorice, plus chocolate overtones. Malty aroma and full finish.

**Ostlers Summer Pale Ale** (OG 1038, ABV 4%) ❧ Light, refreshing and very bitter, with a hint of pepper and a very dry finish.

**Squires Gold Spring Ale** (OG 1042, ABV 4.2%) ❧ A golden spring beer. New Zealand hops give intense bitterness which is followed by a strong chocolate flavour from amber malt. Uncompromising and characterful.

**Innkeeper's Special Reserve** (OG 1045, ABV 4.5%) ❧ A darkish, full-flavoured bitter. Quite fruity, with a strong, bitter aftertaste.

**Posthorn Premium Ale** (OG 1050, ABV 5%) ⬚ ❧ Well-hopped and very fruity, with bitterness and malt also prominent. Hoppy aroma; fruity aftertaste.

**Taverners Autumn Ale** (OG 1050, ABV 5%) ❧ Fruity, bitter, golden ale with a slightly dry aftertaste. A warming, autumnal ale.

**Blunderbus Old Porter** (OG 1055, ABV 5.5%) ⬚ ❧ A super winter beer. The intense roast flavour is backed up by coffee, chocolate and liquorice, and hints of spice and smoke. Very well-hopped with massive mouthfeel. An intense, chewy pint which is surprisingly refreshing and moreish.

### For Joule:

**Old Knotty** (OG 1037, ABV 3.7%)

**Old Priory** (OG 1044, ABV 4.4%)

**Victory Brew** (OG 1050, ABV 5%)

## COBDEN'S

**Richard Cobden's Brewery, Peaches, Wellington Street, Stockport, Cheshire SK1 1JE.** ☎ **(0161) 477 6994**

◻ Brewery housed beneath Peaches nightclub, supplying this and another club in Cheadle, plus customers who come to collect the beer (no deliveries). The club is on the site where Richard Cobden and John Bright repealed the Corn Laws in the 19th century. A cask-conditioned lager has been trialled. Beers: Bitter (ABV 3.6%), Premier Bitter (ABV 4.2%), Festival Bitter (ABV 5%).

## COMBE
Combe Brewery, Ilfracombe, Devon.

Brewery closed.

## COMMERCIAL
Commercial Brewing Co.
Ltd., Worth Brewery, Worth
Way, Keighley,
W. Yorkshire BD21 5LP.
☎ (01535) 611914
[FAX] (01535) 691883

Set up in a former garage, this brewery's first beer was produced in 1992. Its direct free trade now covers 30 outlets in the M62/M1 corridor. A new visitor centre opened at the beginning of 1996, offering tours to groups by arrangement. Shop open normal office hours and Saturday morning. One-off brews are produced for special occasions but bottle-conditioned beers have been discontinued for the present. Occasional/seasonal beers: Hi Summer (OG 1034, ABV 3.2%, June–July), Beckside Mild (OG 1034, ABV 3.4%, May), Wayfarer Mild (OG 1034, ABV 3.4%, May), Queen of the May Mild (ABV 3.9%, May), Harvest Festival (OG 1045, ABV 4.5%, August–Sept), Rampant Spring (OG 1048, ABV 4.8%, March–April), Worth Extra (OG 1049, ABV 5%, May–June), Winter Blues (OG 1048, ABV 5.2%, January February), Ruggie's Russet Nectar (OG 1070, ABV 7.5%, October–November), Santa's Toss (OG 1080, ABV 8%, December).

**Alesman** or **Keighlian Bitter** (OG 1036, ABV 3.7%) ◥ A light-bodied, bitter session beer with some fruit in the aroma and a long, dry finish.

**Wild Boar** (OG 1040, ABV 4%) ◥ Malt, hops and bitterness combine to give a quite refreshing and well-balanced drink with a bitter aftertaste. Brewed to the original Trough Brewery (now defunct) recipe.

**Neary's Stout** (OG 1042, ABV 4.1%) ◥ A strong roast character gives hints of bitter chocolate, coffee and liquorice. The long, dry finish has a citrus tang. It is a shame this fine stout is not more widely available.

**Worth Best Bitter** (OG 1045, ABV 4.5%) ◥ A long, hoppy finish complements a bitter hop taste with underlying malt and fruit. Look for hints of pear in the nose. A tasty and satisfying amber ale.

**Worth Porter** (OG 1045, ABV 4.5%) A true porter, produced October–March.

**Knöbwilter** (OG 1049, ABV 5.2%) A pale wheat beer, with a bitter taste and a dry finish, available April–September. Normally sold fined and therefore clear.

**Old Toss** (OG 1065, ABV 6.5%) A rich, dark brew with plenty of roast in the nose and taste. The finish is long, dry and pleasantly warming. Akin in style to a strong stout.

## CONCERTINA
The Concertina Brewery, The Mexborough
Concertina Band Club, 9A Dolcliffe Road,
Mexborough, S. Yorkshire S64 9AZ.
☎ (01709) 580841

🍺 Brewery in the cellar of a club, which began production in 1993, brewing eight barrels a week and supplying about 25 occasional outlets. Occasional beers: Shot Firers Porter (OG 1040, ABV 4.5%), Bandsman Strong Ale (OG 1048, ABV 5.2%).

**Best Bitter** (OG 1038, ABV 4%) ◥ Paler than before, this mid-brown bitter has lots of hops on the nose, a hoppy taste and a dry finish, plus gentle fruitiness throughout.

**Old Dark Attic** (OG 1038, ABV 4%) A very dark, almost black, bitter.

**Hackett VC** (OG 1040, ABV 4.2%) ◥ A well-balanced, malty ale with a hop underlay and even coffee tastes, though the finish has a bitter edge. Mid-brown to amber in colour.

**KW Special Pride** (OG 1042, ABV 4.5%) ⌑ ◥ A smooth, medium-bodied premium bitter with a fine mixture of grain, fruit and hop in the mouth, followed by a balanced, mellow aftertaste. Easy drinking for a beer of its strength.

**Bengal Tiger** (OG 1043, ABV 4.5%) Pale and hoppy, in the style of an IPA.

**Fitzpatricks Stout** (OG 1043, ABV 4.5%)

## CONISTON
The Coniston Brewing Co. Ltd.,
Coppermines Road, Coniston, Cumbria
LA21 8HL. ☎ (01539) 441133
[FAX] (01539) 441177

🍺 Brewery set up in October 1995 behind the Black Bull pub. The ten-barrel plant was built by Marston Moor and now supplies nine other pubs locally, with Flying Firkin distributing the beers nationwide. A third brew is planned. Tours by arrangement.

**Bluebird Bitter** (OG 1036, ABV 3.6%) A golden, hoppy bitter.

**Opium** (ABV 4%)

**Old Man Ale** (OG 1043, ABV 4.4%) A ruby red ale.

## COTLEIGH
Cotleigh Brewery, Ford
Road, Wiveliscombe,
Somerset TA4 2RE.
☎ (01984) 624086
[FAX] (01984) 624365

Continued growth has taken this brewery a long way from its first home, a stable block at Cotleigh Farmhouse in 1979. It is now housed in specially converted premises in Wiveliscombe, capable of producing 140 barrels a week. Cotleigh supplies 150 outlets direct, mostly in Devon and Somerset, although the beers are also available across

the country via wholesalers. Two beers are produced exclusively for the Kent wholesalers, East-West Ales Ltd.
☎ (01892) 834040. Occasional beers (made available to customers on a monthly rota): Swift (OG 1030, ABV 3.2%), Nutcracker Mild (OG 1036, ABV 3.6%), Harvest Ale (OG 1040, ABV 4%), Hobby Ale (OG 1042, ABV 4.2%), Peregrine Porter (OG 1045, ABV 4.4%), Golden Eagle (OG 1045, ABV 4.5%), Merlin Ale (OG 1048, ABV 4.8%), Osprey (OG 1050, ABV 5%), Powderkeg (OG 1050, ABV 5%), Snowy Ale (OG 1050, ABV 5%), Red Nose Reinbeer (OG 1060, ABV 5.6%, Christmas).

**Harrier SPA** (OG 1035, ABV 3.6%)✎ A straw-coloured beer with a very hoppy aroma and flavour, and a hoppy, bitter finish. Plenty of flavour for a light, low gravity beer.

**Tawny Bitter** (OG 1038, ABV 3.8%)▯ ✎ A mid-brown-coloured, very consistent beer. A hoppy aroma, a hoppy but quite well-balanced flavour, and a hoppy, bitter finish.

**Barn Owl Bitter** (OG 1045, ABV 4.5%)

**Old Buzzard** (OG 1048, ABV 4.8%)▯ ✎ Now only a winter brew: a dark, ruby beer tasting of roast malt balanced with hops. Roast malt continues in the finish, with bitterness.

### For East-West Ales:

**Aldercote Ale** (OG 1042, ABV 4.2%)

**Aldercote Extra** (OG 1046, ABV 4.7%)

## COTTAGE

**Cottage Brewing Company, Little Orchard, High Street, West Lydford, Somerset TA11 7DQ.**
☎ (01963) 240551
FAX (01963) 240383

Brewery founded in 1993 and upgraded to a ten-barrel plant in 1994. Owned by an airline pilot, the company has got off to a flying start, with Norman's Conquest taking the *Champion Beer of Britain* title at the 1995 Great British Beer Festival. The beers are served in over 200 outlets locally, with deliveries made by the company's steam lorry and horse-drawn dray. The names mostly follow a railway theme. Tours by arrangement. Bottle-conditioned beer: Norman's Conquest (OG 1066, ABV 7%).

**Southern Bitter** (OG 1037, ABV 3.7%)

**Wheeltappers Ale** (OG 1040, ABV 4%)

**Somerset & Dorset Ale (S&D)** (OG 1043, ABV 4.4%) Named after the Somerset & Dorset Railway: a well-hopped, malty brew, with a deep red colour.

**Golden Arrow** (OG 1044, ABV 4.5%)

**Our Ken** (OG 1044, ABV 4.5%)

**Great Western Real Ale (GWR)** (OG 1053, ABV 5.4%) Similar to S&D but stronger and darker, with a full-bodied maltiness.

**Norman's Conquest** (OG 1066, ABV 7%)▯ ✎ A dark strong ale, with plenty of fruit flavour and a touch of bitterness.

## COURAGE
See Nationals, Scottish Courage.

## CRANBORNE
**The Cranborne Brewery, Sheaf of Arrows, 4 The Square, Cranborne, Dorset BH21 5PR. ☎ / FAX (01725) 517456**

▯ This new brewery, set up in a stable block behind the Sheaf of Arrows pub, went into production at Easter 1996. A second beer is planned. Shop open 12–3 Wed, Sat and Sun. Tours by arrangement. Beer: Quiver (OG 1038, ABV 3.8%).

## CROPTON

**Cropton Brewery Co., The New Inn, Cropton, near Pickering, N. Yorkshire YO18 8HH.**
☎ / FAX (01751) 417310

▯ Brewery set up in 1984 in the cellar of the New Inn just to supply the pub. The plant was expanded in 1988, but by 1994 it had outgrown the cellar and a purpose-built brewery was installed behind the pub. Cropton's additive-free beers are now supplied to 60 outlets locally, plus wholesalers. A new visitor centre adjoining the pub opened in March 1996, with tours available by arrangement. There are plans to bottle more of the brewery's products. Bottle-conditioned beer: Backwoods Bitter (OG 1053, ABV 5.1%).

**King Billy** (OG 1039, ABV 3.6%)✎ A gold-coloured, beautifully clean, hoppy bitter, light on the palate but with strong hop flavour and bitterness. Long, hoppy and bitter finish, but only a slight aroma.

**Two Pints** (OG 1042, ABV 4%)▯ ✎ A hop aroma precedes a powerful, flowery hop character in the taste with some malt and bitterness. Long, smooth, hoppy and sweet finish. A fine, distinctive bitter.

**Scoresby Stout** (OG 1044, ABV 4.2%)▯ ✎ A rich assault of roast malt and bitterness leads to a long, bitter finish of roast malt and chocolate. Jet black, and a stout in every sense.

**Backwoods Bitter** (OG 1051, ABV 4.7%)

**Special Strong Bitter** (OG 1063, ABV 6%) A powerful ale, produced all year but popular at Christmas.

## CROUCH VALE
**Crouch Vale Brewery Ltd., 12 Redhills Road, South Woodham Ferrers, Chelmsford, Essex CM3 4HJ.**
☎ (01245) 322744 FAX (01245) 329082

Founded in 1981, Crouch Vale has expanded slowly but surely. Growth in the guest beer and wholesale markets has resulted in the building of new offices and the installation of new brewing plant. Tours by arrangement. The introduction of seasonal beers to the range has proved very successful. The brewery's single tied house, the Cap & Feathers at Tillingham, was the CAMRA national *Pub of the Year* in 1989. Crouch Vale currently delivers its wares by liveried dray to 300 free trade outlets in Suffolk, Essex and Greater London. Occasional/seasonal beers: Best Dark Ale (OG 1035, ABV 3.6%), Essex Porter (OG 1051, ABV 5.1%), Santa's Revenge (OG 1055, ABV 5.5%), Fine Pale Ale (OG 1057, ABV 5.9%), Willie Warmer (OG 1060, ABV 6.4%).

**Woodham IPA** (OG 1036, ABV 3.6%) ♦ An amber beer with a fresh, hoppy nose. A good session bitter with a well-balanced malt and hop taste leading to a fruit and hop finish.

**The Golden Duck** (OG 1038, ABV 3.8%) A summer beer.

**Best Bitter** (OG 1040, ABV 4%) ♦ The fruit in the aroma melts into a hoppy malt taste before dominating the finish.

**Millennium Gold** (OG 1042, ABV 4.2%) ▦ ♦ A golden beer with a notable hop nose. The strong hop/fruit presence makes this a deceptively easy drinking premium bitter.

**The Conqueror** (OG 1043, ABV 4.3%) The brewery's autumnal offering.

**Kursaal Flyer** (OG 1045, ABV 4.4%) A seasonal beer for the spring.

**Strong Anglian Special** or **SAS** (OG 1050, ABV 5%) ♦ Well-balanced and full-bodied, this is a sharply bitter beer with a dry aftertaste.

**Santa's Revenge** (OG 1057, ABV 5.7%) A Christmas ale, also sold throughout the year under house names. Despite its strength, it is dry and winey, not sweet.

## CROWN BUCKLEY

Crown Buckley Ltd.,
Gilbert Road, Llanelli,
Carmarthenshire SA15 3PP.
☎ (01554) 777004
[FAX] (01554) 777017

Following several takeovers, Buckley, the oldest brewery in Wales (est. 1767), merged with Crown Brewery (the former United Clubs Brewery) in 1989, with Harp financial backing. This ultimately meant that the new company was owned by Guinness but provided the firm with a genuine lifeline. Crown Buckley subsequently underwent heavy rationalisation and restructuring, before a management buyout in 1993 ensured its true independence once more. Today, all beer production is carried out at the Llanelli (Buckley) site, with kegging and bottling taking place at Pontyclun (the old Crown brewery). A tied estate (mostly Harp houses) of 76 pubs, and a free trade of around 400 outlets, are supplied direct from the brewery. The clubs trade is still important, too. Seasonal beers are now being produced in limited volumes.

**Crown Pale Ale (CPA)** (OG 1033, ABV 3.4%) A light bitter with a subtle hop flavour.

**Buckley's Dark Mild** (OG 1034, ABV 3.4%) ▣ ♦ A very dark, malty mild, fairly sweet with traces of chocolate, followed by a nutty, bitter finish. Very drinkable.

**Buckley's Best Bitter** (OG 1036, ABV 3.7%) ♦ A well-balanced, medium gravity bitter which has a rather sweet, malty flavour and a pleasant, bitter finish.

**Special Best Bitter (SBB)** (OG 1036, ABV 3.7%) ♦ Distinctively malty and clean-tasting, with a pronounced bitter flavour and a rather dry aftertaste.

**Reverend James Original Ale** (OG 1045, ABV 4.5%) ♦ A malty, full-bodied bitter with hoppy and fruity overtones, followed by a bittersweet aftertaste.

## CROWN HOTEL See Scott's.

## CROWN INN

Munslow Brewhouse, The Crown Inn, Munslow, Shropshire SY7 9ET.
☎ (01584) 841205

Pub brewery established in 1994 to supply just the pub itself, using a two-barrel plant and the brewer's own recipes. The brewery can be visited during opening hours. Beers: Boy's Pale Ale (OG 1036, ABV 3.6%), Munslow Ale (OG 1041, ABV 4.1%).

## CUCKMERE HAVEN

The Cuckmere Haven Brewery, Exceat Bridge, Cuckmere Haven, Seaford, E. Sussex BN25 4AB.
☎ (01323) 892247
[FAX] (01323) 893728 (ring first)

This tiny brewhouse went into production in 1994 to serve the Golden Galleon pub (the brewery's owner), plus a dozen other outlets on an occasional basis. Deliveries are made in the brewery's much publicised, 1957 Ford T0 pickup truck. Plans are in hand to expand both the pub and the brewery. Tours by arrangement. Occasional/seasonal beers: Seven Sisters Sussex Special (OG 1044, ABV 4.3%), Velvet Dark Mild (OG 1049, ABV 4.7%), Fuggl'olmullable (OG 1063, ABV 6.2%, a spicy winter ale).

**Best Bitter** (OG 1041, ABV 4.1%) ♦ Malty overtones in the aroma are joined by a hoppy bitterness in the flavour. Hop character increases in the aftertaste.

**Saxon King Stout** (OG 1042, ABV 4.2%)

**Gentlemen's Gold** (OG 1046, ABV 4.5%)

**Guv'ner** (OG 1047, ABV 4.7%) ♦ Pleasant bitter in which malt and roast malt in the aroma give way to a hoppy bitterness in the taste and aftertaste.

**Golden Peace** (OG 1055, ABV 5.5%) An amber-coloured, strong beer.

## CYDER HOUSE INN See Baynards.

## DALESIDE

**Daleside Brewery, Camwal Road, Starbeck, Harrogate, N. Yorkshire HG1 4PT.**
☎ **(01423) 880041**

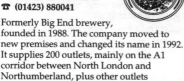

Formerly Big End brewery, founded in 1988. The company moved to new premises and changed its name in 1992. It supplies 200 outlets, mainly on the A1 corridor between North London and Northumberland, plus other outlets nationwide via wholesalers. Bottling began in 1995.

**Nightjar** (OG 1038, ABV 3.7%)

**Country Stile** or **Legover** (OG 1042, ABV 4.1%) ❤ A well-balanced, mid-brown, refreshing beer which leaves a lingering hop and bitter aftertaste.

**Dales Delight** (OG 1042, ABV 4.1%) A full-bodied, light-coloured, hoppy beer.

**Monkey Wrench** (OG 1056, ABV 5.3%) ❤ A powerful strong ale, dark ruby/brown in hue. A strong aroma of fruit leads to a rich assault of malt and roast malt, plus a strong fruit flavour with balancing bitterness. Long, fruity, malty and bitter finish; some sweetness throughout. It can be difficult to find, however.

## DARK HORSE

**Dark Horse Brewing Co. (Hertford) Ltd., Adams Yard, off Maidenhead Street, Hertford SG14 1DR.**
☎ **(01992) 509800**
FAX **(01992) 509801**

Brewery set up in the cellar of the White Horse free house in 1994, but moved in summer 1996 to its own premises, in converted Victorian stables, at the town centre, giving scope for greatly increased output. The White Horse is now the brewery tap, and ten other outlets also take the beers. Occasional/seasonal beers: Fallen Angel (OG 1040, ABV 4.2%, a wheat-based ginger beer), St Elmo's Fire (OG 1048, ABV 4.6%), Black Widow (OG 1048, ABV 4.6%, a stout), Death Wish (OG 1053, ABV 5.3%).

**Dark Horse Ale** (OG 1036, ABV 3.6%) A tasty light bitter, with a hint of roast grain. Slightly more malty than when first produced.

**Sunrunner** (OG 1040, ABV 4.1%) A well-balanced, full-flavoured bitter, with fruit notes and a strong, bitter finish.

## DARK STAR See Skinner's.

## DARLEY See Ward's.

## DARTMOOR

See St Austell and Nationals, Carlsberg-Tetley.

## DARWIN

**Darwin Brewery, Brewlab, University of Sunderland, Darwin Annexe, Chester Road, Sunderland SR1 3SD.**
☎ **(0191) 515 2535**
FAX **(0191) 515 2531**

Brewery founded in 1994 as a research facility for the staff and students at the University of Sunderland. Two local pubs now take the regular beers, as do beer festivals, but numerous experimental beers are also produced. Bottle-conditioned beers are planned.

**Evolution** (OG 1042, ABV 4%) Dark amber, full-bodied bitter with a malty flavour and a clean, bitter aftertaste.

**Saints Sinner** (OG 1052, ABV 5%) A rich, smooth-tasting, ruby red ale with a fruity aroma and hop character in the taste.

**Killer Bee** (OG 1054, ABV 6%) A strong beer made with honey.

## DAVENPORTS

See Nationals, Carlsberg-Tetley, and Pub Groups, Greenalls.

## DAVENPORTS ARMS

**Worfield Brewery, Davenports Arms, Main Street, Worfield, Shropshire WV15 5LF.**
☎ **(01746) 716320**

Pub brewery established in 1994 and currently supplying just the pub itself. In addition to the beers listed below, WB Stout (OG 1040, ABV 4%) is produced. However, this is served under mixed gas dispense. Beers: JLK Pale Ale (OG 1038, ABV 3.8%), Hopstone Bitter (OG 1040, ABV 4%), Reynold's Redneck (OG 1055, ABV 5.5%, a strong mild), Hermitage Barley Wine (OG 1090, ABV 8.8%, occasional).

## DAVIS'ES

See Grainstore.

## DENT

**Dent Brewery, Hollins, Cowgill, Dent, Cumbria LA10 5TQ.**
☎ **(01539) 625326**
FAX **(01539) 625033**

Brewery set up in a converted barn in the Yorkshire Dales in 1990, originally to supply just three local pubs. It now has two tied houses and supplies 12 free trade outlets directly. Its own distribution company, Flying Firkin Distribution –
☎ (01282) 865923 – delivers all over

northern England and is making some inroads into the South, too. All Dent's beers are brewed using the brewery's own spring water. Tours by arrangement (minimum six people).

**Bitter** (OG 1036, ABV 3.7%) ◗ Fruit dominates the aroma, with hops and malt coming through more strongly in the taste and aftertaste. A clean, refreshing and well-balanced bitter.

**Ramsbottom Strong Ale** (OG 1044, ABV 4.5%) ◗ A rich and complex tawny ale, with a warming, dry finish. There are hints of toffee in the nose, while in the taste fruit, caramel and roast vie for attention.

**T'Owd Tup** (OG 1058, ABV 6%) A dark old ale.

## For Flying Firkin:

**Aviator** (OG 1038, ABV 4%) ◗ A distinctively hoppy brew with tangy citrus flavours throughout. Refreshing and highly enjoyable.

**Kamikaze** (OG 1048, ABV 5%) A light-coloured, strong bitter.

## DEVENISH

See Nationals, Whitbread, and Pub Groups, Greenalls.

## DEVON

**Devon Ales, Mansfield Arms, 7 Main Street, Sauchie, Alloa, Clackmannanshire FK10 3JR. ☎ (01259) 722020 FAX (01259) 218409**

Brewery founded at CAMRA's 1993 Scottish *Pub of the Year*, the Mansfield Arms, in spring 1994 which has since been expanded by the addition of two five-barrel fermenters. One other associated pub also takes the beer. Tours by arrangement. Beers: Gold (OG 1037, ABV 3.8%), Original (OG 1037, ABV 3.8%), Thick Black (OG 1040, ABV 4.1%), Pride (OG 1046, ABV 4.6%).

## DONNINGTON

**Donnington Brewery, Stow-on-the-Wold, Gloucestershire GL54 1EP. ☎ (01451) 830603**

Possibly the most attractive brewery in the country, set in a 13th-century watermill in idyllic surroundings. Bought by Thomas Arkell in 1827, it became a brewery in 1865, and is still owned and run by the family. The millhouse is still in excellent condition with the millwheel still employed to drive small pumps and machinery. Unfortunately, the brewery is not open to the public. Donnington supplies its own 15 tied houses, and 12 free trade outlets, with cask ales, although XXX is only available in a few pubs.

**BB** (OG 1036, ABV 3.6%) ◗ Little aroma, but a pleasing, bitter beer, with a good malt/hop balance. Not as distinctive as it used to be.

**XXX** (OG 1036, ABV 3.6%) Again, thin in aroma, but flavoursome. More subtle than others in its class, with some fruit and traces of chocolate and liquorice in the taste, and a notably malty finish.

**SBA** (OG 1040, ABV 3.8%) Malt dominates over bitterness in the flavour of this subtle premium bitter, with just a hint of fruit and a dry, malty finish. Faintly malty aroma.

## DRINKLINK See Hardy.

## DUNN PLOWMAN

**Dunn Plowman Brewery, Queen's Head, Bridge Street, Kington, Herefordshire HR5 3DW. ☎ (01544) 231106**

Pub brewery operating intermittently for over two years, producing three beers: Brewhouse Bitter (ABV 3.8%), Kingdom Bitter (ABV 4.5%), Heavy Horse (ABV 5%, occasional).

## DURHAM

**The Durham Brewery, Units 6D/E, Lindsey Park, Bowburn North Industrial Estate, Bowburn, Co. Durham DH6 5PF. ☎/FAX (0191) 377 1991**

Since this brewery launched its first beers in 1994, Celtic has twice been voted *Best Beer* at CAMRA's Durham Beer Festival. Now, with a full-time brewer employed, several more beers have been added to the range and special brews, as well as bottled beers, are planned. Over 100 outlets are supplied.

**Old Elvet** (OG 1038, ABV 3.6%)

**Sunstroke** (OG 1038, ABV 3.6%) Available April–September.

**Magus** (OG 1039, ABV 3.8%)

**Celtic** (OG 1043, ABV 4.2%) ◗ A mid-brown ale with a slight malty and fruity aroma. The aftertaste is predominantly dry and well-balanced.

**Old Hundred** (OG 1044, ABV 4.4%)

**Black Bishop** (OG 1046, ABV 4.5%)

**Canny Lad** (OG 1046, ABV 4.5%)

**Pagan** (OG 1049, ABV 4.8%)

**Sanctuary** (OG 1058, ABV 6%) An old ale for winter.

## DYFFRYN CLWYD

**Bragdy Dyffryn Clwyd Brewery, Old Buttermarket, Chapel Street, Denbigh LL16 3TJ. ☎ (01745) 815007**

Brewery founded by local pub landlord Ioan Evans in 1994. The beers have bilingual pump clips and are sold in some free houses in North Wales, but are more widely available in England via wholesalers. The bottle-conditioned beers have been discontinued for the present. There are plans to open a small public bar in part of the brewery. Tours by arrangement.

**Dr Johnson's Draught** (OG 1036, ABV 3.6%) 🍺 ◆ Hoppy and fruity, thirst quenching beer, with caramel notes in the taste and nose. Thin aftertaste.

**Archdruid** (OG 1038, ABV 3.9%) ◆ A blend of Dr Johnson and Castell. A smooth, nutty and full-bodied beer, which is well hopped and has a short and very dry aftertaste.

**Cwrw Castell** or **Castle Bitter** (OG 1042, ABV 4.2%) 🍺 ◆ A darkish, smooth bitter, with good hop character. Fairly fruity, with some roast malt flavour. A complex bitter.

**Jolly Jack Tar Porter** (OG 1045, ABV 4.5%) ◆ A smooth, dry porter with good roast malt and chocolate flavours; reasonably well hopped.

**Pedwar Bawd** or **Four Thumbs** (OG 1048, ABV 4.8%) 🍺 ◆ A well-balanced, fruity and sweetish bitter with a hint of caramel. Citrus and caramel aroma; dry aftertaste.

## EARL SOHAM

**Earl Soham Brewery, c/o The Victoria, Earl Soham, Woodbridge, Suffolk IP13 7RL.** ☎ **(01728) 685758**

🚩 Brewery set up behind the Victoria pub in 1985. Brewing has recently been suspended, but the brewer/owner hopes to resume in the near future.

## EASINGWOLD

**Easingwold Brewery, Station Hotel, Knott Lane, Raskels Road, Easingwold, York, N.Yorkshire YO6 3NT.** ☎ **(01347) 822635**

🚩 Brewery set up in a stable block behind an hotel in May 1996, supplying the hotel and beer festivals, though hoping to expand. Two more beers are planned. Tours by arrangement. Beer: Steamcock Bitter (OG 1038, ABV 3.8%)

## EAST-WEST ALES

See Brewery on Sea, Cotleigh and Foxley.

## EASTWOOD'S

**Eastwood's Brewery, Longwood, Huddersfield, W. Yorkshire.** ☎ **(01484) 656024**

Originally set up in Huddersfield, Eastwood's moved to the Walkleys Clogs tourist attraction at Hebden Bridge in 1995, but has since moved yet again. Production was due to restart in Huddersfield as we went to press.

## ECCLESHALL

**Eccleshall Brewery, George Hotel, Castle Street, Eccleshall, Stafford ST21 6DF.** ☎ **(01785) 850300** FAX **(01785) 851452**

🚩 Brewery opened in outbuildings behind the George Hotel in March 1995, producing 'Slaters Ales'. Around 50 other local outlets and wholesalers are also supplied with the beers. Tours by arrangement.

**Slaters Bitter** (OG 1036, ABV 3.6%) ◆ Malt and hops combine with a fruity flavour in this light amber beer.

**Slaters Original** (OG 1040, ABV 4%) A distinctive, creamy amber beer.

**HiDuck** (OG 1041, ABV 4.1%) Available March–June.

**Slaters Premium** (OG 1044, ABV 4.4%) Strong, but light and creamy, dry bitter, darker than the other brews.

**All Mighty** (OG 1053, ABV 5.3%) Available November–March.

## EDGCOTE See Merivales.

## ELDRIDGE POPE See Hardy.

## ELGOOD'S

**Elgood & Sons Ltd., North Brink Brewery, Wisbech, Cambridgeshire PE13 1LN.** ☎ **(01945) 583160** FAX **(01945) 587711**

From its classical Georgian, riverside premises (converted in the 1790s from a mill and granary and acquired by the Elgood family in 1878), this brewery supplies real ale to all but two of its 47 tied houses, and to a free trade of around 100 outlets. In addition, a mini-brewery produces a variety of beers in small volumes for sale as guests. A visitors' centre and brewery museum were opened in 1995. Tours by arrangement.

**Black Dog Mild** (OG 1036, ABV 3.6%) Malt dominates the aroma of this black/red seasonal (spring) mild. Malt and roast grain on the palate are blended with hops and fruit. Dry, roast grain finish.

**Cambridge Bitter** (OG 1036, ABV 3.8%) ◆ An amber beer with an aroma of fresh hops and fruit. The flavour is predominately of hops, with some malt and fruit on a dry base. Very dry finish, with faint hops.

**Pageant Ale** (OG 1043, ABV 4.3%)

**Barleymead** (OG 1048, ABV 4.8%) A summer/autumn brew.

**Greyhound Strong Bitter** or **GSB** (OG 1050, ABV 5.2%) ◆ Preceded by a fruity and faintly malty aroma, the flavour of this mid-brown beer is a blend of fruit, malt and hops on a dry, but slightly sweet, base. Very dry finish, with some malt and fruit.

**North Brink Porter** (OG 1050, ABV 5%) ⬚
◆ This dark red/brown winter beer is a complex blend of roast, malt, grain and fruit, with an underlying dryness. Roast malt and grain in the aroma, with some sulphur; dry, roasty aftertaste, with faint fruit.

**Wenceslas Winter Warmer** (OG 1070, ABV 7.5%) ◆ A robust winter ale with a rich fruity aroma. Bitter chocolate and raisin fruit on the palate leads through to a dry, fruity finish with some roast malt.

## MARTIN ELMS See Nethergate.

## ENVILLE
**Enville Ales, Enville Brewery, Cox Green, Enville, Stourbridge, W. Midlands DY7 5LG.**
☎ (01384) 873728
[FAX] (01384) 873770

Brewery on a picturesque Victorian farm complex. Using the same water source as the original village brewery (closed in 1919), the beers also incorporate over three tons of honey annually, using recipes passed down from the proprietor's great-great aunt. Enville's owner had originally intended to go into full-time beekeeping with brewing as a sideline, but the position is now entirely reversed, and the brewery now grows its own barley, too. Enville (in Staffordshire, despite the postal address) also runs the Victoria Pub Co. Tours by arrangement.

**Bitter** (OG 1038, ABV 3.8%) ◆ A straw-coloured, hoppy and bitter beer which leaves a malty, moreish aftertaste.

**Simpkiss Bitter** (OG 1038, ABV 3.9%) ◆ A medium-bodied, golden bitter. The refreshing, hoppy taste lingers.

**Low Gravity Mild** (OG 1038, ABV 3.8%)

**White** (OG 1042, ABV 4%) ◆ A clean, well-balanced, golden, sweet bitter, light in flavour. An appealing beer.

**High Gravity Mild** (OG 1042, ABV 4.2%)

**Enville Ale** (OG 1045, ABV 4.5%) ◆ A pale gold, medium-bodied bitter. Light hops and sweet fruit in the taste; a hint of honey in the aroma and aftertaste.

**Gothic Ale** (OG 1054, ABV 5.2%) ◆ Malt, hops and caramel combine with a strong roast malt taste in this dark, stout-like beer. Well-balanced, with lurking hints of honey.

## EVENING STAR See Skinner's.

## EVERARDS
**Everards Brewery Ltd., Castle Acres, Narborough, Leicester LE19 5BY.**
☎ (0116) 281 4100
[FAX] (0116) 281 4199

Small, family-owned brewery, founded in 1849 by William Everard, great-great-grandfather of the current chairman, Richard Everard. Over the years Everards beers were brewed in both Leicester and Burton upon Trent, until all production was transferred to Castle Acres in 1991. Its growing tied estate of 153 pubs includes many attractive, historic houses and over 90 per cent of them sell real ale, but with the occasional use of cask breathers. Everards also services some 500 free trade accounts. Brewery tours for groups by arrangement. Occasional/seasonal beers: Spencer's Stout (OG 1041, ABV 4.2%), Daredevil Winter Warmer (OG 1068, ABV 7.1%, December–January).

**Mild** (OG 1036, ABV 3.3%) ◆ A smooth, sweet, dark red beer, malty throughout but with caramel and liquorice also in evidence. Beware: often on a cask breather.

**Beacon Bitter** (OG 1036, ABV 3.8%) ⬚ 🍺
◆ A refreshing, well-balanced, tawny/brown session beer. A bitter, hoppy taste leads to a long, dry, bitter finish that can be sulphurous in character, dependent upon the age of the cask. Very drinkable.

**Tiger Best Bitter** (OG 1041, ABV 4.2%)
◆ Mid-brown and smooth, this bitter has a gentle aroma of malt, hops and fruit, leading to a well-balanced palate and dry finish. Can be sulphurous.

**Old Original** (OG 1050, ABV 5.2%) ◆ A mid-brown beer with a sulphurous, hop/malt aroma and a very complex taste dominated by a bitter maltiness. Equally complex, strong, dry aftertaste; hints of liquorice can also be detected.

### For Whitbread:

**Chester's Best Mild** (OG 1032, ABV 3.5%)

## EVESHAM
**Evesham Brewery, 17 Oat Street, Evesham, Worcestershire WR11 4PJ.**
☎ /[FAX] (01386) 443462

Brewery set up in 1992 in the old bottle store at the Green Dragon Inn in Evesham. The owner and licensee, Steve Murphy, who also owns another pub, currently supplies another four outlets direct. The lack of local market penetration is compensated for by beer swaps with other small breweries and sales via agents. The brewery has become something of a tourist attraction (7,000 visitors were conducted round in 1995); tours by arrangement. 'Asum' is the local pronunciation of Evesham.

**Asum Ale** (OG 1038, ABV 3.8%) ◆ A distinctive malt and hop balance that attacks the palate to leave a fruity aftertaste.

**Asum Gold** (OG 1050, ABV 5.2%) ◆ A thick, fruity and malty strong ale.

445

# THE INDEPENDENTS

## EXE VALLEY

**Exe Valley Brewery, Land Farm, Silverton, Exeter, Devon EX5 4HF.**
☎ **(01392) 860406**

Founded as Barron Brewery in 1984 by Richard Barron, this company's name changed in 1991 with the expansion of the brewery, as Richard was joined as partner by Guy Sheppard. It operates from an old barn (using the farm's own spring water), and new plant was installed in 1993, to treble capacity. The brewery supplies 30 outlets locally and the beers have also been available nationally via wholesalers. Tours for groups by arrangement.

**Bitter** (OG 1038, ABV 3.7%) ◆ A light brown-coloured beer, with a fruit and malt aroma and taste. The finish is a mix of malt and hop bitterness.

**Devon Summer** (OG 1039, ABV 3.9%) A new seasonal beer.

**Dob's Best Bitter** (OG 1040, ABV 4.1%) ◆ Pale brown-coloured, superbly well-balanced beer, with a fruity aroma and taste and a bitter aftertaste.

**Spring Beer** (OG 1043, ABV 4.3%) ◆ A straw-coloured, fruity tasting beer with a bittersweet finish.

**Autumn Glory** (OG 1045, ABV 4.5%) Another new seasonal offering.

**Devon Glory** (OG 1047, ABV 4.7%) ◆ A tawny-coloured beer, with malt and fruit running through from the aroma to the finish.

**Exeter Old Bitter** (OG 1047, ABV 4.8%) ☐ ◆ A creamy, bittersweet, hoppy tasting beer with a flowery nose and a slightly sharp, lemony finish.

**Winter Glow** (OG 1060, ABV 6%) ◆ A dark brown, malty winter brew with plenty of malt and fruit right through the aroma, taste and finish.

## EXMOOR

**Exmoor Ales Ltd., Golden Hill Brewery, Wiveliscombe, Somerset TA4 2NY.** ☎ **(01984) 623798**
**FAX (01984) 624572**

Somerset's largest brewery was founded in 1980 in the old Hancock's brewery, which had been closed since 1959. It quickly won national acclaim, as its Exmoor Ale took the *Best Bitter* award at CAMRA's Great British Beer Festival, the first of over 30 prizes. The brewery has seen many years of continuous expansion and, with steadily increasing demand, growth looks set to continue. Around 250 pubs in the South-West are supplied directly, and others nationwide via wholesalers and pub chains. Tours by arrangement. Occasional/seasonal beers: Dark (OG 1042, ABV 4.1%), Stoat (OG 1044,

ABV 4.2%), Exmas (OG 1050, ABV 5%, Christmas).

**Exmoor Ale** (OG 1039, ABV 3.8%) ◆ A pale brown beer with a malty aroma, a malty, dry taste and a bitter and malty finish. Very drinkable.

**XV** (OG 1043, ABV 4.3%)

**Exmoor Gold** (OG 1045, ABV 4.5%) ☐ ◆ Yellow/golden in colour, with a malty aroma and flavour, and a slight sweetness and hoppiness. Sweet, malty finish.

**Exmoor Stag** (OG 1050, ABV 5.2%) ◆ A pale brown beer, with a malty taste and aroma, and a bitter finish. Slightly sweet. Very similar to Exmoor Ale and drinks as easily.

**Exmoor Beast** (OG 1066, ABV 6.6%) A winter brew, available October–Easter.

## FARMERS ARMS

**Mayhem's Brewery, Lower Apperley, Gloucestershire GL19 4DR.**
☎ **(01452) 780172**
**FAX (01452) 780307**

☐ Brewery opened in 1992 in the grounds of the Farmers Arms, which also produces its own cider. The beers are stored in cellar tanks and are only available at the pub. Tours by arrangement. Beers: Odda's Light (OG 1038, ABV 3.8%), Sundowner (OG 1044, ABV 4.5%).

## FEATHERSTONE

**Featherstone Brewery, Unit 3, King Street Buildings, King Street, Enderby, Leicestershire LE9 5NT.**
☎ **/FAX (0116) 275 0952**

Small brewery which has moved site several times. It specialises in supplying custom beers to pubs for sale under house names and turnover has grown considerably since it started in 1989. Four local outlets take the beers regularly. Occasional beer: Vulcan (OG 1049, ABV 5.1%, brewed to order).

**Hows Howler** (OG 1036, ABV 3.6%)

**Best Bitter** (OG 1042, ABV 4.2%)

**Stage Ale** (OG 1045, ABV 4.8%)

**Kingstone Bitter** (ABV 7.2%)

## FEDERATION

**Federation Brewery Ltd., Lancaster Road, Dunston, Tyne & Wear NE11 9JR.**
☎ **(0191) 460 9023**
**FAX (0191) 460 1297**

Federation was founded as a co-operative by local clubs in 1919, to overcome the post-war beer shortage. It moved to the Oystershell Brewery in 1921, but quickly outgrew that, and moved on to John Buchanan's Brewery in 1930. Expansion some 50 years later led to the company moving out to a green field site at Dunston. The brewery is still owned by local clubs, and their business accounts for the majority of the brewery's trade. Cask beers were reinstated in 1986, but only since the introduction of the Buchanan range in 1991 have sales taken off (90 outlets supplied) in 1995. Tours by arrangement.

**Buchanan's Best Mild** (OG 1033, ABV 3.2%) A recent addition.

**Buchanan's Best Bitter** (OG 1034, ABV 3.6%) ◆ Very difficult to find, especially on top form, when it has a pleasant aroma, a bitter flavour and a well-balanced aftertaste, with a hint of fruit throughout. Really an ordinary bitter, not a best.

**Buchanan's Special** (OG 1040, ABV 4%) ◆ A clean, hoppy and bitter ale, finishing dry, with fruit and hop lingering.

**Buchanan's Original** (OG 1042, ABV 4.4%) ◆ A rich, ruby red bitter with a smooth, creamy taste and lingering mouthfeel. A robust malt character makes this a better than average drinking bitter.

## FELDON
**Feldon Brewery, Coach & Horses, 16 New Street, Shipston-on-Stour, Warwickshire CV36 4EN. ☎ (01608) 661335**

Only opened at the beginning of 1996, Feldon's beer range is still subject to change as customers express their preferences. The beers are currently only available at the Coach & Horses. Beers: At Last (OG 1035, ABV 3.4%), plus a second brew at OG 1042.

## FELINFOEL
**Felinfoel Brewery Co. Ltd., Farmers Row, Felinfoel, Llanelli, Carmarthenshire SA14 8LB. ☎ (01554) 773357 FAX (01554) 752452**

This renowned Welsh brewery was built in 1878, when the village brew pub could no longer keep up with demand. The first brewery in Europe to can beer (in the 1930s), Felinfoel now supplies cask ale to most of its 85 houses (though some use top pressure) and serves roughly 160 free trade outlets. Shop open Mon–Fri 9–3.30. Occasional beer: Festive (OG 1085, ABV 8%).

**Bitter** (OG 1032, ABV 3.2%) ◆ A light brown, slightly malty, bitter beer with a distinct hop flavour and a bitter finish. Very drinkable.

**Dark** (OG 1032, ABV 3.2%) ◆ A dark brown/red mild, rather thin, with a slightly bitter flavour and aftertaste.

**Double Dragon** (OG 1042, ABV 4.2%) ◆ A fine, well-balanced, rich bitter with a nutty malt flavour, a fruity nose and a rounded, bittersweet finish.

## FELLOWS, MORTON & CLAYTON See Nationals, Whitbread.

**FILO** See First In, Last Out.

**FIRKIN** See Nationals, Carlsberg-Tetley.

## FIRST IN, LAST OUT
**FILO Brewery, 14–15 High Street, Old Town, Hastings, E. Sussex TN34 3EY. ☎ (01424) 425079 FAX (01424) 420802**

The First In, Last Out began brewing in 1985 and changed hands three years later. The new father and son partnership introduced their own yeast in 1995, but further developments have been restricted by space, so they still just brew for their own pub. Tours by arrangement. Beers: Crofters (OG 1040, ABV 3.9%), Cardinal (OG 1045, ABV 4.3%).

## FLAGSHIP
**The Flagship Brewery, Unit 2, Building 64, The Historic Dockyard, Chatham, Kent ME4 4TE. ☎ (01634) 832828**

Brewery set up in 1995 in Chatham's preserved Georgian dockyard, now a major tourist site. A new visitor centre at the brewery features a display about beer and the navy. Around 30 outlets are supplied direct, and other pubs throughout the UK take the beer via wholesalers. Tours by arrangement. Occasional beer: Nelson's Blood (OG 1054, ABV 6%).

**Special Ale** (OG 1036, ABV 3.5%) A crisp, light ale with a malty flavour.

**Capstan Ale** (OG 1039, ABV 3.8%) A medium-dry beer with a balanced malt and hop flavour and hints of honey.

**Ensign Ale** (OG 1042, ABV 4.2%) A fruity ale, with a good balance of malt and hops.

**Crow's Nest Ale** (OG 1048, ABV 4.8%) A straw-coloured, sweet and fruity ale with a hoppy aroma.

**Futtock Ale** (OG 1050, ABV 5.2%) A fruity, ruby-coloured ale, with a roast malt aftertaste.

**Gangplank Ale** (OG 1054, ABV 5.8%) A dark, malty winter ale, with balanced malt and hops.

## FLAMINGO
**The Kingston Brewery, 88 London Road, Kingston upon Thames, Surrey KT2 6PX. ☎ (0181) 541 3717**

Previously part of the Firkin chain, but now owned by Saxon Inns, this five-barrel brewhouse is situated behind the Flamingo pub (which is in Greater London, despite the postal address). Some of the beer is stored under mixed gas in cellar tanks. A couple of other pubs are supplied with cask beer. Beers: Fairfield Bitter (OG 1037, ABV 3.4%), Royal Charter (OG 1044, ABV 4.2%), Tiffin Ale (ABV 4.7%, occasional), Coronation (OG 1059, ABV 5.8%), Crucifixion Ale (ABV 6%, Easter), Hogsmill (ABV 6.6%, occasional), Rudolph's Revenge (OG 1070, ABV 7%, Christmas).

### FLOWER POTS INN See Cheriton.

### FLOWERS See Nationals, Whitbread.

### FLYING FIRKIN See Dent.

### FOX & HOUNDS
**Barley Brewery, Barley, Hertfordshire SG8 8HU. ☎ (01763) 848459**

An early member of the pub brewing revival, using a 19th-century brewhouse at what used to be the Waggon & Horses before changing its name. Some special brews are occasionally produced. Beers: Nathaniel's Special (OG 1037, ABV 3.3%), Flame Thrower (OG 1048, ABV 4.2%).

### FOX & HOUNDS
**Woody Woodward's Brewery, c/o The Fox & Hounds, High Street, Stottesdon, Shropshire DY14 8TZ.
☎ (01746) 718222**

Brewing commenced at this pub in 1979 and saw two changes of ownership before Glen Woodward took over in 1992 and started selling to the free trade (currently four outlets). He started trading under the present name in 1994 and now also brews under contract for the Blackbeard Trading Company ☎ (01584) 872908. The brewery can be visited during pub opening hours. The 'wust' and 'bostin' in the beer names are Black Country expressions meaning worst and best. Beers: Wust Bitter (OG 1037, ABV 3.6%), Bostin Bitter (OG 1042, ABV 4.2%), Wild Mild (OG 1042, ABV 4.2%), Gobstopper Bitter (OG 1060, ABV 6%, winter).

### For Blackbeard Trading:

**Brew 37** (OG 1052, ABV 5.1%).

### FOX & NEWT
See Nationals, Whitbread.

### FOXLEY
**Foxley Brewing Company Ltd., Unit 3, Home Farm Workshops, Mildenhall, Marlborough, Wiltshire SN8 2LR. ☎ (01672) 515000**

Brewery founded in 1992, now run by Neil and Louise Collings and directly supplying

around 30 free trade outlets within a 50-mile radius, and pubs further afield via wholesalers. There are plans to increase production of the four regular beers and introduce a summer brew. One beer is brewed occasionally for wholesalers East-West Ales Ltd. ☎ (01892) 834040. Bottle-conditioned beers: Dog Booter (OG 1047, ABV 4.6%), Howling Wolf (OG 1049, ABV 4.8%).

**Best Bitter** (OG 1039, ABV 3.8%) A light, copper-coloured session bitter with a well-balanced flavour. An initial slight sweetness develops into a dry finish. Very easy drinking.

**Barking Mad** (OG 1044, ABV 4.3%) Light and hoppy in aroma, this beer has lots of wheat, giving it plenty of body. Lingering aftertaste that is pleasantly bitter.

**Dog Booter** (OG 1047, ABV 4.6%) This refreshing beer has an initial bite, leading to a long, hoppy finish. A straw-coloured, premium ale that is a true bitter, with plenty of hops.

**Howling Wolf** or **Strong Bitter** (OG 1049, ABV 4.8%) A ruby-red warming ale with a complex aroma. The taste is rich and full and includes strawberry and other fruit sweetness.

### For East-West Ales:

**Roadhog** (OG 1042, ABV 4.2%)

### FRANKLIN'S
**Franklin's Brewery, Bilton Lane, Bilton, Harrogate, N. Yorkshire HG1 4DH.
☎ (01423) 322345**

Brewery set up in 1980 and now run by Leeds CAMRA founder-member Tommy Thomas, supplying guest beers to pubs in North Yorkshire, plus beer festivals. Occasional beers: DTs (OG 1055, ABV 4.7%), Summer Blotto (OG 1055, ABV 4.7%), Winter Blotto (OG 1055, ABV 4.7%).

**Bitter** (OG 1038, ABV 3.8%) A tremendous hop aroma precedes a flowery hop flavour, combined with malt. Long, hoppy, bitter finish. A fine, unusual amber bitter.

### FREEDOM
**The Freedom Brewing Company Ltd., The Coachworks, 80 Parsons Green Lane, Fulham, London SW6 4HU.
☎ (0171) 731 7372 [FAX] (0171) 731 1218**

Brewery opened in 1995 primarily to produce an unpasteurised premium lager, but with some ale production. Beer: Fulham Ale (OG 1043, ABV 4.3%, occasional).

## FREEMINER

**Freeminer Brewery Ltd, The
Laurels, Sling, Coleford,
Gloucestershire GL16 8JJ.**
☎ / FAX **(01594) 810408**

Established at the edge of the
Forest of Dean in 1992, Freeminer is now
brewing to full capacity. It has one tied
house (the Miners Arms in Sling) and
supplies over 50 free trade outlets directly
(including several in Manchester), plus
others nationwide via wholesalers. It also
produces cider and perry and has extended
its range of bottle-conditioned beers. Beers
are also brewed under contract for the
Blackbeard Trading Company
☎ (01584) 872908, and other wholesalers.
Tours by arrangement. Occasional beers
(sometimes badged as Blackbeard brews):
Iron Brew (OG 1044, ABV 4.2%), Hopewell
Special (OG 1050, ABV 5%), Trafalgar IPA
(OG 1060, ABV 6%). Bottle-conditioned
beers: Shakemantle Ginger Beer (OG 1050,
ABV 5%), Slaughter Porter (OG 1050, ABV
5%), Deep Shaft Stout (OG 1060, ABV 6.2%),
Trafalgar IPA (OG 1060, ABV 6%).

**Bitter** (OG 1038, ABV 4%) 🍺 A light, hoppy
bitter with a wonderful hop aroma and a
very dry, hoppy finish. Very moreish.

**Strip and At It** (OG 1038, ABV 4%) A very
pale summer bitter, named after a local
mine.

**Speculation Ale** (OG 1047, ABV 4.8%) 🍺 A
smooth, well-balanced mix of malt and hop,
with a predominantly hoppy finish.

**Shakemantle Ginger Ale** (OG 1050, ABV
5%) An unfined, cloudy summer brew with
a very high wheat content: almost a wheat
beer.

**Slaughter Porter** (OG 1050, ABV 5%) A dark
ale akin to a strong mild, mainly produced
for spring and autumn. The roast malt
flavour is followed by a hoppy finish.

**Deep Shaft Stout** (OG 1060, ABV 6.2%) A
black stout. Roast and malt hit you
immediately, then a very dry, biscuity,
hoppy finish follows.

### For Blackbeard Trading:

**White Riot** (OG 1040, ABV 4%)

**Dead Ringer** (OG 1048, ABV 4.8%)

**Stairway to Heaven** (OG 1050, ABV 5%)

**Low Rider** (OG 1060, ABV 6%)

### For Westbury Ales:

**Neat Rembla** (OG 1050, ABV 5%)

## FREETRADERS
See King & Barnes and Ushers.

## FREMLINS See Nationals, Whitbread.

## FRIARY MEUX
See Nationals, Carlsberg-Tetley.

## FROG & PARROT
See Nationals, Whitbread.

## FROG ISLAND

**Frog Island Brewery, The
Maltings, Westbridge
Street, James Road,
Northampton NN5 5HS.**
☎ (01604) 587772

Based in an old malthouse, once owned by
the defunct Thomas Manning brewery, this
company has been in operation since 1994.
Frog Island is a local name for an area once
prone to flooding. Forty free trade outlets
are currently supplied. Tours by
arrangement.

**Best Bitter** (OG 1040, ABV 3.8%) A fairly
complex beer, with malt, roast malt and
fruit, plus a hint of sulphur, before a
powerful kick of hop bitterness and
astringency in the aftertaste. Pale brown in
colour, and light on the tongue.

**Shoemaker** (OG 1044, ABV 4.2%) The
Cascade hop citrus notes on the tongue are
preceded by a huge malty aroma with
passion fruit and roast characteristics. The
malty aftertaste fades into a dry, nuttiness.
Rich, pale brown and complex.

**Natterjack** (OG 1048, ABV 4.8%)
Deceptively robust, golden and smooth.
Fruit and hop aromas fight for dominance
before the grainy astringency and floral
palate give way to a long, strong, dry
aftertaste with a hint of lingering malt.

**Croak & Stagger** (OG 1057, ABV 5.8%) The
initial honey/fruit aroma is quickly
overpowered by roast malt then bitter
chocolate and pale malt sweetness on the
tongue. Gentle, bittersweet finish. A winter
brew.

## FROMES HILL

**Fromes Hill Brewery,
Wheatsheaf Inn, Fromes
Hill, Ledbury,
Herefordshire HR8 1HT.**
☎ (01531) 640888

Brewery founded in 1993 and now
supplying three pubs of its own. Local
hops are used. Tours by arrangement.

**Buckswood Dingle** (OG 1036, ABV 3.6%)
🍺 Sweet to begin, but the fruitiness comes
through to leave a pleasant and sweet
aftertaste.

**Overture** (OG 1040, ABV 4.2%) 🍺 A
distinctive and well-balanced bitter that
leaves a dry, hoppy taste in the mouth.

**IDK** (OG 1048, 4.8%)

### FRUITERER'S ARMS
See Cannon Royall.

### FULBECK
**Fulbeck Brewery, John O'Gaunt Brewery, John O'Gaunt, Twyford, Leicestershire.**
☎ (01400) 272090 ☐FAX☐ (01400) 273663

Brewery founded in August 1995 and temporarily located in the tiny hamlet of John O'Gaunt, awaiting transfer to the Hare & Hounds in Fulbeck, Lincolnshire, a pub owned by one of the partners. Around a dozen other pubs take the beers. Occasional beer: Bitter or Whippet (OG 1048, ABV 4.8%).

**Beagle** (OG 1036, ABV 3.6%) ◆ Pale brown and malty throughout, with a faint underlying fruitiness. Well-balanced taste, but the aftertaste fails to linger.

**Harrier** (OG 1044, ABV 4.4%) ◆ Fruity to the nose and taste, as citrus meets hops. Malt forges through in the taste and the bitterness is sustained well into the finish.

**Lurcher** (OG 1060, ABV 6%) ◆ Cinnamon, orange and malt are the main characteristics, although hops are never far behind. Sweetness and bitterness feature, with a drying aftertaste.

### FULLER'S
**Fuller, Smith and Turner PLC, Griffin Brewery, Chiswick Lane South, Chiswick, London W4 2QB.**
☎ (0181) 996 2000
☐FAX☐ (0181) 995 0230

Beer has been brewed on the Fuller's site for over 325 years, John Fuller being joined by Henry Smith and John Turner in 1845. Descendants of the original partners are still on the board today. The brewery recently completed a £1.6 million brewhouse redevelopment to cope with growing demand, and the installation of new mash tuns in 1993 led to an increase in capacity of 50%. A new range of seasonal beers has been developed and 1845 Ale, originally brewed to commemorate the brewery's 150th anniversary, is now regularly available as a bottle-conditioned beer. Fuller's owns 200 pubs, roughly half of which are managed and half tenanted, and all but two serve real ale. Fuller's also supplies 700 outlets within a 50-mile radius of Chiswick. Shop open 10–6 Mon–Sat. Tours by arrangement. Occasional/seasonal beers: India Pale Ale (OG 1048, ABV 4.8%, April–May), London Porter (OG 1053, ABV 5%, February–March), Golden Pride (OG 1086, ABV 8.5%, Christmas). Bottle-conditioned beer: 1845 Ale (OG 1062, ABV 6.3%).

**Hock** (OG 1033, ABV 3.2%) ◆ A reddish brown, malty mild with roast notes and a pleasant, dry finish. Available in autumn.

**Chiswick Bitter** (OG 1034, ABV 3.5%) ◆ A distinctively hoppy, refreshing beer, with

underlying maltiness and a lasting bitter finish. *Champion Beer of Britain 1989*.

**Summer Ale** (OG 1037, ABV 3.9%) ◆ A refreshing, golden, hoppy bitter, with balancing malt flavour. Available June–August.

**London Pride** (OG 1040, ABV 4.1%) ☐ ☐ ◆ An award-winning beer with a good, malty base and a rich balance of well-developed hop flavours.

**Old Winter Ale** (OG 1048, ABV 4.8%) ◆ A tawny ale with a moderate malty aroma and flavour. Lightly hopped, with an astringent bitter finish. Available November–January.

**ESB** (OG 1054, ABV 5.5%) ☐ ◆ A strong and aromatic beer of great character. The immediate full-bodied maltiness gives way to a rich hoppiness in the finish.

### FYFE
**Fyfe Brewing Company, 469 High Street, Kirkcaldy, Fife KY1 2SN.**
☎ / ☐FAX☐ (01592) 646211

☐ Established in 1995 behind the Harbour Bar, this is Fife's first brew pub this century, producing the Kingdom's first beer since the 1920s. Most of the output is taken by the pub, the remainder being available to the free trade via Belhaven Brewery and some agencies.

**Rope of Sand** (OG 1035, ABV 3.5%) ◆ Named after the legendary local Rope of Sand, this is a quenching session bitter. Malt and fruit throughout, with a hoppy, bitter finish.

**Auld Alliance** (OG 1040, ABV 4%) ◆ A very bitter beer with a lingering, dry, hoppy finish. Malty, with hop and fruit notes throughout.

### GALE'S
**George Gale & Co. Ltd., The Hampshire Brewery, London Road, Horndean, Hampshire PO8 0DA.**
☎ (01705) 571212
☐FAX☐ (01705) 598641

Hampshire's major brewery, Gale's was founded in 1847. The original building was largely destroyed by fire and a new, enlarged brewery was built on the site in 1869. Still family owned, it has grown slowly and steadily and all 130 tied houses (which include some very attractive old inns) serve real ale. Gale's also supplies around 400 free trade outlets directly, and other pubs via the big breweries. Licensees who join the Gale's Beer Club can take a series of special one-off brews. Shop open 10–5 Mon–Fri. Tours by arrangement. Bottle-conditioned beer: Prize Old Ale (OG 1094, ABV 9%) ☐ ☐.

**Butser Bitter** (OG 1034, ABV 3.4%) Formerly BBB. A light golden chestnut beer with a floral hop aroma and a balanced hop and malt flavour. A quaffing bitter.

**Best Bitter** (OG 1039, ABV 3.8%) A red chestnut beer with a delicate aroma, a lingering hop and malt balance and a hint of fruit.

**IPA** (OG 1042, ABV 4.2%) A refreshing, light amber beer with a hoppy aroma, hop flowers in the clean palate and a hint of pine nuts.

**Winter Brew** (OG 1044, ABV 4.2%) A rich winter ale, partly made from Prize Old Ale. Available November–March.

**Harvest Ale** (OG 1045, ABV 4.5%) Brewed September–November; a hoppy autumn ale.

**HSB** (OG 1050, ABV 4.8%) A medium chestnut beer with a floral hop aroma with hints of Dundee cake. Full-bodied and silky-textured, the taste balances hops, malt and a complex fruit taste.

**Festival Mild** (OG 1052, ABV 4.8%) Black, with a deep red tinge; an unusually strong mild with an aroma of hops and blackcurrants leading to a sweet, fruity flavour and a warming, long, hoppy finish.

### For Whitbread:

**Pompey Royal** (OG 1043, ABV 4.5%) A brown beer with a hint of red. Low in aroma, with the flavour dominated by sweetness and pear fruit. The finish can be a little cloying.

## GIBBS MEW
**Gibbs Mew PLC, Anchor Brewery, Gigant Street, Salisbury, Wiltshire SP1 2AR. ☎ (01722) 411911 FAX (01722) 410013**

Gibbs Mew was established in 1898 by the amalgamation of Salisbury brewers Bridger Gibbs & Sons and Herbert Mew & Co. Charrington bought a stake in the company in the 1960s, which the Gibbs family bought back in 1972, which, in 1992, with CAMRA support, it saw off new predators Brierly Investments. The tied estate is still growing: in 1994 it bought the Centric Pub Company (197 pubs) and in 1995 it exchanged the Castle Leisure Complex in Cardiff for the six pubs formerly owned by Harmony Leisure Group. Real ale is supplied to over half of its 320 pubs (300 of which are tied), and to over 100 free trade outlets in southern England. Tours by arrangement.

**Wiltshire Traditional Bitter** (OG 1036, ABV 3.6%) ❧ A beer with a pleasant enough flavour of malt and hops, and a dry finish.

**Overlord** (OG 1036, ABV 3.6%) Produced to commemorate the 50th anniversary of D-Day and maintained as a regular brew. A mid-brown session bitter, with modest malt flavour initially, and a clean, hoppy finish and aroma.

**Salisbury Best Bitter** (OG 1042, ABV 4%) ❧ A rather chewy, sweet ale, decidedly lacking in bitterness. All the same, a pleasant beer.

**Wake Ale** (OG 1050, ABV 5%) Rich, warming ruby-red winter ale (available October–March). Basically sweet, but with almost herbal hop flavours in the finish.

**Deacon** (OG 1051, ABV 5%) ❧ A pale, golden beer with a faint orange aroma, an initial bitter taste, and a lingering, dry aftertaste.

**The Bishop's Tipple** (OG 1066, ABV 6.5%) ❧ Weaker than the average barley wine, but not lacking in flavour. The full-bodied taste is marvellously malty with a kick that leaves the brain rather less clear than the beer.

## GLASCHU
**The Glaschu Brewery, Glasgow.**

Brewery closed.

## GLENTWORTH
**Glentworth Brewery, Glentworth House, Crossfield Lane, Skellow, Doncaster, S. Yorkshire DN6 8PL. ☎ (01302) 725555 FAX (01302) 724133 (phone first)**

Brewery established in January 1996 in former dairy outbuildings at the owners' home. Around 50 pubs now take the beers.

**Dark Bitter** (OG 1045, ABV 4%) A winter brew.

**Dizzy Blonde** (OG 1050, ABV 4.5%)

**Hoppy Blonde** (OG 1052, ABV 5%)

## GOACHER'S
**P&DJ Goacher, The Bockingford Brewery, Unit 8, Tovil Green Business Park, Tovil, Maidstone, Kent ME15 6TA. ☎ (01622) 682112**

Kent's most successful small independent brewer, set up in 1983 by Phil and Debbie Goacher, producing all-malt ales with Kentish hops for its single free house and around 25 free trade outlets in the Maidstone area. Special, a 75%/25% mix of Light and Dark, is also available to pubs for sale under house names. Tours by arrangement.

**Real Mild Ale** (OG 1033, ABV 3.4%) A full-flavoured malty ale with a background bitterness.

**Fine Light Ale** (OG 1036, ABV 3.7%) A pale, golden brown bitter with a strong, hoppy aroma and aftertaste. A very hoppy and moderately malty session beer.

**Best Dark Ale** (OG 1040, ABV 4.1%) ❧ An intensely bitter beer, balanced by a moderate maltiness, with a complex aftertaste. Lighter in colour than it once was, but still darker than most bitters.

**Gold Star** (OG 1050, ABV 5.1%) A summer pale ale.

**Maidstone Porter** (OG 1050, ABV 5.1%) A dark ruby winter beer with a roast malt flavour.

**Old 1066 Ale** (OG 1066, ABV 6.7%) Black, potent old ale, produced in winter only.

## GODDARDS
**Goddards Brewery, Barnsley Farm, Bullen Road, Ryde, Isle of Wight PO33 1QF.**
☎ **(01983) 294987**
[FAX] **(01983) 293898**

Housed in a picturesque converted 18th-century barn, on a farm near Ryde, this brewery went into production in 1993. Its award-winning beers are supplied to around 45 outlets. A bottled (not bottle-conditioned) version of Fuggle-Dee-Dum has been produced using equipment at Bateman's brewery.

**Special Bitter** (OG 1039, ABV 4%) Well-balanced bitter beer with a good hoppy nose.

**Fuggle-Dee-Dum** (ABV 4.8%) 🍺 ◆ A golden, full-bodied ale with a hoppy aroma, a malty, bitter taste with a little sweetness and a hoppy, bitter finish.

## GOFF'S
**Goff's Brewery Ltd., 9 Isbourne Way, Winchcombe, Gloucestershire GL54 5NS.**
☎ **(01242) 603383**
[FAX] **(01242) 603959**

Family concern which started brewing in 1994, using plant purchased from Nethergate brewery. Its first beer, Jouster, won immediate recognition, as *Champion Beer* at the South Devon Beer Festival. Free trade has grown to 40 outlets, and Goff's plans to widen its delivery area. Tours by arrangement.

**Jouster** (OG 1040, ABV 4%) ◆ A very drinkable, tawny-coloured ale. Malt and fruit dominate the aroma and in the mouth. Some hoppiness in the taste sometimes persists into the aftertaste.

**White Knight** (OG 1046, ABV 4.7%) A light-coloured premium bitter.

**Black Knight** (OG 1053, ABV 5.3%) A dark winter beer.

---

🍺 The empty tankard indicates the beer was a *Good Beer Guide Beer of the Year* in the last three years.

---

## GOLDFINCH
**Goldfinch Brewery, 47 High East Street, Dorchester, Dorset DT1 1HU.**
☎ **(01305) 264020**

Brewery established in 1987 at Tom Brown's Public House, whose theme is broadly based on *Tom Brown's Schooldays*. A second tied house has now been acquired in Salisbury and is also called Tom Brown's. The brewery now supplies these two pubs and ten other free trade outlets direct, plus others via wholesalers. Tours by arrangement.

**Tom Brown's Best Bitter** (OG 1039, ABV 4%) ◆ A pale-coloured bitter which is fruity in both aroma and taste, with hops and some malt. The bittersweet taste gives way to a predominantly bitter finish.

**Flashman's Clout Strong Ale** (OG 1043, ABV 4.5%) ◆ A tawny/mid-brown beer with an attractive, honeyed aroma, and, again, a bittersweet taste with malt and some hops. Hoppiness continues through to give a bitter edge to the aftertaste.

**Midnight Blinder** (OG 1050, ABV 5%) ◆ A ruby red-coloured beer with an intense fruit aroma. Malt, hops and fruit combine to give the familiar bittersweet taste of Goldfinch beers, leading into a marvellous hoppy, bitter finish.

## DOROTHY GOODBODY
See Wye Valley.

## GOOSE EYE
**Goose Eye Brewery, Ingrow Bridge, South Street, Keighley, W. Yorkshire BD21 5AX.**
☎ **(01535) 605807**

After an absence of four years from the brewing scene, Goose Eye was re-opened in 1991 in a converted carpet warehouse. Slowly expanding, it supplies around 50 free trade outlets in North and West Yorkshire and Lancashire, and the beers are also available through national wholesalers and the Tap & Spile pub chain. Goose Eye's seasonal and occasional beers are proving very successful. Tours for small parties by arrangement. Occasional/seasonal beers: Black Goose Mild (OG 1036, ABV 3.6%), Christmas Goose (OG 1045, ABV 4.5%).

**Bitter** (OG 1038, ABV 3.8%) ◆ A pleasantly sweet, refreshing golden bitter, with a fruity nose and a malty taste. The finish is malty, with a growing bitterness.

**Bronte** (OG 1040, ABV 4%) ◆ An amber beer, less well-balanced than the bitter. A predominantly malty flavour, but with a definite fruitiness and a bitter, malty aftertaste.

**Wharfedale** (OG 1045, ABV 4.5%) A copper-coloured best bitter, becoming increasingly hard to find.

**Pommie's Revenge** (OG 1052, ABV 5.2%) A light-coloured, full-bodied and fruity, strong bitter.

## GRAINSTORE

Davis'es Brewing Company Ltd., The Grainstore Brewery, Station Approach, Oakham, Rutland LE15 6QW.
☎ (01572) 770065 [FAX] (01572) 770068

THE **GRAINSTORE** BREWERY
DAVISES BREWING CoLtd.

This new brewery's rather strange company name comes from the fact that it was set up by Tony Davis and Mike Davies. After 30 years in the industry, latterly with Ruddles, Tony decided to set up his own business after finding a derelict Victorian railway building which had the potential of becoming an ideal brewhouse and tap. The tap room was opened first, in August 1995, offering guest beers, then a few months later the brewery went into production and now supplies 35 other outlets. Tours by arrangement.

**Cooking** (OG 1036, ABV 3.6%) ♦ A smooth, copper-coloured beer, full-bodied for its gravity. Malt and hops on the nose; malt and fruit to the taste, with a malty aftertaste.

**Triple B** (OG 1042, ABV 4.2%) ♦ Initially, hops dominate over malt in both the aroma and taste, but fruit is there, too. All three linger in varying degrees in the sweetish aftertaste of this tawny brew.

**Ten Fifty** (OG 1050, ABV 5%) ♦ This full-bodied, tawny beer is very hoppy and fruity right into the aftertaste. A little malt on the nose and in the initial taste, with an undying sweetness and an increasing bitterness.

## GRAND METROPOLITAN

See Nationals, Scottish Courage, and Pub Groups, Inntrepreneur and Spring Inns.

## GRAY'S See Mansfield.

## GREENALLS See Smiles, Nationals, Carlsberg-Tetley, and Pub Groups.

## GREEN DRAGON

Green Dragon Free House & Brewery, 29 Broad Street, Bungay, Suffolk NR35 1EE.
☎ / [FAX] (01986) 892681

The Green Dragon was purchased from Brent Walker in 1991 and the buildings at the rear converted to a brewery. In 1994 the plant was expanded and moved into a converted barn across the car park. The increased capacity has allowed the production of a larger range of ales, including seasonal and occasional brews, but the beers are only available at the pub itself. Tours by arrangement. Beers: Mild (OG 1032, ABV 3.2%), Chaucer Ale (OG 1037, ABV 3.7%), Summer Ale (OG 1045, ABV 4.3%, seasonal), Bridge Street Bitter (OG 1046, ABV 4.5%), Dragon (OG 1060, ABV 5.5%), Wynter Warmer (OG 1065, ABV 6%, seasonal), Alzheimers (OG 1080, ABV 7.8%, occasional).

## GREEN DRAGON See Evesham.

## GREENE KING

Greene King PLC, Westgate Brewery, Westgate Street, Bury St Edmunds, Suffolk IP33 1QT. ☎ (01284) 763222 [FAX] (01284) 706502

East Anglia's largest regional brewery (established 1799), producing cask-conditioned beers at Bury (its Biggleswade brewery is entirely given over to lager production). Recent acquisitions of pubs from Allied have extended the company's tied estate into south-eastern England, while an additional 65 pubs acquired from Bass (bringing its total estate to 865 houses), has strengthened its position in London. In summer 1996, the company agreed to buy the Magic Pub Company chain of 277 pubs for £197.5 million. All Greene King's tied houses take real ale, but many have a cask breather device fitted in the cellar which, happily, some licensees choose not to use. Greene King also supplies some 3,000 free trade outlets. Group tours by arrangement. The seasonal/occasional beers are sold under the 'King's Court' banner. Occasional/seasonal beers: Mad Judge (OG 1042, ABV 4.2%, an autumn beer brewed with cranberries), Royal Raven (OG 1046, ABV 4.6%, a stout, March–April).

**XX Dark Mild** (OG 1033, ABV 3%) ♦ Smooth and sweetish, with a faint, slightly astringent aftertaste. Still under threat, due to low volumes.

**IPA** (OG 1036, ABV 3.6%) ♦ A blandish session bitter. Not unpleasant, it has a weak hop on the nose, with hop and bitterness in the taste, ending in an astringent, bitter finish. Hop oils can be noticeable in the clinging finish.

**Rayments Special Bitter** (OG 1040, ABV 4%) ♦ Different to the other Greene King beers: predominantly malty and sweet, with a complex bitterness and hops lingering in the aftertaste. Now replaced by seasonal beers in most tied houses.

**King's Champion** (OG 1042, ABV 4%) A light-coloured summer beer, available June–September.

**Black Baron** (OG 1044, ABV 4.3%) ♦ A winter beer. A plum red, strong mild, robust and flavoursome, with a complex fruity and sweet taste, developing bitterness in the finish.

**453**

**Sorcerer** (OG 1048, ABV 4.5%) ❧ A spring beer, available April–June. Its aroma gives little indication of the crisp, citrus, hoppy flavour which follows.

**Abbot Ale** (OG 1048, ABV 5%) 🍺 ❧ A medium-bodied, distinctive, fruity brew, with a pleasant bittersweet and hoppy aftertaste. A much improved brew since changes were made in late 1995; it is now fermented longer and is late hopped with hop pellets instead of hop oil.

**Winter Ale** (OG 1060, ABV 6%) ❧ Available November–January. A dark red/brown, warming old ale of substance, like a good wine in many ways. A predominantly fruity nose with some chocolate leads through to a rich blend of fruit, roast malt and some sweetness in the taste. Surprisingly dry aftertaste.

---

## GREEN JACK

**Green Jack Brewing Co. Ltd., Oulton Broad Brewery, Harbour Road Industrial Estate, Oulton Broad, Suffolk NR32 3LZ.**
☎ (01502) 587905

Green Jack opened in 1993, on the site of the closed Forbes Brewery. The attached, newly refurbished Tap Room, along with a single tied house, takes most of the output, with six other outlets supplied directly. The beers are also available via wholesalers. A range of seasonal ales is being introduced, incorporating unusual ingredients such as elderflowers and honey. A planned beer for autumn (OG 1041, ABV 4%) had not been named as we went to press.Tours by arrangement. Occasional/seasonal beers: Moild (OG 1032, ABV 3%), Ripper (OG 1077, ABV 8.5%), plus a Christmas beer which is changed each year.

**Bitter** (OG 1036, ABV 3.5%) ❧ A malty, light bitter with a fresh floral hoppiness.

**Honey Bunny** (OG 1041, ABV 4%) The new spring beer, brewed with honey.

**Summer Dream** (OG 1041, ABV 4%) Also seasonal, brewed with elderflowers.

**Old Thunderbox** (OG 1041, ABV 4%) The winter offering.

**Best Bitter** (OG 1043, ABV 4.2%) ❧ A hoppy bitter with a slightly astringent finish. Noticeably sweeter when young.

**Golden Sickle** (OG 1047, ABV 4.8%) ❧ An uncomplicated light bitter, stronger than it · tastes.

**Norfolk Wolf Porter** (OG 1050, ABV 5.2%) ❧ An excellent, dry, roasty winter porter. Brewed on an alternate basis with Lurcher, so not always available.

**Lurcher Strong Ale** (OG 1056, ABV 6%) ❧ A sharp-tasting, fruity, strong bitter, mostly brewed in winter, alternating with Norfolk Wolf.

## GREENWOOD'S

**Greenwood's Brewery, Bell Farm, Bell Foundry Lane, Wokingham, Berkshire RG40 5QF.**
☎ (01734) 793516
FAX (01276) 675049

It was the fondness for teddy bears of Andrew Greenwood's partner, Helen Glennon, that inspired the logo for this brewery, which was set up in converted farm buildings in 1994. The equipment is gradually being upgraded to cope with the growing demand for the award-winning beers which are supplied direct (but intermittently) to around 50 pubs and also to wholesalers. The list of permanent brews has increased and special beers are brewed to order. Occasional/seasonal beers: Weisse Squad (OG 1043, ABV 4.2%, a wheat beer), Passion Killer (OG 1053, ABV 5.2%, St Valentine's Day).

**Mahogany Mild** (OG 1037, ABV 3.4%) A mild full of dark malt character.

**Hop Pocket Bitter** (OG 1039, ABV 3.8%) A straw-coloured pale ale with hop character.

**Temperance Relief** (OG 1044, ABV 4.3%) A full-bodied, fruity, amber ale.

**Gold Prospector** (OG 1047, ABV 4.6%) A golden summer brew.

**Prohibition** (OG 1048, ABV 4.8%) A complex copper-coloured ale.

**Amber Gambler** (OG 1055, ABV 5.5%) An amber-coloured, fruity and hoppy ale.

**Draught Excluder** (OG 1060, ABV 6%) A rich, dark winter brew.

## GREYHOUND
See Nationals, Scottish Courage.

---

## GRIBBLE

**The Gribble Inn, Oving, Chichester, W. Sussex PO20 6BP.**
☎ / FAX (01243) 786893

Brew pub owned by Hall & Woodhouse (Badger, qv) and, while most of the output is taken by the inn, it sometimes supplies other Badger pubs. Black Adder II is not to be confused with the beer from Mauldons, nor Pig's Ear with the brew from Uley. Tours by arrangement. Beers: Ewe Brew (ABV 3.8%), Gribble Ale (OG 1043, ABV 4.1%), Reg's Tipple (OG 1055, ABV 5%), Plucking Pheasant (OG 1055, ABV 5.2%), Black Adder II (OG 1060, ABV 5.8%), Pig's Ear Old Ale (OG 1060, ABV 6%), Wobbler (OG 1080, ABV 7.2%, winter).

---

**GRIFFIN INN** See Church End.

## GUERNSEY

The Guernsey Brewery Co. (1920) Ltd., South Esplanade, St Peter Port, Guernsey GY1 1BJ. ☎ (01481) 720143 [FAX] (01481) 710658

One of two breweries on this Channel Isle, serving its stronger than average real ales in 13 of its 33 pubs (18 of which are tied). Originally opened as the London Brewery in 1856, it became a Guernsey registered company in 1920 upon the introduction of income tax on the mainland. It was taken over by Ann Street (now Jersey) Brewery in 1988 and Guernsey real ale is still available in selected Jersey Brewery houses. A new micro-brewery produces an ever-changing range of real ales and stouts, and has helped secure the future of Braye Ale. Sadly, more beer is now being sold as keg, dispensed with mixed gas. Six free trade outlets in the Channel Isles are supplied with the real thing. Tours occasionally by arrangement.

**Braye Ale** (OG 1038, ABV 3.7%) 🍺 🍂 Copper-red in colour, with a complex aroma of malt, hops, fruit and toffee. The rich, mellow flavour combines malt, fruit, hops and butterscotch, whilst the finish has malt and hops. Full-flavoured, surprisingly dry and hoppy.

**Sunbeam Bitter** (OG 1045, ABV 4.2%) 🍂 Golden in colour, with a fine malt aroma. Malt and fruit are strong on the palate and the beer is quite dry for its strength. Excellent, dry malt and hop finish.

**McGinty's Stout** (OG 1045, ABV 4.9%)

**Wheat Beer** (OG 1045, ABV 4.9%)

**Summer Ale** (OG 1055, ABV 5.3%)

**Winter Warmer** (OG 1060, ABV 5.8%)

## GUINNESS See Nationals.

## HP&D See Nationals, Carlsberg-Tetley.

## HADRIAN

Hadrian Brewery Ltd., Unit 10, Hawick Crescent Industrial Estate, Newcastle upon Tyne, Tyne & Wear NE6 1AS. ☎ (0191) 276 5302

Brewery founded with a five-barrel plant in 1987. Hadrian's sales are continuing to increase steadily, following expansion of the brewery in 1992. It now supplies 50 free trade outlets with its additive-free beers, whose names follow a Roman theme. It also brews for the Tap & Spile pub chain. Tours by arrangement. Occasional/seasonal beer: Yule Fuel (OG 1060, ABV 6.2%, December).

**Gladiator Bitter** (OG 1038, ABV 3.8%) 🍂 A full-flavoured, hoppy beer, with a clean finish and lasting bitterness.

**Legion Ale** (OG 1042, ABV 4.2%)

**Centurion Best Bitter** (OG 1045, ABV 4.5%) 🍺 🍂 An excellently-balanced bitter, with a prolonged malt and bitter character, balancing a lingering hoppiness. It well deserves its wide acclaim.

**Emperor Ale** (OG 1050, ABV 5%) 🍺 🍂 A beautiful old ale, well-crafted to give lasting flavours. Highly-hopped, with a good balance of fruit and bitterness, finishing rich but dry. A winter beer.

### For Tap & Spile:

**Tap & Spile Bitter** (OG 1036.5, ABV 3.8%)

## HALL & WOODHOUSE
See Badger.

## HALLCROSS See Stocks.

## HAMBLETON

Nick Stafford Hambleton Ales, Holme-on-Swale, Thirsk, N. Yorkshire YO7 4JE. ☎ (01845) 567460 [FAX] (01845) 567741

Hambleton was set up in 1991 in a Victorian barn on the banks of the River Swale, but production soon outgrew the original premises and a new brewery was opened on the same site in March 1996. The brewing capacity has now increased to 150 barrels a week and more and more local pubs are taking the beers which are currently supplied to 100 free trade outlets directly. Hambleton brews beers under contract for the Village Brewer wholesale company ☎ (01325) 371887. Tours by arrangement.

**Bitter** (OG 1036, ABV 3.6%) 🍂 A crisp, satisfying bitter, with early malt character and final dryness. Strong hop aroma; smooth mouthfeel.

**Goldfield** (OG 1040, ABV 4.2%) 🍂 A light amber bitter with good hop character and increasing dryness. A fine blend of malts gives a smooth overall impression.

**Stallion** (OG 1040, ABV 4.2%) 🍂 A premium bitter, moderately hoppy throughout and richly balanced in malt and fruit, developing a sound and robust bitterness, with earthy hop drying the aftertaste.

**Stud** (OG 1041, ABV 4.3%)

**Nightmare** (OG 1048, ABV 5%) 🍺 🍂 Smooth, strong roast malt and liquorice characters predominate, but with more discernible hop than expected for a beer of this type; dry finish. Now available all year.

**Thoroughbred** (OG 1048, ABV 5%) Available in summer.

### For Village Brewer:

**White Boar** (OG 1036, ABV 3.8%) 🍂 A dry-hopped, light, fruity beer, crisp and refreshing. Bitterness develops and dominates the aftertaste.

**Bull** (OG 1039, ABV 4%) 🍺 A fairly thin, but well-hopped, pale session bitter. Some fruit in both the nose and taste.

**Zetland Best Bitter** (OG 1042, ABV 4.2%)

**Old Raby** (OG 1048, ABV 4.8%) 🍺 A full-bodied, smooth, rich-tasting dark ale. A complex balance of malt, fruit character and creamy caramel sweetness offsets the bitterness nicely. A classic old ale.

## HAMPSHIRE

**Hampshire Brewery Ltd., 5 Anton Trading Estate, Andover, Hampshire SP10 2NJ. ☎ (01264) 336699 FAX (01264) 332338**

Brewery set up as a partnership in 1992 and now a limited company. The brewery is thriving, selling around 100 barrels a week to 400 local free trade outlets and a few wholesalers. It also brews for The Beer Seller wholesaler ☎ (01963) 34264. Future plans include a move to larger premises in 1997. Occasional/seasonal beers: Bewitched (ABV 4.6%, Halloween), Hampshire Hare (ABV 5%, Easter), Good King Wenceslas (ABV 5%, Christmas).

**King Alfred's** (OG 1039, ABV 3.8%) 🍺 A session beer. The well-hopped, fruity, slightly perfumed flavour is followed by a lingering bitter finish.

**Edmond Ironside** (OG 1042, ABV 4.2%) A well-balanced, traditional best bitter.

**Richard Lionheart** (OG 1043, ABV 4.2%) A smooth, golden best bitter.

**Arthur Pendragon** (OG 1048, ABV 4.8%) A full-bodied and fruity premium ale.

**William the Conqueror's 1066** (OG 1066, ABV 6%)

### For The Beer Seller:

**Hampshire Hog** (OG 1039, ABV 3.6%)

## HANBY

**Hanby Ales Ltd., New Brewery, Aston Park, Soulton Road, Wem, Shropshire SY4 5SD. ☎ (01939) 232432 FAX (01939) 232432**

Following the closure of Wem Brewery by Greenalls in 1988, the former head brewer, Jack Hanby, set up his own business. Brewing commenced the following spring and by 1990 he had moved into a new, larger brewhouse (which was improved in 1991). Hanby supplies a single tied house, plus more than 100 pubs directly and others via wholesalers. A monthly 'special' is brewed in addition to the regular range. Hanby also brews for Blackbeard Trading ☎ (01584)

872908. Occasional/seasonal beer: Santa's Socka (OG 1050, ABV 5.1%, Christmas).

**Black Magic Mild** (OG 1033, ABV 3.3%) 🍺 A dark, reddish brown mild, which is dry and bitter with a roast malt taste.

**Drawwell Bitter** (OG 1039, ABV 3.9%) 🗍 🍺 A hoppy beer with excellent bitterness, both in taste and aftertaste. Beautiful amber colour.

**All Seasons Bitter** (OG 1042, ABV 4.2%)

**Shropshire Stout** (OG 1044, ABV 4.4%) 🍺 Full-bodied, rich ruby stout, with a very distinctive, chocolate malt, dry flavour.

**Scorpio** (OG 1045, ABV 4.5%)

**Treacleminer Bitter** (OG 1046, ABV 4.6%) 🍺 A pale brown beer which is sweeter and fruitier than the beers above. Slight malt and hop taste.

**Old Wemian Ale** (OG 1049, ABV 4.9%)

**Taverners Ale** (OG 1053, ABV 5.3%)

**Nutcracker Bitter** (OG 1060, ABV 6%) 🍺 A warming, smooth, mid-brown beer, with malt and hops coming through. Definitely more bitter than sweet.

### For Blackbeard Trading:

**Happy Jack** (OG 1030, ABV 3%)

**Black Betty** (OG 1045, ABV 4.4%)

**Cherry Bomb** (OG 1060, ABV 5.9%)

**Joy Bringer** (OG 1060, ABV 5.9%)

**Queen Ann's Revenge** (OG 1080, ABV 7.6%)

**HANCOCK'S** See Nationals, Bass.

**HAND IN HAND** See Kemptown.

**HANSON'S** See Banks's.

## HARDINGTON

**Hardington Brewery, Albany Buildings, Dean Lane, Bedminster, Bristol BS3 1BT. ☎ (0117) 963 6194**

Set up in 1991, Hardington has no connection with the old Somerset brewery of the same name. Demand for its beers continues to grow and it now serves 200 outlets. A third tied house was purchased in 1995, and there are plans for further acquisitions in the local area. All three houses offer a selection of small brewers' products as guest beers, plus Hardington special brews. Tours by arrangement. Occasional/seasonal beers: Special Pale (OG 1035, ABV 3.5%), Rocket Best Bitter (OG 1040, ABV 4%).

**Traditional Bitter** (OG 1036, ABV 3.6%) 🗍 🍺 An amber-coloured, clean, refreshing bitter with a floral hop and citrus fruit aroma. The taste is similar, with balancing malt, some sweetness and occasionally butterscotch. Long, dry, bitter hop finish.

**Best Bitter** (OG 1041, ABV 4.1%) ◆ A crisp, refreshing pale brown best bitter with malt complexity and slight sweetness, becoming bitter and finishing dry. Floral hop and citrus fruit aroma. Moreish.

**Jubilee** (OG 1050, ABV 5%) ◆ A mid-brown, strong bitter, rich in fruit and malt; beautifully balanced with a contrasting dry, bitter finish.

**Moonshine** (OG 1050, ABV 5%) ◆ A yellow/gold beer, with a wheaty malt and slight citrus fruit aroma. The smooth, sweetish taste of pale malt has hints of fruit and spice; dry, bitter finish.

**Old Lucifer** (OG 1055, ABV 5.5%) ◆ A pale brown, smooth and powerful, distinctive strong bitter, sweet, hoppy, fruity and warming, with a complex biscuit and chocolate malt balance and a dry, bitter finish. Full-bodied.

**Old Ale** (OG 1060, ABV 6%) ▢ ◆ A rich, copper-red, full-bodied, warming ale. The fruity, hoppy, roast malt aroma is well-balanced. The similar bittersweet, vinous taste has fruit notes and spices. Complex finish. A powerful, well-crafted old ale.

## HARDY
**Thomas Hardy Brewery, Eldridge, Pope & Co. PLC, Weymouth Avenue, Dorchester, Dorset DT1 1QT. ☎ (01305) 251251** FAX (01305) 258300

Thomas Hardy is the new trading name for the Eldridge Pope Brewery. There has been no change of ownership, but there have been numerous developments within the business, including changes to the beer range. Originally founded by the Eldridge family as the Green Dragon Brewery in 1837, the company is still run by the Pope family who bought into the brewery in 1880. Producing award-winning ales, including Thomas Hardy's Ale which has long been notable as the strongest naturally-conditioned bottled beer in the UK, the company also has a pub division running 195 pubs, 159 of which are tied to Hardy products. Many free trade outlets take the beer in a trading area which extends as far as London, Bristol and Exeter. The brewery also produces occasional beers and brews under licence for Ross (qv), Tavern Wholesaling (formerly Liquid Assets) ☎ (0161) 864 5000, and the Drinklink wholesaler ☎ (01271) 862016. Tours by arrangement. Bottle-conditioned beer: Thomas Hardy's Ale (OG 1125, ABV 12%) ▢ ▇.

**Dorchester Bitter** (OG 1032, ABV 3.3%) ◆ A light session bitter which is hoppy and bitter throughout, with some balancing malt.

**Pope's Traditional** (OG 1036, ABV 3.8%) ◆ Formerly Best Bitter. A mixture of malt and hop with a hint of fruit.

**Country Bitter** (OG 1040, ABV 4.2%) ◆ A dry, hoppy beer with faint undertones of malt and fruit. The taste is smooth despite a bitter edge which continues into the finish.

**Royal Oak** (OG 1048, ABV 5%) ◆ A full-bodied beer with a distinctive banana aroma and a mainly sweet, fruity taste. This is balanced by malt and some hops and there is a fruity finish to this smooth, well-rounded brew.

## For Drinklink:

**Parson's Nose** (OG 1039, ABV 3.7%)

## For Ross:

Bottle-conditioned beer: Saxon Strong Ale (OG 1050, ABV 5%)

## For Tavern Wholesaling:

**Potter's Pride** (ABV 3.8%)

## HARDYS & HANSONS
**Hardys & Hansons PLC, Kimberley Brewery, Nottingham NG16 2NS. ☎ (0115) 938 3611** FAX (0115) 945 9055

Established in 1832 and 1847 respectively, Hardys and Hansons were two competitive breweries until a merger in 1931 produced the present company. Nottingham's last independent brewery is today controlled by descendants of the original Hardy and Hanson families, with all production taking place on the original Hardy site. Ninety per cent of its 254 houses (172 are tied) take its award-winning real ales, although there is still a tendency to spoil them with top pressure (never used on the strong Kimberley Classic). The brewery also supplies around 60 free trade outlets. A range of seasonal ales has been introduced. Tours by arrangement.

**Kimberley Best Mild** (OG 1035, ABV 3.1%) ◆ A deep ruby mild. Some initial sweetness is tempered by moderate hop and fruit. Fruit on the nose and hops in the taste, with chocolate malt always present.

**Kimberley Best Bitter** (OG 1039, ABV 3.9%) ▇ ◆ A fine, flowery hop nose introduces this light brown bitter and a fruity hop flavour dominates the taste. Malt is always there and comes through into the aftertaste, but bitterness wins.

**Kimberley Classic** (OG 1047, ABV 4.8%) ◆ Not as widely available as it ought to be. Hops and fruit dominate the aroma, with malt making its appearance more in the taste. A bitter beer throughout.

## HARPENDEN

**Harpenden Brewery, The Red Cow, 171 Westfield Road, Harpenden, Hertfordshire AL5 4ND.**
☎ (01582) 460156

Brew pub which started production in 1994, but which is restricted to selling only one beer outside the list approved by Inntrepreneur, which owns the pub lease. The licensee is hoping to move the operation to St Albans. Tours available. Beer: Special Ale (OG 1037, ABV 3.8%).

## HART

**Hart Brewery, Cartford Hotel, Cartford Lane, Little Eccleston, Lancashire PR3 0YP.** ☎ (01995) 671686

Brewery founded in 1994, in a small private garage, which moved to premises at the rear of the Cartford Hotel in 1995. With a ten-barrel plant, Hart is supplying a growing number (currently over 30) of local free houses as well as the hotel. Tours by arrangement. Occasional/seasonal beers: Liberator (OG 1039, ABV 3.8%), Mayson Premier (OG 1041, ABV 4%), Second Coming (OG 1046, ABV 4.5%, Easter), Hart's Proposal (OG 1047, ABV 4.5%, St Valentine's Day), Messiah (OG 1057, ABV 5.5%, Christmas).

**Gold Beach** (OG 1035, ABV 3.5%) A golden beer, brewed for spring/summer, featuring a light, semi-sweet, biscuity flavour, combined with a peppery hop flavour and a full aftertaste.

**Fylde Ale** (OG 1040, ABV 4%) A popular session ale, an unusual bronze beer in which hop flavour enhances full, but delicate malt tones.

**Crimin-ale Porter** (OG 1040, ABV 4%) A winter beer.

**Squirrels Hoards** (OG 1042, ABV 4%) Brewed for the Cartford Hotel and CAMRA festivals; bronze, smooth and nutty, with crystal malt flavour. Sweet and moreish.

**High Octane Gold Beach** (OG 1043, ABV 4.2%) Another winter brew; a premium version of Gold Beach, with more body and flavour.

**Nemesis** (OG 1046, ABV 4.5%) A light yellow, sweet, premium beer, fruity, with light hop undertones.

**Andrew's Cobblestone Stout** (OG 1050, ABV 5%) A stout in which dark malt flavours combine with a sharp, sweet hop aroma and bitterness.

**Old Ram** (OG 1050, ABV 5%) A full-bodied, complex, malty brew in which sweet malt flavours balance light hop undertones. Easy to drink for a brew of this gravity.

**Amadeus** (OG 1060, ABV 5.5%) An old ale for winter.

**HARTLEYS** See Robinson's.

## HARVEYS

**Harvey & Son (Lewes) Ltd., The Bridge Wharf Brewery, 6 Cliffe High Street, Lewes, E. Sussex BN7 2AH.**
☎ (01273) 480209
FAX (01273) 483706

**HARVEYS**

Established in the late 18th century by John Harvey, on the banks of the River Ouse, this Georgian brewery was rebuilt in 1881. The Victorian Gothic tower and brewhouse remain a very attractive feature. A major development in 1985 doubled brewing capacity and the further addition of fermenters has seen production rise to more than 30,000 barrels per year. Still a family-run company, Harveys supplies real ale to all its 38 pubs and about 600 free trade outlets in Sussex and Kent. One of the first breweries to introduce seasonal ales, it also frequently produces commemorative beers, which are sometimes available on draught. Tours by arrangement (two-year waiting list!). Shop open 9.30–1, 2–4.45 Mon–Wed, 9.30–4.45 Thu–Sat. Occasional/seasonal beers: Knots of May Light Mild (OG 1030, ABV 3%, May), 1859 Porter (OG 1053, ABV 4.8%, March) 🗍, Tom Paine (OG 1055, ABV 5.5%, July), Christmas Ale (OG 1090, ABV 8.1%, December). Bottle-conditioned beer: 1859 Porter (OG 1053, ABV 4.8%) 🗍.

**Sussex XX Mild Ale** (OG 1030, ABV 3%) 🍺 🔸 A dark, malty brew with slight malt and hops in the aroma and roasted malt and hops coming through in both the flavour and finish.

**Sussex Pale Ale** (OG 1033, ABV 3.5%) 🍺 🔸 An agreeable, light bitter with malt and hops dominating the aroma, whilst a hoppy bitterness develops throughout the taste, to dominate the finish.

**Sussex Best Bitter (BB)** (OG 1040, ABV 4%) 🍺 🔸 A medium-strength bitter with a good balance of malt and strong hops in the flavour, which develops into a bitter, hoppy aftertaste.

**Sussex XXXX** or **Old Ale** (OG 1043, ABV 4.3%) 🔸 Brewed October–May: a rich, dark beer with a good malty nose, with undertones of roast malt, hops and fruit. The flavour is a complex blend of roast malt, grain, fruit and hops with some caramel. Malty caramel finish with roast malt.

**Armada Ale** (OG 1045, ABV 4.5%) 🔸 A full-bodied beer in which hops are dominant throughout. Long, dry finish.

## HARVIESTOUN

**Harviestoun Brewery Ltd., Devon Road, Dollar, Clackmannanshire FK14 7LX.** ☎ (01259) 742141
FAX (01259) 743141

Hand-built in a 200-year-old stone byre, by two home-brew enthusiasts in 1985, this small brewery operates from a former dairy at the foot of the Ochil Hills, near Stirling. A new custom-built brewing plant was installed in 1991 and Harviestoun now serves 70 outlets in central Scotland as well as wholesalers' customers throughout Britain. The most recent development is the installation of a bottling line. Occasional beer: Nouveau (OG 1140, ABV 11%, a barley wine for Christmas).

**Waverley 70/-** (OG 1037, ABV 3.7%) ◆ Light in body, with a malt and fruit aroma. Malt and hops throughout, with a hint of roast in the finish.

**Original 80/-** (OG 1041, ABV 4.1%) ◆ This beer has malt, fruit and hops throughout, with a slight toffeeness in the taste. Faintly sulphurous aroma.

**Montrose** (OG 1042, ABV 4.2%) ◆ A tawny-coloured beer with a complex aroma of malt, roast, caramel and fruit, which remain in the taste, giving way to a slight bitterness.

**Ptarmigan 85/-** (OG 1045, ABV 4.5%) ◆ A well-balanced, bittersweet beer in which fruit and malt dominate. The blend of malt, hops and fruit produces a clean, hoppy aftertaste. Fruity aroma, with malt and hop undertones.

**Schiehallion** (OG 1048, ABV 4.8%) 🍺◆ A cask lager, brewed using a lager yeast and Herrsbrooker hops, and properly lagered. A fruity aroma, with hops and malt, leads to a malty, bitter taste with floral hoppiness and a bittersweet finish.

**Old Manor** (OG 1050, ABV 5%) A winter brew.

## HEATHER
Heather Ale Ltd, 736 Dumbarton Road, Glasgow G11 6RD. ☎ (0141) 339 3479
[FAX] (0141) 337 6298

Bruce Williams started brewing Fraoch (Gaelic for heather) in 1992 at the now closed West Highland Brewery in Argyll, then moved his production to Maclay's Thistle brewery in 1993 from where he supplies almost 40 outlets (Bruce brews the beer himself, using Maclay's equipment). Heather Ale is made with flowering heather, following an ancient tradition, hence its seasonal nature. Pictish is brewed in November using the last crop of heather flowers. Tours by arrangement.

**Fraoch Heather Ale** (OG 1042, ABV 4.1%) 🍺 Available May–November; a beer with a floral, peaty aroma, a spicy, herbal, woody flavour and a dry finish.

**Fraoch Pictish Ale** (OG 1053, ABV 5.4%) Available December–April.

---

🍺The empty tankard indicates the beer was a *Good Beer Guide Beer of the Year* in the last three years.

---

## THE INDEPENDENTS

## HEDGEHOG & HOGSHEAD
Belchers Brewery, 100 Goldstone Villas, Hove, E. Sussex BN3 3RX. ☎ (01273) 324660; 163 University Road, Highfield, Southampton, Hampshire SO17 1TS. ☎ (01703) 581124; Highbury Corner, London N1 1RU. ☎ (0171) 226 4627; 2 High Street, Sutton, Surrey SM1 1HN. ☎ (0181) 661 7525

Brew pub chain established with two outlets (Hove and Southampton) in 1990 by David Bruce (of Firkins fame), who sold them in 1994 to Grosvenor Inns (see Pub Groups) for shares, with Bruce taking a seat on the Grosvenor board. The two London Hedgehogs added later have only recently started brewing. The beers are stored in cellar tanks and a cask breather is used on slower sellers. The products are also supplied to some other outlets. Tours by arrangement. Beers: Belchers Original (OG 1034, ABV 3.4%), Belchers Best Bitter (OG 1042, ABV 4.2%), Old Slug Porter (OG 1042, ABV 4.2%), Bootleg Bitter (OG 1052, ABV 5.2%), New Barbarian (OG 1052, ABV 5.2%, occasional), Hogbolter (OG 1058, ABV 5.8%).

## HENSTRIDGE
Henstridge Brewery, Gibbs Marsh, Bow Bridge Works, Henstridge Trading Estate, Henstridge, Somerset BA8 0TH. ☎ (01963) 363150 [FAX] (01963) 363864

Brewery founded in 1994 and supplying one beer to outlets locally and pubs further afield via an agent.

**Vickery's Brew** (ABV 4%)

## HESKET NEWMARKET
Hesket Newmarket Brewery, Old Crown Barn, Back Green, Hesket Newmarket, Cumbria CA7 8JG. ☎ / (0169 74) 78066

Brewery set up in 1988 in a barn behind the Old Crown pub in an attractive North Lakes village. Since then, sales to other outlets have increased (currently around 30), as has the beer range. The beers are named after local fells, with the notable exception of Doris's 90th Birthday Ale (Doris sadly died in 1995, aged 96). The brewery also produces special beers for individual local pubs. Tours by arrangement. Occasional/seasonal beer: Ayala's Angel (OG 1080, ABV 7%, Christmas).

**Great Cockup Porter** (OG 1035, ABV 2.8%) A refreshing, chocolate-tasting beer.

**Blencathra Bitter** (OG 1035, ABV 3.1%) A predominantly bitter beer, from the start to the dry finish. Malty nose.

**Skiddaw Special Bitter** (OG 1035, ABV 3.7%) A golden session beer, despite its name.

**Doris's 90th Birthday Ale** (OG 1045, ABV 4.3%) A fruity premium ale.

**Catbells Pale Ale** (OG 1052, ABV 5.1%) Initially sweet, strongly aromatic beer developing a bitter finish.

**Old Carrock Strong Ale** (OG 1065, ABV 5.6%) A dark red, powerful ale.

## HEXHAMSHIRE

**Hexhamshire Brewery, Leafields, Ordley, Hexham, Northumberland NE46 1SX.**
☎ (01434) 673031

Brewery set up in a redundant farm building in 1992 by the owner of the Dipton Mill Inn with two partners. No adjuncts are used in the beers, which are produced for the inn and other local outlets. Occasional/seasonal beers: Low Quarter Ale (OG 1035, ABV 3.5%), Blackhall Stout (OG 1043, ABV 4.3%), Old Humbug (OG 1055, ABV 5.5%).

**Shire Bitter** (OG 1037, ABV 3.8%) ◆ Thicker than expected: a bitter beer with a malty overtone.

**Devil's Water** (OG 1041, ABV 4.1%) ◆ A beer of mixed character and an unexpected range of flavours. Malt dominates and bitterness gradually declines, giving a strong, sweet finish.

**Whapweasel** or **Strong** (OG 1048, ABV 4.8%) ◆ This malty bitter has a lasting hoppiness and a smooth mouthfeel.

## HIGH FORCE

**High Force Hotel Brewery, Forest-in-Teesdale, Barnard Castle, Co. Durham DL12 0XH.**
☎ (01833) 622222
FAX (01833) 622264

 This, the first and only brew pub in Co. Durham, went into production in November 1995. It also claims to be the highest brewery in Britain; at 1,060 feet it is situated by the High Force waterfall, a popular tourist attraction. There are plans to bottle-condition the beers, which are available at 30 other outlets. Tours by arrangement.

**Low Force** (OG 1037, ABV 3.5%)

**Teesdale Bitter** (OG 1041.5, ABV 3.8%)

**Forest XB** (OG 1045, ABV 4.2%)

> ▐ The full tankard indicates the beer is one of this year's *Good Beer Guide Beers of the Year*.

## HIGHGATE

**The Highgate & Walsall Brewing Company Ltd., Sandymount Road, Walsall, W. Midlands WS1 3AP.**
☎ (01922) 644453
FAX (01922) 644471

This, once the smallest brewery in the Bass group, had been under threat of closure for some years until a management buyout brought it back into the independent sector in 1995. The traditional Victorian tower brewery still uses equipment dating back to 1898, although there are plans to replace the old cask racking unit. Other projects for the future include a visitor centre. Ten free trade outlets are supplied direct, and the company has a contract to supply Bass for at least three years.

**Dark Mild** (OG 1035, ABV 3.1%) ▐ ▐ ◆ A dark brown, Black Country mild with a good balance of malt and hops and traces of roast flavour following a malty aroma.

**Saddlers Best Bitter** (OG 1042, ABV 4%) A very fruity, pale yellow bitter with a strong hop flavour and a light, refreshing bitter aftertaste.

**Old Ale** (OG 1054, ABV 5.1%) ◆ A winter beer (November–January): a dark brown/ruby-coloured old ale, full-flavoured, fruity and malty, with a complex aftertaste which has touches of malt, roast, hops and fruit.

## HIGH PEAK See Lloyds.

## HIGHWOOD

**Highwood Brewery Ltd., Melton Highwood, Barnetby, Lincolnshire DN38 6AA.**
☎ (01652) 680020
FAX (01652) 680729

Located in a converted granary on the edge of the Lincolnshire Wolds, this brewery went into production in 1995. Now supplying around 80 pubs, Highwood hopes to increase production to 50 barrels a week and other plans include the possible bottling of the stronger beers. The range always includes a seasonal beer, 4–5% ABV. Tours by arrangement.

**Tom Wood Best Bitter** (OG 1036, ABV 3.5%) ◆ A hoppy bitter in all aspects, although malt is also present, especially in the taste. A faint fruitiness can sometimes be detected. Mid-brown in colour.

**Tom Wood Harvest Bitter** (OG 1041, ABV 4.3%)

**Old Timber** (OG 1043, ABV 4.5%) ◆ Hoppy on the nose, but featuring well-balanced malt and hops otherwise. A slight, lingering roast/coffee flavour develops, but this is generally a bitter, darkish brown beer.

## HIGSONS
See Cains and Nationals, Whitbread.

## HILDEN
**Hilden Brewery, Hilden House, Grand Street, Lisburn, Co. Antrim BT27 4TY. ☎ (01846) 663863**

Mini-brewery beside a Georgian country house, set up in 1981 to counter the local Guinness/Bass duopoly. It presently supplies Hilden Ale to just a handful of pubs in Northern Ireland, with the full range of beers exported to some pubs in England. Occasional beers: Special (OG 1037, ABV 3.6%), Festival Ale (OG 1052, ABV 5.2%).

**Great Northern Porter** (OG 1039, ABV 4%) ◆ A beer with a rich, tawny colour and a pronounced malty aroma. Crystal malt is dominant in both the flavour and aftertaste.

**Hilden Ale** (OG 1040, ABV 4%) ◆ An amber-coloured beer with an aroma of malt, hops and fruit. The balanced taste is slightly slanted towards hops, and hops are also prominent in the full, malty finish. Bitter and refreshing.

**Special Reserve** (OG 1048, ABV 4.6%) ◆ Dark red/brown in colour and superbly aromatic – full of dark malts, producing an aroma of liquorice and toffee. Malt, fruit and toffee on the palate, with a sweet, malty finish. Mellow and satisfying, but not always available.

## HOBSONS
**Hobsons Brewery & Co., New House Farm, Tenbury Road, Cleobury Mortimer, Kidderminster, Worcestershire DY14 8RD. ☎ (01299) 270837**

Opened at Easter 1993 in a former sawmill, Hobsons (a Shropshire brewery, despite its postal address) is now located in a characterful building which was once a farm granary. Output is slowly increasing, with the brewery currently working to half its capacity of 60 barrels a week and supplying around 140 outlets with cask ale. A trial bottling of Old Henry is planned. Shop open during working hours. Tours by arrangement.

**Best Bitter** (OG 1038, ABV 3.8%) ◆ A pale brown to amber, medium-bodied beer with strong hop character throughout. It is consequently bitter, but with malt discernible in the taste.

**Town Crier** (OG 1045, ABV 4.5%) A straw-coloured bitter.

**Old Henry** (OG 1052, ABV 5.2%) A winter brew.

## HODGE'S
**Hodge's Brewery, Unit 5A, Castle Close, Crook, Co. Durham DL15 8LU. ☎ (01388) 763200 FAX (01388) 746482**

After an initial ten months of brewing just a single beer, Hodge's (founded in 1994) now produces three ales, mostly for local outlets (around 30 currently supplied off and on), with the beers rarely seen elsewhere in the country. Home deliveries are also made. Tours by arrangement.

**Traditional** (OG 1037, ABV 3.7%)

**Original** (OG 1043, ABV 4%) ◆ A mid-brown brew with a noticeable metallic taste. Low on aroma, but with faint caramel and mild hops. Little aftertaste.

**Best** (OG 1045, ABV 4.5%)

## HOGS BACK
**Hogs Back Brewery, Manor Farm, The Street, Tongham, Surrey GU10 1DE. ☎ (01252) 783000 FAX (01252) 782328**

This purpose-built brewery was set up in a restored farm building (circa 1768) in 1992 and the popularity of its ales – particularly the award-winning TEA – has helped it to expand. It now supplies over 200 outlets and has a well-stocked shop/off-licence on site, offering a wide range of English and foreign (particularly Belgian) bottled beers – open seven days a week, with late closing (8.30) Wednesday and Thursday. Tours by arrangement. Occasional/seasonal beers: Legend (ABV 4%), Friday 13th (ABV 4.2%), BSA or Burma Star Ale (ABV 4.5%), Brewster's Bundle (ABV 7.4%), YES or Your Every Success (ABV 7.4%), Santa's Wobble (OG 1077, ABV 7.5%, Christmas). Bottle-conditioned beer: Wobble in a Bottle (OG 1077, ABV 7.5%).

**Dark Mild** (OG 1036, ABV 3.4%) A deep red, refreshing mild with a malty mouthfeel and a bitter finish.

**APB or A Pinta Bitter** (OG 1037, ABV 3.5%) ◆ A thin, but well-balanced, bitter with an underlying fruitiness.

**TEA or Traditional English Ale** (OG 1044, ABV 4.2%) ☐ ◆ A pale brown, malty bitter with a developing hop balance. Slightly fruity.

**Blackwater Porter** (OG 1046, ABV 4.4%) ◆ A black beer with a good roast malt aroma and a strong roast malt flavour which lasts into the aftertaste.

**Hop Garden Gold** (OG 1048, ABV 4.6%) ◆ A malty, golden beer with a hoppy finish.

**Rip Snorter** (OG 1052, ABV 5%) ◆ A strong, malty and fruity, reddish brown bitter with a slight hop flavour.

**OTT or Olde Tongham Tasty** (OG 1066, ABV 6%) ◆ A black winter ale, with a pleasant fruity, roast malt aroma and flavour. Hops are present in the finish with lingering roast malt and bitterness.

**A over T** or **Aromas Over Tongham** (OG 1091, ABV 9%) A rich, full-flavoured bitter to be drunk with caution.

## HOLDEN'S

**Holden's Brewery Co. Ltd., Hopden Brewery, George Street, Woodsetton, Dudley, W. Midlands DY1 4LN.**
☎ (01902) 880051
[FAX] (01902) 665473

Family brewery going back four generations. Holden's began life as a brew pub when Edwin and Lucy Holden took over the Park Inn (now the brewery tap) in the 1920s. It now produces a good range of real ales for its 21 pubs and around 30 free trade customers. Shop open daily 10.30–2, 4–10 (all day Sat). Tours by arrangement. Occasional/seasonal beer: Old Ale (OG 1072, ABV 6.9%, Christmas).

**Mild** (OG 1037, ABV 3.7%) ❧ A good, red/brown Black Country mild; a refreshing, light blend of roast, malt, hops and fruit, dominated by malt throughout.

**Bitter** (OG 1039, ABV 3.9%) ❧ A medium-bodied, golden ale; a light, well-balanced bitter with a subtle, dry, hoppy finish.

**XB** or **Lucy B** (OG 1041 ABV 4.2%) ❧ Named after Lucy Blanche Holden, this is a sweeter, slightly fuller version of the bitter.

**Special Bitter** (OG 1051, ABV 5.1%) ❧ A sweet, malty, full-bodied amber ale with hops to balance in the taste and in the good, bittersweet finish.

## HOLT

**Joseph Holt PLC, Derby Brewery, Empire Street, Cheetham, Manchester M3 1JD.** ☎ (0161) 834 3285
[FAX] (0161) 834 6458

Successful family brewery, founded in 1849 – not to be confused with Carlsberg-Tetley's Midlands company Holt, Plant & Deakin. The tied estate has been gradually increased over the last 15 years, and now exceeds 120 houses, all serving real ale, with most of the pubs taking hogsheads (54-gallon casks), because the low prices result in a high turnover. The beers are also popular as guests and Holt supplies a free trade of around 60 outlets (plus another 40 or so via an agent).

**Mild** (OG 1032, ABV 3.2%) ❧ A very dark beer with a complex aroma and taste. Roast malt is prominent, but so are hops and fruit. Strong in bitterness for a mild, with a long-lasting, satisfying aftertaste.

**Bitter** (OG 1039, ABV 4%) ❧ A tawny beer with a good hop aroma. Although balanced by malt and fruit, the uncompromising

bitterness can be a shock to the unwary. It has gained a little sweetness in recent years.

**HOLTS** See Nationals, Carlsberg-Tetley.

**HOME** See Mansfield and Nationals, Scottish Courage.

## HOOK NORTON

**The Hook Norton Brewery Co. Ltd., Hook Norton, Banbury, Oxfordshire OX15 5NY.**
☎ (01608) 737210
[FAX] (01608) 730294

Built by John Harris in a former farm maltings in 1850, and still controlled by his family, Hook Norton remains one of the most delightful, traditional Victorian tower breweries in Britain. It retains much of its original plant and machinery, the showpiece being a 25-horsepower stationary steam engine which still pumps the Cotswold well water used for brewing. The brewery boasts some fine old country pubs, with all 35 of its tied houses serving real ale, and some 250 free trade outlets also supplied direct. Brewery shop. Tours by arrangement. Occasional/seasonal beers: Double Stout (OG 1050, ABV 4.8%), Haymaker (OG 1052, ABV 5%, July–August), Twelve Days (OG 1057, ABV 5.5%, December).

**PAB Mild** (OG 1031, ABV 3%) ❧ A dark, red/brown mild with a malty aroma and a malty, sweetish taste, tinged with a faint hoppy balance. Malty in the aftertaste. Highly drinkable.

**Best Bitter** (OG 1035, ABV 3.4%) ❧ An excellently-balanced, golden bitter. Malty and hoppy on the nose and in the mouth, with a hint of fruitiness. Dry, but with some balancing sweetness. A hoppy bitterness dominates the finish.

**Old Hooky** (OG 1048, ABV 4.6%) ❧ An unusual, tawny beer with a strong fruity and grainy aroma and palate, balanced by a hint of hops. Full-bodied, with a bitter, fruity and malty aftertaste.

## HOP BACK

**Hop Back Brewery PLC, Unit 21–23 Batten Road Industrial Estate, Downton, Salisbury, Wiltshire SP5 3HU.** ☎ (01725) 510986
[FAX] (01725) 513116

Originally a brew pub, the Wyndham Arms, set up in 1987 with a five-barrel plant, Hop Back switched most of its production to a new brewery at Downton in 1992. A new 50-barrel plant was installed in 1995 to cope with increased demand, and in the same year a fourth tied house, the Hop Leaf in Reading, was opened (see Reading Lion Brewery). A fifth pub was added to the estate in 1996. Hop Back also sells directly to 85 free trade outlets. A small bottling plant has been installed. Tours by arrangement. Bottle-conditioned beer: Summer Lightning (OG 1049, ABV 5%).

**Mild** (OG 1034, ABV 3.2%) ◆ A dark, well-balanced, very tasty mild, with bags of chocolate malt. Dry, clean-tasting and well-hopped. A very quaffable session ale.

**GFB** (OG 1036, ABV 3.5%) ◆ A golden beer, with the sort of light, clean, tasty quality which makes an ideal session ale. A hoppy aroma and taste lead to a good, dry finish. Refreshing. *Champion Cask-Conditioned Beer* at the Brewing Industry International Awards 1996.

**Special** (OG 1041, ABV 4%) ◆ A medium bitter, slightly sweet, but with a good balance of malt and hops and a long finish. The name and recipe may change.

**Entire Stout** (OG 1045, ABV 4.5%) ◻ ◆ A rich, dark stout with a strong roasted malt flavour and a long, sweet and malty aftertaste. A vegan beer.

**Thunderstorm** (OG 1048, ABV 5%) A softly bitter, easy drinking wheat beer: a replacement for the brewery's original wheat beer.

**Powerhouse** (OG 1049, ABV 5%) A ruby-coloured winter beer with a hoppy nose. The chocolate and crystal malts come through initially, developing into a clean, bitter finish.

**Summer Lightning** (OG 1049, ABV 5%) ◻ ◼ ◆ A very pleasurable pale bitter with a good, fresh, hoppy aroma and a malty, hoppy flavour. Finely balanced, it has an intense bitterness leading to a long, dry finish. Though strong, it tastes like a session ale.

## HOPE & ANCHOR
The Lucifer Live Beer Brewing Company, Hope & Anchor, Clifton, Bristol.

Brewery closed.

## HOP HOUSE
The Hop House Brewery, Harborough Road, Kingsthorpe, Northamptonshire NN2 7AZ. ☎ (01604) 715221.

This new brew pub was opened in December 1995 after the total refurbishment and renaming of the Cock Hotel. Now owned by Enterprise Inns (see Pub Groups), its full mash beers are brewed only for the Hop House, where they are kept under blanket pressure. Occasional special brews are produced. Tours by arrangement. Beers: Hoppers Original (ABV 3.6%), St David's Mercy (ABV 4.5%), Old Cock's Throat Charmer (ABV 5.5%).

**HOP LEAF** See Reading Lion.

**HORSEBRIDGE** See Royal Inn.

## HOSKINS
Tom Hoskins Brewery PLC, Beaumanor Brewery, 133 Beaumanor Road, Leicester LE4 5QE. ☎ (0116) 266 1122 FAX (0116) 261 0150

Established in 1877, this traditional tower brewery was family-owned until 1983, when it was acquired and expanded by TRD Estates Ltd. Following the sale of eight pubs to Wolverhampton & Dudley in 1992, the brewery was taken over by Halkin Holdings in 1993 and in 1995 was subject to a management buyout. It has five tied houses (all serving real ale), and supplies 12 free trade outlets, as well wholesalers. Tours by arrangement.

**Beaumanor Bitter** (OG 1039, ABV 3.7%) ◆ A strange mixture of flavours with astringent bitterness predominant. Light brown and thin, this beer tends to be sulphurous. Early promise is quickly evaporated.

**Penn's Bitter** (OG 1043, ABV 4.6%) ◆ This nearly red-coloured beer is very inconsistent. Sometimes sweet, sometimes bitter, with a metallic taste.

**Premium** (OG 1050, ABV 4.9%) ◆ A stronger version of the bitter.

**Churchill's Pride** (OG 1050, ABV 4.9%)

**Old Nigel** (OG 1059, ABV 5.8%) ◆ A reddish-brown beer that has an unsubtle, strong bitterness with more than a hint of pear drops and cloves in the taste. Roast malt in an astringent finish.

## HOSKINS & OLDFIELD
Hoskins & Oldfield Brewery Ltd., North Mills, Frog Island, Leicester LE3 5DH. ☎ (0116) 251 0532

Brewery set up by two members of Leicester's famous brewing family, Philip and Stephen Hoskins, in 1984, after the sale of the old Hoskins Brewery. The company supplies over 15 outlets directly, and others nationwide via wholesalers. Production of bottle-conditioned beers has been resumed, but only on an occasional basis. Occasional/seasonal beers: Tom Kelly's Christmas Pudding Porter (OG 1052, ABV 5%, Christmas), Reckless Raspberry (ABV 5.5%, a stronger version of the wheat beer with raspberries).

**HOB Best Mild** (OG 1036, ABV 3.5%) An almost black-coloured beer, with malt and hops in the taste. Very difficult to find.

**Brigadier Bitter** (OG 1036, ABV 3.6%) An ordinary bitter.

**HOB Bitter** (OG 1041, ABV 4%) ◆ A tawny-coloured best bitter with a hoppy, malty nose and a more complex, fruity, bittersweet flavour which becomes more hoppy and bitter in the finish. It frequently tastes of pear drops.

**Little Matty** (OG 1041, ABV 4%) A complex brown/red beer.

**White Dolphin** (OG 1041, ABV 4%) A fruity wheat beer.

**Tom Kelly's Stout** (OG 1043, ABV 4.2%) A dark, dry stout.

**Supreme** (OG 1045, ABV 4.4%) A very light gold best bitter.

**Tom Hoskins Porter** (OG 1050, ABV 4.8%) Brewed using honey and oats.

**EXS Bitter** (OG 1051, ABV 5%) A malty, full-bodied premium bitter.

**Ginger Tom** (OG 1053, ABV 5.2%) A ginger beer.

**Old Navigation Ale** (OG 1071, ABV 7%) A strong ruby/black beer.

**Christmas Noggin** (OG 1100, ABV 10%) A strong, russet-coloured beer available throughout the year.

## HUGHES

**Sarah Hughes Brewery, Beacon Hotel, 129 Bilston Street, Sedgley, Dudley, W. Midlands DY3 1JE.**
☎ (01902) 883380

Brewery re-opened in 1987 after lying idle for 30 years, to serve the village pub and a few other local houses, but now also producing beers for 40 outlets in the free trade. A Victorian-style conservatory acts as a reception area for brewery visits. Bottle-conditioned beer: Dark Ruby Mild (OG 1058, ABV 6%).

**Sedgley Surprise** (OG 1048, ABV 5%) ◆ A bittersweet, medium-bodied, hoppy ale with some malt.

**Dark Ruby Mild** (OG 1058, ABV 6%) ◻ ◆ A near-black, strong ale with a good balance of fruit and hops, leading to a pleasant, lingering hops and malt finish.

## HULL

**The Hull Brewery Co. Ltd., 144–148 English Street, Hull, E. Yorkshire HU3 2BT.**
☎ (01482) 586364  FAX (01482) 586365

Hull Brewery was resurrected in 1989 after a 15-year absence, and was taken over by a new owner in 1994. Improvements have since been made to ensure consistency. Hull acquired its first tied house in September 1995 (from Bass) and around 100 free trade outlets throughout northern England are currently supplied directly from the brewery. Tours by arrangement. Occasional/seasonal beers: Summer That (OG 1037, ABV 3.7%), Rack and Ruin (OG

1040, ABV 3.9%), Knocker Dibb (OG 1042, ABV 4.2%), Coal Porter (OG 1048, ABV 4.8%, October–November), Belly Rumbler (OG 1050, ABV 5%, spring), Old Acquaintance (OG 1050, ABV 5%, Christmas).

**Mild** (OG 1034, ABV 3.3%) A smooth and malty dark mild with a long lasting aftertaste and a rich aroma of fruit, hops and roast malt.

**Bitter** (OG 1039, ABV 3.8%) A refreshing copper bitter, with a predominantly hoppy aroma. The initial bitter aftertaste leads to a pleasant lingering maltiness. Complex.

**Ellwood's Best Bitter** (OG 1038, ABV 3.8%) A golden straw-coloured session bitter, smooth and rounded, with subtle hints of hops and malt, and a refreshing aftertaste.

**Amber Ale** (OG 1040, ABV 4%) ◆ A light brown beer with an unusual, dry, malty taste in which amber malt dominates. A slightly fruity aroma is followed by a dry, bitter finish. Some tartness can be evident.

**Northern Pride** (OG 1042, ABV 4.2%) A wonderfully distinctive, full-bodied beer, with a malty aroma.

**The Governor** (OG 1046, ABV 4.4%) A full-bodied, amber-coloured premium ale. Deceptively powerful, it enjoys a great malt attack in the mouth and a deep finish, dominated by hops and tart fruit.

## HYDES' ANVIL

**Hydes' Anvil Brewery Ltd., 46 Moss Lane West, Manchester M15 5PH.**
☎ (0161) 226 1317
FAX (0161) 227 9593

Family-controlled traditional brewery, first established at the Crown Brewery, Audenshaw, Manchester in 1863 and on its present site, a former vinegar brewery, since the turn of the century. It is slowly expanding its tied estate, supplying cask ale to all its 61 tied houses and over 40 free trade outlets. The 4X winter warmer was re-introduced in 1995 and the brewery is experimenting with a series of seasonal brews, producing a different beer for each quarter.

**Dark Mild** (OG 1032, ABV 3.5%) ◆ A mild with a caramel and fruit aroma: quite sweet and fruity, with a pleasant aftertaste. Sold mainly in the company's Welsh pubs, but rare in the Manchester area.

**Mild** (OG 1032, ABV 3.5%) ◆ A light, refreshing and quite fruity drink, with a short, dry aftertaste. This mid-brown beer has a fruity and malty aroma.

**Light** (OG 1034, ABV 3.7%) ◻ ◆ A lightly-hopped session beer, with malt and a refreshing fruitiness dominating before a brief but dry finish.

**Bitter** (OG 1036, ABV 3.8%) ◗ A good-flavoured bitter, with a malty and hoppy nose, fruity background and malt and hops in the finish. A hint of bitterness and astringency throughout.

**4X** (ABV 6.8%) A winter warmer; a full-bodied, smooth dark beer with a good balance of malt, hops and fruitiness. Not too sweet; dangerously drinkable!

## ICENI

**The Iceni Brewery,
3 Foulden Road, Ickburgh,
Mundford, Norfolk
IP26 5BJ. ☎ (01842) 878922
FAX (01842) 811539**

Owner Brendan Moore had a dream one night of opening a brewery. A year later, without any prior experience, but armed with redundancy money and a grant from the Rural Development Commission, he set up a ten-barrel plant and his first brew rolled out in January 1995. The beers, which are named after Celtic queens and the Iceni tribe, have been well received at regional beer festivals and are supplied direct to 25 outlets. Plans are in hand for bottling. Tours by arrangement. Occasional/seasonal beers: Curse of Macha (OG 1034, ABV 3.4%), Queen Maev Stout (OG 1045, ABV 4.9%).

**Boadicea Chariot Ale** (OG 1038, ABV 3.8%) The original brew; a well-balanced session bitter with hop and fruit flavours and a dry aftertaste.

**Celtic Queen** (OG 1042, ABV 4%) A light summer ale, packed with flavour. Voted *Best Bitter* at the 1995 Norwich Beer Festival, on its first outing.

**Deirdre of the Sorrows** (OG 1044, ABV 4.4%) A gold-coloured ale, with a distinctively pleasant taste that lingers. Moreish; a firm local favourite.

**Roisin Dubh** (OG 1044, ABV 4.4%) Roisin Dubh translates as 'dark rose'. The beer is also dark in colour, with a slightly sweet taste. Very smooth.

**Gold** (OG 1046, ABV 5%) A strong ale, sun gold in colour. Crisp taste; smooth and deceptive for its strength.

## IND COOPE

See Nationals, Carlsberg-Tetley.

## ISLAND See Burts.

## ISLE OF MAN See Okells.

◗ The tilted glass indicates CAMRA tasting notes (supplied by a trained CAMRA tasting panel). Beer descriptions not preceded by this symbol are based on limited tastings only or have been obtained from other sources.

## ISLE OF SKYE

**The Isle of Skye Brewing
Company (Leann an Eilein),
The Pier, Uig, Isle of Skye
IV51 9XY. ☎ (01470) 542477
FAX (01470) 542488**

This new brewery was set up in December 1995 by two teachers, as a part-time venture, aiming to go full-time by 1997. The brewery is situated in purpose-built premises at the pier terminal for the Outer Hebrides. Its two main ales are supplemented by occasional brews, such as Extortion Ale (ABV 4.3%) brewed in February 1996 to highlight the campaign against the new Skye Bridge tolls. Thirty outlets are presently supplied. Shop open 12.30–6 Mon–Fri. Tours by arrangement.

**Red Cuillin** (OG 1042, ABV 4.2%)

**Black Cuillin** (OG 1045, ABV 4.5%)

## JENNINGS

**Jennings Bros PLC,
The Castle Brewery,
Cockermouth, Cumbria
CA13 9NE.
☎ (01900) 823214
FAX (01900) 827462**

Founded in 1828, and moved to its present site in 1874, Jennings has gradually expanded over the years (particularly during the 1920s). Although there is no longer any family involvement, many of the company's shares are owned by local people. Around 380 free trade outlets are now supplied from its own Leyland and Newcastle depots, and many more via a network of wholesalers throughout the UK. Real ale is also available at 94 of the 107 tied houses. Shop open 9–4.45 Mon–Fri. Tours by arrangement.

**Dark Mild** (OG 1031, ABV 3.1%) A dark, mellow, malty, sweet mild.

**Bitter** (OG 1035, ABV 3.5%) ◗ A distinctive, red/brown brew with a hoppy, malty aroma. A good, strong balance of grain and hops in the taste, with a moderate bitterness, develops into a lingering, dry, malty finish.

**Cumberland Ale** (OG 1040, ABV 4%) ◗ A light, but hoppy, bitter, with a creamy taste and smooth mouthfeel. The aroma can be sulphury, but the taste ends crisp and dry with a spicy bitterness.

**Cocker Hoop** (OG 1047, ABV 4.8%) A golden bitter. The initial taste of hop, fruit and malt is followed by a refreshingly hoppy, bitter aftertaste.

**Sneck Lifter** (OG 1055, ABV 5.1%) A very dark bitter, with a rich, full malt flavour, followed by a smooth and mellow mixture of malt and hop in the aftertaste.

**La'al Cockle Warmer** (OG 1062, ABV 6.5%) A new winter brew.

## JERSEY

The Jersey Brewery, Ann
Street Brewery Co. Ltd., 57
Ann Street, St Helier, Jersey
JE1 1BZ. ☎ (01534) 31561
FAX (01534) 67033

Jersey (formerly known by its parent
company's title of Ann Street) began
brewing cask beer again in 1990 after a break
of 30 years. It has 50 tied houses, of which 12
take real ale, including beers from its sister
company, Guernsey Brewery. Tours by
arrangement. The beer range is likely to
change.

**Old Jersey Ale** (OG 1036, ABV 3.5%) ◆ An
attractive tawny/copper colour, this bitter
ale packs an immense depth of malt
flavours, the crystal malt giving hints of
barley sugar. The malty bitterness is quite
intense in the aftertaste.

**Winter Ale** (OG 1070, ABV 7.5%) ◆ Very
dark brown, with hues of copper, this is a
complex beer, full of roast barley and malt
flavours, giving glimpses of chocolate, coffee
and butterscotch. Quite bitter for its strength
and very rewarding.

## JOHN THOMPSON INN

John Thompson Brewery, Ingleby,
Derbyshire DE73 1HW. ☎ (01332) 862469

▯ This 15th-century farmhouse was
converted to a pub in 1969. It has brewed
since 1977, with most of the production
supplied to the free trade through Lloyds
Country Beers (see Lloyds), a separate
enterprise. Beers (on sale here): Summer
Gold (OG 1040, ABV 4%), JTS XXX (OG
1042, ABV 4.1%, sold elsewhere as Lloyds
Derby Bitter), JTS Rich Porter (OG 1045,
ABV 4.3%, winter).

## JOLLYBOAT

The Jollyboat Brewery Ltd.,
4 Buttgarden Street,
Bideford, Devon EX39 2AU.
☎ (01237) 424343

Brewery established in April 1995 and
currently supplying around 40 local outlets,
plus wholesalers.

**Buccaneer** (OG 1038, ABV 3.7%)

**Mainbrace Bitter** (OG 1041, ABV 4.2%)

**Plunder** (OG 1048.5, ABV 4.8%)

**Contrabrand** (OG 1058, ABV 5.6%) A porter
available November–March and at other
times on demand.

## JOLLY ROGER

Jolly Roger Brewery, Worcester.

Brewery closed.

**JOULE** See Coach House.

## JUDGES

Judges Brewery, Unit 15A,
Boughton Road, Rugby,
Warwickshire CV21 1BU.
☎ (01788) 535356

Brewery set up by Graham and Anne Judge
in 1992 in a sleepy Warwickshire village, but
since moved to a larger site in Rugby. It is
now at the forefront of a brewing revival in
the county and supplies around 25 local
outlets. Tours by arrangement. Occasional/
seasonal beer: Santa's Surprise (OG 1052,
ABV 5%, a Christmas porter).

**Barristers Bitter** (OG 1038, ABV 3.5%) 🍺
◆ A well-balanced, pale-coloured session
beer; light and easily drinkable.

**Coombe Ale** (OG 1042, ABV 4.2%) Primed
with local honey.

**Old Gavel Bender** (OG 1050, ABV 5%) ◆ A
beer with a complex hop, fruit and malt
aroma, with some caramel. A perfect
bittersweet balance in the taste, but no
significant aftertaste.

**Solicitor's Ruin** (OG 1056, ABV 5.6%)
◆ Dark, strong and full-tasting; a very well
hopped beer, with a smooth, sweetish,
treacly taste, and a bitter finish.

## JUWARDS

Juwards Brewery, c/o Fox
Brothers & Co. Ltd.,
Wellington, Somerset
TA21 0AW.
☎ (01823) 667909

Juwards, the latest venture of Ted Bishop,
former brewer at Cotleigh and Ash Vine,
went into production in 1994, based in an
old wool mill. It supplies around 30 outlets
direct in the West Country, plus others in the
Midlands and North of England via agents.
One beer is brewed for the Lock, Stock and
Barrel wholesaling company ☎ (01364)
644124.

**Bitter** (OG 1040, ABV 3.9%)

**Golden** (OG 1044, ABV 4.4%) Also sold by
Lock, Stock and Barrel as Newt & Abbot Ale.

**Premium** (OG 1048, ABV 4.8%)

### For Lock, Stock and Barrel:

**Pistol Dawn** (ABV 5%) An occasional brew.

## KELHAM ISLAND,

Kelham Island Brewery,
23 Alma Street, Sheffield,
S. Yorkshire S3 8SA.
☎ (0114) 249 4804
FAX (0114) 249 4803

▯ Brewery opened in 1990 at the Fat Cat
pub, serving this, another associated pub
and over 30 outlets in Derbyshire,
Nottinghamshire and South Yorkshire.
Bottle-conditioned beer: Wheat Bier (OG
1050.5, ABV 5%).

**Fat Cat Pale Ale** (OG 1036.5, ABV 3.6%) ❧ A straw-coloured, clean-tasting beer with a powerful hop and fruit aroma, which is reflected in the taste, along with a lingering dry and bitter finish. A good session beer.

**Bitter** (OG 1038.5, ABV 3.8%) ❧ A clean and crisp, pale brown beer of character. The nose and taste are dominated by refreshing hoppiness and fruitiness which last, along with a good bitter dryness, in the aftertaste.

**Golden Eagle** (OG 1042.5, ABV 4.2%) ❧ An excellent hoppy, fruity best bitter of distinction. The aroma is strong in hops with a slight fruitiness which gets stronger in the taste and in the finish, which is moderately bitter.

**Wheat Bier** (OG 1050.5, ABV 5%) ❧ A pale brown, hazy, wheat beer with a complex flavour which is moderately hoppy, with malty sweetness, and a slight, bittersweet finish. A good wheatmalt taste is also in the aftertaste.

**Pale Rider** (OG 1052.5, ABV 5.2%) ❧ A well-bodied, straw-pale ale, with a good fruity aroma and a strong fruit and hop taste. Its well-balanced sweetness and bitterness continue in the finish.

**Bête Noire** (OG 1055.5, ABV 5.4%) ❧ A dark, ruby beer with little aroma. Malt and caramel, along with some fruitiness and dryness, are in the taste, which also has plum notes and chocolate and develops into a dry, but sweet, aftertaste.

## KEMPTOWN

**The Kemptown Brewery Co. Ltd., 33 Upper St James's Street, Kemptown, Brighton, E. Sussex BN2 1JN. ☎ (01273) 699595**

🚪 Brewery established in 1989, built in the 'tower' tradition behind the Hand in Hand, which is possibly the smallest pub in England with its own brewery. It takes its name and logo from the former Charrington's Kemptown Brewery 500 yards away, which closed in 1964. Fifteen free trade outlets are supplied. Tours by arrangement. Occasional beers: Crewsaver (OG 1045, ABV 4.5%), Tipper's Tipple (OG 1045, ABV 4.5%).

**Budget Bitter** (OG 1036, ABV 3.5%) ❧ A refreshing, dry beer, with malt and hops in the flavour and a dry, hoppy finish.

**Bitter** (OG 1040, ABV 4%) ❧ Hops in the aroma lead into a soft, malt flavour with bitterness, which fades in the aftertaste.

**Ye Olde Trout** (OG 1045, ABV 4.5%)

**Staggering in the Dark (SID)** (OG 1050, ABV 5.2%) ❧ A dark, almost black, beer with a vinous nose and a complex flavour, with roast and bitterness giving way to a dry finish.

**Old Grumpy** (OG 1060, ABV 6%) Available November–February.

---

## KING & BARNES

**King & Barnes Ltd.,
The Horsham Brewery,
18 Bishopric, Horsham,
W. Sussex RH12 1QP.
☎ (01403) 270470
[FAX] (01403) 270570**

Long-established brewery, dating back almost 200 years and in the present premises since 1850. It is run by the King family, which united with the Barnes family brewery in 1906. A continuing programme of investment in brewery plant and machinery has meant its 'Fine Sussex Ales' are always in demand. All 57 tied houses take real ale, which is supplied direct to a further 250 other outlets. Twelve Bore Bitter is produced for the Freetraders Group wholesalers ☎ (0181) 965 0222. Brewery shop open 11–7 Mon–Sat. Tours by arrangement. Occasional/seasonal beers: Valentine (ABV 4%, February), Wheat Mash (ABV 4.3%, April), Oatmeal Stout (ABV 4.5%, March), Harvest Ale (OG 1045, ABV 4.5%), Rye Beer (ABV 5.5%, April–May), Corn Beer (ABV 6.5%, October), Christmas Ale (ABV 6.5%). Bottle-conditioned beers: Wheat Mash (ABV 4.3%), Harvest Ale (OG 1045, ABV 4.5%), Festive (OG 1052, ABV 5.3%) 🗄 🍶, Old Porter (OG 1057, ABV 5.5%), Christmas Ale (ABV 6.5%), Corn Beer (ABV 6.5%).

**Mild Ale** (OG 1034, ABV 3.5%) 🗄 ❧ A smooth, very dark mild, with hints of malt in the aroma. The bittersweet flavour, with some malt and hops, leads to a late-developing bitterness in the aftertaste.

**Sussex** (OG 1034, ABV 3.5%) ❧ Whilst hops are still most apparent in the finish of this mid-brown bitter, they are not as evident throughout the beer as they used to be.

**Broadwood** (OG 1040, ABV 4.2%) ❧ A tawny-coloured, well-balanced beer from aroma to finish, with hops winning through in the end.

**Old Ale** (OG 1045, ABV 4.5%) 🗄 ❧ A classic, black old ale. A slightly fruity, roast malt flavour leads to a bittersweet finish, with fruit joining the roast. Lovely roast malt aroma. Available October–March.

**Festive** (OG 1050, ABV 5%) ❧ A red-brown beer, with a fruity aroma. The flavour is also fruity and malty, but with a noticeable hop presence. Malt and fruit dominate the aftertaste.

## For Freetraders:

**Twelve Bore Bitter** (OG 1035, ABV 3.7%) ❧ A thin, mid-brown bitter, with a clean finish. Good balance of malt and hops throughout.

## KING'S HEAD

King's Head Ale House and Brewery, 21 Bretonside, Plymouth, Devon PL4 0BB.
☎ (01752) 665619

Plymouth's first brew pub, founded in January 1994 in the oldest pub in the city. The business has quickly taken off and it now supplies two other tied houses and around 25 other outlets directly, plus more via agencies. Tours by arrangement. Occasional/seasonal beers: Hare Brained (OG 1043, ABV 4.3%, Easter), Santa's Blotto (OG 1058, ABV 6%, Christmas).

**Nicholsons IPA** (OG 1038, ABV 3.8%)

**King's Ransom** (OG 1040, ABV 4%)

**Bretonside's Best (BSB)** (OG 1042, ABV 4.2%)

**Golden Goose** (OG 1050, ABV 5%) ◆ A straw-coloured beer with a hoppy and fruity aroma, taste and finish.

**Ma Husson's Strong Olde Ale** (OG 1056, ABV 5.6%)

## KINGSTON See Flamingo.

## KITCHEN

The Kitchen Brewery, Unit J, Shaw Park Industrial Complex, Ivy Street East, Aspley, Huddersfield, W. Yorkshire HD5 5DJ. ☎ (01484) 534120
[FAX] (01484) 542709

Brewery founded in April 1996 by CAMRA member Robert Johnson in part of Shaw's Pickle Factory in a five-barrel plant. The beers are on sale in local pubs and in pubs in Northamptonshire (Robert's home county).

**Waitress** (ABV 4.2%) The lighter-coloured beer of the two, with a high hop content.

**Maître d'** (ABV 4.5%) A malty, auburn-coloured beer with a hoppy aroma.

## LAKELAND See Masons Arms.

## LARKINS

Larkins Brewery Ltd., Chiddingstone, Edenbridge, Kent TN8 7BB.
☎ (01892) 870328
[FAX] (01892) 871141

Larkins brewery was founded in 1986 by the Dockerty family (who are farmers and hop-growers), with the purchase of the Royal Tunbridge Wells Brewery. Brewing was transferred to a converted barn at the family farm in 1990 and an additional copper and fermenter were acquired in 1991 to keep up with the growing local free trade. The additive-free beers can now be found in around 85 pubs and tourist venues in the South-East. Only Kent hops are used, some from the farm itself. Tours by arrangement for groups of 15 or more people on Saturday mornings.

**Traditional Ale** (OG 1035, ABV 3.4%) A tawny-coloured beer.

**Chiddingstone Bitter** (OG 1040, ABV 4%) A malty and slightly fruity, bitter ale, with a very malty finish. Copper-red in colour. Called Sovereign until Samuel Smith claimed prior ownership of the name.

**Best Bitter** (OG 1045, ABV 4.4%) ◆ Full-bodied, slightly fruity and unusually bitter for its gravity. Dangerously drinkable!

**Porter** (OG 1052, ABV 5.2%) ◆ Each taste and smell of this potent black winter beer reveals another facet of its character. An explosion of roasted malt, bitter and fruity flavours leaves a bittersweet aftertaste.

## LASS O'GOWRIE
See Nationals, Whitbread.

## LASTINGHAM
Lastingham Brewery Co. Ltd., Pickering, N. Yorkshire.

Brewery closed.

## LEAKING BOOT
Leaking Boot Brewery, Grimsby, Lincolnshire.

Brewery closed.

## LEANN AN EILEIN See Isle of Skye.

## LEATHERBRITCHES

Leatherbritches Brewery, Bently Brook, Brewery Yard, Fenny Bentley, Ashbourne, Derbyshire DE6 1LF. ☎ (01335) 350278
[FAX] (01335) 350422

Beer sausages are an unusual sideline at this brewery which keeps its own pigs. Although only founded in 1994, Leatherbritches has already outgrown an initial capacity of five barrels a week, and new plant has been installed. Tours by arrangement. It has now acquired a second tied house and supplies 50 other local outlets, as well as brewing under contract for the non-productive Steamin' Billy Brewery to supply one pub, the Cow & Plough in Leicester. Beers are also brewed for special occasions such as Mother's Day and Burns Night. Occasional/seasonal beers: Robert Catesby (ABV 5.2%, November), Tarebrane (ABV 6.5%, February). Bottle-conditioned beers: Belt 'n' Braces (ABV 3.8%), Robert Catesby (ABV 5.5%).

**Belt 'n' Braces** (ABV 3.8%) A light-coloured, hoppy session beer, with a dry finish.

**Belter** (ABV 4%)

**Stout** (ABV 4%) A beer with a dominant chocolate flavour, smooth and fruity, with a long, satisfying finish.

**Ashbourne Ale** (ABV 4.5%)

**Bespoke** (ABV 5%) A rich, well-balanced, fruity, full-bodied premium bitter.

## For Steamin' Billy:

**Best Bitter** (ABV 4.5%)

## LEDBURY

**Ledbury Brewing Co. Ltd., 5 The Southend, Ledbury, Herefordshire HR8 2EY. ☎ (01531) 632110 FAX (01531) 634761**

This brewery was first established in 1841 and has now been reopened in the original building, some 75 years after its closure in 1921.

**Doghill Goldings Bitter** (OG 1036, ABV 3.6%) ◆ Not much nose, but fruitiness balances the bitterness on the tongue; satisfying, dry aftertaste.

**Challenger SB** (OG 1038, ABV 3.8%) ◆ Bitterness is evident on the tongue, with a rich, malty taste.

**Challenger Premium Best** (OG 1042, ABV 4.2%) ◆ Hops dominate the nose and mouth and a hint of sweetness in the aftertaste gives it a smooth, even finish.

**Exhibition** (ΛBV 5.1%)

**XB** (6.5%)

## LEES

**JW Lees & Co. (Brewers) Ltd., Greengate Brewery, Middleton Junction, Manchester M24 2AX. ☎ (0161) 643 2487 FAX (0161) 655 3731**

Family-owned brewery, founded in 1828 by John Willie Lees, a retired cotton manufacturer, and recently joined by sixth-generation family members. The existing brewhouse dates from 1876 but has been expanded and refitted recently, doubling the capacity. In 1995 Lees took on its first full-time cooper for almost 30 years (half its cask beer is still delivered in traditional oak casks). All the brewery's 172 pubs (most in northern Manchester) serve real ale, which is also supplied to 125 other outlets directly. Tours by arrangement (long waiting list). Occasional beer: Harvest Ale (OG 1142, ABV 12%, a well-matured cask version of a filtered but not pasteurised bottled beer).

**GB Mild** (OG 1032, ABV 3.5%) ◆ Malty and fruity in aroma. The same flavours are found in the taste, but do not dominate in a beer with a rounded and smooth character. Dry, malty aftertaste.

**Bitter** (OG 1037, ABV 4%) ◆ A pale beer with a malty, fruity aroma and a distinctive, malty, dry and slightly metallic taste. Clean, dry Lees finish.

**Moonraker** (OG 1073, ABV 7.5%) ◆ A reddish-brown beer with a strong, malty, fruity aroma. The flavour is rich and sweet, with roast malt, and the finish is fruity yet dry. Only available in a handful of outlets.

## LEYLAND

**Leyland Breweries Ltd., Unit 78, Lawrence Leyland Industrial Estate, Irthlingborough Road, Wellingborough, Northamptonshire NN8 1RT. ☎ (01933) 275215**

Leyland is the name given to the new company established by the merger of the former Nene Valley and Nix Wincott breweries. The beers are still labelled 'Nene' or 'Wincott' and the vast majority of the output is sold via agencies. Occasional beer: Trojan Bitter (OG 1038, ABV 3.8%).

**Old Cock Up Mild** (OG 1032, ABV 3.4%) A black/red mild.

**This Bitter** (OG 1034, ABV 3.4%)

**Unicorn Bitter** (OG 1036, ABV 3.6%) A hoppy bitter also sold under house names.

**Two Henrys Bitter** (OG 1038, ABV 3.9%)

**Griffin** (ABV 4.4%) A malty brew with hop balance.

**Old Black Bob** (OG 1047, ABV 4.7%) A dark, roasty strong mild.

**THAT** (OG 1048, ABV 4.8%) A pale brown, fruity beer.

**Rawhide** (OG 1050, ABV 5%) A full-flavoured, strong bitter.

**Midas** (ABV 5.2%) A pale, hoppy strong bitter.

**Summer Nights** (ABV 6%)

**Winky Wobbler** (OG 1072, ABV 7.5%) A powerful winter brew.

**Medusa Ale** (OG 1080, ABV 8%) A full-flavoured barley wine.

## LICHFIELD

**Lichfield Brewery, 3 Europa Way, Boley Park, Lichfield, Staffordshire WS14 9TZ. ☎ (01543) 419919**

Two CAMRA members began brewing at Lichfield in 1992, bringing production back to the city after 60 years. The brewery has since doubled its capacity and increased its beer range. Over a hundred outlets are supplied either directly or via agencies. Occasional/seasonal beers: Winter Warmer (OG 1055, ABV 5.5%), Mincespired (OG 1060, ABV 5.8%, Christmas).

**Steeplechase** (OG 1037, ABV 3.7%) A summer beer.

**Inspired** (OG 1040, ABV 4%) ◆ Dark and malty, with a proper bitter aftertaste.

**Sheriff's Ride** (OG 1042, ABV 4.2%) A seasonal brew for autumn.

**Resurrection Ale** (OG 1043, ABV 4.3%) A spring beer.

**Steeplejack** (OG 1045, ABV 4.5%) ◆ A refreshing, pale brown, hoppy beer, with a bitter finish.

**Xpired** (OG 1050, ABV 4.8%) ◆ A dark winter bitter, with malt and chocolate flavours.

Gargoyle (OG 1050, ABV 5%)

# LINFIT

**Linfit Brewery, Sair Inn,
Lane Top, Linthwaite,
Huddersfield, W. Yorkshire
HD7 5SG. ☎ (01484) 842370**

Nineteenth-century brew pub which recommenced brewing in 1982, producing an impressive range of ales for sale at the Sair Inn and in the free trade as far away as Manchester (14 regular outlets). New plant installed in 1994 has almost doubled its capacity. Linfit also brews West Riding Bitter for the West Riding Licensed Refreshment Rooms in Dewsbury, as well as special occasion ales. Tours by arrangement. Occasional/seasonal beer: Xmas Ale (OG 1080, ABV 8.6%). Bottle-conditioned beer: English Guineas Stout (OG 1050, ABV 5.5%).

**Summer Ale** (OG 1030, ABV 3.1%)

**Dark Mild** (OG 1032, ABV 3%) ◆ Roast malt dominates in this straightforward dark mild which has some hops in the aroma and a slightly dry flavour. Malty finish.

**Bitter** (OG 1035, ABV 3.7%) ◆ A session beer. A dry-hopped aroma leads to a clean-tasting, hoppy bitterness, balanced with some maltiness. The finish is well-balanced, too, but sometimes has an intense bitterness.

**Special** (OG 1041, ABV 4.3%) ◆ Dry-hopping provides the aroma for this rich and mellow bitter, which has a very soft profile and character: it fills the mouth with texture rather than taste. Clean, rounded finish.

**Janet Street Porter** (OG 1043, ABV 4.5%) A smooth, dry porter with a bitter, roasted malt character.

**Autumn Gold** (OG 1045, ABV 4.7%) A straw-coloured beer with a dominant hop character and a slightly fruity finish.

**English Guineas Stout** (OG 1050, ABV 5.3%) ◆ A fruity, roast aroma preludes a smooth, roasted malt, chocolatey flavour which is bitter but not too dry. Excellent appearance; good, bitter finish.

**Old Eli** (OG 1050, ABV 5.3%) A well-balanced premium bitter with a dry-hopped aroma and a fruity, bitter finish.

**Smoke House Ale** (OG 1050, ABV 5.3%) A German-style 'rauchbier', brewed with Franconian malt.

**Springbok Bier** (OG 1055, ABV 5.7%) A pale amber beer with hops balanced by a subtle maltiness in the taste. Hoppy aroma; bitter finish.

**Leadboiler** (OG 1063, ABV 6.6%) ◆ Flowery and hoppy in aroma, with a very moreish, strong bitter flavour which is well-balanced by a prominent maltiness. Soft mouthfeel; rounded, bitter finish.

**Enoch's Hammer** (OG 1080, ABV 8.6%) ◆ A straw-coloured, vinous bitter with no pretensions about its strength or pedigree. A full, fruity aroma leads on to a smooth, alcoholic-tasting, hoppy, bitter flavour, with an unexpectedly bitter finish.

# LITTLE

**The Little Brewery Co. Ltd., Henley House,
School Lane, Medmenham,
Buckinghamshire SL7 2HJ.
☎ (01491) 576100 FAX (01491) 571764**

Henley House is a business training centre set in an idyllic spot near Marlow. Its brewery was set up in 1995 to produce real ale for delegates attending courses. The tiny plant (producing one barrel a week) is effectively an exhibition piece to show to others wishing to purchase a brewery of a similar size. Tours by arrangement. Beer: Sam Trueman's Tipple (OG 1044, ABV 4.7%).

# LITTLE AVENHAM

**The Little Avenham
Brewery, Arkwright Mill,
Hawkins Street, Preston,
Lancashire PR1 7HS.
☎ (01772) 555305**

Previously based at the CAMRA award-winning Gaston's Real Ale and Fine Wine Pub, this brewery quickly outgrew its original premises and moved in 1995 to a new brewhouse from where it now serves 70 free trade customers. Tours by arrangement. Bottle-conditioned beer: Torchlight (OG 1046, ABV 4.8%).

**Arkwright Ale** (OG 1035, ABV 3.5%) ◆ A mid-brown session beer with a gentle aroma but strong fruit and hop flavours which continue through to the aftertaste. A sourness and wine-like tartness are not unpleasant.

**Arkwright Mild** (OG 1035, ABV 3.5%) ◆ A dark mild with intense fruit flavours and a dry aftertaste.

**Chartist Ale** (OG 1038, ABV 3.8%) A hoppy bitter with a nice amber colour and a touch of fruit and a long biscuit flavour in the mouth. Quite dry aftertaste.

**Clog Dancer** (OG 1038, ABV 4%) ◆ A golden yellow, distinctive bitter. Though well-balanced, complex fruit and hop flavours make it rich and moreish.

**Ace of Spades** (OG 1040, ABV 4%) A black beer, with a complex fruit and hop flavour. Lots of roasted malt and chocolate in the mouth, a hint of biscuit and liquorice, and a dry aftertaste. A good, well-finished beer.

**Porter** (OG 1040, ABV 4%) ◆ An excellent dark beer with hints of ruby red. Thinner than you would expect from its colour, but very satisfying. Chocolate and roast malt flavours are prominent, with a slight hoppiness and a dry aftertaste.

**Pickled Priest** (OG 1043, ABV 4.3%) ◆ A pale, thin and tart bitter in which fruit flavours give way to a lasting dryness in the finish.

**Torchlight** (OG 1046, ABV 4.8%) ◆ A dark to mid-brown premium ale. Malt and fruit are prominent in the aroma and flavour. Enjoyable and distinctive, it is mild and complex in the mouth, with some sweetness.

**Pierrepoints Last Drop** (OG 1061, ABV 7%) ◆ A pale, strong ale with prominent fruit flavours and a dry aftertaste.

## LIVERPOOL
**The Liverpool Brewing Company Ltd., The Brewery, 21–23 Berry Street, Liverpool, Merseyside L1 9DF. ☎ (0151) 709 5055**
FAX (0151) 709 9405

🍺 Brewery with a five-barrel plant, set up in 1990 to brew solely for what was the Black Horse & Rainbow pub, although this was sold and renamed as The Brewery in March 1996. The beer is stored in cellar tanks and the brewing equipment can be viewed both from inside the pub and from the street. There are plans to brew other beers and to supply other pubs. Beer: Celebration Bitter (OG 1050, ABV 4.8%).

## LLOYDS
**Lloyds Country Beers Ltd., John Thompson Brewery, Ingleby, Melbourne, Derbyshire DE7 1HW. ☎ (01332) 863426**

Lloyds is the separate business set up to supply the beers brewed at the John Thompson Inn (qv) to the free trade. It currently has around 250 outlets, mainly in the Midlands. The High Peak brewery in Chinley, Derbyshire, which is yet to go into production, is still using the premises for its own beers: Peak Pale (ABV 3.8%), Bagman's Bitter (OG 1045, ABV 4.5%) and Cracken (ABV 5.5%, Christmas), as well as a 3.8% bitter. Lloyds also produces occasional brews throughout the year (generally ABV 4–5%). Tours by arrangement.

**Country Gold** (OG 1040, ABV 4%) Brewed in summer.

**Derby Bitter** or **JTS XXX** (OG 1042, ABV 4.1%) Full and fruity.

**Scratching Dog** (OG 1045, ABV 4.5%)

**Vixen Velvet** (OG 1045, ABV 4.5%) A winter porter.

**VIP (Very Important Pint)** (OG 1048, ABV 4.8%) A heavier, darker version of the bitter.

## LOCK, STOCK AND BARREL
See Branscombe Vale and Juwards.

## LONDON BEER COMPANY
See Pitfield.

## LONGSTONE
**Longstone Brewery, Belford, Northumberland.**

Brewery closed.

## LUCIFER See Hope & Anchor.

## LUGTON
**Lugton Inn & Brewery, Lugton, Ayrshire KA3 4DZ. ☎ (01505) 850267**
FAX (01505) 850509

🍺 This new brew pub is Ayrshire's only brewery, producing additive-free beers, just for the pub itself, from hops grown without the use of pesticide. Future plans include the installation of a bottling plant. Tours by arrangement. Beers: Best (OG 1042, ABV 3.7%), Gold (OG 1044, ABV 4.2%), Black (OG 1046, ABV 3.9%), John Barleycorn (OG 1046, ABV 4.5%).

## LUNDY
**Lundy Company, Marisco Tavern Brewery, Lundy Island, Bristol Channel.**

Brewery closed.

**LWCC** See Mansfield.

**M&B** See Nationals, Bass.

## McEWAN
See Nationals, Scottish Courage.

## McGUINNESS
**Thomas McGuinness Brewing Company, Cask & Feather, 1 Oldham Road, Rochdale, Gtr Manchester OL16 1UA.**
☎ / FAX (01706) 711476

🍺 Small brewery established in 1991 behind the Cask & Feather pub, by the late Thomas McGuinness and brewer Eric Hoare. It currently supplies real ale to its own two pubs which are free of tie, and 20 other outlets. 'Personalised contract brewing' was introduced in 1996, for pubs wishing to use their own brand name on beers of a requested colour and strength. Tours by arrangement. Occasional/seasonal beers: Nutcrusher Crumple (ABV 4.4%, autumn), Autumn Glory (ABV 4.4%, autumn), Christmas Cheer (ABV 4.6%, winter), Summer Tipple (ABV 4.6%, summer), Utter Nutter (ABV 4.6%, summer), Winter's Revenge (ABV 4.6%, winter).

**Feather Plucker Mild** (OG 1034, ABV 3.4%) A dark brown beer, with roast malt dominant in the aroma and taste. There's a touch of bitterness, too.

**Best Bitter** (OG 1038, ABV 3.8%) ◆ Gold in colour with a hoppy aroma: a clean, refreshing beer with hop and fruit tastes and a hint of sweetness. Bitter aftertaste.

**Special Reserve Bitter** (OG 1040, ABV 4%)
🔷 A tawny beer, sweet and malty, with underlying fruit and bitterness, and a bittersweet aftertaste.

**Stout** (OG 1040, ABV 4%)

**Junction Bitter** (OG 1042, ABV 4.2%)
🔷 Mid-brown in colour, with a malty aroma. Maltiness is predominant throughout, with some hops and fruit in the taste and bitterness coming through in the finish.

**Tommy Todd Porter** (OG 1050, ABV 5%)
🔷 A winter warmer, with a fruit and roast aroma, leading to a balance of malt and roast malt flavours, with a touch of chocolate. Not too sweet for its gravity.

## MACLAY
**Maclay & Co. Ltd., Thistle Brewery, East Vennel, Alloa, Clackmannanshire FK10 1ED.**
☎ **(01259) 723387**
[FAX] **(01259) 216511**

Founded in 1830 and moved to the present Victorian tower brewery in 1869, Maclay still uses traditional brewing methods and direct-fired coppers, with the beers produced using solely bore-hole water (the only Scottish brewery to do so) without any adjuncts. Until 1992, the company was run by descendants of the founder, James Maclay, but is now owned by the family of Evelyn Matthews, Maclay's chief executive in recent years who sadly died in May 1996. Plant improvements have already led to an upturn in sales, and several new beers have been added to the range, though declining volumes have resulted in 60/- being discontinued. All 30 tied houses offer real ale, which is also supplied to over 200 other outlets. Occasional/seasonal beers: Tam O'Shanter (OG 1042, ABV 4.1%, January), Bruce (OG 1048, ABV 4.8%, March–April).

**Jacobite** (ABV 3.2%)

**70/- Ale** (OG 1036, ABV 3.6%) 🔷 A well-rounded, malty, fruity, clean-tasting beer. There is malt in the nose and a dry, but sweet, finish.

**Broadsword** (OG 1038, ABV 3.8%) 🔷 A golden-coloured beer, with a lingering dry finish. Malt and fruit are dominant in the aroma, with a hop character developing in the sweetish taste and becoming dominant in the bitter aftertaste.

**St Nicholas** (OG 1038, ABV 3.8%) A winter beer.

**80/- Export** (OG 1040, ABV 4%) 🔷 A rich, creamy, bittersweet beer, well worth seeking out; plenty of malt, balanced with bitterness in a lingering dry finish.

**Kane's Amber Ale** (OG 1040, ABV 4%)
🔷 Brewed to commemorate the contribution of the late Dan Kane to Scottish brewing: a malty, fruity, bittersweet, amber-coloured

beer with hops in evidence, but not as hoppy and bitter as when first launched.

**Porter** (OG 1040, ABV 4%)

**Oat Malt Stout** (OG 1045, ABV 4.5%)

**Wallace IPA** (OG 1045, ABV 4.5%) 🔷 Hops and fruit are to the fore in the aroma and remain in the taste, with a surprisingly bitter finish.

**Pictish** (OG 1050, ABV 5%) A winter brew.

**Scotch Ale** (OG 1050, ABV 5%)

## McMULLEN
**McMullen & Sons Ltd., The Hertford Brewery, 26 Old Cross, Hertford SG14 1RD.**
☎ **(01992) 584911**
[FAX] **(01992) 500729**

Hertfordshire's oldest independent brewery, founded in 1827 by Peter McMullen. The Victorian tower brewery, which houses the original oak and copper-lined fermenters still in use today, was built on the site of three wells. Real ale is served in all McMullen's 147 pubs in Hertfordshire, Essex and London, and also supplied directly to 180 free trade outlets. Seasonal beers are brewed for a limited period under the banner of McMullen Special Reserve. Tours by arrangement.

**Original AK** (OG 1033, ABV 3.7%) 🔷 A bitter-tasting beer, with a pleasant mix of hops and malt. Distinctive, dry aftertaste.

**Country Best Bitter** (OG 1041, ABV 4.3%)
🔷 A full-bodied beer with a well-balanced mix of malt, hops and fruit flavours and a strong, dry aftertaste.

**Gladstone** (OG 1041, ABV 4.3%) A smooth, refreshing ale with a finely rounded bitterness.

**Stronghart** (OG 1070, ABV 7%) 🔷 A sweetish, rich, dark beer, full of fruit and hop aromas and flavours.

## MALLARD
**Mallard Brewery, 15 Hartington Avenue, Carlton, Nottingham NG4 3NR.**
☎ **(0115) 952 1289**

Phil Mallard still works full-time for BT, so his new brewery is at present just a sideline. He built the tiny (two-barrel) plant himself and currently supplies 20 outlets. Occasional/seasonal beer: Quismas Quacker (OG 1060, ABV 6%).

**Bitter** (OG 1038, ABV 4%) 🔷 Golden brown, fruity and hoppy to the nose, with malt more apparent in the taste than anywhere else. The fruity hop carries through to a bitter, dry finish.

**Duckling** (OG 1039, ABV 4.2%)

**Owd Duck** (OG 1047, ABV 4.8%)
◆ Intensely roasty and strongly bitter, this ruby/brown drink has moderate undertones of fruit and faint hops throughout.

**DA** (OG 1057, ABV 5.8%) A dark, sweetish winter ale.

## MALTON

**Malton Brewery Company Ltd., Suddaby's Crown Hotel, Wheelgate, Malton, N. Yorkshire YO17 0HP.**
☎ (01653) 697580

Malton began brewing in 1985 in a stable block at the rear of the Crown Hotel Owner Geoff Woollons has now been brewing for 50 years and in 1994 was joined in the business by his daughter and his nephew. The additive-free beers are supplied to around ten free trade outlets directly and pubs further afield via wholesalers. There are plans to add two more fermenters to provide greater capacity. Brewery souvenirs are sold at the hotel. Tours by arrangement.

**Pale Ale** (OG 1034, ABV 3.2%) ◆ With a light aroma, but immediately hoppy in the mouth, this is a thin, light, golden yellow brew, with a balanced smoothness ending in a delicate, dry finish.

**Double Chance Bitter** (OG 1038, ABV 3.8%) ◆ A beer with hops on the nose and tongue, and a dry and lightly bitter aftertaste. Less sweet than in the past and fairly malty.

**Nutbrown** (OG 1041, ABV 3.9%) ◆ A full hop nose and a chocolate tone upfront fade into a dry and malty taste with bitter interludes. Little body and no great depth.

**Pickwick's Porter** (OG 1042, ABV 4%) 🍺 ◆ Heavy malt and roast malt in both the nose and the mouth lead to a dry mixture of tart fruit and dark chocolate. Dry and nutty finish.

**Crown Bitter** (OG 1044, ABV 4.4%)

**Owd Bob** (OG 1055, ABV 5.9%) 🍺 ◆ A rich and warming combination of hops and roast malt leads to floral, fruit and chocolate tastes. The roast malt lingers through to the slightly sweet, yet still bitter, finish. Red hints to the dark brown body.

## MANSFIELD

**Mansfield Brewery PLC, Littleworth, Mansfield, Nottinghamshire NG18 1AB.**
☎ (01623) 25691
FAX (01623) 658620

Founded in 1855, and now one of the country's leading regional brewers, Mansfield resumed cask beer production in 1982 after a break of ten years. The purchase of Hull's North Country Brewery in 1985 led to major expansion, and its tied estate has grown considerably in recent years (to around 500 outlets, including clubs), with acquisitions from Courage and S&N. Its award-winning ales, all fermented in traditional Yorkshire squares, are also supplied to over 700 free trade outlets, and Mansfield enjoys a reciprocal trading arrangement with Charles Wells. A contract to brew for Scottish Courage has been negotiated and production of the Home brewery range (including Matthew Brown beers) and some beers from the old Webster's brewery was transferred to Mansfield in the summer of 1996. Mansfield also brews under contract for LWCC wholesalers in Manchester ☎ (0161) 707 7878. Tours by arrangement (second Sunday in the month). Occasional 'Deakin's' beers: White Rabbit (OG 1042, ABV 4.3%, Easter), Red Squirrel (OG 1042, ABV 4.4%, winter), Red Admiral (OG 1043, ABV 4.4%, summer), Royal Stag (OG 1044, ABV 4.5%, autumn), Wild Boar (OG 1052, ABV 5.5%, winter).

**Riding Mild** (OG 1035, ABV 3.5%) ◆ A dark ruby mild, with a chocolate malt nose, backed up by an orange and blackcurrant fruitiness which is more prominent in the taste. The beer then mellows to a dry finish.

**Riding Bitter** (OG 1035, ABV 3.6%) ◆ A hoppy and bitter beer, with hop being the dominant factor throughout. However, malt almost matches hops on the nose and there is a certain amount of fruitiness in the taste.

**Mansfield Bitter** (OG 1038, ABV 3.9%) ◆ Mansfield's Midlands (as opposed to Yorkshire) bitter. Malt and hops are balanced, but with malt getting the upper hand. Sweetness and bitterness in the taste; a well-rounded brew.

**Old Baily** (OG 1045, ABV 4.8%) 🍺 ◆ Coppery-brown, with fruit on the nose and in the taste, and an initial sweetness. The hops come in late and malt is always present. A complex beer with something for everyone.

### For LWCC

**Gray's Mild** (ABV 3.5%)

**Gray's Bitter** (ABV 3.6%)

### For Scottish Courage:

**Matthew Brown Lion Mild** (OG 1030, ABV 3.1%)

**Matthew Brown Lion Bitter** (OG 1034, ABV 3.5%)

**Webster's Yorkshire Bitter** (OG 1035, ABV 3.5%) This beer supplements supplies from Scottish Courage's John Smith's brewery.

**Wilson's Original Bitter** (OG 1035, ABV 3.5%)

**Home Mild** (OG 1036, ABV 3.6%)

**Home Bitter** (OG 1038, ABV 3.8%)

## MANSFIELD ARMS See Devon.

## MARCHES

**Marches Ales, Unit 6, Western Close, Southern Avenue Industrial Estate, Leominster, Herefordshire HR6 0QD. ☎ (01568) 611084**

The Solstice brewery of Kington was taken over by Paul Harris in 1995 and moved to this new purpose-built brewery, which takes its name from its location at the edge of the Marches. Demand for the beers has already led to expansion of the brewery, which currently supplies 20 outlets directly and others nationally via wholesalers. The Black Horse pub in Leominster acts as a brewery tap for the ales. Tours by arrangement Friday evenings.

**Best Bitter** (OG 1036, ABV 3.8%)

**BHB** (OG 1036, ABV 3.8%) ◆ A standard bitter, with well-balanced malt and hops. Bitterness does not linger; subdued aroma.

**Forever Autumn** (OG 1040, ABV 4.2%) ◆ Hop fruitiness predominates in a complex array of flavours, to give a rich aftertaste.

**Priory Ale** (OG 1046, ABV 4.8%)

**Jenny Pipes Summer Ale** (OG 1050, ABV 5.2%)

**Earl Leofric Winter Ale** (OG 1062, ABV 6.2%)

## MARISCO TAVERN See Lundy.

## MARSTON MOOR

**Marston Moor Brewery, Crown House, Kirk Hammerton, York, N. Yorkshire YO5 8DD. ☎ /FAX (01423) 330341**

Small, but expanding brewery, set up in 1983 and moved to the rear of its first tied house, the Crown, in 1988. This pub was closed in 1993 after the acquisition of the Beer Exchange at Woodhouse in Leeds, but more pubs are being sought. The company currently produces 1,000 barrels a year and supplies around 60 free trade outlets. It also installs brewing plants and acts as a consultant to mini-brewers. Tours by arrangement.

**Cromwell Bitter** (OG 1036, ABV 3.6%) ◆ A golden beer with an initial burst of fruit flavours that graduate to a malt and hop taste. A lingering aftertaste is predominantly fruity.

**Brewers Pride** (OG 1042, ABV 4.2%) ◆ A light and fruity, amber-coloured beer with a hoppy, bitter aftertaste.

**Porter** (OG 1042, ABV 4.2%) A seasonal brew (October–May), ruby-coloured and stout-like.

**Merrie Maker** (OG 1045, ABV 4.5%)

**Brewers Droop** (OG 1050, ABV 5.1%) A potent, straw-coloured ale.

**ESB** (OG 1050, ABV 5.1%)

**Trooper** (OG 1050, ABV 5.1%)

## MARSTON'S

**Marston, Thompson & Evershed PLC, Shobnall Road, Burton upon Trent, Staffordshire DE14 2BW. ☎ (01283) 531131 FAX (01283) 510378**

The only brewery still using the Burton Union system of fermentation (for its stronger ales), Marston's reinforced its commitment to this method in 1992 with a £1 million investment in a new Union room. Real ale is available in all the company's 836 pubs, which stretch from Yorkshire to Hampshire. Marston's also enjoys an enormous free trade, thanks to trading agreements with Wolverhampton & Dudley and the fact that many national brewers' houses stock Pedigree Bitter. The Head Brewer's Choice scheme (noted as HBC in *Good Beer Guide* pub entries) offers a range of new brews to selected outlets for two weeks at a time. Shop open 10–2. Tours by arrangement. Bottle-conditioned beer: Oyster Stout (OG 1045, ABV 4.5%)🍷.

**Bitter** (OG 1037, ABV 3.8%) ◆ An amber/tawny session beer which can often be markedly sulphury in aroma and taste. At its best, a splendid, subtle balance of malt, hops and fruit follows a faintly hoppy aroma and develops into a balanced, dry aftertaste.

**Pedigree** (OG 1043, ABV 4.5%) ◆ Strong hop and malt taste and finish. Sulphurous aroma and dry aftertaste.

**Owd Rodger** (OG 1080, ABV 7.6%)🍷 ◆ A dark, ruby-red barley wine, with an intense fruity nose before a deep, winey, heavy fruit flavour, with malt and faint hops. The finish is dry and fruity (strawberries).

### For Tesco:

Bottle-conditioned beer: Tesco Select Ales IPA (OG 1048, ABV 5%)

## MASONS ARMS

**Lakeland Brewing Co., Strawberry Bank, Cartmel Fell, Cumbria LA11 6NW. ☎ (0153 95) 68686 FAX (0153 95) 68780**

Famous pub, known for its large selection of bottled beers, which began brewing in 1990. Beer names are based on books by local author Arthur Ransome. Tours by arrangement. Beers: Amazon Bitter (OG 1038, ABV 4%), Captain Flint (OG 1040, ABV 4%, occasional), Great Northern (OG 1045, ABV 4.5%), Big Six (OG 1060, ABV 6%), Damson Beer (OG 1070, ABV 7%). Bottle-conditioned beers (all occasional, except Damson Beer): Amazon Bitter (OG 1038, ABV 4%), Great Northern (OG 1045, ABV 4.5%), Big Six (OG 1060, ABV 6%), Damson Beer (OG 1070, ABV 9%).

## MAULDONS

Mauldons Brewery,
7 Addison Road, Chilton
Industrial Estate, Sudbury,
Suffolk CO10 6YW.
☎ / FAX (01787) 311055

Company set up in 1982 by former Watney's brewer Peter Mauldon, whose family had its own local brewery in the late 18th century. Its extensive beer list changes frequently and is supplied to 150 free trade outlets in East Anglia, as well as pubs further afield via wholesalers. Occasional/seasonal beers: Broomstick Bitter (OG 1040, ABV 4%, Hallowe'en), Mother's Ruin (OG 1040, ABV 4%, Mothering Sunday), George's Best (OG 1045, ABV 4.4%, St George's Day), Love Potion No. 9 (OG 1045, ABV 4.5%, St Valentine's Day), Bah Humbug (OG 1049, ABV 4.9%, Christmas), Gunpowder Blast (OG 1063, ABV 6%, Guy Fawkes Day), Christmas Reserve (OG 1066, ABV 6.6%).

**May Bee** (OG 1037, ABV 3.7%) Softer than the Best Bitter, with added honey. Available in summer.

**Best Bitter** (OG 1037, ABV 3.8%) ◆ A well-balanced session beer with a crisp, hoppy bitterness balancing sweet malt.

**Midsummer Gold** (OG 1040, ABV 4%) A light-coloured summer beer.

**Eatanswill Old XXXX** (OG 1042, ABV 4%) ◆ Taking its name from the title given to Sudbury by Dickens in *Pickwick Papers*, this is a winter ale of deep red and brown hue, with well-balanced fruit and malt plus a slight sweetness on the palate, ending in a pleasant roast bitterness.

**Original Porter** (OG 1042, ABV 3.8%) ◆ A black beer with malt and roast malt flavours dominating. Some hop in the finish.

**Special Bitter** (OG 1044, ABV 4.2%) ◆ By far the hoppiest of the Mauldons beers, with a good, bitter finish and some balancing malt.

**Squires Bitter** (OG 1044, ABV 4.2%) ◆ A best bitter with a good, malty aroma and a reasonably balanced flavour, which leans towards malt. Hops come through late and crisply into the aftertaste.

**Midwinter Gold** (OG 1045, ABV 4.5%) A winter beer.

**Suffolk Punch** (OG 1050, ABV 4.8%) ◆ A full-bodied, strong bitter. The malt and fruit in the aroma are reflected in the taste and there is some hop character in the finish. Deep tawny/red in colour.

**Black Adder** (OG 1053, ABV 5.3%) ◆ A dark stout. Roast malt is very strong in the aroma and taste, but malt, hop and bitterness provide an excellent balance and a lingering finish. *Champion Beer of Britain* 1991.

**White Adder** (OG 1053, ABV 5.3%) ▯ ◆ A pale brown, almost golden strong ale. A warming, fruity flavour dominates and lingers into a dry, hoppy finish.

**Suffolk Comfort** (OG 1065, ABV 6.6%) ◆ A clean, hoppy nose leads to a predominantly malty flavour in this full-bodied beer. Dry, hoppy aftertaste.

## MAYHEM'S See Farmers Arms.

## MAYPOLE

Maypole Brewery, North
Laithes Farm, Wellow Road,
Eakring, Newark,
Nottinghamshire
NG22 0AN.
☎ (01623) 871690

Brewery established in 1995 with equipment purchased from Springhead Brewery. It supplies four local pubs regularly, which increase to seven in summer, with a further 25 taking the beers as guests. Occasional/seasonal beer: Donner and Blitzed (ABV 5.1%, a stronger version of Poleaxed for Christmas).

**Celebration** (OG 1040, ABV 4%) ◆ A ruddy-brown bitter in which malt dominates. Some fruity hop in the nose and taste, with an initial sweetness that drys into a bitter finish where the fruit and hops meet the malt.

**Mayday** (OG 1046, ABV 4.6%) ▯ ◆ A tawny best bitter, with malt and a hint of dates on the nose. The taste is predominantly fruit and malt again, which becomes more bitter and hoppy in the finish.

**Poleaxed** (OG 1048, ABV 4.8%)

**Old Homewrecker** (OG 1050, ABV 4.7%) A new porter.

## MERIVALES

Merivales Ales Ltd.,
Warden Brewery, Manor
Farm, Chipping Warden,
Banbury, Oxfordshire
OX17 1LH.
☎ (01295) 660090

Company set up in 1994 with a tiny, single-barrel brewplant at Edgcote, and moved early in 1996 to a new brewery, with eight times the capacity, in nearby Chipping Warden (which is in Northamptonshire, despite the postal address). About 20 pubs take the beers but brewing was temporarily suspended in summer 1996. Tours by arrangement. Occasional/seasonal beer: Merrielegs (OG 1042, ABV 4.5%, Christmas).

**Edgecutter** (OG 1037, ABV 3.9%) A hoppy brew with a long finish.

**Chaser-Best** (OG 1044, ABV 4.8%) A sweeter beer, but still hoppy, particularly in the aroma and finish.

**Hurdler** (OG 1048, ABV 5%) A darker, strong beer.

## MERRIMANS

**Merrimans Brewery, Old Fart Ltd., Marpak House, Westland Square, Leeds, W. Yorkshire LS11 5SS.**
☎ (0113) 270 4542
FAX (0113) 270 0778

After the demise of Robinwood Brewery, Tim Fritchley set up this new operation in 1994 with the intention of rejuvenating the 'Old Fart' name. Such has been the demand for its bottled beers, that, apart from the odd appearance at beer festivals, the brewing of cask ales has been suspended until expansion of the plant has been completed. Bottle-conditioned beer: Old Fart (OG 1050, ABV 5%).

## MIDDLETON

**The Middleton Brewery, Unit 6, Stainton Grove Industrial Estate, Barnard Castle, Co. Durham DL12 8TH.** ☎ (01833) 690004

One of the newest breweries in the North-East, set up in spring 1996. It was launched with a single real ale, but there are plans to expand the range as soon as a regular trade is established.

**Leo's** (OG 1038, ABV 3.8%)

## MILDMAY

**The Mildmay Brewery, Holbeton, Plymouth, Devon PL8 1NA.** ☎ (01752) 830302
FAX (01752) 830540

🍺 Mildmay started brewing in 1993, for its tied house, the Mildmay Colours Inn. In 1994, the brewery was expanded to triple its capacity to around 50 barrels per week and the beers can now be found throughout Devon and the South-West (some 70 outlets are supplied directly). There are plans to sell further afield via wholesalers. Tours by arrangement.

**Colours Best** (OG 1040, ABV 3.8%) 🍺 A pale brown, well-balanced beer with a dry malt and fruit flavour and a bitter finish.

**SP** or **Starting Price Ale** (OG 1047, ABV 4.5%) 🍺 A mid-brown bitter with a malty, fruity aroma and taste, and a sharp, bitter aftertaste.

**Tipster** (OG 1052, ABV 5.1%) A strong beer, available April–November.

**50/1** (OG 1052, ABV 5.1%) A porter, brewed November–April.

**Old Horse Whip** (OG 1057, ABV 5.7%)

**Jockey Warmer** (OG 1061, ABV 6.2%) An old ale, brewed November–February.

---

🍺 The pub sign indicates a brew pub: a pub which produces beer on the premises.

---

## MILL

**Mill Brewery, 18C Bradley Lane, Newton Abbot, Devon TQ12 1LZ.**
☎ (01626) 63322

MILL BREWERY

Brewery founded in 1983 on the site of an old watermill and in production on a part-time basis until changing hands in 1994. After running the company full-time for two years on his own, the new owner, Mike Cox, took on a partner in March 1996 and they have reduced the beer range to concentrate on two main beers and a winter brew. Special beers are now brewed bi-monthly. Over 20 outlets take the beers regularly. Tours by arrangement.

**Janner's Ale** (OG 1038, ABV 3.8%) 🍺 A pale brown beer, with a fruity aroma and a bitter taste and aftertaste.

**Old Original** (OG 1048, ABV 5%) A golden beer with plenty of fruit and hops in both aroma and flavour.

**Black Bushel** (OG 1060, ABV 6%) A black beer with a fruity, vanilla aroma, complemented by rich roasted barley and malt flavours. Smooth and dry finish. Available November–December.

## MILLGATE

**The Millgate Brewery, The Millgate, Ashton Road West, Failsworth, Manchester M35 0ES.** ☎/FAX (0161) 688 4910

🍺 Brewery established in 1995 and temporarily closed in summer 1996, pending a move to larger premises.

## MINERVA

See Nationals, Carlsberg-Tetley.

## MITCHELL'S

**Mitchell's of Lancaster (Brewers) Ltd., 11 Moor Lane, Lancaster, Lancashire LA1 1QB.** ☎ (01524) 63773
FAX (01524) 846071

The only surviving independent brewery in Lancaster (est. 1880), wholly owned and run by direct descendants of founder William Mitchell. Real ale is sold in all but one of its 53 pubs and is available virtually countrywide in the free trade. Occasional/seasonal beers, with a 'William' theme, are now being produced, including Lakeland Reserve (ABV 3.6%, William Wordsworth), Just William (ABV 4%, a mild), Tempest (ABV 4.2%, Shakespeare), Rev. William Spooner (ABV 4.5%), Conqueror (ABV 5%), Old Faithful (ABV 5.2%, after William Mitchell's dog).

**William Mitchell's Original Bitter** (OG 1038, ABV 3.8%) A dark gold beer with a light, hoppy aroma, a malty, hoppy taste and a dry finish.

**Lancaster Bomber** (OG 1044, ABV 4.4%) A straw-coloured bitter with an aromatic nose.

Initially sweet on the palate, followed by plenty of hop and a dry finish.

**Single Malt** (OG 1064, ABV 7.2%) 🔶 A winter brew (November–January), mid-brown in colour and suggestive of malt whisky in aroma and flavour. Strongly malty throughout, with a subtle, bittersweet, hoppy balance in the taste.

## MITCHELLS & BUTLERS
See Nationals, Bass.

## MOLE'S
**Mole's Brewery (Cascade Drinks Ltd.), 5 Merlin Way, Bowerhill, Melksham, Wiltshire SN12 6TJ.**
☎ (01225) 704734
[FAX] (01225) 790770

Brewery established in 1982 and run on very traditional lines by former Ushers brewer Roger Catté (the brewery name came from his nickname). All the brewery's 14 tied houses take at least two of the cask ales, which are also supplied directly to 100 other free trade outlets. Mole's also acts as a distributor for other members of the Small Independent Brewers Association (SIBA). Shop open 9–5. Tours by arrangement. Bottle-conditioned beer. Brew 97 (OG 1050, ABV 5%).

**Tap Bitter** (OG 1035, ABV 3.5%) 🔶 A pale brown beer with a trace of malt in the aroma. A gentle, malty, dry flavour with apple and pear fruits follows, then a bitter finish.

**Best Bitter** (OG 1040, ABV 4%) 🔶 A pale brown/golden-coloured beer with a light malt aroma. The taste is clean, dry and malty, with some bitterness and delicate floral hop. A well-balanced, light and subtle ale.

**Landlords Choice** (OG 1045, ABV 4.5%) A dark bitter, not widely available.

**Brew 97** (OG 1050, ABV 5%) 🔶 A mid-brown, full-bodied beer with a gentle malt and hop aroma. The rich flavour is malty, with fruit, hop and traces of vanilla. A wonderfully warming, malty ale.

**XB** (OG 1060, ABV 6%) A winter brew.

## MOOR
**Moor Beer Company, Whitley Farm, Ashcott, near Bridgwater, Somerset TA7 9QW.**
☎ (01458) 210050

Farmer Arthur Frampton, his wife and two partners set up this brewery on a former dairy farm in February 1996. Their five-barrel plant supplies six local outlets. Tours by arrangement.

**Withycutter** (OG 1038)

## MOORHOUSE'S
**Moorhouse's Brewery (Burnley) Ltd., 4 Moorhouse Street, Burnley, Lancashire BB11 5EN.**
☎ (01282) 422864
[FAX] (01282) 838493

Long-established (1865) producer of hop bitters, which in 1978 began brewing cask beer. A succession of owners failed to develop the company until it was taken over in 1985 by Bill Parkinson, since when it has grown considerably, opening the first of six tied houses in 1987. A modern brewhouse was installed in 1988 and a further extension to the brewery was completed in 1996. Special beers are brewed on a monthly basis. Moorhouse's supplies real ale to around 100 free trade outlets. Tours by arrangement.

**Black Cat Mild** (OG 1034, ABV 3.2%) A superb dark mild, brewed in the traditional way. A justifiably popular session beer.

**Premier Bitter** (OG 1036, ABV 3.7%) 🔶 Pale brown in colour, this characterful brew has a superb hop flower aroma, with some fruit and malt. Dry, hoppy finish.

**Yates 1884 Bitter** (OG 1040, ABV 4.1%) The latest addition to the range.

**Pendle Witches Brew** (OG 1050, ABV 5.1%) 🍺 🔶 A good hoppy aroma leads through to a full-bodied, malty sweetness, with a trace of hop bitterness.

**Owd Ale** (OG 1064, ABV 6%) A winter brew, available November–March.

## MORDUE
**Mordue Brewery, Unit 22C Middle Engine Lane, West Chirton North Industrial Estate, North Shields, Tyne & Wear NE29 8SF.**
☎ (0191) 296 1879

The Mordue brewery, founded in 1995, takes its name from an original family brewery which operated in Wallsend in the 19th century. Demand for the beers has grown steadily and the company now supplies 70 outlets directly. Tours by arrangement.

**Five Bridge Bitter** (OG 1038, ABV 3.8%) A crisp, drinkable bitter, with a hoppy bite and sound body.

**Geordie Pride** (OG 1042, ABV 4.2%) 🔶 Hop and fruit dominate this robust ale. Bitterness is light, but lingers long after the last swallow.

**Workie Ticket** (OG 1045, ABV 4.5%)

**Radgie Gadgie** (OG 1048, ABV 4.8%)

---

🍺 The empty tankard indicates the beer was a *Good Beer Guide Beer of the Year* in the last three years.

## MORLAND

Morland PLC, The Brewery,
Ock Street, Abingdon,
Oxfordshire OX14 5BZ.
☎ (01235) 553377
FAX (01235) 540508

Established in 1711, Morland is the second oldest independent brewer in the UK and has been on its present site since 1861. In 1992 it survived a take-over bid by Greene King and in 1995 it purchased the small pub company Unicorn Inns, owner of the Newt & Cucumber mini-chain. Nearly all Morland's 350-plus pubs serve real ale, but in some cases the licensee uses cask-breathers. The company also supplies around 500 free trade outlets around the Thames Valley and Surrey, and has quickly established Old Speckled Hen as one of the UK's best-known guest beers. A recent £5 million investment in the brewery has improved and expanded production facilities. Tours by arrangement. Seasonal beers: Aunt Sally Summer Ale (ABV 3.8%), Bill's Spring Brew (ABV 4.2%), Autumn Beechnut (ABV 4.5%), Winter Warmer Christmas Ale (ABV 6%).

**Independent IPA** (OG 1037, ABV 3.4%)

**Original Bitter** (OG 1035, ABV 4%) ❧ A light amber beer with malty, hoppy nose and a hint of fruitiness. The distinct, but lightish malt and hops carry over to the flavour and leave a sweet but dry, hoppy aftertaste.

**Old Masters** (OG 1040, ABV 4.6%) ❧ A well-balanced tawny/amber beer with not outstandingly strong flavours. The initial aroma of malt and hops leads to a moderately malty, but dry and hoppy flavour, with a hint of fruit which can be faintly sulphurous. Dry, bitter finish.

**The Tanner's Jack** (OG 1042, ABV 4.4%)

**Old Speckled Hen** (OG 1050, ABV 5.2%) ❧ Morland's most distinctive beer, deep tawny/amber in colour. A well-balanced aroma of roasted malt and hops is complemented by a good hint of caramel. An initial sweet, malty, fruity, roast caramel taste soon allows the dry hop flavour through, leaving a well-balanced aftertaste.

### For Scottish Courage:

**Wilson's Original Mild** (OG 1032, ABV 3%)

## MORRELLS

Morrells Brewery Ltd., The
Lion Brewery, St Thomas'
Street, Oxford OX1 1LA.
☎ (01865) 792013
FAX (01865) 791868

MORRELLS BREWERY
Oxford

The oldest brewery in Oxford has been owned or managed by the Morrell family since it opened in 1782. Of its 127 pubs, over 50 are within the city limits and all but one of the outlets serve real ale, though some employ blanket pressure. Some 180 other outlets also stock Morrells beers. The shop is open in conjunction with tours (by arrangement). Occasional/seasonal beer: College Ale (OG 1073, ABV 7.4%, winter).

**Oxford Bitter** (OG 1036, ABV 3.7%) ❧ Golden in colour and light in body, but not in flavour, with a good aroma of hops complemented by malt and fruitiness. An initial dry hop bitterness is well-balanced by malt, which gives way to a refreshing, slightly sweet fruitiness, with a hint of roast caramel. Bittersweet, hoppy finish.

**Oxford Mild** (OG 1037, ABV 3.7%) A full-bodied dark mild.

**Varsity** (OG 1041, ABV 4.3%) ❧ A tawny/amber beer. Malt, hops and fruit are the main features in both aroma and taste, but are well-balanced. The slightly sweet, malty, fruity start fades away to a distinctive, bittersweet finish.

**Graduate** (OG 1048, ABV 5.2%) ❧ An intense malt and roast malt aroma carries through to the taste and is complemented by a moderate hoppiness. Pleasant, bitter finish.

### For Whitbread:

**Strong Country Bitter** (OG 1037, ABV 3.9%)

## MOULIN

Moulin Brewery, The Old
Coach House, Balemund
Road, Moulin, Pitlochry,
Perthshire & Kinross
PH16 5EW.
☎ (01796) 472196

This new brewery was opened in August 1995 at the Moulin Hotel, during celebrations for the hotel's 300th anniversary (it had a brewery when it first opened in 1695, so it was deemed fitting to recommence brewing on the site). The operation has since moved next door to the Old Coach House. It currently supplies six outlets, but the turnover fluctuates with the tourist season. Shop open 12–4. Tours by arrangement.

**Braveheart** (OG 1038, ABV 4%)

**Ale of Atholl** (OG 1043, ABV 4.5%)

**Old Remedial** (OG 1049, ABV 5.2%)

## MUNSLOW See Crown Inn.

## NAG'S HEAD

Nag's Head, Abercych, Boncath,
Ceredigion SA37 0JH. ☎ (01239) 841200

New pub brewery producing just one brew on an occasional basis largely for its own consumption. Beer: Old Emrys (ABV 4.1%).

## NENE VALLEY See Leyland.

## NETHERGATE

**Nethergate Brewery Co. Ltd., 11–13 High Street, Clare, Suffolk CO10 8NY.**
☎ (01787) 277244
FAX (01787) 277123

Small brewer of award-winning beers, set up in 1986, which continues to use traditional methods and no additives. The Umbel beers are infused with coriander seeds, recalling an ancient brewing style, and other brewers have now followed Nethergate in adding herbs and spices to their beers. Two tied houses and 180 free trade outlets are now supplied, most in East Anglia. Tours by arrangement. Two beers are produced for wholesaler Martin Elms Wines ☎ (01245) 478323.

**IPA** (OG 1036, ABV 3.6%) ◗ An apple crisp, refreshing session beer, hoppy throughout, without fully masking the malt. Lingering, bitter aftertaste.

**Umbel Ale** (OG 1039, ABV 3.8%) ■ ◗ Wort is percolated through coriander seeds to give a wonderful, warming, spicy fruit tang to both the taste and aroma. The hops are strong enough to make themselves known and a strong, bitter malt finish hits late.

**Bitter** (OG 1039, ABV 4%) ◫ ◗ A dark bitter in which delightful malt and hop aromas give way to a well-balanced palate. Rich malts and powerful bitterness dominate the flavour, ending in a strong, bitter finish.

**Golden Gate** (OG 1045, ABV 4.5%) A golden bitter using three hop varieties, giving it a fresh aroma and a hoppy finish. Malt and hops are balanced in the taste.

**Old Growler** (OG 1055, ABV 5.5%) ◫ ◗ A complex and satisfying porter, smooth and distinctive. Sweetness, roast malt and fruit feature in the palate, with bitter chocolate lingering. The finish is powerfully hoppy.

**Umbel Magna** (OG 1055, ABV 5.5%) ◗ The addition of coriander to the Old Growler wort completes the original 1750s recipe for this very distinctive dark beer. The powerful spiciness only adds to this porter's appeal.

### For Martin Elms Wines:

**Porters Suffolk Bitter** (ABV 3.5%)

**Porters Sidewinder** (ABV 4.5%)

---

## NEWALE

**Newale Brewing Company Ltd., 6 Viscount Court, South Way, Walworth Industrial Estate, Andover, Hampshire SP10 5NW.**

☎ (01264) 336336 FAX (01264) 333310

Set up in 1993, this brewery has been voted the *Most Environmentally Friendly Company* in Andover. Trade has increased beyond expectation, with over 100 outlets now regularly taking the beers, as well as wholesalers. Brewery shop open 9–5 Mon–Fri. Tours by arrangement.

**New Tun Mild** (OG 1035, ABV 3.5%) A refreshing, nutty dark mild, brewed May–September.

**Amber Ale** (OG 1035, ABV 3.6%) A light amber session bitter.

**Anna Valley Ale** (OG 1040, ABV 4.2%) A light and smooth, malty beer with a high hop content.

**Balksbury Bitter** (OG 1044, ABV 4.5%) A dry, dark red/brown, distinctive bitter.

**Clatford Clout** (OG 1048, ABV 5%) A pale golden, well-hopped premium ale.

**Old Hatch Ale** (OG 1058, ABV 6%) A dark, sweetish, full-bodied strong ale, brewed November–March.

## NEWPORT See Ross.

## NICHOLSON'S
See Nationals, Carlsberg-Tetley.

## NIX WINCOTT See Leyland.

## NORTH DOWNS

**Weltons North Downs Brewery Ltd., The Brewhouse, Rugge Farm, Wigmore Lane, Capel, Dorking, Surrey RH5 4PT.**
☎ / FAX (01403) 242901

Brewery founded in October 1995 by a former beer wholesaler. Now over 60 pubs take the beers. Occasional/seasonal beers: May Gold (OG 1036, ABV 4%, a wheat beer), Red Rooster (ABV 4%, September), Coronation Ale (OG 1043, ABV 4.4%, June), Lion Brew (ABV 4.5%, August), Summer Special (ABV 4.8%, July), Guy Fawkes Revenge (ABV 5%), Wenceslegless (ABV 5%, December), De Frenches Stout (ABV 5.2%, November), Wellington's Cannon (OG 1050, ABV 5.4%, June), Nelson's Trafalgar (ABV 5.6%, October).

**Bitter** (OG 1038, ABV 3.8%) ◗ An amber to pale brown bitter with a hoppy flavour, balanced by underlying malt.

**Old Cocky** (OG 1042, ABV 4.3%) ■ ◗ Malty and fruity in the aroma, with hops developing in the flavour and dominating the aftertaste.

**Tower Power** (OG 1048, ABV 5%) A ruby-coloured, warming beer.

---

## NORTHUMBERLAND

**The Northumberland Brewery Ltd., Unit 14, North Seaton Industrial Estate, Ashington, Northumberland NE63 0YB.**
☎ (01670) 819139

This new brewery went into production in May 1996, producing three traditionally brewed beers.

**Castles Bitter** (ABV 3.8%) A session bitter.

**Best Bitter** (ABV 4.5%) A full-bodied bitter.

**Duke of Northumberland Premium Ale**
(ABV 5%) A dark malted premium bitter.

## NORTH YORKSHIRE

**North Yorkshire Brewing
Co., 80–84 North Ormesby
Road, Middlesbrough,
N. Yorkshire TS4 2AG.
☎ (01642) 226224
FAX (01642) 226225**

Brewery founded in 1990. The traditionally brewed beers are in much demand, and, while the permanent range has been slimmed down, an extra beer is brewed every month to a new recipe. Over 100 free trade outlets are currently supplied. Tours by arrangement. Occasional/seasonal beers: Honey Bunny (OG 1037, ABV 3.8%, an Easter beer with added honey), Love Muscle (OG 1040, ABV 4%, February), Xmas Herbert (OG 1044, ABV 4.4%), Cereal Killer (OG 1045, ABV 4.5%, wheat beer for August).

**Best Bitter** (OG 1036, ABV 3.6%) ♠ Light, very refreshing and surprisingly full-flavoured for a pale, low gravity beer, with a complex, bittersweet mixture of malt, hops and fruit carrying through into the aftertaste.

**Boro Best** (OG 1040, ABV 4%) A full-bodied, northern beer with a malty aroma and a balanced malt and hops taste, with vanilla notes.

**Fool's Gold** (OG 1046, ABV 4.6%) ♠ A well-hopped, lightly malted, golden premium bitter, using Styrian and Goldings hops.

**Flying Herbert** (OG 1046, ABV 4.7%) ♠ A refreshing, red/brown beer with a hoppy aroma. The flavour is a pleasant balance of roast malt and sweetness which predominates over the hops. The malty, bitter finish develops slowly.

**Dizzy Dick** (OG 1080, ABV 7%) ♠ A smooth, strong, dark, aromatic ale with an obvious bite, although too sweet for some. The very full, roast malt and caramel flavour has hints of fruit and toffee. The malty sweetness persists in the aftertaste. A winter brew.

**OAK** See Phoenix.

## OAKHAM

**Oakham Ales, 12–14
Midland Court, Station
Approach, Oakham,
Rutland LE15 6QW.
☎ (01572) 755333**

Established in 1993 in industrial units on a trading estate, with a custom-built, ten-barrel plant, Oakham found a new owner in 1995. It now has a single associated house (Charters Café Bar in Peterborough) and free trade outlets have increased to 60, all within a 50-mile radius of the brewery. Future plans include seasonal special brews and to continue to build up trade via wholesalers. Tours by arrangement.

**Jeffrey Hudson Bitter or JHB** (OG 1038, ABV 3.8%) 🏠 🍺 ♠ A golden bitter with a slightly fruity hop nose. The taste is mainly hoppy, with some malt and a little fruit that fades into a hoppy, bitter finish.

**Hunky Dory** (OG 1045, ABV 4.5%) ♠ A robust, well-balanced beer. The blend of malt and hops on a bitter fruit base is preceded by a subtle aroma of hops, fruit and malt. Dry finish with hops and fruit.

**Bishops Farewell** (OG 1046, ABV 4.6%) A golden, refreshing, fruity beer, with wheat and malt in the taste and a bitter, citrus finish.

**Old Tosspot** (OG 1052, ABV 5.2%) ♠ A tawny, semi-sweet beer with a fruity edge throughout. Malt and hops dominate the taste, with hops remaining in the finish.

## OAKHILL

**Oakhill Brewery, High
Street, Oakhill, Bath,
Somerset BA3 5AS.
☎ (01749) 840134
FAX (01749) 840531**

Situated high in the Mendip Hills in Somerset, this brewery was set up by a farmer in 1984 in an old fermentation room of the original Oakhill Brewery (established in 1767 and burnt down in 1924). To cope with demand from its three tied houses and 100 free trade outlets, Oakhill needs to move to larger premises, and renovation of the old Maltings building in Oakhill, is expected to be complete by summer 1996. Bottle-conditioned beers: Best Bitter (OG 1039, ABV 4%), Yeoman 1767 Strong Ale (OG 1050, ABV 5%).

**Somer Ale** (OG 1035, ABV 3.5%) ♠ An amber, light and refreshing, fruity pale ale, with a pleasant, dry, bitter finish. A spring/summer brew.

**Best Bitter** (OG 1039, ABV 4%) ♠ A clean-tasting, tangy bitter, with a good hop content and citrus fruit and malt balance. Dry finish; light hop aroma. Very quenching.

**Black Magic** (OG 1044, ABV 4.5%) 🏠 ♠ A black/brown bitter stout with roast malt and a touch of fruit in the nose. Smooth roast malt and bitterness in the taste, with mellow coffee and chocolate.

**Mendip Gold** (OG 1045, ABV 4.5%)

**Yeoman 1767** (OG 1050, ABV 5%) ♠ A strong, pale brown, full-bodied bitter, with a floral hop palate and notable fruitiness. Dry, bitter, lasting finish.

**Mendip Tickler** (ABV 6.3%) Brewed for autumn/winter.

**OFFILER'S** See Nationals, Bass.

## O'HANLON'S

**O'Hanlon's Brewing Company Ltd., 8 Tysoe Street, Clerkenwell, London EC1R 4RQ.**
☎ (0171) 278 7238

John O'Hanlon bought the former Three Crowns pub in 1991, changed the name in 1993 and started brewing on the site in March 1996. More brews are planned. Beer: Dry Stout (ABV 4.2%).

## OKELLS

**Okell & Son Ltd., Falcon Brewery, Kewaigue, Douglas, Isle of Man IM2 1QG.** ☎ (01624) 661120
FAX (01624) 625234

Formerly trading as Isle of Man Breweries, this is the main brewery on the island, having taken over and closed the rival Castletown brewery in 1986. Production of Castletown beers ceased completely in 1992 after a period at the old Victorian Falcon Brewery, which itself was closed in 1994, when production moved to a new, purpose-built brewery at Kewaigue. All beers are produced under the unique Manx Brewers' Act 1874 (permitted ingredients: water, malt, sugar and hops only). All but one of the 53 tied houses sell real ale and over 50 free trade outlets are also supplied directly. Tours by arrangement. Occasional/seasonal beers: Doolish Stout (OG 1045, ABV 4.1%), Olde Skipper (OG 1045, ABV 4.5%, May), St Nick (OG 1050, ABV 5%, Christmas).

**Mild** (OG 1034, ABV 3.4%) ◈ A genuine, well-brewed mild ale, with a fine aroma of hops and crystal malt. Reddish-brown in colour, this beer has a full malt flavour with surprising bitter hop notes and a hint of blackcurrants and oranges. Full, malty finish.

**Bitter** (OG 1035, ABV 3.7%) ◈ Golden, malty and superbly hoppy in aroma, with a hint of honey. Rich and malty on the tongue, with a wonderful, dry malt and hop finish. A complex but rewarding beer.

## OLD BEAR

**Old Bear Brewery, 6 Keighley Road, Cross Hills, Keighley, N. Yorkshire BD20 7RN.**
☎ (01535) 632115

Brewery founded in 1993 by former Goose Eye Brewery owner Bryan Eastell, next to his Whitbread tied house, producing beers brewed with local spring water. Four free trade outlets are also supplied and some occasional beers are produced. Tours by arrangement.

**Bitter** (OG 1038, ABV 3.9%) ◈ A clean-tasting and refreshing amber session beer. Malt and sweetness in the taste decline in the finish as a hoppy bitterness takes over.

**Ursa Minor** (ABV 4.6%) A copper-coloured, fruity beer, with a hoppy aroma and dry finish.

**Ursa Major** (ABV 5.8%) A darker, stronger version of Minor, also with a dry finish and a deceptively smooth taste.

## OLD CHIMNEYS

**Old Chimneys Brewery, The Street, Market Weston, Diss, Norfolk IP22 2NZ.**
☎ (01359) 221411

Tiny craft brewery opened in 1995 by former Greene King/Broughton brewer Alan Thomson. The beers are brewed with wild hops gathered from local hedgerows and are mostly named after local endangered species. Despite the postal address, the brewery is in Suffolk. It currently supplies 30 outlets directly and, in addition to the beers listed, a winter warmer is produced to individual customers' requirements. Tours by arrangement. Occasional/seasonal beers: Bittern Bitter (OG 1038, ABV 4.1%, summer), Black Rat Stout (OG 1046, ABV 4.4%, winter).

**Military Mild** (OG 1035, ABV 3.4%) ◈ A moreish dark mild, with good body for its gravity. Light roast bitterness features, with a crisp, dry, malt and hop aftertaste.

**Swallowtail IPA** (OG 1036, ABV 3.6%) ◈ An interesting session bitter, with hop dominating over a toffee, nutty flavour.

**Great Raft Bitter** (OG 1042, ABV 4.2%) ◈ A malty best bitter with a distinctive, spicy fruit and hop character.

**Natterjack Premium Ale** (OG 1050, ABV 5%) ◈ A rich, full-bodied, fruity ale, with roast malt and some hop.

## OLD COTTAGE

**Old Cottage Beer Co., Unit 3, Hall House Industrial Estate, New Hutton, Kendal, Cumbria LA8 0AN.** ☎ (01539) 724444

New brewery in the southern Lake District, producing three real ales, using local spring water.

**Red Pyke** (ABV 3.6%) A gold/amber-coloured session beer.

**Barleycorn** (ABV 4%) A dark brew with hops and malt in the taste.

**Old Hutton** (ABV 4.5%) A dark, malty brew with a hop aroma.

## OLD COURT

**The Old Court Brewhouse, Queen Street, Huddersfield, W. Yorkshire HD1 2SL.**
☎ (01484) 454035

Brew pub opened in 1994 in Huddersfield's former County Court. The building's character has been retained and the brewing copper, protruding from the lower ground floor into the ground floor

481

public bar, provides an unusual talking point. Beers: Coppers' Ale (ABV 3.4%, a mild), M'Lud (OG 1035, ABV 3.5%), 1825 (OG 1045, ABV 4.5%), Maximum Sentence (OG 1055, ABV 5.5%).

## OLDHAM

See Burtonwood and Nationals, Whitbread.

## OLD FORGE

**Pett Brewing Company, The Old Forge Brewery, c/o The Two Sawyers, Pett, Hastings, E. Sussex TN35 4HB. ☎ (01424) 813030**

Brewery established in 1995 in a restored old village forge. Around 50 local outlets now take the beer and the brewery is currently approaching its newly extended capacity. Occasional beers: Hastings Rouser (ABV 4%, November), 101 (ABV 4.7%), White Christmas (ABV 6%, Christmas).

**Brothers Best** (OG 1037, ABV 3.9%) 🍺 A hoppy, amber-coloured, session beer.

**Pett Progress** (OG 1043, ABV 4.6%) 🍺 A mid-brown beer marked by its maltiness which dominates the aroma and taste. Caramel comes through in the aftertaste.

**Summer Eclipse** (ABV 5%) Available in summer only.

**Old Farnes** (OG 1052, ABV 5.3%) A winter brew.

## OLD LUXTERS

**Old Luxters Farm Brewery, Hambleden, Henley-on-Thames, Oxfordshire RG9 6JW. ☎ (01491) 638330 FAX (01491) 638645**

Buckinghamshire brewery (despite the postal address) set up in 1990 in a 17th-century barn by David Ealand, owner of Chiltern Valley Wines. Apart from the brewery and vineyard, the site also houses a fine art gallery and a cellar shop. The brewery supplies 12 local free trade outlets and pubs further afield via wholesalers. Occasional brews are produced to order for other independent breweries, and these are often also supplied bottle-conditioned. Shop open daily 9–5 Mon–Fri, 10–5 Sat–Sun. Tours by arrangement. Bottle-conditioned beer: Barn Ale (OG 1052, ABV 5.4%).

**Barn Ale** (OG 1043, ABV 4.5%) 🍺 Predominantly malty, fruity and hoppy in taste and nose, and tawny/amber in colour. Fairly strong in flavour: the initial, sharp, malty and fruity taste leaves a dry, bittersweet, fruity aftertaste, with hints of black cherry. It can be slightly sulphurous.

---

🍺The full tankard indicates the beer is one of this year's *Good Beer Guide Beers of the Year*.

---

## OLD MILL

**Old Mill Brewery Ltd., Mill Street, Snaith, Goole, E. Yorkshire DN14 9HS. ☎ (01405) 861813 FAX (01405) 862789**

Small brewery opened in 1983 in a 200-year-old former malt kiln and corn mill. A new brewhouse was installed in 1991 to increase the brew length to 60 barrels and the brewery is slowly building up the tied estate (currently 12 houses). Around 150 free trade outlets are also supplied. The beer range has been expanded and other brews are produced for special occasions. Tours by arrangement.

**Traditional Mild** (OG 1035, ABV 3.5%) 🍺 A thin, but easy drinking, dark brown/red brew. The malty aroma has hints of burnt chocolate and the same elements are found on the palate. The dry and nutty finish fades away.

**Nellie Dene** (OG 1035, ABV 3.5%) Available April–October.

**Traditional Bitter** (OG 1038, ABV 3.9%) 🍺 The Old Mill character has returned to this beer, though bitterness remains at a premium. It has a malty nose and initial flavour, with hops hiding until the lingering finish.

**Old Curiosity** (OG 1043, ABV 4.5%)

**Bullion** (OG 1045, ABV 4.7%) 🍺 The malty and hoppy aroma is followed by a neat mix of hop and fruit tastes within an enveloping maltiness. Dark brown/amber in colour.

**Blackjack** (OG 1050, ABV 5%) A winter brew.

## ORANGE

See Nationals, Scottish Courage.

## ORIGINAL

**Original Brewing Company, Hollywood Bowl, Meridian Leisure Park, Braunstone, Leicester LE3 2WX. ☎ (0116) 263 1234 FAX (0116) 263 1102; Hollywood Bowl, Woodside Leisure Park, Kingsway, Garston, Watford, Hertfordshire WD2 6NB. ☎ (01923) 682929 FAX (01923) 682442; Hollywood Bowl, Finchley Leisure Park, Finchley High Road, North Finchley, London N12. ☎ (0181) 446 1958 FAX (0181) 446 0292.**

A new chain of micro-breweries housed in ten-pin bowling alleys. The first opened in Leicester in June 1995, with a brewery visible to the public on the first floor. The company has since opened two further breweries at bowling centres in Garston, near Watford, and North Finchley. Tours by arrangement. The beers are kept under $CO_2$ in cellar tanks. Two lagers are also produced. Beers: VSP (OG 1043, ABV 4.4%), Disciples Brew (OG 1049, ABV 5%).

## ORKNEY

**The Orkney Brewery,
Quoyloo, Orkney
KW16 3LT.**
☎ (01856) 841802
FAX (01856) 841754

The island's first brewery in living memory, set up in 1988 by former licensee Roger White. Initially only brewing keg beer for local outlets, Roger's personal commitment to real ale has resulted in cask ales now representing 90 per cent of sales. The beers are available nationwide via wholesalers. Tours by arrangement.

**Raven Ale** (OG 1038, ABV 3.8%) ❧ A pale brown beer in which malt and fruit are dominant. Roast is evident in the aroma and taste, and hop in the taste and aftertaste. Initially sweet, but with a satisfying dry, bitter aftertaste.

**Dragonhead Stout** (OG 1040, ABV 4%) ❧ A strong, dark malt aroma flows into a complex, dry roast and caramel flavour. The roast malt continues to dominate the aftertaste and blends with chocolate and fruit to develop a strong, dry finish.

**The Red MacGregor** (OG 1042, ABV 4.1%)

**Dark Island** (OG 1046, ABV 4.6%) ⬧ ❧ Dark, beautifully balanced and full of roast malt and fruit. A bittersweet taste leads to a long-lasting, roasted, slightly bitter finish. Full-bodied and deceptively drinkable.

**Skull Splitter** (OG 1080, ABV 8.5%)

## OTTER

**Otter Brewery, Mathayes
Farm, Luppitt, Honiton,
Devon EX14 0SA.**
☎ (01404) 891285

Otter began brewing in 1990 and grew steadily for almost a year, then disaster struck in the shape of yeast problems. Persistence in finding the right strain has since paid off, leading to a major expansion of the brewery in 1994 and improved sales. Now some 75 pubs take the beers, which are produced using local malt and the brewery's own spring water. The business is very much a family affair. Tours by arrangement.

**Bitter** (OG 1036, ABV 3.6%) ⬧ ◼ ❧ A pale brown, pleasant session bitter with a hoppy, fruity aroma and taste and a bitter finish.

**Bright** (OG 1039, ABV 4.3%) A summer beer.

**Ale** (OG 1043, ABV 4.5%) ⬧ ◼ ❧ A pale brown, well-balanced beer with a predominant hop and bitter taste and aftertaste.

**Dark** (OG 1046, ABV 4.8%) ❧ A dark brew with a strong roast malt and fruit taste and finish.

**Head** (OG 1054, ABV 5.8%) ❧ A sweet-tasting, mid-brown beer with a strong malty nose. Plenty of fruit and bitterness in the finish.

## OUTLAW See Rooster's.

## PALMERS

**JC & RH Palmer Ltd., The
Old Brewery, West Bay
Road, Bridport, Dorset
DT6 4JA.** ☎ (01308) 422396
FAX (01308) 421149

Thatched brewery, founded in 1794, situated by the sea in former mill buildings. The company is managed by the great-grandsons of brothers John Cleeves and Robert Henry Palmer, who acquired the brewery in the late 19th century. All its 62 pubs serve real ale, although top pressure and cask breathers are widely in use. A further 35 free trade outlets are serviced directly, but Palmers' beers are reaching a wider audience throughout the South via wholesalers. Shop open 9.30–6 Mon–Thu, 9.30–8 Fri and Sat. Tours by arrangement.

**Bridport Bitter** or **BB** (OG 1030, ABV 3.2%) ❧ A light beer with a hoppy aroma, a bitter, hoppy taste with some malt, and a bitter aftertaste.

**Best Bitter** or **IPA** (OG 1040, ABV 4.2%) ❧ A beer that is hoppy and bitter throughout. Fruit and malt undertones give some balance to the aroma and taste, and there is a lingering bitter aftertaste.

**Tally Ho!** (OG 1046, ABV 4.7%) ❧ A dark and complex brew with a mainly malty aroma. The nutty taste is dominated by roast malt and the aftertaste is malty and bitter. Limited availability, especially in winter.

**200** (OG 1052, ABV 5%) A complex anniversary ale, now a permanent feature.

## PARADISE See Bird in Hand.

## PARISH

**Parish Brewery, The Old
Brewery Inn Courtyard,
High Street, Somerby,
Leicestershire LE14 2PJ.**
☎ (01664) 454781

The first brewery to be established in Somerby since the 16th century, Parish started life at the Stag & Hounds, Burrough on the Hill, in 1983. It moved in 1991, acquiring a new 20-barrel plant to keep up with demand for the beers, which are now supplied to around 20 free trade outlets, as well as the Old Brewery Inn (which is a free house). Parish is listed in the *Guinness Book of Records* as brewer of the strongest beer in the world – Baz's Super Brew (ABV 23%), brewed as a one-off in 1995. A slightly weaker bottled version (not bottle-conditioned) of Baz's Bonce Blower is now brewed by Bateman for London-based beer agency Jacktar Ltd., which has licensed the name from Parish. Tours by arrangement.

**Mild** (OG 1035, ABV 3.6%) 🍶 A thin, smooth, reddish-black brew with caramel dominant throughout. The palate and aftertaste feature a dry maltiness that may be too lactic for some.

**Special Bitter** or **PSB** (OG 1038, ABV 3.8%) 🍶 A thin-bodied beer in which a hoppy bitterness predominates. A refreshing bitter finish follows a pear drop fruitiness. Plenty of yeast.

**Farm Gold** (OG 1040, ABV 4%) 🍶 Brewed principally for the Cow & Plough at Stoughton Farm Park, this is a medium-bodied, refreshing bitter with a good balance of malt and hops.

**Somerby Premium** (OG 1040, ABV 4%) 🍶 A medium-bodied, mid-brown beer with a striking perfumed hop fragrance. The hoppy/malty taste is overtaken by an orange fruitiness and a late, sweet ending.

**Wild John Bitter** (OG 1041, ABV 4%) A summer/autumn brew using only fresh, wild hops.

**Porter** (OG 1048, ABV 4.7%) 🍶 Not bitter enough in the finish to be considered a true porter – more a pleasant, strong mild. This rather sweet, yeasty brew has something of a roast caramel aftertaste that can be astringent.

**Poachers Ale** (OG 1060, ABV 6%) 🍶 This creamy, smooth, full-bodied ale is ruby red in colour, with a pronounced elderberry and liquorice flavour. A bitter, astringent finish is preceded by a complex, malty caramel taste.

**Baz's Bonce Blower** or **BBB** (OG 1100, ABV 10%) 🍶 Almost black, this complex, heavy beer does not taste as strong as its OG. A caramel fruitiness dominates, but it may be spoilt by astringency in the aftertaste.

## PARKER See Cannon.

## PASSAGEWAY
**Passageway Brewing Company, Unit G8, Mariners House, Norfolk Street, Liverpool, Merseyside L1 0BG.**
☎ (0151) 708 0730 [FAX] (0151) 709 0925

THE PASSAGEWAY BREWING Cº

Brewery established in 1994. Its two founders, Steve Dugmore and Phil Burke, who brew on a part-time basis, painstakingly researched the history of St Arnold, the Belgian patron saint of brewing, before beginning production. They use yeast from a Belgian monastic brewery, and a quarter-pint of water from St Arnold's well in Belgium is added to the copper during each brew. Occasional/seasonal beer: Advent (OG 1065, ABV 7%, Christmas).

**Docker's Hook** (1036, ABV 3.6%) 🍶 A mid-brown, full-bodied ale. Banana fruitiness dominates the palate and aftertaste.

**Redemption** (OG 1040, ABV 4%) 🍶 A dry, tart and clean beer brewed with rye, which gives a natural haze.

**Trinity** (OG 1040, ABV 4.2%) A hoppy aroma and a very hoppy, bitter aftertaste are key features of this very pale beer.

**St Arnold** (OG 1048, ABV 5%) 🍶 Deep ruby in colour, this is a very bitter and fruity beer, yet not sweet. Hop, roast malt, chocolate and liquorice flavours also fight for attention in the taste and dry aftertaste. A complex, heavy beer, reminiscent of a Belgian brown ale. Highly drinkable.

## PEMBROKE
**Pembroke Brewery Co., Eaton House, 108 Main Street, Pembroke SA71 4HN.**
☎ (01646) 682517
[FAX] (01646) 682008

Brewery founded in 1994 in former stables behind the proprietors' house. The plant has recently been redesigned to allow for smaller runs and greater flexibility. Pembroke also produces a cask-conditioned lager and other beers are planned. It supplies a single tied house (a converted railway building at Pembroke Dock) and 15 other free trade outlets. Tours by arrangement. Bottle-conditioned beer: Off the Rails (OG 1048, ABV 5.1%)

**Darklin** (OG 1035, ABV 3.5%)

**Dimond Lager** (OG 1040, ABV 4.1%)

**Main Street Bitter** (OG 1040, ABV 4.1%)

**Golden Hill Ale** (OG 1043, ABV 4.5%)

**Off the Rails** (OG 1048, ABV 5.1%) A new winter beer.

## PETT See Old Forge.

## PHOENIX
**Phoenix Brewery Ltd., Phoenix Brewery, Green Lane, Heywood, Gtr Manchester OL10 2EP.** ☎ (01706) 627009

Company established as Oak Brewery in 1982 in Ellesmere Port which moved in 1991 to Heywood and changed its name in 1996. It now supplies over 100 free trade outlets in the North-West and West Yorkshire. Occasional/seasonal beers: Mild (ABV 4%), Shamrock (ABV 4.2%), March Hare (ABV 4.4%), Mayfly (ABV 4.5%), Massacre (ABV 4.7%), Resurrection (ABV 4.7%), Firecracker (ABV 5%), Spooky Brew (ABV 5%), Sticky Wicket (ABV 5.4%).

**Hopwood Bitter** (OG 1035, ABV 3.5%) A pale, easy drinking session beer.

**Bantam Bitter** (ABV 3.5%) Darker and drier than Hopwood, with a slight nutty finish.

**Best Bitter** (OG 1038, ABV 3.9%) ◈ A tawny, hoppy session beer with some balancing malt in the aroma and taste. Strong, dry and hoppy finish.

**Tyke Bitter** (OG 1042, ABV 4.3%) A best bitter, originally for the Yorkshire trade.

**Midsummer Madness** (OG 1044, ABV 4.4%) A pale, hoppy and refreshing, very drinkable beer, available June–August.

**Old Oak Ale** (OG 1044, ABV 4.5%) ◈ A well-balanced, brown beer with a multitude of mellow fruit flavours. Malt and hops balance the strong fruitiness in the aroma and taste, and the finish is malty, fruity and dry.

**Thirsty Moon** (ABV 4.6%) A beer with a slight malty character and a full and crisp hop finish.

**Bonneville** (ABV 4.8%) A very malty beer with a short hop finish.

**Double Dagger** (OG 1050, ABV 5%) ◈ A pale brown, malty brew, more pleasantly dry and light than its gravity would suggest. Moderately fruity throughout; a hoppy bitterness in the mouth balances the strong graininess.

**Porter** (OG 1050, ABV 5%) ◈ The roast malt promised by the aroma is joined in the taste by malt, caramel and hops. Long and pleasant aftertaste. Brewed October–January.

**Wobbly Bob** (OG 1060, ABV 6%) ◈ A red/brown beer with a malty, fruity aroma. Strongly malty and fruity in flavour and quite hoppy, with the sweetness yielding to a dryness in the aftertaste.

**Humbug** (ABV 7%) A rich, dark brown, hoppy beer, available November–January.

## PILGRIM

**Pilgrim Ales, The Old Brewery, West Street, Reigate, Surrey RH2 9BL.**
☎ **(01737) 222651**
[FAX] **(01737) 225785**

Set up in 1982, and moved to Reigate in 1985, Pilgrim has gradually increased its capacity and its beers have won both local and national awards, although sales are mostly concentrated in the Surrey area (around 60 outlets). Tours are available by arrangement on the last Friday of the month in summer. A shop is planned. Occasional/seasonal beers: Autumnal (OG 1045, ABV 4.5%, September–October), Excalibur (OG 1045, ABV 4.5%, Easter), Springbock (OG 1050, ABV 5.2%), The Great Crusader (OG 1063, ABV 6.5%, June–July), Conqueror (OG 1065, ABV 6.5%) ⬚, Pudding (OG 1075, ABV 7.3%, November–December). Bottle-conditioned beers: Springbock (OG 1050, ABV 5.2%), Pudding (OG 1075, ABV 7.3%).

**Surrey Bitter** (OG 1037, ABV 3.7%) ▧ ◈ A clean, well-balanced session bitter. Hop flavour comes through in the finish.

**Porter** (OG 1040, ABV 4%) ◈ A dark beer with a pleasant roast malt flavour, balanced by a faint hoppiness which is also there at the finish. Noticeable roast malt aroma.

**Progress** (OG 1040, ABV 4%) ◈ Reddish-brown in colour, with a predominantly malty flavour and aroma, although hops are also evident in the taste.

**Saracen** (OG 1047, ABV 4.5%) ◈ Roast malt dominates the aroma of this black stout, but hops balance the roast malt flavour, leading to a bitter finish.

**Crusader** (OG 1047, ABV 4.9%) ⬚ ◈ A summer brew; a light, golden beer with a good marriage of malt and hops from aroma through to finish. Very drinkable.

**Talisman** (OG 1050, ABV 5%) ◈ A strong ale with a mid-brown colour, a fruity, malt flavour and a faint hoppiness.

**Springbock** (ABV 5%) ◈ A Bavarian-style wheat beer for spring.

## PIONEER See Rooster's.

## PITFIELD

**Pitfield Brewery, The London Beer Company Ltd., 14 Pitfield Street, Hoxton, London N1 6EY.**
☎ **(0171) 739 3701**

▢ Revived brewery next to The Beer Shop off-licence. Pitfield brands were contract-brewed at Brewery on Sea until Pitfield re-opened with new equipment in new premises in July 1996.

**Bitter** (OG 1036, ABV 3.5%)

**Hoxton Heavy** (OG 1048, ABV 5.5%)

## PLANETS

**HG Wells Planets, Crown Square, Woking, Surrey GU21 1HR.**
☎ **(01483) 727100 ext. 317**
[FAX] **(01483) 723409**

▢ Brewery opened in April 1996 in a leisure complex, supplying its full mash beers only to the house bars. The beers are kept under a blanket of gas in cellar tanks. A lager is also produced. Beers: Newark Abbey Ale (OG 1038, ABV 3.8%), Bobby's Bitter (OG 1042, ABV 4.2%), HG's (OG 1052, ABV 5%).

## PLASSEY

**Plassey Brewery, The Plassey, Eyton, Wrexham LL13 0SP.** ☎ **(01978) 780922**
[FAX] **(01978) 780019**

Brewery founded in 1985 on the 250-acre Plassey Estate, which also incorporates a touring caravan park, craft centres, a golf course and three licensed outlets for Plassey's ales. Twenty free trade outlets also take the beers. Work has now been completed on a new brewery, incorporating a brewery shop (open 11–5 daily), and plans are in hand for a new bottling plant. Tours by arrangement.

**Bitter** (OG 1040, ABV 4%)  A well-hopped, straw-coloured beer, with blackcurrant fruitiness.

**Stout** (OG 1046, ABV 4.6%) A dry, roasty stout, with a long, dry finish and good hop character.

**Cwrw Tudno** (OG 1048, ABV 5%) More malty and sweet and less bitter than the bitter, but with a fairly dry aftertaste.

**Dragon's Breath** (OG 1060, ABV 6%) A fruity, strong bitter, smooth and quite sweet, though not cloying, with an intense, fruity aroma. A dangerously drinkable winter warmer.

## PLOUGH INN
**Bodicote Brewery, Plough Inn, Bodicote, Banbury, Oxfordshire OX15 4BZ.**
☎ (01295) 262327

Brewery founded in 1982 at the Plough, No. 9 High Street (hence the beer name), which has been in the same hands since 1957. Three other outlets are also supplied with its full mash beers. Tours by arrangement. Beers: Bodicote Bitter (OG 1035, ABV 3.3%), Three Goslings (OG 1044, No. 9 (OG 1045, ABV 4.4%), Old English Porter (OG 1046, ABV 4.5%, winter), Triple X (OG 1052, ABV 5.4%, Christmas).

## POOLE
**The Brewhouse Brewery,
68 High Street, Poole,
Dorset BH15 1DA.**
☎ (01202) 682345

Brewery established in 1981, which transferred to the Brewhouse pub in 1987. Extensive alterations took place at the brewery in 1990 and additional fermenting vessels were installed in 1995 and 1996. The brewery now has a capacity of 75 barrels a week and serves a growing free trade through wholesalers. Occasional tours by arrangement.

**Best Bitter** or **Dolphin** (OG 1038, ABV 3.8%) The brewery's original session bitter – amber coloured, and well-balanced.

**Holes Bay Hog** (OG 1044, ABV 4.5%) The latest addition to the range, light amber in colour. It is brewed from pale malt and malted wheat, and has a distinctive, dry hopped character and a refreshing aftertaste.

**Bosun Bitter** (OG 1045, ABV 4.6%) The brewery's top selling beer. A rich amber-coloured beer with a smooth, crisp, powerful malty flavour and a pronounced hoppy aftertaste.

**Double Barrel** (OG 1055, ABV 5.5%) A very pale straw-coloured IPA, smooth, mellow

and deceptively strong. It looks like a Pilsener, but tastes like a traditional bitter.

**Ansty Ale** (OG 1080, ABV 7.6%) Mostly brewed for the Fox at Ansty in Dorset. Packed with flavours, it is a classic strong ale.

## PORTER
**Porter Brewing Co. Ltd.,
Rossendale Brewery, The
Griffin Inn, Hud Rake,
Haslingden, Lancashire
BB4 5AF.**
☎/FAX (01706) 214021

The Griffin Inn was refurbished and re-opened, complete with micro-brewery, by new owner David Porter in 1994. A second tied house was acquired in 1995 and a third is planned. Several other local outlets also take the beer. Tours by arrangement. Occasional/seasonal beers: Sleighed (OG 1064, ABV 6.5%, December–January), Celebration Ale (OG 1068, ABV 7.1%, July–August).

**Dark Mild** (OG 1033, ABV 3.3%) A true dark mild, with a slight maltiness and a good hint of roast in the finish.

**Bitter** (OG 1037, ABV 3.8%) A dark beer for a standard bitter, with a good, sharp, northern bitterness that lingers through to the back of the throat, and a dry finish.

**Rossendale Ale** (OG 1041, ABV 4.2%) An initial slight malty sweetness leads through to a deep, fruity mouthfeel and a lingering fruity finish.

**Porter** (OG 1050, ABV 5%) A rich beer with a slightly sweet, malty start, counterbalanced with sharp bitterness and a very noticeable roast barley dominance.

**Sunshine** (OG 1050, ABV 5.3%) A dangerously drinkable, very pale premium bitter with a light citrus nose and powerful lemon fruit in the taste. Noticeably bitter, lingering finish.

## PORTERS See Nethergate.

## POWELL See Wood.

## PRINCETOWN
**Princetown Breweries Ltd., The Prince of Wales, The Brewery, Tavistock Road, Princetown, Devon PL20 6QF.**
☎ (01822) 890789  FAX (01822) 890719

Brewery established in 1994 by a former Gibbs Mew and Hop Back brewer. It now serves four tied pubs with any surplus beer sold to five local free trade outlets. Princetown also brews under contract for the Westbury Ales wholesaling company ☎ (01458) 850845. Tours by arrangement. Bottle-conditioned beers: Jail Ale (OG 1049, ABV 4.8%), Dartmoor Gold (OG 1051, ABV 5%).

**Dartmoor IPA** or **Best Bitter** (OG 1041, ABV 4%) This beer is sold under both names.

**Jail Ale** (OG 1049, ABV 4.8%) ◆ Hops and fruit predominate in the flavour of this mid-brown beer which has a slightly sweet aftertaste.

**Dartmoor Gold** (OG 1051, ABV 5%)

## For Westbury Ales:

**Jordy** (OG 1043, ABV 4.3%)

## QUAY
**The Quay Brewery, Lapin Noir Ltd., Brewer's Quay, Hope Square, Weymouth, Dorset DT4 8TU. ☎ (01305) 777622 FAX (01305) 761680**

Brewery set up in summer 1996 in the old Devenish and Groves brewery buildings, bringing brewing back to Weymouth after a ten-year absence which followed the closure of Devenish. Although Greenalls owns the complex, the brewery is totally independent and is open to visitors as part of the Timewalk attraction. Bottle-conditioned beers, for sale at the complex, are planned.

**Weymouth Special Pale Ale (SPA)** (OG 1039, ABV 4%)

**Bombshell Bitter** (OG 1044, ABV 4.5%)

**Old Rott** (OG 1049, ABV 5%)

## RCH
**RCH Brewery, West Hewish, Weston-super-Mare, Somerset BS24 6RR. ☎ (01934) 834447 FAX (01934) 834167**

Brewery originally installed in the early 1980s behind the Royal Clarence Hotel at Burnham-on-Sea, but since 1993 brewing has taken place on a commercial basis on a new site. RCH now supplies over 100 outlets through its own wholesaling company and new beers have been added to the range over the last 12 months. Some RCH beers are rebadged for sale by Green Cucumber Wholesale ☎ (01584) 872908. Tours by arrangement. Occasional/seasonal beers: Wheat Beer (OG 1044, ABV 4.4%), Santa Fé (OG 1074, ABV 7.3%, Christmas). Bottle-conditioned beers: Old Slug Porter (OG 1046, ABV 4.5%), Firebox (OG 1060, ABV 6%).

**PG Steam** (OG 1039, ABV 3.9%)

**CH40** (OG 1040, ABV 4%) Known as Bilbo's when sold by Green Cucumber.

**Pitchfork** (OG 1043, ABV 4.3%)

**Old Slug Porter** (OG 1046, ABV 4.5%) ☐ ◆ A traditional-style porter with a nutty, woody flavour and a toffee and honey aroma.

**Fiery Liz** (OG 1049, ABV 5%) Known as Gandalf when sold by Green Cucumber.

**East Street Cream** (OG 1050, ABV 5%)

**Firebox** (OG 1060, ABV 6%)

## For Green Cucumber:
**Thorin** (ABV 4.5%) A blend of CH40 and Fiery Liz.

## RAINBOW
**Rainbow Inn & Brewery, 73 Birmingham Road, Allesley Village, Coventry, W. Midlands CV9 5GT. ☎ (01203) 402888**

Pub brewery, housed in former stables, which opened in 1995 just to serve its own customers. Occasional special beers are brewed. Tours by arrangement. Beers: Piddlebrook (OG 1040, ABV 3.8%), Belcher's Wood (OG 1042, ABV 4.2%), Firecracker (OG 1050, ABV 4.8%).

## RANDALLS
**RW Randall Ltd., Vauxlaurens Brewery, PO Box 154, St Julian's Avenue, St Peter Port, Guernsey GY1 3JG. ☎ (01481) 720134 FAX (01481) 723233**

The smaller of Guernsey's two breweries, purchased by PH Randall from Joseph Gullick in 1868. Successive generations have continued to run the business, except during the period of the German occupation, when it ceased brewing until after the war. Randalls owns 18 pubs, but only three serve real ale. Do not confuse with Randalls Vautier of Jersey, which no longer brews. Shop open 10–5 Mon–Sat. Tours at 2.30 on Thursdays, May–September. Some occasional beers are produced. Bottle-conditioned beers: Bitter (OG 1046, ABV 5%, occasional), Stout (OG 1046, ABV 5.5%, occasional).

**Patois Ale** (OG 1046, ABV 5%) ◆ Formerly Bitter. Amber in colour, with a hoppy aroma. Bitter and hoppy both in the palate and finish.

## RAT & RATCHET
**The Rat & Ratchet Brewery, 40 Chapel Hill, Huddersfield, W. Yorkshire HD1 3EB. ☎ (01484) 516734**

Well-known ale house which began brewing in 1994 to supply just itself and occasional beer festivals. There are no regular beers confirmed to date.

## RAVEN See Wingfields.

## RAYMENTS See Greene King.

## READING LION
**Reading Lion Brewery, The Hop Leaf, 163–165 Southampton Street, Reading, Berkshire RG1 2QZ. ☎ (01734) 314700**

Brewery opened by Hop Back Brewery in 1995 at the Hop Leaf pub, a former

Inntrepreneur house, becoming Reading's first real ale brewery since Courage closed the old Simonds site in the late 1970s. The five-barrel plant came from the Wyndham Arms in Salisbury and beers are stored in both casks and cellar tanks (no blanket pressure). Occasional beers are brewed for other Hop Back pubs and the free trade. Beers: Hop Leaf Bitter (OG 1042, ABV 4%), Entire Stout and Ginger (OG 1042, ABV 4%), Rye & Coriander Beer (OG 1047, ABV 4.5%).

## REBELLION

**Rebellion Beer Company, Unit J, Rose Industrial Estate, Marlow Bottom Road, Marlow, Buckinghamshire SL7 3ND. ☎ / FAX (01628) 476594**

Opened in 1993, Rebellion helps to fill the gap left in Marlow by Whitbread's closure of the Wethered brewery in 1988. Plans are in hand to move to a larger site locally, increasing the brewing capacity from 50 to 100 barrels a week, and to brew further beers. Around 80 local pubs are supplied directly, with others served via wholesalers. Shop open 8–6 Mon–Fri, 9–4 Sat. Tours by arrangement for CAMRA branches. One beer is brewed for Scanlon's Fine Ales (qv). Occasional/seasonal beers: 24 Carat (OG 1048, ABV 4.8%, a wheat beer), Scrooge (OG 1052, ABV 5%, a Christmas spice beer). Bottle-conditioned beer: Mutiny (OG 1052, ABV 5%).

**IPA** (OG 1039, ABV 3.7%) A very clean, refreshing pale ale. A sweet malt character dominates the palate, before a crisp, dry finish. A good session beer.

**Smuggler** (OG 1041, ABV 4.1%) Different hops are added at four stages during the brewing process, resulting in a bittersweet beer with a fresh, fruity late hop flavour and aroma.

**Mutiny** (OG 1046, ABV 4.5%) A reddish, full-bodied beer, with a well-balanced malt and hop taste. Goldings are added for a late hop charge to give a lasting aftertaste.

**Red Oktober** (OG 1050, ABV 4.8%) A new autumn beer in the style of a German Altbier. Brewed using crystal and rye malts and Continental hops, it has a deep reddish hue.

**Old Codger** (OG 1054, ABV 5%) A heart-warming winter ale with a full, dark-roasted malt character. The hops give contrast, but do not overpower the richness of the malt.

### For Scanlon's:

**Spike** (OG 1046, ABV 4.5%)

## RECKLESS

**Reckless Brewing & Supply Co. Ltd., Cilfynydd, Pontypridd, Glamorgan.**

Brewery closed.

## RECTORY

**Rectory Ales Ltd., White House Farm, Station Road, Plumpton Green, Lewes, E. Sussex BN7 3ST. ☎ (01273) 890570**

Unusual brewery founded in summer 1996 by the Rector of Plumpton, Godfrey Proster, to generate profits for the maintenance of the three churches in his parish. Twenty-six churchgoers are shareholders and their financial input purchased the brewing equipment. Some seasonal beers are also produced. Beers: Parson's Porter (OG 1036, ABV 3.6%), Rector's Pleasure (OG 1034, ABV 3.8%), Rector's Revenge (OG 1047, ABV 5.4%).

## RED CROSS

**Red Cross Brewery, Perryfields Lane, Bromsgrove, Worcestershire B61 8QW. ☎ (01527) 871409**

After the resolution of planning permission problems, Red Cross started brewing in 1993 in the old bull pen of Red Cross Farm, a 17th-century yeoman farmhouse. The beer is available at the Hop Pole Inn in Bromsgrove, an M&B pub which is run by Red Cross. Tours by arrangement. Beer: Nailer's OBJ (OG 1046, ABV 4.6%).

## RED LION

**Red Lion Hotel, Long Bridge Street, Llanidloes, Powys SY18 6EE. ☎ (01686) 412270**

Brewery set up in a garage adjoining the Red Lion in spring 1995, brewing just for the pub itself and beer festivals. Witches' Brew is partially made with malt extract. Beers: Blind Cobbler's Thumb (OG 1042), Witches' Brew (ABV 7.5%), Blind Cobbler's Last (ABV 10.5%, Christmas).

## REDRUTH

**Redruth Brewery (1742) Ltd., The Brewery, Redruth, Cornwall TR15 1RB. ☎ (01209) 212244 FAX (01209) 313793**

Since being taken over by Dransfield Group PLC of Hong Kong in 1995, Redruth has ceased production of cask beer, concentrating instead on contract packaging and brewing.

## REEPHAM

**Reepham Brewery, Unit 1, Collers Way, Reepham, Norwich, Norfolk NR10 4SW. ☎ (01603) 871091**

Family brewery, founded in 1983 by a former Watney's research engineer, with a purpose-built plant in a small industrial unit. Reepham now supplies 20 local outlets directly. The latest addition to the range is a genuine wheat beer. Occasional/seasonal beer: Bittern (OG 1050, ABV 5%, spring).

**Granary Bitter** (OG 1038, ABV 3.8%) ✦ An amber beer which is well-balanced and makes easy drinking. The malt and hops are complemented by a pleasing amount of bitterness and hints of fruit.

**Summer Velvet** (OG 1040, ABV 4%)

**Velvet** (OG 1042, ABV 4.2%) ▢ ✦ The fruity, malt aroma of this darkish brown winter stout gives way to a sweet, mellow taste explosion of malt, roast malt, fruit and hops. This subsides to a pleasant aftertaste with hints of liquorice.

**Rapier Pale Ale** (OG 1043, ABV 4.2%) ▢ ✦ A beer with a flowery hop aroma and maltiness in the taste on a fruit and hop background.

**Smugglers Stout** (OG 1045, ABV 4.5%)

**Old Bircham Ale** (OG 1046, ABV 4.6%) ✦ An amber/tawny beer with good body for its gravity. The fruity aroma precedes a complex, malty, hoppy palate which also has a sweetness that dies away in the malty, dry finish. A winter brew.

**Brewhouse** (OG 1055, ABV 5.2%) A strong winter ale.

## REINDEER
See Nationals, Carlsberg-Tetley.

## RIDLEYS
**TD Ridley & Sons Ltd.,
Hartford End Brewery,
Felsted, Chelmsford, Essex
CM3 1JZ. ☎ (01371) 820316
[FAX] (01371) 821216**

Ridleys was established by a miller, Thomas Dixon Ridley, on the banks of the picturesque River Chelmer in 1842, under the influence of his wife who came from a brewing family in Chelmsford. Run today by Thomas's great-great grandson, Nicholas, the company currently supplies 62 tenanted pubs (all in Essex) and 120 local free trade outlets. Ridleys also brews under contract for Tavern Wholesaling (formerly Liquid Assets) ☎ (0161) 864 5000. Shop open 9–5 Mon–Fri. Tours by arrangement. Occasional/seasonal beer: Winter Ale (OG 1055, ABV 5%, Christmas). Bottle-conditioned beer: Chelmer Gold (OG 1051, ABV 5%).

**Champion Mild** (OG 1034, ABV 3.5%) ▢ ✦ A very dark mild, with a light aroma of roast malt and subdued hop. Quite bitter for a mild, with roast malt and fruit in the taste and a balanced, dry finish with hops and roast malt.

**IPA** (OG 1034, ABV 3.5%) ✦ Refreshing and hoppy throughout, well-balanced by a persistent maltiness and delicate fruit in the flavour, with a lingering bitterness.

**ESX Best** (OG 1043, ABV 4.3%) ✦ Harmonious malt and hops dominate the taste of this best bitter, with a hint of fruit. Hops just gain over malt in the finish.

**Witchfinder Porter** (OG 1045, ABV 4.3%) ✦ A dark ruby, bittersweet winter beer, with strong roast malt and light hoppiness.

**Spectacular** (OG 1048, ABV 4.6%) A pale, straw-coloured beer, with a flowery nose. It has a delicate malty flavour and a rather bitter aftertaste.

**Rumpus** (OG 1049, ABV 4.5%) ✦ A tawny, malty beer with a developing fruitiness and a bittersweet balance, becoming dryer with hops in the finish.

### For Tavern Wholesaling:

**Norman's Conquest** (ABV 4.6%) Not to be confused with the *Champion Beer of Britain 1995* from Cottage Brewery.

## RINGWOOD
**Ringwood Brewery Ltd.,
Christchurch Road,
Ringwood, Hampshire
BH24 3AP.
☎ (01425) 471177
[FAX] (01425) 480273**

Ringwood was set up in 1978 and moved in 1986 to attractive 18th-century buildings, formerly part of the old Tunks brewery. A new brewhouse was commissioned at the end of 1994, and a new fermenting room completed in 1995. Famous for its award-winning Old Thumper, Ringwood has relaunched True Glory, originally brewed as a VE Day commemorative beer, and made it a permanent part of the range. The brewery supplies two tied houses and 350 free trade outlets directly. Shop open 10–5 Mon–Fri, 9.30–12 Sat. Tours by arrangement.

**Best Bitter** (OG 1038, ABV 3.8%) ✦ A golden brown, moreish beer, with flavours for all. The aroma has a hint of hops and leads to a malty sweetness, which becomes dry, with a hint of orange. Malt and bitterness in the finish.

**True Glory** (OG 1043, ABV 4.3%) A copper-coloured premium ale, hopped with just Goldings and Fuggles.

**Fortyniner** (OG 1048, ABV 4.8%) ✦ A good premium beer, with malt and hops in good balance. The flavours slowly increase to a fruity finish.

**XXXX Porter** (OG 1048, ABV 4.7%) ✦ Sadly only available October–March: a rich, dark brew with a strong aroma of roasted malt, hops and fruit. Rich in flavour, with coffee, vanilla, damsons, apples and molasses evident. The overall roast maltiness continues into the drying, hoppy, bitter finish.

**Old Thumper** (OG 1058, ABV 5.8%) ✦ A golden beer with a surprisingly bitter aftertaste, which follows a middle period tasting of various fruits. It may be a little sweet for some.

## RISING SUN

**The Rising Sun Inn, Knowle Bank Road, Shraley Brook, Audley, Stoke-on-Trent, Staffordshire ST7 8DS. ☎ (01782) 720600 [FAX] (01782) 721288**

🍺 The brewery at the Rising Sun opened in 1989 and was enlarged in 1994. It supplies the busy pub and 15 other local outlets. A new porter was launched in 1995. Tours by arrangement. Bottle-conditioned beers: Porter (OG 1048, ABV 4.6%), Solar Flare (OG 1100, ABV 11%).

**Rising** (OG 1038, ABV 3.5%) 🍂 A thin, dry bitter with little flavour.

**Setting** (OG 1047, ABV 4.6%) 🍂 A beer with a new recipe. Good body, but little taste or aroma. Some bitter aftertaste.

**Porter** (OG 1048, ABV 4.6%) 🍂 A black, stout-like beer with a strong roast and bitter flavour and a long, dry aftertaste.

**Sunstroke** (OG 1056, ABV 5.6%) 🍂 A dark, red/brown, medium-bodied ale. The aroma has roast malt and some hops, whilst the taste is bittersweet with a dominating maltiness. The aftertaste sees malt, roast malt and hops coming through.

**Total Eclipse** (OG 1072, ABV 6.8%)

**Solar Flare** (OG 1100, ABV 11%) A winter beer.

## RIVERHEAD

**Riverhead Brewery Ltd., 2 Peel Street, Marsden, Huddersfield, W. Yorkshire HD7 6BR. ☎ (01484) 841270**

🍺 Brew pub which opened in October 1995, after two years' work converting an old corn merchant's/grocery store. The pub is on two floors with a window on to the brewing area. Tours by arrangement. No other pubs take the beer at present. Beers: Sparth Mild (OG 1036), Butterley Bitter (OG 1038), Deer Hill Porter (OG 1040), Black Moss Stout (OG 1043), March Haigh Special Bitter (OG 1046), Redbrook Premium Bitter (OG 1055).

## ROBINSON'S

**Frederic Robinson Ltd., Unicorn Brewery, Lower Hillgate, Stockport, Cheshire SK1 1JJ. ☎ (0161) 480 6571 [FAX] (0161) 476 6011**

Major Greater Manchester family brewery, founded in 1838. Robinson's has grown through various pub and brewery acquisitions over the years, including Hartleys of Ulverston in 1982. The Hartleys brewery was closed in 1991 and only Hartleys XB is still brewed (at Stockport). Robinson's now supplies real ale to all its 400 tied houses (most in southern Manchester and Cheshire), and to free trade outlets. Shop open Mon–Fri 9–5.30, 9–5 Sat. Tours by arrangement.

**Dark Best Mild** (OG 1033, ABV 3.3%) 🍂 Toffee/malt tasting, with a slight bitterness. A very quaffable beer with a fruity malt aroma and a dry finish. A very rare find.

**Hatters Mild** (OG 1034, ABV 3.5%) 🍂 A light mild with an unpronounced malty aroma and a refreshing dry, malty flavour. Short bitter/malty aftertaste.

**Old Stockport Bitter** (OG 1034, ABV 3.5%) 🍂 A beer with a refreshing, malty, fruity taste, a characteristic fruity aroma, with a touch of sulphur, and a short, dry finish.

**Hartleys XB** (OG 1040, ABV 4%) 🍂 Little aroma, but malty with some hop bitterness in the taste; dry finish.

**Best Bitter** (OG 1041, ABV 4.2%) 🍂 A pale brown beer with a malty, hoppy nose. There are malt, hops and bitterness in the flavour and the aftertaste is short and bitter.

**Frederics** (OG 1049, ABV 5%)

**Old Tom** (OG 1080, ABV 8.5%) 🍷 🍂 A full-bodied, dark, fruity beer. The aroma is fruity and mouthwatering; the aftertaste is bittersweet, with an alcoholic kick. A beer to sip respectfully by a winter fire.

## ROOSTER'S

**Rooster's Brewery, Unit 20 Claro Court, Claro Business Centre, Claro Road, Harrogate, N. Yorkshire HG1 4BA. ☎ (01423) 561861 [FAX] (01423) 520994**

Brewery set up in 1993 by Sean Franklin, formerly of Franklin's Brewery. Rooster's is now successfully building up its business and expanded the plant in 1994 to cater for increased demand. A subsidiary label, Outlaw (previously known as Pioneer), produces a different, experimental beer every two months for the guest beer market, and those that prove popular are repeated. Occasional/seasonal beer: Nector (ABV 5.8%, mostly for Christmas).

**Jak's** (OG 1039, ABV 3.9%) A pale copper-coloured beer, similar to Rooster's but with less toffee flavour.

**Special** (OG 1039, ABV 3.9%) A pale yellow beer with a fruity, floral aroma and citrus hop in the taste.

**Yankee** (OG 1043, ABV 4.3%) 🍂 A straw-coloured beer with a delicate aroma. The flavour is an interesting mix of malt and hops, with a gentle sweetness and a bite of orange peel, leading to a short, pleasant finish.

**Rooster's** (OG 1047, ABV 4.7%) 🍷 🍂 A light amber beer with a subtle, sweet, slightly hoppy nose. Intense malt flavours, reminiscent of treacle toffee with chocolate and orange undertones, precede an unexpected hoppy finish.

**Cream** (OG 1047, ABV 4.7%) A pale beer with fruity aromas and a soft bitterness.

## ROSE STREET
See Nationals, Carlsberg-Tetley.

## ROSS
**Ross Brewing Company,
The Bristol Brewhouse,
117–119 Stokes Croft,
Bristol BS1 3RW.
☎ (0117) 942 0306
FAX (0117) 942 8746**

Set up in Hartcliffe in 1989, Ross was the first brewery to brew with organic Soil Association barley, initially producing bottle-conditioned beers only. The brewery later moved to the Bristol Brewhouse pub and the one remaining bottled beer, Saxon Strong Ale, is now brewed under contract by Thomas Hardy (qv). In 1994 Ross set up the Newport Brewhouse in South Wales, although this no longer brews and may see its brewery relocated. Ross brews just for its two tied houses, but its range includes many occasional beers. Tours by arrangement. Brewery shop at Brewers Droop, 36 Gloucester Road, Bishopston, Bristol BS7 8AR, open 9–5.30 Mon–Sat. Beers: Hartcliffe Bitter (OG 1045, ABV 4.5%), SPA (OG 1050, ABV 5%), Uncle Igor (ABV 21%).

## ROSSENDALE See Porter.

## ROTHER VALLEY
**Rother Valley Brewing Company, Gate Court, Northiam, E. Sussex TN31 6QT.
☎ / FAX (01797) 252922**

Brewery founded jointly by a hop farmer and a publican, as a part-time venture in 1993. Now brewing full-time, from yeast, hops and water all sourced on site, the company will be using its own barley by the end of 1997. A bottling line has recently been installed. Thirty free trade outlets take the beer directly.

**Level Best** (OG 1040, ABV 4%) 🍺 Light in aroma, this beer has a good, bitter taste, but lacks fullness of flavour for a beer of this gravity.

## ROYAL CLARENCE See RCH.

## ROYAL INN
**Royal Inn & Horsebridge Brewery, Horsebridge, near Tavistock, Devon PL19 8PJ. ☎ (01822) 870214**

Fifteenth-century pub, once a nunnery, which began brewing in 1981. It recently changed hands, but the new owners are continuing to brew all four beers full time. There are plans to expand the brewery and its range and to supply other outlets. Tours

by arrangement. Beers: Tamar Ale (OG 1039, ABV 3.9%), Horsebridge Best (OG 1045, ABV 4.5%), Right Royal (OG 1050, ABV 5%), Heller (OG 1060, ABV 6%).

## RUDDLES
**Ruddles Brewery Ltd., Langham, Oakham, Rutland LE15 7JD.
☎ (01572) 756911
FAX (01572) 756116**

Famous real ale brewery, founded in 1858, which lost its independence when it was taken over by Grand Metropolitan in 1986. Ruddles beers subsequently became national brands. Ownership passed to Courage in the 'pubs for breweries' swap and the company is now owned by Dutch lager giants Grolsch, who acquired the business in 1992. Tours by arrangement.

**Best Bitter** (OG 1037, ABV 3.7%) 🍺 The malty and occasionally sulphurous nose precedes a complex and well-balanced flavour of malt, fruit and hoppy bitterness in this mid-brown beer. Malt in the finish leads to a late astringent bitterness.

**County** (OG 1050, ABV 4.9%) 🍺 A mid-brown, strong bitter with a good mix of malt, hops and fruit in the nose. All these elements appear in a full-bodied, well-balanced taste that leads to a long hoppy, bitter ending.

### For Scottish Courage:
**Webster's Green Label** (OG 1034, ABV 3.2%)

## RUDGATE
**Rudgate Brewery Ltd, 2 Centre Park, Marston Business Park, Rudgate, Tockwith, York, N. Yorkshire YO5 8QF.
☎ (01423) 358382**

Brewery founded in 1992 and subsequently purchased by two former Bass executives. Operating from an old armoury building on a disused airfield, it supplies 150 outlets from Tyneside to Nottingham. The beers are themed around the York Viking connection and are brewed in open square fermenters. A number of house beers are also produced. Tours by arrangement. Occasional/seasonal beers: Sunbeam (OG 1037, ABV 3.8%), Ruby Mild (OG 1041, ABV 4%), Maypole (OG 1045, ABV 4.5%), Pillage Porter (OG 1045, ABV 4.5%), Rudolf's Ruin (OG 1060, ABV 6%).

**Viking** (OG 1038, ABV 3.8%) 🍺 A well-hopped beer with a malty, full-bodied mouthfeel of hops and fruit which lingers well into the aftertaste.

**Battleaxe** (OG 1043, ABV 4.2%) 🍺 A smooth tasting beer, with malt and bitterness predominant throughout. Slightly sweet.

**Thor's Hammer** (OG 1055, ABV 5.5%)

## RYBURN

**Ryburn Brewery, c/o Ram's Head, Wakefield Road, Sowerby Bridge, Halifax, W. Yorkshire HX6 2AZ.**
☎ (01422) 835413
FAX (01422) 836488

Founded in 1990 in a former dye works, this brewery moved in 1994 to larger premises beside the re-opened Rochdale Canal. The equipment has since moved yet again, this time to temporary accommodation in a former textile mill, and the intention is to move very shortly to a permanent home behind the brewery's one tied house. A Pilsener-style beer may be added to the range. Occasional/seasonal beer: Porter (OG 1044, ABV 4.2%, Christmas).

**Best Mild** (OG 1033, ABV 3.3%) ◈ Stout-like in taste and colour, with a rich, roast malt flavour and balancing bitterness, which is reflected in the finish and aroma.

**Best Bitter** (OG 1038, ABV 3.8%)

**Rydale Bitter** (OG 1044, ABV 4.2%) ◈ Mid-brown in colour with little aroma. A smooth, malty bitter with hop character and bitterness, plus some fruit notes. Long, malty and bitter finish.

**Luddite** (OG 1048, ABV 5%) A dark beer.

**Stabbers Bitter** (OG 1052, ABV 5.2%) ◈ A malty aroma leads to a rich maltiness in the mouth, with bittersweet, fruity elements. Malty and bitter finish. A mid-brown, powerful strong ale.

**Coiners** (OG 1060, ABV 6%)

---

**S&N** See Nationals, Scottish Courage.

---

## ST AUSTELL

**St Austell Brewery Co. Ltd., 63 Trevarthian Road, St Austell, Cornwall PL25 4BY.**
☎ (01726) 74444
FAX (01726) 68965

Brewing company set up in 1851 by maltster and wine merchant Walter Hicks. During St Austell's boom years, the business grew quickly and by 1893 had to move to larger premises, which it still occupies. It remains a family business, selling real ale to all its 146 pubs. A further 3,000 free trade outlets are supplied directly from the brewery. Trelawny's Pride is the first new addition to the beer range for some years, but also new are the Carlsberg-Tetley contract brews which are re-creations of beers from the closed Furgusons Plympton brewery. Shop open 9–5 in the visitors' centre (tours by arrangement).

**Bosun's Bitter** (OG 1031, ABV 3.1%) ◈ A refreshing session beer, sweetish in aroma and bittersweet in flavour. Lingering, hoppy finish.

**XXXX Mild** (OG 1031, ABV 3.6%) ▯ ◈ Little aroma, but a strong, malty character. A

caramel-sweetish flavour is followed by a good, lingering aftertaste which is sweet, but with a fruity dryness. Very drinkable.

**Tinners Ale** (OG 1037, ABV 3.7%) ◈ A deservedly popular, golden beer with an appetising malt aroma and a good balance of malt and hops in the flavour. Lasting finish.

**Trelawny's Pride** (OG 1044, ABV 4.4%) A beer served through a swan neck and sparkler which robs it of aroma and taste and keeps aftertaste to a minimum.

**Hicks Special Draught** or **HSD** (OG 1050, ABV 5%) ◈ An aromatic, fruity, hoppy bitter which is initially sweet and has an aftertaste of pronounced bitterness, but whose flavour is fully-rounded. A good premium beer.

**Winter Warmer** (OG 1059, ABV 6%) ◈ A red/brown winter beer, available November–February. Full-bodied, it has a pronounced malty aroma which leads into a palate featuring strong malt and hop flavours.

### For Carlsberg-Tetley:

**Dartmoor Best Bitter** (OG 1038, ABV 3.9%)

**Dartmoor Strong** (OG 1045, ABV 4.6%)

**Dartmoor Cockleroaster** (OG 1059, ABV 6%) A winter warmer.

---

## ST PETER'S

**St Peter's Brewery Co. Ltd., St Peter's Hall, South Elmham, Bungay, Suffolk NR35 1NQ.**
☎ (01986) 782322
FAX (01986) 782505

This new brewery enjoys an enviable, albeit unusual, setting, in the outbuildings of a beautiful 13th-century hall, and is owned by an equally unusual husband and wife team of a businessman and a psychiatry professor. The brewery supplies its own three tied houses in the Waveney Valley, plus free trade outlets. There are plans for speciality, seasonal and fruit beers to complement the regulars. Tours by arrangement.

**Wheat Beer** (OG 1034, ABV 3.4%)

**Hoxne Bitter** (OG 1040, ABV 4%)

**Stout** (OG 1040, ABV 4%)

**Strong Ale** (OG 1050, ABV 5%)

---

## SALOPIAN

**The Salopian Brewing Company Ltd., The Brewery, 67 Mytton Oak Road, Shrewsbury, Shropshire SY3 8UQ.**
☎ / FAX (01743) 248414

This, the first brewery in Shrewsbury in 30 years, began production in August 1995 in a former dairy in Copthorne on the outskirts of the city. Brewer Martin Barry, formerly of the Snowdonia Brewery, produces a wide range of beers, some for individual outlets and some for sale by Green Cucumber Wholesale ☎ (01584) 872908. Twenty outlets are supplied directly with the regular beers. Shop open 10–4 Sat, 2–4 Sun, or by arrangement. Tours by arrangement. Occasional/seasonal beers: Manchester Festival Beer (OG 1043, ABV 4.3%), Parsons Progress (OG 1045, ABV 4.5%), Lemon Bitter (OG 1045, ABV 4.5%), White Wheat Beer (ABV 4.7%). Bottle-conditioned beers: Minsterley Ale (OG 1047, ABV 4.5%), Gingersnap Wheat Beer (OG 1047, ABV 4.7%), Ironbridge Stout (OG 1050, ABV 5%).

**Bitter** (OG 1035, ABV 3.5%) A hoppy, fruity bitter.

**Monkmoor Bitter** (OG 1040, ABV 4%) A dark, malty beer utilising four hop strains.

**Choir Porter** (OG 1045, ABV 4.5%) A smooth, traditional porter.

**Minsterley Ale** (OG 1045, ABV 4.5%) A premium bitter using three kinds of hops.

**Ironbridge Stout** (OG 1050, ABV 5%) A rich, complex beer.

**Shropshire Spires Strong Bitter** (OG 1050, ABV 5%) A red, very malty strong ale.

**Hollybush Winter Ale** (OG 1060, ABV 6%) A deeply malty winter warmer.

### For Green Cucumber:

**Dark Wheat Beer** (OG 1037, ABV 3.7%, occasional) A dark, fruity wheat beer.

**Pale White** (OG 1050, ABV 5%, occasional) A pale bitter with little hop.

## SCANLON'S

**Scanlon's Fine Ales, Scanlon's Brewery, Unit 8D Waterside House, Rainbow Industrial Estate, Trout Road, Yiewsley, Gtr London UB7 7RN. ☎ (01895) 256270**

Brewery founded in October 1995, with its first beer, Spike, brewed under contract by Rebellion Brewery (qv). In summer 1996, Scanlon's own plant went into operation, producing the two beers below, with Spike still contract brewed at Rebellion. Over 30 outlets take the beers.

**Middlesex Gold** (OG 1039, ABV 3.8%)

**Colne Valley Bitter** (OG 1040, ABV 4.1%)

## SCOTTISH & NEWCASTLE
See Nationals, Scottish Courage.

## SCOTT'S

**Scott's Brewing Company, Crown Street East, Lowestoft, Suffolk NR32 1HR. ☎ (01502) 537237**

Founded in 1988, in former stables at the rear of the Crown Hotel, Scott's is on the

site of a brewery owned by William French 400 years ago. Having recently added a fourth fermenter to increase capacity, Scott's now supplies cask ale to five pubs owned by its parent company, Scott's Inns, and to over 70 other outlets. Tours by arrangement.

**Golden Best Bitter** (OG 1033, ABV 3.4%) ◆ A golden beer with a reasonable balance of malt and (pungent) hop, the latter dominating the aftertaste.

**Blues & Bloater** (OG 1036, ABV 3.7%) ◆ This pleasant, malty, fruity beer has some hop bitterness in the aftertaste.

**East Point Ale** or **EPA** (OG 1040, ABV 4%) A balanced bitter with a sweet start followed by hoppiness throughout.

**Strong Mild** (OG 1043, ABV 4.4%) A dark, full-bodied mild, almost a porter.

**Hopleaf** (OG 1045, ABV 4.5%) A dry hopped (Challenger) strong ale.

**William French** (OG 1048, ABV 5%) ◆ A full and beautifully-balanced beer. A faint, malty aroma leads into strong malt and hop flavours, with considerable fruitiness. Full and balanced aftertaste, too.

**Dark Oast** (OG 1048, ABV 5%) ◆ Red/brown in colour, with less body than its gravity would suggest. The taste has roast malt as its main characteristic, with hoppiness prominent in the aftertaste.

## SELBY
**Selby (Middlebrough) Brewery Ltd., 131 Millgate, Selby, N. Yorkshire YO8 0LL. ☎ (01757) 702826**

Old family brewery which resumed brewing in 1972 after a gap of 18 years and is now mostly involved in wholesaling. Its beers, which are brewed on an occasional basis, are available, while stocks last, through its Brewery Tap off-licence in Selby (open 10–2, 6–10, Mon–Sat) and not at the company's single pub. Beers: No. 1 (OG 1040, ABV 4%), No. 3 (OG 1040, ABV 4%), Old Tom (OG 1065, ABV 6.5%).

## SHARDLOW          shardlow
**Shardlow Brewery Ltd., British Waterways Yard, Cavendish Bridge, Leicestershire DE72 2HL. ☎ (01322) 799188**

This brewery opened in 1993 in the old kiln house of the original Cavendish Bridge Brewery, which closed in the 1920s. It stands on the River Trent, opposite Shardlow Marina, and currently supplies 50 free trade outlets. Its beer range has been almost completely revised within the last 12 months. Brewery tours are planned. Occasional beer: Alternative Lager (OG 1052, ABV 5.2%, cask-conditioned lager).

**Chancellor's Revenge** (OG 1036, ABV 3.6%)

**Abu Derby** (OG 1040, ABV 4.1%)

**Reverend Eaton's Ale** (OG 1045, ABV 4.5%)

**Whistle Stop** (OG 1050, ABV 5%)

**Sleighed** (OG 1058, ABV 5.8%) A winter warmer.

## SHARP'S

**Sharp's Brewery, Pityme
Industrial Estate, Rock,
Wadebridge, Cornwall
PL27 6NU.**
☎ (01208) 862121
FAX (01208) 863727

Three years old, Bill Sharp's brewery now supplies some 250 outlets and there are also plans for bottling. Tours by arrangement.

**Cornish Coaster** (OG 1038, ABV 3.6%) A light, refreshing session beer with a hoppy nose and a dry finish.

**Doom Bar Bitter** (OG 1040, ABV 4%) A mid brown, hoppy bitter with a hint of nuttiness.

**Own** (OG 1044, ABV 4.4%) A red/brown beer with good body which is very malty but balanced by hops. Hoppy aroma; dry finish.

**Special Ale** (OG 1053, ABV 5.2%) Light brown, very hoppy beer with a very dry aftertaste.

## SHEPHERD NEAME
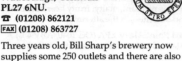

**Shepherd Neame Ltd., 17
Court Street, Faversham,
Kent ME13 7AX.**
☎ (01795) 532206
FAX (01795) 538907

Kent's major independent brewery is believed to be the oldest continuous brewer in the country (since 1698), but records show brewing commenced as far back as the 12th century. The same water source is still used today, steam engines are employed and the mash is produced in two teak tuns which date from 1910. A visitors' reception hall is housed in a restored medieval hall (tours by arrangement). The company has 390 tied houses in the South-East, all selling real ale, but tenants are encouraged to keep beers under blanket pressure if the cask is likely to be on sale for more than three days. Over 500 other outlets are also supplied directly. Shop open 9–5. Occasional/seasonal beer: Goldings Harvest Ale (OG 1050, ABV 5%, September). Bottle-conditioned beer: Spitfire (OG 1047, ABV 4.7%) 🍷 🍶.

**Master Brew Bitter** (OG 1037, ABV 3.7%) 🍴 A very distinctive bitter, mid-brown in colour, with a very hoppy aroma. Well-balanced, with a nicely aggressive bitter taste from its hops, leaving a hoppy/bitter finish, tinged with sweetness.

**Best Bitter** (OG 1041, ABV 4.1%) 🍴 Mid-brown, with less marked characteristics than the bitter. However, the nose is very well-

balanced and the taste enjoys a malty, bitter smokiness. Malty, well-rounded finish.

**Spitfire Premium Ale** (OG 1047, ABV 4.7%) A commemorative brew (Battle of Britain) for the RAF Benevolent Fund's appeal, now a permanent feature.

**Bishops Finger** (OG 1052, ABV 5.2%) A well-known bottled beer, introduced in cask-conditioned form in 1989.

**Original Porter** (OG 1052, ABV 5.2%) 🍴 A rich, black, full-bodied winter brew. The good malt and roast malt aroma also has a fine fruit edge. The complex blend of flavours is dominated by roast malt, which is also present in a very dry aftertaste.

## SHIP & PLOUGH See Blewitts.

## SHIPSTONE'S See Nationals, Carlsberg-Tetley, and Pub Groups, Greenalls.

## SKINNER'S

**The Dark Star Brewing
Company (incorporating
Skinner's of Brighton) Ltd.,
The Evening Star, 55–56
Surrey Street, Brighton,
E. Sussex BN1 3PB.** ☎ (01273) 328931

🍺 Brewing started in 1994 in the cellar of the Evening Star with a tiny plant designed by Rob Jones, formerly of Pitfield Brewery, who has now added his own Dark Star range to the output. The beers are supplied to Peter Skinner's two pubs (the other being the Gardener's Arms in Lewes), and a handful of other outlets. Numerous special brews are produced. Skinner's beers: Ale Trail Roast Mild (OG 1035, ABV 3.5%), Summer Ale (OG 1035, ABV 3.5%), Flintknapper (OG 1036, ABV 3.6%), Pale Ale (OG 1037, ABV 3.7%), Brighton Rock (OG 1040, ABV 4%), Forty Two (OG 1042, ABV 4.2%, winter), Old Ale (OG 1042, ABV 4.2%, winter), Penguin Stout (OG 1042, ABV 4.2%, winter), Golden Gate Bitter (OG 1043, ABV 4.3%), Dunroamin' (OG 1045, ABV 4.5%), Surrey Street Special (OG 1045, ABV 4.5%), Old Familiar (OG 1050, ABV 5%), Cliffe Hanger (OG 1055, ABV 5.5%), Pavilion Beast (OG 1060, ABV 6%). Dark Star beers: Solstice (OG 1040, ABV 4%), Summer Haze (OG 1041, ABV 4.1%, a wheat beer), Pulsar (OG 1045, ABV 4.5%), Zingiber (OG 1045, ABV 4.5%, a ginger beer), Dark Star (OG 1050, ABV 5%), Critical Mass (OG 1060, ABV 6%), Melt Down (OG 1060, ABV 6%, a ginger beer).

## SLATERS See Eccleshall.

🍺 The pub sign indicates a brew pub: a pub which produces beer on the premises.

## SMILES

**Smiles Brewing Co. Ltd.,
Colston Yard, Colston
Street, Bristol BS1 5BD.
☎ (0117) 929 7350
FAX (0117) 925 8235**

Established in 1977 to supply a local restaurant, Smiles commenced full-scale brewing a year later. Under the ownership of Ian Williams, who acquired the company in 1991, the tied estate has since increased to 15 houses, all selling real ale, and there are plans to add more. Noted for its good, traditional pubs (winners of three CAMRA *Pub Design* awards), the brewery also supplies over 250 other outlets. Tours by arrangement. Occasional/seasonal beers: March Hare (OG 1041, ABV 4%, March–April), Indian Summer (OG 1046, ABV 4.4%, September–October), Holly Hops (OG 1052, ABV 5%, Christmas).

**Brewery Bitter** (OG 1036, ABV 3.7%) ◆ A golden amber, lightly malted beer. Its sweet fruit palate is followed by a slightly bitter, dry finish. Gentle fruit and hop aroma.

**Best Bitter** (OG 1040, ABV 4.1%) ◆ A mid-brown beer with some malt and hops in both nose and taste, plus a slight bittersweetness. Briefly hoppy, dry finish.

**Mayfly** (OG 1046, ABV 4.5%) A light golden summer ale (May–September), with a delicate balance of malt and hops.

**Bristol Stout** (OG 1048, ABV 4.7%) ◆ A dark, red/brown stout with a roast malt and coffee aroma. The predominantly rich roast malt taste features some hops and fruit. Roast, bitter, dry finish. Available September–March.

**Exhibition Bitter** (OG 1051, ABV 5.2%) ◆ A dark, copper brown ale, with a chocolate malt, hop and fruit taste, turning to a dry, roast malt and bitter finish.

### For Greenalls:

**Cheshire Cat** (OG 1046, ABV 4.5%, occasional)

## JOHN SMITH'S

See Nationals, Scottish Courage.

## SAMUEL SMITH

**Samuel Smith Old Brewery
(Tadcaster), High Street,
Tadcaster, N. Yorkshire
LS24 9SB. ☎ (01937) 832225
FAX (01937) 834673**

Small company operating from the oldest brewery in Yorkshire, dating from 1758 and once owned by John Smith. Unlike John Smith's, however, Sam's is still family owned and fiercely independent. The beer is brewed from well water without the use of adjuncts and all cask beer is fermented in Yorkshire stone squares before being racked into wooden casks made by the brewery's

own cooper. Tours by arrangement. Real ale is sold in most of its 200 tied houses, but many of Sam's London pubs no longer stock cask beer. This move, together with the decision to axe Museum Ale in autumn 1995 and to place more emphasis on nitrokeg Sovereign Bitter, was greeted with dismay by beer lovers.

**Old Brewery Bitter** (OBB) (OG 1040, ABV 4%) ◆ Malt dominates the aroma, with an initial burst of malt, hops and fruit in the taste which is sustained in the aftertaste.

## SOLSTICE See Marches.

## SOLVA

**The Solva Brewing Co. Ltd., Panteg, Solva, Haverfordwest, Carmarthenshire
SA62 6TL. ☎ (01437) 720350**

⬛ Brewery not in operation as we went to press but hoping to resume brewing in 1997.

## SOUTH YORKSHIRE See Barnsley.

## SP SPORTING ALES

**SP Sporting Ales Ltd., Cantilever Lodge, Stoke Prior, Leominster, Herefordshire
HR6 0LG. ☎/FAX (01568) 760226**

Small brewery opened in April 1996, producing just one beer for sale under various names, including Hole-in-One and Little Dove (OG 1040, ABV 4%).

## SPIKES

**Spikes Brewery, The Wine
Vaults, 43–47 Albert Road,
Southsea, Portsmouth,
Hampshire PO5 2SF.
☎ (01705) 864712**

⬛ Brewery installed above the Wine Vaults pub in 1994. There are plans to move to a different site in order to supply a wider market beyond this one pub. Tours by arrangement. Beers: Impaled Ale (ABV 3.6%), Porter (ABV 4%), Stinger (ABV 4.5%).

## SPRINGHEAD

**Springhead Brewery, Unit
3, Sutton Workshops, Old
Great North Road, Sutton-
on-Trent, Newark,
Nottinghamshire
NG23 6QS. ☎/FAX (01636) 821000**

Springhead started out as the country's smallest brewery, set up in the owner's home, but was forced to move to larger premises in 1994. Around 100 free trade outlets are supplied directly. Tours by arrangement. Occasional beer: Cromwell's Hat (OG 1060, ABV 6%).

**Hersbrucker Weizenbier** (OG 1034, ABV 3.6%) A spring/summer wheat beer.

**Bitter** (OG 1042, ABV 4%) ◆ This pale copper beer has both malt and hops on the nose, the hops complemented by a slight fruitiness which is more apparent in the taste. Malt and hops dominate throughout, with a slow, dying dryness.

**Leveller** (OG 1047, ABV 4.8%) ◻ ◆ A roast amber malt is used to give Leveller its distinctive coffee taste and aroma. Roast and malt dominate all through this dark, smoky beer which has a slight toffee sweetness and a bitter finish.

**1661** (OG 1049, ABV 5%) ◆ Malty, in a nutty way, competing with a plum fruitiness, with hops and bitterness always there in the background. This deep copper beer is now a welcome addition to the range, having started as a Christmas special.

**Roaring Meg** (OG 1052, ABV 5.5%) ◻ ◆ A strong bitter in the blonde style. Hops and a citrus fruitiness dominate the aroma and taste, whilst malt takes equal billing in the dry, lasting finish. Dangerously drinkable.

## STAG
See Abel Brown's and Nationals, Scottish Courage.

## STAG & GRIFFIN
**Stag & Griffin Brewery, Oxford Road, Tatling End, Gerrards Cross, Buckinghamshire SL9 7AL.**
☎ (01753) 883100 [FAX] (01753) 891616

▢ A micro-brewery was installed at this free house (run by the new owner of Viking Brewery) early in 1996 and its first beer was launched at the pub's beer festival over the May Bank Holiday. There are plans to increase the range with a mild (Griffin Dark, ABV 3.2%) and a pale ale (SPA, ABV 4.5%). Beer: Stiffin Ale (ABV 3.8%).

## STANWAY
**Stanway Brewery, Stanway, Cheltenham, Gloucestershire GL54 5PQ.**
☎ (01386) 584320

Small brewery, founded in 1993 with a five-barrel plant, which confines its sales to the Cotswolds area (around 25 outlets). Occasional/seasonal beers: Lords-a-Leaping (OG 1045, ABV 4.5%, winter), Old Eccentric (OG 1052, ABV 5.5%).

**Stanney Bitter** (OG 1042, ABV 4.5%) ◆ A light, refreshing, amber-coloured beer, dominated by hops in the aroma, with a bitter taste and a hoppy, bitter finish.

## STEAMIN' BILLY
See Leatherbritches.

## STEAM PACKET
**The Steam Packet Brewery, The Bendles, Racca Green, Knottingley, W. Yorkshire WF11 8AT.**
☎ / [FAX] (01977) 674176

▢ Pub brewery which began producing beers for its own bar in 1990, but which has expanded to supply 50 outlets regularly (and more on an occasional basis), mainly in the North-West. New brews (including fruit beers) are regularly added to the range.

**Gamekeeper Bitter** (OG 1036, ABV 3.6%) ◆ Bitter and dry, light brown beer, with little aroma. Good, malty taste, but an unbalanced, weak aftertaste. Little hop content.

**Blow Job** or **Bitter Blow** (OG 1038, ABV 3.8%) ◆ A gold-coloured beer with a harsh bitter, strongly fruity taste, echoing the aroma. The moderately malty flavour doesn't last. There is an underlying sourness throughout.

**Ginger Minge** (OG 1039, ABV 4%) ◻ ◆ A wonderfully refreshing and clean-tasting ginger beer with a good hop and fruit taste and well-balanced ginger flavour. The bittersweet aftertaste doesn't linger and gives way to gingerness.

**Porter** (OG 1040, ABV 4%) A dark porter with a strong malt content and a lingering woody flavour.

**Brown Ale** (OG 1045, ABV 4.5%) ◆ A malty brown ale, with a hoppy, fruity nose and a good balance of caramel, malt, hops, sweetness and bitterness in the taste, which fades slightly in the finish.

**Poacher's Swag** (OG 1050, ABV 5%) ◆ A full-bodied, sweetish mid-brown beer, with a moderately fruity aroma, leading to a bitter, slightly fruity and malty taste, and a very dry astringency which dominates the aftertaste. Some yeastiness.

**Craam Stout** (OG 1050, ABV 5%) ◆ A strong blend of roast malt and malt abounds in this beer, with a moderate hoppiness and some fruit, leading to a lingering, dry, bitterness. Black in colour. Note: the OG varies.

## STOCKS
**Stocks Brewery, The Hallcross, 33–34 Hallgate, Doncaster, S. Yorkshire DN1 3NL.** ☎ (01302) 328213 [FAX] (01302) 329776

▢ Brewery founded in 1981 as the Hallcross brew pub and growing steadily until summer 1996, when it was taken over by Century Inns (see Pub Groups). It supplies one other tied house and a free trade of around 20 outlets, including some Tap & Spile pubs.

**Pillory** (OG 1035, ABV 3.5%) A golden brown session beer, initially bitter, giving way to a pleasant, hoppy finish.

**Best Bitter** (OG 1037, ABV 3.9%) 🍺 A thin session beer, with malty overtones and little else. Dry, but weak, in the aftertaste.

**Select** (OG 1044, ABV 4.7%) 🍺 A tawny-coloured drink with little aroma. Malt dominates, with a short, bittersweet finish.

**Golden Wheat** (OG 1044, ABV 4.7%) Straw-coloured, with initially a bitter taste, giving way to a strong, grainy finish.

**St Leger Porter** (OG 1050, ABV 5.1%) 🍺 Black, with ruby hues, this beer is thin for its gravity. A nutty and malty aroma develops into a malty taste and then a weak roast malt finish. Winter only.

**Old Horizontal** (OG 1054, ABV 5.4%) 🍺 This used to be the pick of the bunch, but even this is now a thin, bland-tasting beer. However, roasted malt can be detected in the aroma and taste of this dark brown ale, which has a dry, malty aftertaste.

**STONES** See Nationals, Bass.

## STRONG
See Morrells and Nationals, Whitbread.

## SUMMERSKILLS
**Summerskills Brewery, Unit 15 Pomphlett Farm Industrial Estate, Broxton Drive, Billacombe, Plymouth, Devon PL9 7BG.** ☎ /[FAX] (01752) 481283

Originally set up in a vineyard in 1983, but closed after two years, Summerskills was relaunched by new owners in 1990 with plant from the old Penrhos brewery. Production of its award-winning beers continues to grow at a steady rate, with 35 free trade outlets supplied directly and others nationally via wholesalers. Tours by arrangement. Occasional/seasonal beers: Menacing Dennis (ABV 5%), Turkey's Delight (OG 1051, ABV 5.1%, Christmas). Bottle-conditioned beers: Best Bitter (OG 1042, ABV 4.3%), Indiana's Bones (OG 1056, ABV 5.6%).

**Best Bitter** (OG 1042, ABV 4.3%) 🍺 A mid-brown beer, with plenty of malt and hops through the aroma, taste and finish. A good session beer.

**Tamar Best Bitter** (OG 1043, ABV 4.3%)

**Whistle Belly Vengeance** (OG 1046, ABV 4.7%) 🍺 A red/brown beer with a beautiful malt and fruit taste and a pleasant, malty aftertaste.

**Ninjabeer** (OG 1049, ABV 5%) 🍺 A dark gold beer, with a strong, fruity aroma and a predominantly fruity taste and aftertaste. Very drinkable. Brewed October–April.

**Indiana's Bones** (OG 1056, ABV 5.6%) 🍺 🍺 A mid-brown beer with a good balance of fruit and malt in the aroma and taste, and a sweet, malty finish.

## SUTTON
**Sutton Brewing Company, 31 Commercial Road, Coxside, Plymouth, Devon PL4 0LE.** ☎ /[FAX] (01752) 255335.

This brewery was built alongside the Thistle Park Tavern, near Plymouth's Sutton Harbour, in 1993. It went into production the following year to supply that pub and one other. It now sells to over 50 outlets in and around Plymouth, and a bigger plant and additional fermenters have been installed to cope with demand. Tours by arrangement. Occasional/seasonal beers: Hopnosis (OG 1045, ABV 4.5%), Weetablitz (OG 1050, ABV 5%, summer), Sleigh'd (OG 1058, ABV 5.8%, Christmas).

**Dartmoor Pride** (OG 1038, ABV 3.8%)

**XSB** (OG 1042, ABV 4.2%) 🍺 A mid-brown beer with a fruity nose and a strong, bitter taste and finish.

**Gold** (OG 1044, ABV 4.4%)

**Jinja** (OG 1045, ABV 4.5%)

**Eddystone Light** (OG 1050, ABV 5%)

**Old Pedantic** (OG 1050, ABV 5%)

**Knickadroppa Glory** (OG 1055, ABV 5.5%)

**Plymouth Porter** (OG 1056, ABV 5.5%) 🍺 Brewed November–February; a dark brown beer with a distinct roast malt aroma, taste and finish.

**Winter Warmer** (OG 1059, ABV 6%)

## SWALE
**The Swale Brewery Co., Unit 2, Periwinkle Court, Milton Regis, Sittingbourne, Kent ME10 2JZ.** ☎ (01795) 426871

The first brewery in Milton Regis since the closure of Hartridges in 1895, Swale was opened in December 1995 by experienced home brewer John Davidson. His 15-barrel plant supplies cask ale to 25 free trade outlets in Kent and South-East London. Seasonal brews are planned. Tours by arrangement.

**Tiddleywinkle** (OG 1040, ABV 3.8%) A spring offering.

**Copperwinkle** (OG 1040, ABV 4%) A copper-coloured bitter, predominantly hoppy through to the finish.

**Old Dick** (OG 1052, ABV 5.2%) A strong, dark winter bitter, with a smooth taste. Brewed around Christmas.

## SWANSEA

**Swansea Brewing Company, 74 Hawthorne Avenue, Uplands, Swansea SA2 0LY. ☎ (01792) 290197**

Founded in April 1996, this is the first commercial brewery in the Swansea area for almost 30 years. Based in the Joiners Arms, Bishopston, it is currently brewing mainly for this outlet but the beer is also available in a limited number of free houses. Beer: Bishops Wood Bitter (ABV 4.3%).

## TALLY HO!

**Tally Ho! Country Inn and Brewery, 14 Market Street, Hatherleigh, Devon EX20 3JN. ☎ (01837) 810306**

The Tally Ho! recommenced brewing at Easter 1990, reviving the tradition of the former New Inn brewery on the same site. New owners took over in December 1994. Its beers are produced from a full mash, with no additives, and, as well as sales at the pub itself, beer agencies now take the beers. Tours by arrangement. Beers: Potboiler's Brew (OG 1036, ABV 3.5%), Master Jack's Mild (OG 1039, ABV 3.5%, summer), Tarka's Tipple (OG 1042, ABV 4%), Nutters Ale (OG 1048, ABV 4.6%), Thurgia (OG 1060, ABV 6%), Jollop (OG 1066, ABV 6.8%, winter). Bottle-conditioned beers: Hunter's Ale (OG 1048, ABV 4.6%), Tarka's Tipple (OG 1048, ABV 4.6%), Thurgia (OG 1060, ABV 6%).

## TAYLOR

**Timothy Taylor & Co. Ltd., Knowle Spring Brewery, Keighley, W. Yorkshire BD21 1AW. ☎ (01535) 603139 FAX (01535) 691167**

Timothy Taylor began brewing in Keighley in 1858 and moved to the site of the Knowle Spring in 1863. The business was continued by his sons and remains an independent family-owned company to this day. Its prize-winning ales are served in all 26 of the brewery's pubs as well as a wide free trade. The company also owns an ale shop in Raglan Road, Leeds.

**Golden Best** (OG 1033, ABV 3.5%) ◆ A very drinkable, refreshing light mild with a hoppy nose and a tangy flavour. The dry, bitter finish is disappointingly short.

**Dark Mild** (OG 1034, ABV 3.5%) ◆ Caramel masks the aroma and taste of the Golden Best from which this beer is derived, giving a rather weak toffee flavour and long, sweetish aftertaste. Hard to find.

**Porter** (OG 1041, ABV 3.8%) ◆ Some hops are apparent in the aroma but caramel dominates, combining in both the taste and finish with dark sugar flavours to give an overpoweringly sweet yet smooth drink.

**Best Bitter** (OG 1037, ABV 4%) 🗍 ◆ Well-balanced and clean, with a tangy fruitiness in the aroma and taste. Hoppy throughout, particularly in the long finish. Satisfying and highly recommended.

**Landlord** (OG 1042, ABV 4.3%) 🗍 ◆ An initial burst of hops quickly turns fruity, leading to a long, dry, bitter finish. Citrus notes throughout. Instantly recognisable. *Champion Beer of Britain 1994.*

**Ram Tam** (XXXX) (OG 1043, ABV 4.3%) ◆ A dark brown ale with red hints which has an initial malty sweetness giving way to the hops and fruit of the underlying Landlord. The long finish is dry and satisfying.

## TAYLOR WALKER
See Nationals, Carlsberg-Tetley.

## TEIGNWORTHY

**Teignworthy Brewery, The Maltings, Teign Road, Newton Abbot, Devon TQ12 4AA. ☎ (01626) 332066**

Brewery founded in June 1994 with a 15-barrel plant by former Oakhill and Ringwood brewer John Lawton, using part of the historic Victorian malthouse of Edward Tucker & Sons. About 50 other outlets take the beer. Brewery (Tucker's Maltings) shop open 10–5, April–October. Maltings and brewery tours available. Occasional/seasonal beer: Cracker (OG 1060, ABV 6%, Christmas). Bottle-conditioned beer: Reel Ale (OG 1039, ABV 4%), Spring Tide (OG 1043.5, ABV 4.3%), Beachcomber (OG 1045, ABV 4.5%), Maltster's Ale (ABV 5%).

**Reel Ale** (OG 1039.5, ABV 4%)

**Spring Tide** (OG 1043.5, ABV 4.3%) Available in spring.

**Beachcomber** (OG 1045, ABV 4.5%) Available May–July.

**Maltster's Ale** (OG 1048.5, ABV 4.8%) Available October–January. The first beer made from the new barley variety Regina.

## TENNENT See Nationals, Bass.

## TETLEY See Nationals, Carlsberg-Tetley.

## THEAKSTON
See Nationals, Scottish Courage.

## THOMPSON'S

**Thompson's Brewery, London Hotel, West Street, Ashburton, Devon TQ13 7DT. ☎ (01364) 652478 FAX (01364) 659039**

Brewery which began operation in 1981 by brewing for the London Inn in

Ashburton. By 1992, demand from other outlets in the South-West had increased so much that a new brew-house with a 5,000-barrel capacity was commissioned. Tours by arrangement.

**Best Bitter** (OG 1040, ABV 4.2%) ◆ A pale brown beer with a hoppy aroma and taste. Bitter finish.

**Black Velvet Stout** (OG 1040, ABV 4.2%)

**IPA** (OG 1044, ABV 4.6%) ◆ A mid-brown-coloured ale with a distinct hoppy aroma and a bitter taste and finish.

**Man 'O' War** (OG 1050, ABV 5%) ◆ A golden, summer beer with a fruity sweet taste and aftertaste.

**Figurehead** (OG 1050, ABV 5.2%) ◆ A dark brown, full-bodied winter beer with a malty nose and a roasty, bitter taste and finish.

**Celebration Porter** (ABV 6%)

## THREE TUNS
**The Three Tuns Brewery, Salop Street, Bishop's Castle, Shropshire SY9 5BW.**
☎ (01588) 638797

Historic brew pub which first obtained a brewing licence in 1642. It ceased brewing in 1996 but new owners took over in the summer and they may re-open the brewery.

## THWAITES
**Daniel Thwaites PLC, PO Box 50, Star Brewery, Blackburn, Lancashire BB1 5BU.** ☎ (01254) 54431
FAX (01254) 681439

Lancashire brewery, founded by excise officer Daniel Thwaites in 1807 and now run by his great-great grandson. It still uses shire horse drays and nearly all its 420 pubs serve real ale. A substantial free trade (about 750 outlets) is also supplied. Tours by arrangement. Occasional beers (the monthly Connoisseur Cask Ale Collection): Court Jester (ABV 4%), Snigbrook Ale (OG 1040, ABV 4%), Highwayman (ABV 4.2%), Scallywag (OG 1043, ABV 4.5%), Thunderbolt (OG 1043, ABV 4.5%), Town Crier (OG 1045, ABV 4.5%), Musketeer (ABV 5%), Daniels Hammer (OG 1048, ABV 5.2%), Smugglers Grog (ABV 5.5%).

**Best Mild** (OG 1033, ABV 3.3%) ◆ A rich, dark mild presenting a smooth, malty flavour and a pleasant, slightly bitter finish.

**Bitter** (OG 1036, ABV 3.6%) ◆ A gently-flavoured, clean-tasting bitter. Malt and hops lead into a full, lingering, bitter finish.

**Craftsman** (OG 1042, ABV 4.5%) A hoppy, golden premium ale.

## TIGERTOPS
**Tigertops Brewery, 22 Oakes Street, Flanshaw Lane, Flanshaw, Wakefield, W. Yorkshire WF2 9LN.**
☎ (01924) 378538

Micro-brewery established in September 1995 by two CAMRA enthusiasts. The one-barrel plant is housed in a garden outhouse and the operation remains part-time at present. Several local free houses take the beer, but owners Lynda and Stuart Johnson hope to buy a pub and resite the brewery on the premises. Occasional beer: Lot 47 (OG 1037, ABV 3.1%, a mild).

**Fleur-de-Lys** (OG 1036, ABV 3.8%) A refreshing, amber-coloured session bitter with good hop character and a balancing sweetness.

**Flanshaw Flyer** (OG 1045, ABV 4.5%) An amber/golden best bitter with a sweet start, plenty of hop taste and good body.

**Kinghorn** (OG 1046, ABV 4.7%) A wheat beer with a yellow hue and a full, wheaty mouthfeel and aftertaste.

**Pot Black** (OG 1045, ABV 5%) A stout with plenty of roast malt and malt in the taste, complemented by a liquorice flavour which lasts.

**Chantry Challenge** (OG 1049, ABV 5%) A complex, mid brown, light-bodied premium bitter with hops and malt in balance.

## TIPSY TOAD
**The Tipsy Toad Brewery, St Peter, Jersey JE3 7AA.**
☎ (01534) 485556; **The Tipsy Toad Townhouse and Brewery, 57–59 New Street, St Helier, Jersey JE2 3RB.** ☎ (01534) 615002
FAX (01534) 615003

Following refurbishment of the Star pub, brewing began on these premises in spring 1992. Four other outlets (including one on Alderney) are now supplied on a regular basis with the full mash brews. The brewery opened a second brew pub, The Tipsy Toad Townhouse and Brewery, in St Helier in 1994, but this brewery is not at present in use. Tours by arrangement. Some one-off brews are produced. Beers: Tipsy Toad Ale (OG 1038, ABV 3.8%), Jimmy's Bitter (OG 1040, ABV 4%), Black Tadger (OG 1045, ABV 4.4%, a porter), Horny Toad (OG 1050, ABV 5%), Star Drooper (OG 1060, ABV 6%, winter).

## TISBURY
**Tisbury Brewery Ltd., Church Street, Tisbury, Wiltshire SP3 6NH.**
☎ (01747) 870986
FAX (01747) 871540

Housed in the old Wiltshire Brewery buildings (originally a workhouse), Tisbury began production in April 1995, providing beer for over 100 free trade outlets. One beer, named after the guru of micro-brewing in the UK, Peter Austin, is produced for The Beer Seller wholesaler ☎ (01963) 34264. Tours by arrangement.

**Best Bitter** (OG 1038, ABV 3.8%) A burnt amber-coloured, full-flavoured session bitter.

**Archibald Beckett** (OG 1043, ABV 4.3%) A premium bitter with a dark amber colour, a caramel aroma and a dry, fruity finish.

**Old Wardour** (OG 1048, ABV 4.8%) A full-bodied, mahogany-hued bitter named after Wardour Castle.

## For The Beer Seller:

**Peter Austin's Original Formula** (ABV 4%).

## TITANIC

The Titanic Brewery, Unit G, Harvey Works, Lingard Street, Burslem, Stoke-on-Trent, Staffordshire ST6 1ED. ☎ (01782) 823447 FAX (01782) 812349

This brewery, named in honour of the *Titanic*'s Captain Smith, who hailed from Stoke, was founded in 1985 but fell into difficulties until rescued by the present owners. A move to larger premises took place in 1992 and new brewing plant was installed in 1995. The brewery now supplies over 100 free trade outlets, as well as two pubs of its own (which also sell other Independents' guest beers). Tours by arrangement. Bottle-conditioned beers: Stout (OG 1046, ABV 4.5%), Captain Smith's (OG 1054, ABV 5.2%), Christmas Ale (OG 1080, ABV 7.8%).

**Best Bitter** (OG 1036, ABV 3.5%) ◆ A crisp, clean, refreshing bitter with a good balance of fruit, malt and hops. Bitter finish.

**Lifeboat Ale** (OG 1040, ABV 3.9%) ◆ A fruity and malty, dark red/brown beer, with a fruity finish.

**Premium** (OG 1042, ABV 4.1%) ⬜◆ An impressive, well-balanced pale brown bitter with hops and fruit in the aroma which develop into a full flavour and a dry, hoppy finish.

**Stout** (OG 1046, ABV 4.5%) ◆ A dark combination of malt and roast with some hops. Strongly flavoured and well-balanced.

**White Star** (OG 1050, ABV 4.8%) ◆ A bittersweet amber ale with a very fruity taste and a long fruit aftertaste.

**Captain Smith's** (OG 1054, ABV 5.2%) ◆ A full-bodied, dark red/brown beer, hoppy and bitter with malt and roast malt flavours, and a long, bittersweet finish.

**Wreckage** (OG 1080, ABV 7.8%) ◆ A dark winter brew, full-flavoured with a rich bittersweet finish.

## TOLLY COBBOLD

Tollemache & Cobbold Brewery Ltd., Cliff Road, Ipswich, Suffolk IP3 0AZ. ☎ (01473) 231723 FAX (01473) 280045

One of the oldest breweries in the country, founded by Thomas Cobbold in 1723 at Harwich. Tolly moved to Ipswich in 1746 and celebrated 250 years in the town in 1996. In 1989, Brent Walker took over the company, closed the Cliff Brewery and transferred production to Camerons in Hartlepool. However, a management buyout saved the day and Tolly Cobbold Ipswich-brewed ales were back on sale in 1990. The new company acquired no pubs from Brent Walker, but secured a long-term trading agreement with Pubmaster (the company which runs former Brent Walker pubs), supplying a total of 525 outlets. It opened a brewery tap, the only tied house, in 1992. Brewery tours (daily) have become a major attraction and another feature is the Bottlers Room, containing a display of 1,800 commemorative bottled beers. Brewery shop open lunchtimes in the tourist season. Some seasonal ales are produced.

**Mild** (OG 1032, ABV 3.2%) ⬜ ◆ A tasty mild with fruit, malt and roast malt characters. Pleasing aftertaste. It tends to lose complexity when forced through a sparkler.

**Bitter** (OG 1035, ABV 3.5%) ◆ A light, mid-brown-coloured malty beer lacking bitterness.

**Original Best Bitter** (OG 1038, ABV 3.8%) ◆ A slightly stronger bitter with assertive hop character throughout. The finish is bitter, but with a good balancing maltiness. Disappointingly hard to find.

**IPA** (OG 1045, ABV 4.2%) A best bitter, full of citrus fruit flavours and flowery hoppiness.

**Old Strong Winter Ale** (OG 1048, ABV 5%) ◆ Available November–February. A dark winter ale with plenty of roast character throughout. Lingering and complex aftertaste.

**Conquest** (OG 1051, ABV 5%)

**Tollyshooter** (OG 1052, ABV 5%) ◆ A reddish premium bitter with a full, fruity flavour and a long, bittersweet aftertaste. Good hop character, too. Named after the Sir John Harvey-Jones TV series, *Troubleshooter*, in which Tolly featured.

## TOMINTOUL

Tomintoul Brewery Co. Ltd., Mill of Auchriachan, Tomintoul, Ballindalloch, Banffshire AB37 9EQ. ☎ (01807) 580333 FAX (01807) 580358

Brewery opened in November 1993 in an old watermill, in an area better known for malt whisky and snow-blocked roads. Around 30 outlets are currently supplied. Bottle-conditioned beers are planned. Tours by arrangement. Occasional/seasonal beers: 80/- (OG 1040, ABV 4.2%).

**Laird's Ale** (OG 1038, ABV 3.8%)

**Stag** (OG 1039.5, ABV 4.1%)

**Ginger Tom** (OG 1043, ABV 4.5%) Available in summer.

**Wild Cat** (OG 1049.5, ABV 5.1%)

**Highland Hammer** (OG 1065, ABV 7.3%) A winter beer.

## TOMLINSON'S
Tomlinson's Old Castle Brewery, Unit 5, Britannia Works, Skinner Lane, Pontefract, W. Yorkshire WF8 1HU. ☎ (01977) 780866

Marking a return to brewing in Pontefract after over 60 years, Tomlinson's was built in 1993 and is run by a former pipe fitter and fabricator. The award-winning brews take their names from various local historical connections. Some 40 outlets are now supplied. Tours by arrangement. Occasional/seasonal beers: Hermitage Mild (OG 1036, ABV 3.7%) 🍺, Down With It! (OG 1042, ABV 4.3%), Femme Fatale (OG 1043, ABV 4.5%), Fractus XB (OG 1045, ABV 4.5%).

**Sessions** (OG 1038, ABV 4%) 🍺 A dry, bitter beer with a light, hoppy, smoky aroma leading to a well-hopped and slightly fruity taste and aftertaste, which is also dry. Light brown/copper in colour.

**De Lacy** (OG 1044, ABV 4.6%) 🍺 An enjoyable amber, bitter, dry beer with a good, hoppy, fruity nose and a well-balanced strong hop and fruit taste with some sweetness. Dry, slightly yeasty aftertaste.

**Deceitful Rose** (OG 1048, ABV 5%) 🍺 🍺 Superbly dry, hoppy, straw-coloured beer in the style of an India Pale Ale. Very bitter and dry in the taste and finish, with a clean, hoppy and slightly fruity flavour which lingers.

**Richard's Defeat** (OG 1050, ABV 5%) 🍺 A black, strong porter in which roast flavour dominates throughout along with a moderate fruitiness and some hoppiness, with a good bitter/sweet balance leading to a bitter finish.

**Double Helix** (OG 1055, ABV 5.5%) 🍺 A full-bodied, mid-brown strong bitter of character. An intense malt and hop aroma is followed by a strong chocolatey, malty taste with a good balance of hops, fruit and bitterness, which lasts.

**Three Sieges** (OG 1058, ABV 6%) A liquorice beer, brewed in winter.

## TOWNES
Townes Brewery, Bay 9, Suon Buildings, Lockoford Lane, Chesterfield, Derbyshire S41 7JJ. ☎ (01246) 277994

Brewery established in an old bakery in May 1994 by photographer Alan Wood, bringing brewing back to Chesterfield after nearly 40 years. Now some 40 outlets are supplied and brewing capacity has been increased accordingly. One-off brews feature regularly and a series of six, monthly 'Townes & Country' beers (all at 4.2% ABV and all named after American country song titles) has also been produced.

**Sunshine** (OG 1036, ABV 3.6%) A light-coloured session beer with a full finish.

**Muffin Ale** (OG 1038, ABV 3.8%) A brown session ale with a dry finish.

**Best Lockoford Bitter** (OG 1040, ABV 4%) A golden-coloured bitter with hop character.

**GMT** (OG 1042, ABV 4.2%) A pale, spicy ale with a malty base and a hoppy finish.

## TRAQUAIR
Traquair House Brewery, Innerleithen, Peeblesshire EH44 6PW. ☎ (01896) 830323 FAX (01896) 830639

This 18th-century brewhouse is situated in one of the wings of Traquair House (over 1,000 years old) and was rediscovered by the 20th Laird, Peter Maxwell Stuart, in 1965. He began brewing again using all the original equipment (which remained intact, despite having lain idle for over 100 years). The brewery passed to Catherine Maxwell Stuart in 1990. All the beers are oak-fermented and 60 per cent of production is exported (mostly bottled Traquair House Ale). About five outlets take the beer in the UK. Tours by arrangement, April–September. Shop open daily April–October, 10.30–5.30. Occasional/seasonal beers: Festival Ale (OG 1045, ABV 4%), Fair Ale (OG 1055, ABV 6%).

**Bear Ale** (OG 1050, ABV 5%) 🍺 A powerful, malt/fruit aroma precedes a deep, rich taste bursting with fruit, which lingers and subtly changes into a long-lasting, dry finish.

**Traquair House Ale** (OG 1070, ABV 7.2%)

**Jacobite Ale** (OG 1075, ABV 8%)

## TRING
The Tring Brewery Company Ltd., 81–82 Akeman Street, Tring, Hertfordshire HP23 6AF. ☎ (01442) 890721 FAX (01442) 890740

Established in 1992, bringing brewing back to this Hertfordshire town after over 50 years, Tring now supplies around 80 outlets.

Tours by arrangement on weekday
evenings. Occasional/seasonal beers:
Golden Grail (ABV 4.5%, Easter), Death or
Glory Ale (OG 1070, ABV 7.2%, brewed
October 25 to commemorate the Charge of
the Light Brigade in 1854 and sold
December–January). Bottle-conditioned
beer: Death or Glory Ale (OG 1070, ABV
7.2%).

**Finest Summer Ale** (OG 1037, ABV 3.7%)
Available June–September; a refreshing
summer ale with a proportion of wheat malt
in the mash.

**The Ridgeway Bitter** (OG 1039, ABV 4%)
🍺 A beer with a pleasant mix of hop and
malt flavours in the aroma and taste, leading
to a dry, often flowery hop, aftertaste.

**Old Cantankerous** (OG 1048, ABV 4.8%) A
winter porter, available October–December.

**Old Icknield Ale** (OG 1049, ABV 5%) 🍺 A
beer with a distinct, hoppy flavour and a
dry, bitter aftertaste.

## TYNLLIDIART ARMS
**Tynllidiart Arms, Capel Bangor,
Aberystwyth, Ceredigion SY23 3LR.
☎ (01970) 880248**

🍺 Pub brewery set up in July 1996,
supplying just the pub itself. Beer:
Rheidol Reserve (ABV 4.5%).

## ULEY
**Uley Brewery Ltd., The Old
Brewery, Uley, Dursley,
Gloucestershire GL11 5PD.
☎ (01453) 860120**

Brewing at Uley began in 1833, but Price's
Brewery, as it was then, remained inactive
for most of this century. Work commenced
on restoring the premises in 1984 and Uley
Brewery was reborn in 1985. The brewery
has no pubs of its own but now serves 50
free trade outlets in the Cotswolds area.
Occasional/seasonal beer: Pigor Mortis (OG
1060, ABV 6%, November–December).

**Hogshead Bitter** (OG 1035, ABV 3.5%)

**Bitter** (OG 1040, ABV 4%) 🍺 Copper-
coloured beer with malt, hops and fruit in
the aroma and a malty, fruity taste,
underscored by a hoppy bitterness. The
finish is dry, with a balance of hops and
malt.

**Old Ric** (OG 1045, ABV 4.5%)

**Old Spot Prize Ale** (OG 1050, ABV 5%) 🍺 A
fairly full-bodied, red/brown ale with a
fruity aroma, a malty, fruity taste (with a
hoppy bitterness), and a strong, balanced
aftertaste.

**Pig's Ear Strong Beer** (OG 1050, ABV 5%)
🍺 A pale-coloured, light beer, deceptively
strong. Notably bitter in flavour, with a
hoppy, fruity aroma and a bitter finish.

## UNITED BREWERIES
See Pub Groups, Inn Business.

## USHERS
**Ushers of Trowbridge PLC,
Directors House, 68 Fore
Street, Trowbridge,
Wiltshire BA14 8JF.
☎ (01225) 763171
FAX (01225) 753661**

This famous West Country brewery was
founded in 1824, but lost its identity after
being swallowed up by Watney (later Grand
Met) in 1960. A successful management
buyout, purchasing the brewery and 433
pubs from Courage in 1991, gave Ushers
back its independence. It has since invested
in pubs and plant, with over £5 million spent
on the brewery. Ushers supplies real ale to
nearly all its 550 houses (most tenanted and
all in the South, South-West and South
Wales) and also to Scottish Courage/Grand
Met Inntrepreneur pubs. Keg and bottled
products are brewed for Scottish Courage,
one cask beer is produced for the Tap &
Spile chain (see Pub Groups, Pubmaster)
and one for the Freetraders wholesaling
company ☎ (0181) 965 0222. Tours by
arrangement Mon–Thu evenings.
Occasional/seasonal beers: January'Sale
(OG 1031, ABV 3%, January), Summer
Madness (OG 1040, ABV 4%), Spring Fever
(OG 1040, ABV 4%), Autumn Frenzy (OG
1041, ABV 4%), 1824 Particular (OG 1062.5,
ABV 6%, winter).

**Best Bitter** (OG 1037.5, ABV 3.8%) 🍺 An
amber/pale brown, light bitter with malt
and hoppy bitterness in the flavour followed
by a dry, bitter finish.

**Founders Ale** (OG 1046, ABV 4.5%) 🍺 A
pale brown beer with a bitter hop taste,
balanced by sweet maltiness and faint citrus
fruit. Predominantly bitter finish.

### For Freetraders:
**Chadwicks Finest** (OG 1037, ABV 3.7%)

### For Tap & Spile:
**Tap & Spile Premium** (OG 1041, ABV 4.3%)

## VALE
**Vale Brewery Company,
Thame Road, Haddenham,
Buckinghamshire
HP17 8BY.
☎ (01844) 290008
FAX (01844) 292505**

After many years working for large regional
breweries and allied industries, brothers
Mark and Phil Stevens combined their
experience and opened a small, purpose-
built brewery in Haddenham. This revived
brewing in a village where the last brewery
closed at the end of World War II. Around
150 local outlets now take the beers, which

are brewed from premium barley and whole hops. Tours by arrangement.

**Notley Ale** (ABV 3.3%)

**Wychert Ale** (OG 1040, ABV 3.9%)

**Hadda's Summer Glory** (ABV 4%)

**Edgar's Golden Ale** (ABV 4.3%)

**Grumpling Old Ale** (OG 1046.5, ABV 4.6%)

**Hadda's Headbanger** (ABV 5.5%)

## VAUX
**Vaux Breweries Ltd., The Brewery, Sunderland, Tyne & Wear SR1 3AN.**
☎ (0191) 567 6277
FAX (0191) 514 0422

First established in 1837 and now one of the country's largest regional brewers, Vaux remains firmly independent. It owns Ward's of Sheffield, but sold off Lorimer & Clark in Edinburgh to Caledonian in 1987. Real ale is sold in over 500 of its 939 houses (which include those run by Ward's and Vaux Inns Ltd.) and is also provided to its 700 free trade customers. Tours by arrangement. Vaux Waggle Dance (OG 1047, ABV 5%) is produced at Ward's (qv), whilst Vaux Mild is Ward's Mild rebadged.

**Lorimer's Best Scotch** (OG 1036, ABV 3.6%) 🍺 A replica of the original Scottish Scotch. Aroma is often lacking, but, when fresh, there can be a subtle hop character to balance a sweet and malty taste.

**Bitter** (OG 1038, ABV 3.9%) 🍺 A light and drinkable bitter with low bitterness and some fruit evident. Aroma is easily lost, but can be hoppy.

**Samson** (OG 1041, ABV 4.2%) 🍺 A very light bitter with a grainy aftertaste, and a sulphury aroma when fresh. Bitterness is moderate and sweetness may persist in the taste.

**Double Maxim** (OG 1048, ABV 4.7%) 🍺 A smooth brown ale, rich and well-balanced, with lasting fruit and good body.

## VIKING
**Viking Ales, t/a Viking Brewery, Unit 5, Blenheim Close, Broadstairs, Kent CT10 2YF.** ☎ (01843) 865211
FAX (01843) 603933

Brewery founded in August 1995 with the help of a Government grant, and sold to the owners of the Stag & Griffin brew pub in May 1996. It supplies around 30 regular outlets directly, plus others via wholesalers. Occasional/seasonal beer: Summer Solstice (ABV 3.5%).

**Island Dark Mild** (ABV 3.5%)

**Viking Ale** (OG 1039, ABV 3.9%)

**Thor's Thunder** (OG 1044, ABV 4.4%)

## VILLAGE See Hambleton.

## WADWORTH
**Wadworth & Co. Ltd., Northgate Brewery, Devizes, Wiltshire SN10 1JW.**
☎ (01380) 723361
FAX (01380) 724342

Delightful market town tower brewery set up in 1885 by Henry Wadworth. Though solidly traditional (with its own dray horses), it continues to invest in the future and to expand, producing up to 2,000 barrels a week to supply a wide-ranging free trade in the South of England, as well as its own 200 tied houses. All the pubs serve real ale and 6X remains one of the South's most famous beers, with national distribution now achieved via the Whitbread guest ale portfolio. Shop (reception) open in office hours. Some tours by arrangement. Occasional/seasonal beers: Valentine's Oat Malt Ale (OG 1044, ABV 4.5% February), Easter Ale (OG 1044, ABV 4.5%), Malt & Hops (OG 1044, ABV 4.5%, September).

**Henry's Original IPA** (OG 1034, ABV 3.8%) 🍺 A golden brown-coloured beer with a gentle, malty and slightly hoppy aroma, a good balance of flavours, with maltiness gradually dominating, and then a long-lasting aftertaste to match, eventually becoming biscuity. A good session beer.

**6X** (OG 1040, ABV 4.3%) 🍺 Mid-brown in colour, with a malty and fruity nose and some balancing hop character. The flavour is similar, with some bitterness and a lingering malty, but bitter finish. Full-bodied and distinctive.

**SummerSault** (OG 1044, ABV 4.5%) The summer beer, now available April–September; a pale, refreshing beer made with Saaz lager hops.

**Farmers Glory** (OG 1046, ABV 4.5%) 🍺 This dark beer can be delightfully hoppy and fruity, but varies in flavour and conditioning. The aroma is of malt and it should have a dryish, hoppy aftertaste.

**Old Timer** (OG 1055, ABV 5.8%) 🍺 Available from October–March only: a rich, copper-brown beer with a strong, fruity, malty aroma. The flavour is full-bodied and complete, with hints of butterscotch and peaches, beautifully balanced by a lasting, malty, dry finish.

## WALKER
See Nationals, Carlsberg-Tetley.

## WARDEN See Merivales.

## WARD'S

Ward's Brewery,
Ecclesall Road, Sheffield,
S. Yorkshire S11 8HZ.
☎ (0114) 275 5155
FAX (0114) 275 1816

Established in 1840 by Josiah Kirby, Ward's has been a subsidiary of Vaux of Sunderland since 1972. Since the closure of the neighbouring Thorne brewery in 1986, it has also produced Darley's beers. Real ale is available in 160 of the brewery's 220 tied houses and around 300 free trade outlets are supplied directly. Tours by arrangement.

**Mild** or **Darley's Dark Mild** (OG 1034, ABV 3.4%) 🍺 Also sold as Vaux Mild. This beer's rich dark brown and red hue promises more than is delivered. A strong malt nose precedes a roast malt taste, with hints of chocolate. The dry finish can be tinged with sweetness, if it lasts long enough.

**Thorne Best Bitter** (OG 1038, ABV 3.8%) 🍺 Recently improved, this malty-nosed, mid-brown beer has a hoppy bitterness but is well-balanced throughout, including well into the finish.

**Best Bitter** (OG 1040, ABV 4%) 🍺 The rich, malty aroma of this pale brown bitter has been toned down, but it still has a malty base and a bittersweet aftertaste.

### For Vaux:

**Waggle Dance** (OG 1049, ABV 5%) 🍺 A beer brewed with honey, gold in colour. A malty drink with a gentle bitterness and a dry, malty finish. Better for not being as sweet as before.

## WARWICKSHIRE

The Warwickshire Brewery Ltd., Princes Drive, Kenilworth, Warwickshire CV8 2EG. ☎ (01926) 863346

Brewery established in December 1995, bringing brewing back to the locality after a break of nearly 30 years. Around 40 pubs and clubs now take the beer. Bottling is planned. Tours by arrangement.

**Best Bitter** (OG 1037, ABV 3.9%)

**King's Champion** (OG 1046, ABV 4.6%)

**Kingmaker Ale** (OG 1049, ABV 5.5%)

**King's Ruin** (OG 1055, ABV 6%)

## WATKIN

Tomos Watkin & Sons Ltd.,
The Castle Brewery, 113
Rhosmaen Street, Llandeilo,
Carmarthenshire SA19 6EN.
☎ /FAX (01558) 824140

Professionally-planned new brewery established by Simon Buckley (formerly of Buckley and Ushers breweries), adopting the name of a Llandovery brewery which ceased production in 1928. Brewing commenced in December 1995 and the beers

were officially launched on St Valentine's Day 1996. The attached craft centre opened in spring 1996, whilst the brewery's one initial pub was due to be joined by three others in the first year of operation. Tours of the brewery by arrangement.

**Bitter** (OG 1041, ABV 4%)

**OSB (Old Style Bitter)** (OG 1046, ABV 4.5%)

## WATNEY

See Nationals, Scottish Courage.

## WEBSTER'S

See Mansfield, Ruddles and Nationals, Scottish Courage.

## WEETWOOD

Weetwood Ales Ltd.,
Weetwood Grange,
Weetwood, Tarporley,
Cheshire CW6 0NQ.
☎ (01829) 752377

Brewery set up at an equestrian centre in 1993, with the first brew on sale in March of that year. Around 40 regular customers are now supplied.

**Best Cask Bitter** (OG 1038.5, ABV 3.8%) 🍺 A clean, dry and fruity bitter.

**Old Dog Bitter** (OG 1045, ABV 4.5%) 🍺 A fuller-bodied version of the bitter: fruitier, with a dry, lingering aftertaste and a sulphurous nose.

**Oasthouse Gold Bitter** (OG 1050, ABV 5%) 🍺 A golden, sweetish, fruity bitter which lacks body for its strength.

## WELLS

Charles Wells Ltd., The
Eagle Brewery, Havelock
Street, Bedford MK40 4LU.
☎ (01234) 272766
FAX (01234) 279000

Successful, family-owned brewery, established in 1876 and still run by descendants of the founder. The brewery has been on this site since 1976 and now 270 of its 290 tied pubs serve cask ale, though about 50 per cent apply cask breathers. Wells also supplies around 550 other outlets direct and owns the Ancient Druids brew pub in Cambridge (qv). A new bottling line was added in 1996. Tours by arrangement.

**Eagle IPA** (OG 1035, ABV 3.6%) 🍺 A refreshing session beer that too often has its hoppy aroma knocked out by the use of a tight sparkler. Citrus fruit hop character dominates throughout, with some sulphur. Dry finish.

**Bombardier Premium Bitter** (OG 1042, ABV 4.3%) 🍺 Citrus fruits are again present but malt balances this beer, making it more rounded than Eagle. Long, dry finish.

**Fargo** (OG 1050, ABV 5%) 🍺 A beer to search for. Hops, fruit and sulphur are prominent on the nose, followed by a bitter, citrus fruit flavour with a little malt to add a slight sweetness. Hops and fruit in the long, dry finish.

## WELSH BREWERS
See Nationals, Bass.

## WELTONS See North Downs.

## WEST BERKSHIRE
**The West Berkshire Brewery Company, Pot Kiln Lane, Frilsham, Yattendon, Berkshire RG18 0XX.**
☎ / FAX (01635) 202638

Brewery established in September 1995 in converted farm buildings in the grounds of the Pot Kiln pub, although the businesses remain separate. Around ten outlets take the beers regularly and they guest in other pubs. Brick Kiln Bitter (OG 1041, ABV 4%) is only available at the Pot Kiln. Occasional beer: Graft (OG 1041, ABV 4%).

**Good Old Boy** (OG 1041, ABV 4%) A well-balanced, malty, fruity and hoppy bitter.

**Hartslock No. 1** (OG 1043, ABV 4.2%) A dark bitter, dry-hopped, with chocolate hints and a bitter finish.

**Talon** (OG 1048, ABV 4.9%) A rich ruby bitter with sweetness but a bitter finish.

## WESTBURY ALES
See Freeminer and Princetown.

## WETHERED See Nationals, Whitbread.

## WHEAL ALE See Bird in Hand.

## WHEATSHEAF INN See Fromes Hill.

## WHIM
**Whim Ales, Whim Farm, Hartington, Buxton, Derbyshire SK17 0AX.**
☎ (01298) 84991

Brewery opened in 1993 in redundant outbuildings at Whim Farm by Giles Litchfield who, in August 1995, purchased Broughton Brewery (qv). There are plans for the two breweries to distribute each other's beers in their local areas. Whim's beers, meanwhile, are available in about 50 outlets. Some one-off brews are produced. Occasional/seasonal beers: Hell's Mouth (OG 1059, ABV 6.5%), Black Christmas (OG 1062, ABV 7%, a more attenuated version of Black Bear Stout, available all year at Whim's one tied pub).

**Magic Mushroom Mild** (OG 1042, ABV 3.8%) A well-balanced mild with a complex mix of flavours. Black/ruby in colour.

**Hartington Bitter** (OG 1038, ABV 4%) Light, golden, hoppy bitter with a dry finish.

**Magic Mushroom Ale** (OG 1042, ABV 4.2%) A porter-like ale based on Magic Mushroom Mild but without lactose, giving less sweetness and a dry finish.

**High Peak Pale Ale** (OG 1041, ABV 4.3%) A smooth, single-malt pale ale lightly hopped with German hops.

**Schnee Weiss** or **Snow White** (OG 1043, ABV 4.5%) A Bavarian-style wheat beer.

**Special** (OG 1045, ABV 4.7%) Full-bodied bitter. Good balance of fruit and hops; dry, crisp finish.

**Old Izaak** (OG 1052, ABV 5.2%) A dry, dark brown beer with good flavour balance. Dry, bitter finish.

**Black Bear Stout** (OG 1062, ABV 6.2%)

## WHITBREAD See Nationals.

## WHITBY'S
**Whitby's Own Brewery Ltd., St Hilda's, The Ropery, Whitby, N. Yorkshire YO22 4ET.**
☎ (01947) 605914

Brewery opened in a former workhouse in 1988 and moved 50 yards in 1992 into newer, larger premises. Free trade (mostly as guest beers) extends from Newcastle upon Tyne to Huddersfield and takes in roughly 40 outlets. Tours by arrangement.

**Wallop** (OG 1036, ABV 3.5%) ◆ Formerly known as Ammonite Bitter. A light, refreshing beer, pleasant and fruity, with a hoppy aftertaste. Difficult to track down, but well worth the effort.

**Nut Brown Ale** (OG 1045, ABV 4.5%) A full-bodied, nutty/chocolatey beer.

**Woblle** (OG 1045, ABV 4.5%) ◆ A copper-red, full-bodied, malty bitter, with a burnt roast flavour and a dry, hoppy finish.

**Force Nine** (OG 1055, ABV 5.5%) ◆ Strong and dark, with a well-balanced blend of contrasting flavours: sweet and fruity, dry and malty, with a strong, bitter finish. A beer of the winter ale type, excellent in its class.

**Demon** (OG 1066, ABV 6.6%) A strong pale ale.

## WHITE
**White Brewing Company, The 1066 Country Brewery, Pebsham Farm Industrial Estate, Pebsham Lane, Bexhill, E. Sussex TN40 2RZ.** ☎ (01424) 731066

Brewery founded in May 1995 by husband and wife David and Lesley White to serve local free trade outlets and a wholesaler. Visits by appointment only.

**1066 Country Bitter** (OG 1040, ABV 4%)

# THE INDEPENDENTS

## WHITEWATER
**Whitewater Brewing Co.,
40 Tullyframe Road,
Kilkeel, Newry, Co. Down
BT34 4RZ.**
☎ /FAX (0139 67) 26370

Brewery founded in summer 1996 and now supplying four outlets in Northern Ireland. Beer: Mountain Ale (OG 1043, ABV 4.2%).

## WHITWORTH HALL
**Whitworth Hall Brewery, Spennymoor, Co. Durham.**

Brewery closed.

## WICKWAR
**The Wickwar Brewing Co.,
Arnolds Cooperage, The
Old Cider Mill, Station
Road, Wickwar,
Gloucestershire GL12 8NB.**
☎ (01454) 294168

WICKWAR BREWING CO

Brewery launched on the 'Glorious First of May 1990' (guest beer law day) by two Courage tenants with the aim of providing guest ales for their three tenancies. The business proved so successful that they dropped the pubs to concentrate on supplying their other regular outlets (now totalling over 100). The brewery operates from the cooper's shop of the old Arnold, Perret & Co. Ltd. brewery. Tours by arrangement.

**Coopers' WPA** (OG 1036.5, ABV 3.5%) ◆ A yellow/gold, well-balanced, light, refreshing brew with hops, citrus fruit, peardrop flavour and notable malt character. Bitter, dry finish.

**Brand Oak Bitter (BOB)** (OG 1038.5, ABV 4%) ◆ A distinctive blend of hops, malt and citrus fruits. The slightly sweet taste turns into a fine, dry bitterness with a similar lasting finish. Moreish.

**Olde Merryford Ale** (OG 1048, ABV 4.8%) ◆ A pale brown, full-flavoured, well-balanced beer, with malt, hops and fruit elements throughout. Slightly sweet, with a long lasting, malty, dry finish.

**Station Porter** (OG 1059.5, ABV 6.1%) ◆ A smooth, warming, dark brown ale with an aroma of roast malt, coffee and rich fruit. It has a similar, complex and spicy, rich, bittersweet taste and a long, smooth, roast finish. Available October–December.

## WILD'S
**Wild's Brewery, Unit 3E,
Spa Field Industrial Estate,
Slaithwaite, Huddersfield,
W. Yorkshire HD7 5BB.**
☎ (01484) 648387

Brewery founded in March 1994 by Pete and Wendy Wild, beginning serious production

in August that year after five months of experimentation. At present, around 20 outlets are supplied. Tours are available for groups by prior arrangement.

**Wild Session** (OG 1038, ABV 3.8%)

**Wild Oats** (OG 1041, ABV 4.1%)

**Wild Blonde** (OG 1045, ABV 4.5%)

**Wild Redhead** (OG 1045, ABV 4.5%)

**Wild Thing** (OG 1050, ABV 5%)

## JAMES WILLIAMS See Pub Groups.

## WILLY'S
**Willy's Pub and Brewery, 17
High Cliff Road,
Cleethorpes, Lincolnshire
DN35 8RQ.**
☎ (01472) 602145
FAX (01472) 603578

🍺 Seafront pub brewery opened in 1989, also supplying a second local outlet and some free trade. Old Groyne is popular as a guest beer through wholesalers. Some occasional beers are brewed. Tours by arrangement. Occasional beer: Burcom Bitter (OG 1044, ABV 4.2%).

**Original Bitter** (OG 1038, ABV 3.7%) ◆ A tawny beer with a raisin fruit and hop nose, the fruit getting the better in the taste which also has malt and bitterness.

**Last Resort** (OG 1042, ABV 4.3%) A light summer beer.

**Coxswains Special Bitter** (OG 1049, ABV 4.9%)

**Old Groyne** (OG 1060, ABV 6.2%) Fruit and malt in the nose lead to fruit and malt in the taste, but with hop character present throughout. Bittersweet finish.

## WILSON'S
See Mansfield, Morland, and Nationals, Scottish Courage.

## WINGFIELDS
**Wingfields Brewery, The Raven, Bedford Street, Portsmouth, Hampshire PO5 4BT.**
☎ (01705) 829079

🍺 Very small pub brewery set up in November 1995, just serving the pub itself. A lager is planned but this will be kept under gas pressure. Beers: Mild (ABV 3.5%), Bitter (ABV 3.7%), Stout (ABV 3.8%), Winter Brew (ABV 4.5%).

## WOLF
**The Wolf Brewery Ltd.,
10 Maurice Gaymer Road,
Attleborough, Norfolk
NR17 2QZ.**
☎ (01953)457775
FAX (01953) 457776

Brewery founded by the former owner of the Reindeer Brewery in 1996, using a 20-barrel plant housed on the site of the old Gaymers cider orchard. About 60 customers take the beer.

**Bitter** (ABV 3.9%)

## WOLVERHAMPTON & DUDLEY See Banks's and Camerons.

## WOOD

**The Wood Brewery Ltd., Wistanstow, Craven Arms, Shropshire SY7 8DG.**
☎ (01588) 672523
FAX (01588) 673939

A village brewery, founded by the Wood family in 1980, in buildings adjacent to the Plough Inn. The brewery has enjoyed steady growth in recent years and now supplies around 200 other outlets (locally, and further afield via wholesalers). Sam Powell beers have been brewed here since the Powell brewery in Newtown went into receivership in 1991. One pub is owned at present, but more may be acquired. Tours by arrangement. Occasional/seasonal beers: Summer That (OG 1038, ABV 3.9%), Saturnalia (OG 1042, ABV 4.2%, January–February), Woodcutter (OG 1042, ABV 4.2%, autumn), Get Knotted (OG 1045, ABV 4.7%, February), Hopping Mad (OG 1048, ABV 4.8%, March), Anniversary Ale (OG 1050, ABV 5%, April), Christmas Cracker (OG 1060, ABV 6%, November–December). Bottle-conditioned beer: Shropshire Lad (OG 1050, ABV 5%).

**Wallop** (OG 1035, ABV 3.4%)

**Sam Powell Original Bitter** (OG 1038, ABV 3.7%)

**Parish Bitter** (OG 1039, ABV 4%) ◆ A blend of malt and hops with a bitter aftertaste. Pale brown in colour.

**Special Bitter** (OG 1042, ABV 4.2%) ◆ A tawny brown bitter with malt, hops and some fruitiness.

**Shropshire Lad** (OG 1046, ABV 4.5%)

**Sam Powell Old Sam** (OG 1047, ABV 4.6%)

**Wonderful** (OG 1048, ABV 4.8%) ◆ A mid-brown, fruity beer, with a roast and malt taste.

## WOODFORDE'S

**Woodforde's Norfolk Ales (Woodforde's Ltd.), Broadland Brewery, Woodbastwick, Norwich, Norfolk NR13 6SW.**
☎ (01603) 720353 FAX (01603) 721806

Founded in late 1980 in Norwich, to bring much-needed choice to a long Watney-dominated region, Woodforde's moved to a converted farm complex, with greatly increased production capacity, in the picturesque Broadland village of Woodbastwick in 1989. It brews an extensive

range of beers and runs two tied houses, with some 200 other outlets supplied on a regular basis. Tours for groups by arrangement on weekday evenings. Visitor centre and shop open 11–6 Tue–Fri, 11–5 Sat and 11–3.30 Sun. Occasional beer: John Browne's Ale (OG 1043, ABV 4.3%). Bottle-conditioned beers: Norfolk Ale (OG 1048, ABV 4.7%), Norfolk Nips (OG 1085, ABV 8.6%).

**Broadsman Bitter** (OG 1035, ABV 3.5%) ◆ A session beer which is a straightforward combination of malt and hops, with hints of sweetness and fruit. Hops and bitterness dominate the aftertaste.

**Mardler's Mild** (OG 1035, ABV 3.5%) 🛱 ◆ A red/brown mild which is fairly dry (for a mild), smooth and malty. Well-balanced, with some subtle fruitiness. The aftertaste is pleasant but short.

**Wherry Best Bitter** (OG 1038, ABV 3.8%) 🍺 ◆ This award-winning, amber beer has a distinctly hoppy nose and a well-balanced palate with pronounced bitterness and, usually, a flowery hop character. A long-lasting, satisfying, bitter aftertaste.

**Old Bram** (OG 1043, ABV 4.1%) ◆ A distinctly fruity old ale, full-bodied and flavoursome. Roast malt and hints of chocolate feature.

**Norfolk Stout** (OG 1042, ABV 4.2%) A traditional black Norfolk ale with a milk chocolate-coloured head.

**Great Eastern Ale** (OG 1043, ABV 4.3%) A refreshing, light straw-coloured bitter with a slightly sweetish, malty taste.

**Nelson's Revenge** (OG 1045, ABV 4.5%) ◆ This premium bitter has quite a strong, pleasant, malty, fruity, hoppy aroma which the rounded and complex, malty palate doesn't quite live up to. The hoppiness and bitterness come through more distinctly at the end to give a good, lasting aftertaste.

**Norfolk Nog** (OG 1049, ABV 4.6%) 🛱 ◆ A full-bodied red/brown beer with plenty of flavour and aroma. Roast malt balances the sweeter components of the palate. A very good, dark winter brew. *Champion Beer of Britain 1992.*

**Baldric** (OG 1052, ABV 5.6%) ◆ An amber/golden, light beer, with almost delicate hopping. A pleasing combination of malt, hops and fruit, with some sweetness in the palate and bitterness in the finish.

**Headcracker** (OG 1069, ABV 7%) 🛱 ◆ This fairly pale brown barley wine is full-bodied and fruity throughout. The sweetness in the palate is balanced by the hoppiness and bitterness, and the aftertaste is warming.

## WOODY WOODWARD'S
See Fox & Hounds.

## WORLDHAM

**Worldham Brewery,
Smith's Farm, East
Worldham, Alton,
Hampshire GU34 3AT.**
☎ **(01420) 83383**
FAX **(01420) 83600**

It took 18 months for experienced brewer
Hugo Sharpe to convert a hop kiln into a
ten-barrel brewery, using plant acquired
from a number of different breweries.
Worldham eventually launched its first beer
at the 1991 CAMRA Farnham Beerex and
now serves around 30 free trade outlets.
Tours by arrangement.

**Old Dray Bitter** (OG 1044, ABV 4.4%)
🔶 Mid- to deep brown beer, low in aroma
and with a dry flavour with some grain.
Strong on hops in the slightly cloying finish.

**Golden Summer Bitter** (OG 1046, ABV
4.6%)

**Barbarian Bitter** (OG 1052, ABV 5.2%) A
well-hopped premium bitter.

## WORTH See Commercial.

## WORTHINGTON
See Nationals, Bass.

## WORTLEY

**Wortley Arms Brewery,
Wortley Arms Hotel,
Halifax Road, Wortley,
Sheffield, S. Yorkshire
S30 7DB.** ☎ **(0114) 288 2245**

Full mash brewery opened in 1991 in the
cellar of the Wortley Arms Hotel. Tours
by arrangement. Very limited outside trade.
Beers: Bitter (OG 1036, ABV 3.6%), Earls Ale
(OG 1044, ABV 4.2%), Countess Ale (OG
1056, ABV 5.4%, winter).

## WYCHWOOD

**Wychwood Brewery Ltd.,
The Eagle Maltings, The
Crofts, Corn Street, Witney,
Oxfordshire OX8 7AZ**
☎ **(01993) 702574**
FAX **(01993) 772553**

Formerly Glenny Brewery, set up in 1983 in
the old maltings of the extinct Clinch's
brewery. It moved to a new site in 1987 and
was radically revamped during 1992, when
nine pubs were acquired (leased from Allied
or Inntrepreneur) by its sister company
Hobgoblinns Ltd. The company now runs 30
managed pubs (ten free, the rest tied to
Scottish Courage), in various towns across
the South and South-West, all restyled in the
bare boards and breweriana idiom, most
renamed Hobgoblin and all taking real ale.
Wychwood also supplies about 80 other
outlets. As a consequence of the extra
demand, the brewery moved back to the old

Clinch's site in 1994. Tours by arrangement.
Shop open 9–5 Mon–Fri (ring Sat).

**Fiddlers Elbow** (OG 1040, ABV 4%) Brewed
May–September, a straw-coloured beer
containing barley and wheat malts.

**Special** (OG 1042, ABV 4.2%) 🔶 Formerly
Wychwood Best: a mid-brown, full-
flavoured premium bitter. Moderately
strong in hop and malt flavours, with
pleasing, fruity overtones which last
through to the aftertaste.

**Old Devil** (OG 1047, ABV 4.7%)

**Black Wych Stout** (OG 1050, ABV 5%) A
rich black stout, available Halloween–
Christmas.

**The Dog's Bollocks** (OG 1051, ABV 5.2%) A
full-bodied, hoppy, golden brew,
incorporating Styrian hops and wheat.

**Hobgoblin** (OG 1055, ABV 5.5%)
🔶 Powerful, full-bodied, copper-red, well-
balanced brew. Strong in roasted malt, with
a moderate, hoppy bitterness and a slight
fruity character.

## WYE VALLEY

**Wye Valley Brewery,
69 St Owen Street, Hereford
HR1 2JQ.** ☎ **(01432) 342546**
FAX **(01432) 266553**

Brewery which started
production in 1985 and moved to its
present address in 1986. New plant was
installed in 1992 to increase capacity and
cater for a rapidly growing free trade
(currently 150 outlets). Tours by
arrangement. The company now also has
three pubs of its own and produces seasonal
beers under the Dorothy Goodbody name.
Occasional/seasonal beer: Father Christmas
Ale (OG 1080, ABV 8%, December; also
bottle-conditioned).

**Bitter** (OG 1036, ABV 3.5%) 🔶 A beer whose
aroma gives little hint of the bitter hoppiness
which follows right through to the aftertaste.

**Dorothy Goodbody's Springtime Bitter**
(OG 1040, ABV 4%) Available March–May; a
full, malt-flavoured beer with bitterness and
a hop aroma.

**Hereford Pale Ale** or **HPA** (OG 1040, ABV
4%) 🔶 A pale, hoppy, malty brew with a
hint of sweetness before a dry finish.

**Dorothy Goodbody's Golden Summertime
Ale** (OG 1042, ABV 4.2%). Available June–
August; a golden ale with a light malt
flavour.

**Supreme** (OG 1044, ABV 4.3%) 🔶 A rich,
fruity, malt aroma leads to a sweet, malt and
fruit taste which lingers to the finish.

**Dorothy Goodbody's Glowing Autumn
Ale** (OG 1045, ABV 4.5%). Available
September–November; a dry, full-flavoured
beer with a deep colour.

**Dorothy Goodbody's Wholesome Stout**
(OG 1046, ABV 4.6%) 🔶 Available

November–April. A very smooth and satisfying stout without a bitter edge to its roast flavours. The finish combines roast grain and malt.

**Dorothy Goodbody's Wintertime Ale** (OG 1056, ABV 5.6%) ♦ Available December–February. A sweet winter ale with a fruity, hoppy taste and a rich, fruity aftertaste.

**Brew 69** (OG 1055, ABV 5.6%) ♦ A pale premium beer named after the brewery's street number. Its hoppy taste has a hint of malt; slightly bitter aftertaste.

## WYLYE VALLEY
**Wylye Valley Brewery, Dove Inn, Corton, Warminster, Wiltshire BA12 0SZ.**
☎ / FAX (01985) 850159

Pub brewery hand-built in an old stable block by the landlord of the Dove Inn. It began commercial production in February 1996 and about a dozen other pubs now take the beer. Cellar tanks (no gas blankets) supplement cask storage at the Dove itself. Tours by arrangement.

**Pale Ale** (OG 1037, ABV 4%)

**Sledgehammer** (OG 1046, ABV 5%)

## WYRE PIDDLE
**Wyre Piddle Brewery, Unit 21, Craycombe Farm, Fladbury, Evesham, Worcestershire WR10 2QS.**
☎ (01386) 860473

Brewery established by a former publican and master builder in autumn 1994. Over 80 outlets now take the beer from time to time, in locations throughout the southern Midlands. Occasional/seasonal beer: Piddle in the Snow (OG 1050, ABV 5.2%, December–January).

**Piddle in the Hole** (OG 1039, ABV 3.9%) ♦ A beer dominated by strong malty tastes throughout.

**Piddle in the Wind** (OG 1045, ABV 4.5%) ♦ A malty ale with a sweet aftertaste.

## YATES
**Yates Brewery, Ghyll Farm, Westnewton, Aspatria, Cumbria CA5 3NX.**
☎ (0169 73) 21081

Small, traditional brewery set up in 1986 by Peter and Carol Yates in an old farm building on their smallholding, where a herd of pedigree goats makes good use of the brewery's by-products. Brewing award-winning beers to their capacity of 34 barrels a week during summer and other peak times, they also serve over 20 free trade outlets and own one pub.

**Bitter** (OG 1035, ABV 3.7%) ♦ A fruity, bitter, straw-coloured ale with malt and hops in the aroma and a long, bitter aftertaste.

**Premium** (OG 1048, ABV 5.5%) ♦ Available at Christmas and a few other times of the year. Straw-coloured, with a strong aroma of malt and hops, and full-flavoured, with a slight toffee taste. The malty aftertaste becomes strongly bitter.

**Best Cellar** (OG 1052, ABV 6%) ♦ Brewed only in winter and the strength changes from year to year. An excellent, red/brown beer with a fruity aroma and a sweet, malty flavour, contrasted by a hoppy bitterness. The finish is a bittersweet balance, with grain and some hops.

## YORK
**The York Brewery Co. Ltd., 12 Toft Green, Micklegate, York, N. Yorkshire YO1 1JT.**
☎ (01904) 621162
FAX (01904) 621216

Brewery which began production in May 1996, the first brewery in the city for over 40 years. The plant came from the closed Lion's brewery in Burnley and was installed in a former carpet (and later motorbike) showroom on the York Tourist Trail, within the city walls. Planning the brewery was undertaken with the visitor very much in mind (daily tours).

**Stonewall** (ABV 3.7%)

**Yorkshire Terrier** (ABV 4.2%)

## YORKSHIRE GREY
See Nationals, Scottish Courage.

## YORK TAVERN
**York Tavern, 1 Leicester Street, Norwich, Norfolk NR2 2AS.** ☎ (01603) 620918
FAX (01603) 761046

Full mash pub brewery founded in spring 1996 and supplying only itself in the main. Beers: Old Duke (OG 1038, ABV 4%), Old Nick (OG 1047, ABV 4.7%).

## YOUNGER
See Nationals, Scottish Courage.

## YOUNG'S
**Young & Co.'s Brewery PLC, The Ram Brewery, High Street, Wandsworth, London SW18 4JD.**
☎ (0181) 875 7000
FAX (0181) 875 7100

Brewery founded in 1675 by the Draper family, and bought by Charles Young and Anthony Bainbridge in 1831. Their partnership was dissolved in 1884 and the business was continued by the Young family. Though a public company since 1898, Young's is still very much a family affair and was the only London brewer not to join the keg revolution in the 1970s. It still brews award-winning beers in the traditional manner, with some of its pub deliveries made by horse-drawn drays. Around 500 free trade outlets are supplied, mostly within the M25 ring, though the brewery's presence is extending westward, and the brewery's tied estate now stands at 169 houses. The Bill Bentley's wine bar chain is also part of the business. Tours by arrangement. Occasional/seasonal beers: Best Mild Ale (ABV 3.2%, April–May), Dirty Dick's (ABV 4.1%, September–October).

**Bitter** (OG 1036, ABV 3.7%) ❧ A distinctive amber beer. A strong, hoppy bitterness is followed by a delightfully astringent and hoppy, bitter aftertaste. An underlying malt balance is present throughout.

**Wheat Beer** (ABV 4.1%) Available June–August. A naturally cloudy, straw-coloured beer with a mostly fruity aroma, an orangey fruit taste, moderate sweetness and a slight bitterness. Notably dry aftertaste.

**Special** (OG 1046, ABV 4.6%) 🗍 ❧ A strong, full-flavoured, bitter beer with a powerful hoppiness and a balancing malt flavour. Hops persist in the aftertaste.

**Ram Rod** (ABV 5%) ❧ Mid-brown beer with a malty aroma which leads to a strong malt flavour and a slightly sweet, malty aftertaste. Only a faint hint of hops throughout.

**Winter Warmer** (OG 1055, ABV 5%) 🗍 ❧ A dark reddish-brown ale with a malty, fruity aroma, a sweet, malty flavour and a sweet, fruity finish, plus a hint of caramel throughout. Available October–March.

# NOTES

# BASS

**Bass Brewers Ltd., 137 High Street, Burton upon Trent, Staffordshire DE14 1JZ ☎ (01283) 511000 [FAX] (01283) 513435**

Founded in 1777, Bass is Britain's second largest brewer, with some 23 per cent of all beer production, though, if its planned takeover of Carlsberg-Tetley is given the go-ahead, it will once more be the country's largest beer-maker. It produces the country's biggest selling beer brand, Carling Black Label lager, and two of its ale brands (Stones Bitter and Worthington Bitter) feature amongst the top five sellers. Draught Bass, promoted as its flagship brand, is still the biggest-selling premium cask ale, although volumes are thought to be in decline, thanks mainly to the company's major innovation of the last decade, Caffrey's Ale. The first of the new breed of nitrokeg beers (brewery-conditioned, pasteurised beers which are served under a mixture of $CO_2$ and nitrogen), Caffrey's has also had an impact on Bass's regional ales, with Charrington IPA and Bass Special already discontinued. In addition, Bass has enjoyed success with its Cask Master 'guest' beer scheme, for which special brews have been produced at its Birmingham, Cardiff and Sheffield breweries.

Following the closures of the breweries in Edinburgh (Heriot), Sheffield (Hope) and Wolverhampton (Springfield), and the sale of Highgate Brewery in Walsall to a management buyout team (see Independents), Bass now brews at just eight sites, with those at Alton, Belfast and Tadcaster producing only keg beer. There is a cask ale facility at Glasgow and this has attempted a few brews in recent years, though with little success in the Scottish market place. Bass also has interests in China and in the Czech Republic (through Staropramen, which Bass imports into the UK, and Ostrova).

Half of Bass's production goes into the free trade. On its pub side, the company runs around 4,200 houses (74 per cent taking cask beer), of which about two-thirds are managed and the balance tenanted or leased. Many pubs still bear the liveries of former Bass trading divisions like Charrington, M&B (Mitchells & Butlers) and Welsh Brewers. The Harvester chain of food pubs has now been acquired and this follows the disposal by Bass of about 2,700 pubs in recent years to comply with the DTI Beer Orders, which restricted the number of tied houses run by national brewers. However, many of these pubs were sold to pub chains which then agreed to take their beer from Bass.

## BIRMINGHAM

**Cape Hill Brewery, PO Box 27, Smethwick, Birmingham, W. Midlands B16 0PQ.
☎ (0121) 558 1481**

One of the largest cask beer production centres in the country, subject of a £61 million investment programme in recent years. Bottle-conditioned beer: Worthington White Shield (OG 1050.5, ABV 5.6%) 🗗 🍺.

**M&B Mild** (OG 1034.5, ABV 3.2%) 🍺 A dark brown quaffing mild with roast and malt flavours. Dry, slightly bitter finish.

**M&B Brew XI** (OG 1039.5, ABV 3.9%) 🍺 A sweet, malty beer with a hoppy, bitter aftertaste.

## BURTON

**Burton Brewery, Station Street, Burton upon Trent, Staffordshire DE14 1JZ.
☎ (01283) 513578**

The original home of Bass, producing one of Britain's most famous ales, available throughout its estate and the free trade. **Draught Bass** (OG 1043, ABV 4.4%) 🍺 A malty beer with underlying hops and a dry finish. The classic taste is still occasionally found but modern dispense methods diminish the aroma, taste and finish.

🗗 The empty tankard indicates the beer was a *Good Beer Guide* Beer of the Year in the last three years.

## CARDIFF
**The Brewery, Crawshay Street, Cardiff CF1 1TR. ☎ (01222) 233071**
FAX (01222) 372668

The Hancock's brewery (founded in 1884) which was taken over by Bass Charrington in 1968. Tours by arrangement. Occasional beer: Hancock's IPA (OG 1038, ABV 3.6%).

**Worthington Dark Mild** (OG 1034.5, ABV 3%) ◆ A dark brown, creamy mild with a somewhat malty flavour, followed by a sweet finish. Popular in the Swansea area.

**Hancock's HB** (OG 1038, ABV 3.6%) ◆ A pale brown, slightly malty, bittersweet beer with some fruitiness. A consistent regional beer.

**Worthington Draught Bitter** (OG 1038, ABV 3.6%) ◆ A light brown, slightly malty beer, with a bitter taste and some dryness in the finish. A very consistent national brand.

## MUSEUM
**Museum Brewing Company, The Bass Museum, PO Box 220, Horninglow Street, Burton upon Trent, Staffordshire DE14 1YQ. ☎ (01283) 511000**
FAX (01283) 513509

Active brewery housed within Bass's popular museum, producing around 50 barrels a week of the beers listed below for sale on site and in other outlets. The beer recipes are taken from the Bass archives. A range of IPAs in the ABV range of 4.9–5.4% is also produced for sale as pub house beers, and two beers are re-creations of the defunct Offiler's Brewery ales under contract for the Headless Beer Company wholesaler ☎ (01332) 203955. Bottle-conditioned beers are produced to order for private and public celebrations and can be purchased from the museum shop. Museum open 10–5 (last entries 4); shop open 10–6, all week. The bar on site is open until 7 for visitors already inside. Occasional beer: Premium Pale Ale (OG 1063, ABV 6.5%, winter).

**Quaffing Ale** (OG 1038, ABV 4%)

**Masterpiece IPA** (OG 1048, ABV 4.9%)

**P2 Imperial Stout** (OG 1078, ABV 8%) A black, sweetish, complex stout.

**No.1 Barley Wine** (OG 1105, ABV 10.5%, winter) A dark ruby beer brewed in summer and fermented in casks for six months.

### For Headless Beer Company:

**Offiler's Mild** (OG 1037, ABV 4%)

**Offiler's Bitter** (OG 1038, ABV 4%)

## SHEFFIELD
**Cannon Brewery, 43 Rutland Road, Sheffield, S. Yorkshire S3 8BE.**
**☎ (0114) 272 0323** FAX **(0114) 272 6442**

The original home of William Stones Ltd., dating from at least 1860. It was taken over by Bass in 1968 and, following much investment in recent years, is now the company's specialist cask beer brewery. Tours by arrangement.

**Cask Mild** (OG 1032, ABV 3.1%) ◆ A pleasant, smooth, dark mild with a faint aroma of caramel, which leads to a caramel and roast rich taste, with complementing sweetness and bitterness. A good, long, satisfying, roast malt and caramel-sweet finish.

**Toby Cask** (OG 1032, ABV 3.2%) ◆ An amber-coloured mild: a lightly-flavoured blend of malt, sweetness and bitterness. At its best, it has a delicate, pleasing, flowery taste, but can too often be bland. A disappointing, short, sweetish finish and little aroma.

**Worthington Draught Bitter** (OG 1038, ABV 3.6%) This supplements supplies from the Cardiff brewery.

**Stones Bitter** (OG 1039, ABV 3.9%) ◆ Although generally more hoppy than recently, this golden straw-coloured brew retains a careful balance of malt, hop and fruit on the nose, mellow tastes in the mouth and a clean and bitter finish.

# CARLSBERG-TETLEY
**Carlsberg-Tetley Brewing Ltd., 107 Station Street, Burton upon Trent, Staffordshire DE14 1BZ. ☎ (01283) 512222**
FAX **(01283) 502357**

The story of Britain's third largest brewing company, Carlsberg-Tetley, can be traced back to 1961 when Ansells, Tetley Walker and Ind Coope joined forces to become Allied Breweries. In 1992 Allied merged with Danish lager giant Carlsberg and Carlsberg-Tetley was born. Brewing trade analysts immediately predicted brewery closures and brand rationalisation as Carlsberg's modern Northampton brewery was added to Allied's already under-capacity sites. These predictions were realised in 1996, when the closures of Tetley Walker's Warrington brewery and the Plympton brewery in Plymouth were announced. The Warrington brews have been dispersed throughout the Carlsberg-Tetley empire and Plympton's Dartmoor beers are now brewed under contract by St Austell (see Independents). It is unlikely that this will be the end of the rationalisation and the historic lager plant at Wrexham still looks vulnerable, especially if the company is taken over by Bass, as seems likely.

Carlsberg-Tetley is effectively only a brewing company. The former Allied pubs, which are mostly still tied to Carlsberg-Tetley beers, are held by Allied-Domecq. Local brewery liveries still decorate many of the pubs, with the old brewing names of Tetley, Peter Walker, Friary Meux, Benskins, ABC, Halls and Ansells still in evidence. In London, the Taylor Walker division is complemented by the small Nicholson's chain of upmarket pubs. The Firkin chain of brew pubs was acquired from Stakis Leisure in 1991. There have also been many pub disposals, with hundreds of Allied pubs sold or leased to regional breweries and pub chains, some with the Carlsberg-Tetley beer tie still in place. The current Allied stock stands at around 4,100 pubs.

## ALLOA

**Carlsberg-Tetley Alloa Ltd., Alloa Brewery, Whins Road, Alloa, Clackmannanshire FK10 3RB. ☎ (01259) 723539**

The company's Scottish arm, established in 1819, which was taken over by Archibald Arrol in 1866. It fell to Ind Coope & Allsopp's in 1951, becoming part of Allied in the 1961 merger. Over £2.5 million has been invested in the site in recent years. Less than half of Alloa's 310 pubs sell real ale. Tours by arrangement. Occasional beer: Arrol's 90/- (ABV 4.9%).

**Arrol's 80/-** (OG 1041, ABV 4.4%) ❧ A fruity Scottish heavy, dominated by malt, fruit and hops, with increasing hoppiness in the aftertaste. Well worth seeking out when in top form.

## ALLSOPP

**Samuel Allsopp Brewery Company, 107 Station Street, Burton upon Trent, Staffordshire DE14 1BZ. ☎ (01283) 502284 FAX (01283) 502209**

Specialist cask ale brewery on the site of the main Burton complex. Reviving the old Allsopp's name, the brewery was re-opened in 1994 to produce limited edition, mid–high strength beers for Carlsberg-Tetley's Tapster's Choice 'guest' beer scheme (each available for about six weeks). These have included Single Malt Ale (ABV 4.1%), Harvest Ale (ABV 4.2%, summer), Sam's Stout (OG 1040, ABV 4.2%), IPA (OG 1041, ABV 4.2%), Old Ruby (OG 1041, ABV 4.2%), Double Diamond Cask (OG 1041.5, ABV 4.3%), Summer Golden Ale (ABV 4.4%), Treason Ale (OG 1046, ABV 4.7%), Devil's Kiss (OG 1050.5, ABV 5.2%), Sam's Porter (ABV 5.2%), Triple Diamond (ABV 5.3%) and Winter Warmer (OG 1052, ABV 5.5%).

## For HP&D:

**HP&D Mild** (OG 1036, ABV 3.7%)

## BURTON

**Carlsberg-Tetley Burton Brewery Ltd., 107 Station Street, Burton upon Trent, Staffordshire DE14 1BZ. ☎ (01283) 531111**

Brewery established by the merger of the adjoining Allsopp's and Ind Coope breweries in 1934. It currently has a capacity of two and a half million barrels a year and primarily brews real ales for the South and the Midlands, providing beer for the Ansells, Ind Coope Retail and Nicholson's trading divisions of Allied-Domecq. These 'local' beers are largely derived from two mashes: ABC and Friary from one, Benskins and Nicholson's from the other. Tours by arrangement.

**Ansells Mild** (OG 1033, ABV 3.4%) ❧ A dark red/brown beer with a smooth mouthfeel. Good caramel and liquorice aroma and taste.

**ABC Best Bitter** (OG 1035, ABV 3.7%) A light, refreshing bitter, owing much of its character to dry hopping but with malt and fruit on the tongue.

**Ansells Bitter** (OG 1035, ABV 3.7%) ❧ A pale brown, clean and sharp bitter with a good hop bite. Hop and fruit aroma; dry finish.

**Benskins Best Bitter** (OG 1035, ABV 3.7%) ❧ A predominantly hoppy session beer, which can be a very suppable pint but sometimes suffers from an astringent aftertaste.

**Friary Meux Best Bitter** (OG 1035, ABV 3.7%) ❧ Malt just dominates over hops in the aroma and flavour of this beer, and a strange, fruity taste lurks in the background.

**Nicholson's Best Bitter** (OG 1035, ABV 3.7%)

**Ind Coope Burton Ale** (OG 1047, ABV 4.8%) ❧ Full-tasting hoppy beer with a dry finish and a fruity aroma. *Champion Beer of Britain 1990.*

### For Greenalls:

**Greenalls Mild** (OG 1032, ABV 3.3%)

**Shipstone's Mild** (OG 1034, ABV 3.4%)

**Davenports Traditional Bitter** (OG 1037, ABV 3.7%)

**Greenalls Bitter** (OG 1036, ABV 3.8%)

**Shipstone's Bitter** (OG 1037, ABV 3.9%)

**Thomas Greenall's Original Bitter** (OG 1045, ABV 4.6%)

### For Little Pub Company:

**Little Lumphammer** (OG 1039, ABV 3.5%)

## HP&D
**Holt, Plant & Deakin Ltd., Dudley Road, Wolverhampton, W. Midlands, WV2 3AF.**
☎ **(01902) 450504**

Brewery trading under the name of Holts, but do not confuse it with Manchester's Joseph Holt brewery (to help differentiate, the beers are listed in *Good Beer Guide* pub entries under HP&D). This is a Black Country company set up in 1984 and now running 23 traditional pubs, all serving real ale. Holts Mild is now brewed at Allsopp in Burton and Holts Bitter is brewed by Tetley in Leeds, following the closure of the Tetley Walker Warrington plant.

**Entire** (OG 1043, ABV 4.4%) ✦ A tawny, strongly bitter beer in which fruit and hops dominate the flavour. The long, bitter aftertaste can be metallic.

**Deakin's Downfall** (OG 1060, ABV 6.1%) ✦ A dark brown, full-bodied winter ale. Malt dominates the taste and aftertaste.

## TETLEY
**Carlsberg-Tetley Brewing Ltd., Joshua Tetley & Son, PO Box 142, The Brewery, Leeds, W. Yorkshire LS1 1QG.**
☎ **(0113) 259 4594**

Yorkshire's best-known brewery, purchased in 1822 by maltster Joshua Tetley. The brewery site covers 20 acres and includes a brewhouse opened in 1989 to handle the increased demand for Tetley Bitter (Carlsberg-Tetley's biggest cask ale brand). Fifteen new Yorkshire Square fermenting vessels were commissioned in June 1996, making the brewery the largest cask ale site in the group. A £6 million visitor centre and museum, Tetley's Brewery Wharf, opened in 1994. Occasional/seasonal beer: Autumn Ale (ABV 4.7%).

**Dark Mild** (OG 1032, ABV 3.2%)

**Mild** (OG 1032, ABV 3.3%) 🛑 ✦ A red/mid-brown, smooth beer with a light malt and caramel aroma. A well-balanced taste of malt and caramel follows, with good bitterness and a dry, satisfying finish.

**Bitter** (OG 1035.5, ABV 3.7%) ✦ A variable, light, malty beer with a slight malt and hop aroma leading to a moderate bitterness and a dry finish. Pale brown in colour.

**Imperial** (OG 1042, ABV 4.3%) ✦ A complex, creamy, copper-coloured beer. A light malt and fruit nose is followed by a well-rounded taste of malt, hops and fruit, leading to a short-lived dry, bitter finish.

**Wild Rover** (OG 1055, ABV 5.6%)

### For HP&D:

**HP&D Bitter** (OG 1036, ABV 3.7%)

## TETLEY WALKER
**Tetley Walker Ltd., Warrington, Cheshire.**

Brewery founded by the Walker family in 1852 which merged with Joshua Tetley in 1960 and was closed by Carlsberg-Tetley in 1996. Its numerous beers (including those brewed for Greenalls) have been mostly transferred to Burton upon Trent and Leeds, however, as we went to press, it had not been declared where Walker Mild (OG 1032, ABV 3.2%), Walker Bitter (OG 1033, ABV 3.6%), Walker Best Bitter (OG 1036, ABV 3.7%) and Walker Winter Warmer (OG 1060, ABV 6.2%) are to be produced.

# Carlsberg-Tetley/Allied-Domecq Brew Pubs:

## FIRKIN
**The Firkin Brewery, Tamebridge House, Aldridge Road, Perry Barr, Birmingham, W. Midlands B42 2TZ.** ☎ **(0121) 344 2597**
[FAX] **(0121) 344 2579**

🛑 This famous pub brewery chain was founded by David Bruce in 1979, relaunching the brew pub concept in what used to be run-down national brewers' houses. The pubs were refurbished in a back-to-basics fashion and were given in-house breweries, tucked away behind viewing windows. The Bruce's Brewery chain rapidly grew in number until 1988, when he sold all the pubs to Midsummer Leisure (later European Leisure), which, in turn, sold them to Stakis Leisure in 1990. Since 1991, the chain has been owned by Allied-Domecq, through its subsidiaries Taylor Walker, Ind Coope Retail, Ansells Retail and Tetley Pub Co. Much expansion has taken place, with new sites opened in university towns. The destruction of some classic Midlands pubs to create new Firkins has caused much resentment amongst local drinkers. The estate currently runs to over 60 pubs, but only 38 of them brew. The remainder are supplied by the brew pubs (mainly the Falcon & Firkin in London), so only the actual brew pubs are listed here. Four basic brews are available, usually sold under house names, a 1034 OG/3.4% ABV mild, 1036 OG/3.5% ABV bitter, a stronger bitter at 1043/4.3%, and Dogbolter (OG 1057, ABV 5.6%). Some pubs offer extra one-off brews, including summer and winter ales, and also seen are Stout (OG 1047, ABV 4.6%) and Golden Glory (OG 1051, ABV 5%). All the brews are full mash and most pubs now offer some cask-conditioned beer with no additional gas applied. However, cellar tanks with mixed gas breathers are still used in some outlets. The Flamingo & Firkin in Kingston now belongs to Saxon Inns (see Independents, Flamingo).

Current brew pubs:

Faculty & Firkin, Holt Street, Aston University Campus, Gosta Green, Birmingham, W. Midlands B7 4BD.
☎ (0121) 359 4520

Falcon & Firkin, 360 Victoria Park Road, Hackney, London E9 7BT. ☎ (0181) 985 0693

Feast & Firkin, 229 Woodhouse Lane, Leeds, W. Yorkshire LS2 3AP. ☎ (0113) 245 3669

Fedora & Firkin, Chapel Street, Luton, Bedfordshire LU1 2SE. ☎ (01582) 20427

Ferret & Firkin, 114 Lots Road, Chelsea, London SW10 0RJ. ☎ (0171) 352 6645

Fiddler & Firkin, 14 Southend, Croydon, Surrey CR0 1DL. ☎ (0181) 680 9728

Fielder & Firkin, 346 High Street, Sutton, Surrey SM1 1PR. ☎ (0181) 642 9018

Fieldmouse & Firkin at the Fighting Cocks, St Mary's Row, Moseley, Birmingham, W. Midlands B13 8HW. ☎ (0121) 449 0811

Finch & Firkin, 467 Smithdown Road, Liverpool, Merseyside L15 5AF.
☎ (0151) 733 2403

Firefly & Firkin, 38 Holdenhurst Road, Bournemouth, Dorset BH8 8AD.
☎ (01202) 293569

Fish & Firkin, 53 Alexandra Street, Southend-on-Sea, Essex SS2 6ES.
☎ (01702) 391984

Fizgig & Firkin, St Anne's Well, Lower North Street, Exeter, Devon EX4 3ET.
☎ (01392) 437667

Flamingo & Firkin, 1–7 Becket Street, Derby DE1 1HU. ☎ (01332) 45948

Flea & Firkin, 137 Grosvenor Street, Manchester M1 7DZ. ☎ (0161) 274 3682

Flicker & Firkin, 1 Dukes Street, Richmond, Surrey TW9 1HP. ☎ (0181) 332 7807

Flounder & Firkin, 54 Holloway Road, Holloway, London N7 8JP.
☎ (0171) 609 9574

Fly & Firkin, 18 Southfield Road, Middlesbrough, N. Yorkshire TS1 3BZ.
☎ (01642) 244792

Flyer & Firkin, 53 Blagrave Street, Reading, Berkshire RG1 1PZ. ☎ (01734) 569151

Flyman & Firkin, 166–170 Shaftesbury Avenue, London WC2H 9JB.
☎ (0171) 240 7109

Font & Firkin, South Lanes, Brighton, E. Sussex BN1 1HB. ☎ (01273) 747727

Forger & Firkin, 55–56 Woodridge Road, Guildford, Surrey GU1 4RF.
☎ (01483) 578999

Forrester & Firkin, 3 Eastgate Street, Stafford, ST16 2NQ. ☎ (01785) 223742

Fort & Firkin, The Promenade, Windsor, Berkshire SL4 1QX. ☎ (01753) 869897

Foundry & Firkin, 240 West Street, Sheffield, S. Yorkshire S1 4EU. ☎ (0114) 275 7805

Fowl & Firkin, 1–2 The Butts, Coventry, W. Midlands CV1 3GR. ☎ (01203) 221622

Fox & Firkin, 316 Lewisham High Street, Lewisham, London SE13 3HL.
☎ (0181) 690 8925

Fresher & Firkin, 16 Chesterton Road, Cambridge CB4 3AX. ☎ (01223) 324325

Friar & Firkin, 120 Euston Road, Euston, London NW1 2AL. ☎ (0171) 387 2419

Friesian & Firkin, 87 Rectory Grove, Clapham, London SW4 0DR.
☎ (0171) 622 4666

Fuzz & Firkin, Albert Road, Southsea, Portsmouth, Hampshire PO5 2SH.
☎ (01705) 294353

Phantom & Firkin, Leicester Road, Loughborough, Leicestershire LE11 2AG.
☎ (01509) 263226

Pharoah & Firkin, 90–90A High Street, Fulham, London SW6 3LJ. ☎ (0171) 731 0732

Philanderer & Firkin, Walton Street, Oxford OX2 6AE. ☎ (01865) 54502

Philanthropist & Firkin, 11–13 Victoria Street, St Albans, Hertfordshire AL1 3JJ.
☎ (01727) 847021

Philosopher & Firkin, 288 Cowley Road, Oxford OX4 1UR. ☎ (01865) 244386

Phoenix & Firkin, 5 Windsor Walk, Camberwell, London SE5 3BB.
☎ (0171) 701 8282

Photographer & Firkin, 23–25 Ealing High Street, London W3 6ND. ☎ (0181) 567 1140

Physician & Firkin, 58 Dalkeith Road, Edinburgh EH16 5AD. ☎ (0131) 667 1816

### MINERVA
**Minerva Hotel, Nelson Street, Hull,**
**E. Yorkshire HU1 1XE. ☎ (01482) 326909**

Full mash operation, set up in 1983 and refurbished in 1995. The beer is stored under mixed gas blanket pressure in cellar tanks. Special brews are produced for special occasions. Tours by arrangement. Beers: Sea Fever (OG 1040, ABV 4%, August), Pilots Pride (OG 1042, ABV 4.2%).

### REINDEER
**The Reindeer, 10 Dereham Road, Norwich,**
**Norfolk NR2 4AY. ☎ (01603) 666821**

Brew pub which opened in 1987 and was taken over by Allied-Domecq as part of the Firkin group in June 1995, though the identity of the brewery has remained unaltered. Only the pub itself now takes the beers, which are kept in cellar tanks with no gas blankets. Beers: Moild (OG 1034, ABV 3.5%), RPA (OG 1037, ABV 3.8%), Bevy (OG 1041, ABV 4%), Reindeer (OG 1047, ABV 5%), Dogbolter (OG 1057, ABV 5.6%), Sanity Clause (OG 1065, ABV 7%, Christmas).

### ROSE STREET
**Rose Street Brewery, 55 Rose Street,**
**Edinburgh EH2 2NH. ☎ (0131) 220 1227**

Founded in 1983 and run by Alloa Brewery, supplying six other Alloa outlets with beers produced from malt extract. Beers: Auld Reekie 80/- (OG 1043, ABV 4.1%), Auld Reekie 90/- (OG 1055, ABV 5.2%).

# GUINNESS
**Guinness Brewing GB, Park Royal Brewery, London**
**NW10 7RR. ☎ (0181) 965 7700 [FAX] (0181) 963 5120**

One of the brightest developments in the last year has been the decision by Guinness to rejoin the family of real ale brewers. In 1993, at a time when interest in bottle-conditioned beers was reviving, and with stout making an overdue comeback in many breweries, the company decided to axe its naturally-conditioned, bottled stout, Guinness Original. (Guinness Original is still on sale, but only in a brewery-conditioned, pasteurised version, which lacks the complexity and freshness of the bottle-conditioned beer.) However, in 1996, the company launched a new cask-conditioned porter, named after the father of London porter, Ralph Harwood. Brewed at Park Royal, it is distributed by Carlsberg-Tetley and has been on sale in around 100 pubs. The porter apart, all Draught Guinness sold in the UK is keg. In Ireland, Draught Guinness (OG 1038, brewed at Arthur Guinness, St James's Gate, Dublin 8) is not pasteurised but is served with gas pressure.

**Harwood's Porter Ale** (OG 1046, ABV 4.8%)

# SCOTTISH COURAGE
**Scottish & Newcastle PLC, 111 Holyrood Road, Edinburgh,**
**Lothian EH8 8YS. ☎ (0131) 556 2591 [FAX] (0131) 558 1165**

Scottish & Newcastle was formed in 1960, as a merger between Scottish Brewers Ltd. (the former Younger and McEwan breweries) and Newcastle Breweries Ltd. In May 1995, it was announced that S&N had agreed to purchase Courage from its Australian owner, Foster's. Courage had been a brewer with no pubs since 1991, following the sale of its pub estate to Inntrepreneur Estates (see Pub Groups), a company Foster's jointly owns with Grand Metropolitan. The Government allowed the S&N takeover to go through without reference to the Monopolies and Mergers Commission, despite the fact that it created Britain's largest brewing company, with nearly 30 per cent of the market in beer production. The consequences for the UK industry were obvious. Brewery rationalisation has already taken place, with the loss of hundreds of jobs and fears for the future of many beer brands. Home Brewery in Nottingham was top of the closures list, along with the Fountain Head brewery at Halifax. This leaves the company with five major UK cask ale breweries, plus keg beer plants in Manchester, Reading and Mortlake (a joint venture with American giant Anheuser-Busch known as The Stag Brewing Company and producing Budweiser). The company also owns the Beamish & Crawford brewery in Cork, Ireland.

Scottish & Newcastle (Retail) at present operates over 2,600 pubs nationwide, around 1,900 being managed houses and some 80 per cent selling cask beer. The pubs are controlled by five regional divisions: Scottish, Tyne, Pennine, Trent and Southern Inns. Themed outlets include the T&J Bernard and Barras & Co. ale houses and the Rat & Parrot chain. Scottish Courage also continues to have a massive presence in the free trade (particularly through McEwan and Theakston brands and Newcastle Brown Ale), and also dominates many free houses through the loan-tie system of offering financial loans in return for beer sales.

## BRISTOL

**The Bristol Brewery, Counterslip, Victoria Street, Bristol BS1 6EX. ☎ (0117) 929 7222** **FAX** **(0117) 927 6150**

The former Georges brewery (established 1788), acquired by Courage in 1961 and now Scottish Courage's only real ale brewery in the South. Though Courage Best and Directors are very well promoted nationally, Georges Bitter Ale sales are confined mostly to the West Country and South-East Wales. However, these three beers are all diluted versions of the same original high-gravity brew. In 1995 a bottle-conditioned version of Directors was launched to wide acclaim but was sadly withdrawn a year later. A new range of occasional beers has been introduced, based on recipes from the Courage archives and beginning with Woodham's Old Chopper (OG 1040, ABV 4.1%).

**Georges Bitter Ale** (OG 1031, ABV 3.3%) ◆ A pale, light-bodied session bitter, with a slightly grainy taste, a hoppy aroma and a dry, bitter finish. There are occasional subtle fruit flavours, too.

**Courage Best Bitter** (OG 1039, ABV 4%) ◆ A pale brown bitter with a grainy malt taste. The aroma is hoppy; the finish is bitter and dry with some hops.

**Courage Directors** (OG 1046, ABV 4.8%) ◆ A well-balanced, full-bodied, mid-brown malty ale, with hops and fruit in the nose. The grainy malt taste has some fruit and develops into a powerful, bitter, dry finish.

## FOUNTAIN

**Fountain Brewery, 159 Fountainbridge, Edinburgh EH3 9YY. Tel (0131) 229 9377** **FAX** **(0131) 229 1282**

The Scottish production centre, formerly the home of William McEwan & Co. Ltd, founded in 1856. Its beers are sold under two separate names – McEwan and Younger, depending on the trading area. Younger Best Bitter was brewed at the late Home Brewery,

but will now have to find a new site. Occasional/seasonal beers: Gillespie's Porter (OG 1042, ABV 4.2%), McEwan Export (OG 1043, ABV 4.5%), Raeburn's Edinburgh Ale (OG 1042, ABV 4.7%), McEwan 90/- (OG 1052, ABV 5.5%).

**McEwan 70/-** or **Younger Scotch Bitter** (OG 1036, ABV 3.7%) A well-balanced, sweetish brew, becoming more and more rare. Often competitively priced in Wetherspoon pubs.

**McEwan 80/-** or **Younger IPA** (OG 1042, ABV 4.5%) ◆ Thin-bodied beer with a cloying metallic aftertaste. Once a classic, now bland and sweet with some maltiness.

**Younger No. 3** (OG 1042, ABV 4.5%) ◆ A malty and thin-bodied beer, like McEwan 80/- with added caramel.

## FOUNTAIN HEAD

**Fountain Head Brewery, Halifax, W. Yorkshire.**

The original Samuel Webster brewery, merged by Watney in 1985 with Wilson's of Manchester, a move which saw the closure of Wilson's own brewery. Now this brewery, too, has felt the axe. Wilson's Mild has long been contracted out to Morland and Ruddles has taken over production of Webster's Green Label. Wilson's Original Bitter is contract brewed by Mansfield, whilst Webster's Yorkshire Bitter is chiefly brewed at John Smith's, with supplies supplemented by Mansfield if necessary (see Independents).

## HOME

**Home Brewery, Daybrook, Nottingham.**

Founded in 1875 and acquired by S&N in 1986, the Home brewery, along with the Webster's site in Halifax, was the first production centre to face closure following the S&N takeover of Courage in 1995. The Home and Matthew Brown brands, which were produced here, have now been transferred to Mansfield Brewery (see Independents).

## JOHN SMITH'S

**John Smith's Tadcaster Brewery, Tadcaster, N. Yorkshire LS24 9SA. ☎ (01937) 832091** [FAX] **(01937) 833766**

A business founded at the Old Brewery in 1758 and taken over by John Smith (brother of Samuel Smith – see Independents) in 1847. The present brewery was built in 1884 and became part of the Courage empire in 1970. Tours by arrangement. John Smith's Bitter is Scottish Courage's best known ale, thanks to extensive television advertising. Bottle-conditioned beer: Imperial Russian Stout (OG 1098, ABV 10%, occasional) 🗂 🍶.

**Webster's Yorkshire Bitter** (OG 1035, ABV 3.5%)

**Bitter** (OG 1036, ABV 3.8%) 🍶 Copper-coloured beer with a pleasant mix of hops and malt in the nose. Malt dominates the taste but hops take over in the finish. The brewery's quality control for this beer is excellent. Widely available nationally.

**Magnet** (OG 1040, ABV 4%) 🍶 A well-crafted beer, almost ruby coloured. Hops, malt and citrus fruit can be identified in the nose and there are complex flavours of nuts, hops and fruit, giving way to a long, malty finish.

## THEAKSTON

**T&R Theakston Ltd., Wellgarth, Masham, Ripon, N. Yorkshire HG4 4DX.**
**☎ (01765) 689544** [FAX] **(01765) 689769**

Company formed in 1827 and based at this brewery since 1875. Theakston became part of S&N in 1987 when its parent company, Matthew Brown, was swallowed up. More than £1 million has been spent on this brewery in the last few years, reflecting the 'national' status its brews have been given by Scottish Courage, yet most of Theakston's production now takes place in Newcastle. The same pump clips are used for Masham and Newcastle beers, so the consumer is not told whether the beer actually comes from Theakston's brewery. There is a brewery shop (ring for opening hours) and tours can be taken by arrangement. Occasional/

seasonal beers: Lightfoot (OG 1035, ABV 3.7%), Hogshead Bitter (OG 1041, ABV 4.1%), Masham Ale (OG 1065, ABV 6.6%).

**Mild Ale** (OG 1035, ABV 3.5%) 🗂 🍶 A rich and smooth mild ale with a creamy body and a rounded liquorice taste. Dark ruby/amber in colour, with a mix of malt and fruit in the nose and a dry, hoppy aftertaste.

**Black Bull Bitter** (OG 1037, ABV 3.9%) 🍶 A fruity, hoppy bitter with a smooth, malty body and liquorice character.

**Best Bitter** (OG 1038, ABV 3.8%) 🍶 A light drinking bitter with little body or aftertaste. Hoppiness rapidly declines, leaving a low bitterness and little to remember.

**XB** (OG 1045, ABV 4.6%) 🍶 Although often lacking character, this can be a good drinking bitter, with hop and fruit character, and a smooth, slightly creamy aftertaste.

**Old Peculier** (OG 1057, ABV 5.7%) 🗂 🍶 A deservedly acclaimed old ale with a distinctive and unforgettable character. Look for a smooth, rich beer with malt, roast grain and underlying fruitiness.

## TYNE

**Tyne Brewery, Gallowgate, Newcastle upon Tyne, Tyne & Wear NE99 1RA.**
**☎ (0191) 232 5091** [FAX] **(0191) 261 6297**

The home of Newcastle Breweries Ltd., formed in 1890 as an amalgamation of five local breweries. In recent years it brewed no real ale, until most of Theakston's production was transferred here, but no indication is given at the point of sale or in advertising that Theakston beers are brewed in Newcastle (for tasting notes, see Theakston).

**Theakston Mild Ale** (OG 1035, ABV 3.5%)

**Theakston Best Bitter** (OG 1039, ABV 3.8%)

**Newcastle Exhibition** (OG 1040, ABV 4.4%)

**Theakston XB** (OG 1045, ABV 4.6%)

**Theakston Old Peculier** (OG 1057, ABV 5.7%)

# Scottish Courage Brew Pubs:

## ABINGTON PARK

**Abington Park Brewery Co., Wellingborough Road, Northampton NN1 4EY. ☎ (01604) 31240**

🚪 A Victorian-styled brew pub, opened in 1984 by Chef & Brewer and now owned by S&N Retail (Trent Inns Ltd.) Equipped with a five-barrel plant, the pub stores its beer in cellar tanks under mixed nitrogen/$CO_2$ at atmospheric pressure. Beers: Cobblers Ale (OG 1037, ABV 3.3%), Becket (brewed with malt, wheat and maize, OG 1042, ABV 3.6%), Extra (OG 1047, ABV 4.3%).

## GREYHOUND

**Greyhound Brewery Company Ltd., 151 Greyhound Lane, Streatham Common, London SW16 5NJ.**
**☎ (0181) 677 9962**

🚪 Set up in 1984, the Greyhound brew pub was acquired by Scottish & Newcastle in November 1993. Improvements to the plant began in 1994. Cellar tanks, with a blanket of $CO_2$, are used at the pub. Beers: Special (OG 1037, ABV 3.6%), Streatham Strong (OG 1047, ABV 4.3%), Dynamite (OG 1055, ABV 4.9%).

### ORANGE

Orange Brewery, 37–39 Pimlico Road,
Pimlico, London SW1W 8NE.
☎ (0171) 730 5984

🍺 Brewery opened in 1983, which, like its fellow brew pubs the Greyhound and the Yorkshire Grey, is now part of the Scottish Courage group. It was refurbished in April 1995. The full mash brews are mostly stored in cellar tanks and are kept under blanket pressure. Tours by arrangement. Beers: SW1 (OG 1038, ABV 3.8%), Pimlico Passport (OG 1042, ABV 4.1%), Pimlico Porter (OG 1046, ABV 4.5%), SW2 (OG 1048, ABV 4.8%), Spiritual Reunion (OG 1060, ABV 5.9%, a winter brew

containing orange blossoms).

### YORKSHIRE GREY

Yorkshire Grey, 2–6 Theobalds Road,
Holborn, London WC1X 8PN.
☎ (0171) 405 2519

🍺 Brew pub on the corner of Gray's Inn Road which was extensively refurbished in November 1995. The beers are now produced from full mashes but a $CO_2$ blanket is applied to the cellar tanks which store the finished products. Numerous one-off and occasional beers are brewed each year. Beers: Barristers Best Bitter (OG 1040, ABV 3.8%), QC Best Bitter (OG 1046, ABV 4.5%), Supreme Old Ale (OG 1050, ABV 5%).

---

# WHITBREAD

**The Whitbread Beer Company, Whitbread PLC, Porter Tun House, Capability Green, Luton, Bedfordshire LU1 3LS.**
☎ (01582) 391166 [FAX] (01582) 397397

The name of Whitbread conjures up just one image for many beer drinkers, that of brewery closures. By destroying the likes of Strong's of Romsey, Wethered of Marlow, Fremlins of Faversham, Chester's of Salford and Higsons of Liverpool in the 1970s and 1980s, Whitbread effectively raised two fingers to local preference and killed off an important part of many beer drinkers' lives. The most recent closure was the Exchange Brewery in Sheffield in 1993. Since then Whitbread seems to have rediscovered cask-conditioned beer and has been investing heavily in its cask ale portfolio, though keeping track of what is brewed where remains difficult. The retail side of the company has turned dozens of pubs into Tut 'n' Shive and Hogshead 'ale houses' to support this initiative and there have also been some noteworthy special brew promotions, involving limited edition beers brewed in Cheltenham and Castle Eden. In addition to the cask ale breweries, the company operates keg beer factories in Magor in South Wales and Samlesbury in Lancashire.

Whitbread's 3,850 pubs are controlled by two divisions: Whitbread Inns (managed houses) and Whitbread Pub Partnerships (pubs leased out, usually on 20-year terms).

### BODDINGTONS

Strangeways Brewery, PO Box 23,
Strangeways, Manchester M60 3WB.
☎ (0161) 828 2000 [FAX] (0161) 828 2213

Brewery established in 1778 and acquired by by Whitbread in 1990 when the Boddingtons company, which had already taken-over and closed Oldham Brewery, retreated to pub owning and other leisure enterprises. Now Whitbread is pushing Boddingtons Bitter relentlessly nationwide and the beer takes up 90 per cent of the brewery's already expanded production capacity. To create room, Oldham Best (OB) Bitter (OG 1037.5, ABV 3.8%) has been transferred to Burtonwood Brewery (see Independents).

**Boddingtons Mild** (OG 1032, ABV 3%) 🍺 A thin, dark mild with a sweet caramel and

malt flavour, and a short aftertaste. It has now disappeared from many tied houses.

**OB Mild** (OG 1032, ABV 3%) 🍺 Reddish brown beer with a malty aroma. A smooth roast malt and fruit flavour follows, then a malty and surprisingly bitter aftertaste.

**Boddingtons Bitter** (OG 1034.5, ABV 3.8%) 🍺 A pale beer in which the grainy malt, hop and bitter character can be spoiled by a rather cloying sweetness.

---

🍺The full tankard indicates the beer is one of this year's *Good Beer Guide Beers of the Year.*

## CASTLE EDEN

**Castle Eden Brewery, PO Box 13, Castle
Eden, Co. Durham TS27 4SX.
☎ (01429) 836007**

Originally attached to a 17th-century
coaching inn, the old Nimmo's brewery
(established in 1826) was purchased by
Whitbread in 1963. It has found a niche
within the Whitbread group and now
produces some of the company's better
quality beers. In addition, the Higsons beers
from Sheffield, Wethered Bitter from
McMullen and Fremlins Bitter from
Cheltenham are all now brewed here and
Castle Eden is also responsible for many of
the Whitbread limited-edition brews.

**Higsons Mild** (OG 1034, ABV 3.4%) ❧ A
fruity, dark mild with some roast malt and
caramel. Fairly bitter and dry.

**Fremlins Bitter** (OG 1035.5, ABV 3.5%)

**Wethered Bitter** (OG 1035, ABV 3.6%)

**Eden Bitter** (OG 1036, ABV 3.6%)
❧ Smooth-drinking bitter, malty and sweet,
with a developing dry bitterness in the
aftertaste. Very little aroma.

**Higsons Bitter** (OG 1038, ABV 3.8%) ❧ A
hoppy and fruity bitter with some sweetness
and vanilla notes. Thin, inoffensive and
bland.

**Castle Eden Ale** (OG 1042, ABV 4.2%) ❧ A
light, creamy, malty, sweet ale which
develops a bitter finish, although malt
predominates. It appreciates good
cellarmanship.

**Old Dambuster** (OG 1043, ABV 4.3%) A
commemorative beer (50th anniversary of
the Dambusters raids) which has become a
permanent feature.

**Fuggles Imperial IPA** (OG 1055, ABV 5.5%)
Pale but robust beer which oozes hops and
has a citrus flavour.

**Winter Royal** (OG 1055, ABV 5.5%) ❧ The
former Wethered winter ale. A rich, fruity
and full-flavoured beer with a malty palate,
tasting even stronger than its gravity
suggests.

## FLOWERS

**The Flowers Brewery, Monson Avenue,
Cheltenham, Gloucestershire GL50 4EL.
☎ (01242) 265415 FAX (01242) 265404**

Brewery established in 1760 by banker John
Gardner, which became the Cheltenham
Original Brewery when rebuilt in 1898. It
merged in 1958 with Stroud Brewery to form
West Country Breweries Ltd. and was
acquired by Whitbread in 1963. The Flowers
brewing operation and title were transferred
from Stratford-upon-Avon in 1968. In
recent years it has become the centre for Whitbread
cask ale in the South, absorbing for a while
beers from the closed Wethered, Strong and
Fremlins breweries. These beers have since
been moved again, Strong Country Bitter to
Morrells (see Independents) and Wethered
Bitter (via McMullen) and Fremlins Bitter to
Castle Eden. In addition to the beers listed
below, Whitbread Pompey Royal is now
brewed by Gale's (see Independents).
Cheltenham has also taken over production
of Royal Wessex Bitter (for Greenalls), and
Bentley's and Trophy (following the closure
of the Exchange brewery in Sheffield). One-
off special brews feature regularly.

**West Country Pale Ale (WCPA)** (OG 1030,
ABV 3%) ❧ Hoppy in aroma, but not as
distinctive as it used to be. Light, refreshing
and hoppy, with a clean, dry finish.

**Bentley's Yorkshire Bitter** (OG 1036, ABV
3.6%)

**Flowers IPA** (OG 1035.5, ABV 3.6%) ❧ Pale
brown, with little aroma, perhaps a faint
maltiness. Moderately dry taste and finish,
but no discernible hoppiness. Thin and
uninspiring.

**Trophy Bitter** (OG 1036, ABV 3.8%)

**Whitbread Best Bitter** (OG 1035, ABV 3.6%)
Also available in keg form.

**Flowers Original** (OG 1045, ABV 4.5%)
❧ Hoppy aroma and hops in the taste, with
some malt and a hint of fruit. A notably
bitter finish.

**The Abroad Cooper** (OG 1049, ABV 5.1%)

### For Greenalls:

**Royal Wessex Bitter** (OG 1040.5, ABV 4%)

---

# Whitbread Brew Pubs:

## ALFORD ARMS

**Alford Arms Brewhouse, Frithsden, Hemel
Hempstead, Hertfordshire HP1 3DD.
☎ (01442) 864480**

🍺 Whitbread's original brew pub, opened
in 1981, but only brewing again since
1993, after a long break. It is now working at
full capacity, with possible plans to expand,
supplying malt extract beers to 20 other
outlets. Tours by arrangement. Beers: Dark
Mild (OG 1031, ABV 2.8%), New Cherry
Pickers (OG 1040, ABV 3.9%), Olde
Frithsden (OG 1042, ABV 4.2%), Pickled
Squirrel (OG 1045, ABV 4.5%), Rub of the
Brush (OG 1049, ABV 5%), Rudolf's
Revenge (OG 1055, ABV 5.8%, winter),
500 Special Ale (OG 1057, ABV 6%,
winter).

🍺 The pub sign indicates a brew
pub: a pub which produces beer
on the premises.

## FELLOWS, MORTON & CLAYTON
Fellows, Morton & Clayton Brewhouse Company, 54 Canal Street, Nottingham NG1 7EH. ☎ (0115) 950 6795
FAX (0115) 955 1412

This pub began brewing in 1980 and still uses malt extract. Tours by arrangement. Beers: Samuel Fellows Bitter (OG 1040, ABV 3.7%), Matthew Clayton's Original Strong Ale (OG 1054, ABV 5%), New Year Nectar (ABV 6%, winter), Winter Warmer (ABV 6%).

## FOX & NEWT
Fox & Newt, 9 Burley Street, Leeds, W. Yorkshire LS9 1LD.
☎ (0113) 243 2612

Malt extract brew pub which also sells to other outlets. Tours by arrangement. Beers (not all available at once): Billy's Special (ABV 3.8%), Sherwoon Arms No. 1 (ABV 3.8%), Diesel (ABV 4.1%, a stout), Cushtie (ABV 4.2%), Black and Amber (ABV 4.5%), Ghostbuster (ABV 5.1%), The Bitch (ABV 6.5%).

## FROG & PARROT
Frog & Parrot, 64 Division Street, Sheffield, S. Yorkshire S1 4SG. ☎ (0114) 272 1280

Malt extract brew pub. Beers are kept in casks and are sometimes available in a handful of other pubs. Tours available by arrangement, with all proceeds going to charity. Beers: Reckless (OG 1045, ABV 4.6%), Swamp Monster (ABV 5.2%), Conqueror (OG 1066, ABV 6.2%), Roger & Out (OG 1125, ABV 12.5%).

## LASS O'GOWRIE
Lass O'Gowrie Brewhouse, 36 Charles Street, Manchester M1 7DB.
☎ (0161) 273 6932

Victorian pub, revamped and re-opened as a malt extract brew pub in 1983. The brewery in the cellar is visible from the bar and the beer is now stored in casks. One or two other outlets have taken Lass O'Gowrie beers on a trial basis and sales to other pubs may now be expanded. Some one-off beers are produced to commemorate the end of student terms. Beers: LOG 35 (OG 1038, ABV 3.8%), LOG 42 (OG 1042, ABV 4.7%).

NOTES

# Pub Groups

## ALLIED-DOMECQ
See Nationals, Carlsberg-Tetley.

## ASCOT ESTATES
**Ascot Estates Ltd., Bury House, 31 Bury Street, London EC3A 5AR.**
☎ (0171) 815 0805 [FAX] (0171) 815 0808

Pub-owning company established as Belhaven Inns (a division of Control Securities) in 1987 with 68 pubs. The number rose to over 600 but has now been reduced to 184. These are run for Ascot by Mayfair Taverns (a company which purchased 251 Ascot pubs in 1996) but may be sold soon.

## BEARDS
**Beards of Sussex Ltd., West End, Herstmonceux, E. Sussex BN27 4NN.**
☎ (01323) 832777 [FAX] (01323) 832833

Former brewing company (founded in 1797) which opted out of production in 1959. After contracting out its beers to Harveys from 1960 to 1986, Beards then abandoned brewing altogether and became a cask ale wholesaler as well as a pub company. The wholesaling division was sold off in 1994 and Beards currently runs 46 traditional pubs in Sussex (11 managed, 34 tenanted and one joint venture with Whitbread/Beefeater), which can sell any beers from the wide list offered by The Beer Seller wholesaler and from Scottish Courage. A new beer, Beards Best Bitter, is now brewed for the company by Arundel Brewery (see Independents).

## CM GROUP
**CM Group Ltd., Magnet House, Station Road, Tadcaster, N. Yorkshire LS24 9JF.**
☎ (01937) 833311 [FAX] (01937) 834236

Eighty-strong pub chain in North-East England, expanded from ten in 1992. Most of the pubs have been leased from Whitbread, with half tenanted, half managed. No guest beers are available to managers or tenants, with supplies coming from Whitbread, Scottish Courage, Bass and Carlsberg-Tetley.

## CAFE INNS
**Café Inns PLC, 3 St Thomas's Road, Chorley, Lancashire PR7 1HP.**
☎ (01257) 262424 [FAX] (01257) 260497

Company established in 1987 and now running 61, mostly tenanted pubs in the North-West. Fifty pubs leased from Burtonwood and operated under the Vantage Inns banner, a company jointly owned by Café Inns and Burtonwood, have now been returned to Burtonwood. Pubs sell beers from Bass and Scottish Courage (Matthew Brown).

## CENTURY INNS
**Century Inns PLC, Belasis Business Centre, Coxwold Way, Billingham TS23 4EA.**
☎ (01642) 343426 [FAX] (01642) 345603

Company formed in 1991 by Camerons employees with the purchase of 185 pubs from Bass. The intention was to establish a pub estate for a buyout of the Camerons brewery, but this was scuppered by Brent Walker. The number of pubs now stands at 320, ten managed and the rest traditionally tenanted (three-year agreements), with pubs located down the north-eastern side of the country, from Tyneside to Lincolnshire. Beer sales are still confined to Bass, Scottish Courage and Carlsberg-Tetley products (plus the guest ales these companies supply), though the managed pubs also take some beers from smaller breweries. The two pubs formerly owned by North Yorkshire Brewery are now part of the estate and, in summer 1996, Century took over Stocks Brewery in Doncaster. Century Inns was floated on the Stock Market in 1995.

## CONQUEST INNS
**Conquest Inns Ltd., The Old Vicarage, 10 Church Street, Rickmansworth, Hertfordshire WD3 1BS.**
☎ (01923) 711118 [FAX] (01923) 711128

Company set up to obtain 59 pubs from Bass in 1994, backed by Jersey's Ann Street brewery. About half the current total of 57 pubs (nearly all three-year tenanted) are in London, with small pockets of houses in Sussex, the Midlands and East Anglia. Beers come solely from Bass and Scottish Courage, and tenants have no guest beer rights.

## JT DAVIES
**JT Davies & Sons Ltd., 7 Aberdeen Road, Croydon, Surrey CR0 1EQ.**
☎ (0181) 681 3222 [FAX] (0181) 760 0390

Wine merchants now controlling 35 tenancies and eight managed houses in the South-East. Its main suppliers are Bass and Scottish Courage, with some beers taken from Fuller's and Harveys.

## DAVYS
**The Davy Group, 59–63 Bermondsey Street, London SE1 3XF.**
☎ (0171) 407 9670 [FAX] (0171) 407 5844

Long established (1870) wine merchants which has been opening wine bars and ale and port houses in the City since 1965, taking previously unlicensed properties (largely basements) and creating a Dickensian, sawdust, nooks and crannies type of establishment. Two beers are sold:

Davy's Ordinary Bitter (ABV 4%) and Davy's Old Wallop (ABV 4.8%), both re-badged brews of undeclared origin (though Courage Best and Directors fit the bill). The company currently runs 55 outlets, including the White Hart Hotel in Exeter.

## DISCOVERY INNS

**Discovery Inns Ltd., Discovery House, 502 Worle Parkway, Worle, Weston-super-Mare, Somerset BS22 0WA.**
☎ (01934) 520400  FAX (01934) 520401

Company founded in 1992 and now running 285 pubs most of which it picked up from Whitbread on a freehold basis. Of these, 238 are tenanted on three-year agreements and 47 are managed. Only a limited choice from Whitbread's portfolio, with some Bass, Scottish Courage and regional brewers' beers, is offered to licensees. Many of the pubs are in the West Country and South Wales, with others in the North and London.

## ENTERPRISE INNS

**Enterprise Inns Ltd., Friars Gate, Stratford Road, Solihull, W. Midlands B90 4BN.**
☎ (0121) 733 7700  FAX (0121) 733 6447

Midlands-based company founded in 1991 with the purchase of 372 pubs from Bass. The total now stands at 947, following the purchase of John Labatt Retail and 50 'Wirral Taverns' which Paramount was running for Whitbread. About half the pubs are run on a 21-year lease basis and the remainder are tenanted, with beers provided by Bass, Whitbread, Carlsberg-Tetley, Scottish Courage and Wolverhampton & Dudley. Licensees are not allowed to buy beers outside the company. The pubs are situated in the Midlands and the North. One former Labatt pub, the Hop House, in Kingsthorpe, Northamptonshire is a brew pub (see Independents) and was planned as first of a national chain.

## FAMOUS PUB COMPANY

**Famous Pub Company PLC, 21 Queen Anne's Place, Bush Hill Park, Enfield EN1 2QB.**
☎ (0181) 360 5377  FAX (0181) 360 6563

Expanding pub company established with the purchase of 37 pubs from Whitbread in February 1996 and floated on the stock market the same day. The pubs are traditionally tenanted (one-year contracts) and are supplied with beer by Whitbread. Some tenants are allowed a guest beer.

## FITZGERALD'S

**Sir John Fitzgerald Ltd., Café Royal Buildings, 8 Nelson Street, Newcastle upon Tyne, Tyne & Wear NE1 5AW.**
☎ (0191) 232 0664  FAX (0191) 222 1764

Long-established, family-owned, property and pubs company, dating from the end of the last century. Its pubs convey a 'free

house' image, most offering a decent choice of cask beers, including guest ales. All 30 pubs (28 managed, two tenanted) are located in the North-East.

## GRAY

**Gray & Sons (Chelmsford) Ltd., Rignals Lane, Galley Wood, Chelmsford, Essex CM2 8RE.**
☎ (01245) 475181  FAX (01245) 475182

A brewery which ceased production at its Chelmsford brewery in 1974 and which now supplies its 49 tied, tenanted pubs in Essex with beers from Greene King (XX Mild, IPA, Rayments Special and Abbot Ale) and Shepherd Neame (Master Brew Bitter), as well as various guest ales.

## GREENALLS

**Greenalls Group PLC, PO Box 2, Greenalls Avenue, Warrington, Cheshire WA4 6RH.**
☎ (01925) 651234  FAX (01925) 444734

Former brewing giant which destroyed many fine independent breweries before turning its back on brewing in 1991. On a 1980s rampage, Greenalls stormed the Midlands, taking over and closing the Wem, Davenports, Simpkiss and Shipstone's breweries. Since the closure of its own Warrington brewery, Greenalls brands have been brewed by Carlsberg-Tetley, initially at Warrington and now at Burton upon Trent. The company further demonstrated its contempt for brewing and pub traditions by bulldozing the famous Tommy Ducks pub in Manchester under the cover of night in 1993, ignoring local planning legislation. Following its acquisition of Devenish in the same year, and the takeover of The Boddington Pub Company in 1995, the company now operates around 2,500 pubs, about 1,200 of which are tenanted. The Boddingtons acquisition included the Liquid Assets wholesaling arm and this, together with Greenalls own Tavern distribution company, has made Greenalls the country's largest beer wholesaler. Pubwise, the former Devenish beer, Royal Wessex Bitter (brewed by Whitbread), can be found in the former Devenish estate, alongside Whitbread beers,which are also sold in the former Boddingtons pubs. Guest beers across the country include Tetley Bitter, Stones Bitter, Worthington Bitter and, in a few outlets, ales from Cains, Adnams, Greene King, Young's and Coach House. Various theme outlets have been established, including Irish pubs, Jungle Bungles and Ale & Hearty food pubs.

## GROSVENOR INNS

**Grosvenor Inns PLC, The Old Schoolhouse, London Road, Shenley, Hertfordshire WD7 9DX.**
☎ (01923) 855837  FAX (01923) 857992

Group running 53 (46 managed, seven tenanted) pubs in the South-East, many of which are leased from Inntrepreneur or other companies and are tied to Scottish Courage beers. The other pubs take beers from Whitbread, Fuller's and Wadworth, as well as Scottish Courage. Certain licensees are now able to purchase guest beers from a list of approved wholesalers. Once known as Cromwell Taverns, Grosvenor is now a publicly-quoted company and plans to develop its estate, establishing more of its Slug & Lettuces (currently 13 pubs) and Bar Central houses (currently three). David 'Firkin' Bruce has joined the board and his Hedgehog & Hogshead brew pubs (see Independents) are also part of the Grosvenor empire.

## HEAVITREE

**Heavitree Brewery PLC, Trood Lane, Matford, Exeter, Devon EX2 8YP.**
☎ (01392) 58406 [FAX] (01392) 411697

West Country brewery (established 1790) which gave up production in 1970 to concentrate on running pubs. The current estate (largely in Devon) stands at 113 – 11 managed, and the rest tenanted or leased out (mostly on 21-year contracts). The pubs are tied to taking beers from The Whitbread Cask Collection, with some products from Bass and Thomas Hardy.

## INN BUSINESS

**Inn Business Ltd., Tingewick Road, Buckingham, MK18 1GD.**
☎ (01280) 822663 [FAX] (01280) 823728

Inn Business Ltd. is now a subsidiary company of Inn Business Group PLC (formerly United Breweries, the company which took over and closed the Premier Ales and Wiltshire Brewery operations). The company runs 280 pubs, which are tied to Whitbread, Bass and Scottish Courage products.

## INN KENT LEISURE

**Inn Kent Leisure Ltd., Victoria Hotel, 141 Week Street, Maidstone, Kent ME14 1RE.**
☎ (01622) 661782 [FAX] (01622) 661717

Pub group with an enterprising guest beer and price promotion policy in its 42 pubs.

## INNTREPRENEUR

**Inntrepreneur Pub Company Ltd., Mill House, Aylesbury Road, Thame, Oxfordshire OX9 3AT.**
☎ (01844) 262000 [FAX] (01844) 261332

The pub-owning company formed by Courage (Foster's) and Grand Metropolitan as part of a pubs-for-breweries swap in 1991. In the deal, Courage bought up all Grand Met.'s (Watney's) breweries, with most of Courage's pubs taken over by Inntrepreneur. Inntrepreneur has led the way with the long lease (20 years) as a replacement for the traditional tenancy, a move which has sadly seen many valued former Courage tenants leave the trade. Belatedly, the company installed a new management team in 1995 in an effort to improve relations with its lessees. Following the sale of 1,410 pubs to a new company, Spring Inns (qv), in 1996, Inntrepreneur currently operates 2,900 pubs, some of which are free houses, though most are tied to Scottish Courage until 1998. These pubs have the right to stock a guest beer of their own choosing, in addition to any guests supplied by Inntrepreneur/Scottish Courage.

## KINGSTON INNS

**The Kingston Inn Company Ltd., Phoenix House, Forstal Road, Aylesford, Maidstone, Kent ME20 7AN.**
☎ (01622) 719200 [FAX] (01622) 719300

Holding company controlling 47 pubs spread largely down the eastern side of the UK.

## THE MAGIC PUB COMPANY

See Independents, Greene King.

## MAYFAIR TAVERNS

**Mayfair Taverns Ltd., Bury House, 31 Bury Street, London EC3A 5AR.**
☎ (0171) 815 0805 [FAX] (0171) 815 0808

Company established with a management buyout from Ascot Estates and the purchase of 251 Ascot pubs in April 1996. The pubs are spread throughout most of the UK, as far north as Bradford and Manchester, and are either three-year tenanted or leased out on 20-year contracts. Beers are supplied entirely by Scottish Courage and Carlsberg-Tetley. A new head office in Banbury was about to open as we went to press. Mayfair also runs Ascot's remaining 184 pubs.

## MERCURY TAVERNS

**Mercury Taverns PLC, Mercury House, Amber Business Village, Amington, Tamworth, Staffordshire B77 4RP.**
☎ (01827) 310000 [FAX] (01827) 310530

Company running 133 pubs (116 tenanted, most others managed), scattered from Cumbria and the North-East to South Wales. Most have come from Bass, which, together with Carlsberg-Tetley, Scottish Courage and Banks's in some places, supplies the beer. Twenty-one north-eastern pubs were acquired in the last year from Thornaby Leisure. Part of the group is the Irish-themed Dublin Pub Company (three outlets and more planned).

## PARAMOUNT

**Paramount PLC, St Werburghs Chambers, Godstall Lane, Chester, Cheshire CH1 2EP.**
☎ (01244) 321171 [FAX] (01244) 317665

Ambitious company founded in 1987 as Silver Bear, a games manufacturing company, becoming Paramount in 1988 when it began acquiring pubs. The company is now part-owned by Greenalls (25%), Allied-Domecq (20%, the former Burtonwood shares) and Bass (10%), and now runs 277 pubs. The pubs are centred within 80 miles of Chester and 52 are leased out on long contracts. Licensees are generally restricted to the Burtonwood, Bass, Whitbread and Scottish Courage lists. Two pubs acquired from The Boddington Pub Company continue as 'ale houses', with a greater choice, and there are plans for more such establishments. The 50 pubs formerly managed for Whitbread under the Wirral Taverns banner have now been sold to Enterprise Inns.

## PHOENIX INNS

**Phoenix Inns Ltd., Units 1 & 2, Thame Business Park, Wenman Road, Thame, Oxfordshire OX9 3XA.**
☎ (01844) 262200 [FAX] (01844) 262208

Company running around 1,700 former Inntrepreneur Estates pubs in England and Wales, of which 860 are leased out, the rest being tenanted. All the pubs are officially 'free of tie', with the choice of beers left to the licensees.

## PUB ESTATE COMPANY

**Pub Estate Company Ltd., 3–5 Ashfield Road, Chorley, Lancashire PR7 1LH.**
☎ (01257) 266299 [FAX] (01257) 233918

Company established with the purchase of 230 pubs (23 managed, the rest tenanted) from S&N. These are located nationwide and are still tied to Scottish Courage, but with guest beer rights for tenants. At the same address is Second Pub Estate Company Ltd. which is partly funded by Scottish Courage and which purchased 22 former S&N pubs (five managed, 17 tenanted) from bus operator Go-Ahead Leisure in 1996. The pubs still stock Scottish Courage beers. This company also owns 105 pubs (12 managed, the remainder tenanted), acquired from Allied-Domecq, and these remain tied to Carlsberg-Tetley beers. Third Pub Estate Company (again, same address) controls 18 pubs in the North-West which used to belong to Trust Inns Ltd. and which stock beers from all the national brewers.

## PUBMASTER

**Pubmaster Ltd., Greenbank, Hartlepool TS24 7QS.**
☎ (01429) 266699 [FAX] (01429) 278457

Company formed in 1991 to take over the pub estate of Brent Walker (ex-Camerons and Tolly Cobbold pubs). In 1992, 734 houses were leased from Allied, and other acquisitions have been made from Whitbread and Bass. Pubmaster currently runs 1,650 pubs across the country, 1,540 of which are tenanted (three-year contracts). Its most famous trading name is Tap & Spile, a growing chain (60+) of traditional alehouses offering an excellent choice of beers, including two house brews, Tap & Spile Bitter (ABV 3.8%, produced by Hadrian) and Tap & Spile Premium (ABV 4.3%, from Ushers). The Tap & Spile name is likely to spread quickly now that franchising arrangements have been finalised. Pubmaster's other chain, the BieRRex collection of four European-style bars, specialises in continental beers. Other, non-branded Pubmaster pubs stock beers from Bass, Carlsberg-Tetley, Whitbread and some regional independents.

## RANDALLS VAUTIER

**Randalls Vautier Ltd., PO Box 43, Clare Street, St Helier, Jersey JE4 8NZ.**
☎ (01534) 887788 [FAX] (01534) 888350

Brewery which ceased production in 1992. It now runs 29 pubs (14 managed, the rest tenanted with three-year agreements) on Jersey which sell beers from Bass, Whitbread and Marston's. Not to be confused with Randalls of Guernsey (see Independents).

## REGENT INNS

**Regent Inns PLC, Northway House, 1379 High Road, Whetstone, London N20 9LP.**
☎ (0181) 445 5016 [FAX] (0181) 446 0896

Company founded in 1980 and now owning 57 managed pubs in London and the Home Counties. Further acquisitions are continually sought and expansion into the Midlands is taking place. The pubs are generally allowed to preserve their individual identities and a wide range of beers are sold (the company has contracts with Bass, Scottish Courage and Whitbread, plus half a dozen regional breweries, but licensees can also take beer from The Beer Seller wholesaler). In May 1996 Regent Inns acquired over six per cent of shares in the 26-strong pub chain Surrey Free Inns.

## RYAN

**Ryan Elizabeth Holdings PLC, Ryan Precinct, 33 Fore Street, Ipswich, Suffolk IP4 1JL.**
☎ (01473) 217458 [FAX] (01473) 258237

This company's 54 pubs in East Anglia (many bought from national brewers) are leased to individual operators on 35-year contracts. Most are free, but around 15 per cent have a tie to Bass. A subsidiary company, Elizabeth Hotels, currently runs six pubs.

## SCORPIO INNS

**Scorpio Inns Ltd., Commerce House, Abbey Road, Torquay, Devon TQ2 5PJ.**
☎ **(01803) 296111** FAX **(01803) 296202**

Pub group formed in 1991 and now running 116 pubs leased from Whitbread (nine managed, the rest tenanted out). These stock beers from Whitbread and Bass and are located in South Wales, the Bristol and Hereford areas and along the M4 corridor to Swindon.

## SECOND PUB ESTATE COMPANY See Pub Estate Company.

## SPRING INNS

**Spring Inns Management Ltd., Mill House, Aylesbury Road, Thame, Oxfordshire OX9 3AT.**
☎ **(01844) 262000** FAX **(01844) 261332**

Holding company set up in May 1996 to purchase 1,410 pubs from Inntrepreneur, allowing Inntrepreneur to target its resources on a smaller estate. The eventual aim is to sell the pubs on to other concerns. The company is 98 per cent owned by Royal Exchange Trust Co. Ltd., with Grand Metropolitan and Foster's having one per cent each. All the pubs carry the old Inntrepreneur Scottish Courage tie and vary in location from Cornwall to Kent.

## SYCAMORE TAVERNS

**Sycamore Taverns Ltd., 1 Guildford Street, Chertsey, Surrey KT16 9BG.**
☎ **(01932) 571545** FAX **(01932) 571562**

Company formed in 1992 and operating 240 traditionally-tenanted pubs across most areas of England, from Lancashire south. The stock originally came from Allied (296 pubs), but the estate has now been rationalised. Tenants are allowed a guest beer from the Bass and Whitbread lists, though the main supplier is still Carlsberg-Tetley.

## THIRD PUB ESTATE COMPANY See Pub Estate Company.

## TOM COBLEIGH

**Tom Cobleigh PLC, Phoenix House, Oak Tree Lane, Mansfield, Nottinghamshire NG18 4LF.**
☎ **(01623) 21414** FAX **(01623) 28255**

Company established in 1992 with two pubs. Since then the estate has grown to 81, 38 tenanted, the remainder managed. The pubs, which aim to conform to the company's slogan of 'unspoilt pubs for nice people', are located in Yorkshire and the East Midlands. The tenanted pubs were acquired from

Whitbread in 1994, though these are signed as belonging to The Nice Pub Company. Licensees choose beers from a head office range of national and regional ales, with Marston's, Whitbread, Bass and Scottish Courage the main suppliers. A guest beer list is updated monthly. The company was floated on the Stock Exchange in 1995.

## TRENT TAVERNS

**Trent Taverns Ltd., PO Box 1061, Gringley on the Hill, Doncaster, S. Yorkshire DN10 4ED.**
☎ **(01777) 817408** FAX **(01777) 816487**

Company set up by a former S&N employee. Its 86 pubs in the Midlands and the South are mostly leased from Whitbread, with some freehold acquisitions. They sell only beers from the Whitbread and Scottish Courage lists.

## THE VINTAGE PUB COMPANY

**The Vintage Pub Company, First Floor, North Barn, Tempest Court, Broughton Hall Business Park, Skipton, N. Yorkshire BD23 3AE.**
☎ **(01756) 798700** FAX **(01756) 798613**

Company running 66 pubs (nearly all in Yorkshire), on a mixture of short leases and tenancies, with one managed house. Formed in 1992 as Pub Management Co. Ltd., with the purchase of 32 Bass pubs and 38 Allied pubs, the company is still aiming to expand. Beers sold come from the Carlsberg-Tetley list.

## WETHERSPOONS

**JD Wetherspoon PLC, Wetherspoon House, Central Park, Reeds Crescent, Watford, Hertfordshire WD1 1QH.**
☎ **(01923) 477777** FAX **(01923) 219810**

Ambitious group, founded by Tim Martin, which opened its first pub in 1979 and went public in 1992. It currently owns over 150 managed pubs in and around London and in new locations throughout England and Wales. The company continues to add about 25 pubs a year to its stock, many of which are conversions from shops, featuring standard wood and granite decor and common names like JJ Moon's and other 'Moon' titles. No music is played in any of the pubs, all offer no-smoking areas and food is served all day. There are four standard beers from Scottish Courage available to managers: Theakston Best, XB, Younger Scotch and Directors. Regional variants come from the likes of Banks's, Cains and Wadworth. Additional beers from micro-breweries are chosen by managers from a quarterly list of 30 guest products.

## WHARFEDALE TAVERNS

**Wharfedale Taverns Ltd., Croft House, Audby Lane, Wetherby, W. Yorkshire LS22 4DN.**
☎ (01937) 580805 FAX (01937) 580806

Company set up in 1993 by former Tetley employees to lease 90 pubs from that company. The estate total currently stands at 60 pubs, 25 of which are traditionally tenanted (three-year agreements). The main beer range still comes from Carlsberg-Tetley. The pubs are situated in Yorkshire, the North-West and the northern Midlands.

## WHITE ROSE INNS

**White Rose Inns PLC, Chantrell House, 1 Chantrell Court, The Calls, Leeds, W. Yorkshire LS2 7HA.**
☎ (0113) 246 1332 FAX (0113) 246 1350

Group with 35 tenancies and seven managed houses in Yorkshire. The main supplier is Carlsberg-Tetley.

## WILLIAMS

**James Williams (Narberth), 7 Spring Gardens, Narberth, Pembrokeshire SA67 7BP.**
☎ (01834) 860318 FAX (01834) 860358

Privately-owned concern, founded in 1830 and operating 51 pubs in Pembrokeshire and Carmarthenshire (all tenanted). Tenants are chiefly supplied by Brains, Crown Buckley, Tomos Watkin, Bass, Carlsberg-Tetley and Whitbread. Worthington Bitter is a permanent feature in all pubs and a cask ale of the month features beers from the likes of Jennings, Wells and Everards. Two house ales, James Williams IPA and BB, are brewed by regional brewers (names undeclared).

## YATES'S

**Yates's Wine Lodges Ltd., Peter Yates House, Manchester Road, Bolton, Gtr Manchester BL3 2PY.**
☎ (01204) 373737 FAX (01204) 388383

Company founded in Oldham in 1884 by wine merchant Peter Yates. It now runs 56 branded, managed pubs, in locations from Scotland to London, and is keen to acquire more outlets. The pubs have a Victorian styling and feature bold, vivid colours in their decor. Beers are mainly from Scottish Courage and Bass, with some regional ales also featured.

**Other notable chains (operated by, or divisions of, brewing companies or pub groups):**

Artist's Fare (Morland)
Barras & Co. (Scottish Courage)
Bar Central (Grosvenor Inns)
Beefeater (Whitbread)
Bert's Bars (Alloa)
BieRRex (Pubmaster)
Big Steak (Allied-Domecq)
Bill Bentley's Wine Bars (Young's)
Bootsy Brogan's (Glendola Leisure)
Brewer's Fayre (Whitbread)
Calendars (Allied-Domecq)
Countryside Hotels (Greene King)
Dublin Pub Company (Mercury Taverns)
Exchanges (Taylor Walker)
Firkin (Allied-Domecq)
Fork & Pitcher (Bass)
Harvester (Bass)
Hedgehog & Hogshead (Grosvenor Inns)
Henry's Café Bars (Greenalls)
Henry's Tables (Greenalls)
High Street Taverns (Grosvenor Inns)
Hobgoblinns (Wychwood)
Hogshead Ale Houses (Whitbread)
Hudsons (Greenalls)
Hungry Horse (Greene King)
JJ Moon's (Wetherspoon)
Jungle Bungle (Greenalls)
King's Fayre (Greene King)
Lacon Inns (Adnams)
Landlord's Table (Mansfield)
Maxwells (Allied-Domecq)
Milestone Restaurants and Taverns (Wolverhampton & Dudley)
Millers Kitchen (Greenalls)
Mr Q's (Allied-Domecq)
Newt & Cucumber (Morland)
Nice Pub Company (Tom Cobleigh)
O'Neills (Bass)
Pickled Newt (Greene King)
Pitcher & Piano (Marston's)
Pizza Hut (Whitbread)
PJ Pepper (Whitbread)
Quincey's (Greenalls)
Rat & Carrot (Greene King)
Rat & Parrot (Scottish Courage)
Roast Inns (Greenalls)
Scruffy Murphy's (Allied-Domecq)
Shamus O'Donnell's (Discovery)
Slug & Lettuce (Grosvenor Inns)
T&J Bernard's (Scottish Courage)
Tap & Spile (Pubmaster)
TGI Friday (Whitbread)
Toby Restaurants (Bass)
Tut 'n' Shive (Whitbread)
Vantage Inns (Burtonwood)
Wayside Inns (Whitbread)
Wirral Taverns (Enterprise Inns)

---

Keep up to date with events in the brewery world. Join CAMRA and read *What's Brewing* every month.

# The Beers Index

The Beers Index is your quick guide to the real ales of the United Kingdom. Nearly 2000 brews are highlighted in the following pages, from Abbot Ale to Zingiber, together with page references to the breweries section, where you can find out more about each beer.

# THE BEERS INDEX

Fodder *Cannon* 436
Fool's Gold *North Yorkshire* 480
Force Nine *Whitby's* 505
Forest XB *High Force* 460
Forever Autumn *Marches* 474
Formidable Ale *Cains* 435
44 Special *Blackawton* 427
Fortyniner *Ringwood* 489
Forty Two *Skinner's* 494
Founders Ale *Ushers* 502
4Bs *Berrow* 426
Four Thumbs *Dyffryn Clwyd* 444
4X *Hydes' Anvil* 465
Fractus XB *Tomlinson's* 501
Fraoch Heather Ale *Heather* 459
Fraoch Pictish Ale *Heather* 459
Frederics *Robinson's* 490
Fred's Cap *Bank Top* 423
Fremlins Bitter *Whitbread* 520
Friary Meux Best Bitter *Carlsberg-Tetley* 513
Friday 13th *Hogs Back* 461
Frostbite *B&T* 422
Fruiterers Mild *Cannon Royall* 436
Fuggle-Dee-Dum *Goddards* 452
Fuggles Imperial IPA *Whitbread* 520
Fuggl'olmullable *Cuckmere Haven* 441
Fulham Ale *Freedom* 448
Futtock Ale *Flagship* 447
Fylde Ale *Hart* 458

# G

Gamekeeper Bitter *Steam Packet* 496
Gandalf *Green Cucumber (RCH)* 487
Gangplank Ale *Flagship* 447
Gargoyle *Lichfield* 470
GB Mild *Lees* 469
Gem *Bath* 424
Genesis *Bull's Head* 432
Gentlemen's Gold *Cuckmere Haven* 441
Geordie Pride *Mordue* 477
George's Best *Mauldons* 475
Georges Bitter Ale *Scottish Courage* 517
Get Knotted *Wood* 507
GFB *Hop Back* 463
The Ghillie *Broughton* 431
Ghostbuster *Fox & Newt (Whitbread)* 521
Gillespie's Porter *Scottish Courage* 517
Ginger Minge *Steam Packet* 496
Gingersnap Wheat Beer *Salopian* 493
Ginger Tom *Hoskins & Oldfield* 464
    *Tomintoul* 501
Gladiator Bitter *Hadrian* 455
Gladstone *McMullen* 472
GMT *Townes* 501
Gobstopper Bitter *Fox & Hounds* 448
Gold *Arundel* 421
    *Devon* 443
    *Exmoor* 446
    *Iceni* 465
    *Lugton* 471
    *Sutton* 497
Gold Beach *Hart* 458
Gold Brew *Bullmastiff* 432
Golden *Juwards* 466
Golden Arrow *Cottage* 440
Golden Best *Taylor* 498
Golden Best Bitter *Scott's* 493
Golden Bine *Ballard's* 423
Golden Bitter *Archers* 420
The Golden Duck *Crouch Vale* 441
Golden Eagle *Cotleigh* 440
    *Kelham Island* 467
Golden Gate *Nethergate* 479
Golden Gate Bitter *Skinner's* 494
Golden Glory *Firkin (Carlsberg-Tetley)* 515
Golden Goose *King's Head* 468
Golden Grail *Tring* 502
Golden Hill Ale *Pembroke* 484

Golden Peace *Cuckmere Haven* 442
Golden Pride *Fuller's* 450
Golden Promise *Caledonian* 435
Golden Sickle *Green Jack* 454
Golden Summer Bitter *Worldham* 508
Golden Wheat *Stocks* 497
Goldfield *Hambleton* 455
Goldings Harvest Ale *Shepherd Neame* 494
Gold Prospector *Greenwood's* 454
Gold Star *Goacher's* 452
Good King Wenceslas *Hampshire* 456
Good Old Boy *West Berkshire* 505
Gothic Ale *Enville* 445
The Governor *Hull* 464
Graduate *Morrells* 478
Graft *West Berkshire* 505
Granary Bitter *Reepham* 489
Gravediggers *Church End* 437
Gray's Bitter *LWCC (Mansfield)* 473
Gray's Mild *LWCC (Mansfield)* 473
Great Cockup Porter *Hesket Newmarket* 459
The Great Crusader *Pilgrim* 485
Great Eastern Ale *Woodforde's* 507
Great Northern *Masons Arms* 474
Great Northern Porter *Hilden* 461
Great Raft Bitter *Old Chimneys* 481
Great Western Real Ale *Cottage* 440
Greenmantle Ale *Broughton* 431
Greyhound Strong Bitter *Elgood's* 444
Gribble Ale *Gribble* 454
Griffin *Leyland* 469
Grumpling Old Ale *Vale* 503
GSB *Elgood's* 444
Gunpowder Blast *Mauldons* 475
Gunpowder Strong Mild *Coach House* 438
Guv'ner *Cuckmere Haven* 441
Guy Fawkes Bitter *B&T* 422
Guy Fawkes Revenge *North Downs* 479
GWR *Cottage* 440

# H

Hackett VC *Concertina* 439
Hadda's Headbanger *Vale* 503
Hadda's Summer Glory *Vale* 503
Hammerhead *Clark's* 438
Hampshire Hare *Hampshire* 456
Hampshire Hog *Beer Seller (Hampshire)* 456
Hancock's HB *Bass* 512
Hancock's IPA *Bass* 512
Hanson's Mild *Banks's* 423
Happy Jack *Blackbeard (Hanby)* 456
Hare Brained *King's Head* 468
Harrier *Fulbeck* 450
Harrier SPA *Cotleigh* 440
Hartcliffe Bitter *Ross* 491
Hartington Bitter *Whim* 505
Hartleys XB *Robinson's* 490
Hartslock No. 1 *West Berkshire* 505
Hart's Proposal *Hart* 458
Harvest Ale *Cotleigh* 440
    *Gale's* 451
    *King & Barnes* 467
    *Lees* 469
Harvest Festival *Commercial* 439
Hastings Rouser *Old Forge* 482
Hatters Mild *Robinson's* 490
Haymaker *Hook Norton* 462
Head *Otter* 483
Headcracker *Woodforde's* 507
Head Off *Blewitts* 428
Headstrong *Blackawton* 427
Heart of Oak *Cannon Royall* 436
Hearty Ale *Burton Bridge* 432
Heavy Horse *Dunn Plowman* 443
Heller *Royal Inn* 491
Hell's Mouth *Whim* 505
Hemlock Bitter *Bramcote* 429
Henry's Original IPA *Wadsworth* 503

## O

# READERS' RECOMMENDATIONS

*Suggestions for pubs to be included or excluded*

All pubs are surveyed by the local branches of CAMRA. If you would like to comment on a pub already featured, or any you think should be featured, please fill in the form below (or a copy of it) and send it to the address indicated. Your views will be passed on to the branches concerned.

Pub Name:

Address:

Reason for recommendation/criticism:

Pub Name:

Address:

Reason for recommendation/criticism:

Your name and address:

**Please send to: Good Beer Guide, CAMRA, 230 Hatfield Road, St Albans, Hertfordshire AL1 4LW**

# CAMRA BOOKS AND GIFTS

CAMRA produces a wide range of books and other items to complement the *Good Beer Guide*. The major items are listed below, but a full catalogue of CAMRA products (including local guides) is available on request. Tear out or copy this form for ease of ordering. All prices include UK postage and packing.

| | Quantity | Price each | Amount |
|---|---|---|---|
| **CAMRA BOOKS** | | | |
| Good Beer Guide to Prague and the Czech Republic | | £7.99 | |
| Good Beer Guide to Belgium and Holland (2nd edition) | | £9.99 | |
| Good Beer Guide to Munich and Bavaria | | £8.99 | |
| Room at the Inn (guide to pub accommodation) | | £8.99 | |
| Good Pub Food (4th edition) | | £9.99 | |
| The CAMRA Guide to Real Cider | | £7.99 | |
| Known Treasures and Hidden Gems (guide to London pubs) | | £7.99 | |
| The CAMRA Guide to Home Brewing | | £6.99 | |
| Brew Your Own Real Ale at Home | | £6.99 | |
| Brew Classic European Beers at Home | | £8.99 | |
| **OTHER PRODUCTS** | | | |
| CAMRA Tie | | £7.50 | |
| CAMRA Lapel Badge | | £2.50 | |
| CAMRA T-shirt (white: M, L, XL, XXL – state size) | | £7.50 | |
| | | **Total** | £ |

Please send to CAMRA, 230 Hatfield Road, St Albans, Hertfordshire AL1 4LW (cheques made payable to CAMRA must accompany all orders). Allow 21 days for delivery.

To place a credit card order, phone (01727) 867201 and ask for the Products Secretary.

Name

Address

Post Code

# CAMRA–FREE TRIAL MEMBERSHIP!

*Help protect traditional breweries and real pubs
by joining our successful Campaign*

You may have considered joining CAMRA for some time but have never taken the plunge. Perhaps a membership form has not been placed in front of you. Nearly 50,000 beer drinkers consider CAMRA membership to be well worthwhile, so why not take this opportunity to join them? We are offering our usual free trial membership to all *Good Beer Guide* readers, so, if you don't like it, you can opt out after three months and pay nothing!

■ For three-months', no strings, trial membership, just fill in the direct debit form overleaf, sign the application form below and pop them in the post to us (photocopies will do). If, after the three months are up, you do not wish to remain a CAMRA member, simply write to us returning your membership card and you will owe nothing.

■ As a CAMRA member (even for these three months), you will be able to enjoy generous discounts on all CAMRA products (including the *Good Beer Guide*) and you will receive the highly-rated monthly newspaper, *What's Brewing*, to keep you up to date with events in the pub and brewing world. You will also obtain the CAMRA members' handbook, packed with useful facts and figures about real ale, and can take advantage of free or reduced-price admission at many beer festivals.

■ As a CAMRA member you can help to save pubs and breweries, enjoy local social events and brewery trips, and assist with surveying for the *Good Beer Guide* and other CAMRA activities.

If you do not want to take up this offer, but wish to join anyway, just fill in the application form below and return it to us with a cheque for your first year's subscription. Do not fill in the direct debit form. To pay by credit card, contact the Membership Secretary on (01727) 867201.

------------------------------------------------------------

■ Full annual membership £14 ■ Life membership rates on application
■ Joint annual membership (living partners) £16

*Please delete as appropriate:*

☐ I/We wish to take advantage of the trial membership,
and have completed the instructions overleaf.

☐ I/We wish to become members of CAMRA.

☐ I/We agree to abide by the memorandum and articles of
association of the company.

☐ I/We enclose a cheque/p.o. for £          (payable to CAMRA)

Name(s) _____

Address _____

_____

Signature(s) _____

To: CAMRA, 230 Hatfield Road, St Albans, Hertfordshire AL1 4LW

# INSTRUCTIONS TO YOUR BANK TO PAY DIRECT DEBITS

Please complete parts 1 to 4 to instruct your bank to make payments directly from your account.

Return the form to Campaign for Real Ale Limited, 230 Hatfield Road, St Albans, Hertfordshire AL1 4LW

**To the Manager**

                                                                    **Bank**

_____

_____

**1** Please write the full postal address of your bank branch in the box.

**2** Name(s) of account holder(s)

_____

Address _____

_____

                                        Post Code _____

**3** Account number

| | | | | | | | | |
|-|-|-|-|-|-|-|-|-|

_____

*Banks may refuse to accept instructions to pay direct debits from some types of account.*

*Direct debit instructions should only be addressed to banks in the United Kingdom.*

CAMRA Computer Membership No. (for office use only)

| | | | | | |
|-|-|-|-|-|-|

Originator's Identification No.

| 9 | 2 | 6 | 1 | 2 | 9 |
|---|---|---|---|---|---|

**4** Your instructions to the bank, and signature.

- I instruct you to pay direct debits from my account at the request of Campaign for Real Ale Limited.
- The amounts are variable and are to be debited annually.
- I understand that Campaign for Real Ale Limited may change the amount only after giving me prior notice.
- PLEASE CANCEL ALL PREVIOUS STANDING ORDER INSTRUCTIONS IN FAVOUR OF CAMPAIGN FOR REAL ALE LIMITED.
- I will inform the bank in writing if I wish to cancel this instruction.
- I understand that if any direct debit is paid which breaks the terms of this instruction, the bank will make a refund.

Signature(s) _____

_____

Date _____